THE OPTICAL PROPERTIES OF ORGANIC COMPOUNDS

Alexander N. Winchell
Emeritus Professor of Mineralogy
The University of Wisconsin

SECOND EDITION, ENLARGED AND COMPLETELY REVISED

1954
ACADEMIC PRESS INC., PUBLISHERS
New York, N. Y.

ACADEMIC PRESS INC.
125 East 23rd Street
New York 10, N. Y.

Library of Congress Catalog Card Number: 54-6347

Preface

In the first edition of this volume about sixteen hundred organic substances were described and about one thousand were placed on the diagram for the determination of compounds. In the brief time since that volume was published about seven hundred organic compounds have been described, as to optical properties, in scientific publications, and the American Cyanamid Company has generously released for publication in this volume data on the optical properties of about two hundred other organic compounds. Therefore, in this edition more than twenty five hundred substances are described and nearly two thousand are placed on one or both of the two diagrams for the determination of compounds.

In preparing the second edition of this volume the aim has been to include all organic compounds whose optical properties were described prior to October first, 1952, but there are undoubtedly some omissions, since such data are almost never indexed.

It is a pleasure to acknowledge the helpful cooperation of many persons in this work. The second Plate was prepared at the suggestion of Professor Horace Winchell of Yale University. Useful suggestions and data on optical properties of certain organic compounds have been supplied very generously by many colleagues, including W. L. Bond, Glenn Coven, R. L. Gilbert, F. T. Jones, C. L. Johnson, G. L. Keenan, Alan F. Kirkpatrick, W. J. McCrone, Charles Maresh, John Mitchell, E. M. Plein, C. F. Poe, T. G. Rochow, R. W. Stafford, and E. F. Williams.

Some organic compounds have structures which are not yet fully determined or are entirely unknown. Such substances are described after the others in a separate group ("Unclassified") in two parts (with and without nitrogen) each one arranged alphabetically according to the parent compound.

The classification of the many compounds added in the second edition was accomplished largely by the aid of Dr. Elga R. Wasserman.

It seems reasonable to include a brief description of carbon, as found in nature, as a sort of introduction to the description of organic compounds.

Alexander N. Winchell

88 Vineyard Road
Hamden 17, Conn.

Table of Contents

Descriptions of Substances

PRELIMINARY

I. Acyclic Compounds

II. Isocyclic Compounds

III. Heterocyclic Compounds

IV. Organic Compounds Not Assigned Places in the Three Preceding Groups

Introduction

The aim has been to include all organic compounds whose optical properties are sufficiently well known to permit identification by optical methods. In general it has been found that correct identification requires (as a minimum) an accurate knowledge of the indices of refraction. Therefore this volume includes, so far as they are known, all organic compounds whose indices of refraction have been measured.

The compounds are arranged according to the method by which organic compounds are classified in the fourth edition of Beilstein's *Handbuch der organischen Chemie*, published by the German Chemical Society (deutsche chemische Gesellschaft). The Beilstein system is founded on the premise that every definite compound can be expressed in a structural formula. The system contains the following four main divisions:

Division I: Acyclic stem nuclei. The carbon atoms are joined in open chains only. (Volumes I–IV of Beilstein's *Handbuch*.)

Division II: Isocyclic stem nuclei. The carbon atoms are joined in closed rings which do not include other kinds of atoms as ring components. (Volumes V–XVI of Beilstein's *Handbuch*.)

Division III: Heterocyclic stem nuclei. The carbon atoms are joined in closed rings which include one or more other kinds of atoms as ring components. (Volumes XVII–XXVII of Beilstein's *Handbuch*.)

Division IV: Natural products not assigned places in the three preceding divisions. (Vols. XXX *et seq.* of Beilstein's *Handbuch*.)

The first three divisions are based on the structural formulas; the fourth includes natural products of indefinite composition or incompletely known structure.

Each of the four main divisions is further subdivided. Division I (acyclic) and Division II (isocyclic) each include some thirty-odd classes. For the most part corresponding classes are numbered the same in each division. Division III (heterocyclic) is classified first into subdivisions according to the kind and number of heterocyclic atoms; each of these subdivisions is then divided into classes in the same manner as Divisions I and II above. Division IV is arbitrarily divided into nine subdivisions.

Class I of Division I, Class I of Division II, and Class I of each subdivision of Division III may all be defined as stem nuclei and each subdivided according to the decreasing saturation of the several series of hydrocarbons which it includes, thus:

Division I. Acyclic Compounds

Class I. Compounds with no functional group

Subclass A. Saturated C_nH_{2n+2}
Subclass B. Unsaturated C_nH_{2n}
Subclass C. Unsaturated C_nH_{2n-2}, etc.

Division II. Isocyclic Compounds

Class I. Compounds with no functional group

Subclass A. Saturated C_nH_{2n}
Subclass B. Unsaturated C_nH_{2n-2}
Subclass C. Unsaturated C_nH_{2n-4} etc.

Division III. Heterocyclic Compounds

Subdivision I. Compounds with one oxygen atom in the cycle

Class I. Compounds with no functional group

Subclass A. Saturated $C_nH_{2n}O$
Subclass B. Unsaturated $C_nH_{2n-2}O$
Subclass C. Unsaturated $C_nH_{2n-4}O$, etc.

The classes containing one or more functional groups in the molecule need to be further subdivided. For Class 2 (hydroxy compounds), which contains the hydroxy group, the subclasses in each division (except IV) are determined by the number of such groups in the molecule, thus:

Division I. Acyclic Compounds

Class 2. Hydroxy compounds

Subclass A. Monohydroxy compounds
Subclass B. Dihydroxy compounds
Subclass C. Trihydroxy compounds, etc.

Division II. Isocyclic Compounds

Class 2. Hydroxy compounds

Subclass A. Monohydroxy compounds, etc.

Division III. Heterocyclic Compounds

Subdivision 1. Compounds with one oxygen atom in the cycle

Class 2. Hydroxy compounds

Subclass A. Monohydroxy compounds, etc.

The same method of subdivision is employed for the further division of the subclasses as for Class 1 -- that is, according to the decreasing saturation of its component series, thus:

Division I. Acyclic Compounds

Class 2. Hydroxy compounds

Subclass A. Monohydroxy compounds

Section 1. Monohydroxy compounds $C_nH_{2n+2}O$
Section 2. Monohydroxy compounds $C_nH_{2n}O$
Section 3. Monohydroxy compounds $C_nH_{2n-2}O$, etc.

Each subclass is further arranged in a homologous series of groups of isomers in the order of increasing numbers of carbon atoms.

Carbonyl compounds (class 3 in Divisions I, II, and III) include aldehydes, ketones, ketenes, quinones, etc.

The numbers and letters used for classes and subclasses, respectively, are those given in Beilstein's *Handbuch*. It will be observed that many of the classes and subclasses found in Beilstein are not included here, the reason being that no representatives of these classes have been measured optically.

For a complete description of the classification system the reader is referred to the introduction of volume I of the principal work and to Huntress' excellent monograph[1].

Every principal volume of the fourth edition covers the chemical literature up to January 1, 1910. The First Series of supplementary volumes covers the literature published between 1910 and 1919. As the present work was being prepared, the principal and supplementary volumes covering Divisions I, II, and III (Volumes I–XXVII inclusive) and Volumes XXX (rubber and carotenoids) and XXXI (carbohydrates I) were available. For Division IV (Volumes XXX *et seq.*) the principal and first supplementary volumes are combined. Volumes XXVIII and XXIX are devoted to an alphabetical index to the preceding volumes. The numerous compounds not included in the volumes of Beilstein thus far published have been placed where they will presumably appear in future supplementary volumes.

In one detail the classification used in this book differs from that of Beilstein. He arranges the salts of each acid in the following order: NH_4, NH_3OH, NH_3, NH_2, Li, Na, K, Rb, Cs, Cu, Ag, Be, Mg, Ca, Sr, Ba, Ra, Zn, Cd, Hg, B, Al, Ga, In, Tl, Sc, Y, La, Ce, Pr, Nd, Ta, As, Sb, Bi, Cr, Mo, W, U, Mn, Fe, Co, Ni, Ru, Rh, Pd, Os, Ir, Pt. Acid salts precede neutral salts, which are followed by basic salts. Salts containing two or more metals are always listed with the salts of the metal which comes last in the series. All hydrated salts are included with the corresponding anhydrous salts. This arrangement however, does not always bring together those salts which are isomorphous and are therefore so closely related that in some cases they can intercrystallize in any proportions to form homogeneous crystals. Since such intercrystallizations are common in nature and can be recognized by their optical properties, it seems highly advantageous to modify the classification so as to bring them together. To do this it is necessary to deal with anhydrous and hydrated salts separately and to modify somewhat the order of the metals. Accordingly the anhydrous salts of all the metals are listed first, and these are followed by the monohydrates of all the metals, the dihydrates, the trihydrates, etc. Moreover, the order in which the anhydrous salts, for example, are listed must sometimes be modified to bring the isomorphous salts together. Thus ammonium salts are never isomorphous with lithium salts so far as known, but are frequently isomorphous with potassium salts, and in some cases both of these are miscible with sodium salts, as illustrated in certain tartrates like Seignette salts.

---

[1] Huntress, *A Brief Introduction to the Use of Beilstein's Handbuch der organischen Chemie*, 2d ed., John Wiley, 1938.

It seems reasonable to include a brief description of carbon, as found in nature, as a sort of introduction to the description of organic compounds.

Since the nomenclature of organic chemistry is still unsettled, the choice of names for given compounds in this volume is necessarily somewhat arbitrary. Wherever possible, the name adopted by the International Commission on the Reform of the Nomenclature of Organic Chemistry[1] is given first; this is followed by such other names as seem to have attained wide usage. Compounds such as the sugars and their derivatives, as well as double salts and some naturally occurring compounds which are not readily named according to the systematic scheme, are listed only by their common names.

In abbreviating citations to the original literature, the usage of *Chemical Abstracts* has been followed.

According to George L. Keenan[2] indices of 3,5-dinitrobenzoyl derivatives of various organic compounds may be determined most readily and satisfactorily by the immersion method (see J. Assoc. Official Agr. Chem. 13, 389, 1930) in solutions of potassium mercuric iodide in glycerol and water, although for rapid determinative work oily liquids consisting of mixtures of mineral oils, monochlornaphthaline and methylene iodide can be used.

W. M. D. Bryant[3] used liquids as follows:
$N_D = 1.36–1.40$, glycerol-glycol-water.
$N_D = 1.40–1.72$, potassium mercuric iodide-glycerol-water.
$N_D = 1.74–1.78$, methylene iodide-sulfur.
$N_D = 1.85–2.10$, methylene iodide-arsenic trisulfide.

In 1910 Bolland[4] published optic data for about 450 substances which had not previously been measured; of these more than half (275) were organic compounds. This is a far greater number of new measures than have been reported by any other writer at any time, but the value of Bolland's work is seriously impaired by its imperfections. Thus he usually studied the crystallized substance only in the position in which it happened to lie, which was often on the largest face (or cleavage surface). Accordingly he described the extinction as "parallel" if it was parallel with the edges of that face. Moreover, he called the extinction parallel if it were approximately so, 20° being the smallest angle he recognized as a deviation from the parallel. Any monoclinic crystal which is platy or tabular on any face parallel to *b* has "parallel extinction" in Bolland's usage, and a monoclinic or triclinic crystal having an extinction angle of less than 20° in its platy crystals is described in the same way.

Bolland determined the sign of elongation from a single plate, so that it is always reported as plus or as minus, never as $\pm$.

For only a few substances does Bolland give three indices of refraction; nearly always he gives only the two indices that can be measured in the position of the plates. He does not give these as N_X and N_Z, but later writers, including

[1] Patterson, J. Am. Chem. Soc., 55, 3905 (1933).
[2] J. Am. Chem. Soc. 63, 1924 (1931).
[3] J. Am. Chem. Soc. 64, 3758 (1932).
[4] Sitzber. Akad. Wiss. Wien. 119, Abt. II, b, 275 (1910); Monatsh. 31, 387 (1910).

Landolt-Bornstein and the compilers of the International Critical Tables, quote Bolland's figures as referring to biaxial crystals and as being N_X and N_Z. Actually they might be (1) the two indices of a uniaxial crystal, (2) any two of the three chief indices of a biaxial crystal, or even (3) any two values intermediate between N_X and N_Z. They are the indices for the fast ray and the slow ray normal to the plate studied, whatever its orientation may be. Some other workers have used the same system, notably Kley, Mayrhofer, and Gatewood. In this book such measures are given as values of N_1 and N_2 to distinguish them from true values of the principal indices.

Bolland's data for refractive indices, since they are not very accurate, are not always included in this book when other data are at hand. But for many substances no other measures have been published. To give a clear idea of the range of accuracy in Bolland's data, Table I has been prepared, which shows how his values compare with more accurate measures in certain cases which are believed to be representative.

Kofler[1] has shown that some of the early measures of indices of refraction seem to be incorrect not because of errors in those measures but because they were made on material not accurately described; for example, anhydrous substances were not distinguished from hydrous in the case of caffeine, codeine, morphine, and orthoform; or different crystal phases of a single substance were not distinguished, as in the case of veronal and morphine. Table II illustrates these points.

The first edition of this volume was the result of several years' work supported by grants from the Wisconsin Alumni Research Foundation. It is a pleasure to acknowledge the aid of many persons in the work. Data on optical properties of certain compounds were kindly supplied by W. M. D. Bryant, R. C. Emmons, H. W. Hartline (unpublished thesis received from N. W. Buerger), G. L. Keenan, C. W. Mason, C. F. Poe, C. D. West, R. E. Wilcox, and Mary L. Willard. Optical measures of some compounds were made at the University of Wisconsin by R. G. Comer, R. C. Emmons, and J. J. Marais. The classification of the compounds was accomplished chiefly with the aid of Drs. E. Leon Foreman, Minnie Meyers, and Ivan Wolff, and the final editing was done by Dr. Leonard T. Capell, associate editor of *Chemical Abstracts*.

---

[1]Mikro. Meth. Mikroch., 1936, pp. 91 and 92.

Table I. *Comparison of Data.*

Substance	Crystal System	Chief form	Extinction		Recent Data*	Bolland		Recent Data*	Bolland	Bolland		Recent Data*
			Bolland	In 010	N_X	N_1	N_X	N_Y	N_Y	N_Z	N_2	N_Z
$Li_2SO_4 \cdot H_2O$	Mono.	{$\bar{1}$01}	Parallel	—36°	1.459	1.48		1.477			1.49	1.488
Na_2SO_3	Hex.				1.515	1.54					1.57	1.565
$Na_3PO_4 \cdot 12\ H_2O$	Trig.				1.4458	1.44					1.45	1.4524
KCNS	Mono.	{110}	Parallel	16°	1.532		1.605	1.660	1.645	1.73		1.730
$KClO_3$	Mono.	{001}			1.410	1.47		1.517			1.54	1.524
H_2KPO_4	Tet.	{100}	Parallel	0°	1.4684	1.47					1.51	1.5095
$HKCO_3$	Mono.	{101}	Parallel	+30°	1.380	1.48		1.482			1.57	1.578
$K_2Cr_2O_7$	Tri.	{010}	Parallel		1.7202		1.75	1.7380	1.95	1.95+		1.8197
K_2CrO_4	Orth.	Varied	Parallel		1.6873			1.7245 D				1.7305 C
					1.7087	1.72		1.7261			1.74	1.7304
HKC_2O_4	Mono.	{001}, {010}	Inclined		1.415		1.46	1.545	1.54	1.55		1.565
$HRbC_4H_4O_6$	Orth.	{010}, {001}	Parallel		1.5101	1.52		1.5495			1.58	1.5833
$CuSO_4 \cdot 5\ H_2O$	Tri.	{11$\bar{1}$}	Parallel	Incl.	1.5141	1.53		1.5368			1.54	1.5434
$AgNO_3$	Orth.	{001}			1.729	1.73		1.744			>1.75	1.788
$Na_6Mg(SO_4)_4$	Mono ?				1.485	1.485		1.488			1.49	1.489
$H_2Ca(C_4H_4O_5)_2 \cdot 6\ H_2O$	Orth.	{110}, {010}	Parallel		1.493	1.51		1.507			1.545	1.545
$BaCl_2O_6 \cdot H\ O$	Mono.	{001}, {110}	Parallel		1.562	1.58		1.577			1.63	1.635
$HgCl_2$	Orth.	{011}, {001}	Parallel		1.725		1.63	1.859	1.74	1.95		1.965
$Hg(CN)_2$	Tet.	{110}	Parallel		1.492	1.60					1.65	1.645±

* Believed to be accurate.

Table II. *Refractive Indices*

Substance	Bolland[1], 1910	Behrens-Kley	Mayrhofer	Kofler
Caffeine		1.54 1.66		Anhydrous: 1.446; 1.70 *ca.* Hydrous: 1.421; 1.661 *ca.*; 1.689 *ca.*
Codeine		1.56 1.66		Anhydrous: 1.616 *ca.*; 1.622 *ca.*; 1.645 *ca.* Hydrous: 1.542 > 1.660
Morphine		1.62 1.63		Anhydrous, Phase I: 1.653; 1.657; 1.671 Anhydrous, Phase II: 1.573; 1.625; 1.630 Hydrous: 1.582; 1.623; 1.644
Orthoform			1.515 1.523 (1.528; 1.587)	Anhydrous: 1.622; 1.658 Hydrous: 1.515; 1.523
Veronal			1.436; 1.552; 1.577	Phase I (Stable): 1.526; 1.570 Phase II (Unstable): 1.473; 1.558; 1.580 Phase III (Unstable): 1.473 *ca.*; 1.573 *ca.*
Narcotine	1.54 1.69	1.54 1.69		1.525; 1.687 *ca.*; 1.697 *ca.*
Arabinose	1.545 1.56			α-D 1.551; 1.567; 1.571 β-D 1.555; 1.573; 1.577; E. T. Wherry: J.A.C.S., XL, 1852
Fructose or Levulose	1.55 1.56			1.558; ?; 1.561 G.L. Keenan: J.W.A.S., XVI, 433
Urea	1.485 1.61		1.485 1.600	1.484; 1.602 E. T. Wherry: J.W.A.S., VIII, 277
Phenacetin	1.54; 1.58; 1.59		1.523; 1.532; 1.587	
Santonin	1.61 1.62		1.589; 1.592; 1.639	1.590; 1.630; 1.640 — Int. Crit. Tables, I, 256, 280

[1] Sitz. Akad. Wiss. Wien, 119, II, b, 275 (1910); 117, II, b, 671 (1908).

List of Abbreviations and Symbols

(Names of periodicals and symbols of chemical elements not included.)

A, B = optic axes of biaxial crystals.

A, B, C, D, E, F, G, H (after indices of refraction) = various types of monochromatic light.

Å = Ångstrom (one hundred-millionth of a centimeter).

a = front and rear crystal axis.

α = angle between crystal axes *b* and *c* in the positive octant.

[α] = specific rotation, or the angle through which the plane of polarization is turned by a liquid or solution containing one gram of substance in one cc. of liquid in a layer one decimeter deep.

B = birefringence.

b = right and left crystal axis.

B.P. = boiling point.

β = angle between crystal axes *a* and *c* in the positive octant.

C, see A, B, etc., above.

c = concentration.

c = vertical crystal axis.

ca. = about.

calc. = calculated.

γ = angle between crystal axes *a* and *b* in the positive octant.

D = density.

E = extraordinary ray.

E, see A, B, etc., above.

2 E = apparent optic angle measured in air.

F, see A, B, etc., above.

G, see A, B, etc., above.

H = hardness. See also A, B, etc., above.

2 H = the apparent optic axial angle measured in oil.

Li (after index of refraction) = lithium (red) light.

λ = a wave length of monochromatic light.

M.P. = melting point or fusion temperature.

N = index of refraction.

Na (after index of refraction) = sodium (yellow) light.

N_E = index of refraction for the extraordinary ray.

N_i = an intermediate index of refraction.

N_O = index of refraction for the ordinary ray.

N_X = index of refraction for the ray vibrating along X = $\mathfrak{a}$ of some writers.

$N_{X'}$ = index of refraction for the fast ray in a certain position.

N_Y = index of refraction for the ray vibrating along Y = $\mathfrak{b}$ of some writers.

N_Z = index of refraction for the ray vibrating along Z = $\mathfrak{c}$ of some writers.

$N_{Z'}$ = index of refraction for the slow ray in a certain position.
N_1 = one index of refraction; it may have any value from N_X to N_Y.
N_2 = a second index of refraction; it may have any value from N_Y to N_Z unless N_3 is also given, when it is merely an intermediate value.
N_3 = a third index of refraction (the highest one measured).
n = an indefinite number.
0 > E or 0 < E = absorption greater (or less) for the 0 ray than for the E.
$r > v$ or $r < v$ (after the optic angle) signifies that the optic angle in red light is greater than or less than the optic angle in violet light.
Ref = Reference. See the List of References, pages 319–336.
Tl (after index of refraction) = thallium (green) light.
U.C. = unit cell.
2 V = the true angle between the optic axes.
X = the vibration direction of the fastest ray. = $\mathfrak{a}$ of German writers.
Y = the vibration direction of the intermediate ray. = $\mathfrak{b}$ of German writers.
Z = the vibration direction of the slowest ray. = $\mathfrak{c}$ of German writers.
X > Y, etc. = absorption greater for light vibrating along X than for light vibrating along Y, etc.
° = degree of temperature (Centigrade) or an angle whose unit is measured by one 360th of a circle.
$\wedge$ = angle; for example, $Z \wedge c$ = the angle between Z and c.
> = greater than.
< = less than.
$\perp$ = normal to.
$\|$ = parallel; this is often omitted, as in the statement: the optic plane is 010; or it is replaced by =, as in $X = a$.
$\therefore$ = therefore.
100, 010, 001, 110, 101, etc. = Miller symbols of crystal directions.
{100}, {010}, {001}, {110}, etc. = Miller symbols of crystal forms.

The optic sign of a substance is expressed by (+) or (—) before the expression for the optic angle; for example, (+) 2 V = 50° signifies that the true acute angle between the optic axes is 50° and that this is measured about Z so that the optic sign is positive.

The sign of elongation of crystals is positive if Z (the vibration direction of the slow ray) is parallel with, or less than 45° from, the direction of elongation; it is negative if X (the vibration direction of the fast ray) occupies this position; it is plus or minus (±) if Y occupies the position named.

In monoclinic crystals the extinction angle is commonly measured from the vertical axis to Z, if that is possible; if not, the measure may be to X. This angle is sometimes considered positive (+) if it is measured in the obtuse angle β between the axes a and c; and negative (-) if it is in the acute angle β. It seems better to consider this angle as positive (+) if it is measured (when the observer is looking from a position in the positive octant bounded by $+a$, $+b$, and $+c$ toward the negative octant) by turning the crystal on the stage clockwise from an extinction position to a crystal direction (usually c, the long direction of the crystal).

THE OPTICAL PROPERTIES OF ORGANIC COMPOUNDS

I. ACYCLIC COMPOUNDS

Carbon

Carbon (C) has at least two crystal phases[1]. One (the diamond) is isometric, commonly in octahedrons; also dodecahedral or cubic; perfect 111 cleavage. H = 10. D 3.52. Infusible. Insoluble. Isotropic with N = 2.4135 Li, 2.4195 Na, 2.4278 Tl. Colorless or tinted. Another phase is hexagonal (graphite) with $c/a = 2.760$. a 2.46, c 6.80 Å. U.C. 4. Crystals rounded hexagonal lamellae with perfect 0001 cleavage. H = 1 - 2. D 2.25. Infusible. Insoluble. Opaque in thin section, but translucent in greenish-gray light in flakes made on a streak plate. Uniaxial negative with N between 1.93 and 2.07. Birefringence not strong. Color black; streak on smooth porcelain greenish black. When treated with HNO_3 and $KClO_3$ it changes to graphitic acid which has nearly the same optic properties, but is pleochroic with O = dark green and E = almost colorless. On heating it changes back to graphite.

Coal

The carbon in coal is not diamond nor graphite, although in anthracite it is nearly pure. Recent work has shown that the refractive index of vitrain is a good indication of the quality of the coal. Thus, Fisher found that vitrain

Material	Source	Fixed Carbon	N ⊥ Bedding	N ∥ Bedding	Properties
Vitrain	Leicester	61.3	1.67	1.67	Free burning and coking coals
Vitrain	Warwick	63.1	1.70	1.70	
Vitrain	Lancaster	63.8	1.77	1.77	
Vitrain	S. Wales	74.5	1.87	1.81	Coking coals
Vitrain	Kent	80.8	1.84	1.84	
Vitrain	S. Wales	86.2	1.91	1.86	Steam coals
Vitrain	S. Wales	88.8	1.90	1.89	
Vitrain	S. Wales	93.6	1.90	1.80	Anthracites
Vitrain	Kilkenny	97.1	1.91	1.77	

[1] Graphite and diamond are minerals, but graphite (also diamond ?) is derived from organic matter at least in some cases, and coal is clearly of organic origin.

of bituminous coal had N = 1.76 and vitrain of semibituminous coal had N = 1.87. Also Cannon and George found the results tabulated on page 1 and shown in Fig. 1.

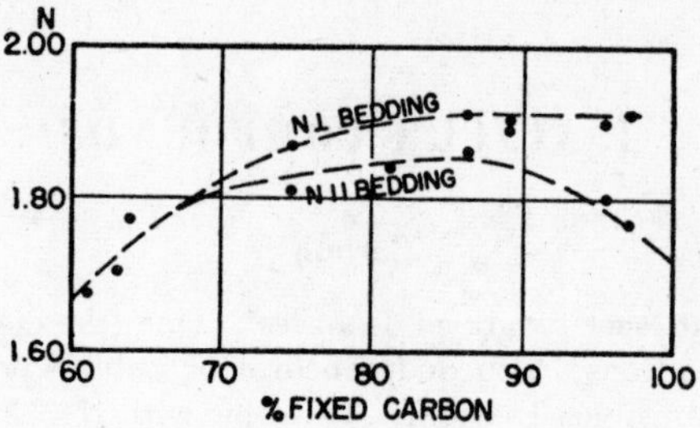

Fig. 1. Optic properties of vitrain.

McCabe and Quirke furnish the following data:

Material	Source	Fixed Carbon	Volatile Matter	Mois- ture	B.T.U.	N
1. Woody lignite	Hernando, Miss.	31.2	32.9	32,1	7048	1.632
2. Vitrain	Lafayette, Colo.	46.4	29.5	21.7	10265	1.703
3. Vitrain	Pershing, Iowa	45.6	34.4	18.7	11540	1.715
4. Vitrain	Middle Grove, Ill.	49.74	33.61	16.0	12188	1.723
5. Vitrain	Roanoke, Ill.	49.6	33.5	15.7	12303	1.723
6. Vitrain	Booneville, Ind.	49.50	40.60	9.18	13240	1.750
7. Vitrain	Harrisburg, Ill.	58.0	35.7	3.7	14160	1.768
8. Vitrain	Gibsonia, Ill.	55.9	40.1	2.3	14769	1.768
9. Vitrain	Hartshorne, Okla.	73.28	23.92	0.56	15680	1.795

Ref: 429a, 459, 465, 549, 556.

ACYCLIC COMPOUNDS

Class 1. Compounds Containing No Functional Group.

Tri-iodomethane or iodoform (CHI_3) is hexagonal pyramidal with $c/a = 1.104$. Space group $C6_3$. *a* 6.92, *c* 7.69 Å. U.C. 2. Crystals basal tablets (Fig. 2) or prisms. No distinct cleavage. D 4.1. M.P. 119°. Uniaxial negative with $N_O = 1.800$, $N_E = 1.750$, $N_O - N_E = 0.050$. Also $N_O = 2.11 \pm 0.02$, $N_E = 1.766$ Na, $N_O - N_E = 0.344 \pm .02$. Color yellow; absorption O > E,

Ref: 117, 152, 349, 498, 524, 621.

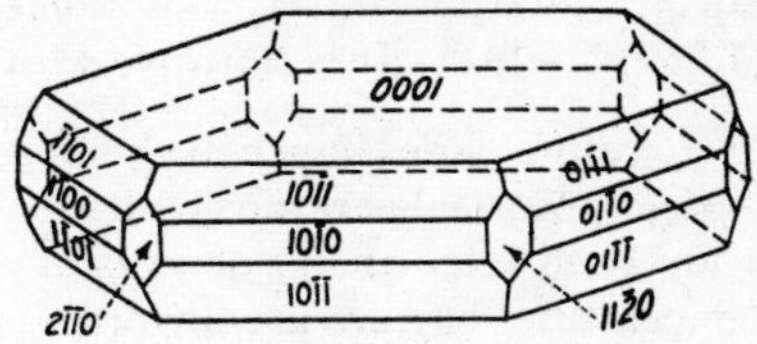

Fig. 2. Iodoform.

Sulfur-iodoform solvate ($CHI_3 \cdot 3S_8$) is hexagonal with $c/a = 0.366$; it has ditrigonal pyramidal symmetry. Uniaxial negative with $N_O = 2.2528$, $N_E = 1.7951$, $N_O - N_E = 0.4577$ for $\lambda = 589$, and $N_O = 2.2285$, $N_E = 1.7860$, $N_O - N_E = 0.4425$ for $\lambda = 650$. Ref: 349.

Hexachloroethane ($Cl_3C \cdot CCl_3$) has three crystal phases. One is orthorhombic with $a{:}b{:}c = 0.568{:}1{:}0.316$. Crystals {100} tablets with {101} and {110}. No cleavage found. D 2.09. M.P. (closed tube) 187°; B.P. 185° - 186°. The optic plane is 100; X = *c*. (–) 2 E = 66° 28′ Na, r > v; 2 V = 38°. $N_X = 1.590$, $N_Y = 1.598$ calc., $N_Z = 1.668$, $N_Z - N_X = 0.078$. Colorless. This form inverts at 43° to a triclinic phase, which inverts to an isometric phase at 71° (with D = 1.90). Ref: 117, 348.

Hexabromoethane ($Br_3C \cdot CBr_3$) is probably trimorphous. One phase is orthorhombic dipyramidal with $a{:}b{:}c$[1] $= 0.887{:}1{:}0.558$. Space group *Pmnb*; *a* 10.64, *b* 12.00, *c* 6.69 Å. U.C. 4. Crystals {010} tablets with {100}, {110}, {011}, etc. No good cleavage. D 3.82. The optic plane is 010; X = *c*. (–) 2 E = 79° 30′; 2 V = 37° Na, r > v. $N_X = 1.7400$, $N_Y = 1.8466$, $N_Z = 1.8626$, $N_Z - N_X = 0.1226$. This phase inverts to a (triclinic ?) phase at 140° - 147°, which becomes isotropic (isometric ?) at about 210° C, some degrees below the temperature of disintegration. Ref: 117, 593.

1,2-Dibromo-1,1,2,2-tetrachloroethane or *s*-dibromotetrachloroethane ($Cl_2BrC \cdot CBrCl_2$) is orthorhombic with $a{:}b{:}c = 0.565{:}1{:}0.313$. Crystals {100} tablets with {110}, {101}, etc. No distinct cleavage. D 2.713. Decomposes at 200°. The optic plane is 100; X = *c*. (–)2V = 48° *ca.* Na. $N_X = 1.6308$, $N_Y = 1.6978$, $N_Z = 1.7132$, $N_Z - N_X = 0.0824$. Ref: 117, 152.

[1] *a b c* changed to *b a c* to make *b* > *a* > *c*.

1,2-Di-iodoethane or ethylene iodide ($ICH_2 \cdot CH_2I$) is pseudo-orthorhombic with $a:b:c = 0.588:1:0.450$, $\beta = 90°12'$. Space group *Cmca*; *a* 7.582, *b* 12.897, *c* 5.810 Å. U.C. 4. The monoclinic cell has $a:b:c = 0.369:1:0.370$, $\beta = 105°5'$; *a* 4.768, *b* 12.897, *c* 4.784 Å. U.C. 2. Crystals {010} plates. Twinning on 100. Perfect 100 and 010 cleavages. M.P. 81.2°, D 3.30. Extinction on 010 at about 8° to *c*. $N_X = 1.66$, $N_Y > 1.95$, $N_Z > 1.95$, $N_Z - N_X > 0.30$.
Ref: 34, 117, 531.

Dinitroethane $\{(NO)_2C_2H_4\}$ is tetragonal with $c = 0.834$. Crystals dipyramidal. Uniaxial negative with $N_O = 1.553$, $N_E = 1.483$, $N_O - N_E = 0.070$.
Ref: 568a.

2,2,3,3-Tetramethylbutane or di-*tert*-butyl (or bi-*tert*-butyl) or hexamethylethane $[(CH_3)_3C \cdot C(CH_3)_3]$ is isometric at ordinary temperature with D 0.81. M.P. 103 – 104°. It is isotropic with N = 1.480. The solid is plastic. Ref: 348.

Paraffin varies much in composition, but always has a formula which is C_nH_{2n+2}. Normal paraffins with $n > 15$ are waxy solids at ordinary temperatures. They have more than one crystal phase; if crystallized from solution at room temperature they are usually orthorhombic, but may be hexagonal. They invert to another phase (hexagonal?) at about 5° below their melting point. They have been described as uniaxial and positive with the following optic properties:

Sample	M.P.	Inferred Comp.	Temp.	N_O	N_E	$N_E - N_O$
1	49.4°	$C_{23.55}H_{49.1}$	20°	1.4960	1.5422	0.0462
2	52.2°	$C_{24.1}H_{50.2}$	20°	1.4995	1.5420	0.0425
3	55.0°	$C_{25.2}H_{52.4}$	20°	1.4985	1.5465	0.0480
4	57.8°	$C_{26.4}H_{54.8}$	20°	1.5022	1.5487	0.0465
5	60.6°	$C_{26.7}H_{55.4}$	20°	1.5040	1.5505	0.0465

However, crystals are thin basal plates with an angle between 110 and $1\bar{1}0$ varying from about 60° to about 75°. Octacosane ($C_{28}H_{58}$ – at least 98% pure) has a prismatic angle of 74°, while dotriacontane ($C_{32}H_{66}$) has a similar angle of 68°, and other types have angles of 64°, 65°, or 66.5°. Twinning is common on 100, 110, 310, or 010. Curved surfaces are common on mix crystals. In all cases the optic plane is 100 and the positive acute bisectrix is normal to the base. Orthorhombic crystals produce dextrorotatory polarization and must therefore belong to the pyramidal class. The rotatory polarization produces a larger optic angle in the NW position than in the NE position of the optic plane, and also produces maximum light at an angle varying a few degrees from 45° from extinction. For paraffins ranging from $C_{21}H_{44}$ to $C_{32}H_{66}$, N_Y is between 1.50 and 1.52, $N_Z - N_X$ is weak, 2 E is between 20° and 40° and 2 V is between 13° and 26°. Mix crystals often appear uniaxial or very nearly so. All paraffins tend to change to a hexagonal phase near their melting points.
Ref: 495, 564.

Hatchettite ($C_{38}H_{78}$) is a kind of paraffin in thin plates or massive. H 1. D 0.96. M.P. 80°. Soluble in oils, but not in acids. Nearly uniaxial and positive with $N_O = 1.480$, $N_E = 1.502$, $N_E - N_O = 0.022$; also biaxial and probably orthorhombic with $(+)2V = 10° \pm$, $r < v$ weak to distinct; also $(+)2V = 0° - 33°$, $r < v$ strong, $N_X = 1.518$ calc., $N_Y = 1.523$, $N_Z = 1.588$, $N_Z - N_X = 0.070$ Li on $C_{38}H_{78}$ with one good cleavage normal to Z, and M.P. 79°. When crushed under a cover glass all fragments become oriented normal to Z. On recrystallization the fibers have negative elongation. Ref: 70, 97, 250.

Dotriacontane or dicetyl (or bicetyl) $\{CH_3(CH_2)_{30}CH_3\}$ has two crystal phases. One phase, stable below 64.6° is uniaxial and positive at 20°: $N_O = 1.5148$, $N_E = 1.5645$, $N_E - N_O = 0.0497$; at 40°: $N_O = 1.5096$, $N_E = 1.5593$, $N_E - N_O = 0.0497$: at 64.6°: $N_O = 1.4971$, $N_E = 1.5472$, $N_E - N_O = 0.0501$. A second phase, stable only between 64.6° and the melting point (69.6°) is also uniaxial and positive; at 64.6°: $N_O = 1.4788$, $N_E = 1.5290$, $N_E - N_O = 0.0502$: at 69.6°: $N_O = 1.4756$, $N_E = 1.5257$, $N_E - N_O = 0.0501$. The liquid has $N = 1.4358$ at 69.6°. Ref: 346.

cis-Ethyleneamminodichloroplatinum ($C_2H_4NH_3PtCl_2$) is tetragonal with $c/a = 2.352$. Crystals are greenish yellow needles. Uniaxial positive with $N_O = 1.732$, $N_E > 1.785$, $N_E - N_O > 0.063$. Ref: 414aa.

cis Ethyleneamminodibromoplatinum ($C_2H_4NH_3PtBr_2$) is tetragonal. Crystals show only {001} and {100}. Uniaxial positive with $N_O = 1.770$, $N_E > 1.790$, $N_E - N_O > 0.020$. Ref: 418aa.

Ammonium ethylenetrichloroplatinate ($C_2H_4NH_4PtCl_3$) forms a yellow powder. $(-)2V = 63°$ calc. $N_X = 1.595$, $N_Y = 1.724$, $N_Z = 1.78$, $N_Z - N_X = 0.195$. Ref: 418aa.

Potassiumtrichloroplatinum butylene ($K_2Cl_3PtCH_2CH:CHCH_2PtCl_3$) forms needles with X $\|$ elongation. $(-)2V = 70°$, $N_X = 1.675$, $N_Y = 1.724$, $N_Z = 1.750$, $N_Z - N_X = 0.075$. X = dark yellow, Y and Z = colorless. Ref: 418aa.

Class 2. Hydroxy Compounds

Tetramethyl alcohol cobalt chloride [$4(CH_3OH) \cdot CoCl_2$] is isometric. D 1.39. $N = 1.712 \pm .005$. Color purple-blue. Ref: 631.

Ethyl alcohol cobalt bromide [$CH_3CH_2OH \cdot CoBr_2$] is isometric. D 2.59. $N = 1.72 \pm .05$. Color sky blue. Ref: 631.

Calcium ethyl sulfate dihydrate [$(C_2H_5 \cdot SO_4)_2Ca \cdot 2H_2O$] is monoclinic with $a:b:c = 1.548:1:1.491$, $\beta = 104°55'$. Crystals {100} tablets with {110}, {100}, {111}, or short prismatic. Perfect 100 and distinct 110 cleavages. D 1.63. The optic plane is 010; $X \wedge c = +49°$. $(-)2V = 67°40'$. $N_X = 1.4455$ Li, 1.4358 Na; $N_Y = 1.4672$ Li, 1.4624 Na; $N_Z = 1.4927$ Li, 1.4859 Na; $N_Z - N_X = 0.0501$ Na. (Groth considers these index values "quite impossible"). Ref: 78, 117.

Strontium ethyl sulfate dihydrate $[(C_2H_5 \cdot SO_4)_2Sr \cdot 2H_2O]$ is monoclinic with $a:b:c = 1.043:1:1.066$, $\beta = 93°44'$. Crystals {010} tablets with {001}, {110}, {101}, {310}, etc. Fig. 3. Very perfect 010 cleavage. D 2.03. The optic plane and Z are normal to 010; $X \wedge c = +70°$. $(-)2V = 75°4'$ calc. $N_X = 1.4972$, $N_Y = 1.5047$, $N_Z = 1.5098$, $N_Z - N_X = 0.0126$ Na. Ref: 117.

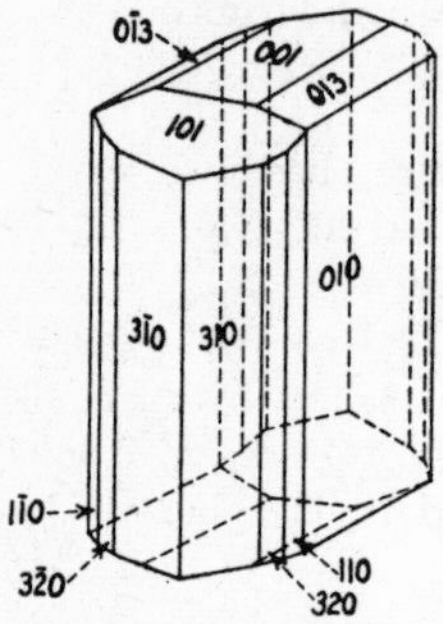

Fig. 3. Strontium ethyl sulphate dihydrate.

Yttrium ethyl sulfate octadecahydrate $[(C_2H_5 \cdot SO_4)_6 Y_2 \cdot 18H_2O]$ is hexagonal dipyramidal with $c/a = 0.507$. Space group $C6_3/m$. a 13.90, c 7.05 Å. U.C. 2. Crystals show $\{10\bar{1}0\}$, $\{11\bar{1}0\}$, $\{11\bar{2}0\}$, etc. Perfect $10\bar{1}0$ cleavage. D 1.764. Uniaxial negative with $N_O = 1.493$ D, $N_E = 1.480$, $N_O - N_E = 0.013$. Colorless or pale pink. Ref: 157, 528.

Lanthanum ethyl sulfate octadecahydrate $[(C_2H_5 \cdot SO_4)_6La_2 \cdot 18H_2O]$ is hexagonal dipyramidal with $c/a = 0.505$. Space group $C6_3/m$. a 14.08, c 7.05 Å. U.C. 2. Crystals show $\{11\bar{2}0\}$, $\{10\bar{1}1\}$, $\{10\bar{1}0\}$, etc. Perfect $10\bar{1}0$ cleavage. D 1.845. Uniaxial negative with $N_O = 1.482$ D, $N_E = 1.473$. $N_O - N_E = 0.009$. Colorless. Ref: 157, 528.

Cerium ethyl sulfate octadecahydrate $[(C_2H_5 \cdot SO_4)_6Ce_2 \cdot 18H_2O]$ is hexagonal dipyramidal with $c/a = 0.506$. Crystals varied but often equant with $\{10\bar{1}0\}$, $\{10\bar{1}1\}$, $\{11\bar{2}0\}$, $\{11\bar{2}1\}$, etc. Perfect $10\bar{1}0$ cleavage. D 1.930. Uniaxial negative with $N_O = 1.482$, $N_E = 1.474$, $N_O - N_E = 0.008$. Colorless. Ref: 157, 528.

Praseodymium ethyl sulfate octadecahydrate $(C_2H_5 \cdot SO_4)_6Pr_2 \cdot 18H_2O)$ is hexagonal dipyramidal with $c/a = 0.506$. Space group $C6_3/m$. a 14.01, c 7.09 Å. U.C. 2. Crystals often have two opposite faces of $\{10\bar{1}0\}$ enlarged, with $\{10\bar{1}0\}$, $\{11\bar{2}1\}$, etc. Perfect $10\bar{1}0$ cleavage. D 1.876. Uniaxial negative with $N_O = 1.486$, $N_E = 1.479$, $N_O - N_E = 0.007$. Emerald green color. Ref: 157, 528.

Neodymium ethyl sulfate octadecahyrate $[(C_2H_5 \cdot SO_4)_6Nd_2 \cdot 18H_2O]$ is hexagonal dipyramidal with $c/a = 0.505$. Space group $C6_3/m$. a 13.99, c 7.07 Å. U.C. 2. Crystals varied in habit with $\{10\bar{1}0\}$, $\{10\bar{1}1\}$, $\{11\bar{2}1\}$, etc. Perfect $10\bar{1}0$ cleavage. D 1.883. Uniaxial negative with $N_O = 1.487$, $N_E = 1.479$, $N_O - N_E = = 0.008$. Red with weak pleochroism. Ref: 157, 528.

Samarium ethyl sulfate octadecahydrate $[(C_2H_5 \cdot SO_4)_6Sm_2 \cdot 18H_2O]$ is hexagonal dipyramidal with $c/a = 0.5070$. Space group $C6_3/m$. a 13.96, c 7.08 Å. U.C. 2. Crystals show $\{11\bar{2}1\}$, $\{10\bar{1}0\}$, $\{10\bar{1}1\}$, etc. Perfect $10\bar{1}0$ cleavage. D 1.904. Uniaxial negative with $N_O = 1.490$, $N_E = 1.481$, $N_O - N_E = 0.009$. Color yellow. Ref: 157, 528.

Europium ethyl sulfate octadecahydrate $[(C_2H_5 \cdot SO_4)_6Eu_2 \cdot 18H_2O]$ is hexagonal dipyramidal with $c/a = 0.5058$. Crystals varied with $\{10\bar{1}0\}$, $\{10\bar{1}1\}$, etc. Perfect $10\bar{1}0$ cleavage. D 1.909. Uniaxial negative with $N_O = 1.494$, $N_E = 1.484$, $N_O - N_E = 0.010$. Colorless. Ref: 157.

Gadolinium ethyl sulfate octadecahydrate $[(C_2H_5 \cdot SO_4)_6Gd_2 \cdot 18H_2O]$ is hexagonal dipyramidal with $c/a = 0.507$. Space group $C6_3/m$. *a* 13.93, *c* 7.06 Å. U.C. 2. Crystals varied with $\{10\bar{1}0\}$, $\{10\bar{1}1\}$, $\{11\bar{2}1\}$, etc. Perfect $10\bar{1}0$ cleavage. D 1.919. Uniaxial negative with $N_O = 1.490$, $N_E = 1.482$, $N_O - N_E = 0.008$. Colorless. Ref: 157, 528.

Dysprosium ethyl sulfate octadecahydrate $[(C_2H_5 \cdot SO_4)_6Dy_2 \cdot 18H_2O]$ is hexagonal dipyramidal with $c/a = 0.506$. Space group $C6_3/m$. *a* 13.91, *c* 7.04 Å. U.C. 2. Crystals show $\{10\bar{1}0\}$, $\{10\bar{1}1\}$, $\{11\bar{2}1\}$, etc. Perfect $10\bar{1}0$ cleavage. D 1.942. Uniaxial negative with $N_O = 1.495$, $N_E = 1.482$, $N_O - N_E = 0.013$. Colorless to pale yellow. Ref: 157, 528.

Erbium ethyl sulfate octadecahydrate $[(C_2H_5 \cdot SO_4)Er_2 \cdot 18H_2O]$ is hexagonal dipyramidal with $c/a = 0.5053$. Crystals show $\{10\bar{1}1\}$, $\{11\bar{2}1\}$, $\{10\bar{1}0\}$, $\{11\bar{2}0\}$, etc. Perfect $10\bar{1}0$ cleavage. D 1.948. Uniaxial negative with $N_O = 1.497$, $N_E = 1.486$, $N_O - N_E = 0.011$. Colorless to pink. Ref: 157.

Thulium ethyl sulfate octadecahydrate $[(C_2H_5 \cdot SO_4)_6Tm_2 \cdot 18H_2O]$ is hexagonal dipyramidal with $c/a = 0.5044$. Crystals short prisms with $\{10\bar{1}0\}$, $\{11\bar{2}1\}$, etc. Perfect $10\bar{1}0$ cleavage. D 2.001. Uniaxial negative with $N_O = 1.492$, $N_E = 1.486$, $N_O - N_E = 0.006$. Colorless. Ref: 157.

Ytterbium ethyl sulfate octadecahydrate $[(C_2H_5 \cdot SO_4)_6Yb_2 \cdot 18H_2O]$ is hexagonal dipyramidal with $c/a = 0.5079$. Crystals varied with $\{10\bar{1}0\}$, $\{11\bar{2}1\}$, $\{11\bar{2}0\}$, $\{10\bar{1}1\}$, etc. Perfect $10\bar{1}0$ cleavage. D 2.019. Uniaxial negative with $N_O = 1.494$, $N_E = 1.482$, $N_O - N_E = 0.012$. Colorless. Ref: 157.

1,1,1-Trichloroisopropyl alcohol or isopral $[CH_3CH(OH)CCl_3]$ is monoclinic. Crystals columnar; hygroscopic. M.P. 51°. Easily soluble in index liquids. $Z' \parallel$ length. $(-)2V = 74°$. N_Y and N_Z between 1.588 and 1.603. Ref: 123.

Diethylmethylsulfonium chloroplatinate $\{[(C_2H_5)_2CH_3SCl]_2PtCl_4\}$ is monoclinic with M.P. 210°. $N_X = 1.687$, $N_Y = 1.687$, $N_Z = 1.704$, $N_Z - N_X = 0.017$; $(+)2V = 0°$ *ca.* Ref: 152.

Triethylsulfonium chloroplatinate $\{[(C_2H_5)_3SCl]_2PtCl_4\}$ is monoclinic with $N_Y = 1.637$. Ref: 152.

bis (2-Chloroethyl)-selenide dichloride or β,β'-dichlorodiethyl selenide dichloride $[(CH_2Cl \cdot CH_2)_2SeCl_2]$ is monoclinic with $a{:}b{:}c = 0.635{:}1{:}0.839$, $\beta = 101°10'$. Crystals prisms with $\{110\}$, $\{001\}$, $\{111\}$. No observed cleavage. M.P. 122.5°. The optic plane and X are normal to 010; $Z \wedge c = +22°$. $(+)2H = 31°13'$ (in oil with $N = 1.65$), $r > v$ moderate. $N_X > 1.64$, $N_Y = 1.65$, $N_Z = 1.75$ calc., $N_Z - N_X < 0.11$. $\therefore 2V = 31°13'$. Ref: 200.

tert-Butyl ester of tetrathiosilicic acid or *tert*-butyl tetrathiosilicate $\{Si[SC(CH_3)_3]_4\}$ is tetragonal with $c/a = 0.84$. Crystals short $\{110\}$ prisms with $\{101\}$. D 1.09. Uniaxial positive with $N_O = 1.604$ Na, 1.607 (546), $N_E = 1.612$ Na, 1.615 (546), $N_E - N_O = 0.008$ Na. Ref: 194a.

tert-Butyl ester of tetrathiogermanic acid or *tert*-butyl tetrathiogermanate $\{Ge[SC(CH_3)_3]_4\}$ is tetragonal with $c/a = 0.83$. D 1.21. Uniaxial positive with $N_O = 1.622$, $N_E = 1.628$, $N_E - N_O = 0.006$ Na. Ref: 194a.

tert-Butyl ester of tetrathiostannic acid or *tert*-butyl tetrathiostannate $\{Sn[SC(CH_3)_3]_4\}$ is tetragonal with $c/a = 0.82$. D 1.34. Uniaxial positive with $N_O = 1.640$, $N_E = 1.643$, $N_E - N_O = 0.003$. Ref: 194a.

Tri-*tert*-butyl monoisopropyl tetrathiosilicate $\{(CH_3)_2CHS \cdot Si[SC(CH_3)_3]_3\}$ is tetragonal with $c/a = 0.85$. D 1.07. Uniaxial positive with $N_O = 1.589$, $N_E = 1.600$, $N_E - N_O = 0.011$ D. Ref: 194a.

Cetyl alcohol $\{CH_3(CH_2)_{14}CH_2OH\}$ forms flexible crystals (between 10° and 42°) which are uniaxial positive with (at 40°) $N_O = 1.470$, $N_E = 1.520$, $N_E - N_O = 0.050$, and (at 25.5°) $N_O = 1.4805$, $N_E = 1.5285$, $N_E - N_O = 0.048$. Ref: 611.

1,4-Dichloro-2,3-butanediol or dichloro-2,3-butylene glycol $[CH_2Cl \cdot (CHOH)_2 \cdot CH_2Cl]$ is trigonal with $c/a = 1.356$. Crystals resemble a combination of cube and dodecahedron. No observed cleavage. M.P. 126°. Uniaxial negative with $N_O = 1.5497$ Li, 1.5535 Na, 1.5568 Tl, $N_E = 1.5119$ Li, 1.5149 Na, 1.5175 Tl, $N_O - N_E = 0.0386$ Na. Ref: 117.

Sodium α-glycerophosphate tetrahydrate $(CH_2OHCHOHCH_2OPO_3Na_2 \cdot 4H_2O)$ is monoclinic in {100} plates with $a:b:c = 1.809:1:0.997$, $\beta = 99°30'$. Often twinned on 100. $N_Y = 1.471$. Colorless. Ref: 245a.

Sodium α-glycerophosphate hexahydrate $(CH_2OHCHOHCH_2OPO_3Na \cdot 6H_2O)$ forms monoclinic prisms with $a:b:c = 1.098:1:0.952$. $\beta = 106°15'$. D 1.634. The optic plane is 010. $(+)2V = 85°$. $N_X = 1.444$, $N_Y = 1.455$, $N_Z = 1.468$, $N_Z - N_X = 0.024$. Colorless. Ref: 245a.

Sodium α-glycerophosphate pentahydrate $(CH_2OHCHOHCH_2OPO_3Na_2 \cdot 5H_2O)$ is monoclinic sphenoidal with $a:b:c = 0.666:1:0.516$, $\beta = 106°50'$. D 1.718. $(-)2V = 79°$. $N_X = 1.474$, $N_Y = 1.489$, $N_Z = 1.499$, $N_Z - N_X = 0.025$. Colorless. Ref: 245a.

Magnesium tetracyanoplatinate glycerol pentahydrate $[MgPt(CH)_4 \cdot C_3H_8O_3 \cdot 5H_2O]$ is monoclinic with $a:b:c = 0.965:1:0.492$, $\beta = 94°4'$. Crystals acicular with {110}, {001}, {100}, {010}, etc. Good 001 cleavage. The optic plane is normal to 010 in red light and parallel thereto in yellow to blue light; $Z = b$; $X \wedge c = -28°$ Li, $-30°6'$ Na, $-34°30'$ Tl, $-46°30'$ F. $(-)2V = 0°$ red, 17°39′ Na, 34°10′ Tl, 59°53′ blue. Horizontal dispersion in red light and strong inclined dispersion in yellow to blue light. $N_Y = 1.584$ Na, 1.589 Tl, 1.598 blue. Ref: 280.

dl-1,2,3,4-Butanetetrol or *dl*-erythritol $[CH_2OH \cdot (CHOH)_2 \cdot CH_2OH]$ is tetragonal dipyramidal with $c/a = 0.376$; space group $I4_1/a$; *a* 12.76, *c* 6.83 Å. U.C. 8. Crystals equant with {100}, {111}, {131}, etc. No distinct cleavage. D 1.45. Uniaxial negative with $N_O = 1.5419$ Li, 1.5444 Na, 1.5495 blue, $N_E = 1.5184$ Li, 1.5210 Na, 1.5266 blue, $N_O - N_E = 0.0234$. Ref: 117, 428.

Tetrakis(hydroxymethyl)methane or 2,2-*bis*(hydroxymethyl)-1,3-propanediol or tetrahydroxyneopentane or pentaerythritol or 2,2-dimethylol-1,3-propanediol [$C(CH_2 \cdot OH)_4$] is tetragonal disphenoidal with $c/a = 1.43$. Space group $I\bar{4}$; *a* 6.10, *c* 8.73 Å. U.C. 2. Crystals short prismatic with {110}, {100}, {11$\bar{1}$}, {001}, etc. Perfect 001 and distinct 100 and 110 cleavages. Inverts to another phase at 192° and melts at 253°. D 1.39. Uniaxial negative with $N_O = 1.5588$, $N_E = 1.5480$ Na, $N_O - N_E = 0.0108$; also $N_O = 1.554$ (668), 1.5562 D, 1.562 (502), $N_E = 1.513$ (668), 1.5154 D, 1.521 (502), $N_O - N_E = 0.0408$ D. Again: $N_O = 1.539$, $N_E = 1.511$, $N_O - N_E = 0.028$. For $\lambda = 5461$: $N_O = 1.560$, $N_E = 1.519$, $N_O - N_E = 0{,}041$. Often shows optic anomalies with variable optic angle and position of the optic plane. Ref: 117, 235, 316, 356, 541, 544, 556a.

Tetrahydroxyneopentane tetra-acetate or pentaerythritol tetra-acetate [$C(CH_2 \cdot O \cdot CO \cdot CH_3)_4$] is tetragonal with $c/a = 0.459$. Space group $P4_2/n$. *a* 12.00, *c* 5.50 Å. U.C. 2. Crystals show {100} and {111}. Perfect 001 cleavage. M.P. 84°. D 1.213. Uniaxial positive with $N_O = 1.433$, $N_E = 1.483$, $N_E - N_O = 0.050$. Again for $\lambda = 5461$: $N_O = 1.471$, $N_E = 1.483$, $N_E - N_O = 0.012$.
Ref: 198, 471, 556a.

Tetrahydroxyneopentane tetranitrate or pentaerythritol tetranitrate [$C(CH_2 \cdot O \cdot NO_2)_4$] is tetragonal scalenohedral with $c/a = 0.713$. Space group $P\bar{4}2_1/c$. *a* 9.45, *c* 6.74 Å. U.C. 2. Crystals show {110} and {101}. Imperfect 110 cleavage. D 1.773. Uniaxial negative with $N_O = 1.554$, $N_E = 1.553$, $N_O - N_E = 0.001$.
Ref: 198, 466.

Tetrakis (*tert*-butylmercaptomethyl) methane or pentaerythritol tetra-*tert*-butyl thioether {$C[CH_2 \cdot SC(CH_3)_3]_4$} has two crystal phases. Phase I is monoclinic with $a:b:c = 1.7373:1:1.605$, $\beta = 99°42'$. Crystals show {001}, {111}, {1$\bar{1}$1}, {100}, etc. D 1.038. Perfect 001 cleavage. The crystals are pseudorhombohedral and sensibly uniaxial and negative with $N_O = 1.5586$ D, $N_E = 1.5455$, $N_O - N_E = 0.0131$. Phase II is trigonal with $c/a = 1.375$. Crystals {0001} plates with {10$\bar{1}$1}, etc. D 1.033. Uniaxial positive with $N_O = 1.5497$ D, $N_E = 1.5571$, $N_E - N_O = 0.0074$. [α] = 61°14′. Ref: 17.

2,2,5,5-Tetrahydroxymethylcyclopentanone $\left\{OC\begin{matrix} C(CH_2OH)_2\text{–}CH_2 \\ C(CH_2OH)_2\text{–}CH_2 \end{matrix}\right\}$ is orthorhombic with $a:b:c = 0.687:1:1.328$. Crystals pyramidal or tabular. Basal cleavage. $Y = b$, $Z = c$. (+)2E = 46°10′, $N_X = 1.528$, $N_Y = 1.545$, $N_Z = 1.647$ calc. $N_Z - N_X = 0.117$ calc. 2V = 29°20′ calc. Ref: 568a.

Adonitol [$CH_2OH \cdot (CHOH)_3 \cdot CH_2OH$] fuses at 102°; it has parallel extinction and negative elongation with $N_1 = 1.54$, $N_2 = 1.545$, $N_2 - N_1 = 0.005$.
Ref: 34.

l-Rhamnitol trihydrate ($C_6H_{14}O_5 \cdot 3H_2O$) is orthorhombic disphenoidal with $a:b:c = 0.995:1:1.175$. Crystals {001} tablets or elongated along *a* with {001}, {021}, {001}, {101}, {100}, etc. No cleavage observed. M.P. 69°. The optic plane is 100; X = *c*. (-)2V = 52.5° Na, r < v distinct. $N_X = 1.442$ Na, $N_Y = 1.492$, $N_Z = 1.505$ calc., $N_Z - N_X = 0.063$. The *d*-form has the same indices. Ref: 262.

Sorbitol ($C_6H_{14}O_6$) has parallel extinction and positive elongation with $N_1 = 1.51$, $N_2 = 1.54$, $N_2 - N_1 = 0.03$. Ref: 34.

Xylitol ($C_5H_{12}O_5$) is known in two phases. The metastable phase (I) melts at 61 - 65° C. It forms lath shaped colorless crystals resembling gypsum. It is monoclinic with (+)2V = 32° ± 5°, r > v weak. $N_X = 1.519$, $N_Y = 1.521$, $N_Z = 1.548$, $N_Z - N_X = 0.029$. The stable phase (II) melts at 93 - 94.5°. It forms colorless tablets with symmetrical pointed ends. It is orthorhombic with (+)2V = 38° ± 5°, r < v weak. $N_X = 1.549$, $N_Y = 1.551$, $N_Z = 1.566$, $N_Z - N_X = 0.017$. Ref: 430.

d-Mannitol [$CH_2OH \cdot (CHOH)_4 \cdot CH_2OH$] is orthorhombic disphenoidal with *a*:*b*:*c* = 0.511:1:0.329. Space group $P2_12_12_1$; *a* 8.65, *b* 16.90, *c* 5.56 Å. U.C. 4. Crystals {010} tablets with {110}, {011}, etc. Perfect 010 and good 100 cleavages. D 1.497. M.P. 166°. The optic plane is 100; X = *b*. (-)2V = 60° calc., r > v weak. $N_X = 1.532$, $N_Y = 1,545$ calc. $N_Z = 1.550$, $N_Z - N_X = 0,018$. Measures by J. J. Marais gave: (-) 2 V = 44°, $N_X = 1.5175$, $N_Y = 1.5530$, $N_Z = 1.5592$, $N_Z - N_X = 0.0417$, but large crystals (apparently mannitol) from an alderberry wine cask gave: (+)2V = 85°, $N_X = 1.5482$, $N_Y = 1.5512$, $N_Z = 1.5550$, $N_Z - N_X = 0.0068$, suggesting that impurities produce marked changes in the indices (especially N_X), the birefringence, the optic angle, and the optic sign. (α) = - 0.49° (in water), + 28.3° (in borax solution). A second phase is known. Ref: 117, 239, 545, 551.

Dulcitol or melampyrin [$CH_2OH \cdot (CHOH)_4 \cdot CH_2OH$] is monoclinic prismatic with *a*:*b*:*c* = 0.737:1:0.774, β = 113°45′. Space group $P2_1/c$; *a* 8.61, *b* 11.60, *c* 9.05 Å. U.C. 4. Crystals prisms with {110}, {111}, {00$\bar{1}$}, {021}, etc. Perfect 021 cleavage. M.P. 188°. The optic plane and X are normal to 010; Z ∧ *c* = - 77°8′ red, - 77°2′ yellow, - 76°50′ blue. (-)2E = 151°10′ red, 150°0′ blue. $N_1 = 1.535$, $N_2 = 1.545$, $N_2 - N_1 = 0.010$. Ref: 34, 117.

D-α-Guloheptitol [$CH_2OH(CHOH)_5CH_2OH$] forms grains apparently with inclined extinction and negative elongation. D 1.560. M.P. 140°. (+)2V = 75° *ca*. $N_X = 1.554$, $N_Y = 1.560$, $N_Z = 1.570$, all ± 0.003, $N_Z - N_X = 0.016$. Ref: 215, 355.

D-β-Guloheptitol [$CH_2OH(CHOH)_5CH_2OH$] forms pointed rods with inclined extinction and ± elongation. D 1.585. M.P. 128°. (+)2V = 60° *ca*. $N_X = 1.565$, $N_Y = 1.570$, $N_Z = 1.586$, all ± 0.002, $N_Z - N_X = 0.021$. Ref: 215, 355.

D-α-Glucoheptitol [$CH_2OH \cdot (CHOH)_6CH_2OH$] forms pointed rods with extinction at 40° and ± elongation. D 1.520. M.P. 128°. (+) 2 E = large, 2V = 53° calc. $N_X = 1.548$, $N_Y = 1.550$, $N_Z = 1.558$, all ± 0.003, $N_Z - N_X =$ = 0.010. Ref: 85, 355.

D-β-Glucoheptitol [$CH_2OH \cdot (CHOH)_5CH_2OH$] forms plates and rods with parallel extinction and positive elongation. D 1.510. M.P. 128° - 129°. (-)2V = 50° *ca.* $N_X = 1.542$, $N_Y = 1.550$, $N_Z = 1.552$, all ± 0.003, $N_Z - N_X = 0.010$.
Ref: 270, 355.

D-α-Mannoheptitol [$CH_2OH \cdot (CHOH)_5CH_2OH$] forms minute needles with parallel extinction and negative elongation. D 1.485. M.P. 180°. (-)2V = large. $N_X = 1.538$, $N_Y = 1.545$, $N_Z = 1.549$, all ± 0.005, $N_Z - N_X = 0.011$.
Ref: 234, 355.

D-β-Mannoheptitol [$CH_2OH \cdot (CHOH)_5CH_2OH$] forms needles in radial groups. Parallel extinction and positive elongation. D 1.470. M.P. 125°. $N_X = 1.533$, $N_Y = 1.54$ *ca.*, $N_Z = 1.545$, all ± 0.005, $N_Z - N_X = 0.012$.
Ref: 274, 355.

D-α-Sedoheptitol [$CH_2OH \cdot (CHOH)_5CH_2OH$] forms rods and needles with parallel extinction and positive elongation. D 1.520. M.P. 151°. (+) 2 V = 80° *ca.* $N_X = 1.550$, $N_Y = 1.555$, $N_Z = 1.562$, all ± 0.003, $N_Z - N_X = 0.012$.
Ref: 216, 355.

D-β-Sedoheptitol [$CH_2OH \cdot (CHOH)_5CH_2OH$] forms plates and rods with 120° angles, parallel extinction, and negative elongation. D 1.590. M.P. 128°. (+) 2V = 65° *ca.* $N_X = 1.564$, $N_Y = 1.570$, $N_Z = 1.584$, all ± 0.002, $N_Z - N_X = 0.020$.
Ref: 216, 355.

Hexamethylenetetramine or hexamine or urotropine or methenamine ($C_6H_{12}N_4$) is isometric hextetrahedral. Space group $I\bar{4}3m$; *a* 7.02 Å. U.C. 2. Crystals are dodecahedrons, often tabular, with no distinct cleavage. D 1.339. Isotropic with N = 1.5856 (667.6), 1.5893 (587.6). Ref: 119, 138, 423.

Class 3. Carbonyl Compounds

2,2-*bis*(Ethylsulfonyl)propane or diethylsulfon-dimethylmethane or sulfomethane or sulfonal [$(CH_3)_2{:}C{:}(SO_2 \cdot C_2H_5)_2$] is monoclinic in prisms. Tabular crystals form from chloroform. M.P. 124° - 126°. $N_X = 1.518$, $N_Y = 1.541$, $N_Z = 1.572$, $N_Z - N_X = 0.054$. ∴ (+)2V = 80° calc. Colorless.
Ref: 239, 343c, 524.

2,2-*bis*(Ethylsulfonyl)butane or 2-butanone diethyl sulfone or sulfonethylmethane or trional [$CH_3 \cdot C \cdot (SO_2 \cdot C_2H_5)_2 \cdot C_2H_5$] is monoclinic in lamellar or platy crystals, nearly tetragonal, with symmetrical extinction. Easily soluble in alcohol or ether. M.P. 76° - 77°. $N_X = 1.504$, $N_Y = ?$, $N_Z = 1.549$, $N_Z - N_X = 0.045$. Again: $N_1 = 1.509$, $N_2 = 1.56$, $N_2 - N_1 = 0.051$.
Ref: 239, 524.

3,3-*bis*(Ethylsulfonyl)pentane or 3-pentanone diethyl sulfone or tetronal [$(C_2H_5)_2{:}C{:}(SO_2 \cdot C_2H_5)_2$] forms slightly elongated rectangular or six-sided plates. M.P. 85°. $N_1 = 1.501$, $N_2 = 1.55$, $N_2 - N_1 = 0.049$. Ref: 239.

Metaldehyde or meta-acetaldehyde $[(CH_3 \cdot CHO)_4]$ is tetragonal with $c/a = 0.381$. Spaces group probably $I4mm$; a 10.34, c 4.10 Å. U.C. 8. Crystals acicular with perfect 110 cleavage. Sublimes with partial decomposition at $112° - 116°$. Uniaxial negative with $N_O = 1.530$, $N_E = 1.430$, $N_O - N_E = 0.100$.
Ref: 117, 152, 481.

Chloral hydrate $[CH(OH)_2 \cdot CCl_3]$ is monoclinic prismatic with $a:b:c =$ $= 1.915:1:1.589$, $\beta = 120°7'$. Space group $P2/c$; a 11.57, b 6.04, c 9.60 Å. U.C. 4. Crystals plates with perfect 001 cleavage. D 1.90. M.P. 51.7°. The optic plane is 010; $X \wedge c = -59°$. $(-)2V = 20°50'$. $N_X = 1.5383$, $N_Y = 1.5995$, $N_Z = 1.6017$, $N_Z - N_X = 0.0634$ Na.
Ref: 117, 453.

Bromal hydrate monohydrate $[CBr_3 \cdot CH(OH)_2 \cdot H_2O]$ is monoclinic with $a:b:c = 1.786:1:1.305$, $\beta = 121°32'$. Crystals show {100}, {001}, {101}, {011}. Easily loses H_2O. Very soluble in H_2O. M.P. $50° - 52°$. The optic plane and Z are normal to 010; X somewhat inclined to a normal to 100 toward $10\bar{1}$. $(-)2V =$ rather large. Bolland gives for bromal-hydrate (with or without H_2O ?): $N_1 = 1.66$, $N_2 = 1.69$, $N_2 - N_1 = 0.03$.
Ref: 34, 117.

2-Propanone oxime or 2-oximinopropane or acetoxime or acetone oxime $[(CH_3)_2 \cdot C:NOH]$ melts at $59° - 60°$. D 0.97. The mean index of refraction is 1.4156.
Ref: 152.

Copper dimethylglyoxime is monoclinic with $a:b:c = 0.573:1:0.824$, $\beta = 107°6'$. $Z = b$; $X \wedge c = 24°$, $N_X = 1.498$, $N_Y = 1.764$, $N_Z = 1.81$, $N_Z - N_X = 0.392$. $\therefore (-)2V = 40°$ calc. Pleochroic with X = clear violet, Y = brown, Z = dark brown.

$$\begin{bmatrix} CH_3 \cdot C:N \cdot O & O-N:C \cdot CH_3 \\ & \diagdown \diagup \\ & Cu \\ & \diagup \diagdown \\ CH_3 \cdot C:N & N:C \cdot CH_3 \end{bmatrix}$$

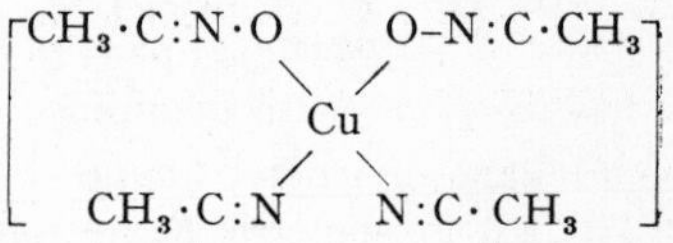

Ref: 588d.

Copper dimethylglyoxime dichloride is triclinic pinacoidal with $a:b:c = 0.983:1:0.931$, $\alpha = 100°23'$, $\beta = 109°42'$, $Y = 109°18'$. Space group $P1$; a 7.96, b 8.10, c 7.54 Å. U.C. 2. Crystals are {010} tablets often elongated along c. D 1.98. Soluble in chloroform

$$\begin{bmatrix} & & OH \\ CH_3 \cdot C:N & \diagup & Cl \\ & \diagdown & \diagup \\ & Cu \\ CH_3 \cdot C:N & \diagup & Cl \\ & & OH \end{bmatrix}$$

and benzene; decomposed by water. $N_Z - N_X =$ very strong. Minimum index in 010 is 1.57 (for $\lambda = 546.1$) and is found at 29° to a in the obtuse angle β. Strong absorption for Z of deep green color.
Ref: 62, 440.

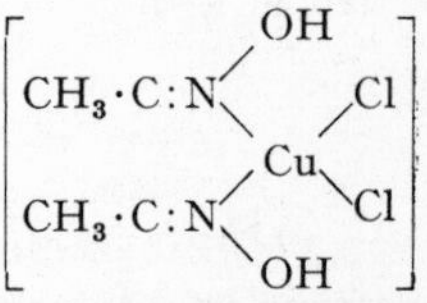

Iridium dichloro(dimethylglyoximic)acid is monoclinic. $(+)2V = 82°$ calc. $N_X = 1.707$, $N_Y = 1.734$, $N_Z = 1.768$, $N_Z - N_X = 0.061$. Extinction angle is 20°. X = yellow, Z = orange.

$$\begin{bmatrix} H \begin{bmatrix} Ir \begin{bmatrix} CH_3C = NO \\ CH_3C = NOH \end{bmatrix}_2 Cl_2 \end{bmatrix} \end{bmatrix}$$

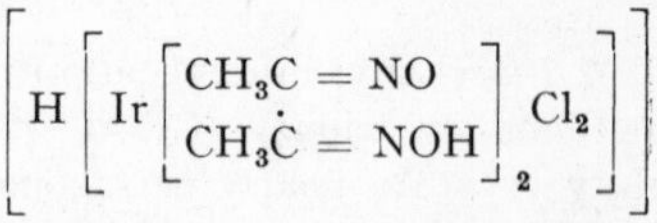

Ref: 418a.

Cupric salt of 2,4-pentanedione or cupric acetylacetonate $[C_5H_7O_2)_2Cu]$ is monoclinic prismatic with $a:b:c = 2.402:1:2.188$, $\beta = 92°0'$. Space group $P2_1/m$; a 11.24, b 4.68, c 10.24 Å. U.C. 2. Crystals elongated along b with {100}, {101}, {10$\bar{1}$}. D 1.57. The optic plane and X are normal to 010. $N_X = 1.59$, $N_Y = ?$, $N_Z \geqslant 1.69$, $N_Z - N_X \geqslant 0.10$. Color blue.
Ref: 64.

Lauron $\{CH_3(CH_2)_{10}CO(CH_2)_{10}CH_3\}$ forms radiating fibrous crystalline masses with (at 41°) $N_1 = 1.508$, $N_2 = 1.555$, $N_2 - N_1 = 0.047$. Ref: 611.

3-Hydroxy-3-methyl-2-butanone oxime nitrate or 3-oximino-2-methyl-*sec*-butyl nitrate or amylene nitrosate $[(CH_3)_2 \cdot C(NO_3) \cdot C(:N \cdot OH) \cdot CH_3]$ is monoclinic with $a:b:c = 0.977:1:1.449$, $\beta = 96°28'$. Crystals short prismatic with {110}, {001}, {011}. Imperfect 100 cleavage. M.P. 96° - 97°. The optic plane and X are normal to 010, Z ∧ c = - 7° *ca.* (-)2V = 64°32′ Li, 62°55′ Na, $N_Y = 1.4985$ Li, 1.5088 Na. (Measurements were probably on the oximino form, but the nitroso form is possible). Ref: 117.

Dihydroxyacetone $(HO \cdot CH_2 \cdot CO \cdot CH_2 \cdot OH)$ is monoclinic or triclinic. Crystals flat plates with rhomboidal outline. M.P. 82°. Plates normal to X have Z ∧ elongation = 4°. Plates normal to Z have Y ∧ elongation = 5°. (-) 2 V = 21°, r < v. $N_X = 1.450$, $N_Y = 1.575$, $N_Z = 1.581$, $N_Z - N_X = 0.131$ (for $\lambda = 5461$). Ref: 556a.

Class 4. Carboxylic acids

Subclass A. Monocarboxylic Acids and Derivatives

Salts of Methanoic or Formic Acid

Sodium formate (CO_2HNa) is monoclinic prismatic with $a:b:c = 0.921:1:0.966$, $\beta = 121°42'$. Space group $C2/c$. U.C. 4. D 1.909. Flat plates and compact prisms with common twinning. M.P. 253°. $N_1 = 1.378$, $N_2 = 1.462$, $N_3 = 1.537$, $N_3 - N_1 = 0.159$. Again: (+)2V = 89° *ca.*, $N_X = 1.370$, $N_Y = 1.460$, $N_Z = 1.563$, $N_Z - N_X = 0.193$ for $\lambda = 5461$. Ref: 556a, 598, 630.

Calcium formate $[(HCO_2)_2Ca]$ is orthorhombic dipyramidal with $a:b:c = 0.760:1:0.468$. Space group $Pcab$: a 10.163, b 13.381, c 6.271 Å. U.C. 8. Crystals pyramidal or {010} tablets with pyramids or prisms and pyramids. D 2.02. No distinct cleavage. The optic plane is 010; Z = a. For B: (+)2V = 26°30′, $N_X = 1.5067$, $N_Y = 1.5100$, $N_Z = 1.5731$; for D: (+)2V = 26°47′, $N_X = 1.5100$, $N_Y = 1.5135$, $N_Z = 1.5775$, $N_Z - N_X = 0.0675$; for E: (+)2V = 26°49′, $N_X = 1.5132$, $N_Y = 1.5167$, $N_Z = 1.5819$. Ref: 117, 560b.

Strontium formate $[(HCO_2)_2Sr]$ is orthorhombic sphenoidal with $a:b:c = 0.785:1:0.829$. Space group $P2_12_12_1$; a 6.86, b 8.73, c 7.25 kX. Crystals short prismatic or {010} tablets with imperfect 011 cleavage. D 2.69. The optic plane is 100; Z = b.

(+)2V	N_X	N_Y	N_Z	$N_Z - N_X$	Author
74°50′	1.5549	1.5712	1.5943	0.0394 Li	Plathan
74°14′	1.5586	1.5743	1.5980	0.0394 Na	Plathan
73°25′	1.5601	1.5800	1.6048	0.0447 Tl	Plathan
73°	1.543	1.552	1.574	0.031 D	Ashton

Ref: 7, 117, 560c.

Barium formate $[(HCO_2)_2Ba]$ is orthorhombic sphenoidal with $a:b:c$ = 0.765:1:0.864. Crystals short prismatic with {110}, {101}, {011}, etc., with distinct 011 cleavage. D 3.24. The optic plane is 010; Z = *a*.

(+)2V	N_X	N_Y	N_Z	$N_Z - N_X$	Author
71°51′	1.5679	1.5918	1.6310	0.0631 B	Schrauf
76°	1.567	1.587	1.627	0.060 D	Ashton
77°54′	1.5729	1.5970	1.6361	0.0632 D	Schrauf
78°32′	1.5777	1.6024	1.6412	0.0635 E	Schrauf

Ref: 7, 117, 290.

Cadmium formate $[(HCO_2)_2Cd]$ is orthorhombic; crystals show {010}, {111}, {110}, {100}. The optic plane is 100. Z = *b*. (+)2V = 26°. N_X = 1.588, N_Y = 1.607, N_Z = 1.685, $N_Z - N_X$ = 0.097 Na. Ref: 7.

Lead formate $[(HCO_2)_2Pb]$ is orthorhombic disphenoidal with $a:b:c$ = 0.746:1:0.848. Space group $P2_12_12_1$; *a* 6.50, *b* 8.75, *c* 7.50 Å. U.C. 4. Crystals prismatic with {110}, {010}, {011}, etc. Very poor 011 cleavage. D 4.63. The optic plane is 010; X = *c*.

(–)2V	N_X	N_Y	N_Z	$N_Z - N_X$	Author
71°28′	1.7806	1.8448	1.8809 calc.	0.1003 Li	Plathan
70°34′	1.7889	1.8545	1.8901 calc.	0.1012 Na	Plathan
69°50′	1.7905	1.8670	1.9018 calc.	0.1113 Tl	Plathan
	1.789	1.852	1.877	0.088 D	Int. Crit. T.

Ref: 117, 152, 478.

Gadolinium formate $[(HCO_2)_3Gd]$ is rhombohedral with c/a = 0.375. Crystals prismatic with $\{11\bar{2}0\}$, $\{10\bar{1}1\}$, $\{02\bar{2}1\}$. D 3.8. Uniaxial negative with N_O = 1.7379 D, 1.7497 F, N_E = 1.7091 D, 1.7194 F, $N_O - N_E$ = 0.0288 D. Ref: 266.

Lithium formate monohydrate $(HCO_2Li \cdot H_2O)$ is orthorhombic with $a:b:c$ = 0.651:1:0.485. Crystals show {010}, {110}, {021}, {111}, etc. D 1.44 – 1.48. The optic plane is 010; X = *a*. (–) 2 V = ?. N_1 = 1.47, N_2 = 1.54, $N_2 - N_1$ = 0.07. Plates are {010}, therefore N_X = 1.47, N_Y > 1.505, N_Z = 1.54, $N_Z - N_X$ = 0.07. Ref: 34, 35, 117.

Copper formate dihydrate $[(HCO_2)_2Cu \cdot 2H_2O]$ is monoclinic prismatic with $a:b:c$ = 1.330:1:1.225, β = 96°38′. Space group $P2_1/c$; *a* 8.952, *b* 6.726, *c* 8.235 Å. U.C. 4. Crystals {001} tablets with {110}, {201}, {100}, etc. Perfect 100 and imperfect 010 cleavages. Parallel extinction and negative elongation with N_1 = 1.54, N_2 = 1.55, $N_2 - N_1$ = 0.01 for "copper formate" (with $2H_2O$?). Ref: 34, 35, 117, 570.

Zinc formate dihydrate [$(HCO_2)_2Zn \cdot 2H_2O$] is monoclinic with $a:b:c$ = 1.307:1:1.221, β = 97°19′. Crystals equant or elongated along b with {110}, {001}, {20$\bar{1}$}, {11$\bar{1}$}, etc. D 2.3. (+)2V = 38°, N_X = 1.513, N_Y = 1.526, N_Z = 1.566, $N_Z - N_X$ = 0.043 Na. The optic plane is probably 010.
Ref: 7, 117.

Magnesium formate dihydrate [$(HCO_2)_2Mg \cdot 2H_2O$] is monoclinic in crystals similar to those of zinc formate dihydrate. An optic axis is inclined 6° to the normal to a pinacoid (001 ?). (+)2V = 42°, r > v. N_X = 1.468, N_Y = 1.476, N_Z = 1.518, $N_Z - N_X$ = 0.050 Na.
Ref: 7.

Strontium formate dihydrate [$(HCO_2)_2Sr \cdot 2H_2O$] is orthorhombic disphenoidal with $a:b:c$ = 0.609:1:0.594. Crystals short prismatic with {110}, {010}, {011}, etc. D 2.25. Cleavage on 010 and 011 in traces. Loses $2H_2O$ at 72°, The optic plane is 010; X = c. For B: (-)2V = 66°36′, N_X = 1.4806. N_Y = 1.5174, N_Z = 1.5342; for D: (-) 2 V = 66°59′, N_X = 1.4838, N_Y= 1.5210, N_Z = 1.5382, $N_Z - N_X$ = 0.0544; for E: (-) 2 V = 67°24′, N_X = 1.4869, N_Y = 1.5244, N_Z = 1.5420. Also (-)2V = 65°, N_X = 1.484, N_Y = 1.518, N_Z = 1.537, $N_Z - N_X$ = 0.053 D.
Ref: 7, 117.

Cadmium formate dihydrate [$(HCO_2)_2Cd \cdot 2H_2O$] is monoclinic with $a:b:c$ = 1.325:1:1.225, β = 97°19′. Crystals equant or {001} tablets with {110}, {11$\bar{1}$}, {20$\bar{1}$}, {111}, etc. D 2.43. The optic plane is 010; an optic axis is inclined 16° to the normal to a pinacoid (001 ?) and a bisectrix is at 26.5°. (+) 2 V = 40°. N_X = 1.496, N_Y = 1.506, N_Z = 1.547, $N_Z - N_X$ = 0.051 Na.
Ref: 7, 117.

Barium cadmium formate dihydrate [$(HCO_2)_4BaCd \cdot 2H_2O$] is monoclinic with $a:b:c$ = 0.898:1:0.540, β = 90°28′. Crystals prismatic with {010}, {110}, {011}, etc. Perfect 010 cleavage. The optic plane and X are normal to 010; Z $\wedge$ c = + 46°23′. (+)2V = 66°51′ red, N_Y = 1.518 red; (+)2V = 67°36′ Na, N_Y = 1.5325 Na.
Ref: 117.

Copper formate tetrahydrate [$(HCO_2)_2Cu \cdot 4H_2O$] is monoclinic prismatic with $a:b:c$ = 1.004:1:0.774, β = 101°5′. Space group $C2m$; a 8.156, b 8.128, c 6.29 Å. U.C. 2. Crystals vermicular with {001}, {110}, {111}, etc. Twinning common on 001. Perfect 001 cleavage. D 1.83. The optic plane is 010; X $\wedge$ c = - 23°35′. (-)2V = 34°54′. N_X = 1.4133, N_Y = 1.5423, N_Z = 1.5571, $N_Z - N_X$ = 0.1438 for D. (-)2V = 34°40′. N_Y = 1.5483 for Tl.
Ref: 117.

Strontium copper formate octahydrate [$(HCO_2)_6CuSr_2 \cdot 8H_2O$] is triclinic with $a:b:c$ = 0.744:1:1.010, α = 104°44′, β = 95°52′, Y = 88°18′. Crystals {010} tablets with {100}, {001}, {110}, etc. Perfect 010 and distinct 100 cleavages. N_X = 1.500, N_Y = 1.520, N_Z = 1.580, $N_Z - N_X$ = 0.080, ∴ (+)2V = 60° *ca.*
Ref: 7, 117.

Scandium basic formate monohydrate [$(HCO_2)_2ScOH \cdot H_2O$] is monoclinic with $a:b:c$ = 1.376:1:1.455, β = 105°38′. Crystals equant with {001}, {111}, {11$\bar{1}$}, {100}, {011}. D 1.946. The optic plane is 010; X $\wedge$ c = - 1°. (-)2V > 67°. N_X < 1.507, N_Y = 1.573, N_Z > 1.607, $N_Z - N_X$ > 0.10.
Ref: 167.

Salts of Ethanoic or Acetic Acid

Sodium acid acetate ($CH_3CO_2Na \cdot CH_3CO_2H$) is isometric. Crystals cubic with {211}. Isotropic with N = 1.457. Ref: 152.

Ammonium uranyl acetate [$(CH_3CO_2)_3NH_4UO_2$] is tetragonal trapezohedral with $c/a = 2.001$. Space group $I4_1/2$; *a* 13.79, *c* 27.60 Å. U.C. 16. Crystals prismatic with {100}, {101}, {103}, etc. Cleavage on 110. Uniaxial positive with $N_O = 1.4754$ B, 1.4808 D, 1.4862 E, $N_E = 1.4877$ B, 1.4933 D, 1.4987 E, $N_E - N_O = 0.0125$ D. Color yellow with O > E; green fluorescence. Ref: 117.

Sodium uranyl acetate [$(CH_3CO_2)_3NaUO_2$] is isometric tetartoidal. Space group $P2_1/3$; *a* 10.69 Å. U.C. 4. Crystals tetrahedral or dodecahedral. Twinning on 111, 211, and 110. D 2.56. Isotropic with N = 1.5014. Also anisotropic. Color yellow with green fluorescence. Ref: 117.

Calcium acetate [$(CH_3CO_2)_2Ca$] is biaxial with $N_X = 1.55$, $N_Y = 1.56$, $N_Z = 1.57$, $N_Z - N_X = 0.02$. Ref: 152.

Copper acetate monohydrate [$(CH_3CO_2)_2Cu \cdot H_2O$] is monoclinic with $a:b:c = 1.532:1:0.811$, $\beta = 116°26'$. Crystals {110} tablets with {001}, {100}, {$20\bar{1}$}, etc. Perfect 001 and distinct 110 cleavages. D 1.88. M.P. 115°. Extinction is at 20°. Strongly pleochroic from clear green to dark blue. Copper acetate pentahydrate [$(CH_3COO)_2Cu \cdot 5H_2O$] is orthorhombic with $a:b:c = 0.631:1:0.579$. Crystals show {110}, {011}, {101}, {001}. Bolland gives for "copper acetate" (H_2O or $5H_2O$?): parallel extinction and negative elongation with $N_1 = 1.545$, $N_2 = 1.55$, $N_2 - N_1 = 0.005$. Ref: 34, 35, 117, 206.

Barium acetate monohydrate [$(C_2H_3O_2)_2Ba \cdot H_2O$] is triclinic with $a:b:c = 0.939:1:0.652$, $\alpha = 74°36'$, $\beta = 107°31'$, Y = 109°40′. Crystals prismatic with perfect 100 cleavage. D 3.19. The optic plane makes an angle of 60° in 100 with *c* in acute α and 50° in 010 with *c* in acute β. (-)2V = 70°, calc. $N_X = 1.500$, $N_Y = 1.517$, $N_Z = 1.525$, $N_Z - N_X = 0.025$. Colorless. Ref: 117.

Lithium acetate dihydrate ($CH_3CO_2Li \cdot 2H_2O$) is orthorhombic with $a:b:c = 0.620:1:?$. Crystals {110} prisms with {100}, {001}. Twinning common on 110. Perfect 110 cleavage. The optic plane is 010; X = *a*. (-)2E = 134°18′ red, 137°24′ green. $N_1 = 1.40$, $N_2 = 1.50$, $N_2 - N_1 = 0.10$. Ref: 34, 35, 117.

Zinc acetate dihydrate [$(C_2H_3O_2)_2Zn \cdot 2H_2O$] is monoclinic with $a:b:c = 2.73:1:2.05$, $\beta = 99°36'$. *a* 14.53, *b* 5.33, c 10.91 Å. U.C. 4. Crystals {100} tablets and rods along *b*. Twinning on 100. M.P. just below 100°. D 1.74. Y = *b*; $Z \wedge c = 13°$ in acute β. (+)2V = 87°, r > v. $N_X = 1.432$, $N_Y = 1.492$, $N_Z = 1.553$, $N_Z - N_X = 0.121$. Ref: 553a.

Uranyl acetate dihydrate [$(CH_3CO_2)_2UO_2 \cdot 2H_2O$] is orthorhombic with $a:b:c = 0.782:1:0.355$. Crystals show {110}, {100}, {101}, etc. Perfect 120 and good 110, 100, and 010 cleavages. For vibrations along *b*, N = 1.521; for vibrations along *c*, N = 1.490 Na. For "uranacetate" (with no H_2O ?)

Bolland gives: parallel extinction and positive elongation with $N_1 = 1.545$, $N_2 = 1.63$, $N_2 - N_1 = 0.085$. Also: $N_1 = 1.53$, $N_2 = 1.64$, $N_2 - N_1 = 0.11$. Color greenish yellow with distinct pleochroism. Ref: 34, 35, 117, 259.

Sodium acetate trihydrate ($CH_3CO_2Na \cdot 3H_2O$) is monoclinic with $a{:}b{:}c = 1.181{:}1{:}0.996$, $\beta = 111°43'$. Crystals short prismatic or {101} plates with 110 and 001 cleavages. Fig. 4. D 1.45. The optic plane and Z are normal to 010; $X \wedge c = +55°$ *ca.* (-)2V = 62°50', $N_Y = 1.464$. Also $N_X = 1.4164$, $N_Y = 1.4630$, $N_Z = 1.4817$, $N_Z - N_X = 0.0653$ Na. Ref: 117, 393.

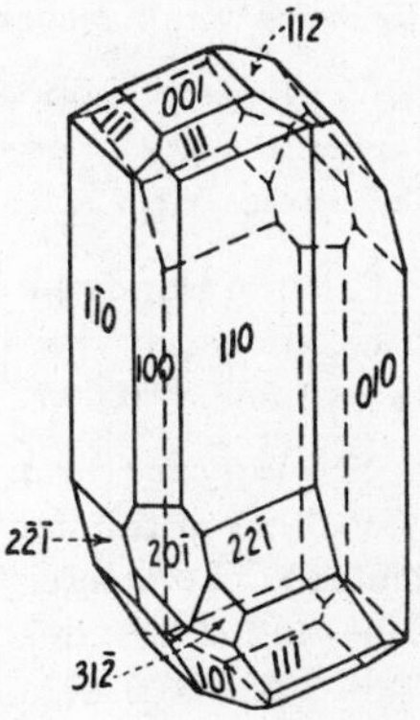

Fig. 4. Sodium acetate trihydrate.

Barium acetate trihydrate [$(CH_3CO_2)_2Ba \cdot 3H_2O$] is monoclinic with $a{:}b{:}c = 2.136{:}1{:}1.222$, $\beta = 113°27'$. Crystals show {001}, {100}, {101}, {110}, etc. Perfect 001 and good 100 cleavages. D 2.02. Bolland gives for "barium acetate" ($3H_2O$?): $N_X = 1.55$, $N_Y = 1.56$, $N_Z = 1.57$, $N_Z - N_X = 0.02$. 2V = large. Ref: 34, 35, 117.

Zinc acetate trihydrate [$(CH_3CO_2)_2Zn \cdot 3H_2O$] is monoclinic with $a{:}b{:}c = 1.557{:}1{:}1.843$, $\beta = 105°34'$. Crystals $\{10\bar{1}\}$ tablets or elongated parallel to *b*. Common twinning on $10\bar{1}$. Very perfect $10\bar{1}$ cleavage. D 1.72. The optic plane is 010, $Z \wedge c = 55°$. (+)2V = 84°30'. $N_Y = 1.494$. Ref: 117.

Lead acetate trihydrate [$(CH_3CO_2)_2Pb \cdot 3H_2O$] is monoclinic with $a{:}b{:}c = 2.179{:}1{:}2.479$, $\beta = 109°48'$. Crystals thick {001} tablets with {100}, {110}, etc.; 100, 001, and 010 cleavages. Fig. 5. D 2.55. The optic plane is 010; $Z \wedge c = -55°18'$. (+)2V = 83°27' red, 83°55' Na, 87°24' blue. $N_Y = 1.570$ red, 1.576 yellow, 1.584 blue. Ref: 71, 117.

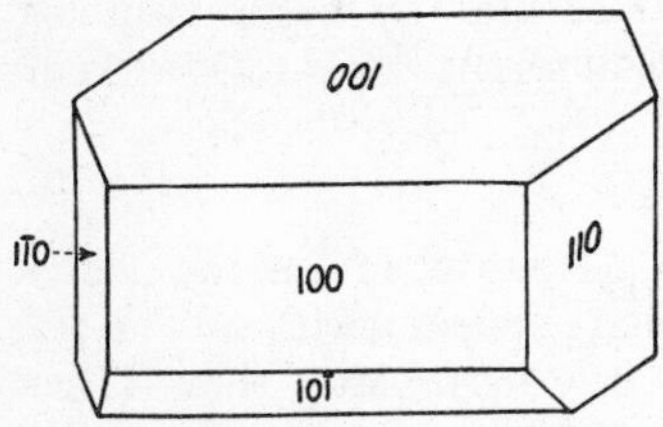

Fig. 5. Lead acetate trihydrate.

Magnesium acetate tetrahydrate [$(CH_3CO_2)_2Mg \cdot 4H_2O$] is monoclinic with $a{:}b{:}c = 0.713{:}1{:}0.403$, $\beta = 95°37'$. Crystals short prisms with {110}, {001}, and {111}. D 1.45. The optic plane is 010; $X \wedge c = +48°$ (-)2V = 56°34', r > v, $N_Y = 1.488$ red, 1.491 Na, 1.493 green. Absorption: Y > Z > X. Ref: 117.

Cobaltous acetate tetrahydrate [$(CH_3CO_2)_2Co \cdot 4H_2O$] is monoclinic with $a{:}b{:}c = 0.718{:}1{:}0.402$, $\beta = 94°43'$. Crystals prismatic with {110}, {100}, {001}, and $\{11\bar{1}\}$. Twinning on 100. D 1.70. The optic plane is 010; $X \wedge c = +54°$. (-)2V = 30°43'. $N_Y = 1.538$ red, 1.542 Na, 1.546 green. Pleochroic with X = rose red, Y = carmine, Z = pale rose red. Ref: 117.

Gadolinium acetate tetrahydrate [$(CH_3CO_2)_3Gd \cdot 4H_2O$] is triclinic and isomorphous with yttrium acetate tetrahydrate. Crystals show {100}, {010}, {001}, $\{11\bar{1}\}$, $\{0\bar{1}1\}$, etc. The isomorphous salt has perfect 010, 100, and $11\bar{1}$

cleavages. D 1.997. Optic orientation given by Pabst: Z nearly parallel with *a*. (+)2V = 85° calc. $N_X = 1.482$, $N_Y = 1.493$, $N_Z = 1.506$, $N_Z - N_X = 0.024$, all ± 0.002. Ref: 117, 266.

Calcium copper acetate hexahydrate $[(CH_3CO_2)_4CaCu \cdot 6H_2O]$ is tetragonal with $c/a = 1.032$. Crystals eight-sided prisms with {110}, {100}, {001}, {111}. Perfect 110 and 100 cleavages. D 1.42. Uniaxial negative with $N_O = 1.4860$, $N_E = 1.4396$, $N_O - N_E = 0.0464$ E; $N_O = 1.4887$, $N_E = 1.4473$ F Color blue with weak pleochroism (O some-what more greenish than E). Ref: 117.

Verdigris or copper basic acetate $[CuO \cdot (CH_3CO_2)_2Cu\ ?]$ in irregular crystal fragments has 2V very large and $N_X = 1.53$, $N_Y = ?$, $N_Z = 1.56$, $N_Z - N_Y = 0.03$. Pleochroic with X = deep green-blue, Z = light blue-green. Ref: 556.

Calcium aluminum basic acetate octahydrate $[3CaO \cdot Al_2O_3 \cdot Ca(CH_3CO_2)_2 \cdot 8H_2O]$ is hexagonal in basal plates. Uniaxial negative with $N_O = 1.549 \pm 0.003$, $N_E = 1.538 \pm 0.003$, $N_O - N_E = 0.011$. Ref: 256.

Sodium zinc uranyl acetate hexahydrate $[NaZn(UO_2)_3(CH_3CO_2)_9 \cdot 6H_2O]$ is monoclinic in tabular crystals elongated along *b*; cyclic rhombohedral twinning common. It intercrystallizes in all proportions with the Li salt. The optic plane and Z are normal to 010; $X \wedge c$ = about 20°. $N_X = 1.475$, $N_Y = ?$, $N_Z = 1.480 \pm 0.002$, $N_Z - N_X = 0.005$ Na. Ref: 151.

Potassium zinc uranyl acetate hexahydrate $[KZn(UO_2)_3(CH_3CO_2)_9 \cdot 6H_2O]$ is tetragonal in prisms with first and second order pyramids. Perfect 110 cleavage. Uniaxial positive with $N_O = 1.477$ Na, $N_E = 1.487 \pm 0.002$, $N_E - N_O = 0.010$. Ref: 151.

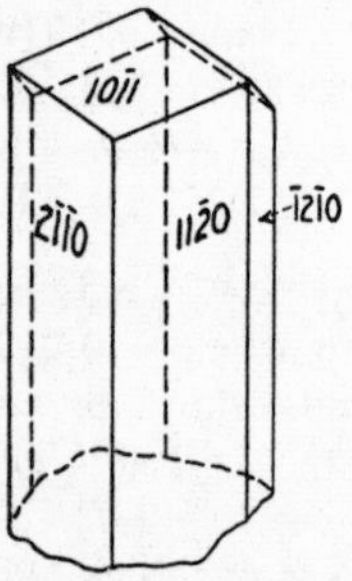

Fig. 6. Acetamide.

Lithium zinc uranyl acetate hexahydrate $[LiZn(UO_2)_3(CH_3CO_2)_9 \cdot 6H_2O]$ is monoclinic in tabular crystals elongated along *b*. Often pseudorhombohedral by cyclic twinning. The optic plane and Z are normal to 010. $N_X = 1.495 \pm 0.002$, $N_Y = ?$, $N_Z = 1.503 \pm 0.002$, $N_Z - N_X = 0.008$ Na. Ref: 151.

Ethanamide or acetamide $(CH_3 \cdot CONH_2)$ has two phases. The stable phase (I) is ditrigonal pyramidal with $c/a = 0.592$. Space group *R*3*c*; *a* 8.06 Å. U.C. 6. Crystals show $\{11\bar{2}0\}$ and $\{10\bar{1}1\}$. No distinct cleavage. Fig. 6. M.P. 82°. D 1.159. Uniaxial negative with $N_O = 1.54$, $N_E = 1.46$, $N_O - N_E = 0.08$. Also $N_O = 1.507$, $N_E = 1.461$, $N_O - N_E = 0.046$. But crystals prepared by Ray Wilcox at the University of Wisconsin from solution in alcohol are hexagonal prisms with prismatic cleavage and parallel extinction. (–)2V = 0° (or near 0°). $N_O = 1.497$, $N_E = 1.455$, $N_O - N_E = 0.042$. An unstable phase is orthorhombic with[1] $a:b:c = 0.402:1:0.185$. Crystals prisms with {110}, {010}, {001}, etc. Perfect 010 cleavage. D 1.10. M.P. 69.1°. The optic plane is 100; X = *c*? (–)2V = 85° *ca.* calc. $N_X = 1.370$, $N_Y = 1.485$, $N_Z = 1.585$, $N_Z - N_X = 0.215$. Ref: 117, 152, 376, 377c.

[1] *a* and *b* interchanged to make $b > a > c$.

Barium monofluoracetate [$(CH_2FCO_2)_2Ba$] forms equant monoclinic crystals with extinction parallel and inclined to prism faces. $(+)2V = 56°$ calc. $N_X = 1.520$, $N_Y = 1.533$, $N_Z = 1.578$, $N_Z - N_X = 0.058$. Ref: 452a.

Barium monofluoracetate monohydrate [$(CH_2FCO_2)_2Ba \cdot H_2O$] forms monoclinic prisms; extinction inclined. $(-?)2V$ = very large, $N_X = 1.475$, $N_Y = 1.498$, $N_Z = 1.524$, $N_Z - N_X = 0.049$. Ref: 452a.

2-Chloroethanoic acid or chloroacetic acid ($CH_2Cl \cdot CO_2H$) has three crystal phases, all monoclinic. The α-phase has $a:b:c = 0.818:1:0.563$, $\beta = 99°17'$. Crystals {010} tablets with {210}, {011}, {111}. Perfect 010 and good 100 cleavage. M.P. 62.4°. The optic plane is 010; an extinction (Z) is nearly parallel to the {111} pyramid edge. Bolland gives (for this phase?) parallel extinction and positive elongation with $N_1 = 1.41$, $N_2 = 1.63$, $N_2 - N_1 = 0.22$.
Ref: 34, 35, 117.

Barium monochloroacetate {$Ba(CH_2ClCO_2)_2$} forms six-sided plates with parallel extinction and negative elongation. $N_1 = 1.582$, $N_2 = 1.611$, $N_2 - N_1 = 0.029$. Ref: 620.

Cadmium monochloroacetate hexahydrate [$(CH_2Cl \cdot CO_2)_2Cd \cdot 6H_2O$] is orthorhombic with $a:b:c = 0.621:1:0.456$. Crystals prisms with {110}, {010}, {111}, {031}, {011}, etc. D 1.94. The optic plane is 001; $X = b$. $(-)2V = 32°9'$ Li, $32°14'$ Na, $31°14'$ blue. $N_X = 1.466$ Li, 1.467 Na, 1.477 blue; $N_Y = 1.532$ Li, 1.533 Na, 1.545 blue; $N_Z = 1.538$ Li, 1.539 Na, 1.551 blue; $N_Z - N_X = 0.072$ Na.
Ref: 221.

Cobalt monochloroacetate hexahydrate [$(CH_2Cl \cdot CO_2)_2CO \cdot 6H_2O$] is orthorhombic with $a:b:c = 0.629:1:0.471$. Crystals prisms with {110}, {010}, {111}, {131}, {011}, etc. The optic plane is 001; $X = b$. $(-)2V = 22°13'$ Li, $21°47'$ Na. $N_X = 1.482$ Li, 1.490 Na; $N_Y = 1.537$ Li, 1.545 Na; $N_Z = 1.539$ Li, 1.547 Na; $N_Z - N_X = 0.057$ Na. Color red with X = raspberry red, Y = orange yellow, Z = violet red. Ref: 221.

Calcium dichloroacetate decahydrate {$(C_2H_3O_2)_2Ca_2Cl_2 \cdot 10H_2O$} is dimorphous. One phase (I) is probably orthorhombic; D 1.48. Soluble in water. $Z = c$ (elongation). $(+)2V = 80°$. $N_X = 1.468$, $N_Y = 1.484$, $N_Z = 1.515$, $N_Z - N_X = 0.047$. An alteration product forming on fossils in oak drawers with plywood bottoms; it has been called *calclacite*. A second phase (II) is monoclinic. It crystallizes from solution. D 1.53. $Z \wedge c = 18°$. $(-)2V = 58°$. $N_X = 1.468$, $N_Y = 1.502$, $N_Z = 1.523$, $N_Z - N_X = 0.055$. Ref: 609.

Trichloroacetic acid ($CCl_3 \cdot CO_2H$) is lamellar to tabular. Hygroscopic. $(+)2V < 10°$, $N_X = 1.510$, $N_Y = 1.512$–5, $N_Z = 1.555$, $N_Z - N_X = 0.045$.
Ref: 529.

Trichloroacetamide (CCl_3CONH_2) is monoclinic prismatic with $a:b:c = 1.748:1:0.849$, $\beta = 101°24'$. Crystals {100} tablets with {001}, {010}. M.P. 141°. Perfect 100 cleavage; also 001 and 010. $Y = b$, Z nearly $= c$. $(+)2E = 59°$, $2V = 36°$, $N_X = 1.546$, $N_Y = 1.558$, $N_Z = 1.643$, $N_Z - N_X = 0.097$.
Ref: 117, 529.

Barium monobromoacetate $\{(CH_2BrCO_2)_2Ba\}$ is monoclinic; crystals prismatic. Z || elongation. $N_X = 1.548$, $N_Y = ?$, $N_Z = 1.705$, $N_Z - N_X = 0.157$. Ref: 452a.

Barium monoiodoacetate $\{(CH_2ICO_2)_2Ba\}$ is monoclinic; crystals prismatic with Z || elongation. (-)2V = large, $N_X = 1.633$, $N_Y = 1.75$, $N_Z = 1.85$, $N_Z - N_X = 0.217$. Ref: 452a.

Tetra(thioacetamide)cuprous chloride $\left[\left[S{:}C\langle^{CH_3}_{NH_2}\right]_4 \cdot CuCl\right]$ is tetragonal disphenoidal with $c/a = 0.444$. Space group $I\bar{4}$. *a* 12.43, *c* 5.52 Å. U.C. 2. Crystals columnar with {100}, {110}, {101}. D 1.56. Uniaxial negative with $N_O = 1.775$, $N_E = 1.755 \pm 0.005$, $N_O - N_E = 0.02$. Ref: 63.

Salts of Propanoic or Propionic Acid

Strontium dicalcium propionate $[(CH_3CH_2 \cdot CO_2)_6SrCa_2]$ is tetragonal with $c/a = 0.976$. Crystals pseudo-octahedral with {100}. Fig. 7. Imperfect 111 and 001 cleavages. Uniaxial positive with $N_O = 1.4839$ Li, 1.4871 Na, 1.4897 Tl, $N_E = 1.4917$ Li, 1.4956 Na, 1.4987 Tl, $N_E - N_O = 0.0085$ Na. Ref: 117.

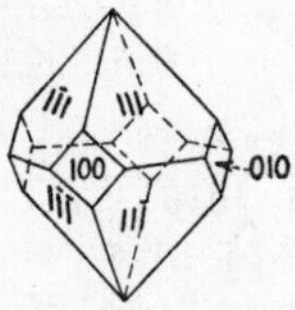

Fig. 7. Strontium dicalcium propionate.

Barium dicalcium propionate $[(CH_3 \cdot CH_2 \cdot CO_2)_6BaCa_2]$ is isometric hexoctahedral. Space group *Fd3m*. *a* 18.20 Å. U.C. 8. Crystals octahedral. N = 1.4442 Na. Ref: 117, 561.

Lead dicalcium propionate $[(CH_3 \cdot CH_2 \cdot CO_2)_6PbCa_2]$ is tetragonal with $c/a = 0.979$. Crystals like the strontium dicalcium salt with rather distinct 111 cleavage. Uniaxial positive with $N_O = 1.5241$ Li, 1.5268 Na, 1.5310 Tl; $N_E = 1.5341$ Li, 1.5389 Na, 1.5436 Tl; $N_E - N_O = 0.0121$ Na. Ref: 117.

There is a discontinuous series of mix-crystals between barium dicalcium propionate and lead dicalcium propionate whose optical properties are shown in Fig. 8.

Barium propionate monohydrate $[(CH_3 \cdot CH_2 \cdot CO_2)_2Ba \cdot H_2O]$ is orthorhombic with $a{:}b{:}c = 0.881{:}1{:}0.949$. Crystals short prismatic terminated by {011}, {221}, {001}. 010 and 110 cleavages. The optic plane is 100; X = *b*. (-)2V = 81°36′, r < v weak. $N_Y = 1.5175$ Na. Ref: 117.

Gadolinium propionate trihydrate $[(CH_3 \cdot CH_2 \cdot CO_2)_3Gd \cdot 3H_2O]$ is monoclinic with $a{:}b{:}c = 0.629{:}1{:}0.824$, $\beta = 101°31′$. Crystals {001} tablets with {111}, {110}, {11$\bar{1}$}, etc. D 1.809. The optic plane and Z are normal to 010; X nearly normal to 001. (-)2V = 45°30′ obs.; r < v and strong horizontal dispersion. $N_X = 1.493$, $N_Y = 1.495$, $N_Z = 1.496$, $N_Z - N_X = 0.003$, all ± 0.001. Ref: 266.

Propionamide ($CH_3 \cdot CH_2 \cdot CONH_2$) is orthorhombic[1] with $a:b:c = 0.700:1:0.188$. Crystals (somewhat volatile) often {010} plates with {110} and {011}. Perfect 010 cleavage. D 1.04. M.P. 79°. $X = b$, $Y = a$, $Z = c$. (+)2V = 53°, $N_X = 1.445$, $N_Y = 1.461$, $N_Z = 1.530$, $N_Z - N_X = 0.085$. Ref: 117, 377c.

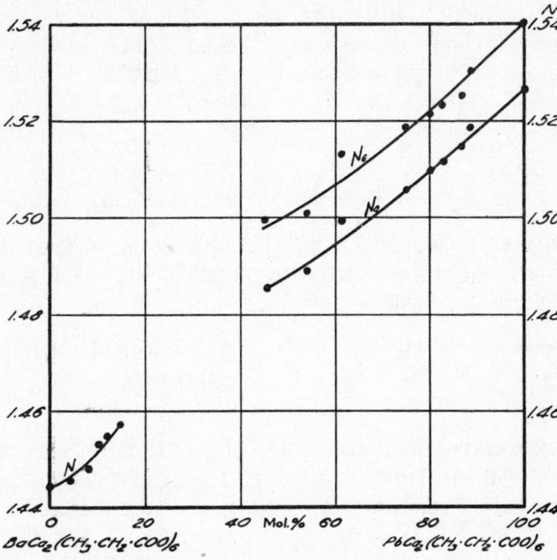

Fig. 8. Barium dicalcium propionate to lead dicalcium propionate. See F. Sansoni: Zeit. Kryst. 6, 67 (1882).

Tetracalcium butyrate pentalead propionate dodecahydrate $[4(CH_3 \cdot CH_2 \cdot CH_2 \cdot CO_2)_2Ca \cdot 5(CH_3 \cdot CH_2 \cdot CO_2)_2Pb \cdot 12H_2O]$ is isometric with distinct 110 cleavage. Crystals cubic with {110}, {211}. Isotropic with N = 1.5131 Li, 1.5176 Na, 1.5215 Tl. Colorless. Ref: 117.

Salts of 3-Methylbutanoic or Isovaleric Acid

Sodium-*n*-valerate $\{CH_3(CH_2)_3CO_2Na\}$ forms liquid crystals (between 229° and 252°) which are uniaxial positive with (at 231°) $N_O = 1.3976$, $N_E = 1.4100$, $N_E - N_O = 0.0124$. Ref: 218.

Sodium-*i*-valerate $\{(C_4H_9)CO_2Na\}$ forms liquid crystals (between 170° and 240°) which are uniaxial positive with (at 180°) $N_O = 1.4036$ and (at 181°) $N_E = 1.4041$, $N_E - N_O = 0.0005$. Ref: 218.

Ammonium valerate[2] $[C_4H_9CO_2NH_4(2H_2O\,?)]$ has an extinction angle of 33° and $N_1 = 1.46$, $N_2 = 1.485$, $N_2 - N_1 = 0.025$. Ref: 34, 35.

---

[1] *a b c* changed to *b a c* to make $b > a$.

[2] Possibly a salt of pentanoic or *n*-valeric acid.

Zinc valerate $[(C_4H_9CO_2)_2Zn]$ (with H_2O?) has parallel extinction and negative elongation with $N_1 = 1.495$, $N_2 = 1.515$, $N_2 - N_1 = 0.02$.
Ref: 34, 35, 343c.

3-Methylbutanamide or isovaleramide $[(CH_3)_2CH \cdot CH_2 \cdot CO \cdot NH_2)]$ is monoclinic in {100} plates with {110}, {10$\bar{1}$}. 110 $\wedge$ 100 = 60° ±; 10$\bar{1}$ $\wedge$ 100 = 78° ±. Perfect 100 cleavage shows a bisectrix. D 0.965. The optic plane is 010. $N_X = 1.438$, $N_Y = 1.450$, $N_Z = 1.457$, $N_Z - N_X = 0.019$. ∴ (-)2V = 70° calc. Also: (+)2V = 57°, $N_X = 1.458$, $N_Y = 1.466$, $N_X = 1.498$, $N_Z - N_Y = 0.040$. (Which is correct?)
Ref: 101, 162, 377c.

Salts of Butanoic or Butyric Acid

Sodium-*n*-butyrate $\{CH_3(CH_2)_2CO_2Na\}$ forms liquid crystals (between 250° and 300°) which are uniaxial positive with (at 267°) $N_O = 1.3874$ (and at 263°) $N_E = 1.3962$, $N_E - N_O \approx 0.0088$.
Ref: 218.

Zinc butyrate $\{(CH_3CH_2CH_2CO_2)_2Zn\}$ is monoclinic with $N_X = 1.480$, $N_Y = 1.500$, $N_Z = 1.530$, $N_Z - N_X = 0.050$; therefore (+)2V = 80° *ca.*
Ref: 152.

Gadolinium butyrate dihydrate $[(CH_3 \cdot CH_2 \cdot CH_2CO_2)_3Gd \cdot 2H_2O]$ is monoclinic with $a:b:c = 0.631:1:1.143$, $\beta = 112°31'$. Crystals {001} tablets with {110}, {11$\bar{1}$}. D 1.616. Very soft. Perfect 001 cleavage. The optic plane is 010; Z nearly normal to 001. (+)2V = 70° ±. $N_X = 1.471$, $N_Y = 1.475$, $N_Z = 1.480$, $N_Z - N_X = 0.009$.
Ref: 266.

Butyramide $(CH_3 \cdot CH_2 \cdot CH_2 \cdot CONH_2)$ is orthorhombic with[1] $a:b:c = 0.580:1:0.294$. Crystals often {010} plates with {110}, {011}. Prism faces vertically striated. Perfect 010 cleavage. D 1.032. M.P 115°. X = *b*, Y = *a*, Z = *c*. (+)2V = 63°. $N_X = 1.465$, $N_Y = 1.482$, $N_Z = 1.530$, $N_Z - N_X = 0.065$.
Ref: 117, 355c.

Valeramide $[CH_3 \cdot (CH_2)_3 \cdot CONH_2]$ is monoclinic with $a:b:c = 1.766:1:0.397$, $\beta = 92°8'$. Crystals {100} tablets with {110}, {101}, and {10$\bar{1}$}. Perfect 100 cleavage. D 1.023. M.P. 101°. The optic plane is 010; a bisectrix of a large optic angle is nearly normal to 100. (+)2V = 74°. $N_X = 1.466$, $N_Y = 1.488$, $N_Z = 1.530$, $N_Z - N_X = 0.064$.
Ref: 117, 377c.

2,2-*bis*(Bromomethyl)propanoic acid or dibromotrimethylacetic acid or β, β′-dibromopivalic acid $[CH_2Br \cdot C(CH_2Br)(CH_3) \cdot CO_2H]$ is orthorhombic, probably hemimorphic, with $a:b:c = 0.895:1:0.779$. Crystals pyramidal with {111}, {100}, {001}, {010{, {021}, etc. Imperfect 100 and 010 cleavages. D 2.078. (+)2V = 35°40′. $N_X = 1.5676$, $N_Y = 1.5729$ calc., $N_Z = 1.6242$, $N_Z - N_X = 0.0566$.
Ref: 146.

[1] *a* and *b* interchanged to make *b* > *a*.

2-Bromo-2-ethylbutanamide or α-bromo-α-ethylbutyramide or bromodiethylacetamide or neuronal $[(C_2H_5)_2\cdot C\cdot Br\cdot CO\cdot NH_2]$ is monoclinic with $\beta \approx 90°$. Good 001 (?) cleavage. M.P. 66° to 67°. The optic plane is 010; $X \wedge c = 22°$. (+)2V = 64°, $N_X = 1.516$, $N_Y = 1.533$ calc., $N_Z = 1.583$, $N_Z - N_X = 0.067$. Again: $N_1 = 1.515$, $N_2 = 1.59$, $N_2 - N_1 = 0.075$. Colorless. Ref: 123, 239.

Hexadecanoic or Palmitic Acid and Derivatives

α-Palmitic acid $(C_{15}H_{31}CO_2H)$ is monoclinic with $a:b:c = 1.912:1:9.198$, $\beta = 129°10'$. a 9.54, b 4.99, c 45.9 Å. U.C. 4. M.P. 63° - 64°. The optic plane is 010. (+)2V = large. The indices measured in 001 are $N_Y = 1.508$, $N_Z' = 1.533$. Ref: 333, 450, 589.

Potassium palmitate $(C_{15}H_{31}\cdot CO_2K)$ is probably triclinic; soft like talc. Thin plates are nearly rectangular and show small extinction angles. A cleavage is normal to the plates and extinction is at 21° to the cleavage. The optic plane is at an angle of about 40° to the plates. (+)2V = medium. $N_X = 1.500$, $1.52 > N_Y > 1.51$, $N_Z = 1.561$, all = ± 0.004, $N_Z - N_X = 0.061$. On plates: $N_1 = 1.500$, $N_2 = 1.521$. Ref: 80.

Magnesium palmitate $[(C_{15}H_{31}\cdot CO_2)_2Mg]$ is probably orthorhombic. M.P. 105° - 112°. Rods show parallel extinction and negative elongation. Index normal to elongation is sometimes less than 1.548. 2V = biaxial. $N_X = 1.510$, N_Y = ?, $N_Z = 1.548$, both ± 0.003, $N_Z - N_X = 0.038$. The glass has N = 1.493. Ref: 80.

Sodium acid palmitate $[(C_{15}H_{31}CO_2)_2HNa]$ is dimorphous. The α-phase (I) is monoclinic prismatic with $a:b:c = 1.351:1:6.192$, $\beta = 93°$. Space group $P2_1/a$; a 9.97, b 7.38, c 45.7 kX. U.C. 4. Crystals {010} tablets elongated along a with consequent + elongation when viewed normal to the tablet. Perfect 001 and 010 cleavages. Glide plane 001 in many directions. D 1.05 calc. X = b. Y ≈ a, Z ≈ c. (+)2E = 78°, 2V = 49°, r > v marked. $N_X = 1.506$, $N_Y = 1.513$, $N_Z = 1.57$ calc. $N_Z - N_X = 0.064$ calc. The β-phase has not been measured. Ref: 427.

Sodium palmitate hemihydrate or β-sodium palmitate $[C_{15}H_{31}CO_2Na\cdot 0.5H_2O$?] has variable tenor of H_2O (from 0.2 to about 3%). It is monoclinic prismatic with $a:b:c = 1.140:1:11.467$, $\beta = 94°$. Space group $A2/a$ (?); a 9.13, b 8.01, c 91.85 kX. Crystals {001} tablets elongated along b. Perfect 001 and 010 cleavages. Glide plane 001 in direction ⊥ 010. X = b, Y ≈ a, Z ≈ c. With 0.5 H_2O: (+)2V = 50°, r > v strong, $N_X = 1.505$, $N_Y = 1.517$, $N_Z = 1.57$ calc., $N_Z - N_X = 0.065$ calc. Again: $N_X = 1.492$, $N_Y = 1.514$. With only 0.2% H_2O: $N_X = 1.500$, $N_Y = 1.522$. Ref: 427, 458.

Calcium palmitate $[(C_{15}H_{31}\cdot CO_2)_2Ca]$ is probably orthorhombic. M.P. 153° - 156°. Rods show parallel extinction and negative elongation. 2V = biaxial. $N_X = 1.503$, N_Y = ?, $N_Z = 1.548$, both ± 0.004, $N_Z - N_X = 0.045$. The glass has N = 1.506. Ref: 80.

Methyl palmitate ($C_{15}H_{31} \cdot CO_2CH_3$) forms liquid crystals (between 23° and 30°) which are biaxial; they have (at 25.5°) $N_1 = 1.4981$, $N_2 = 1.5580$, $N_2 - N_1 = 0.0599$. M.P. 30°. Ref: 611.

Ethyl palmitate ($C_{15}H_{31} \cdot CO_2C_2H_5$) forms liquid crystals (between 17° and 19°) which are uniaxial positive with (at 18.5°) $N_O = 1.4630$, $N_E = 1.5179$, $N_E - N_O = 0.0549$. M.P. 24°. Ref: 611.

Propyl palmitate ($C_{15}H_{31} \cdot CO_2C_3H_7$) forms liquid crystals (between 12° and 19°) which are uniaxial positive with (at 16°) $N_O = 1.464$, $N_E = 1.517$, $N_E - N_O = 0.053$. M.P. 20 - 22°. Ref: 611.

Isopropyl palmitate ($C_{15}H_{31} \cdot CO_2C_3H_7$) forms liquid crystals (between 5° and 9°) which are uniaxial positive with (at 5°) $N_O = 1.4648$, $N_E = 1.517$, $N_E - N_O = 0.0522$. Ref: 611.

Butyl palmitate ($C_{15}H_{31} \cdot CO_2C_4H_9$) forms liquid crystals (between 10° and 12°) which are uniaxial positive with (at 12°) $N_O = 1.4629$, $N_E = 1.5169$, $N_E - N_O = 0.054$. M.P. 16°. Ref: 611.

Octadecanoic or Stearic Acid and Derivatives

β-Stearic acid ($C_{17}H_{35}CO_2H$) is monoclinic with $a:b:c = 0.769:1:6.609$, $\beta = 116°22'$; a 5.68, b 7.39, c 48.84 Å. U.C. 4. The optic plane and X are normal to 010. $Z \wedge c$ = moderate. (+)2V = moderate. The indices in 001 are: $N_X = 1.510$, $N_Z' = 1.535$. Also $N_1 = 1.516$, $N_2 = 1.533$. Another phase is also monoclinic, but has a 9.46, b 4.96, c 49.15 Å. $\beta = 125°48'$. U.C. 4. D 1.008. Ref: 333, 343c, 450, 589, 605.

Magnesium stearate [$(C_{17}H_{35} \cdot CO_2)_2Mg$] is probably orthorhombic in rods and plates, with M.P. 120°. Parallel extinction and negative elongation. (+)2V = small to moderate, $N_X = 1.498$ Na, $N_Y = 1.520$, $N_Z = 1.542$, $N_Z - N_X = 0.044$. (The reported optic angle and indices are inconsistent-A.N.W.) The amorphous substance has N = 1.491 Na. Ref: 80.

Calcium stearate [$(C_{17}H_{35} \cdot CO_2)_2Ca$] is probably orthorhombic in rods with M.P. 150 - 154°. Parallel extinction and negative elongation. $N_X = 1.501$ Na, N_Y = ?, $N_Z = 1.552$, $N_Z - N_X = 0.051$. The amorphous substance has N = 1.505 Na. Ref: 80.

Barium stearate [$\{CH_3(CH_2)_{16}CO_2\}_2Ba$] forms films which are uniaxial and positive with $N_O = 1.491$, $N_E = 1.551$, $N_E - N_O = 0.060$. Ref: 31.

Calcium magnesium stearate [$(CaMg)(C_{17}H_{35} \cdot CO_2)_2$?] is probably orthorhombic in rods and plates with parallel extinction and negative elongation. Rhombic plates with an acute angle of 70° show cleavage parallel to both diagonals. Such plates are normal to Z and the optic plane bisects the obtuse angle of the rhombs. (+)2V = small to moderate. $N_X = 1.504$ (another measure = 1.508), $N_Y = 1.522$, $N_Z = 1.553$, $N_Z - N_X = 0.049$. The amorphous substance has N = 1.493 Na. Ref: 80.

Sodium acid stearate $[(C_{17}H_{35}CO_2)_2HNa]$ is dimorphous; the α-phase (I) is monoclinic prismatic with $a:b:c = 1.351:1:6.192$, $\beta = 93°$. Space group $P2_1/a$; *a* 9.97, *b* 7.38, *c* 45.7 kX. U.C. 4. Crystals {010} tablets or needles, elongated along *a* with positive elongation. Perfect 001 and 010 cleavages. Glide plane 001 in many directions. D 1.05. X = *b*, Y ≈ *a*, Z ≈ *c*. (+)2E = 78°. 2V = 49°, r > v marked. $N_X = 1.506$, $N_Y = 1.516$, $N_Z = 1.56$ calc., $N_Z - N_X = 0.054$ calc. This phase forms below about 50° C. The β-phase (II) is triclinic with $a:b:c = 0.872:1:4.380$, $\alpha = 90°45'$, $\beta = 90°$, $\gamma = 94°$. Space group $P1$ or $P\bar{1}$. *a* 9.98, *b* 11.46, *c* 50.2 kX. U.C. 6. This is the stable phase above about 50° C. Crystals {001} flakes. Perfect 001 and 110 cleavages. Glide plane 001. D 1.02, X ∧ *b* = + 40°, Y ∧ *a* = + 36°, Z ≈ *c*. (+)2E = 66°. 2V = 42°, r > v marked. $N_X = 1.498$ calc., $N_Y = 1.510$, $N_Z = 1.59$ calc., $N_Z - N_X = 0.092$ calc.
Ref: 427.

Methyl stearate $(C_{17}H_{35}\cdot CO_2CH_3)$ forms liquid crystals (between 22° and 38°) which are biaxial; they have (at 24.5°) $N_1 = 1.5015$, $N_2 = 1.5587$, $N_2 - N_1 = 0.0572$.
Ref: 611.

Ethyl stearate $(C_{17}H_{35}\cdot CO_2C_2H_5)$ forms liquid crystals (between 20° and 33°) which are uniaxial positive with (at 26°) $N_O = 1.4658$, $N_E = 1.5212$, $N_E - N_O = 0.0554$. M.P. 33°.
Ref: 611.

Propyl stearate $(C_{17}H_{35}\cdot CO_2C_3H_7)$ forms liquid crystals (between 21° and 30°) which are uniaxial positive with (at 25.5°) $N_O = 1.465$, $N_E = 1.520$, $N_E - N_O = 0.055$. M.P. 30°.
Ref: 611.

Isopropyl stearate $(C_{17}H_{35}\cdot CO_2C_3H_7)$ forms liquid crystals (between 10° and 28°) which are uniaxial positive with (at 18°) $N_O = 1.468$, $N_E = 1.521$, $N_E - N_O = 0.053$.
Ref: 611.

Butyl stearate $(C_{17}H_{35}\cdot CO_3C_4H_9)$ forms liquid crystals (between 19° and 28°) which are uniaxial positive with (at 22°) $N_O = 1.4673$, $N_E = 1.5162$, $N_E - N_O = 0.0489$. M.P. 28°.
Ref: 611.

Isobutyl stearate $(C_{17}H_{35}\cdot CO_2C_4H_9)$ forms liquid crystals (between 10° and 22.5°) which are uniaxial positive with (at 17°) $N_O = 1.4658$, $N_E = 1.517$, $N_E - N_O = 0.0512$. M.P. 22.5°. Another phase melts at 29°.
Ref: 611.

Calcium *trans*-2-butenoate or calcium crotonate $[(CH_3—\underset{C}{H}=\underset{H}{C}—CO_2)_2Ca]$ is biaxial with $N_X = 1.450$, $N_Y = 1.567$, $N_Z = 1.600$, $N_Z - N_X = 0.150$. (-)2V = 55° *ca.* calc.
Ref: 152.

Potassium *cis*-9-octadecanoate or potassium oleate $[CH_3\cdot(CH_2)_7\cdot CH=CH\cdot(CH_2)_7\cdot CO_2K]$ is tetragonal. Soft and flexible. $N_1 = 1.452$, $N_2 = 1.465$, $N_2 - N_1 = 0.013$.
Ref: 117, 152.

Elaidic acid $\{CH_3(CH_2)_7CH:CH(CH_2)_7CO_2H\}$ forms liquid crystals (between 25° and 40°) which are uniaxial positive with (at 30°) $N_O = 1.5119$, $N_E = 1.5867$, $N_E - N_O = 0.0748$. M.P. 50°.
Ref: 611.

Eruca acid $\{CH_3(CH_2)_7CH:CH(CH_2)_{11}CO_2H\}$ forms liquid crystals (between 10° and 22°) which are uniaxial positive with (at 15°) $N_O = 1.500$, $N_E = 1.537$, $N_E - N_O = 0.037$. Ref: 611.

2,4-Hexadienoic acid or sorbic acid or 1,3-pentadiene-1-carboxylic acid $[CH_3 \cdot (CH)_4 \cdot CO_2H]$ has parallel extinction and negative elongation. $N_1 = 1.46$, $N_2 > 1.95$, $N_2 - N_1 > 0.49$. Ref: 34,35.

t,t,$\Delta^{9,11}$ Linoleic acid $[(CH)_3 \cdot (CH_2)_4 \cdot (CH)_2 \cdot CH_2(CH)_2 \cdot (CH_2)_7CO_2H]$ is monoclinic with *a* 95.7, *b* 4.95, *c* 7.31 kX, $\beta = 90°36'$. Crystals are {100} plates with {011}. D 1.01. Y = *b*. Z $\wedge$ *a* = 17°23′. One optic axis normal to 100. (+)2V = 34°36′. 2E = 54°18′. $N_Y = 1.527$. Ref: 620b.

Subclass B. Dicarboxylic Acids and Derivatives

Ethanedioic Acid or Oxalic Acid and Derivatives

Ethanedioic acid or oxalic acid $(C_2O_4H_2)$ is dimorphous; the α-phase (I) is orthorhombic dipyramidal with *a*:*b*:*c* = 0.830:1:0.768. Space group *Pcab*; *a* 6.46, *b* 7.79, *c* 6.02 Å. U.C. 4. Crystals pyramidal or elongated along *b* with {111}, {100}, {101}, etc. Fig. 9. Perfect 100 cleavage. D 1.90. The optic plane is 001; Z = *b*. 2V = 90° (obs.), $N_X = 1.445$, $N_Y = 1.540$, $N_Z = 1.635$, $N_Z - N_X = 0.190$. Again: (-)2V = 81°, r < v. $N_X = 1.431$, $N_Y = 1.540$, $N_Z = 1.636$, $N_Z - N_X = 0.205$. The β-phase (II) is monoclinic prismatic with *a*:*b*:*c* = 0.870:1:0.944, $\beta = 115°30'$. Space group $P2_1/c$; *a* 5.30, *b* 6.09, *c* 5.51 Å. U.C. 2. Perfect 100 cleavage. D 1.895. The optic plane and X are normal to 010; Z $\wedge$ *a* = 11°. (+)2V = 84° *ca.* $N_X = 1.445$, $N_Y = 1.523$, $N_Z = 1.631$, $N_Z - N_X = 0.186$. Again: $N_X = 1.440$, $N_Y = 1.475$, $N_Z = 1.625$, $N_Z - N_X = 0.185$. Ref: 117, 123a, 137, 152, 433b.

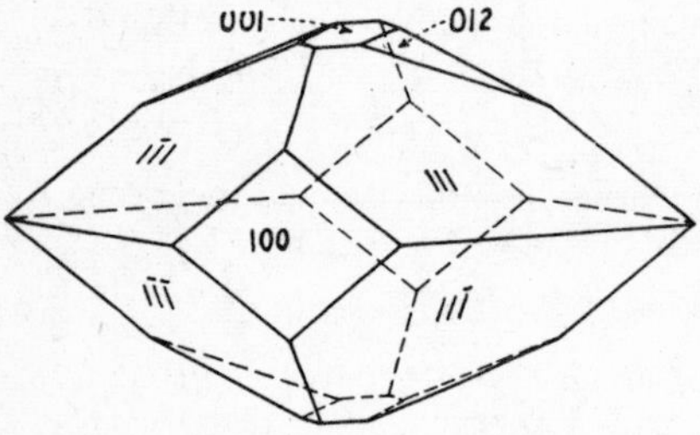

Fig. 9. Oxalic acid.

Oxalic acid dihydrate $(H_2C_2O_4 \cdot 2H_2O)$ is monoclinic prismatic with *a*:*b*:*c* = 1.695:1:3.336, $\beta = 106°12'$. Space group $P2_1/n$. *a* 6.12, *b* 3.60, *c* 12.03 Å. U.C. 2. Crystals {001} tablets with {10$\bar{1}$}, {101}, {110}, etc. 110 cleavage. D 1.64 *ca.* The optic plane and X are normal to 010 and Z $\wedge$ *c* = 14°42′ in the obtuse angle β. (-)2V = 68°. $N_X = 1.422$, $N_Y = 1.495$, $N_Z = 1.547$, $N_Z - N_X = 0.125$. Also $N_X = 1.445$, $N_Y = 1.505$, $N_Z = 1.540$, $N_Z - N_X = 0.095$. Again: $N_X = 1.417$, $N_Y = 1.506$, $N_Z = 1.550$, $N_Z - N_X = 0.133$.
Ref: 117, 136a, 137, 152, 433b.

Potassium acid oxalate or potassium bioxalate $[(CO_2)_2KH]$ is monoclinic prismatic with *a*:*b*:*c* = 0.335:1:0.801, $\beta = 133°29'$. Space group $P2_1/c$. *a* 4.32, *b* 12.88, *c* 10.32 Å. U.C. 4. Crystals show {001}, {010}, {110}, {100}, {011}, etc. Perfect 100 and distinct 010 cleavages. D 2.0. The optic plane and Z are normal to 010 X nearly normal to 100. (-)2V = 37°13′, r < v very weak. N_Y = 1.4945 (Groth). N_X = 1.415, N_Y = 1.545, N_Z = 1.565, $N_Z - N_X$ = 0.150, (-)2V = 52° *ca.* Also (-)2V = 34°, N_X = 1.382, N_Y = 1.553, N_Z = 1.573, $N_Z - N_X$ = 0.191. Ref: 117, 136a, 137, 152, 582.

Rubidium acid oxalate or rubidium bioxalate [$(CO_2)_2RbH$] is monoclinic prismatic with $a:b:c$ = 0.315:1:0.762, β = 133°15′. Space group $P2_1/c$; a 4.30, b 13.63, c 10.39 Å. U.C. 4. Crystals striated prisms with {110}, {001}, {011}, {010}, etc. D 2.55. The optic plane is 010; X nearly normal to 100; (-)2V = 36°, N_X = 1.386, N_Y = 1.555, N_Z = 1.583, $N_Z - N_X$ = 0.197.
Ref: 117, 136a, 152.

Sodium acid oxalate monohydrate or sodium bioxalate monohydrate [$(CO_2)_2NaH \cdot N_2O$] is triclinic with $a:b:c$ = 0.575:1:0.590, α = 95°26′, β = 104°48′, γ = 70°6′. Crystals {010} tablets with {001}, {110}, {$1\bar{1}0$}, etc. Perfect 110 and $1\bar{1}0$ cleavages. D 1.925. (-)2V = 52° calc. N_X = 1.386, N_Y = 1.533, N_Z = 1.576, $N_Z - N_X$ = 0.190. Ref: 117, 136a, 152.

Ammonium acid dioxalate dihydrate or ammonium tetraoxalate dihydrate [$(CO_2)_4NH_4H_3 \cdot 2H_2O$] is triclinic with $a:b:c$ = 0.602:1:0.687, α = 85°49′, β = 97°50′, γ = 79°43′. Crystals equant or pinacoidal tabular with {100}, {110}, {001}, {011}, etc. Perfect 001, distinct 100, and fair 110 cleavages. D 1.655. The optic plane is nearly normal to the zone $\bar{1}10:\bar{1}11$; it makes an angle of 30°23′ with c. (-)2V = 39°55′ Na, with strong dispersion. N_X = 1.4237 Na, N_Y = 1.5500, N_Z = 1.5687, $N_Z - N_X$ = 0.1450. Ref: 117, 278.

Potassium acid dioxalate dihydrate or potassium tetraoxalate dihydrate [$(CO_2)_4KH_3 \cdot 2H_2O$] is triclinic with $a:b:c$ = 0.600:1:0.664, α = 86°2′, β = 100°4′, γ = 78°42′. Crystals equant or pinacoidal tabular with {010}, {100}, {001}, {011}, {110}, etc. Perfect 001 and 100 and distinct 110 cleavages. D 1.860. The optic plane is nearly normal to the zone $\bar{1}10:\bar{1}11$. The optic plane makes an angle of 32° with c. (-)2V = 45°54′ Na, with strong dispersion. N_X = 1.4152 Na, N_Y = 1.5364, N_Z = 1.5604, $N_Z - N_X$ = 0.1452. Ref: 278.

Rubidium acid dioxalate dihydrate or rubidium tetraoxalate dihydrate [$(CO_2)_4RbH_3 \cdot 2H_2O$] is triclinic with $a:b:c$ = 0.591:1:0.677, α = 85°20′, β = 97°43.5′, γ = 79°36′. Crystals equant or pinacoidal tabular with {001}, {010}, {110}, {100}, {011}, etc. Perfect 001 and 100 and distinct 110 cleavages. D 2.124. The optic plane is nearly normal to the zone $\bar{1}10:\bar{1}11$. The optic plane makes an angle of 29°30′ with c; it is nearly parallel to the edge $\bar{1}\bar{1}1:\bar{1}\bar{1}0$. (-)2V = 38°51′ Na, with strong dispersion. N_X = 1.4210, N_Y = 1.5428, N_Z = 1.5595, $N_Z - N_X$ = 0.1385. Ref: 278.

Caesium acid dioxalate dihydrate or caesium tetraoxalate dihydrate [$(CO_2)_4CsH_3 \cdot 2H_2O$] is triclinic with $a:b:c$ = 0.583:1:0.692, α = 85°23′, β = 95°13′, γ = 80°34′. Crystals equant or pinacoidal tabular with {010}, {001}, {100}, {110}, {011}, etc. Good 001, fair 100 and 110 cleavages. D 2.352. The optic plane is nearly normal to the zone $\bar{1}10:\bar{1}11$, and makes an angle of 30°56′ with c. (-)2V = 30°36′ Na, with strong dispersion. N_X = 1.4365 Na, N_Y = 1.5523, N_Z = 1.5621, $N_Z - N_X$ = 0.1256. Ref: 278.

Thallous acid dioxalate dihydrate or thallous tetraoxalate dihydrate [$(CO_2)_4TlH_3 \cdot 2H_2O$] is triclinic with $a:b:c = 0.585:1:0.686$, $\alpha = 84°58'$, $\beta = 96°59'$, $\gamma = 80°4'$. Crystals equant or pinacoidal tabular with {010}, {100}, {110}, {001}, {011}, etc. Fair 001, 100, and 110 cleavages. D 2.992. The optic plane is nearly normal to the zone 010:001 and makes an angle of 49°52′ with *c*. (-)2V = 43°49′ Na, r < v very strong. $N_X = 1.5097$ Na, $N_Y = 1.6319$, $N_Z = 1.6538$, $N_Z - N_X = 0.1441$. Ref: 278.

Tetrapotassium trioxalate dihydrate [$(CO_2)_6K_4H_2 \cdot 2H_2O$] is orthorhombic with D 1.213. $N_X = 1.48$, $N_Y = 1.52$, $N_Z = 1.55$, $N_Z - N_X = 0.07$. (-)2V = 80° *ca.* Ref: 126.

Sodium oxalate [$(CO_2)_2Na_2$] is monoclinic in acicular forms often spherulitic. D 2.335. (-)2V = 70° calc. $N_X = 1.410$, $N_Y = 1.528$, $N_Z = 1.587$, $N_Z - N_X = 0.177$. Ref: 136a.

Lithium oxalate [$(CO_2)_2Li_2$] is orthorhombic with $a:b:c = 0.853:1:0.790$. D 2.12. (+)2V = 65° calc. $N_X = 1.465$, $N_Y = 1.53$, $N_Z = 1.696$, $N_Z - N_X = 0.231$. Ref: 136a.

Ammonium oxalate monohydrate [$(CO_2)_2(NH_4)_2 \cdot H_2O$] is orthorhombic disphenoidal with $a:b:c = 0.780:1:0.370$. Space group $P2_12_12$. *a* 8.04, *b* 10.27, *c* 3.82 Å. U.C. 2. Crystals prismatic to acicular with {010}, {100}, {001}, etc.; also sphenoidal. Imperfect 001 cleavage. H = soft. D 1.48 *ca.* Soluble in water. The optic plane is 100; X = *c*. (-)2V = 60°48′ red, 61°44′ Na, 63°14′ green. $N_X = 1.4369$ red, 1.4383 Na, 1.4400 green; $N_Y = 1.5470$ red, 1.5475 Na, 1.5486 green; $N_Z = 1.5904$ red, 1.5950 Na, 1.5966 green; $N_Z - N_X = 0.1567$ Na. The natural substance is called "oxammite". Ref: 117, 136a, 485b.

Potassium oxalate monohydrate [$(CO_2)_2K_2 \cdot H_2O$] is monoclinic with $a:b:c = 1.477:1:1.710$, $\beta = 110°58'$. Space group $C2/c$. *a* 9.32, *b* 6.17, *c* 10.65 Å. U.C. 4. Crystals {001} tablets with {111}, {11$\bar{1}$}, {100}, etc. D 2.15. The optic plane is 010; X ∧ *c* = − 40°45′. (-)2H = 97° (Groth). $N_X = 1.440$, $N_Y = 1.485$, $N_Z = 1.550$, $N_Z - N_X = 0.110$, (+)2V = 83° *ca.* Also (+)2V = 86°, $N_X = 1.434$, $N_Y = 1.493$, $N_Z = 1.560$, $N_Z - N_X = 0.126$.
Ref: 117, 136a, 137, 152, 485a.

Rubidium oxalate monohydrate [$(CO_2)_2Rb_2 \cdot H_2O$] is monoclinic prismatic with $a:b:c = 1.514:1:1.755$, $\beta = 110°30'$. Space group $C2/c$; *a* 9.66, *b* 6.38, *c* 11.20. U.C. 4. Crystals show {11$\bar{1}$}, {111}, {001}, {10$\bar{1}$}. D 2.76. The optic plane is 010: X ∧ *c* = 41°45′. $N_X = 1.438$, $N_Y = 1.485$, $N_Z = 1.557$, $N_Z - N_X = 0.119$. (+)2V = 80° calc. Ref: 117, 136a, 137.

Caesium oxalate monohydrate [$(CO_2)_2Cs_2 \cdot H_2O$] is biaxial. D 3.23. (+)2V = 80° calc. $N_X = 1.493$, $N_Y = 1.540$, $N_Z = 1.612$, $N_Z - N_X = 0.119$. Ref: 136a.

Calcium oxalate monohydrate [$(CO_2)_2Ca \cdot H_2O$] is monoclinic with $a:b:c = 0.870:1:1.370$, $\beta = 107°18'$. Crystals with {110}, {120}, {010}, {001}, etc. Frequent twinning on 10$\bar{1}$. 001, 010, 110, and 10$\bar{1}$ cleavages. H 2.5. D 2.23. Soluble in acid. The optic plane and X are normal to 010; Z ∧ *c* = − 29°.

(+)2E = 84°, r < v weak. (+)2V = 51°. N_X = 1.490, N_Y = 1.555, N_Z = 1.650, $N_Z - N_X$ = 0.160. Colorless. The natural substance is called *whewellite*.
Ref: 117, 357.

d-Potassium rhodium oxalate monohydrate $[(CO_2)_3RhK_3 \cdot H_2O]$ is trigonal trapezohedral with c/a = 0.894. Crystals may resemble quartz with $\{10\bar{1}0\}$, $\{01\bar{1}1\}$, $\{10\bar{1}1\}$, {0001}, etc. No distinct cleavage. Uniaxial negative with N_O = 1.6052, N_E = 1.5804, $N_O - N_E$ = 0.0248. Also slightly biaxial. Pleochroic with O = blood red, E = orange. [α] = + 21° (638), - 62° Na, - 85° (542); the *l*-form has the same indices. Ref: 155.

Oxalmolybdic acid monohydrate, or molybdenum oxalate monohydrate $[(CO_2)_2(MoO_3) \cdot H_2O]$ is monoclinic with $a:b:c$ = 0.917:1:1.073, β = 93°52′. Crystals short prisms with {210}, {001}, $\{11\bar{1}\}$, etc. N_X = 1.52, N_Y = 1.53, N_Z = 1.55, $N_Z - N_X$ = 0.03. (+)2V = 70° calc. Ref: 34, 35, 117.

Calcium oxalate dihydrate $[(CO_2)_2Ca \cdot 2H_2O]$ is tetragonal with c/a = 0.594. Crystals pyramidal, encrusting. H 4. D 1.94? Uniaxial positive with N_O = 1.523, N_E = 1.544, $N_E - N_O$ = 0.02 *ca*. The natural substance is called *weddellite*. Ref: 19.

Ferrous oxalate dihydrate $[(CO_2)_2Fe \cdot 2H_2O]$ is orthorhombic with $a:b:c$ = 0.773:1:1.104. Crystals prismatic with perfect 110 and distinct 100 and 010 cleavages. H 2. D 2.28. Soluble in acid. The optic plane is 010; Z = *c*. (+)2V = large. N_X = 1.494, N_Y = 1.561, N_Z = 1.692, $N_Z - N_X$ = 0.198 (nat. cryst.). Color yellowish with X = pale yellowish green, Y = pale greenish yellow, Z = intense yellow. The natural substance is called "*humboldtite*" or "*oxalite*". Ref: 232.

Beryllium oxalate trihydrate $[(CO_2)_2Be \cdot 3H_2O]$ is orthorhombic with $a:b:c$ = 0.853:1:1.663. Crystals pyramidal with {111}, {001}, {011}, {101}. No distinct cleavage. The optic plane is 010; Z = *a*. (+)2V = 84°26′, no noticeable dispersion. N_Y = 1.4869 D. Ref: 117.

Calcium oxalate trihydrate $[(CO_2)_2Ca \cdot 3H_2O]$ is tetragonal with c/a = 0.412. Crystals pyramidal with {111}, {301}, {110}, etc. Twinning on 201. D 2.122. Uniaxial positive with N_O = 1.552, N_E = 1.583, $N_E - N_O$ = 0.031. Bannister argues that tetragonal calcium oxalate is actually the dihydrate, but his conclusion is not accepted. Ref: 19, 91, 117, 194.

Strontium oxalate hemipentahydrate $[(CO_2)_2Sr \cdot 2.5H_2O]$ is tetragonal dipyramidal with c/a = 0.580. Space group $I4/m$; *a* 12.795, *c* 7.509 Å. Crystals show {100} and {101}. D 2.384. Uniaxial positive with N_O = 1.517, N_E = 1.535, $N_E - N_O$ = 0.018. Ref: 194.

Calcium chloro-oxalate dihydrate $[(Cl_2C_2O_4Ca_2 \cdot 2H_2O)]$ is monoclinic in prismatic crystals with β = about 95°. The optic plane is 010; X $\wedge$ *c* = + 40°. (-)2V = 87° (calc), 85° (est.), r < v weak. N_X = 1.571, N_Y = 1.648, N_Z = 1.718, $N_Z - N_X$ = 0.147. N_1 (common view) = 1.596, N_2 = 1.698. Colorless.
Ref: 507.

Calcium chloro-oxalate heptahydrate $[(Cl_2C_2O_4Ca_2 \cdot 7H_2O)]$ is monoclinic in thin {010} plates with β = about 102°. The optic plane and X are normal to 010; $Z \wedge c = +23°$. (-)2V = 71°, r < v weak. $N_X = 1.500$, $N_Y = 1.545$, $N_Z = 1.568$, $N_Z - N_X = 0.068$. Colorless. Ref: 507.

Potassium aluminum oxalate hexahydrate $[(CO_2)_{12}Al_2K_6 \cdot 6H_2O]$ is monoclinic with $a:b:c = 1.006:1:0.396$, $\beta = 93°23'$. Crystals show {110}, {230}, {111}, etc. $10\bar{1}$ parting. D 2.026. The optic plane is 010; $Z \wedge a = -11°$. (+)2H = 70°44′ Li, 71°12′ Na, 71°36′ Tl (in benzene, N = 1.50). $N_X = 1.49$, $N_Y = 1.493$ calc., $N_Z = 1.50$, $N_Z - N_X = 0.01$. (+)2V = 71° calc. Marked inclined dispersion. Ref: 197.

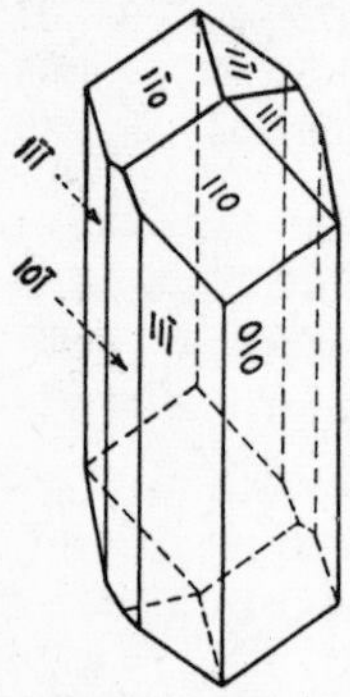

Fig. 10. Potassium ferric oxalate hexahydrate.

Potassium ferric oxalate hexahydrate $[(CO_2)_{12}Fe_2K_6 \cdot 6H_2O]$ is monoclinic with $a:b:c = 0.992:1:0.390$, $\beta = 94°14'$. Crystals often {010} plates or prisms with $\{11\bar{1}\}$, {110}, {010}, {111}, etc. Fig. 10. 111 parting. D 2.133. The optic plane is 010; $X \wedge c = -2°$. (-)2V = 79°36′ Li, 78°49′ Na, 77°53′ Tl. $N_X = 1.5019$ Na, $N_Y = 1.5558$, $N_Z = 1.5960$, $N_Z - N_X = 0.0941$. Also: $N_X = 1.51$, $N_Y = 1.55$ $N_Z = 1.605$, $N_Z - N_X = 0.095$. Marked inclined dispersion. Color green; pleochroic; X < Z. Ref: 34, 117, 197.

Sodium ammonium aluminum oxalate hexahydrate $[(CO_2)_{12}Al_2(NH_4, Na)_6 \cdot 6H_2O]$ is triclinic* with $a:b:c = 0.975:1:0.956$, $\alpha = 97°10'$, $\beta = 78°53'$, $\gamma = 108°52'$. Crystals show {010}, {001}, {100}, {110}, {032}, etc. Good 001 cleavage. D 1.708. X is nearly normal to 001. The optic plane makes an angle of 25° with *a* and 46°10′ with *b*. (-)2E = 138°, r > v. $N_X = 1.465$, $N_Y = 1.48$, $N_Z = 1.50$, $N_Z - N_X = 0.035$. (-)2V = 78°40′ calc. Ref: 307.

Rubidium aluminum oxalate hexahydrate $[(CO_2)_{12}Al_2Rb_6 \cdot 6H_2O]$ is monoclinic with $a:b:c = 1.019:1:0.405$, $\beta = 95°2'$. Crystals {010} tablets or prismatic with {010}, {110}, {111}, $\{11\bar{1}\}$, etc. The optic plane is 010; $Z \wedge c = 5°$ *ca.* (-)2V = 80°32′. $N_Y = 1.494$, $N_Z - N_X$ = very strong. Ref: 117.

Sodium ammonium aluminum oxalate heptahydrate $[(CO_2)_{12}Al_2(Na, NH_4)_6 \cdot 7H_2O]$ is monoclinic with $a:b:c = 0.535:1:0.186$, $\beta = 90°17'$. Crystals show {010}, {210}, {650}, {412}, etc. 010 and $\bar{1}\bar{1}1$ cleavages. D 1.749. $N_X = 1.47$, $N_Y = 1.48$, $N_Z = 1.50$, $N_Z - N_X = 0.03$. The same compound is described by Wyrouboff as monoclinic with $a:b:c = 0.607:1:0.428$, $\beta = 90°30'$. Crystals often {010} tablets with $\{11\bar{1}\}$ and {101}. Perfect 010 cleavage. The optic plane and X are normal to 010; $Z \wedge c = -76°$. (-)2E = 134°, r < v weak. (If $N_Y = 1.48$, 2V must be 77° - A.N.W.). Heat does not change these properties until loss of water ($6H_2O$) occurs (at 110°); then the birefringence decreases, the optic plane becomes normal to *c*, and the optic angle decreases, becoming

---

[1] *a* and *b* interchanged to make *b* > *a*.

nearly zero with complete dehydration. Loss of $2H_2O$ (over H_2SO_4) has little effect on the properties. Ref: 117, 307, 394.

Sodium ferric oxalate decahydrate $[(CO_2)_{12}Fe_2Na_6 \cdot 10H_2O]$ is monoclinic with $a:b:c = 1.369:1:1.201$, $\beta = 100°15'$. Crystals {001} tablets or short prismatic with {001}, {110}, {111}, {11$\bar{1}$}, etc. Distinct 001 cleavage. The optic plane is 010; $X \wedge c = -12°$. (-)2V = 30°, r > v. $N_Y = 1.534$ red, 1.537 yellow, 1.542 green. Pleochroic with X = greenish yellow, Y and Z = deep grass-green. Ref: 117.

Lanthanum oxalate decahydrate $\{La_2(C_2O_4)_3 \cdot 10H_2O\}$ is monoclinic with $a:b:c = 1.233:1:1.084$, $\beta = 119°$. *a* 11.91, *b* 9.66, *c* 10.47 Å. U.C. 2. D 2.30. Cleavage on 010. Twinning on 100. $X = b$, $Z \wedge c = -63.5°$. (-)2V = 77°, $N_X = 1.473$, $N_Y = 1.548$, $N_Z = 1.601$, $N_Z - N_X = 0.128$. Ref: 553d.

Potassium *trans*-diaminodinitro-oxalato-cobaltiate monohydrate $[K[Co(NH_3)_2(NO_2)_2C_2O_4] \cdot H_2O]$ is monoclinic with $a:b:c = 1.156:1:0.939$, $\beta = 92°47'$. Crystals show {120}, {001}, {100}, etc. No cleavage observed. D 2.093. The optic plane is 010; $X \wedge c$ = very small. (+)2V = large. $N_X = 1.56$, $N_Y = 1.65$, $N_Z > 1.74$ and < 1.77, $N_Z - N_X = 0.2$ *ca.* Color reddish brown with X > Y > Z. Ref: 197.

Barium *cis*-diaminodinitro-oxalato-cobaltiate trihydrate $[Ba[Co(NH_3)_2(NO_2)_2(CO_2)_2] \cdot 3H_2O]$ is hexagonal scalenohedral with $c/a = 0.659$. No cleavage observed. D 2.142. Uniaxial negative with N_O = very high, $N_E = 1.5607$, $N_O - N_E$ = ?. Ref: 197.

Potassium iridium oxalate potassium chloride octahydrate $[2(CO_2)_3IrK_3 \cdot KCl \cdot 8H_2O]$ is rhombohedral with $c/a = 0.912$. Crystals rhombohedral with {10$\bar{1}$1}, {0001}, {20$\bar{2}$1}. Uniaxial negative with $N_O = 1.5681$ D, $N_E = 1.4498$, $N_O - N_E = 0.1183$. Color yellow. Ref: 73.

Potassium iridium chloro-oxalate monohydrate $[(CO_2)_4Cl_2IrK_3 \cdot H_2O]$ is monoclinic with $a:b:c = 1.197:1:1.200$, $\beta = 99°40'$. Crystals imperfect with {101}, {10$\bar{1}$}, etc. Perfect 10$\bar{1}$ cleavage. The optic plane is 010; $Z \wedge c = -14°$. (+)2V = 76°23′. $N_Y = 1.592$ Na. Color deep red with little pleochroism. An optic axis nearly normal to 101. Ref: 117.

Potassium iridium dichlorodinitro-oxalate dihydrate $[(CO_2)_2(NO_2)_2Cl_2IrK_3 \cdot 3H_2O]$ is orthorhombic with $a:b:c = 0.591:1:0.815$. Crystals thick {010} tablets or short prisms with {110}, {010}, {011}, etc. No distinct cleavage. The optic plane is 100; $Z = b$. (+)2V = 38°49′, r < v strong. $N_X = 1.5689$, $N_Y = 1.5791$, $N_Z = 1.6692$, $N_Z - N_X = 0.1003$ Na. Color yellow. Ref: 117.

Potassium platinum nitrito-oxalate monohydrate $[(CO_2)_2(NO_2)_2PtK_2 \cdot H_2O]$ is monoclinic with $a:b:c = 0.889:1:0.789$, $\beta = 93°11'$. Crystals thick {010} tablets with {210}, {102}, etc. Perfect 10$\bar{2}$ cleavage. The optic plane is normal to 010 and X makes an angle with *c* of + 21°45′ Li, + 24° Na, + 26°50′ Tl. 2V (meas. about Z or *b*) = 90°40′ Li, 89°40′ Na, 88°29′ Tl. $N_X = 1.5343$ Li,

1.5450 Na, 1.5579 Tl; N_Y = 1.6319 Li, 1.6414 Na, 1.6510 Tl; N_Z = 1.7478 Li, 1.7600 Na, 1.7698 Tl, $N_Z - N_X$ = 0.2150 Na. Color clear yellow, only weakly pleochroic in yellow. Ref: 117.

Potassium platinum oxalate dihydrate [$K_2Pt(C_2O_4)_2 \cdot 2H_2O$] is dimorphous. One phase is monoclinic prismatic with $a:b:c = 0.471:1:0.434$, $\beta = 112°53'$. Space group $P2_1/c$. a 6.68, b 14.03, c 6.15 Å. U.C. 2. Basal cleavage. D 3.03. The optic plane is 010; $Z \wedge c = 23°$ (in obtuse β). (Dufet). (+)2V = 81.5°, r > v, N_X = 1.437, N_Y = 1.555, N_Z = 1.774, $N_Z - N_X$ = 0.337 for λ = 578 and N_X = 1.450, N_Y = 1.575, N_Z = 1.824, $N_Z - N_X$ = 0.374 for λ = 436. Color yellow with X = orange yellow, Z = pale yellow to colorless (Dufet). Not pleochroic (Lambot). Ref: 449, 538.

Potassium nickel dithio-oxalate [$K_2Ni(COS)_4$] is dimorphous. One phase (I) crystallizing below 10° forms needles; it inverts at about 10° to phase II which forms equant pyramidal crystals that are monoclinic prismatic with $a:b:c$ = 1.764:1:2.866, β = 109°4′. Perfect 100 and poor 010 cleavages. D 2.13. N = 1.54 for light vibrating normal to 100. Parallel extinction. Strongly pleochroic with [100] = deep red, b = pale brown, c = black. Ref: 479.

Monomethyl oxalate [$H(CO_2)_2CH_3$] is biaxial with D 1.42. M.P. 54°. (+)2V = 70° calc. N_X = 1.4162, N_Y = 1.4603, N_Z = 1.5502, $N_Z - N_X$ = 0.134. Ref: 152.

Methyl oxalate or dimethyl oxalate [$(CO_2)_2(CH_3)_2$] is monoclinic with $a:b:c$ = 0.332:1:0.523, β = 103°22′. Crystals {010} tablets with {110}, {011}, or {120}, {021}. Perfect 010 cleavage. Plates normal to X have Z parallel with elongation. M.P. 54°. Parallel extinction with N_X = 1.43, N_Y = 1.55, N_Z = 1.58, $N_Z - N_X$ = 0.15, (-)2V = 70° calc. Again: (+)2V = 74°, N_X = 1.418, N_Y = 1.468, N_Z = 1.559, $N_Z - N_X$ = 0.141 (for λ = 5461). Ref: 34, 35, 117, 556a.

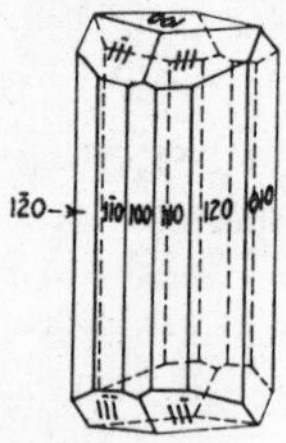

Fig. 11. Sodium bimalonate monohydrate.

Ethyl ethanamic acid or ethyl oxamate or oxamethan [$NH_2 \cdot CO \cdot CO_2(C_2H_5)$] is orthorhombic with $a:b:c$ = 0.577:1: 0.713. Crystals {010} plates with {110}, {011}, have parallel extinction and negative elongation. Biaxial with N_1=1.545+, N_2 = 1.620, $N_2 - N_1$ = 0.075–. Ref: 93, 117.

Malonic acid ($C_3H_4O_4$) is triclinic in lath-shaped to acicular crystals. M.P. 135.5°. Positive elongation. (+)2V = 27°, r < v weak. N_X = 1.448, N_Y = 1.488, N_Z = 1.578, $N_Z - N_X$ = 0.130. (2V from indices is 69°). Ref: 433b.

Sodium acid propanedioate monohydrate or sodium acid malonate monohydrate or sodium bimalonate monohydrate [$CH_2(CO_2)_2NaH \cdot H_2O$] is orthorhombic with $a:b:c$ = 0.639:1:0.418. Crystals short prismatic with {010}, {120}, {110}, {100}, {001}, {111}. Fig. 11. Perfect 001 and distinct 100 cleavages. The optic plane is 100; X = c. (-)2V = 39°20′. N_X = 1.4069, N_Y = 1.5237, N_Z = 1.5408, $N_Z - N_X$ = 0.1339 Na. Ref: 117.

Ammonium salt of 2-cyano-2-nitroethanamide or ammonium salt of α-cyano-α-nitroacetamide or ammonium fulminurate $[(NH_4)C(NO_2)(CN)\cdot CONH_2]$ is monoclinic with $a:b:c = 1.821:1:2.402$, $\beta = 100°54'$. Crystals show {001}, {10$\bar{1}$}, {100}, {101}, {111}. Refringence, dispersion, and birefringence very strong. $N_Y = 1.755$ *ca.* Ref: 117.

Butanedioic Acid, or 1,2-Ethanedicarboxylic Acid, or Succinic Acid and Derivatives

Succinic acid $(CO_2H\cdot CH_2\cdot CH_2\cdot CO_2H)$ has two crystals phases. The α-phase (I), stable above 137°, is triclinic with $a:b:c = 0.835:1:1.105$, $\alpha = 106°10'$, $\beta = 116°$, $\gamma = 83°20'$. Space group $P\bar{1}$; *a* 5.72, *b* 6.85, *c* 7.57 Å. U.C. 2. Often twinned on 010 to pseudo-monoclinic forms. Z nearly parallel with *c* (elongation of needles). $N_X = 1.513$, $N_Y = ?$, $N_Z = 1.597$, $N_Z - N_X = 0.084$ Na. The β-phase (II), stable below 137°, is monoclinic prismatic with $a:b:c = 0.574:1:0.857$, $\beta = 133°37'$. Space group $P2_1/a$: *a* 5.10, *b* 8.88, *c* 7.61 Å. U.C. 2. Crystals six-sided {001} tablets with {111}, {110}, {010}, {011}. Common twinning on 001. Perfect 010 and good 111 cleavages. D 1.56. M.P. 185°. The optic plane is 010; $X \wedge c = 47°$. (-)2V = 87° calc. $N_X = 1.450$, $N_Y = 1.534$, $N_Z = 1.610$, $N_Z - N_X = 0.160$. Again: (-)2V = 85°, r > v, weak. $N_X = 1.448$, $N_Y = 1.531$, $N_Z = 1.610$, $N_Z - N_X = 0.162$.
Ref: 75, 117, 152, 240, 433b, 575, 610.

Ammonium acid succinate $[(CH_2CO_2)_2HNH_4]$ is triclinic with 010, 001, and 1$\bar{1}$0 cleavages. Crystals show {011}, {0$\bar{1}$1}, {001}, {010}, {110}, etc. $110 \wedge 1\bar{1}0 = 44°6'$; $010 \wedge 001 = 89°7'$; $100 \wedge 110 = 20°30'$. Extinction at 37° and $N_1 = 1.52$, $N_2 = 1.59$, $N_2 - N_1 = 0.07$ (on acid or neutral salt?).
Ref: 35, 117.

Potassium acid succinate dihydrate $[(CH_2CO_2)_2HK\cdot 2H_2O]$ is orthorhombic with $a:b:c = 0.502:1:1.016$. Crystals prismatic with {110}, {010}, {011}, {100}, etc. Perfect 110 cleavage. D 1.62. The optic plane is 001; X = *a*. (-)2V = very small. $N_X = 1.417$, $N_Y = 1.5295$, $N_Z = 1.533$, $N_Z - N_X = 0.116$ Na.
Ref: 117.

Barium succinate $[(CH_2\cdot CO_2)_2Ba]$ forms tetragonal prisms or basal tablets with bipyramid faces. Prisms have positive elongation and parallel extinction. Uniaxial positive with $N_O = 1.580$, $N_E = 1.633$, $N_E - N_O = 0.053$. Colorless.
Ref: 450a.

Calcium succinate trihydrate $[(CH_2CO_2)_2Ca\cdot 3H_2O]$ is biaxial with (-)2V = 87° calc., $N_X = 1.460$, $N_Y = 1.540$, $N_Z = 1.610$, $N_Z - N_X = 0.150$. Ref: 152.

Sodium succinate hexahydrate $[(CH_2CO_2)_2Na_2\cdot 6H_2O]$ is monoclinic with $a:b:c = 0.983:1:1.669$, $\beta = 103°21'$. Crystals show {110}, {10$\bar{1}$}, {001}, {011}, etc. Also described as triclinic. "Bernsteinsaures Natrium" has parallel extinction and positive elongation with $N_1 = 1.40$, $N_2 = 1.49$, $N_2 - N_1 = 0.09$. Is this the hexahydrate? Ref: 34, 35, 117.

Butanedinitrile disilver nitrate or succinonitrile disilver nitrate or ethylene dicyanide disilver nitrate [$(CH_2CN)_2 \cdot 2AgNO_3$] is orthorhombic disphenoidal with $a:b:c = 0.728:1:2.543$. Sphenoidal faces often prominent. Fig. 12. No distinct cleavage. D 3.35. The optic plane is 001; $X = b$. (-)2V = 42°3′ Li, 42°36′ Na. $N_Y = 1.6598$ Li, 1.6657 Na. Ref: 117.

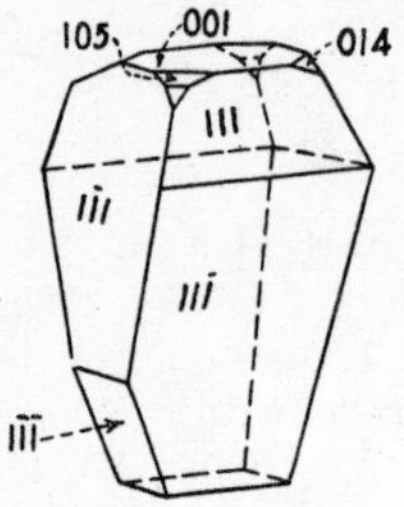

Fig. 12. Ethylene dicyanide disilver nitrate.

Succinonitrile ($NC \cdot CH_2 \cdot CH_2 \cdot CN$) is probably isometric. Crystals equant. D 1.02. M.P. 57.7° C. N = 1.440. Ref: 405a.

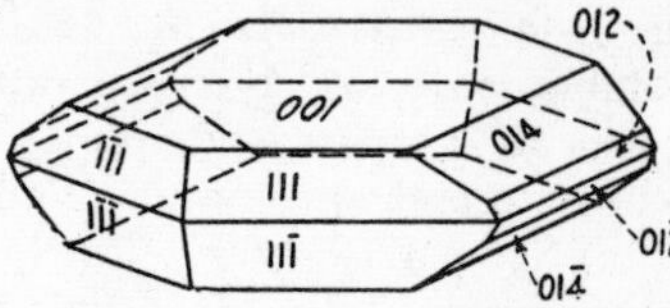

Fig. 13. Ethylene dicyanide tetrasilver nitrate.

Butanedinitrile tetrasilver nitrate or succinonitrile tetrasilver nitrate or ethylene dicyanide tetrasilver nitrate [$(CH_2CN)_2 \cdot 4AgNO_3$] is orthorhombic with $a:b:c = 0.762:1:2.649$. Crystals {001} tablets with {111}, {014}, etc. Fig. 13. Distinct 110 cleavage. D 3.24. The optic plane is 001; $X = a$. (-)2V = 42°32′ Li, 43°41′ Na. $N_Y = 1.6438$ Li, 1.6543 Na. Ref: 117.

Glutaric acid ($C_5H_8O_4$) is monoclinic with $a:b:c = 2.148:1:3.573$, $\beta = 132°36'$ a 10.06, b 4.87, c 17.40 Å. U.C. 4. Crystals acicular. M.P. 98°. D 1.40. $Y = b$, $Z \wedge c = 8°$. Positive elongation. (+)2V = 80°, r > v weak. $N_X = 1.451$, $N_Y = 1.502$, $N_Z = 1.585$, $N_Z - N_X = 0.134$. Ref: 433b.

2-Methylbutanedioic acid or methylsuccinic acid or pyrotartaric acid [$HO_2C \cdot CH(CH_3) \cdot CH_2 \cdot CO_2H$] has parallel extinction and positive elongation with $N_1 = 1.49$, $N_2 = 1.58$, $N_2 - N_1 = 0.09$. Ref: 34, 35.

2,2-Dimethylpropanedioic acid or dimethylmalonic acid [$(CH_3)_2C(CO_2H)_2$] is tetragonal trapezohedral with $c/a = 1.283$. Crystals pyramidal with {101}, {001}, {100}, {112}, etc. D 1.357. No good cleavage. Uniaxial positive with $N_O = 1.197$, $N_E = 1.266$, $N_E - N_O = 0.069$ D. (These indices seem to be too low–A.N.W.) Ref: 72.

Adipic acid or hexanedioic acid or 1,4-butanedicarboxylic acid [$CO_2H(CH_2)_4 \cdot CO_2H$] is monoclinic prismatic with $a:b:c = 1.990:1:1.942$, $\beta = 137°5'$. Space group $P2_1/c$. a 10.27, b 5.16, c 10.02 Å. U.C. 2. D 1.36. M.P. 152°. Crystals {001} tablets long || b. X nearly normal to 100; $Y = b$. $Z \wedge c = 3°$ in acute β. (+)2V = 74°, r < v weak. $N_X = 1.488$, $N_Y = 1.505$, $N_Z = 1.593$, $N_Z - N_X = 0.105$ (for $\lambda = 5461$). $N_X = 1.466$, $N_Y = 1.506$, $N_Z = 1.590$, $N_Z - N_X = 0.124$ (for $\lambda = 5893$). Again: $N_X = 1.464$, $N_Z = 1.592$. Ref: 117, 433b, 553, 556a.

2,2-Dimethylpropanediamide or α,α-dimethylmalonamide [$C(CH_3)_2(CONH_2)_2$] is orthorhombic with $a:b:c = 0.524:1:0.896$. Crystals thick prismatic with

{110}, {010}, {001}, etc. Perfect 110 and imperfect 010 and 001 cleavages. M.P. 198°. The optic plane is 010, X = *c*. (+)2V = 37°44′ Na. N_X = 1.500 calc., N_Y = 1.5100, N_Z = 1.6073 Na, $N_Z - N_X$ = 0.107 calc. Ref: 117.

Pimelic acid or heptanedioic acid {$HO_2C \cdot (CH_2)_5 \cdot CO_2H$} is monoclinic prismatic with *a*:*b*:*c* = 4.551:1:2.043, β = 131°. Space group $P2_1/c$. *a* 22.12, *b* 4.86, *c* 9.93 Å. U.C. 4. Crystals {001} tablets or rods with {100}, {120}. D. 1.32. M.P. 103 - 105°. X = *b*, Z ∧ *c* = 2° in obtuse β. (+)2V = 67°, r < v, N_X = 1.460, N_Y = 1.492, N_Z = 1.580, $N_Z - N_X$ = 0.120. Again: N_X = 1.458, N_Y = 1.492, N_Z = 1.579. Ref: 433b, 552, 553a.

Suberic acid ($C_8H_{14}O_4$) is monoclinic in lamellar crystals. M.P. 144°. (+)2V = 72°, r < v. N_X = 1.469, N_Y = 1.507, N_Z = 1.587, $N_Z - N_X$ = 0.118. Ref: 433b.

Decanedioic acid or sebacic acid [$HOOC(CH_2)_8COOH$] is monoclinic prismatic. Space group $P2_1/c$. *a* 10.05, *b* 4.96, *c* 15.02 Å. β = 133°50′. U.C. 2. (Caspari); Crystals lamellar and tabular. N_1 = 1.53, N_2 = 1.54, $N_2 - N_1$ = 0.01 (Bolland). (+)2E = 96°, 2V = 59°, N_X = 1.483, N_Y = 1.510, N_Z = 1.578, $N_Z - N_X$ = 0.095 (Kirkpatrick). Again: (+)2V = 71°, r > v weak. N_X = 1.470, N_Y = 1.507, N_Z = 1.589, $N_Z - N_X$ = 0.119.
Ref: 34, 35, 431, 433b, 529, 579, 589.

Azelaic acid ($C_9H_{16}O_4$) is monoclinic in tabular crystals. M.P. 106°. (+)2V = 63°, r < v. N_X = 1.466, N_Y = 1.495, N_Z = 1.582, $N_Z - N_X$ = 0.166. Ref: 433b.

Fumaric acid $\left[\begin{array}{r} HC \cdot CO_2H \\ HO_2C \cdot \ddot{C}H \end{array}\right]$ is monoclinic prismatic with *a*:*b*:*c* = 0.513:1:0.438, β = 117°5′. Space group $P2_1/c$; *a* 7.60, *b* 15.11, *c* 6.61 Å. U.C. 6. D 1.625. M.P. 293 - 295°. Crystals prisms, needles or plates, usually irregular, with an angle of about 70°; Y bisects this angle and Z is normal to the plates. Twinning common. N_X = 1.387 ± .003, N_Y = 1.614 ± .003. Ref: 573a, 599.

Sodium fumarate $\left[\begin{array}{r} HC \cdot CO_2Na(H_2O\,?) \\ NaO_2C \cdot \ddot{C}H \end{array}\right]$ is monoclinic. Crystals columnar along *c*. X ∧ *c* near 10°. (-)2V = (*ca*. 40° A.N.W.), N_1 = 1.430 (N_X ?), N_2 = 1.620 (N_Y ?), N_3 = 1.648 (N_Z ?), $N_3 - N_1$ = 0.218 ($N_Z - N_X$?). Ref: 529.

Dipotassium fumarate $\left[\begin{array}{r} HC{-}CO_2K \\ KO_2C{-}\ddot{C}H \end{array}\right]$ forms needles with N_1 = 1.420, N_2 = 1.530, $N_2 - N_1$ = 0.090. Ref: 597

Calcium *trans*-butenedioate dihydrate or calcium fumarate dihydrate [$(CHCO_2)_2Ca \cdot 2H_2O$] is orthorhombic with *a*:*b*:*c* = 0.397:1:0.377. Crystals {010} tablets with {110}, {011}. D 1.71. The optic plane is 001; X = *a*. (-)2V = 22°24′. N_X = 1.413, N_Y = 1.602, N_Z = 1.611, all ± .003, $N_Z - N_X$ = 0.198. Ref: 362.

Maleic acid $\begin{bmatrix} HC\cdot CO_2H \\ \ddot{HC}\cdot CO_2H \end{bmatrix}$ is monoclinic prismatic with $a:b:c = 0.738:1:0.702$, $\beta = 117°7'$. U.C. 4. Crystals prismatic with twinning on 100. Perfect 001 cleavage. D 1.59. M.P. 130°. X nearly normal to 001; Y = b. Optically positive. $N_X = 1.45$ est., $N_Y = 1.561 \pm .003$, $N_Z = 1.745 \pm .005$ ($N_Z - N_X = 0.30$ est. A.N.W.). Ref: 599, 631.

Sodium maleate $\left[\begin{matrix} HC\cdot CO_2Na \\ \ddot{HC}\cdot CO_2Na \end{matrix}\left(\cdot\frac{1}{2}H_2O\,?\right)\right]$ forms equant crystals. (−)2E = $122° \pm 5°$, $2V = 70° \pm 2°$, $N_X = 1.463$, $N_Y = 1.527$, $N_Z = 1.572$, $N_Z - N_X = 0.109$. Ref: 529.

Dipotassium maleate $\begin{bmatrix} HC\text{–}CO_2K \\ \ddot{HC}\text{–}\ddot{C}O_2K \end{bmatrix}$ forms laths with $N_1 = 1.513$, $N_2 = 1.610$, $N_2 - N_1 = 0.097$. Ref: 597.

Calcium *cis*-butenedioate monohydrate or calcium maleate monohydrate [$(CHCO_2)_2Ca\cdot H_2O$] is orthorhombic with $a:b:c = 0.779:1:0.643$. Crystals show {110}, {011}, {010}, etc. D 1.84. The optic plane is 010; X = c. (−)2V = 77°36′. $N_X = 1.495$, $N_Y = 1.580$, $N_Z = 1.640$, all $\pm .003$, $N_Z - N_X = 0.145$. Ref: 362.

trans-2-Methylbutenedioic acid or methylfumaric acid or mesaconic acid [$HO_2C\cdot CH:C(CH_3)CO_2H$] melts at 204.5°. It has parallel extinction and ± elongation. (−)2V < 50° calc. $N_X < 1.445$, $N_Y = 1.690$, $N_Z = 1.740$, $N_Z - N_X > 0.295$. Colorless rods. Ref: 253.

trans-2-Methylbutenedioic acid dihydrazide or mesaconic dihydrazide [$H_2N\cdot NH\cdot CO\cdot CH:C(CH_3)\cdot CO\cdot NH\cdot NH_2$] melts at 217° – 218°. It forms glassy rods with (+)2V = 65° calc., $N_X = 1.583$, $N_Y = 1.610$, $N_Z = 1.680$, all $\pm$ 0.003, $N_Z - N_X = 0.097$. Ref: 253.

Zinc *trans*-2-bromo-3-methylbutenedioate octahydrate or zinc bromomesaconate octahydrate [$CO_2\cdot C(CH_3)\cdot C(Br)\cdot CO_2Zn\cdot 8H_2O$] is monoclinic with $a:b:c = 1.417:1:0.859$, $\beta = 92°16'$. Crystals equant with {110}, {111}, {210}, {100}, {11$\bar{1}$}, etc. Distinct 100 cleavage. The optic plane and Z are normal to 010; X ∧ c = − 14°. (−)2V = 71°21′, $N_Y = 1.4743$ Na. Ref: 117.

Subclass C. Tricarboxylic Acids and Derivatives

Aconitic acid ($C_6H_6O_6$) forms needles or plates. M.P. 195°. Biaxial with $N_X = 1.475$, $N_Y = ?$, $N_Z = 1.642$, $N_Z - N_X = 0.165$. Ref: 527.

Monopotassium aconitate ($C_6H_3O_6KH_2$) forms thin plates with $N_X = 1.459$, $N_Y = ?$, $N_Z = 1.657$, $N_Z - N_X = 0.198$. Ref: 405.

Calcium propene-1,2,3-tricarboxylate or calcium aconitate [$[CO_2CH_2C(CO_2):CHCO_2]_2Ca_3$] is biaxial with D 1.85, $N_X = 1.515$, $N_Y = 1.535$, $N_Z = 1.575$, $N_Z - N_X = 0.060$. ∴ (+)2V = 70° calc. (Probably this is a hydrate.) Ref: 152.

Sodium calcium aconitate dihydrate ($C_6H_3O_6CaNa \cdot 2H_2O$) forms fragments and wedges with $N_X = 1.457$, $N_i = 1.572$, $N_Z = 1.626$, $N_Z - N_X = 0.169$. Ref: 405.

Magnesium dicalcium aconitate hexahydrate [$(C_6H_3O_6)_2Ca_2Mg \cdot 6H_2O$] forms rhombs and prisms showing uncentered interference figures. $N_X = 1.504$, $N_Y = 1.560$, $N_Z = 1.643$, $N_Z - N_X = 0.139$. ∴ (+)2V = 80° calc. Ref: 405.

Tricalcium aconitate trihydrate [$(C_6H_3O_6)_2Ca_3 \cdot 3H_2O$] forms rods and plates with parallel extinction and $N_X = 1.520$, $N_Y = ?$, $N_Z = 1.639$, $N_Z - N_X = 0.119$. Ref: 405.

Magnesium acid aconitate tetrahydrate ($C_6H_3O_6MgH \cdot 4H_2O$) forms small prisms with $N_X = 1.447$, $N_Y = ?$, $N_Z = 1.660$, $N_Z - N_X = 0.213$. Ref: 405.

Zinc acid aconitate tetrahydrate ($C_6H_3O_6ZnH \cdot 4H_2O$) forms small prisms with $N_X = 1.468$, $N_Y = ?$, $N_Z = 1.690$, $N_Z - N_X = 0.222$. It loses water at 60° and decomposes at 110°. Ref: 405.

Tricalcium aconitate hexahydrate [$(C_6H_3O_6)_2Ca_3 \cdot 6H_2O$] forms rhomblike or six-sided prisms (often showing optic axis interference figures) with $N_X = 1.497$, $N_Y = 1.545$, $N_Z = 1.620$, $N_Z - N_X = 0.123$. ∴ (+)2V = 80° calc. Ref: 405.

Tricadmium aconitate hexahydrate [$(C_6H_3O_6)_2Cd_3 \cdot 6H_2O$] forms prisms showing optic axis interference figures. $N_X = 1.590$, $N_Y = 1.602$, $N_Z = 1.620$, $N_Z - N_X = 0.030$. ∴ (+)2V = 80° calc. Ref: 405.

Subclass D. Tetracarboxylic Acids and Derivatives

3,3-Diethanoicpentanedioic acid or *β,β-bis*(carboxymethyl) glutaric acid or methanetetra-acetic acid [$C(CH_2 \cdot CO_2H)_4$] is tetragonal with $c/a = 0.56$. Crystals pyramidal with {111} and {110}. No cleavage observed. D = 1.46. Uniaxial positive with $N_O = 1.487$, $N_E = 1.518$, $N_E - N_O = 0.031$. Ref: 198.

Subclass L. Hydroxy Carboxylic Acids and Derivatives

Ammonium carbamate ($NH_2CO_2NH_4$) forms tabular crystals with ragged edges. M.P. > 135° and < 140°. (+)2E = 104°, 2V = 62°, $N_X = 1.495$, $N_Y = 1.520$, $N_Z = 1.59$ (calc. A.N.W.), $N_Z - N_X = 0.095$ calc. Ref: 529.

Sodium carbamate (NH_2CO_2Na) is orthorhombic in prismatic to acicular crystals with X = *c*, Y = *b*, Z = *a*. (+)2V = 75°. $N_X = 1.467$, $N_Y = 1.584$, $N_Z = 1.594$, $N_Z - N_X = 0.127$. Ref: 396a.

Sodium carbamate trihydrate ($NH_2CO_2Na \cdot 3H_2O$) is triclinic in grains or short prisms with $X \wedge a = 33°$, $Y \wedge c = 22°$. (−)2V = 44°, $N_X = 1.413$, $N_Y = 1.446$, $N_Z = 1.510$, $N_Z - N_X = 0.097$. Ref: 396a.

Butyl carbamate ($NH_2CO_2C_4H_9$) is monoclinic in elongated plates. Y ∥ elongation in red and Z ∥ elongation in violet. M.P. 54°. The optic plane is 010 for violet and normal thereto for red (Z = *b*). (-)2E = 23.5° (4358), 15° (4916), 0° (at about 5300), 7° (5461), 13° (5780), 19° (6234), 23° (6908). N_X = 1.435, N_Y = 1.481, N_Z = 1.482, $N_Z - N_X$ = 0.047 (5461). Ref: 39a.

Ethyl (2,2,2-trichloro-1-hydroxyethyl) carbamate or chloral urethan [$CCl_3 \cdot CH(OH) \cdot NH \cdot CO_2 \cdot C_2H_5$] has parallel extinction and positive elongation with M.P. 103° and N_1 = 1.54, N_2 = 1.55, $N_2 - N_1$ = 0.01. Ref: 34, 35.

1-Methylbutyl carbamate or 2-pentyl carbamate or methylpropylcarbinyl urethan [$NH_2 \cdot CO_2CH(CH_3) \cdot (C_3H_7)$] is acicular or irregular. M.P. 76°. Easily soluble in hot water. N_1 = 1.46, N_2 = 1.47, $N_2 - N_1$ = 0.01. Ref: 239.

Potassium cyanate (KCON) is tetragonal with *c*/*a* = 0.577. Crystals tabular with D 2.056. M.P. 315° C. Uniaxial negative with N_O = 1.552, N_E = 1.337, $N_O - N_E$ = 0.175. Ref: 405a.

Urea or carbamide [$CO(NH_2)_2$] is tetragonal scalenohedral with *c*/*a* = 0.833. Space group $P\bar{4}2_1/m$; *a* 5.67, *c* 4.73 Å. U.C. 2. Crystals thin prisms with {110}, {111}, {001}, etc. Perfect 110 and distinct 001 cleavages. D 1.335. M. P. 132°. Uniaxial positive with N_O = 1.484, N_E = 1.602, $N_E - N_O$ = 0.118 D. Also: N_O = 1.485, N_E = 1.600, $N_E - N_O$ = 0.115 D. Again: N_O = 1.4743, N_E = 1.6005. Ref: 117, 239, 248, 356, 483.

Urea nitrate [$CO(NH_2)_2 \cdot HNO_3$] is monoclinic with *a*:*b*:*c* = 1.156:1:0.901, β = 123°55′. Crystals show {001}, {110}, {010}, {100}. D 1.635. Perfect 001 cleavage. The optic plane is 010; X nearly normal to 001. (-(2E = 21°10′ red, 23°10′ yellow, 24°30′ green; (-)2V = 14°. N_X = 1.375, N_Y = 1.647, N_Z = 1.654, $N_Z - N_X$ = 0.279 D. Ref: 99, 117.

Urea phosphate [$CO(NH_2)_2 \cdot H_3PO_4$] is orthorhombic with *a*:*b*:*c* = 0.831:1:0.981. Crystals {001} tablets or pyramidal with {101}, {110}, {100}, {112}, etc. Good 001 cleavage. D 1.76. The optic plane is 001; X = *a*. (-)2E = 80° *ca.* N_X = 1.506, N_Y = ?, N_Z = 1.540, $N_Z - N_X$ = 0.034, all ± 0.003. ∴ (-)2V = 50° *ca.* N_Y = 1.533. Ref: 238.

Urea-hydrogen peroxide or hyperol [$CO(NH_2)_2H_2O_2$] is orthorhombic* with *a*:*b*:*c* = 0.531:1:0.374. *a* 6.86, *b* 12.92, *c* 4.83. D 1.39. Good 100 and 101 cleavages. The optic plane is 001, X = *a*. (+)2V = 65° calc. N_X = 1.480, N_Y = 1.500, N_Z = 1.550, $N_Z - N_X$ = 0.070. Ref: 229.

Sodium chlorocarbamide monohydrate {$NaCO(NH_2)_2Cl \cdot H_2O$} is orthorhombic(?) with *a*:*b*:*c* = 0.805:1:2.708. *a* 5.24, *b* 6.51, *c* 17.62 Å. U.C. 4. Crystals short colorless rods. D 1.52. X = *a*, Y = *c*. (+)2V = 35°36′. N_X = 1.479, N_Y = 1.485, N_Z = 1.543, $N_Z - N_X$ = 0.064. Ref: 530a.

Sodium bromocarbamide monohydrate {$NaCO(NH_2)_2Br \cdot H_2O$} is dimorphous. Phase I is orthorhombic (?) with *a*:*b*:*c* = 0.807:1:2.741. *a* 5.30, *b* 6.57, *c* 18.01 Å. U.C. 4. Crystals twinned or in groups. Colorless. D 1.85. X = *a*,

---

[1] *b* and *c* interchanged to make *b* > *a* > *c*.

Y = b. (+)2V = 40°. N_X = 1.481, N_Y = 1.490, N_Z = 1.553, $N_Z - N_X$ = 0.072. Phase II is tetragonal with c/a = 4.27. a 8.43, c 36.02 Å. U.C. 16. Crystals colorless plates or short rods. D 1.85. Uniaxial positive (but somewhat abnormal) with N_O = 1.490, N_E = 1.555, $N_E - N_O$ = 0.065. Ref: 530a.

Urea ethanedioate or urea oxalate [$2CO(NH_2)_2 \cdot C_2H_2O_4$] is monoclinic prismatic with $a:b:c$ = 0.564:1:0.411, β = 97°50′. Space group $P2_1/m$; a 7.02, b 12.42, c 5.08 Å. U.C. 2. Crystals {010} tablets with {110} or {210}, {011}, etc. Perfect 20$\bar{1}$ cleavage. Twinning on 20$\bar{1}$. D 1.585. The optic plane is 010; X is nearly normal to 20$\bar{1}$. (-)2V = 19°17′. N_X = 1.3885, N_Y = 1.6116, N_Z = 1.6165, $N_Z - N_X$ = 0.2280. Ref: 99, 117, 542.

Calcium sulfate urea {$CaSO_4 \cdot 4CO(NH_2)_2$} is triclinic pinacoidal with $a:b:c$ = 0.984:1:0.865, α = 92°6′, β = 90°22′, γ = 86°50′. Space group $P1$; a 14.74, b 14.95, c 6.47 Å. U.C. 4. Crystals equant with {110}, {1$\bar{1}$0}, {001}, {100}, {010}, etc. No cleavage. D 1.80. X is nearly parallel with c. Z is nearly normal to 110. (-)2V = 70°, N_X = 1.523 (D), N_Y = 1.583, N_Z = 1.615, $N_Z - N_X$ = 0.092. Ref: 484.

2-Bromo-3-methylbutanoylcarbamide or α-bromoisovaleryl urea or bromural [$H_2N \cdot CO \cdot NH \cdot CO \cdot CHBr \cdot CH(CH_3)_2$] has two crystal phases. The α-phase (I) is triclinic in lamellar crystals (from methanol) at about 146° with* $a:b:c$ = 0.478:1:0.373, α = 101°26′, β = 106°10′, γ = 97°20′. Perfect 010 cleavage. D 1.622. (-)2V = 68°. N_1 = 1.526, N_2 = 1.58, $N_2 - N_1$ = 0.054. Also N_1 = 1.526, N_2 = 1.586. (Probably N_Y = 1.57 *ca.*, N_Z = 1.586 – A.N.W.) It inverts slowly to the β-phase (II) at 90°, very rapidly at 130°; the inversion is not reversible. The β-phase (II) is orthorhombic pyramidal with $a:b:c$ = 0.629:1:0.303. Distinct 110 cleavage. D 1.561. M.P. 153 – 154°. X = a, Y = b, Z = c. N_X = 1.52, N_Y = 1.55, N_Z = 1.576, $N_Z - N_X$ = 0.056. Acicular crystals have (-)2V = 50° *ca.* calc. N_X = 1.519, N_Y = 1.583, N_Z = 1.599, $N_Z - N_X$ = 0.080. Colorless. Soluble in index liquids. Ref: 239, 343b, 343c.

2-Bromo-2-ethylbutanoylcarbamide or (α-bromo-α-ethylbutyryl) urea or bromodiethylacetylurea or carbromal or adaline [$H_2N \cdot CO \cdot NH \cdot CO \cdot CBr(C_2H_5)_2$] is dimorphous. The α-form (I) is orthorhombic in prismatic crystals with $a:b:c$ = 0.663:1:0.692. Soluble in some index liquids. D 1.596. X = c, Y = a, Z = b. (-)2V = 86°. N_X = 1.529, N_Y = 1.575, N_Z = 1.618, $N_Z - N_X$ = 0.089. The β-form (II) is monoclinic in needles with $a:b:c$ = 1.053:1:0.738, β = 114°58′. D 1.544. M.P. 118°. X = b, Z $\wedge$ c = + 6.5°. (+)2V = 28°. N_X = 1.527, N_Y = 1.532, N_Z = 1.603, $N_Z - N_X$ = 0.076. Ref: 239, 343c, 343d.

Biuret or allophanamide ($H_2N \cdot CO \cdot NH \cdot CO \cdot NH_2$) is probably monoclinic. Crystals long plates. M.P. 205°. Plates normal to X have Z parallel with elongation and plates normal to Z have X $\wedge$ elongation = 28° ± 3°. (Z probably = b) (-)2V = 16°, r > v. N_X = 1.403, N_Y = 1.616, N_Z = 1.624, $N_Z - N_X$ = 0.221 (for λ = 5461). Ref: 556a.

---

[1] b and c interchanged to make $b > a$.

Cyanamide ($H_2N \cdot CN$) forms elongated six-sided colorless crystals which are probably monoclinic. D 1.073. M.P. 44 - 45°. Maximum extinction angle is 10°. $Z \wedge c = 80°$. $N_1 = 1.412$, $N_2 = 1.556$, $N_3 = 1.675$, $N_3 - N_1 = 0.263$. (+)2V = 30 - 40°, r < v weak. Ref: 280a.

Sodium dicyanimide [$N(CN)_2Na$] is orthorhombic (?). Crystals lamellar. Z normal to plates. (+)2E = 86°, 2V = 55°, $N_X = 1.410$, $N_Y = 1.489$ ($N_Z = 1.75$ calc., $N_Z - N_X = 0.34$ calc. A.N.W.). Ref: 529.

Zinc dicyanimide [$\{N(CN)_2\}_2Zn$] is orthorhombic in stout columns with {100}, {010}, {001}, {110}, {101}. Z || length. (-)2E = 24°, 2V = 14°, $N_X = 1.445$, $N_Y = 1.698$, $Z_Z = 1.702$, $N_Z - N_X = 0.257$. Ref: 529.

Calcium dicyanamide dihydrate [$\{N(CN)_2\}_2Ca \cdot 2H_2O$] is monoclinic (?). Crystals columnar. Perfect cleavage parallel to *b* (001 ?). X || *b* (= elongation). (+)2E = 86°, 2V = 55°, $N_X = 1.405$, $N_Y = 1.480$, $N_Z = 1.82$, $N_Z - N_X = 0.415$. Ref: 529.

Guanidinium chloride or guanidine hydrochloride [$CNH(NH_2)_2 \cdot HCl$] is orthorhombic dipyramidal with[1] $a:b:c = 0.706:1:0.594$. Space group *Pbca*; *a* 9.22, *b* 13.06, *c* 7.76 Å. U.C. 8. $N_1 = 1.54$, $N_2 = 1.64$, $N_2 - N_1 = 0.10$. Ref: 34, 35, 604.

Guanidinium iodide or guanidine hydroiodide [$CNH(NH_2)_2HI$] is hexagonal with $c/a = 1.711$. Space group *C6mc*; *a* 7.19, *c* 12.30 Å. U.C. 4. Crystals show $\{10\bar{1}0\}$, {0001}, $\{10\bar{1}1\}$, $\{20\bar{2}1\}$. Perfect 0001 cleavage. D 2.243. M. P. 195°. Strongly piezoelectric. Uniaxial negative with $N_O = 1.745$ D, $N_E = 1.549$, $N_O - N_E = 0.196$. Ref: 332.

Guanidine nitrate [$CNH(NH_2)_2 \cdot HNO_3$] melts at 214° C. Crystals have parallel extinction and positive elongation with $N_1 = 1.40$ *ca.*, $N_2 = 1.605$, $N_2 - N_1 = 0.205$ *ca.* Again: (-)2E = 37°, 2V = 23°, $N_X = 1.450$, $N_Y = 1.575$, $N_Z = 1.580$, $N_Z - N_X = 0.130$. Ref: 34, 35, 468.

Guanidine sulfate [$NH_2C(NH)NH_2 \cdot H_2SO_4$] is isometric. Crystals equant octahedral. Isotropic with N = 1.462. Ref: 584.

Guanidine carbonate [$[CNH(NH_2)_2]_2 \cdot H_2CO_3$] is tetragonal trapezohedral with $c/a = 2.885$. Space group $P4_12_12$ or $P4_322$; *a* 6.95, *c* 19.45 Å. U.C. 4. Crystals pyramidal with {111}, {001}, {100}. Perfect 001 cleavage. D 1.25. M.P. 197°. Uniaxial negative with $N_O = 1.4922$ Li, 1.4963 Na, 1.5003 Tl, $N_E = 1.4818$ Li, 1.4864 Na, 1.4899 Tl. $N_O - N_E = 0.0099$ Na. May show optic anomalies. Rotation of polarization plane for 1 mm is 12°35′ Li, 14°35′ Na, 17°4′ Tl. Also reported to have: $N_O = 1.499$, $N_E = 1.49$. Ref: 117, 152, 429.

Guanidine *dl*-lactate [$CNH(NH_2)_2 \cdot CH_3 \cdot CH(OH) \cdot CO_2H$] is orthorhombic with $a:b:c = 0.774:1:0.730$. Crystals show {010}, {110}, {111}, {021}, etc. Imperfect 001 and 010 cleavages. M.P. 162°. The optic plane is 100; Z = *b*. (+)2V = 79°18′ Li, 79°12′ Na, 79°4′ Tl. $N_X = 1.510$, $N_Y = 1.5467$, $N_Z = 1.600$, $N_Z - N_X = 0.090$ Na. Ref: 117, 391.

[1] *a b c* changed to *b c a* to make $b > a > c$.

Guanidine rhodanate or guanidine thiocyanate $[CNH(NH_2)_2 \cdot HSCN]$ is granular with $N_1 = 1.625$, $N_2 = 1.63$, $N_2 - N_1 = 0.005$. Ref: 34, 35, 117.

Guanylurea nitrate $(C_2H_6 \cdot ON_4 \cdot NO_3)$ is probably triclinic in equant to tabular crystals. D 1.579. M.P. 230° C. (-)2V = 36°, $N_X = 1.393$, $N_Y = 1.660$, $N_Z = 1.701$, $N_Z - N_X = 0.308$. Ref: 405a.

Guanylurea sulfate dihydrate $(C_2H_6ON_4 \cdot SO_4 \cdot 2H_2O)$ is probably triclinic in columnar crystals. D 1.609. M.P. 192°. (-)2V = 45°, $N_X = 1.432$, $N_Y = 1.585$, $N_Z = 1.615$, $N_Z - N_X = 0.183$. Ref: 405a.

Guanylurea phosphate $(C_2H_6ON_4 \cdot H_3PO_4)$ is probably triclinic in tabular crystals. D 1.614. M.P. 184°. (-)2V = 64°, $N_X = 1.423$, $N_Y = 1.553$, $N_Z = 1.616$, $N_Z - N_X = 0.193$. Ref: 405a.

Dicyanodiamide or cyanoguanidine $[H_2NC(:NH)NH \cdot CN]$ is monoclinic prismatic with $a:b:c$[1] = 3.378:1:2.955, $\beta = 115°20'$. Space group $C2c$; a 15.00, b 4.44, c 13.12 Å. U.C. 8. Crystals $\{\bar{1}01\}$ plates elongated along b with {101}, {100}, etc. Perfect 100 and good 001 cleavages. D 1.40. M.P. 205°. The optic plane is 010; $Z \wedge c = -12°39'$. (+)2V = 38°31′ D with very strong dispersion, $r < v$. $N_X = 1.5177$ C, 1.5212 D, 1.5321 F, $N_Y = 1.5454$ C, 1.5493 D, 1.5579 F, $N_Z = 1.8354$ C, 1.8471 D, 1.8697 F, $N_Z - N_X = 0.3259$ D. Again: $N_Y = 1.547$, $N_Z = 1.88 \pm 0.02$. Ref: 18, 117, 143, 280a, 496, 497.

Dicyanodiamide monohydrochloride $\{NH_2C(NH)NHCN \cdot HCl\}$ is probably orthorhombic in tablets with {110}, {101}, {001}, {010}. X parallel with elongation. Y parallel with width. (-)2E = 73°, 2V = 41° calc. $N_X = 1.620$, $N_Y = 1.645$, $N_Z = 1.663$, $N_Z - N_X = 0.043$. Ref: 529.

Dicyanodiamide dihydrochloride $\{NH_2C(NH)NHCN \cdot 2HCl\}$ is orthorhombic with twinning on 110. Crystals tabular with {100}, {010}, {110}, {101}. Good 010, 100, and 001 cleavages, X (|| width) = b, Z = a, (+)2V = 70 - 80°, 2E > 150°. $N_Y = 1.608$. Ref: 529.

Cyanoguanidine nitrate or dicyanodiamide nitrate $\{NH_2C(NH)NHCN \cdot HNO_3\}$ is monoclinic prismatic. Crystals equant with {110}, {001}, $\{10\bar{1}\}$, Y = b, $Z \wedge c = 17°$. (-)2E = 63°, 2V = 38°, $N_X = 1.362$, $N_Y = 1.615$, $N_Z = 1.687$, $N_Z - N_X = 0.325$. Ref: 529, 563a.

Dicyanodiamide sulfate $\{NH_2C(NH)NHCN \cdot H_2SO_4\}$ is probably triclinic. Crystals tabular. One optic axis nearly normal to tabular face. (-)2E = 82°, 2V = 48°, N (parallel to elongation) = 1.571, $N_Y = 1.567$. Ref: 529.

Dicyanodiamide oxalate $\{NH_2C(NH)NHCN \cdot (COOH)_2\}$ is monoclinic (?). Crystals tabular with an angle ($a \wedge c$?) of 97°. Y $\wedge$ elongation = 6°. (+)2E = 41°, 2V = 29°, $N_Y = 1.541$. Colorless. Ref: 529, 563a.

---

[1] b axis only one third the goniometer value.

Dicyanodiamide maleate $\{H_2NC(NH)NHCN \cdot C_2(COOH)_2\}$ is monoclinic prismatic. Crystals equant pyramids with good 010 cleavage. X = *b*, Z ∧ *c* = 10° *ca.* (-)2E = 29°, 2V = 17°, $N_X = 1.390$, $N_Y = 1.692$, $N_Z = 1.700$, $N_Z - N_X = 0.310$. Ref: 529, 563a.

Dicyanodiamide ethyl sulfonate $\{NH_2C(NH)CNC_2H_5O \cdot HSO_3\}$ is monoclinic prismatic. Crystals tabular with {100}, {010}, {001}. Good 100 and 001 cleavages. Complicated twinning on 100 and 010. Y ∧ *c* = 3°. (-)2E = 90°, 2V = 54°, $N_X = 1.497$, $N_Y = 1.551$, $N_Z = 1.569$, $N_Z - N_X = 0.072$. Ref: 529, 563a.

Ethyl cyanoguanidinecarboxylate or carbethoxydicyandiamide or carbethoxycyanoguanidine $(C_5H_8O_2N_4)$ is monoclinic, commonly twinned. Crystals {010} tablets with terminal angle (100 ∧ 001?) = 54° ± 2°. X ∧ *c* = 42°. Z = *b*. (+)2V = large, $N_X = 1.395$, $N_Y = 1.633$, $N_Z = 1.85$ (est. - A.N.W.), $N_Z - N_X = 0.46$ (est. - A.N.W.). Again: $N_X = 1.432$, $N_Z = 1.618$; is this another phase? Ref: 275, 529.

Ammonium dicyanoguanidine $(C_3H_2N_5 \cdot NH_4)$ is probably orthorhombic in elongated tabular crystals. X || elongation. $N_X = 1.435$, $N_Y = 1.701$, N_Z = ?. Ref: 405a.

Potassium dicyanoguanidine $(C_3H_2N_5K)$ is probably orthorhombic in equant to stout columnar crystals. M.P. 265°. (-)2V = 75°, $N_X = 1.435$, $N_Y = 1.638$, $N_Z = 1.830$, $N_Z - N_X = 0.395$. Ref: 405a.

Lead dicyanoguanidine $\{(C_3H_2N_5)_2Pb\}$ is probably orthorhombic in elongated tabular crystals. Y || elongation. Optic sign - ? $N_X = 1.565$, $N_Y = 1.794$, $N_Z > 1.9$, $N_Z - N_X > 0.335$. Ref: 405a, 528a.

Calcium dicyanoguanidine tetrahydrate $\{(C_3H_2N_5)_2Ca \cdot 4H_2O\}$ is orthorhombic in equant to stout columnar crystals. (-)2V = 70°, $N_X = 1.435$, $N_Y = 1.642$, $N_Z = 1.816$, $N_Z - N_X = 0.381$. Ref: 405a.

Biguanide sodium ferricyanide $\{NH_2C(NH)NHC(NH)NH_2H_2NaFe(CN)_6\}$ has $N_1 = 1.582$, $N_2 = 1.606$, $N_3 = 1.662$, $N_3 - N_1 = 0.080$. Ref: 598.

Biguanidine disodium ferrocyanide $\{NH_2C(NH)NHC(NH)NH_2HNa_2Fe(CN)_6\}$ is tetragonal. Crystals equant pyramids or tablets. Uniaxial negative. $N_O = 1.613$, N_E' (on pyramid face) = 1.533, $N_O - N_E' = 0.080$. Ref: 598.

3,7-Dimethyl-2,6-octadienal semicarbazone, neral semicarbazone, geranial semicarbazone, or citral semicarbazone $[(CH_3)_2 \cdot C{:}CH \cdot (CH_2)_2C(CH_3){:}(CH)_2{:}N \cdot NH \cdot CONH_2]$ melts at 132°. It is biaxial (?) with $N_X = 1.560$, N_Y = ?, $N_Z = 1.660$, $N_Z - N_X = 0.100$, all ± 0.003. Probably a mixture of α- and β-forms. Ref: 378.

2-Tridecanone semicarbazone or methyl undecyl ketone semicarbazone $[CH_3(CH_2)_{10}C{:}[N \cdot NH \cdot (CO)NH_2]CH_3]$ melts at 123°. (-)2V = 50° calc. $N_X = 1.480$, $N_Y = 1.560$, $N_Z = 1.580$, all ± 0.003, $N_Z - N_X = 0.100$. Ref: 378.

Nitroaminoguanidine $\{H_2NC(NH)NHNHNO_2\}$ is orthorhombic in tabular crystals with good 001 cleavage. X = *c*; Y = *b*. (-)2E = 78°, N_X = ?, N_Y = 1.74 *ca.*, $N_Z > 1.83$, ∴ 2V = 42° calc. Colorless. Ref: 529.

Lead nitroaminoguanidine $\{[NH_2C(NH)NHNNO_2]_2Pb\}$ is probably orthorhombic. Crystals yellow tablets. (+)2E = 80° *ca.*, $N_X > 1.70$, $N_Y > 2.0$, $N_Z > 2.0$. Ref: 529.

Nitroguanidine $(NH_2CNHNHNO_2)$ is said to have two phases, one in long flat needles having $N_X = 1.518$, $N_Y = 1.668$, $N_Z > 1.768$, $N_Z - N_X > 0.250$, and another in elongated six-sided plates having $N_X = 1.525$, $N_Z = 1.710$. These orthorhombic needles (long ‖ *c*) show {100} and {010}, with cleavage lengthwise and M.P. 232°; they have X = *c*, Y = *b*, (-)2V = ?, $N_X = 1.531$, $N_Y = 1.705$, $N_Z > 1.760$, $N_Z - N_X > 0.23$. But Doll and Grison found only one phase (in two crystal habits) which is orthorhombic with *a*:*b*:*c* = 0.713:1:0.147. *a* 17.47, *b* 24.50, *c* 3.59. U.C. 16. Crystals acicular along *c*. D 1.80. M.P. 246°. (-)2V = 74°, $N_X = 1.530$ calc., $N_Y = 1.715$, $N_Z = 1.86$, $N_Z - N_X = 0.330$ calc. Again: (-)2V = 80°, $N_X = 1.526$, $N_Y = 1.694$, $N_Z = 1.81$, $N_Z - N_X = 0.284$. Ref: 67, 446a, 553c, 619.

Guanylazide nitrate $[N_3C(NH)NH_2 \cdot HNO_3]$ is monoclinic prismatic with $\beta = 99°$. Crystals {001} or {010} tablets. M.P. 127 - 129°. Perfect 010 and good 001 cleavages. X = *b*, Z ∧ *c* = 12° *ca.* in obtuse *β*. (+)2V = 81°, $N_X = 1.425 \pm 0.003$, $N_Y = 1.535 \pm 0.003$, $N_Z = 1.731 \pm 0.005$, $N_Z - N_X = 0.306$. Ref: 619.

Caesium silver barium thiocyanate $\{Cs_3Ag_2Ba(CNS)_7\}$ is tetragonal with *c* = 0.906. Crystals prismatic. Perfect 001 cleavage. D 3.026. Uniaxial negative with $N_O = 1.7761$, $N_E = 1.6788$, $N_O - N_E = 0.0973$. Ref: 568a.

Caesium cuprous barium thiocyanate $\{Cs_3Cu_2Ba(CNS)_7\}$ is tetragonal with *c* = 0.918. Crystals prismatic. Perfect 001 cleavage. D 2.924. Uniaxial negative with $N_O = 1.8013$, $N_E = 1.6882$, $N_O - N_E = 0.1131$. Ref: 568a.

Caesium cuprous strontium thiocyanate $\{Cs_3Cu_2Sr(CNS)_7\}$ is tetragonal with *c* = 0.916. Crystals dipyramidal. Perfect 001 cleavage. D 2.882. Uniaxial negative with $N_O = 1.8525$, $N_E = 1.6982$, $N_O - N_E = 0.1543$. Ref: 568a.

Thiourea or thiocarbamide $[CS(NH_2)_2]$ is orthorhombic dipyramidal with *a*:*b*:*c* = 0.716:1:1.116. Space group *Pnma*. *a* 5.50, *b* 7.68, *c* 8.57 Å. U.C. 4. Crystals {001} tablets with {010}, {110}, etc. Perfect 010 and 101 cleavages. D 1.40. M.P. 182°. X = *b*, Y = *c* above λ = 3780. (Y = *a* below λ = 3780.) (-)2H = 48° (6908), 44° (5461), 40° (4916), 32.5° (4358), 22° (4047), 0° (3780), 25° (3650). For λ = 5461: (-)2V = 32°, $N_X = 1.634$, $N_Y = 1.789$, $N_Z = 1.806$, $N_Z - N_X = 0.172$. (Bryant). For white light: (-)2V = 36°, $N_X = 1.630$, $N_Y = 1.742$, $N_Z = 1.76 \pm 0.01$, $N_Z - N_X = 0.13 \pm 0.01$ (Kirkpatrick). Ref: 425, 529, 556a, 625.

Trithiocarbamide cuprous chloride or trithiourea cuprous chloride $[[CS(NH_2)_2]_3 \cdot CuCl]$ is ditetragonal dipyramidal with *c*/*a* = 1.451. Space group

P4/mmm; *a* 9.50, *c* 13.81 Å. U.C. 4. Crystals prisms with {100}, {110}, {101}, {111}, M.P. 168°. D 1.73. H 2.5. Uniaxial negative with $N_O = 1.7719$, $N_E = 1.7581$, $N_O - N_E = 0.0138$ D. Ref: 245.

Trithiocarbamide bismuth chloride or trithiourea bismuth chloride $[[CS(NH_2)_2]_3BiCl_3]$ has two phases. One (I) is red and trigonal pyramidal with $c/a = 0.527$. Space group *R*3; *a* 13.29, *c* 7.02 Å. Crystals equant with $\{10\bar{1}0\}$, $\{10\bar{1}1\}$, $\{01\bar{1}0\}$, $\{11\bar{2}0\}$, $\{2\bar{1}\bar{1}0\}$, $\{\bar{1}01\bar{1}\}$. Uniaxial negative with $N_O = 1.46$, $N_E = 1.38$, $N_O - N_E = 0.08$. Commonly optically abnormal with rectangular systems of twinning bands in basal sections, and evidence of a small optic angle. The other (yellow) phase (II) is triclinic. Distinct 100 cleavage. Not measured optically. Ref: 113, 474.

Allylthiourea or thiosinamine $(CH_2CHCH_2NHCSNH_2)$ is monoclinic prismatic with $a:b:c = 1.14:1:0.976$, $\beta = 120°36'$. Crystals tablets or rods long || *b*, with {001}, {100}, {110}, etc. D 1.25. M.P. 77 - 78°. Y = *b*, Z ∧ *c* = 15° in acute *β*. (-)2V = 77°, r < v. $N_X = 1.602$, $N_Y = 1.684$, $N_Z = 1.74$, $N_Z - N_X = 0.138$. Ref: 553a.

Azidodithiocarbonic acid or dithiocarbonic acid azide $(HSCSN_3)$ is monoclinic with $\beta = 124°$ *ca.* and 110 ∧ $1\bar{1}0$ in 001 = 83°. Common twinning on 001. Crystals show {001}, {010}, {110}. The optic plane and Z are probably normal to 010; X ∧ *c* = 30°. (+)2E = large. $N_X = 1.35 +$ (at 30° to *c* - C.W. Mason), $N_Y = 1.6$ (est.), N_Z = ?, $N_Z - N_X$ = extreme. Ref: 236, 237.

Dithiobiuret $(C_2H_5N_3S_2)$ is monoclinic (or orthorhombic ?) in columnar crystals. D 1.522. M.P. 181°. X || elongation. (-)2V = 52°, with strong axial dispersion. $N_X = 1.654$, $N_Y = 1.880$, $N_Z = 1.95$ calc., $N_Z - N_X = 0.296$ calc. Ref: 405a.

Glycolic acid or hydroxyethanoic acid or hydroxyacetic acid $\{HOCH_2CO_2H\}$ is dimorphous; the α-phase (I) is monoclinic prismatic with $a:b:c = 1.77:1:1.34$, $\beta = 115°$. Crystals {010} plates with {110} and {011}. M.P. 79°. Plates normal to Z show Y ∧ elongation = 35° *ca.* (-)2V = 33°, r > v. $N_X = 1.434$, $N_Y = 1.511$, $N_Z = 1.518$, $N_Z - N_X = 0.084$ (for $\lambda = 5461$). The *β*-phase (below 63°) is probably monoclinic. (+)2H = 85° ± 2°, $N_Z - N_X$ = strong. Ref: 117, 556a.

Diglycolic acid monohydrate or oxydiethanoic acid monohydrate or oxydiacetic acid monohydrate $\{O(CH_2CO_2H)_2 \cdot H_2O\}$ is monoclinic prismatic with $a:b:c = 1.324:1:0.463$, $\beta = 90°$ *ca.* Crystals prismatic. M.P. 148°. Plates normal to X show Z ∧ elongation = 23°, X = *b*. (-)2V = 74°, r > v with weak crossed dispersion. X = *b*. $N_X = 1.458$, $N_Y = 1.525$, $N_Z = 1.57$ calc., $N_Z - N_X = 0.11$ (for $\lambda = 5461$). Ref: 117, 556a.

dl-Mandelic acid $(C_6H_5 \cdot CHOH \cdot COOH)$ is orthorhombic with $a:b:c = 0.576:1:0.614$. *a* 9.66, *b* 16.20, *c* 9.94 Å. U.C. 8. D 1.29. M.P. 118 - 119°. Crystals {010} tablets with good 100 cleavage. Y = *a*; Z = *b*. (-)2V = 84°, $N_X = 1.526$, $N_Y = 1.564$, $N_Z = 1.620$, $N_Z - N_X = 0.094$. Ref: 585a.

Calcium *d*-2,3-dihydroxypropanoate dihydrate or calcium *d*-glycerate dihydrate $[[CH_2(OH) \cdot CH(OH) \cdot CO_2]_2Ca \cdot 2H_2O]$ is monoclinic sphenoidal with $a:b:c = 1.447:1:0.669$, $\beta = 110°54'$. Crystals short prismatic with {110}, {100}, {001}, {011}, etc. Good 001 cleavage. The optic plane and X are normal to 010; $Z \wedge c = + 23°$. (+)2V = 34°56′ Li, 35°28′ Na, 36°16′ Tl, $N_Y = 1.4496$ Li, 1.4521 Na, 1.4545 Tl. Ref: 117.

2,2-*bis*(Hydroxymethyl)propanoic acid or β,β'-dihydroxypivalic acid $[CH_3 \cdot C(CH_2OH)_2 \cdot CO_2H]$ is rhombohedral with $c/a = 1.255$. Crystals acute rhombohedral, sometimes tetartohedral, with $\{01\bar{1}0\}$, $\{02\bar{2}1\}$, {0001}, $\{10\bar{1}0\}$, etc. D 1.329. M.P. 179 - 182°. Uniaxial positive with $N_O = 1.516$, $N_E = 1.521$, $N_E - N_O = 0.005$. Ref: 146.

2,3,4-Trihydroxypentanamide or methyltetronamide $[CH_3(CHOH)_3CONH_2]$ is biaxial with M.P. 135°. $N_X = 1.510$, $N_Y = 1.530$, $N_Z = 1.566$, $N_Z - N_X = 0.056$. (+)2V = 74° *ca.* calc. $(\alpha)_D = + 54.8$ (water). Ref: 152.

2-Hydroxypropanedioic acid or tartronic acid $[CH(OH) \cdot (CO_2H)_2]$ is granular with $N_1 = 1.505$, $N_2 = 1.605$, $N_2 - N_1 = 0.100$. Ref: 34, 35.

Zinc *d*-lactate dihydrate $[(CH_3CHOHCO_2)_2Zn \cdot 2H_2O]$ is orthorhombic* with $a:b:c = 0.825:1:0.408$. Crystals show {010}, {110}, {111}. Good 010 cleavage. (-)2V = 26°30′. $N_X = 1.515$, $N_Y = 1.535$, $N_Z = 1.540$, $N_Z - N_X = 0.025$. Ref: 84a.

Zinc *d*-(or *l*-)lactate trihydrate $[(CH_3CHOHCO_2)_2Zn \cdot 3H_2O]$ is monoclinic with $a:b:c = 1.860:1:3.346$, $\beta = 92°0'$. Crystals tabular with {100}, {001}, {110}, {120}, D 1.656. (+)2V = 74°38′. $N_X = 1.4742$, $N_Y = 1.4971$, $N_Z = 1.5392$, $N_Z - N_X = 0.065$. Ref: 35, 84a.

Calcium lactate trihydrate $[(C_3H_5O_3)_2Ca \cdot 3H_2O]$ melts at 100°. It has $N_1 = 1.485$, $N_2 = 1.515$. Again: $N_1 = 1.470$, $N_2 = 1.510$. Ref: 343c, 518.

Ferrous lactate (trihydrate?) $[(C_3H_5O_3)_2Fe(\cdot 3H_2O\,?)]$ has parallel extinction and $N_1 = 1.49$, $N_2 = 1.53$. Also $N_1 = 1.49$, $N_2 = 1.50$. Optically negative. Ref: 34, 343c.

Magnesium lactate (trihydrate?) $[(C_3H_5O_3)_2Mg(\cdot 3H_2O\,?)]$ has parallel extinction with $N_1 = 1.45$, $N_2 = 1.46$, $N_3 = 1.50$, $N_3 - N_1 = 0.05$. Ref: 35.

Cerous lactate (trihydrate?) $[(C_3H_5O_3)_2Ce(\cdot 3H_2O\,?)]$ has $N_1 = 1.53$, $N_2 = 1.54$, $N_3 = 1.57$. Ref: 343c.

2-Hydroxybutanedioic Acid or Malic Acid and Derivatives*

Malic acid $[CO_2H \cdot CH(OH) \cdot CH_2 \cdot CO_2H]$ has parallel extinction and positive elongation with $N_1 = 1.51$, $N_2 = 1.56$, $N_2 - N_1 = 0.05$. Ref: 34, 35.

---

[1] Salts of *d*-malic acid have the same indices of refraction as those of *l*-malic acid. Some papers are not clear as to which isomer was used; in such cases no separation will be made.

Ammonium acid *d*-malate or ammonium *d*-bimalate [$HO_2C \cdot CHOH \cdot CO_2NH_4$] is orthorhombic disphenoidal with $a:b:c = 0.723:1:0.777$. Crystals thick {010} tablets with {110}, {011}, {012}, {001}. Perfect 001 and imperfect 010 and 110 cleavages. D 1.51. The optic plane is 010; X = *c*. (-)2V = 47°34′, r < v weak. $N_Y = 1.503$. Also $N_1 = 1.46$, $N_2 = 1.56$, $N_2 - N_1 = 0.10$. (If N_1 and N_2 are N_X and N_Z, the sign should be +: A.N.W.) Ref: 34, 35, 117.

Hydracrylamide ($HOCH_2CH_2CONH_2$) is orthorhombic. Crystals equant with {110}, {111}, {011}, {001}. Hygroscopic. X = *c*, Y = *b*. (-)2E = 58°, 2V = 37°, $N_X = 1.485$, $N_Y = 1.558$, $N_Z = 1.570$, $N_Z - N_Y = 0.085$. Ref: 529.

α-Hydroxyisobutyric acid [$(CH_3)_2C(OH)CO_2H$)] forms elongated tablets with parallel extinction and the obtuse bisectrix normal to the tablets. N_1 (|| width) = 1.463, N_2 (|| length) = 1.495, $N_2 - N_1 = 0.032$. Ref: 468.

Lithium acid *l*-malate hexahydrate or lithium bimalate hexahydrate [$C_2H_3(OH) \cdot (CO_2)_2LiH \cdot 6H_2O$) is monoclinic sphenoidal with $a:b:c = 0.392:1:0.490$, $\beta = 138°48'$. Crystals equant with {100}, {010}, {0$\bar{1}$0}, {001}, {110}, {1$\bar{1}$0}, {11$\bar{1}$}, {1$\bar{1}\bar{1}$}, etc. Distinct 010 cleavage. The optic plane is 010; strong inclined dispersion. $N_X = 1.530$, $N_Y = 1.560$, $N_Z = 1.590$?, $N_Z - N_X = 0.060$?. 2V = 90° *ca.* Ref: 117, 152.

Calcium acid *d*-malate hexahydrate or calcium bimalate hexahydrate [$\{C_2H_3(OH) \cdot (CO_2)_2\}_2CaH_2 \cdot 6H_2O$] is orthorhombic disphenoidal with $a:b:c = 0.942:1:1.056$. Crystals prismatic with {110}, {210}, {010}, {011}, etc. Cleavage on 010. The optic plane is 100; Z = *c*. (+)2E = 109°6′ red, 105°15′ violet. $N_X = 1.493$, $N_Y = 1.507$, $N_Z = 1.545$, $N_Z - N_X = 0.052$; ∴ (+)2V = 62° *ca.* calc. Ref: 117, 152.

Calcium *l*-malate trihydrate [$C_2H_3OH \cdot (CO_2)_2Ca \cdot 3H_2O$] is orthorhombic disphenoidal with $a:b:c = 0.438:1:1.093$. Crystals {010} tablets with {110}, {011}, {112}, etc. The optic plane is 010; Z = *a*. (+)2V = 70° *ca.* calc. $N_X = 1.545$, $N_Y = 1.555$, $N_Z = 1.575$, $N_Z - N_X = 0.030$. Ref: 117, 152.

Magnesium *l*-malate pentahydrate [$C_2H_3OH \cdot (CO_2)_2Mg \cdot 5H_2O$] is orthorhombic disphenoidal with $a:b:c = 0.748:1:0.410$. Crystals prismatic with {110}, {111}, {101}, etc. The optic plane is 001; Z = *b*. (-)2V = 48°29′ C, 48°31′ D, 48°31′ F. $N_X = 1.4704$ C, 1.4735 D, 1.4789 F; $N_Y = 1.4945$ C, 1.4969 D, 1.5022 F; $N_Z = 1.4985$ C, 1.5015 D, 1.5079 F; $N_Z - N_X = 0.0280$ D. Rotation of polarization plane by 1 cm, plate is 6°30′ C, 12°4′ D, 20°15′ ($\lambda = 527$). Ref: 117, 166, 249.

Potassium boromalate monohydrate ($C_8H_8O_{10}BK \cdot H_2O$) is monoclinic with $a:b:c = 0.828:1:?$, $\beta = 97°40'$. Crystals {001} tablets with {110}. D 1.69. The optic plane is 010; X ∧ ⊥ 001 = 8°38′. (-)2V = 87°32′. dispersion weak. $N_X = 1.482$, $N_Y = 1.51$, $N_Z = 1.536$, $N_Z - N_X = 0.054$. Ref: 384.

Cadmium bromide cadmium xylonate dihydrate [$CdBr_2 \cdot (C_5H_9O_6)_2Cd \cdot 2H_2O$] is orthorhombic disphenoidal. Crystals prisms usually lying on {110}. Parallel extinction and positive elongation. Z = *c*. (-)2V = small. $N_X = 1.615$, $N_Y = 1.633$, $N_Z = 1.638$, $N_Z - N_X = 0.023$. Ref: 251.

[1] *a* and *b* interchanged to make *b* > *a*.

2,3-Dihydroxybutanedioic Acid or Tartaric Acid and Derivatives*

Tartaric acid [$HO_2C\cdot(CHOH)_2\cdot CO_2H$] is monoclinic sphenoidal with $a:b:c = 1.273:1:1.025$, $\beta = 92°53'$. Space group $P2_1$; a 7.68, b 6.03, c 6.18 Å. U.C. 2. Crystals equant with {100}, {001}, {110}, {1$\bar{1}$0}, {011}, {101}, {10$\bar{1}$}, etc., or {100} plates. Fig. 14. Twinning on c. Perfect 100 cleavage. D 1.76. M.P. 168 – 172°. The optic plane and X are normal to 010; $Z \wedge c = +71°18'$ red, $+72°10'$ blue.

(+)2V	N_X	N_Y	N_Z	$N_Z - N_X$	Authority
	1.4957	1.5352	1.6045	0.1088 Na	Perrot
	1.4958	1.5353	1.6049	0.1091 Na	Schwietring
77°4′	1.4961	1.5359	1.6055	0.1094 Na	Cornu
	1.4951	1.5355	1.6047	0.1103 Na	Kohlrausch
75°36′ r > v	1.500	1.540	1.6052	0.1052 $\lambda = 5461$	Bryant

Optical rotation of d-$C_4H_6O_6$ per mm. along either optic axis 10.8°.

Ref: 117, 225a, 293, 410, 556a.

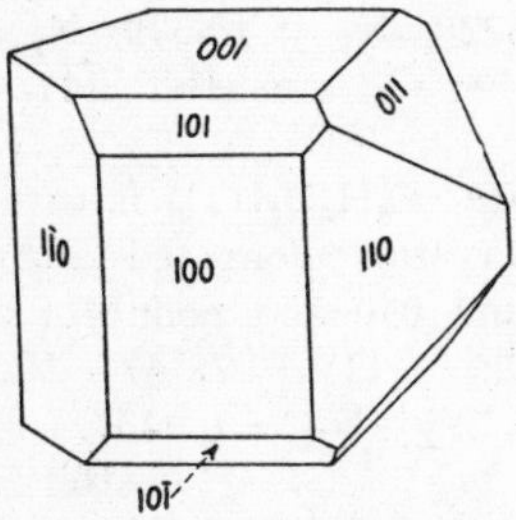

Fig. 14. d-or l-Tartaric acid.

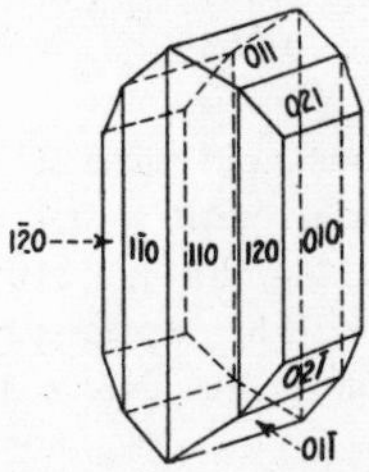

Fig. 15. Ammonium bitartrate.

Ammonium acid tartrate or ammonium bitartrate [$H(NH_4)C_4H_4O_6$] is orthorhombic disphenoidal with $a:b:c = 0.695:1:0.717$. Crystals short brachydomatic or prismatic with {010}, {001}, {011}, {021}, {111}, etc. Fig. 15. Perfect 001 and very good 010 and 011 cleavages. D 1.673. The optic plane is 001: X = b.

(–)2V	N_X	N_Y	N_Z	$N_Z - N_X$	Authority
	1.5168	1.5577	1.5861	0.0693 C	Topsøe
79°54′	1.5188	1.5614	1.5910	0.0722 D	Topsøe
80°16′	1.5201	1.5611	1.5904	0.0703 D	Porter
	1.5279	1.5689	1.6000	0.0721 F	Topsøe

Ref: 117, 279, 334.

* All the following salts are probably salts of d-tartaric acid.

Potassium acid tartrate or potassium bitartrate [$C_4H_4O_6HK$] is orthorhombic disphenoidal with $a:b:c = 0.714:1:0.732$. a 7.614, b 10.70, c 7.80 Å. U.C. 4. Crystals of varied habit often somewhat elongated parallel to a, with {010}, {110}, {111}, {001}, {101}, etc. Perfect 001 and distinct 010 and 011 cleavages. D 1.984. The optic plane is 001; X = b. (-)2V = 88°2′ Na, r > v. $N_X = 1.5105$ Na, $N_Y = 1.5498$, $N_Z = 1.5900$, $N_Z - N_X = 0.0795$.
Ref: 117, 279, 457.

Rubidium acid tartrate or rubidium bitartrate [$C_4H_4O_6HRb$] is orthorhombic disphenoidal with $a:b:c = 0.697:1:0.724$. Crystals often somewhat elongated parallel to a with {010}, {001}, {011}, {111}, {110}, etc. Perfect 001 and distinct 010 and 011 cleavages. D 2.314. The optic plane is 001; X = b. (-)2V = 83°44′ Na, r > v. $N_X = 1.5101$ Na, $N_Y = 1.5495$, $N_Z = 1.5833$, $N_Z - N_X = 0.0732$.
Ref: 177, 279.

Caesium acid tartrate or caesium bitartrate [$C_4H_4O_6HCs$] is orthorhombic disphenoidal with $a:b:c = 0.662:1:0.695$. a 7.66, b 11.58, c 8.03 Å. U.C. 4. Crystals {010} tablets elongated along a with {011}, {001}, {110}, {111}, etc. Perfect 001 and distinct 010 and 011 cleavages. D 2.586. The optic plane is 001; X = b. (-)2V = 81°6′ Na, r > v. $N_X = 1.5206$ Na, $N_Y = 1.5558$, $N_Z = 1.5820$, $N_Z - N_X = 0.0614$. For $\lambda = 546$: $N_X = 1.5220$, $N_Y = 1.5579$, $N_Z = 1.5850$, $N_Z - N_X = 0.0630$.
Ref: 117, 133, 279.

Thallous acid tartrate or thallous bitartrate [$C_4H_4O_6HTl$] is orthorhombic disphenoidal with $a:b:c = 0.695:1:0.723$. Crystals elongated along a with {010}, {011}, {001}, {110}, etc. Good 001 and 010 and poor 011 cleavages. D 3.491. The optic plane is 001; X = b. (-)2V = 78°47′ Na, r < v. $N_X = 1.6609$ Na, $N_Y = 1.6872$, $N_Z = 1.7046$, $N_Z - N_X = 0.0437$.
Ref: 117, 279.

Sodium acid tartrate monohydrate or sodium bitartrate monohydrate [$C_4H_4O_6HNa \cdot H_2O$] is orthorhombic disphenoidal with $a:b:c = 0.818:1:0.683$. Crystals prismatic with {110}, {100}, {011}, {111}, etc. Good 100 cleavage. The optic plane is 100; Z = c. (+)2V = 51°31′ red, 52°18′ blue. $N_Y = 1.533$ red, 1.537 blue. Also: $N_X = 1.53$, $N_Y = 1.54$, $N_Z = 1.60$, $N_Z - N_X = 0.07$.
Ref: 34, 35, 117.

Lithium acid tartrate sesquihydrate or lithium bitartrate sesquihydrate [$C_4H_4O_6HLi \cdot 1.5H_2O$] is orthorhombic disphenoidal with $a:b:c = 0.541:1:0.432$. Crystals {010} tablets with {110}, {011}, {001}, etc. Imperfect 001 cleavage. Parallel extinction and positive elongation with $N_1 = 1.54$, $N_2 = 1.58$, $N_2 - N_1 = 0.04$.
Ref: 34, 35, 117.

Antimony acid tartrate tetrahydrate or antimony bitartrate tetrahydrate [$(C_4H_4O_6)_3H_3Sb \cdot 4H_2O$?] is orthorhombic disphenoidal with $a:b:c = 0.430:1:0.466$. Crystals prisms with {110}, {250}, {010}, {011}, etc. $N_1 = 1.62$, $N_2 = 1.645$, $N_2 - N_1 = 0.025$. (These data are for "antimony tartrate," but which one is unknown.)
Ref: 34, 35, 117.

Ammonium *d*-tartrate $[C_4H_4O_6(NH_4)_2]$ is monoclinic sphenoidal with $a:b:c = 1.151:1:1.438$, $\beta = 92°23'$. Crystals short columnar parallel to *b* with {100}, {001}, {10$\bar{1}$}, {101}, {01$\bar{1}$}, etc. Fig. 16. D 1.60. Perfect 001 cleavage. The optic plane is 010; $X \wedge c = -18°41'$ D, 18°48′ blue. (−)2V = 39°32′ red, 39°36′ yellow, 40°0′ blue. $N_Y = 1.579$ red, 1.581 yellow, 1.592 blue. Int. Crit. Tables, p. 280, gives $N_X = 1.55$, whence $N_Z = 1.585$ and $N_Z - N_X = 0.035$. Bolland gives $N_1 = 1.55$, $N_2 = 1.59$. Ref: 34, 35, 117, 152.

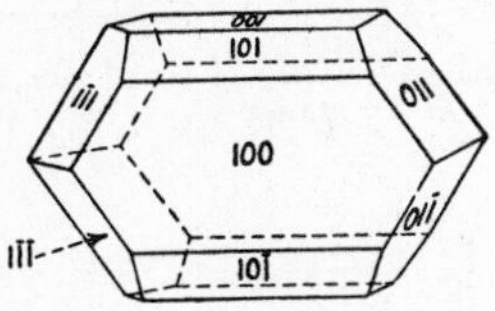

Fig. 16. Ammonium tartrate.

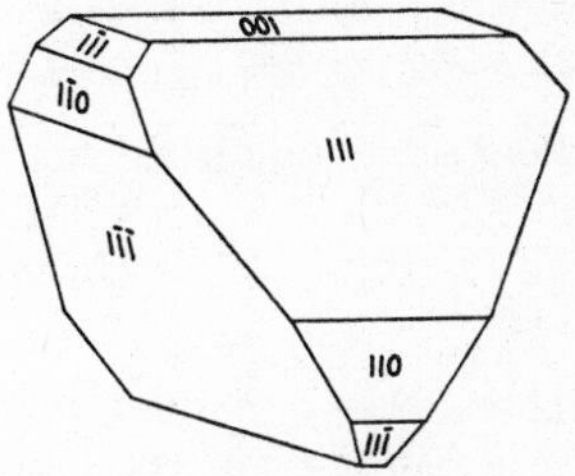

Fig. 17. Potassium antimonyl tartrate monohydrate.

Thallous *d*-tartrate $[C_4H_4O_6)Tl_2]$ is trigonal with $c/a = 1.853$. Crystals rhombohedral with no distinct cleavage. D 4.80. Uniaxial positive with $N_O = 1.7583$ Li, 1.7677 Na, 1.7763 Tl, $N_E = 1.8006$ Li, 1.8115 Na, 1.8218 Tl, $N_E - N_O = 0.0438$ Na. Crystals 1 mm. thick rotate the plane of polarization to the left 34.2° (644), 43.3° Na, 55° Tl. Ref: 117, 141.

Potassium antimonyl tartrate monohydrate or tartar emetic $[C_4H_4O_6K(SbO) \cdot H_2O]$ is orthorhombic disphenoidal with $a:b:c = 0.958:1:1.105$. Crystals sphenoidal with {001}, {110}, etc. Fig. 17. Perfect 001 and distinct 100 and 010 cleavages. D 2.56 − 2.61. The optic plane is 001; $X = b$. (−)2V = 75°30′, r > v. $N_X = 1.6148$ C, 1.6199 D, 1.6325 F, $N_Y =$ 1.6306 C, 1.6360 D, 1.6497 F, $N_Z = 1.6322$ C, 1.6375 D, 1.6511 F, $N_Z - N_X = 0.0176$ D. Ref: 117, 152, 252, 334.

Strontium antimonyl tartrate $[(C_4H_4O_6)_2Sr(SbO)_2]$ is dihexagonal pyramidal with $c/a = 0.844$. Crystals simple prismatic with pyramid terminations. Fig. 18. Uniaxial negative with $N_O = 1.6827$ red,. $N_E = 1.5874$, $N_O - N_E = 0.0953$. Ref: 117.

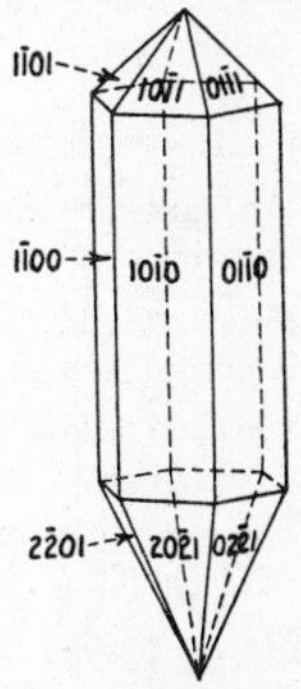

Fig. 18. Strontium antimonyl tartrate.

Potassium tartrate hemihydrate $[C_4H_4O_6K_2 \cdot 0.5H_2O]$ is monoclinic sphenoidal with $a:b:c = 3.087:1:3.970$, $\beta = 90°50'$. Crystals nearly equant with {001}, {100}, {10$\bar{1}$}, {111}, etc. D 1.98. Perfect 100 and 001 cleavages. The optic plane and Z are normal to 010; $X \wedge c =$ 21°20′ in acute angle β. (−)2V = 62° *ca.*, r < v. $N_X = 1.494$, $N_Y = 1.526$, $N_Z = 1.535$, $N_Z - N_X = 0.041$. Ref: 34, 35, 117, 343c, 418b.

Lithium ammonium tartrate monohydrate [$C_4H_4O_6NH_4Li \cdot H_2O$] is orthorhombic disphenoidal with $a:b:c = 0.539:1:0.440$. Crystals short prismatic with {010}, {110}, {120}, {001}, {111}, etc. Perfect 010 cleavage. The optic plane is 001; Z = b. (+)2V = 87°6′, r > v weak. $N_Y = 1.5673$. Ref: 117.

Lithium potassium tartrate monohydrate [$C_4H_4O_6LiK \cdot H_2O$] is orthorhombic disphenoidal with $a:b:c = 0.548:1:0.443$. Crystals thick {010} tablets with {110}, {120}, {001}, {1$\bar{1}$1}, etc. Perfect 010 and imperfect 001 cleavages. The optic plane is 010; X = a. (-)2V = 80°48′, r < v. $N_Y = 1.570$. Also reported as (+)2V = 73°58′ red, $N_Y = 1.5226$. Ref: 117.

Lithium rubidium tartrate monohydrate [$C_4H_4O_6LiRb \cdot H_2O$] is orthorhombic disphenoidal with $a:b:c = 0.541:1:0.436$. Crystals with {010}, {110}, {120}, {001}, {101}, etc. D 2.28. The optic plane is 001; X = a. (-)2V = 57°10′ red. $N_Y = 1.552$. Ref: 117.

Sodium tartrate dihydrate ($C_4H_4O_6Na_2 \cdot 2H_2O$) is orthorhombic disphenoidal with $a:b:c = 0.779:1:0.335$. Crystals show {100}, {010}, {110}, {101}, etc. Imperfect 110 cleavage. D 1.794. Parallel extinction and positive elongation with $N_1 = 1.49$, $N_2 = 1.545$, $N_2 - N_1 = 0.055$ (on the dihydrate?). Ref: 34, 35, 117.

Sodium ammonium tartrate tetrahydrate ($C_4H_4O_6NaNH_4 \cdot 4H_2O$) is orthorhombic disphenoidal with $a:b:c = 0.823:1:0.420$. Crystals short prismatic with {100}, {010}, {110}, {120}, {001}, {011}, etc. D 1.587. The optic plane is 100; X = c. (-)2V = 65°22′ red, 59°52′ yellow, 55°0′ green. $N_X = 1.4953$ Na, $N_Y = 1.4985$, $N_Z = 1.4996$, $N_Z - N_X = 0.0043$. This is known as ammonium Seignette or ammonium Rochelle salt. A plate 1 cm. thick rotates the plane of polarization - 14.5° for Na light. Ref: 117, 379.

Sodium potassium tartrate tetrahydrate or Seignette salt or Rochelle salt ($C_4H_4O_6NaK \cdot 4H_2O$) is dimorphous; one phase (1) is probably monoclinic sphenoidal, but apparently orthorhombic disphenoidal from twinning; it is stable between - 18° and + 23.7° C. Average extinction angle is 1.5°. Another phase (II), stable above 24° C., is orthorhombic disphenoidal with $a:b:c = 0.832:1:0.430$. Space group $P2_12_12$; a 11.85, b 14.25, c 6.21 Å. U.C. 4. Crystals short prismatic with {100}, {010}, {110}, {120}, {001}, {011}, etc. Imperfect 100 and 001 cleavages. D 1.79. M.P. 74°. The optic plane is 010; Z = a. (+)2V = 72°29′ at 16°, 76°46′ at 45°. $N_X = 1.4900$, $N_Y = 1.4920$, $N_Z = 1.4954$, $N_Z - N_X = 0.0054$. A plate 1 cm. thick rotates the plane of polarization + 22.4° for yellow light (D). Ref: 117, 379, 503, 613.

$C_4H_4O_6NaK \cdot 4H_2O$ and $C_4H_4O_6NaNH_4 \cdot 4H_2O$ form a continuous series of mix-crystals in which the optic angle passes through 90° with change of sign from + to -, and then through 0° with a change of the optic plane from 010 to 100. These changes are shown in Fig. 19; the data in some cases cannot be accurate. Mix-crystals show microscopic evidences of imperfect homogeneity, but slowly become homogeneous. In freshly prepared crystals the optic planes for different colors do not coincide with either 010 or 100.

$C_4H_4O_6NaK \cdot 4H_2O$ and $C_4H_4O_6NaRb \cdot 4H_2O$ also form mix-crystals with similar characteristics.

$C_4H_4O_6NaNH_4 \cdot 4H_2O$ and $C_4H_4O_6NaRb \cdot 4H_2O$ form a continuous series of mix-crystals which also show microscopic evidences of imperfect homogeneity, slowly disappearing. Their properties are shown in Figs. 20 and 21.

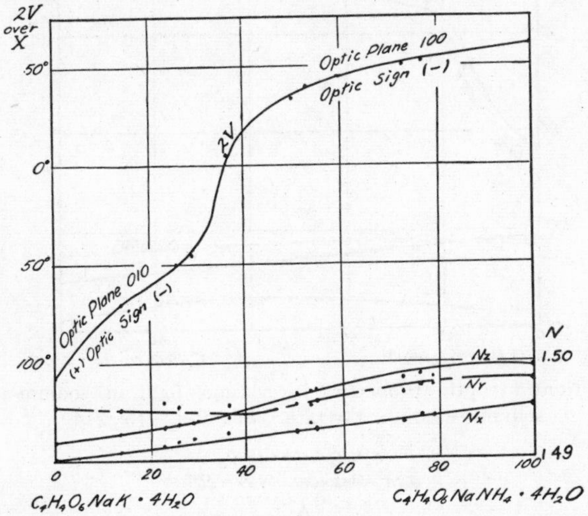

Fig. 19. Variations of optic properties for $\lambda=589$ in Seignette salts. See Ref. 43, 44.

Buckley has demonstrated also the existence of the following series of tetrahydrate tartrates isomorphous with Seignette salt:

Sodium ammonium to potassium ammonium
Potassium ammonium to sodium potassium
Sodium ammonium to diammonium
Sodium ammonium to disodium
Sodium potassium to dipotassium

Variations in the optic angle in some of these series, and also in the sodium ammonium, sodium potassium, and potassium ammonium ternary system are shown in Figs. 22 – 27. Ref: 43, 44, 214, 379.

Sodium rubidium tartrate tetrahydrate ($C_4H_4O_6NaRb \cdot 4H_2O$) is orthorhombic disphenoidal with $a:b:c = 0.833:1:0.43$. Crystals {001} tablets with {110}, {210}, {100}, {010}, {001}, {011}, etc. The optic plane is 010; $X = c$. (−)2V = 51°32′ C, 50°23′ D, 47°16′ F. $N_X = 1.4888$ C, 1.4909 D, 1.4971 F, $N_Y = 1.4924$ C, 1.4948 D, 1.5012 F, $N_Z = 1.4947$ C, 1.4975 D, 1.5044 F, $N_Z - N_X = 0.0066$ D. Ref: 117, 213.

Calcium *d*-tartrate tetrahydrate ($C_4H_4O_6Ca \cdot 4H_2O$?) is orthorhombic disphenoidal with $a:b:c = 0.845:1:0.875$. Space group $P2_12_12_1$; *a* 9.20, *b* 10.54, *c* 9.62 Å. U.C. 4. Crystals equant with {110}, {011}, {101}, D 1.85. Z || elongation. $N_X = 1.525$, $N_Y = 1.535$?, $N_Z = 1.550$, $N_Z - N_X = 0.025$, (+)2V = 80° *ca* ? Ref: 117, 152, 454, 567b.

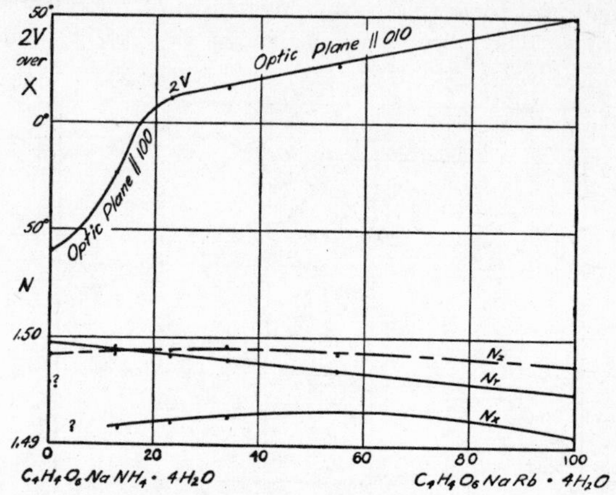

Fig. 20. Variations in optic properties in sodium light in sodium-ammonium to sodium-rubidium tartrate. See Ref. 213, 214.

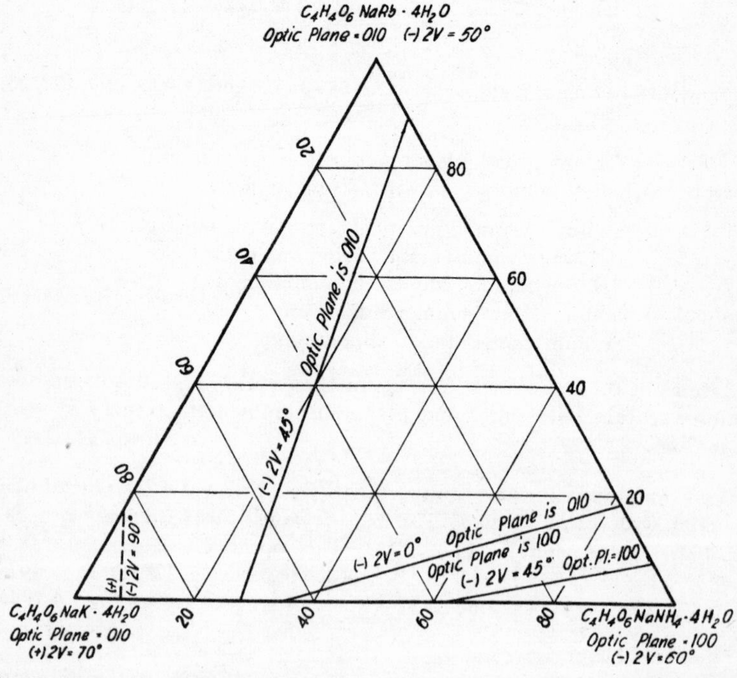

Fig. 21. Variations of optic angle, sign and optic plane in the NaK–$NaNH_4$–NaRb system of tartrates. See Ref. 44, 214.

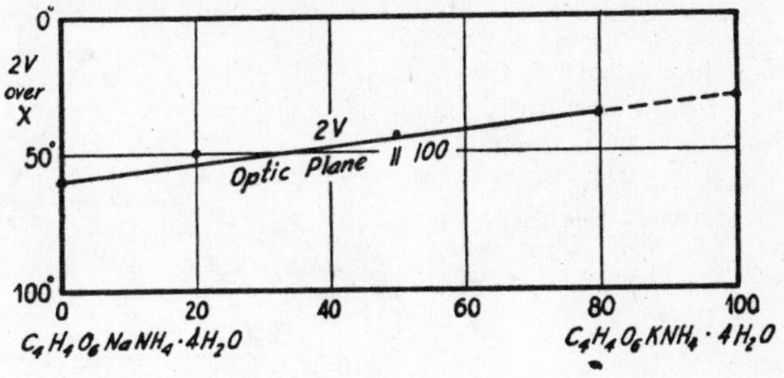

Fig. 22. Variations of optic angle for $\lambda = 578$ in the $NaNH_4$ to KNH_4 tartrates. See Ref. 44.

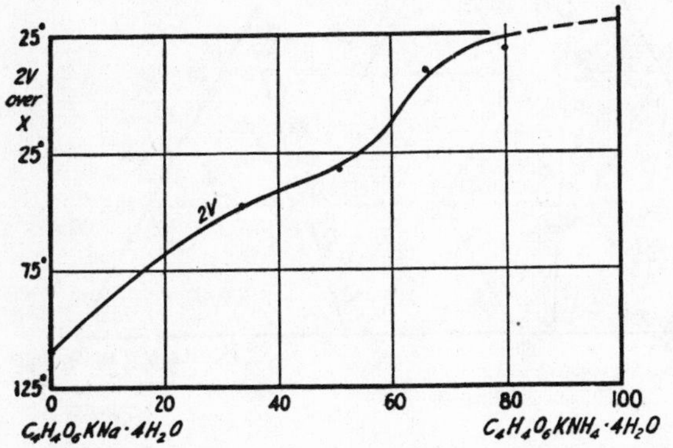

Fig. 23. Variations of optic angle for $\lambda = 578$ in KNa to KNH_4 tartrates. See Ref. 44.

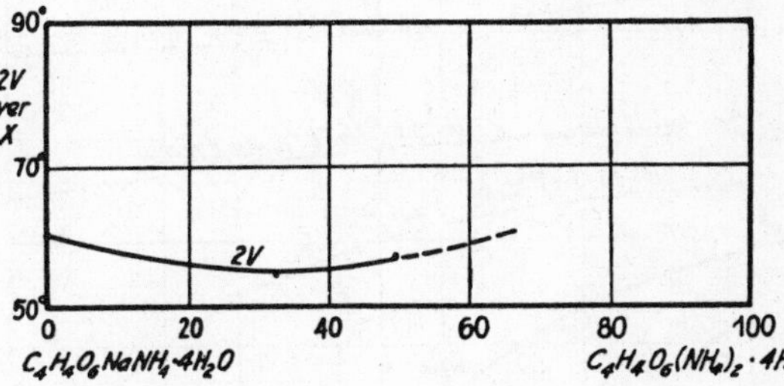

Fig. 24. Optic angle for $\lambda = 578$ in ammonium to sodium-ammonium series of tartrates. See Ref. 44.

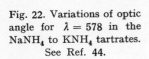

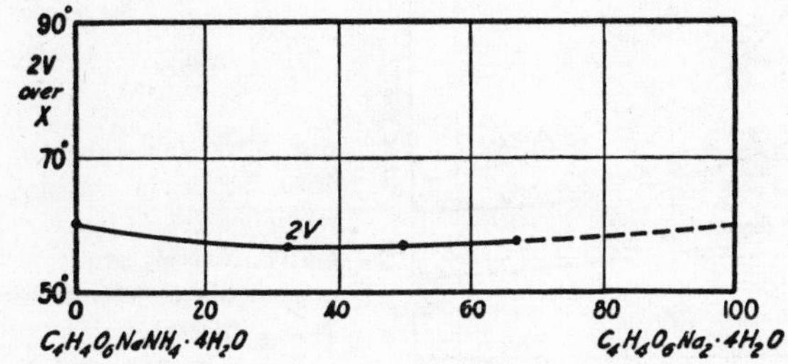

Fig. 25. Optic angle for $\lambda = 578$ in sodium to sodium-ammonium series of tartrates. See Ref. 44.

Fig. 26. Variations of optic angle, sign, and optic plane for $\lambda = 578$ in the KNH_4–NaK–$NaNH_4$ system of tartrates. See Ref. 44.

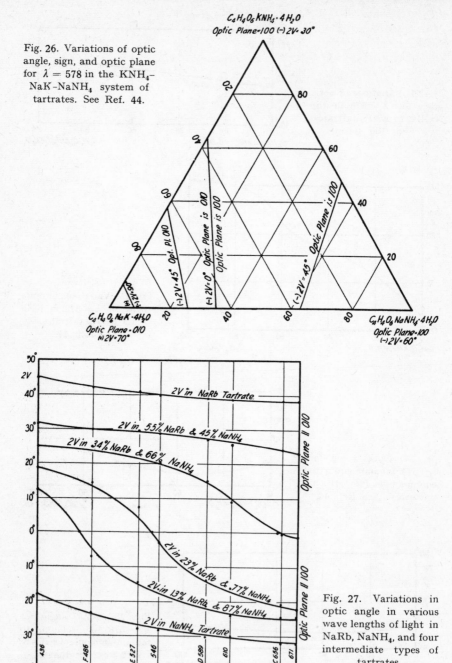

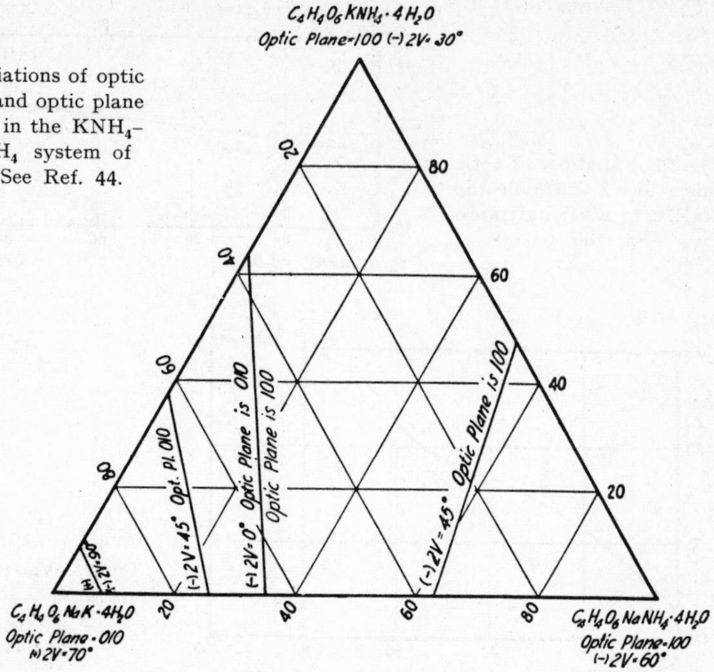

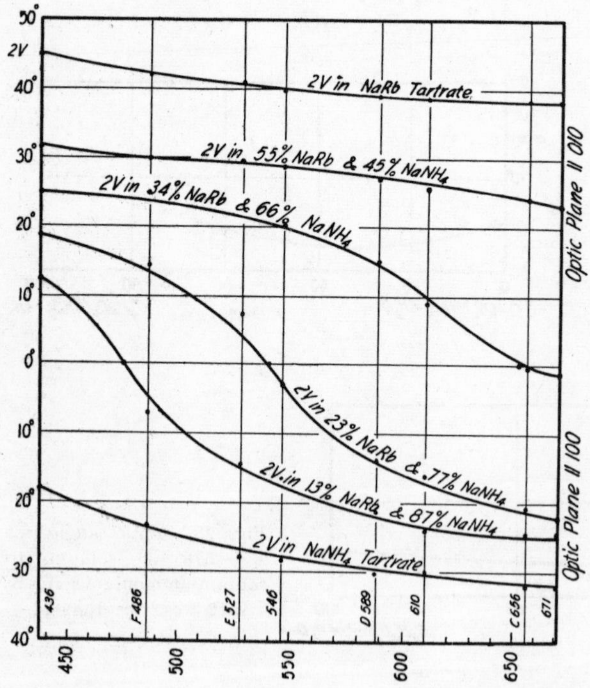

Fig. 27. Variations in optic angle in various wave lengths of light in NaRb, $NaNH_4$, and four intermediate types of tartrates. See Ref. 213, 214.

Calcium *d*-tartrate hexahydrate ($C_4H_4O_6Ca \cdot 6H_2O$) is monoclinic in fine needles elongated along *b* with good 001, 100, 010 and 110 cleavages. $100 \wedge 001 = 104°$. D 1.7 *ca.* Y = *b*, with ± elongation. Imperfect extinction on 010 due to dispersion. (-)2V = small, $N_X = 1.487$, $N_Y = 1.50$, $N_Z = 1.517$, $N_Z - N_X = 0.03$. (Indices and 2V are inconsistent.) Colorless. Not very stable. Ref: 567b.

dl-Tartaric Acid or Racemic Acid and Derivatives

Racemic acid monohydrate [$HO_2C(CHOH)_2CO_2H \cdot H_2O$] is triclinic with $a:b:c = 0.807:1:0.479$, $\alpha = 76°2'$, $\beta = 96°58'$, $\gamma = 120°8'$. Crystals short prismatic with {1$\bar{1}$0}, {010}, {110}, {100}, {101}, {0$\bar{1}$1}, etc. Twinning on 110. D 1.70. Very perfect 010 and distinct 0$\bar{1}$1 and 110 cleavages. The optic plane is nearly parallel with 110; the acute bisectrix makes an angle of about 43° with a normal to 1$\bar{1}$0 and about 90° with the edge 101:1$\bar{1}$0. 2V = 67°10′. $N_Y = 1.526$. Ref: 117.

Ammonium racemate [$(C_4H_4O_6)_2(NH_4)_4$] is monoclinic with $a:b:c = 1.200:1:0.598$, $\beta = 90°19'$. Crystals prismatic with {100}, {110}, {210}, {111}, etc. D 1.60. No distinct cleavage. The optic plane is 010; $Z \wedge c = -12°$ to $-13°$. (+)2V = 60°54′, r < v. $N_Y = 1.564$ red. Distinct inclined dispersion. Ref: 117.

Thallous racemate [$(C_4H_4O_6)_2Tl_4$] is monoclinic with $a:b:c = 1.457:1:0.775$, $\beta = 90°20'$. Crystals variable, prismatic, or equant with {110}, {101}, {10$\bar{1}$}, {001}, etc. Perfect 10$\bar{1}$ cleavage. D 4.80; 4.66. The optic plane is 010; $Z \wedge c = -84°44'$ Na. Distinct inclined dispersion. (+)2V = 88°30′ red, 88°22′ yellow. $N_Y = 1.80$ red, 1.81 yellow, $N_Z - N_X$ = very strong. $(C_4H_4O_6)_2Tl_4$ has another monoclinic phase; the indices have not been measured, but the optic plane is 010; $Z \wedge c = -76°35'$ red, 76°29′ yellow, 76°1′ blue. (+)2V = very large. $N_Z - N_X$ = very strong. Ref: 117.

Lithium ammonium racemate monohydrate [$C_4H_4O_6LiNH_4 \cdot H_2O$] is monoclinic with $a:b:c = 1.918:1:1.003$, $\beta = 115°1'$. Crystals short prismatic or thick {100} tablets with {110}, {310}, {001}, {101}, {111}, etc. Twinning on 100. The optic plane is 010; $Z \wedge c = -77°$. (+)2V = 81°42′; very weak dispersion. $N_Y = 1.5287$. Ref: 117.

Sodium ammonium racemate monohydrate [$C_4H_4O_6NaNH_4 \cdot H_2O$] is monoclinic with $a:b:c = 2.028:1:3.004$, $\beta = 94°24'$. Crystals short prismatic with {100}, {110}, {001}, etc. D 1.74. Perfect 100 cleavage. The optic plane and Z are normal to 010; $X \wedge c = -81°$. (-)2V = 44°20′, r < v very weak. Horizontal dispersion weak. $N_Y = 1.473$ red. Ref: 117.

Lithium sodium racemate dihydrate ($C_4H_4O_6LiNa \cdot 2H_2O$) is monoclinic with $a:b:c = 2.328:1:1.794$, $\beta = 131°28'$. Crystals thick {100} tablets with {001},

{110}, {310}, etc. Indistinct 100 and 110 cleavages. The optic plane is 010; X ∧ c = - 34.5°. (-)2V = 68°57′ calc. N_Y = 1.4904. Distinct inclined dispersion. Ref: 117.

Rubidium racemate dihydrate ($C_4H_4O_6Rb_2 \cdot 2H_2O$) is monoclinic with $a:b:c$ = 0.902:1:0.632, β = 91°42′. Crystals {001} tablets with {021}, {201}, {110}, etc. Perfect 010 and $20\bar{1}$ cleavages. The optic plane is 010, X ∧ c = +82°18′. (-)2V = 56°6′, r > v very weak. N_Y = 1.488. Ref: 117.

Barium racemate pentahydrate ($C_4H_4O_6Ba \cdot 5H_2O$) is monoclinic with $a:b:c$ = 3.346:1:1.444, β = 92°5′. Crystals {100} tablets with {010}, {001}, {101}, etc. Distinct 001 cleavage. The optic plane and Z are normal to 010; X ∧ c = - 73°. (+)2V = 86°59′, r < v. N_Y < 1.7429, N_Z = 1.7886. Ref: 117, 255.

Dimethyl racemate diacetate or dimethyl 2,3-diacetoxybutanedioate $[[CH(O \cdot C_2H_3O) \cdot CO_2(CH_3)]_2]$ is orthorhombic with $a:b:c$ = 0.810:1:0.673. Crystals {010} tablets with {110}, {111}. Imperfect 010 cleavage. M.P. 86°. The optic plane is 001; Z = b. (+)2V = 62°36′ Na, r < v distinct. N_Y = 1.5115 Na. $N_Z - N_X$ = moderate. Ref: 117.

i-2,3-Dihydroxybutanedioic Acid or Mesotartaric Acid and Derivatives

Mesotartaric acid monohydrate or antitartaric acid monohydrate or *i*-2,3-dihydroxybutanedioic acid monohydrate ($C_4H_6O_6 \cdot H_2O$) is triclinic[1] with $a:b:c$ = 0.780:1:0.647, α = 75°18′, β = 106°47′, γ = 90°24′. Crystals prismatic with {011}, {010}, {100}, {110}, etc. Imperfect 001 and 010 cleavages. Extinction on 010 at 61°42′ to 100 in the acute angle between 001 and 100. Extinction on 001 at 69°30′ to 100 in the acute angle between 100 and 010. An optic axis is nearly normal to 001; on 010 an optic axis emerges near the edge of the field of view. The optic angle is about 90°. The trace of the optic plane makes an angle on 001 of about 33° with 100 and about 56° with 010. The trace of the optic plane makes an angle on 010 of about 22° with 100 and about 61° with 001. N_X = 1.478, N_Y = 1.516 calc., N_Z = 1.554, $N_Z - N_X$ = 0.076. Ref: 3.

Thallous mesotartrate ($C_4H_4O_6Tl_2$) is triclinic with $a:b:c$ = 0.815:1:0.470, α = 75°42′, β = 86°20′, γ = 82°44′. Crystals have {100}, {010}, {110}, {111}, etc. Perfect 010 and $1\bar{1}1$ cleavages. D 5.11. The optic plane makes an angle of 104° with the edge $0\bar{1}0:1\bar{1}0$ and 20° with the edge $0\bar{1}0:1\bar{1}\bar{1}$; Z ∧ ⊥ 010 = 15° *ca.* (+)2V = 73°54′, r < v. N_Y = 1.707. Ref: 117, 152.

Rubidium mesotartrate monohydrate ($C_4H_4O_6Rb_2 \cdot H_2O$) is triclinic with $a:b:c$ = 0.597:1:0.351, α = 89°43′, β = 89°58′, γ = 89°14′. Crystals elongated parallel to a with {011}, {$0\bar{1}1$}, {010}, {100}, etc. Perfect 010 cleavage. D 2.58.

---

[1] a b c changed to b c a to make $b > a > c$.

The optic plane makes an angle of 19° with c; Z $\wedge \perp 1\bar{1}0$ = 15°. (−)2V = 75°18′, r < v. N_Y = 1.510. Ref: 117.

Calcium mesotartrate trihydrate ($C_4H_4O_6Ca \cdot 3H_2O$) is triclinic (?) or monoclinic with $a:b:c$ = 0.886:1:0.962, β = 91°37′. Crystals {100} tablets with {011}, {010}, {110}, etc. Perfect 100 cleavage. The optic plane is 010; extinction on 011 at 38° to the edge 011:100. (−)2V = 73° calc. N_X = 1.470, N_Y = 1.525, N_Z = 1.555, $N_Z - N_X$ = 0.085. Ref: 117, 152, 255.

2,3,4,5,6-Pentahydroxyhexanoic Acid or Gluconic Acid and Derivatives

Ammonium gluconate [$CH_2OH(CHOH)_4CO_2NH_4$] is biaxial with N_X = 1.510, N_Y = 1.555, N_Z = 1.577, $N_Z - N_X$ = 0.067, all ± 0.003. (−)2E = 65° ± 5°, r < v. (−)2V = 40° calc. Ref: 192.

Sodium gluconate [$CH_2OH(CHOH)_4CO_2Na$] is biaxial in grains with no definite shape. (−)2V = 70° calc. N_X = 1.523, N_Y = 1.569, N_Z = 1.589, $N_Z - N_X$ = 0.066, all ± 0.003. Grains often lie normal to an optic axis. Ref: 192.

Potassium gluconate [$CH_2OH(CHOH)_4CO_2K$] is probably orthorhombic in rods with parallel extinction and positive elongation. (+)2V = 80° calc. N_X = 1.523, N_Y = 1.548, N_Z = 1.565, $N_Z - N_X$ = 0.042, all ± 0.003. Ref: 192.

Lead gluconate [$[O_2C \cdot (CHOH)_4 \cdot CH_2OH]_2Pb$] is biaxial often in six-sided plates. (−)2V = 10° ± 2°. N_X = 1.624, N_Y = 1.633, N_Z = 1.635, $N_Z - N_X$ = 0.011, all ± 0.003. Ref: 192.

Barium gluconate monohydrate [$[O_2C \cdot (CHOH)_4 \cdot CH_2OH]_2Ba \cdot H_2O$] is biaxial in grains, some of which are roughly six-sided. Only partial biaxial interference figures were obtained. N_1 = 1.570, N_2 = 1.613, $N_2 - N_1$ = 0.043, all ± 0.003. Ref: 192.

1-Hydroxy-1,2,3-propanetricarboxylic acid or isocitric acid [$CH(OH) \cdot (CO_2H) \cdot CH(CO_2H) \cdot CH_2CO_2H$] crystallizes from ethyl acetate as rods (and fragments) with parallel extinction and positive elongation. (+)2V = 60° *ca.* N_X = 1.519, N_Y = 1.527, N_Z = 1.548 (all ± 0.003), $N_Z - N_X$ = 0.029. It melts at about 105°, but softens at a lower temperature. Ref: 189.

1-Hydroxy-1,2,3-propanetricarbohydrazide or isocitric trihydrazide ($C_6H_{14}N_6O_4$) forms rods and needles with parallel extinction and positive elongation. It melts at 199°. N_X = 1.540, N_Y = ?, N_Z = 1.632, both ± 0.003, $N_Z - N_X$ = 0.092. Ref: 189.

2-Hydroxy-1,2,3-propanetricarboxylic acid monohydrate or citric acid monohydrate [$HO_2C \cdot CH_2 \cdot C \cdot (OH)(CO_2H)CH_2 \cdot CO_2H \cdot H_2O$] is orthorhombic with $a:b:c$ = 0.674:1:1.662. Crystals brachydomatic with {011}, {110}, {101}, {111}, etc. Fig. 28. D 1.55. Perfect 001 cleavage (also 102 and 100?). The optic plane is 100; Z = *b*. (+)2V = 66°24′ B, 65°42′ D, 62°48′ H. N_X = 1.4896 B, 1.4932 D, 1.5098 H, N_Y = 1.4943 B, 1.4977 D, 1.5140 H, N_Z = 1.5054 B, 1.5089 D, 1.5254 H, $N_Z - N_X$ = 0.0157 D. Also: N_X = 1.498, N_Y = 1.507, N_Z = 1.513, $N_Z - N_X$ = 0.015. Ref: 117, 239.

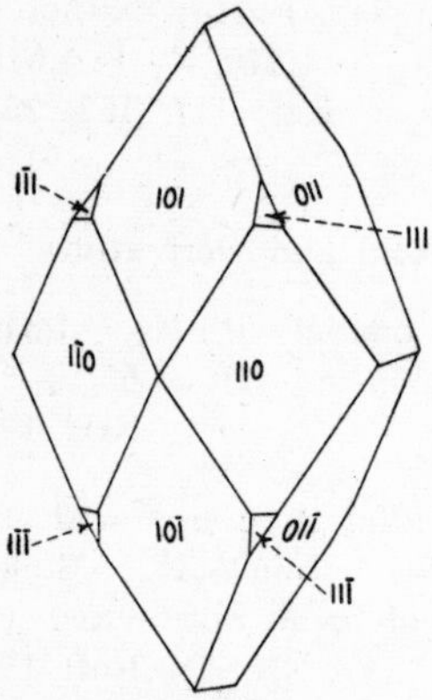

Fig. 28.
Citric acid monohydrate.

Lithium citrate [$C_6H_5O_7Li_3 \cdot (H_2O\ ?)$] has parallel extinction and positive elongation with N_1 = 1.48, N_2 = 1.53, $N_2 - N_1$ = 0.05. Ref: 34, 35.

Sodium citrate dihydrate {$C_3H_4OH \cdot (CO_2Na)_3 \cdot 2H_2O$} is monoclinic prismatic with *a*:*b*:*c* = 0.892:1:1.365, β = 115°55′. Crystals equant with {001}, {010}, {110}, {10$\bar{1}$}, etc. Good 110 and 10$\bar{1}$ cleavages. Soluble in water. (-)2V = moderate, N_1 = 1.470, N_2 = 1,500, N_3 = 1.510, $N_3 - N_1$ = 0.040. Colorless. Ref: 518.

Calcium citrate tetrahydrate [$(C_6H_5O_7)_2Ca_3 \cdot 4H_2O$] is biaxial with D 1.95 and N_X = 1.515, N_Y = 1.530, N_Z = 1.580, $N_Z - N_X$ = 0.065, (+)2V = 60° ± calc. The natural substance has been found in deep-sea deposits and named "earlandite". Ref: 19, 152.

Agaric acid [$C_{19}H_{36}OH(CO_2H)_3 \cdot 1.5H_2O$] forms needles with M.P. 141.5°. N_X = 1.510, N_Y = 1.525. Ref: 343c.

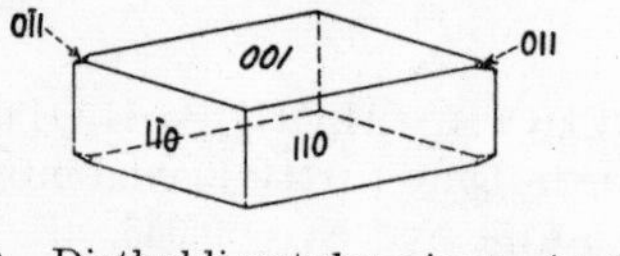

Fig. 29. Diethyldiacetylsuccinate (stable).

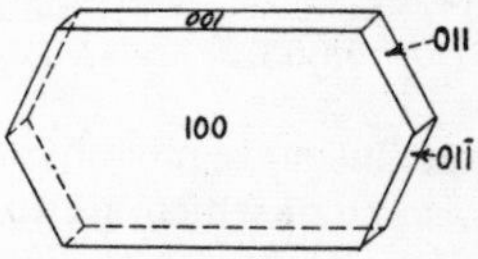

Fig. 30. Diethyldiacetylsuccinate (metastable).

Sodium uroxanate octahydrate [$(NH_2 \cdot CO \cdot NH)_2C(CO_2Na)_2 \cdot 8H_2O$] forms thin six-sided plates with symmetrical extinction and positive elongation with the optic plane parallel to plates. N_X = 1.51, N_Y = ?, N_Z = 1.52 to 1.53, $N_Z - N_X$ = 0.01 to 0.02. Heated to 110°, crystals become cloudy with N_X = 1.53 to 1.54, N_Y = ?, N_Z = 1.54 to 1.55, $N_Z - N_X$ = 0.01 to 0.02. Ref: 338.

Diethyl 2.5-diketo-3,4-hexanedicarboxylate or diethyl α,β-diacetylsuccinate [$(C_2H_5)O_2C \cdot CH(CO \cdot CH_3) \cdot CH(CO \cdot CH_3) \cdot CO_2(C_2H_5)$] is dimorphous: one phase (I) is monoclinic with *a*:*b*:*c* = 0.876:1:0.793, β = 106°5′. Crystals short prismatic or {001} tablets with {110}, {010}, etc. Fig. 29. D 1.21. M.P. 89 - 90°. Perfect 010 and poor 110 cleavages. The optic plane is 010; extinction at - 61° to *c* in 010. (+)2V = 64° *ca*. N_X = 1.4790, N_Y = 1.4955, N_Z = 1.5243, $N_Z - N_X$ = 0.0453 Na. Another phase (II) is also monoclinic with *a*:*b*:*c* = ?:1:3.130, β = 100°38′. Crystals acicular parallel to *b* with {100}, {001}, {011}, etc. Fig. 30.

Imperfect 001 and 100 cleavages. D 1.18. The optic plane is 010; an optic axis is visible in 100 and also in 001. Optic angle in oil = 62.5°, $N_X = 1.4705$, $N_Y = 1.4790$, $N_Z = 1.5190$, $N_Z - N_X = 0.0485$ Na. (+)2V = 50° calc. Ref: 117.

Potassium acid *d*-2,3,4,5-tetrahydroxyhexanedioate or potassium acid *d*-saccharate or potassium *d*-disaccharate [$HO_2C \cdot (CHOH)_4 \cdot CO_2K$] is monoclinic in {100} tablets elongated along *c*. An optic axis is nearly normal to 100; the optic plane is 010; $X \wedge c = -42°$. (-)2V = 45° calc. $N_X = 1.483$, $N_Y = 1.571$, $N_Z = 1.586$, $N_Z - N_X = 0.103$ Na. Ref: 251.

i-2,3,4,5-Tetrahydroxyhexanedioic acid or mucic acid [$HO_2C[CH(OH)]_4 \cdot CO_2H$] is triclinic in rhombic {001} tablets with angles of 86° and 94°. The optic plane makes an angle of 40° with the elongation. X is nearly normal to 001. (-)2V = medium. $N_X = 1.490$, $N_Y = 1.600$, $N_Z = 1.610$ (approx.), $N_Z - N_X = 0.120$. Ref: 251.

Subclass M. Carbonyl Carboxylic Acids and Derivatives

1,2-Dioximino-1-hydroxypropane or hydroxymethylglyoxime or oxime of pyruvohydroxamic acid [$CH_3C(:NOH)C(NOH)OH$] is tetragonal with $c/a = 0.247$. Crystals prismatic with {100}, {110}, {410}, {101}, {211}. Uniaxial and negative with $N_O = 1.590$, $N_E = 1.511 \pm 0.001$, $N_O - N_E = 0.079$. Ref: 289a.

2,2-Dicarbamidopropanedioic acid or diureidomalonic acid or uroxanic acid [$(NH_2 \cdot CO \cdot NH)_2C(CO_2H)_2$] forms irregular four-sided solids with $N_1 = 1.5316$, $N_2 = 1.6005$, $N_2 - N_1 = 0.0689$. Ref: 248.

Potassium acid uroxanate or potassium biuroxanate [$(NH_2 \cdot CO \cdot NH)_2 C(CO_2H)(CO_2K)$] forms long needles with parallel extinction and positive elongation. $N_1 = 1.4676$, $N_2 = 1.620 +$, $N_2 - N_1 = 0.152 +$. Ref: 248.

Class 6. Sulfonic Acids and Derivatives

Subclass E. Keto Sulfonic Acids and Derivatives

Ammonium methanedisulfonate [$CH_2 \cdot (SO_3NH_4)_2$] is monoclinic with $a:b:c = 1.638:1:0.970$, $\beta = 91°42'$. Crystals pyramidal or prismatic, easily formed from solution in water. Distinct 001 cleavage. D 1.83. The optic plane and X are normal to 010; $Z \wedge c = -39°$. (-)2V = 79°34′, r < v. $N_Y = 1.5504$ Na, $N_Z - N_X$ = rather strong. Ref: 117.

Potassium methanedisulfonate [$CH_2 \cdot (SO_3K)_2$] is monoclinic with $a:b:c = 1.616:1:0.936$, $\beta = 90°11'$. Crystals short prismatic or {010} tablets. Perfect 001 cleavage. D 2.38. The optic plane is normal to 010. The acute bisectrix makes an angle of 41° with *c* in the obtuse angle β. (-?)2V = 72°, $N_Y = 1.539$ Na. Ref: 117.

Sodium ammonium methanedisulfonate [$CH_2(SO_3)_2NaNH_4$] is orthorhombic with $a:b:c = 0.916:1:1.016$. Crystals show {110} and {111}. Often twinned on 110. N (in direction of c) = 1.534. Ref: 317.

Sodium methanedisulfonate dihydrate [$CH_2(SO_3)_2Na_2 \cdot 2H_2O$] intercrystalizes in all proportions with silver methane disulfonate dihydrate [$CH_2(SO_3)_2Ag_2 \cdot 2H_2O$]. In the proportion of 3 Na to 4 Ag, the crystals are monoclinic with $a:b:c = 1.419:1:1.392$, $\beta = 95°34'$. Crystals show {111}, {$\bar{1}11$}, {001}, {201}, etc. The optic plane is 010. (+)2V = 75° *ca.* calc. $N_X = 1.568$, $N_Y = 1.577$, $N_Z = 1.590$, $N_Z - N_X = 0.022$ D. Ref: 317.

Lead methanedisulfonate dihydrate ($CH_2S_2O_6Pb \cdot 2H_2O$) is orthorhombic with $a:b:c = 0.888:1:1.601$. Crystals tabular. Good 001 cleavage. X = c, Y = b. (-)2V = 89°. $N_X = 1.632$ *ca.*, $N_Y = 1.650$, $N_Z = 1.666$, $N_Z - N_X = 0.034$ *ca.* Ref: 568a.

Potassium chloromethanedisulfonate [$CHCl(SO_3K)_2$] is monoclinic with $a:b:c = 1.380:1:0.962$, $\beta = 107°3'$. Crystals show {110}, {101}, {100}, {$\bar{1}01$}, {120}, etc. The optic plane is 010; one optic axis is almost normal to 101; the other makes an angle of 29° with a normal to 100. (-)2V = 69°20'. $N_X = 1.503$, $N_Y = 1.531$, $N_Z = 1.545$, $N_Z - N_X = 0.042$. Ref: 318.

Thallous chloromethanedisulfonate [$CHCl(SO_3Tl)_2$] is monoclinic with: $a:b:c = 1.341:1:0.932$, $\beta = 109°5'$. Crystals show {110}, {101}, {$\bar{1}01$}, {100}, {001}, etc. The optic plane is 010; the optic axes are nearly normal to 100 and 101. Therefore $X \wedge c = -65°$. (-)2V = 47°30'. $N_X = 1.693$, $N_Y = 1.734$, $N_Z = 1.742$, $N_Z - N_X = 0.049$. Ref: 318.

Caesium methanetrisulfonate monohydrate [$CH(SO_3Cs)_3 \cdot H_2O$] is monoclinic with $a:b:c = 0.802:1:0.760$, $\beta = 102°35'$. Crystals show {100}, {011}, {$\bar{1}01$}, {110}, etc. The optic plane is 010; (+)2V = 45° calc. $N_X = 1.549$ yellow, 1.551 green, 1.560 blue, $N_Y = 1.552$ yellow, 1.554 green, 1.562 blue, $N_Z = 1.570$ yellow, 1.572 green, 1.582 blue, $N_Z - N_X = 0.021$. Ref: 320.

Thallous methanetrisulfonate monohydrate [$CH(SO_3Tl)_3 \cdot H_2O$] is orthorhombic disphenoidal with $a:b:c = 0.997:1:1.301$. Crystals show {110}, {101}, {011}, {$1\bar{1}1$}, etc. The optic plane is 001; Z = b. (+)2V = 24°, r > v. $N_Y = 1.739$ (578), 1.743 (546), 1.768 (436). Ref: 319.

Potassium methanetrisulfonate monohydrate [$CH(SO_3K)_3 \cdot H_2O$] is orthorhombic disphenoidal with $a:b:c = 0.998:1:1.306$. Crystals show {001}, {101}, {010}, {100}, {110}, {111}, etc. The optic plane is 001; X = a. (-)2V = 51°45', r < v. $N_X = 1.5130$, $N_Y = 1.5235$, $N_Z = 1.5270$, $N_Z - N_X = 0.0140$. Ref: 319.

Rubidium methanetrisulfonate monohydrate [$CH(SO_3Rb)_3 \cdot H_2O$] is orthorhombic with $a:b:c = 0.995:1:1.130$. Crystals show {001}, {101}, {110}, {111}. The optic plane is 010; X = c. (-)2V = about 80° calc. $N_X = 1.521$ calc. (Hg green), $N_Y = 1.528$, $N_Z = 1.533$, $N_Z - N_X = 0.012$ *ca.* calc. Intercrystallizes freely with the K salt. Ref: 320.

Potassium bromomethanetrisulfonate monohydrate [$BrC(SO_3K)_3 \cdot H_2O$] is tetragonal with $c/a = 1.149$. Crystals simple pyramids. Uniaxial negative with (for $\lambda = 589$): $N_O = 1.5520$, $N_E = 1.5433$, $N_O - N_E = 0.0087$; for $\lambda = 546$: $N_O = 1.5543$, $N_E = 1.5454$, $N_O - N_E = 0.0089$. Ref: 328.

Rubidium bromomethanetrisulfonate monohydrate [$BrC(SO_3Rb)_3 \cdot H_2O$] is ditetragonal pyramidal with $c/a = 1.153$. Crystals complex pyramids. Twinning on 001. D 3.037. Uniaxial negative with $N_O = 1.5488$ D, $N_E = 1.5416$, $N_O - N_E = 0.0072$. Also monoclinic. Ref: 324.

Barium 2-keto-1-butanesulfonate or barium 2-butanone-1-sulfonate [$(SO_3 \cdot CH_2 \cdot CO \cdot C_2H_5)_2Ba$] is orthorhombic with $a:b:c = 0.8195:1:1.282$. Crystals {100} plates with {011} and {110}. Very soluble in water. The optic plane is 010; $Z = c$. (+)2V = ?. $N_X = 1.472$ (Hg) yellow, 1.474 (Hg green), 1.479 (Hg blue), N_Y = ?, $N_Z = 1.477$ (Hg yellow), 1.478 (Hg green), 1.483 (Hg blue), $N_Z - N_X = 0.005$. Ref: 14.

Barium 2-keto-4-butanesulfonate or barium 2-butanone-4-sulfonate [$(CH_3 \cdot CO \cdot CH_2 \cdot CH_2 \cdot SO_3)_2Ba$] is orthorhombic with $a:b:c = 0.976:1:3.423$. Crystals {001} tablets with {012}, {100}, {111}. Perfect 001 cleavage. The optic plane is 100; $X = c$. (-)2V = 75°. $N_X = 1.54$ calc., $N_Y = 1.553$, $N_Z = 1.561$ calc., $N_Z - N_X = 0.021$ calc. Ref: 14.

Class 8. Amines and Derivatives.

Methylamine chloroplatinate [$(CH_3NH_2)_2 \cdot PtCl_2$?] forms thin six-sided plates which melt at 233°; they are isotropic with N = 1.74. Color yellow. Ref: 93.

Methylammonium chlororhodate [$(CH_3NH_3)_3RhCl_6CH_3NH_3Cl$] is orthorhombic with $a:b:c = 0.793:1:0.570$. Crystals rod-like; rose colored to black. (+)2V = 79°, $N_X = 1.672$, $N_Y = 1.680$, $N_Z = 1.692$, $N_Z - N_X = 0.020$. Ref: 418a.

Methylammonium chloroiridate [$(CH_3NH_3)_3IrCl_6CH_3NH_3Cl$] is orthorhombic with $a:b:c = 0.79:1:0.56$. Crystals dirty green flakes. (+)2V = 63°. $N_X = 1.638$, $N_Y = 1.656$, $N_Z = 1.704$ calc. $N_Z - N_X = 0.066$. Ref: 418a.

Dimethylammonium hexachlorostannate [$[NH_3(CH_3)_2]_2SnCl_6$] is hexagonal scalenohedral with $c/a = 1.507$. Crystals six-or three-sided {0001} plates. D 1.989. Uniaxial positive according to Hjortdahl, but Wendekamm gives: $N_O = 1.614$, $N_E = 1.567$, $N_O - N_E = 0.047$. Ref: 615.

Indium chloride tetrakis(methylamine hydrochloride) or indium chloride tetrakis(methylammonium chloride) ($4CH_3NH_3Cl \cdot InCl_3$) is tetragonal in short prisms said to have negative elongation although the optic sign is positive. M.P. above 300°. $N_O = 1.582$, $N_E = 1.595$, $N_E - N_O = 0.013$. Ref: 76.

Indium chloride tetrakis(dimethylamine hydrochloride) or indium chloride tetrakis(dimethylammonium chloride) $[4(CH_3)_2NH_2Cl \cdot InCl_3]$ is orthorhombic in plates with ± elongation and M.P. 215° - 217°. (+)2V = 80° calc. $N_X = 1.550$, $N_Y = 1.560$, $N_Z = 1.575$, $N_Z - N_X = 0.024$. Ref: 76.

Indium chloride tris(trimethylamine hydrochloride) or indium chloride tris(trimethylammonium chloride) $[3(CH_3)_3NHCl \cdot InCl_3]$ is tetragonal in flat prisms with M.P. 196° - 198° and positive elongation. Uniaxial and positive with $N_O = 1.546$, $N_E = 1.549$, $N_E - N_O = 0.003$. Ref: 76.

Trimethylamine hexachlorostannate $[[NH_4(CH_3)_3]_2SnCl_6]$ is isometric with N = 1.535 D. Ref: 615.

Trimethylamine chloroplatinate $[[(CH_3)_3N]_2 \cdot H_2PtCl_6]$ is isometric with D 2.015; M.P. 245°, with decomposition. Isotropic with N = 1.600. Ref: 152.

Trimethylamine aluminum sulfate dodecahydrate $[NH(CH_3)_2Al(SO_4)_2 \cdot 12H_2O]$ is isometric. Isotropic with N = 1.4506 C, 1.4531 D, 1.4584 F. Ref: 615.

Di-trimethyl ammonium hexachlorostannate $\{(NH(CH_3)_3)_2SnCl_6\}$ is isometric in cubes and octahedrons. D 1.652. Isotropic with N = 1.535 D. Ref: 615.

Indium chloride *bis*(tetramethylammonium chloride) $[2(CH_3)_4NCl \cdot InCl_3]$ is monoclinic in twinned prisms and plates with M.P. above 300°. (-)2V = large. $N_X = 1.54+$, $N_Y = 1.550$, $N_Z = 1.555$, $N_Z - N_X < 0.015$. Ref: 76.

Indium bromide *bis*(tetramethylammonium bromide) $[2(CH_3)_4NBr \cdot InBr_3]$ is isometric, in pseudo-prisms with M.P. 236° - 238°. Isotropic with N = 1.559. Ref: 76.

Di-tetramethylammonium hexachlorostannate $\{(N(CH_3)_4\}_2SnCl_6\}$ is isometric in octahedrons with octahedral cleavage. D 1.508. Isotropic with N = 1.509 D. Ref: 615.

Di-(tetramethylammonium) uranium hexachloride $\{[(CH_3)_4N]_2UCl_6\}$ is orthorhombic with *a* 13.03 kX. U.C. 4. Crystals cubic or octahedral. Good 111 cleavage. D 1.79. N = 1.511. Color green. Ref: 599.

Di-(tetramethyl ammonium) plutonium hexachloride $\{[(CH_3)_4N]_2PuCl_6\}$ is isometric with *a* 12.94 kX. U.C. 4. Crystals cubic or octahedral. Good 010 cleavage. D 1.83. N = 1.526. Color orange yellow. Ref: 599.

Di-(tetramethyl ammonium) uranyl tetrachloride $\{[(CH_3)_4N]_2UO_2Cl_4\}$ is tetragonal with $c/a = 1.29$. *a* 9.12, *c* 11.77 kX. U.C. 2. Crystals show {001}, {110}, {101}. Good 101 cleavage. Uniaxial positive with $N_O = 1.516$, $N_E = 1.526$, $N_E - N_O = 0.010$. Color yellow with O < E. Ref: 599.

Di-(tetramethyl ammonium) plutonyl tetrachloride $\{[(CH_3)_4N]_2PuO_2Cl_4\}$ is tetragonal with $c/a = 1.29$. *a* 9.2, *c* 11.9 kX. U.C. 2. Crystals show {001}, {110}, {101}. Good 101 cleavage. Uniaxial positive with $N_O = 1.526$, $N_E = 1.541$, $N_E - N_O = 0.015$. Color yellow with O < E. Ref: 599.

Di-(tetraethyl ammonium) uranium hexachloride $\{[(C_2H_5)_4N]_2UCl_6\}$ is orthorhombic with $a:b:c = 0.966:1:0.905$. *a* 14.2, *b* 14.7, *c* 13.3 kX. U.C. 4. Inverts to an isotropic form at 94°. Crystals show {111}, {100}, {010}, {001}. D 1.69. Good 111 cleavage. X = *c*, Y = *a*. (-)2V = 35°, r > v. $N_X = 1.548$, $N_Y = 1.555$, $N_Z = 1.556$, $N_Z - N_X = 0.008$. Color light green, with X < Y = Z. Ref: 599.

Di-(tetraethyl ammonium) plutonium hexachloride $\{[(C_2H_5)_4N]_2PuCl_6\}$ is orthorhombic with $a:b:c = 0.979:1:0.935$. *a* 14.2, *b* 14.5, *c* 13.56 kX. U.C. 4. Crystals show {111}, {100}, {010}, {001}. Good 111 cleavage. X = *c*, Y = *a*. (-)2V = 24°, r > v extreme (19° at 470 and 27° at 664 mμ). $N_X = 1.560$, $N_Y = 1.568$, $N_Z = 1.569$, $N_Z - N_X = 0.009$. Color yellow with X < Y = Z. Ref: 599.

Di-(tetraethyl ammonium) uranyl tetrachloride $\{[(C_2H_5)_4N]_2UO_2Cl_4\}$ is monoclinic with $a:b:c = 1.63:1:1.29$, $\beta = 142°$. *a* 16.3, *b* 10.0, *c* 12.9 kX. U.C. 2. Crystals show {001}, {110}, {010}, {101}, {$\bar{1}$01}. D 1.72. Good 011, 101, and $\bar{1}$01 cleavages. $X \wedge c = 10°$, Y = *b*. (-)2V = 33°, r > v. $N_X = 1.531$, $N_Y = 1.558$, $N_Z = 1.559$, $N_Z - N_X = 0.028$. Color yellow with X < Y = Z. Ref: 599.

Di(tetraethyl ammonium) plutonyl tetrachloride $\{[(C_2H_5)_4N]_2PuO_2Cl_4\}$ is tetragonal with *c* = 1.29. *a* 10.0, *c* 12.9 kX. U.C. 2. Crystals show {001}, {110}, {101}. Good 111 cleavage. Uniaxial negative with $N_O = 1.568$, $N_E = 1.539$, $N_O - N_E = 0.027$. Color yellow with O > E. Ref: 599.

bis(Ethylamine sulfate) di-indium sulfate heptahydrate or di(ethylamine sulfate) di-indium sulfate heptahydrate $[2(C_2H_5NH_3)_2SO_4 \cdot 2In_2(SO_4)_3 \cdot 7H_2O]$ is monoclinic in prisms with ± elongation and M.P. above 300°. (+)2V = 80° calc. $N_X = 1.537$, $N_Y = 1.552$, $N_Z = 1.575$, $N_Z - N_X = 0.038$. Ref: 76.

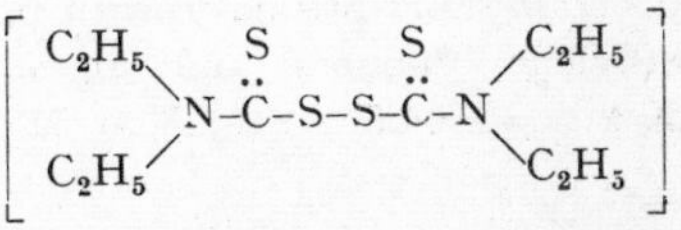

Tetraethyl thiuram disulfide or antabase is monoclinic prismatic with $a:b:c = 0.870:1:0.545$, $\beta = 126°$. *a* 13.84, *b* 15.90, *c* 8.66 Å. U.C. 4. D 1.292. M.P. 70°, Y = *b*; $Z \wedge c = 33°$ in obtuse β (-)2V = 84°, r < v. $N_X = 1.590$, $N_Y = 1.67 \pm 0.01$, $N_Z = 1.740 \pm 0.005$, $N_Z - N_X = 0.15$. Ref: 474a.

Triethylamine hexachlorostannate $[[NH(C_2H_5)_3]_2SnCl_6]$ is biaxial with $N_X = 1.574$, $N_Y = 1.585$, $N_Z = 1.60$ *ca.* $N_Z - N_X = 0.026$, and (+)2V = large. Ref: 344a.

Triethylamine aluminum sulfate dodecahydrate $\{NH(C_2H_5)_3Al\,(SO_4)_2 \cdot 12H_2O\}$ is isometric. Isotropic with N = 1.4594 D. Ref: 615.

Indium chloride *bis*(tetraethylammonium chloride) $[2(C_2H_5)_4NCl \cdot InCl_3]$ is tetragonal in basal plates with positive elongation and M. P. 275° - 277°. Uniaxial and negative with $N_O = 1.583$, $N_E = 1.565$, $N_O - N_E = 0.018$. Ref: 76.

Indium bromide tetraethylammonium bromide [$(C_2H_5)_4NBr \cdot InBr_3$] is hexagonal in prisms with M.P. 289° - 291°. Uniaxial positive with $N_O = 1.609$, $N_E = 1.614$, $N_E - N_O = 0.005$. Ref: 76.

Tuamine sulfate ($C_7H_{17}N \cdot H_2SO_4$) forms irregular units which are uniaxial and positive. $N_O = 1.458$, $N_E = 1.468$, $N_E - N_O = 0.010$. Ref: 523e.

1,2-Diaminoethane dihydrochloride or ethylenediamine dihydrochloride [$(NH_2)_2C_2H_4 \cdot 2HCl$] is monoclinic with $a:b:c = 1.444:1:0.644$, $\beta = 91°35'$. Crystals long prismatic with perfect 001 cleavage. Fig. 31. The optic plane is 010; $X \wedge c = +6°$. (-)2V = 80°16′ red, 81°4′ Na, 82°56′ blue. $N_Y = 1.629$ red, 1.633 Na, 1.643 blue. Ref: 117.

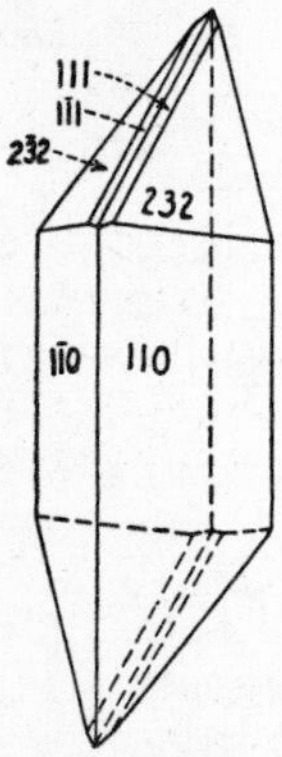

Fig. 31. Ethylene diamine dihydrochloride.

Ethylenediammino(methylammino)(nitrochloronitro)-platinum chloride [$Pt[C_2H_4(NH_2)_2(CH_3NH_2)NO_2ClNO_2]Cl$] forms yellow platelets. (-)2V = 40°, $N_X = 1.670$, $N_Y = 1.740$, $N_Z = 1.750$, $N_Z - N_X = 0.080$. Ref: 418aa.

l-(Ethylenediammino)nitrochloro(methylammino)chloroplatinumchloride sesquihydrate [$C_2H_4(NH_2)_2NO_2ClCH_3NH_2PtCl \cdot 1.5H_2O$] is monoclinic with $a:b:c = 1.593:1:1.821$, $\beta = 101°34'$. (-)2V = 78°, $N_X = 1.660$, $N_Y = 1.690$, $N_Z = 1.710$, $N_Z - N_X = 0.050$. Color yellow. Ref: 418a.

d-(Ethylenediammine)amminodinitrochloroplatinum nitrate [$C_2H_4(NH_2)_2 \cdot NH_3Cl(NO_2)_2PtNO_3$] forms yellow crystals. (-)2V = 60°, $N_X = 1.643$, $N_Y = 1.734$, $N_Z = 1.770$, $N_Z - N_X = 0.127$. Ref: 418a.

1,2-Diaminoethane dithiocyanate or ethylenediamine dithiocyanate [$(NH_2)_2C_2H_4 \cdot 2HCNS$] is monoclinic with $a:b:c = 1.026:1:0.453$, $\beta = 100°40'$. Crystals short prismatic with perfect 100 cleavage. M.P. 145°, decomposing to ethylene thiourea and ammonium thiocyanate. The optic plane is 010; $X \wedge c = -64.5°$. (-)2V = 51°. $N_Y = 1.635$. An optic axis normal to 100. Ref: 117.

Ethylenediamine *d*-tartrate ($C_2H_8N_2 \cdot C_4H_6O_6$?) is monoclinic sphenoidal with $a:b:c = 1.019:1:0.677$, $\beta = 105°10'$. Space group $P2_1$. *a* 8.974, *b* 8.803, *c* 5.959 Å. U.C. 2. Crystals {001} tablets with {100}, {110}, {1$\bar{1}$0}, etc. Twinning on 100. Good 001 cleavage. D 1.54. $X \wedge c = 25°$ in acute β. Z = *b*. (-)2V = 21°, r < v, with strong horizontal dispersion. Optic angle decreases to 0° at 120° C. $N_X = 1.5086$, $N_Y = 1.5893$, $N_Z = 1.5930$, $N_Z - N_X = 0.0844$. Ref: 418a, 599a.

Ethylenediamine *d*-tartrate monohydrate ($C_6H_{14}O_6N_2 \cdot H_2O$) is orthorhombic sphenoidal with $a:b:c = 0.769:1:0.386$. Space group probably $P2_12_12_1$. *a* 11.56, *b* 15.04, *c* 5.80 Å. U.C. 4. D 1.52. X = *a*, Y = *c*. (-)2V = 26° (at 18°; uniaxial at -34°). $N_X = 1.542$, $N_Y = 1.552$, $N_Z = 1.552$, $N_Z - N_X = 0.010$. Ref: 599b.

Ethylene dinitramine ($C_2H_6O_4N_4$) is orthorhombic with $a:b:c$ = 0.812:1:0.571. a 8.80, b 10.84, c 6.19 Å. U.C. 4. Crystals pyramidal with {111}, {001}, and {110}. M.P. 178°. D 1.73. X = c, Y = b. (-)2V = 44°, r < v weak. N_X = 1.427, N_Y = 1.686, N_Z = 1.73, $N_Z - N_X$ = 0.303. Ref: 553d.

Tris(2-aminoethyl)amine tetrahydrochloride monohydrate [$N(C_2H_4 \cdot NH_2)_3 \cdot 4HCl \cdot H_2O$] is hexagonal with c/a = 3.093. Crystals hexagonal prisms with {10$\bar{1}$1}. D 1.39. M.P.169° with loss of $HCl + H_2O$, forming the trihydrochloride. Distinct 0001 cleavage. Uniaxial negative with N_O = 1.5949, N_E = 1.5813, $N_O - N_E$ = 0.0136 Na. This substance is described by Jaeger and Beintema as triaminotriethylamine trichloride hydrochloride monohydrate. They find that it is hexagonal pyramidal hemimorphic with c/a = 3.226. Crystals often twinned on 0001. D 1.37. Uniaxial negative with N_O = 1.598, N_E = 1.584, $N_O - N_E$=0.014 for Hg green line. Ref: 158.

Hexamethylenediamine picrate ($C_6H_{16}N_2 \cdot C_6H_3O_7N_3$) is monoclinic. Crystals lamellar or columnar. M.P. 228°. Plates normal to X are elongated along Z and plates normal to Z have Y $\wedge$ elongation = 25° ± 3°. (-)2V = 21°, r > v, with strong crossed dispersion. N_X = 1.462, N_Y = 1.842, N_Z = 1.861, $N_Z - N_X$ = 0.399 (for λ = 5461). Ref: 556a.

Ethanolamine hydrogen d-tartrate ($C_{16}H_{13}O_7N$) is monoclinic sphenoidal with a 8.83, b 7.51, c 7.60 Å., β = 92°. U.C. 8. Crystals sphenoidal. D 5.51. Excellent 001 cleavage. Y very nearly parallel with a. Z = b. (-)2V = 19.5°. N_X = 1.485, N_Y = 1.549, N_Z = 1.551, $N_Z - N_X$ = 0.066. Ref: 599b.

racemic-Diacetyl-α-2,4-diaminopentane ($CH_3 \cdot CHNH_2 \cdot CH_2 \cdot CHNH_2 \cdot CH_3$) is tetragonal with c/a = 1.093. Crystals dipyramidal. Good 111 cleavage. D 1.126. M.P. 168°. Uniaxial negative with N_O = 1.515, N_E = 1.514, $N_O - N_E$ = 0.001. Ref: 568a.

Stearoylcholine bromide {$CH_3(CH_2)_7CH_3NOHCH_2CH_2Br$} is dimorphous. The β-phase (II) is triclinic[1] with a = 7.18, b = 9.27, c [001] = 31.17 Å. Z inclined 27° on 001; the optic plane inclined 6° on 100. 2V = 72°, N_1 = 1.551, N_2 = 1.560, $N_2 - N_1$ = 0.009. Ref: 600.

Lauroylcholine bromide {$CH_3(CH_2)_{10}CH_3NOHCH_2CH_2Br$} is dimorphous. The α-phase (I) is triclinic with a = 8.01, b = 9.21, c [001] = 27.61 Å. Two interaxial angles are 93.3° and 90°. 2V = 32°, N_1 = 1.523, N_2 = 1.527. The β-phase is also triclinic with a = 5.63, b = 7.38, c [001] = 24.67 Å. Ref: 600.

Palmitoylcholine bromide [$CH_3(CH_2)_{14}CH_3NOHCH_2CH_2Br$] is dimorphous. The α-phase (I) is triclinic with a = 8.0, b = 9.2, c [001] = 32.56 Å. Two interaxial angles are 97° and 93°. Crystals nearly rectangular {001} plates with extinction at 15°. 2V = 27°, N_1 = 1.525, N_2 = 1.530. The β-phase is also triclinic with a = 9.25, b = 7.14, c [001] = 28.9 Å. Ref: 600.

---

[1] a and b interchanged to make $b > a$.

1,3-Diamino-2-propanone oxime dihydrochloride or diaminoacetoxime dihydrochloride $[(HCl\cdot NH_2\cdot CH_2)_2C\cdot NOH]$ is monoclinic with $a:b:c = 0.909:1:0.882$, $\beta = 121°11'$. Crystals prismatic with {100}, {110}, {011}. No observed cleavage. D 1.525. (+)2V=large. $N_X = 1.55$, $N_Y = 1.56$, $N_Z = 1.58$, $N_Z - N_X = 0.03$. Ref: 161.

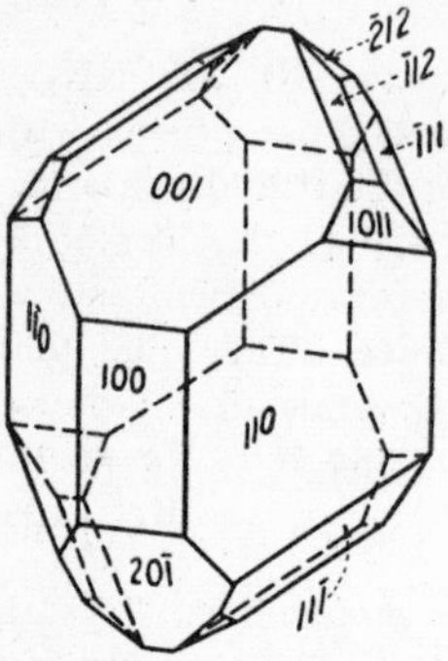

Fig. 32. Triacetone diamine dihydrochloride zinc chloride trihydrate.

2,6-Diamino-2,6-dimethyl-4-heptanone dihydrochloride zinc chloride trihydrate or 2,6-dimethyl-4-keto-2,6-heptanediamine dihydrochloride zinc chloride trihydrate or triacetonediamine dihydrochloride zinc chloride trihydrate $[ZnCl_2\cdot C_9H_{20}ON_2\cdot 2HCl\cdot 3H_2O]$ is monoclinic with $a:b:c = 1.492:1:1.321$, $\beta = 123°27'$. Crystals equant with {110}, {001}, {100}, {201}, {011}, etc. Fig. 32. Loses water at 110° and decomposes at 208°. The optic plane and X are normal to 010; $Z \wedge c = -49°$; both optic axes visible through 001. (+)2V = 35°53′ Li, 36°14′ Na, 38°39′ Tl. $N_X = 1.5627$ Li, 1.5661 Na, 1.5704 Tl, $N_Y = 1.5649$ Li, 1.5688 Na, 1.5736 Tl, $N_Z = 1.5857$ Li, 1.5944 Na, 1.6031 Tl, $N_Z - N_X = 0.0283$ Na. Ref: 117.

D-Glucosamine hydrochloride $[HCOH\cdot CH(NH_2\cdot HCl)\cdot (CHOH)_2CH\cdot CH_2OH]$ (ring O linking HCOH and CH) is monoclinic sphenoidal with $a:b:c = 0.871:1:0.924$, $\beta = 129°25'$. Crystals equant with {110}, {001}, {011}, {101}. Perfect $10\bar{1}$ cleavage. The optic plane is 010; $X \wedge c = -40°$. (-)2H = 73°48′, r > v. Parallel extinction and positive elongation with $N_1 = 1.555$, $N_2 = 1.565$, $N_2 - N_1 = 0.010$. $(\alpha)_D = +44°$ (in water). Ref: 34, 35, 117.

Aminoacetic acid or glycine or glycocoll $[CH_2(NH_2)\cdot CO_2H]$ has two crystal phases; the α-phase (I) is monoclinic prismatic with $a:b:c = 0.426:1:0.456$, $\beta = 111°38'$. Space group $P2_1c$; *a* 5.10, *b* 11.96, *c* 5.45 Å U.C. 4. Crystals equant or brachydomatic with {110}, {011}, {010}, {210}, etc. Perfect 010 and distinct 001 cleavage. D 1.61. Darkens at 228° and melts at 232° – 236° with evolution of gas. The optic plane is nearly parallel to 001; X = *b*; Z nearly parallel to *a*.

	(-)2V	N_X	N_Y	N_Z	$N_Z - N_X$	Authority
For λ=686.7	61°50′	1.4985	1.6115	1.6588	0.1603	Lebedev
For λ=589		1.495	1.615	1.650	0.155	Keenan
For λ=486	61°52′	1.5065	1.6255	1.6758	0.1695	Lebedev
Daylight		1.502	1.618	1.670	0.168	Bowen

The β-phase (II) is monoclinic domatic with $a:b:c = 0.838:1:0.856$, $\beta = 114°20'$. Space group *Pc*; *a* 5.18, *b* 6.18, *c* 5.29 Å. U.C. 2. Crystals acicular parallel to *b*. Good 010 cleavage. Inverts easily to the α-phase. D 1.59. X = *b*; Z nearly parallel to *c*. (-)2V = 62° calc. $N_X = 1.490$, $N_Y = 1.608$, $N_Z = 1.652$, $N_Z - N_X = 0.162$. Ref: 28a, 35a, 117, 169, 223, 404.

Cupric 2-aminoacetate monohydrate or copper glycine salt [$(O_2C{\cdot}CH_2NH_2)_2Cu{\cdot}H_2O$] forms needles with parallel extinction and negative elongation. $N_1 = 1.589$, $N_2 = 1.652$, $N_2 - N_1 = 0.063$. Color blue. Ref: 66.

Calcium pantothenate ($C_{18}H_{32}O_{10}N_2Ca$) forms small rods with Z parallel with elongation. (+ ?)2V = large, $N_X = 1.487$, $N_Y = 1.505$, $N_Z = 1.525$, $N_Z - N_X = 0.038$. Colorless. Ref: 517.

2-Aminopropanoic acid or α-aminopropionic acid or α-alanine [$CH_3CH(NH_2){\cdot}CO_2H$] is orthorhombic disphenoidal with $a:b:c = 0.997:1:0.495$. Space group $P2_12_12_1$; *a* 6.0, *b* 12.1, *c* 5.75 Å. U.C. 4. Crystals show {110}, {120}, {101}. Cleavage on 100 (?). M.P. for *d*- and *l*-alanine is 297°, with decomposition. The optic plane is 001. $N_X = 1.515$, $N_Y = 1.540$, $N_Z = 1.575$, $N_Z - N_X = 0.060$. (+)2V = 80° *ca.* Parallel extinction and positive elongation of rods. (α) *l* = – 9.68° (*c* = 9.3 per cent). Ref: 28a, 117, 169.

β-Aminopropionic acid or β-alanine ($H_2N{\cdot}CH_2{\cdot}CH_2{\cdot}CO_2H$) is orthorhombic with $a:b:c: = 0.714:1:0.441$. *a* 9.86, *b* 13.81, *c* 6.09 Å. Crystals are {010} tablets. Good 010 cleavage. D 141. M.P. 196°. X = *b*; Y = *c*. (–)2V = 48°, r > v. $N_X = 1.519$, $N_Y = 1.591$, $N_Z = 1.600$, $N_Z - N_X = 0.081$. Ref: 535c

Cupric 2-aminopropionate monohydrate or copper alanine salt monohydrate [$(CH_3)_2{\cdot}(O_2C{\cdot}CHNH_2)Cu{\cdot}H_2O$] forms coarse needles with oblique ends, parallel extinction, and negative elongation. $N_1 = 1.527$, $N_2 = 1.630$, $N_2 - N_1 = 0.103$. Color violet. Ref: 66.

Betaine hydrochloride or trimethylglycine ($C_5H_{11}O_2N{\cdot}HCl$) is monoclinic in plates and prisms. Z ∧ elongation = 35°, but the extinction is usually parallel or symmetrical. (–)2V = 62° calc., r > v weak. $N_X = 1.515$, $N_Y = 1.535$, $N_Z = 1.594$, $N_Z - N_X = 0.079$. Again: $N_X = 1.505$, $N_Y = 1.533$, $N_Z = 1.595$, $N_Z - N_X = 0.090$. Ref: 523f, 557e.

Betaine hydrochloride with gold chloride ($C_5H_{11}O_2N{\cdot}HCl$ with $AuCl_3$) forms prisms with Z ∥ elongation. (– ?)2V = 70° calc. $N_X = 1.530$, $N_Y = 1.660$, $N_Z \geqslant 1.734$, $N_Z - N_X \geqslant 0.204$. Ref: 523f.

dl-1-Carboxyethyl trimethylammonium chloroplatinate or *dl-N,N,N*-trimethyl-*dl*-alanine chloroplatinate or *dl*-homobetaine chloroplatinate [$[NCl{\cdot}(CH_3)_3{\cdot}CH(CH_3){\cdot}CO_2H]_2PtCl_4$] is monoclinic with $a:b:c = 0.846:1:0.746$, β = 105°41′. Crystals thick {100} tablets with {110} {011}, etc. M.P. 210° – 212°, with decomposition. The optic plane is 010; Z ∧ *c* = – 99°. (+)2V = 80°39′ Li, 88°12′ Na, $N_Y = 1.6464$ Li, 1.6555 Na. Optic sign is (–) for green Ref: 117.

Di(2-cyanoethyl)amine hydrochloride [$NH_2(C_2H_4CN)_2{\cdot}HCl$] is probably monoclinic. Crystals {010} tablets or lamellar. X ∧ *c* = 22°, Z = *b*. (+)2E = 110°, 2V = 75°, $N_X = 1.517$, $N_Y = 1.537$, $N_Z = 1.581$, $N_Z - N_X = 0.064$. Ref: 529.

dl-2-Acetamidopropanoic acid or *N*-acetyl-*dl*-alanine [$CH_3{\cdot}CH(NH{\cdot}CO{\cdot}CH_3){\cdot}CO_2H$] is orthorhombic with $a:b:c = 0.773:1:1.098$. Crystals short prismatic with {110}, {100}, {001}. Fig. 33. Perfect 001 cleavage. M.P. 133°. The optic plane is 100; X = *c*. (-)2V = 36°12′ Li, 36°9′, Na, 36°37′ Tl. N_X = 1.410 Li, 1.413 Na, 1.415 Tl, N_Y = 1.517 Li, 1.520 Na, 1.524 Tl, N_Z = 1.584 Li, 1.589 Na, 1.596 Tl, $N_Z - N_X$ = 0.176 Na. Ref: 117.

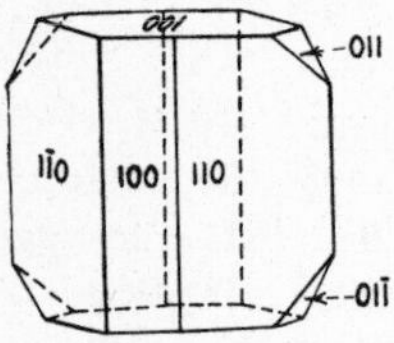

Fig. 33. α-Acetamidopropanoic acid.

Cupric *l*-2-aminopentanoate or copper α-aminovalerate or copper norvaline salt [$[O_2C \cdot CHNH_2 \cdot (CH_2)_2 \cdot CH_3]_2Cu$] forms elongated six-sided plates with extinction at 29° and positive elongation. N_1 = 1.534, N_2 = 1.570, $N_2 - N_1$ = 0.036. Ref: 66.

Cupric (*dl* ?) 2-aminopentanoate or copper α-aminovalerate or copper norvaline salt [$[CH_3(CH_2)_2CHNH_2 \cdot CO_2]_2Cu$] forms elongated ragged plates with parallel extinction and negative elongation. N_1 = 1.530, N_2 = 1.542, $N_2 - N_1$ = 0.012. Ref: 66.

l-2-Amino-3-methylbutanoic acid or *l*-α-aminoisovaleric acid or *l*-valine [$(CH_3)_2CH \cdot CH(NH_2) \cdot CO_2H$] forms rods with parallel extinction and positive elongation. M.P. 315°. N_X = 1.495, N_Y = ?, N_Z = 1.565, $N_Z - N_X$ = 0.070. [α] = - 5.71° (*c* = 5.43 per cent). Ref: 169.

α-Amino-δ-guanidovaleric acid or *d*-arginine [$H_2N \cdot C(:NH)NH(CH_2)_3 \cdot CHNH_2 \cdot CO_2H$] forms thin colorless plates with irregular ends. Optic plane parallel with plates. (+)2V = moderate, N_X = 1.548, N_Y = 1.562, N_Z = 1.610, $N_Z - N_X$ = 0.062. Ref: 514.

α-Amino-δ-guanidovaleric acid dihydrate or *d*-arginine dihydrate [$H_2N \cdot C(:NH)NH(CH_2)_3CHNH_2 \cdot CO_2H \cdot 2H_2O$] forms tablets. (+)2V = large, N_X = 1.528, N_Y = 1.549, N_Z = 1.579, $N_Z - N_X$ = 0.051. Cleavage about normal to an optic axis. Ref: 514.

Cupric 2-amino-3-methylbutanoate or copper valine salt [$[O_2C \cdot CHNH_2 \cdot CH(CH_3)_2]_2Cu$] forms elongated irregular plates with parallel extinction and negative elongation. N_1 = 1.534, N_2 = 1.555, $N_2 - N_1$ = 0.021. Ref: 66.

d- or *l*-2-Aminohexanoic acid or *d*- or *l*-α-aminocaproic acid or *d*- or *l*-norleucine [$CH_3(CH_2)_3 \cdot CH(NH_2) \cdot CO_2H$] is orthorhombic[1] with *a*:*b*:*c* = 0.486:1:0.349. Crystals {011} tablets with {101}, {001}, etc. The optic plane is 100; Z = *b*. (+)2V = 36°, N_X = 1.5074, N_Y = 1.5104, N_Z = 1.5400, $N_Z - N_X$ = 0.0326. For *l*-norleucine [α] = - 21.5°. For *d*-norleucine, [α] = + 18.3°. Ref. 312.

d-2-Formamidohexanoic acid or *N*-formyl-*d*-norleucine [$CH_3(CH_2)_3 \cdot CH \cdot (NHCHO)CO_2H$] is probably orthorhombic with *a*:*b*:*c* = 0.192:1:?. Crystals {110} plates. M.P. 115 - 116°. The optic plane is 100; Z = *c*. (+)2V = 68°28′. N_X = 1.4833, N_Y = 1.5068, N_Z = 1.5616, $N_Z - N_X$ = 0.0783. Ref: 395.

---

[1] *b* and *c* interchanged to make $b > a > c$.

Cupric 2-aminohexanoate or copper norleucine salt $[[O_2C \cdot CHNH_2 \cdot (CH_2)_3 \cdot CH_3]_2Cu]$ forms diamond-shaped plates with extinction parallel to the long diagonal and negative elongation. $N_1 = 1.541$, $N_2 = 1.552$, $N_2 - N_1 = 0.011$. Ref: 66.

2-Amino-4-methylpentanoic acid or α-aminoisocaproic acid or *d*- or *l*-leucine $[(CH_3)_2 \cdot CH \cdot CH_2 \cdot CH(NH_2) \cdot CO_2H]$ is orthorhombic[1] with $a:b:c = 0.662:1:0660$. Crystals {110} tablets with {100}, {010}, {112}, etc. D 1.29. M.P. 295°. The optic plane is 010; X = *a*. (+)2V = 47°. $N_X = 1.5331$, $N_Y = 1.5361$, $N_Z = 1.5514$, $N_Z - N_X = 0.0183$. For *l*-leucine [α] = + 15.51°. For *d*-leucine [α] = − 11.16°. Also for *l*-leucine: $N_X = 1.525$, $N_Y = 1.535$, $N_Z = 1.560$, $N_Z - N_X = 0.035$. ∴ (+)2V = 65°. Ref: 169, 312.

l-2-Formamido-4-methylpentanoic acid or *N*-formyl-*l*-leucine $[(CH_3)_2CH \cdot CH_2CH(NHCHO) \cdot CO_2H]$ is orthorhombic with $a:b:c = 0.975:1:0.925$. Crystals short prisms with {110}, {100}, {001}, {011}, etc. The optic plane is 001; the acute bisectrix = *a*. Described as negative, but the indices require a positive sign. 2V = 73°50′. $N_X = 1.5004$, $N_Y = 1.5070$, $N_Z = 1.5182$, $N_Z - N_X = 0.0178$. Ref: 395.

Cupric 2-amino-4-methylpentanoate or copper leucine salt $[[O_2C \cdot CHNH_2 \cdot CH_2 \cdot CH(CH_3)_2]_2Cu]$ forms very small plates with $N_1 = 1.564$, $N_2 = 1.612$, $N_2 - N_1 = 0.048$. Color bluish. Ref: 66.

Cupric 2-amino-3-methylpentanoate or copper α-amino-β-methylvalerate or copper isoleucine salt $[[O_2C \cdot CHNH_2 \cdot CH(CH_3) \cdot CH_2 \cdot CH_3]_2Cu]$ forms diamond-shaped plates with extinction parallel with the diagonal and negative elongation. $N_1 = 1.534$, $N_2 = 1.547$, $N_2 - N_1 = 0.013$. Ref: 66.

l-2-Aminobutanedioic acid or aminosuccinic acid or aspartic acid $[HO_2C \cdot CH_2 \cdot CH(NH_2) \cdot CO_2H]$ forms spherulites and fragments, probably triclinic. Fibers have negative elongation in two types and positive in a third type. D 1.59. M.P. 270°. (+)2V = 80° calc. $N_X = 1.515$, $N_Y = 1.560$, $N_Z = 1.630$, $N_Z - N_X = 0.115$ D. Ref: 98, 117, 169.

Cupric 2-aminobutanedioate or aspartate $[O_2C \cdot CH(NH_2) \cdot CH_2CO_2Cu \cdot 5H_2O(?)]$ forms small needles with positive elongation and parallel extinction. $N_1 = 1.522$, $N_2 = 1.538$, $N_2 - N_1 = 0.016$. Ref: 66.

2-Amino-3-carbamylpropanoic acid monohydrate or α-aminosuccinamic acid monohydrate or asparagine monohydrate $[CO(NH_2) \cdot CH_2 \cdot CH(NH_2) \cdot CO_2H \cdot H_2O]$ is orthorhombic disphenoidal with $a:b:c = 0.474:1:0.836$. Space group $P2_12_12_1$; *a* 5.6, *b* 11.8 *c* 9.86 Å U.C. 4. Crystals short brachydomatic with {021}, {110}, {001}, {011}, {1$\bar{1}$1}, etc. Imperfect 001 cleavage. Loses water at 100°. D 1.54. The optic plane is 010; Z = *c*. *d*- and -*l* forms have the same optical properties (except optical rotation), as shown by the following data:

[1] *a b c* changed to *b c a* to make $b > a > c$.

d-form		*l*-form				
Grattiola	Gaubert	Schrauf	Groth	Grattiola	Gaubert	
$(+)2V = 86°32'$ -87°16'			86°30′ red 86°40′ D			
$N_X = 1.5474$	1.5477	1.5476	1.5489	1.5489	1.5480	1.5477
$N_Y = 1.5799$	1.5804	1.5800	1.5829		1.5808	1.5805
$N_Z = 1.6188$	1.6191	1.6190	1.6246	1.6185	1.6196	1.6192
$N_Z - N_X = 0.0714$	0.0714	0.0714	0.0757	0.0696	0.0716	0.0715

Ref: 28a, 98, 117, 152, 290.

d- or *l*-2-Aminopentanedioic Acid, or Glutamic Acid and Derivatives

l-2-Aminopentanedioic acid or *l*-glutamic acid or α-aminoglutaric acid [$HO_2C \cdot CH(NH_2) \cdot (CH_2)_2 \cdot CO_2H$] is orthorhombic disphenoidal with $a:b:c = 0.685:1:0.850$. Space group $P2_12_12_1$; *a* 7.06, *b* 10.3, *c* 8.75 Å. U.C. 4. Crystals varied, sphenoidal, or short prismatic with {110}, {111}, {1$\bar{2}$1}, {1$\bar{1}$1}, {011}, {001}, etc. Twins of dextro- and levo-forms common. Distinct 001 cleavage. M.P. 227° (213°). The optic plane is 010; X = *a*. $(-)2V = 40°5'$, $r < v$ weak. $N_X = 1.480$ calc., $N_Y = 1.6015$, $N_Z = 1.6187$, $N_Z - N_X = 0.138$ *ca.* calc. Also: $N_X = 1.490$, $N_Y = 1.605$, $N_Z = 1.620$, $N_Z - N_X = 0.130$. Ref: 28a, 117, 169.

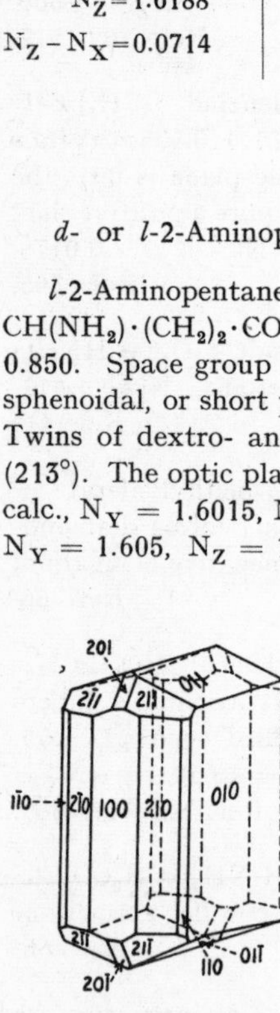

Fig. 34. *d*-or *l*-Glutamic acid hydrochloride.

Sodium acid *d*-glutamate or sodium biglutamate [$HO_2C \cdot (CH_2)_2 \cdot CH(NH_2) \cdot CO_2Na$] is monoclinic sphenoidal with $a:b:c = 1.013:1:0.864$, $\beta = 97°59'$. Crystals columnar parallel to *b* with {001}, {100}, {10$\bar{2}$}, {110}, {120}, etc. Perfect 001 and less perfect 100 cleavages. The optic plane and Z are normal to 010. X ⊥ 10$\bar{2}$. $(-)2V = 63°4'$. $N_Y = 1.5107$ Na. Ref: 117.

Sodium acid *l*-glutamate monohydrate or monosodium-*l*-glutamate monohydrate [$HO_2C \cdot (CH_2)_2 \cdot CH (NH_2) \cdot CO_2Na \cdot H_2O$] is monoclinic. Crystals columnar parallel to *b*. X = *b*. Optic axis interference figure often seen. $(-)2V = 85°$ calc. $N_X = 1.500$, $N_Y = 1.550$, $N_Z = 1.592$, $N_Z - N_X = 0.092$. Colorless. Ref: 527e.

Glutamic acid hydrochloride [$HO_2C \cdot CH(NH_2) \cdot (CH_2)_2 \cdot CO_2H \cdot HCl$] is orthorhombic disphenoidal with $a:b:c = 0.886:1:0.387$. Crystals show {100}, {010}, {110}, {210}, {010}, {201}, etc. Fig. 34. Perfect 100 cleavage. D 1.525. M.P. 193°. The optic plane is 100; Z = *b*. Dispersion, $r > v$ weak.

	2V	N_X	N_Y	N_Z	$N_Z - N_X$	Authority
d-form		1.547	1.558	1.582	0.035	Takayama
d-form	(+)71°7′	1.551	1.561	1.588	0.037	Kaplanova
inactive	(+)71°23′	1.550	1.562	1.588	0.038	Kaplanova
or		1.548	1.561	1.583	0.035	Takayama
dl-form	(+)70°44′	1.5461	1.5587	1.584 calc.	0.038 calc.	Artini
λ=5461	(+)78°	1.552	1.567	1.590 calc.	0.038 calc.	Bryant

Ref: 6, 117, 163, 313, 556a.

Glutamic acid hydrobromide [$HO_2C \cdot CH(NH_2) \cdot (CH_2)_2 \cdot CO_2H \cdot HBr$] is orthorhombic with $a:b:c = 0.878:1:0.403$. Crystals {010} tablets with {110}, {210}, {011}, etc. Perfect 100 cleavage. The optic plane is 100; Z = *b*.

	D	(+)2V	N_X	N_Y	N_Z	$N_Z - N_X$
d-form	1.790	80°21′	1.570	1.582	1.599	0.029
inactive (*dl*)	1.814	80°33′	1.570	1.582	1.598	0.029

Ref: 117, 163.

d-Glutamic acid hydroiodide [$HO_2C \cdot CH(NH_2) \cdot (CH_2)_2CO_2H \cdot HI$] is orthorhombic with $a:b:c = 0.884:1:0.432$. Crystals show {010}, {100}, {001}, {210}, {021}. Imperfect 100 and 021 cleavages. D 1.982. The optic plane is 001; Z = *b*. (+)2H = 60°32′ (in oil with N = 1.6055). Average refractive index = 1.62 *ca*, $N_Z - N_X$ = very strong. The inactive *d*-form is triclinic with perfect 001 cleavage. D 2.03. It has very strong birefringence and an average refractive index of 1.62. In 010 an optic axis is nearly centered and the optic plane is inclined 15° to *c*. (+)2V = considerable. Ref: 163.

l-2-Amino-3-hydroxypropanoic acid or β-hydroxyalanine or *l*-serine [$CH_2(OH) \cdot CH(NH_2) \cdot CO_2H$] is monoclinic with $a:b:c = 1.141:1:0.524$, $\beta = 100°44'$. Crystals equant with {100}, {011}, {110}, {010}, etc., or {100} tablets. Perfect 100 cleavage. M.P. 228°. The optic plane is 010; an optic axis is nearly normal to 100. (-)2V = 45° calc. $N_X = 1.515$, $N_Y = 1.575$, $N_Z = 1.586$, $N_Z - N_X = 0.071$. Ref: 117, 169.

Cupric 2-amino-3-hydroxypropionate or copper serine salt [$[O_2C \cdot CH(NH_2) \cdot CH_2OH]_2Cu$] forms six-sided plates with extinction parallel with the diagonal. $N_1 = 1.536$, $N_2 = 1.599$, $N_2 - N_1 = 0.063$. Ref: 66.

Threo-α-amino-β-hydroxy-*n*-butyric acid or L_8-threonine ($C_4H_9O_2N$) is orthorhombic[1] with $a:b:c = 0.568:1:0.378$. *a* 7.75, *b* 13.64, *c* 5.16 Å. U.C. 4. Crystals {110} prismatic rods. Good 010 cleavage. D 1.463. Decrepitates at 225 - 245°. X = *a*, Y = *b*. (-)2V = 37°, r < v strong. $N_X = 1.521$, $N_Y = 1.591$, $N_Z = 1.600$, $N_Z - N_X = 0.079$. Ref: 435a.

[1] *a* and *b* interchanged to make $b > a > c$.

l-3,3′-Dithiobis(2-aminopropanoic acid) or *β,β*-dithiodialanine or *l*-cystine $[[S\cdot CH_2\cdot CH(NH_2)\cdot CO_2H]_2]$ is hexagonal trapezohedral with $c/a = 1.070$. Space group $C6_12$; *a* 5.40, *c* 5.78 Å. U.C. 6. Crystals {0001} tablets. Perfect basal cleavage. H 2. D 2.06. M.P. 258°. Uniaxial negative with $N_O = 1.700$, $N_E = 1.640$, $N_O - N_E = 0.060$. Brun gives $N_O = 1.683$ D. Ref: 28a, 36, 169, 573.

l-Cystine hydrochloride $[[S\cdot CH_2\cdot CH(NH_2\cdot HCl)\cdot CO_2H]_2]$ is monoclinic sphenoidal with $a:b:c = 3.394:1:1.347$, $\beta = 98°58'$. Crystals orthodomatic with {101}, {10$\bar{1}$}, {100}, {011}, {110}, etc. Perfect 100 cleavage. The optic plane and X are normal to 010; Z $\perp$ 10$\bar{1}$. (+)2E = 0° Li, 3°16′ Na, 8°1′ Tl, 13°54′ blue. (+)2V = 2°8′ Na. $N_X = N_Y = 1.584$, $N_Z = 1.618$, $N_Z - N_X = 0.034$ Na. Ref: 117.

Cupric 2-amino-4-methylmercaptobutanoate or copper methionine salt $[[O_2C\cdot CHNH_2\cdot (CH_2)_2\cdot S\cdot CH_3]_2Cu]$ forms roughly rectangular plates with parallel extinction and negative elongation. $N_1 = 1.572$, $N_2 = 1.630$, $N_2 - N_1 = 0.058$. Color blue. Ref: 66.

Class 10. Hydrazines

Tetra-acetylhydrazine $[(CH_3\cdot CO)_2N\cdot N(CO\cdot CH_3)_2]$ is orthorhombic with $a:b:c = 0.736:1:0.557$. Crystals have {100}, {010}, {110}, {021}, and {111} with perfect 010 cleavage. M.P. 86°. The optic plane is 001; Z = *b*. (+)2V = 47°5′, r < v. $N_X = 1.4871$, $N_Y = 1.4988$, $N_Z = 1.5657$, $N_Z - N_X = 0.0786$. Ref: 117, 152.

Class 19. Carbon-Phosphorus Compounds

3-(Allylimino)-2,2,2-triethyl-2,2-dihydrothiaphosphirane $[(C_2H_5)_3\overset{S}{\overbrace{P-C}}:NCH_2\cdot CH:CH_2]$ is monoclinic with $a:b:c = 2.764:1:2.089$, $\beta = 115°15'$. Crystals six-sided with {001}, {100}, {10$\bar{1}$}, {110}, etc. Perfect 100 and 001 cleavages. M.P. 68°. The optic plane is 010; X $\wedge$ *c* = + 24°. (−)2V = 72.5°. $N_Y = 1.657$. Ref: 117.

Tetraethylphosphonium iodide $\{(C_2H_5)_4PI\}$ is hexagonal with $c/a = 1.472$. Crystals dipyramidal. Uniaxial positive with $N_O = 1.660$, $N_E = 1.668$, $N_E - N_O = 0.008$. Ref: 568a.

Triethylphosphine sulfide $[P(C_2H_5)_3S]$ is hexagonal with $c/a = 0.701$. Crystals thin hexagonal prims. M.P. 94°. Very plastic. Uniaxial positive with $N_O = 1.59$, $N_E = 1.65$ *ca*, $N_E - N_O = 0.06$ *ca*. Ref: 117.

Class 20. Carbon-Arsenic Compounds

Methanearsonic acid or methylarsenic acid $[CH_3AsO(OH)_2]$ is monoclinic with $a:b:c = 1.532:1:1.258$, $\beta = 98°59'$. Crystals {001} plates often elongated along *b*, with {100}, {20$\bar{1}$}, {11$\bar{1}$}, {011}, {110}, etc. Perfect 001 cleavage. Soft and pliable like talc. The optic plane and Z are normal to 010; X $\wedge$ *c* = + 53°.

(-)2V = 9°5′ Li, 14°24′ Na, 17°46′ Tl. N_X = 1.5037 Li, 1.5074 Na, 1.5105 Tl, N_Y = 1.5415 Li, 1.5457 Na, 1.5490 Tl, N_Z = 1.5417 Li, 1.5463 Na, 1.5499 Tl, $N_Z - N_X$ = 0.0389 Na. Ref: 117.

2-Arsonobutanoic acid or α-arsonobutyric acid [$CH_3 \cdot CH_2 \cdot CH(AsO_3H_2) \cdot CO_2H$] is triclinic with $a:b:c$ = 0.901:1:1.391, α = 72°16′, β = 103°6′, γ = 88°28′. Crystals {001} plates with {$\bar{1}$01}, {100}, {111}, {010}, {011}, {110}. Perfect 001 cleavage. D 1.89. M.P. 127°. The optic plane is nearly parallel with 001. (-)2V = 81° *ca.* N_X = 1.509 D, N_Y = 1.559, N_Z = 1.603, $N_Z - N_X$ = 0.094. Colorless. Ref: 10.

(Carboxymethyl)methylpropylarsine sulfide or methylpropyl (carboxymethyl)-arsine sulfide [$(HO_2CCH_2)(CH_3)(C_3H_7)As:S$] is monoclinic sphenoidal with $a:b:c$ = 1.448:1:1.449, β = 104°50′. Crystals show {100}, {001}, {$\bar{1}$01}, {210}, {2$\bar{1}$0}, etc. Perfect 100 and distinct 001 cleavages. The optic plane and Z are normal to 010; X almost exactly = *c*. Y ∧ *a* = − 15°. (+)2V = 26°18′. N_X = 1.604, N_Y = 1.606, N_Z = 1.645, $N_Z - N_X$ = 0.041 Na. Ref: 231a.

Class 32. Carbon-Thallium Compounds

Dimethyl thallium bromide {$(CH_3)_2TlBr$} is tetragonal with *c* = 3.078. Crystals tabular or dipyramidal. D 3.79. Uniaxial negative with N_O = 1.808, N_E = 1.785, $N_O - N_E$ = 0.023. Ref: 568a.

II. ISOCYCLIC COMPOUNDS

Class I. Compounds Containing no Functional Group

1,2,3,4,5,6-Hexachlorocyclohexane or benzene hexachloride ($C_6H_6Cl_6$) has at least five phases. The α-phase is orthorhombic. Crystals rod-like. M.P. 160°. (-)2V = 30°. N_X = 1.60, N_Y = 1.602 calc., N_Z = 1.626, $N_Z - N_X$ = 0.026. The β-phase is isometric. Sublimes at about 200°. Crystals equant, often octahedral or dodecahedral. N = 1.630. The γ-phase (also called gammexane) is monoclinic prismatic with $a:b:c$ = 0.830:1:1.357, β= 121°16′. *a* 8.52, *b* 10.27, *c* 13.94 Å. U.C. 4. (+)2V = 60°, N_X = 1.62, N_Y = 1.64 calc., N_Z = 1.67, $N_Z - N_X$ = 0.05. In another orientation it is described as monoclinic with $a:b:c$ = 1.51:1:1.35, β = 109°. *a* 6.77, *b* 4.66, *c* 6.94 Å. D 1.86. M.P. 114°. Sublimes at about 215°. Crystals rode or plates with good 010 cleavage. X ∧ *c* = 10° in acute β. Z = *b*. (+)2V = 55°. N_X = 1.630, N_Y = 1.633, N_Z = 1.644, $N_Z - N_X$ = 0.014. The Δ-phase is orthorhombic (?). Crystals platy. M.P. 138°. (+)2V = ?, N_X = 1.576, N_Y = ?, N_Z = 1.674, $N_Z - N_X$ = 0.098. The ϵ-phase is monoclinic. Crystals rods and plates. D 1.85. M.P. 114°. (+)2V = 75°, r < v. N_X = 1.60, N_Y = 1.612 calc., N_Z = 1.635, $N_Z - N_X$ = 0.035. Ref: 117, 443a, 553a, 610a.

trans-1,4-Dichloro-1,4-dinitrosocyclohexane [$C_6H_8(NO)_2Cl_2$] is monoclinic with $a:b:c$ = 1.568:1:1.601, β- = 102°49′. Crystals thick {001} tablets with

{100}, {111}, and {11$\bar{1}$}. M.P. 108°. The optic plane and X are normal to 010; $Z \wedge c = +40.5°$. (+)2V = 61°58′ blue. $N_Y = 1.594$. Distinctly pleochroic (violet to deep blue). Ref: 117.

Perhydro-7-isopropyl-1-methylphenanthrene or perhydroretene ($C_{18}H_{32}$) is monoclinic sphenoidal with $a:b:c = 1.433:1:1.756$, $\beta = 126°47'$. Crystals {001} tablets elongated parallel to *b* with {100}, {10$\bar{1}$}, {110}, etc. Twinning on 001. Perfect 001 and distinct 10$\bar{1}$ cleavages. H 1. D 1.01. M.P. 46°. Soluble in ether. The optic plane is 010; $Z \wedge c = -13°$. (-)2V = 87°20′ Na. $N_X = 1.544$, $N_Y = 1.572$, $N_Z = 1.60$ calc. $N_Z - N_X = 0.055$ *ca.* Color white. The substance as found in wood of fossil conifers is called *fichtelite.* The corrected formula is given as $C_{19}H_{34}$. Ref: 65a, 117, 379a.

1,4-Dibromobenzene or *p*-dibromobenzene ($C_6H_4Br_2$) is monoclinic prismatic with $a:b:c = 3.76:1:1.41$, $\beta = 112°38'$. Space group $P2_1/c$; *a* 15.46, *b* 4.11, *c* 5.80 Å. U.C. 2. Crystals {100} plates elongated along *b* with {001}, {110}. Twinning on 100. Cleavage on 100 (and 10$\bar{1}$?). D 2.29. The optic plane is 010; the acute bisectrix makes an angle of about 40° with *c*. 2V = small. For λ = 667.6: $N_X = 1.5642$. $N_Y = 1.7375$. For λ = 587.6: $N_X = 1.5682$, $N_Y = 1.7437$. For λ = 546.1: $N_X = 1.5716$, $N_Z = 1.7498$. Ref: 118, 138, 485.

1,4-Dinitrobenzene or *p*-dinitrobenzene [$C_6H_4(NO_2)_2$] is monoclinic prismatic with $a:b:c = 2.038:1:1.043$, $\beta = 90°18'$. Space group $P2_1/n$; *a* 11.05, *b* 5.42, *c* 5.65 Å. U.C. 2. Crystals long prisms with {110}, {$\bar{1}$01}, {100}, etc., or {001} or {100} tablets. Imperfect $\bar{1}$01, 001, and 100 cleavages. D 1.64. M.P. 172°. The optic plane is 010; extinction at + 38.5° to *c*. (+)2V = 65° calc. $N_X = 1.616$ Na, $N_Y = 1.647$, $N_Z = 1.725$, $N_Z - N_X = 0.109$. Ref: 118, 160.

2,4-Dinitrobenzene or *m*-dinitrobenzene [$C_6H_4(NO_2)_2$] is orthorhombic with $a:b:c = 0.944:1:0.272$. *a* 13. 27, *b* 14.06, *c* 3.82 Å. The optic plane is 010, X = *a*. For λ = 589: $N_X = 1.432$, $N_Y = 1.766$, $N_Z = 1.839$, $N_Z - N_X = 0.407$; ∴ (-)2V = 50° calc. Ref: 443b.

o-Chloronitrobenzene ($C_6H_4ClNO_2$) is monoclinic with $a:b:c = 1.353:1:?$, $\beta = 110°30'$. Crystals prismatic with no end faces. Good 100 and poor 010 cleavages. D 1.56. M.P. 33°. The optic plane is normal to 010 for red to green, but parallel to 010 for blue. $X \wedge c = 16°$. (-)2V = very small, $N_X = 1.481$, N_Y (nearly) = $N_Z = 1.70 - 1.71$, $N_Z - N_X = 0.22 - 0.23$. Ref: 118, 444.

m-Chloronitrobenzene ($C_6H_4ClNO_2$) is orthorhombic pyramidal with $a:b:c = 0.560:1:0.5004$. Crystals {010} hemimorphic tablets with {110}, {101}, {011}, etc. Perfect 010 cleavage. M.P. 44.5°. The optic plane is 100; X = *c*. (-)2E = 91°23′ Na, $r < v$. (From 2E and N_Y, 2V = 48°34′ calc.) $N_X = 1.675$ calc. $N_Y = 1.74$, $N_Z = 1.753$, $N_Z - N_X = 0.078$ calc. Ref: 118, 444.

p-Chloronitrobenzene ($C_6H_4ClNO_2$) is monoclinic prismatic with $a:b:c = 1.966:1:1.126$, $\beta = 97°21'$. Crystals variable in habit with {100}, {001}, or {10$\bar{1}$} dominant. Poor 001 and 110 cleavages. D 1.52, M.P. 83.5°. The optic plane is 010; $X \wedge c = 20°$ (Steinmetz), 13° (Davies). (-?)2V = ?, $N_X = 1.5115$, $N_2 = 1.72$. Ref: 118, 444.

o-Bromonitrobenzene ($C_6H_4BrNO_2$) is monoclinic in prisms with no end faces. M.P. 41°. Obtuse bisectrix apparently normal to 010; $X \wedge c = 14.5°$. (-)2V = ?, $N_X = 1.515$, N_Y (or N_Z?) = 1.71, $N_Y - N_X = 0.195$. Pleochroic with X = pale green, Y (or Z?) = deep yellowish green. Ref: 118, 444.

m-Bromonitrobenzene ($C_6H_4BrNO_2$) is orthorhombic pyramidal with $a:b:c$ = 0.549:1:0.493. Crystals {010} tablets with {110}, {101}, {011}, etc. Perfect 010 and good 100 cleavages. D 1.97. M.P. 56°. The optic plane is 100; X = *c*. (-)2H = 84°; $N_X = 1.670$, N_Y (or N_Z?) = 1.70 - 1.71. Ref: 118, 444.

p-Bromonitrobenzene ($C_6H_4BrNO_2$) is triclinic with $a:b:c = 1.04:1:0.39$. $\alpha = 91°$, $\beta = 107.5°$, $\gamma = 92.5°$. Crystals acicular; twinning common on 010. Good 010 cleavage. M.P. 127°. Elongated plates have $X \wedge$ elongation = 14°. (+?)2V = large. $N_1 = 1.480$, $N_2 = 1.72 - 1.74$. Ref: 118, 444.

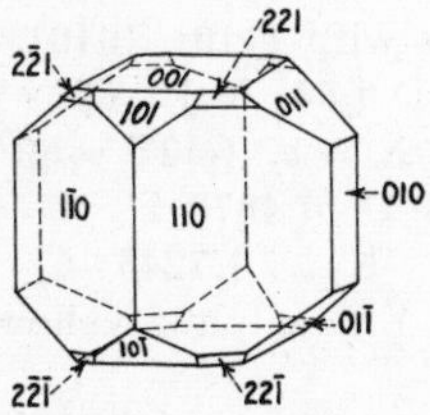

Fig. 35. 1-Bromo-2,4-dinitrobenzene.

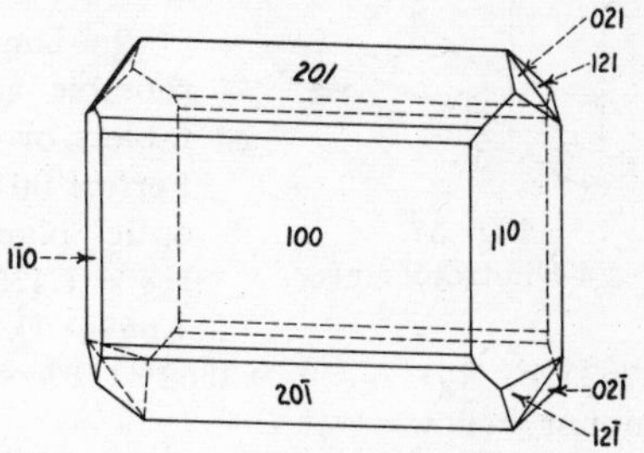

Fig. 36. 1,5-Di-iodo-2,4-dinitrobenzene.

1-Bromo-2,4-dinitrobenzene or bromo-*m*-dinitrobenzene [$C_6H_3Br(NO_2)_2$] is orthorhombic (?) in crystals showing {010}, {101}, {011}, {110}, etc. Fig. 35. Intercrystallizes with the chloro-compound. The optic plane is 001. (+)2V = 51°5 red, 54° blue. $N_X = 1.640$, $N_Y = 1.670$, $N_Z = 1.810$, $N_Z - N_X = 0.170$. The indices are the same (as nearly as can be measured) for crystals, half bromo- and half chloro-. Ref: 118.

1,5-Di-iodo-2,4-dinitrobenzene [$C_6H_2I_2(NO_2)_2$] is orthorhombic disphenoidal[1] with $a:b:c = 0.455:1:0.322$. Crystals {100} tablets or domatic with {021}, {010}, {110}, {201}, etc. Fig. 36. D 2.73 - 2.74. M.P. 158°. Distinct 010 cleavage. The optic plane is 010; Z = *c*. (+)2V = 61°26′ Li, 63°26′ Na, 66°35′ Tl. N_X = 1.7625 Na, N_Y = 1.7687 Li, 1.7873 Na, 1.8073 Tl, N_Z = 1.8361 Li, 1.8568 Na, 1.8791 Tl, $N_Z - N_X = 0.0943$ Na. Ref: 118.

p-Nitrotoluene ($C_6H_4NO_2CH_3$) is orthorhombic dipyramidal with $a:b:c$ = 0.911:1:1.097. Crystals {010} plates with {001}, {211}, etc; perfect 010 cleavage. M.P. 54°. The optic plane is 100; X = b. (-)2E = 94° Na, r > v. 2V = 48° (calc.), $N_X = 1.475$, $N_Y = 1.670$, $N_Z = 1.71$; $N_Z - N_X = 0.235$. Ref: 118, 444.

---

[1] *a* and *b* interchanged to make $b > a$.

3-Fluoro-4-nitrotoluene [$C_6H_3 \cdot (CH_3)(F)(NO_2)$] is monoclinic with $a:b:c$ = 0.994:1:?, β = 123°25′. Crystals prismatic with {110}, {210}, {100}, {001}, etc. Good 110? cleavage. D 1.44. M.P. 53.2°. The optic plane is 010; $X \wedge c = -29°$. (-)2V < 30°. $N_X = 1.42$, $N_Y < 1.73$, $N_Z > 1.74$, $N_Z - N_X > 0.32$. Ref: 83.

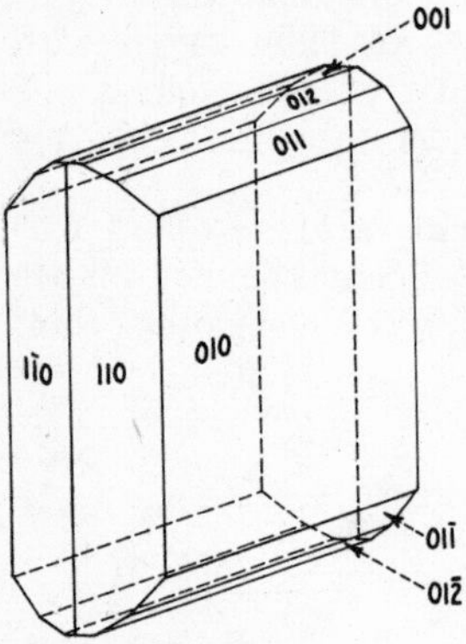

Fig. 37.
2,4-Dinitrotoluene.

2,4-Dinitrotoluene [$C_6H_3(NO_2)_2 \cdot CH_3$] is monoclinic with $a:b:c$ = 0.859:1:0.541, β = 94°48′. Crystals short prismatic with {110}, {101}, {120}, {010}, {100}, etc. Fig. 37. Imperfect 001 cleavage. D 1.52. M.P. 70.5°. The optic plane and Z are normal to 010; $X \wedge c = -32°$. (-)2V = 70° *ca.* calc. N_X = 1.4394 C, 1.4423 D, 1.4527 F, N_Y = 1.6567 C, 1.6619 D, 1.6771 F, N_Z = 1.7440 C, 1.7556 D, 1.7884 F, $N_Z - N_X$ = 0.3133 D Ref: 118.

2,6-Dinitrotoluene [$C_6H_3(NO_2)_2 \cdot CH_3$] is orthorhombic with $a:b:c$ = 0.571:1:0.541. Crystals {010} tablets or short prisms with {110}, {010}, {001}, etc. Perfect 001 cleavage. D 1.54. M P. 60° - 60.5°. The optic plane is 100; X = *c*. (-)2V = 60° *ca.* calc. N_X = 1.4755 C, 1.4788 D, 1.4875 F, N_Y = 1.6625 C, 1.6694 D, 1.6893 F, N_Z = 1.7245 C, 1.7340 D, 1.7621 F, $N_Z - N_X$ = 0.2552 D. Pleochroic with Y = sulphur yellow, Z = pale sulphur yellow. Ref: 118.

2,4,6-Trinitrotoluene or TNT [$C_6H_2CH_3(NO_2)_3$] is orthorhombic with $a:b:c$ = 0.375:1:0.153. *a* 14.99, *b* 40.0, *c* 6.10 Å. U.C. 16. D 1.65, M.P. 81°. Crystals are rods or tablets or plates bounded by {010}, {110}, {061}, elongated along *a* or *c*. X = *b*, Y = *c*. (-)2V = 60°, r < v. N_X = 1.543, N_Y = 1.674, N_Z = 1.717, $N_Z - N_X$ = 0.174. Ref: 553a.

bis-Dimethylfulvene (C_8H_{10}) is orthorhombic with $a:b:c$ = 0.605:1:0.441. Crystals prisms with {110}, {010}, {011}, etc. No distinct cleavage. M.P. 83°. The optic plane is 001; X = *a*. (-)2V = 78° *ca.* red, 76° *ca.* blue. N_X = 1.557, N_Y = 1.657, N_Z = 1.734, $N_Z - N_X$ = 0.177 red. Ref: 118.

2-Bromo-1,3,5-trimethyl-4,6-dinitrobenzene or bromodinitromesitylene [$C_6Br(NO_2)_2(CH_3)_3$] is monoclinic prismatic with $a:b:c$ = 1.205:1:1.216, β = 118°47′. Crystals {100} tablets elongated parallel to *b* with {001}, {010}, etc. Perfect 010 and distinct 001 cleavages. M.P. 190° *ca.* The optic plane and X are normal to 010; $Z \wedge c = -14.5°$. (-)2V = 42°19′ Na, r > v weak. N_X = 1.535, N_Y = 1.744 calc., N_Z = 1.784, $N_Z - N_X$ = 0.245. Colorless and clear. Ref: 118.

1,2,4,5-Tetramethylbenzene or durene [$C_6H_2(CH_3)_4$] is monoclinic prismatic with $a:b:c$ = 2.005:1:1.179, β = 113°18′. Space group $P2_1/a$; *a* 11.57, *b* 5.77, *c* 7.03 Å. U.C. 2. Crystals columnar along *b* with {100}, {001}, {10$\bar{1}$}, {11$\bar{1}$}.

Fig. 38. Common twinning on 100. Perfect 100 and distinct $10\bar{1}$ cleavage. D 1.03. M.P. 79° - 80°. The optic plane is 010; X $\wedge$ c = - 0°54′ with weak dispersion. (-)2V = 87°22′, r > v. N_Y = 1.6148 Na. Ref: 118, 579.

Pentamethylbenzene $[C_6H(CH_3)_5]$ is biaxial with D 1.005. (+)2V = 81°50′ (578). For λ = 667.6: N_X = 1.5508, N_Y = 1.5789, N_Z = 1.6188, $N_Z - N_X$ = 0.0680; for λ = 578: N_X = 1.5571, N_Y = 1.5858, N_Z = 1.6266, $N_Z - N_X$ = 0.0695; for λ = 546.1: N_X = 1.5602, N_Y = 1.5892, N_Z = 1.6304, $N_Z - N_X$ = 0.0702. Ref: 118, 138.

Hexamethylbenzene $[C_6(CH_3)_6]$ is triclinic with $a:b:c$ = 1.0095:1:0.5987, α = 44°27′, β = 116°43′, γ = 119°34′, Space group $P\bar{1}$; a 9.019, b 8.926, c 5.344 Å. U.C. 1. Crystals show {100}, {001}, {010}, {221}, etc. Very good 001 cleavage. D 1.042. M.P. 164°. In spite of triclinic symmetry the optic plane is 010 and X is normal to 001. For λ = 587: (-)2V=50° calc., N_X = 1.5032. N_Y = 1.7475, N_Z = 1.8012, $N_Z - N_X$ = 0.2980. Later, more accurate, measures give very different results: D 1.063 at 24.8°. (-)2V = 50°48′ (λ = 578). For λ = 667.6: N_X = 1.4773, N_Y = 1.6713, N_Z = 1.7114, $N_Z - N_X$ = 0.2341; for λ = 587.6: N_X = 1.4805, N_Y = 1.6791, N_Z = 1.7199, $N_Z - N_X$ = 0.2394. Ref: 30, 138, 226.

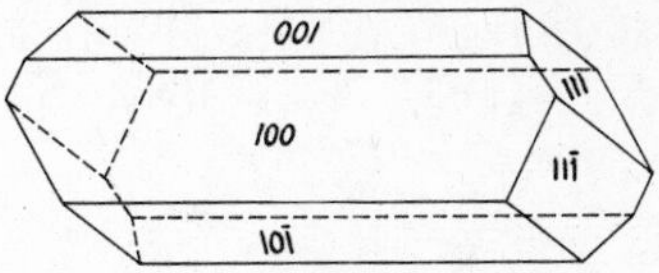

Fig. 38.
1,2,4,5-Tetramethylbenzene.

Hexa(chloromethyl)benzene or hexakis(chloromethyl)benzene $[C_6(CH_2Cl)_6]$ is rhombohedral with c/a = 0.315. Crystals show $\{11\bar{2}0\}$, $\{10\bar{1}1\}$, etc. Uniaxial negative with N_O = 1.726 (Hg green), N_E = 1.600, $N_O - N_E$ = 0.126. Ref: 323.

Hexa(bromomethyl)benzene or hexakis(bromomethyl)benzene $[C_6(CH_2Br)_6]$ is rhombohedral with c/a = 0.328. Space group $R\bar{3}$; hexagonal cell: a 16.37, c 5.38 Å. U.C. 3. Crystals show $\{11\bar{2}0\}$, $\{10\bar{1}1\}$, etc. Imperfect $10\bar{1}1$ cleavage. D 2.50. M.P. 297°. Uniaxial negative with N_O = 1.799 (Hg yellow), 1.806 (Hg green), N_E = 1.679 (Hg yellow), 1.683 (Hg green), $N_O - N_E$ = 0.120 (Hg yellow). Ref: 26.

Hexaethylbenzene $[C_6(C_2H_5)_6]$ is triclinic with $a:b:c$ = 1.004:1:0.610, α = 58.5°, β = 103°54′, γ = 123°43′. a 9.90, b 9.84, c 6.10 Å U.C. 1. Crystals {010} tablets or vertical columns. D 0.994. For λ = 587.6 at 23.5°: (-)2V = 71°, N_X = 1.4901, N_Y = 1.5358, N_Z = 1.6135, $N_Z - N_X$ = 0.1234; for λ = 501.6 at 23.1°: N_X = 1.4791, N_Y = 1.5358, N_Z = 1.6259, $N_Z - N_X$ = 0.1288. Ref: 138, 565.

cis-Styreneamminodichloroplatinum $[PtC_8H_8NH_3Cl_2]$ seems to be triclinic. (-)2V = 45°, N_X = 1.668, N_Y > 1.790, $N_Z \gg$ 1.790, $N_Z - N_X$ > 0.122. Ref: 418aa.

Naphthalene $(C_{10}H_8)$ is monoclinic prismatic with $a:b:c$ = 1.378:1:1.436, β = 122°49′. Space group $P2_1/c$; a 8.34, b 5.98, c 8.68 Å. U.C. 2. Crystals {001} plates with {110}, {201}. Fig. 40. Perfect 001 cleavage. D 1.179. M.P. 80°. The optic plane is 010; Z $\wedge$ c = - 9.5°. (-)2V = 83°, strong inclined dispersion.

N_X = 1.442 D, 1.525 (546), N_Y = 1.775 D, 1.722 (546), N_Z = 1.932 D, 1.945 (546), $N_Z - N_X$ = 0.490 D, 0.420 (546), Also for λ = 667.6: N_X = 1.5188; N_Y = 1.7077; for λ = 587.6 N_X = 1.5238, N_Y = 1.7182; for λ = 546.1: N_X = 1.5291, N_Y = 1.7255. Naphthalene forms a continuous isomorphous series with β-naphthol and also with β-napthylamine.
Ref: 118, 138, 310, 533, 558.

Napththalene tetrachloride ($C_{10}H_4Cl_4$) is monoclinic. X = *b*, Z $\wedge$ *a* = 2°16′ for λ = 546, 1°28′ for λ = 589 and 0°34′ for λ = 656. For λ = 589, N_X = 1.528, N_Y = 1.766, N_Z = 1.786, $N_Z - N_X$ = 0.258.{∴ (−)2V = 30° *ca.*}. Ref: 443b.

1,8-Dinitronaphthalene II ($C_{10}H_6O_4N_2$) is orthorhombic with *a*:*b*:*c* = 0.758: 1:0.359. *a* 11.37, *b* 15.00, *c* 5.38 Å. U.C. 4. Crystals {100} or {001} plates. D 1.587. M.P. 173°. Inverts to I at 110°. Y = *c*, Z = *b*. (−)2V = 80°, r < v strong. N_X = 1.634, N_Y = 1.763, N_Z = 1.86 calc. $N_Z - N_X$ = 0.326. Ref: 553c.

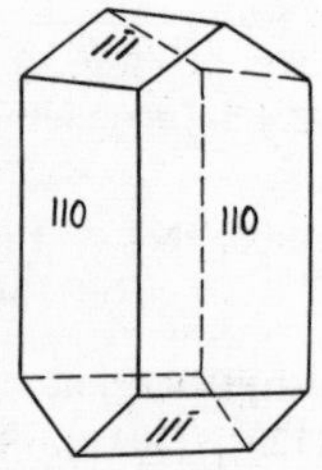

Fig. 39. *d*-α-Amyrilene.

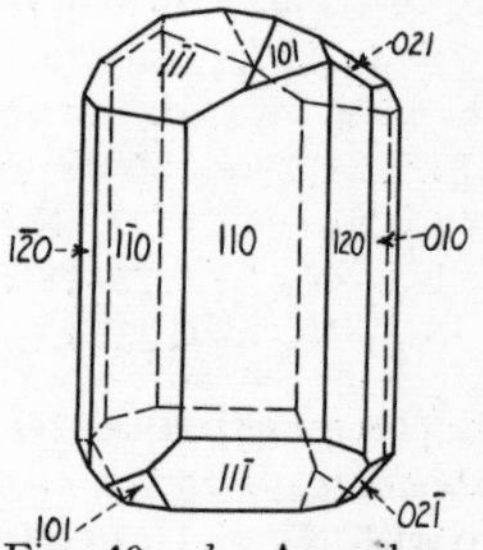

Fig. 40. *d*-α-Amyrilene.

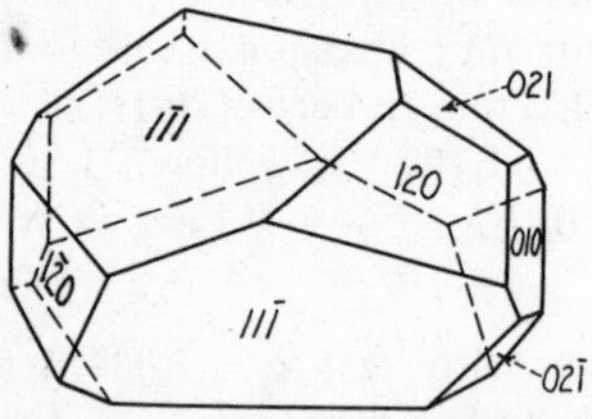

Fig. 41. *d*-α-Amyrilene.

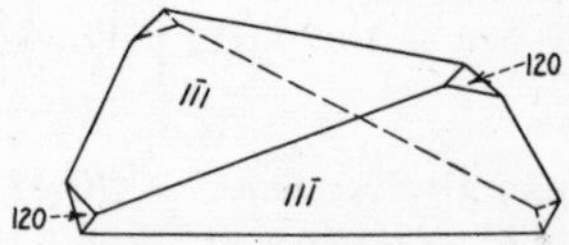

Fig. 42. *d*-α-Amyrilene.

2-Methylnaphthalene ($C_{10}H_7 \cdot CH_3$) is monoclinic with a:*b*:*c* = 3.110:1:1.472, β = 103°16. Crystals rounded with very rare faces, and 100 cleavage. D 1.09. M.P. 38°. Z = *a*. (−)2V = 81°, r > v. N_X = 1.494, N_Y = 1.640, N_Z = 1.77, $N_Z - N_X$ = 0.276. Ref: 552a.

d-α-Amyrilene ($C_{30}H_{48}$) is orthorhombic disphenoidal with *a*:*b*:*c* = 0.667: 1:0.405. Crystals varied in habit with {110}, {120}, {01̄1}, {101}, {021}, {010}. Figs. 39–42. M.P. 134 – 135°. The optic plane is 001; Z = *a*. (+)2V = 72°12′ Na, r > v weak. N_X = 1.5405, N_Y = 1.5814, N_Z = 1.6232, $N_Z - N_X$ = 0.0827 Na.
Ref: 117.

d-β-Amyrilene ($C_{30}H_{48}$) is orthorhombic disphenoidal with $a:b:c = 0.917:1:0.540$. Crystals prismatic with {210}, {110}, {010}, {101}, {011}. Fig. 43. M.P. 175° - 178°. The optic plane is 001; Z = *b*. (+)2V = 23°37′ red, 22°22′ Na. $N_X = 1.5655$, $N_Y = 1.5698$, $N_Z = 1.5941$, $N_Z - N_X = 0.0286$ Na. Ref: 117.

Biphenyl, diphenyl, or phenylbenzene ($C_6H_5 \cdot C_6H_5$) is monoclinic prismatic with $a:b:c = 1.443:1:1.670$, $\beta = 94°46'$. Space group $P2_1/c$; *a* 8.38, *b* 5.82, *c* 9.47 Å. U.C. 2. Crystals {001} plates with {110}, {101}, {010}, etc. Fig. 44. Perfect 001 and distinct 010 and 100 cleavages. Soft and flexible. D 1.189. M.P. 70°. The optic plane is 010; $Z \wedge c = -20.5°$. (+)2V=68.8°, r > v. $N_X = 1.561$, $N_Y = 1.658$, $N_Z = 1.945$, $N_Z - N_X = 0.384$, all for $\lambda = 546$. $N_X = 1.5598$ D, $N_Y = 1.6542$ D, $N_Z > 1.90$ D. Ref: 119, 138, 310, 446.

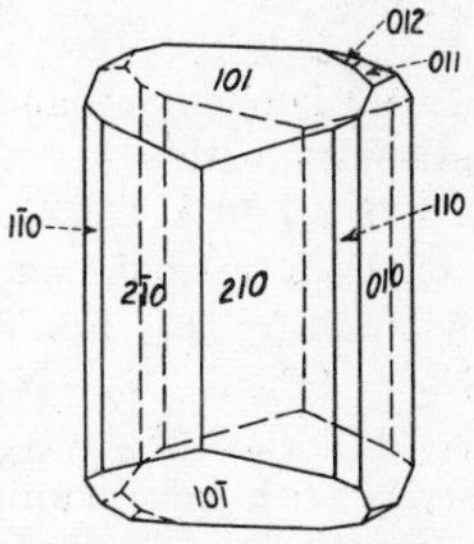

Fig. 43. *d*-β-Amyrilene.

Diphenyliodonium chloride [$(C_6H_5)_2 \cdot I \cdot Cl$] is monoclinic sphenoidal with $a:b:c = 1.220:1:1.187$, $\beta = 102°15'$. Crystals {001} tablets with {100}, {101} {10$\bar{1}$}, {1$\bar{3}$4}, etc. Fig. 45. Perfect 100 cleavage. D 1.67. Decomposes at 230°. The optic plane is 010. Large optic angle. $N_Y = 1.74$, $N_Z - N_X = 0.02$. Ref: 119.

2,2′-Difluorobiphenyl or 2,2′-difluorodiphenyl ($FC_6H_4 \cdot C_6H_4F$) is orthorhombic and pseudotetragonal with $a:b:c = 0.913:1:0.870$. Crystals elongated along *c* with {010}, {100}, {110} {111}, etc. Good 010, 100, and 001 cleavages. D 1.39. M.P. 117°. The optic plane is 001; Z = *b*. (+)2V = 65°, r > v strong. $N_X = 1.623$ D, $N_Y = 1.648$, $N_Z = 1.713$, $N_Z - N_X = 0.090$. Ref: 83.

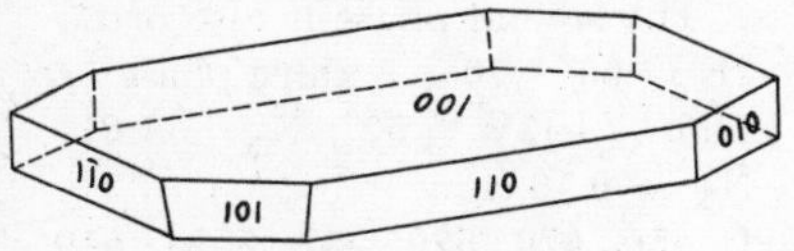

Fig. 44. Diphenyl.

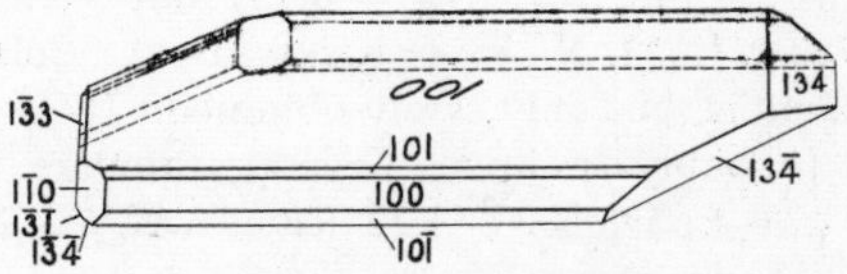

Fig. 45. Diphenyl iodonium chloride.

4,4′-Difluoro-2-nitrobiphenyl or 4,4′-difluoro-2-nitrodiphenyl [$FC_6H_4 \cdot C_6H_3 \cdot (F)(NO_2)$] is orthorhombic with $a:b:c = 0.704:1:0.375$. Crystals show {110}, {011}, {001}, etc. No cleavage observed. D 1.488. M.P. 95°. The optic plane is 001; Z = *b*. (+)2V = 63°19′ C, 63°48′ D, 65°26′ F. $N_X = 1.5285$ C, 1.5336 D, 1.5466 F, $N_Y = 1.5874$ C, 1.5944 D, 1.6134 F, $N_Z = 1.7754$ C, 1.7871 D, 1.8194 F, $N_Z - N_X = 0.2505$ D. Ref: 83.

4,4-Dinitrodiphenyl with 4-bromodiphenyl $(O_2NC_6H_4C_6H_4NO_2)_7$ with $(HC_6H_4C_6H_4Br)_2$ is monoclinic with $a:b:c = 2.105:1:2.716$, $\beta = 100°$. *a* 20.0, *b* 9.5, *c* 25.8 Å. M.P. 192 - 220°. D 1.52. Z = *b*. (+)2V = 37°. $N_X = 1.60$, $N_Y = 1.64$, $N_Z = 2.39$, $N_Z - N_X = 0.79$. Color cream. Ref: 588b.

4,4-Dinitrodiphenyl with 4-iododiphenyl $(O_2NC_6H_4C_6H_4NO_2)_7$ with$(HC_6H_4 \cdot C_6H_4I)_2$ is monoclinic with $a:b:c = 2.105:1:2.716$, $\beta = 100°$. *a* 20.0, *b* 9.5,

c 25.8 Å. M.P. 192 – 220°. D 1.56. Z = b. (+)2V = 34°. $N_X = 1.62$, $N_Y = 1.65$, $N_Z = 2.13$, $N_Z - N_X = 0.51$. Color pale yellow. Ref: 588b.

Acenaphthene ($C_{10}H_6 \cdot CH_2CH_2$) is orthorhombic dipyramidal with $a:b:c$ = 0.590:1:0.516. Space group *Pcmm*; a 8.32, b 14.15, c 7.26 Å. U.C. 4. Crystals prismatic or {010} tablets with {110}, {010}, {100}, {111}, {101}. Perfect 010 and imperfect 001 cleavages. M.P. 95°. The optic plane is 100; Z = b. (+)2V = 70°26′ Na, r < v weak. $N_X = 1.4065$, $N_Y = 1.4678$, $N_Z = 1.6201$, $N_Z - N_X$ = 0.2136 Na. Ref: 119, 414.

1,2-Diphenylethane or bibenzyl or dibenzyl ($C_6H_5CH_2 \cdot CH_2C_6H_5$) is monoclinic prismatic with $a:b:c$ = 2.081:1:1.252, β = 115°54′. Space group $P2_1/c$; a 12.77, b 6.12, c 7.70 Å. U.C. 2. Crystals {001} tablets or equant with {001}, {$20\bar{1}$}, {$11\bar{1}$}, etc. Poor prismatic and 010 cleavages. M.P. 52°. The optic plane is 010; $Z \wedge c$ = + small angle. For λ = 587.6: (+)2V = 88°42′, $N_X = 1.5292$, $N_Y = 1.6286$, $N_Z = 1.7566$, $N_Z - N_X = 0.2274$; for λ = 546.1: $N_X = 1.5329$, $N_Y = 1.6330$, $N_Z = 1.7638$, $N_Z - N_X = 0.2309$. Dibenzyl forms a continuous isomorphous series with benzylamine Ref: 119, 138, 420, 580.

1,1,1-Trichloro-2,2-*bis*-(*p*-chlorophenyl)-ethane [$CCl_3CH(C_6H_5Cl)_2$] commonly known as DDT, is polymorphous; one phase is orthorhombic with $a:b:c$ = 0.520:1:0.408; space group[1] *Pbc* or *Pbcm*; a 9.96, b 19.14, c 7.85 Å. UC. 4. Crystals acicular or plates long ‖ c with {100}, {120}, {010} and {111}. Twinning common. M.P. 108° C. D = 1.556. X = a, Y = c. Parallel extinction and ± elongation. (+)2V = 30° (calc.). $N_X = 1.618$, $N_Y = 1.626$, $N_Z = 1.755$, $N_Z - N_X$ = 0.137 (Gooden); (+)2E = 46°, 2V = 28° calc., $N_X = 1.617$, $N_Y = 1.624$, $N_Z = 1.748$, $N_Z - N_X = 0.131$ (McCrone); (+)2V = 26° (meas.), $N_X = 1.617$, $N_Y = 1.622$, N_Z = ? (Kirkpatrick). Colorless. The second phase is also orthorhombic, but only rarely obtained. It has (+)2E = 60° – 70°. A third phase (?) is probably triclinic. Crystals tabular. D 1.556. (+)2V = 52°, $N_X = 1.619$, $N_Y = 1.639$, $N_Z = 1.72$ (calc.-A.N.W.) $N_Z - N_X = 0.10$.
Ref: 456, 470, 529, 552, 552a, 619.

4,4′-Difluoro-3,3′-dimethyldiphenyl or 4,4′-difluoro-3,3′-ditolyl [$(F)(CH_3) \cdot C_6H_3 \cdot C_6H_3(F)(CH_3)$] is orthorhombic with $a:b:c$ = 0.956:1:0.604. Crystals elongated along c with {010}, {100}, {110}, {111}, etc. Imperfect 001, 100, and 010 cleavages. D 1.345. M.P. 59°. The optic plane is 100; X = c. (–)2V = 72°2′ C, 71°38′ D, 70°52′ F. N_X = 1.5034 C, 1.5070 D, 1.5170 F, N_Y = 1.691 C, 1.698 D, 1.721 F, N_Z = 1.802 C, 1.816 D, 1.858 F, $N_Z - N_X$ = 0.309 D. Ref: 83.

4,4′-Dichloro-3,3′-bitolyl or 4,4′-dichloro-3,3′-ditolyl [$(Cl)(CH_3)C_6H_3 \cdot C_6H_3 \cdot (Cl)(CH_3)$] is monoclinic (?) Crystals thin plates with no observed cleavage. D 1.330. M.P. 58° – 58.5°. The optic plane and Z make an angle of 70° with the plates. (–)2V = ?. N_X = 1.507 D, N_Y = ?, N_Z = 1.729 (20° from Z), $N_Z - N_X$ > 0.222D. Ref: 83.

---

[1] a and b interchanged to make $b > a$.

2,3′-Dimethyl-2′-nitrobiphenyl ($CH_3 \cdot C_6H_4 \cdot C_6H_3 \cdot CH_3 \cdot NO_2$) is dimorphous. The α-phase is monoclinic with $a:b:c = 1.583:1:1.027$, $\beta = 116°31'$. a 11.81, b 7.46, c 7.66 Å. U.C. 2. D 1.214. (+)2V = 44°42′. $N_X = 1.5717$, $N_Y = 1.5903$, $N_Z = 1.7229$, $N_Z - N_X = 0.1512$. Ref: 588b.

2,4,6′-Trimethyl-2′-nitrobiphenyl {$(CH_3)_2 \cdot C_6H_3 \cdot C_6H_3 \cdot CH_3 \cdot NO_2$} is monoclinic prismatic with $a:b:c = 1.3797:1:0.5213$, $\beta = 99°47'$. a 21.28, b 15.46, c 8.09 Å. U.C. 8. Crystals prismatic. D 1.214. Y = b. (-)2V = 65°52′. $N_X = 1.5720$, $N_Y = 1.6529$, $N_Z = 1.6898$, $N_Z - N_X = 0.1178$. Ref: 456b.

Acenaphthylene ($\overline{C_{10}H_6 \cdot CH:CH}$) is orthorhombic with $a:b:c = 0.593:1:0.500$. Crystals thin prismatic with {110}, {010}, {100}, {101}, etc. Perfect 010 cleavage. M.P. 93°. The optic plane is 100; Z = b. (+)2V = 70°16′ Na. $N_X = 1.4017$, $N_Y = 1.4634$, $N_Z = 1.6172$, $N_Z - N_X = 0.2155$ Na; 2E = 113°15′ red, 114°46′ yellow. Ref: 119.

Fluorene ($\overset{CH_2}{C_6H_4 \cdot C_6H_4}$) is orthorhombic with $a:b:c = 1.486:1:3.311$. Space group *Pna* (or *Pnam*); a 8.47, b 5.70, c 18.87 Å. U.C. 4. Crystals {001} plates. The optic plane is 010; Z = c. (+) 2 V = 67.5°. $N_X = 1.578$, $N_Y = 1.663$, $N_Z = 1.919$, $N_Z - N_X = 0.341$, all for $\lambda = 546$. Colorless when pure; usually impure with violet fluorescence. Ref: 310, 501.

9,10-Dihydro-9,9,10,10-tetraisobutylanthracene ($C_{30}H_{44}$) is triclinic with $a:b:c = 0.944:1:1.074$. $\alpha = 118°34'$, $\beta = 111°48'$, $\gamma = 72°4'$. Crystals {001} tablets with {100}, {110}, {010}, {10$\bar{1}$}, {0$\bar{1}$1}. Poor 001 cleavage. (+ ?) 2 V = 90° *ca.* $N_1 = 1.548$, $N_2 = 1{,}603$ (both measured on 001), $N_2 - N_1 = 0.055$. Ref: 302.

Anthracene ($\overset{CH}{\underset{CH}{C_6H_4\ C_6H_4}}$) is monoclinic prismatic with $a:b:c = 1.422:1:1.878$, $\beta = 124°24'$. Space group $P2_1/a$; a 8.58, b 6.02, c 11.18 Å. U.C. 2. Crystals {001} plates or tablets with {201}, {110}, etc. Fig. 46. M.P. 216.5°. D 1.25. Perfect 001 and distinct 010 cleavages. The optic plane is 010; Z ∧ c = 7.5°. (-) 2 V = 72°, $N_X = 1.556$, $N_Y = 1.786$, $N_Z = 1.959$, $N_Z - N_X = 0.403$, all for $\lambda = 546$. Again: 2 V = 90°, $N_X = 1.57$, $N_Y = 1.817$, $N_Z = 2.22$, $N_Z - N_X = 0.65$, for $\lambda = 546$, and (-)2V = 85°, $N_X = 1.59$, $N_Y = 1.86$, $N_Z = 2.26$, $N_Z - N_X = 0.67$ for $\lambda = 490$ and (-)2V = 67°, $N_X = 1.64$, $N_Y = 2.07$, $N_Z = 2.41$, $N_Z - N_X = 0.77$ for $\lambda = 420$. When pure, colorless with violet fluorescence; often impure and yellow with green fluorescence. Ref: 119, 310, 562a, 578.

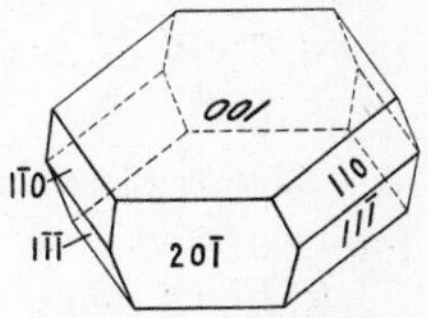

Fig. 46. Anthracene.

Phenanthrene ($\overline{C_6H_4 \cdot CH:CH \cdot C_6H_4}$) is monoclinic prismatic with $a:b:c = 1.409:1:3.149$, $\beta = 98°15'$. Space group $P\,2_1/a$; a 8.66, b 11.5, c 19.24 Å. Crystals {001} plates with {110}?, {100}?. M.P. 99°. The optic plane is 010; Z ∧ c = − 19°. (-)2V = 83.5°. $N_X = 1.548$, $N_Y = 1.724$, $N_Z = 1.920$, $N_Z - N_X = 0.372$, all for $\lambda = 546$. Ref: 119, 310, 417.

p-Diphenylbenzene or terphenyl $(C_6H_5 \cdot C_6H_4 \cdot C_6H_5)$ is monoclinic prismatic with $a : b : c = 1.443 : 1 : 2.427$, $\beta = 91°55'$. Space group $P\,2_1/a$; *a* 8.14, *b* 5.64, *c* 1.41 Å. U.C. 2. Crystals {001} plates. D 1.213. M.P. 211°. The optic plane is 010; $Z \wedge c = +14°$. $(+)2V = 68.5°$. $N_X = 1.584$, $N_Y = 1.687$, $N_Z = 2.004$, $N_Z - N_X = 0.420$, all for $\lambda = 546$.
Ref: 273, 310, 492.

a, β-Diphenylethylene or (*trans*)-stilbene $\left[\begin{array}{l} C_6H_5 \cdot CH \\ \quad\quad \ddot{HC} \cdot C_6H_5 \end{array}\right]$ is monoclinic prismatic with $a : b : c = 2.170 : 1 : 1.400$, $\beta = 114°6'$. Space group $P\,2_1/a$; *a* 12.35, *b* 5.70, *c* 15.92 Å. U.C. 4. Crystals basal tablets with {100}, {110}, {201}. D 1.16. M.P. 125°. X = *b*, $Z \wedge c = +60°$. Optically positive except in the blue below $\lambda = 4070$ at which 2 V = 90°. Data follow:

$\lambda = 6908$	6234	5780	5461	4916	4358	4070 ± 50	3650
$2V_Z = 40°$	45°	51°	56°	64°	78°	90°	127°
$N_X = 1.691$	1.699	1.706	1.712	1.726	1.751	1.769	1.797
$N_Y = 1.708$	1.721	1.732	1.743	1.772	1.823	1.864	1.975
$N_Z = 1.818$	1.835	1.848	1.860	1.893	1.940	1.973	2.03
$N_Z - N_X = 0.127$	0.136	0.142	0.148	0.167	0.189	0.204	0.233

Ref: 425, 583.

Triphenylmethane or tritan $[(C_6H_5)_3CH]$ has two crystal phases, both orthorhombic. Phase I has $a : b : c = 0.5716 : 1 : 0.5867$. Space group *Pna*; *a* 14.71, *b* 25.72, *c* 7.55 Å. U.C. 8. Crystals are columnar with {100}, {010} {110}, etc. Indistinct 011 cleavage. D 1.14. The optic plane is 001, Z = *b*. Birefringence positive. Obtuse optic angle in oil = 139.5° Na. Phase II (metastable) has $a : b : c = 0.789 : 1 : 0.696$. Crystals from alcohol at low temperature are prisms with {110}, {011}, {101}, etc. The optic plane is 001; the acute bisectrix is *b*. But triphenylmethane is said to be monoclinic or triclinic with $Y \wedge c = 4°$ and (+) 2 V = 70°, r > v; $N_X = 1.642$, $N_Y = 1.655$, $N_Z = 1.685$, $N_Z - N_X = 0.043$. Ref: 119, 120, 397, 398, 569.

Chlorotriphenylmethane $[(C_6H_5)_3CCl]$ is monoclinic or triclinic. The extinction angle, $X \wedge c$, is 32°. (–) 2 V = 55°, r < v. $N_X = 1.631$, $N_Y = 1.67$, $N_Z = 1.686$, $N_Z - N_X = 0.055$. Ref: 397, 398.

(2,5-Dimethylphenyl)diphenylmethane or diphenyl-2,5-xylylmethane or 2,5-dimethyltritan $[C_6H_3(CH_3)_2CH(C_6H_5)_2]$ is monoclinic with $a : b : c = 0.910 : 1 : 0.203$, $\beta = 119°53.5'$. Crystals show {001}, {100}, {110}. Imperfect 010 cleavage. M.P. 92°. (+) 2 V = 57°43′ Na. $N_Y = 1.7171$ Na. Ref: 119.

Chrysene $\left[\begin{array}{l} C_6H_4 \cdot CH \\ \dot{C}_{10}H_6 \cdot \ddot{C}H \end{array}\right]$ is monoclinic with $a : b : c = 1.349 : 1 : 4.045$, $\beta = 115°48'$. Space group *C2c* or *Cc*; *a* 8.34, *b* 6.18, *c* 25.0 Å. U.C. 4. D 1.27. M.P. 250°. Crystals {001} plates. The optic plane is 010; $Z \wedge c = -9°$

(–)2V = 88°. N_X = 1.585, N_Y = 1.787, N_Z = 2.068, $N_Z - N_X$ = 0.483, all for λ = 5460. Again: (–) 2 V = 84°30′, r > v. N_X = 1.578, N_Y = 1.775, N_Z = 2.01, $N_Z - N_X$ = 0.432. Ref: 119, 150, 310, 535b.

3-Methylcholanthrene (20-methylcholanthrene) ($C_{21}H_{16}$) is polymorphous. Phase I (stable above 140° C.) is monoclinic; X = *b*; Z nearly normal to 001. Basal plates are rhombic, and the plane of symmetry bisects the acute angle of 68°. (+) 2 V = 60° *ca.* r < v marked. N_X = 1.62 calc., N_Y = 1.640 *ca.*, N_Z = 1.7 *ca.*, $N_Z - N_X$ = 0.08 calc. Another phase (II) is monoclinic with *a* : *b* : *c* = 0.429 : 1 : 2.449, β = 116°30′. Space group $P2_1/c$; *a* 4.86, *b* 11.31, *c* 27.7 Å. U.C. 4. Crystals acicular along *a*. D 1.277. Y = *b*; Z ∧ ⊥ 001 ± 27°. A phase (III) stable at room temperature is probably triclinic in needles with a maximum extinction angle of about 20°. Abnormal interference colors. (+)2V = 75° or more, r > v marked. N_X = 1.51 *ca.*, N_Y = 1.63 *ca.*, N_Z = 1.75 or more, $N_Z - N_X$ = 0.24 or more. Ref: 236a, 500.

3-Ethylcholanthrene (20-ethylcholanthrene) [$C_{22}H_{20}$] is apparently monoclinic, basal rhombic plates having an angle of 70°. Edge views give inclined extinction. The optic plane is 010; Z inclined to a normal to 001. (+)2V=40° *ca.* r<v marked. N_X = 1.64 *ca.* N_Y = 1.660, N_Z = 1.80 calc., $N_Z - N_X$ = 0.16 calc. Ref: 236a.

3-Isopropylcholanthrene (20-isopropylcholanthrene [$C_{23}H_{20}$] is probably orthorhombic in rectangular lath-shaped crystals with parallel extinction. Z is normal to the plates. (+)2V = 40° *ca.* N_X = 1.67, N_Y = 1.69, N_Z = 1.72 *ca.*, $N_Z - N_X$ = 0.05 *ca.* Ref: 236a.

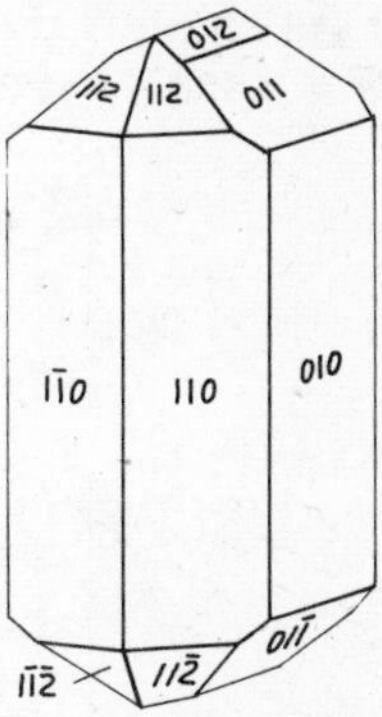

Fig. 47. Triphenyl benzene.

1,3,5-Triphenylbenzene [$(C_6H_5)_3C_6H_3$] is orthorhombic pyramidal with *a*:*b*:*c* = 0.568:1:0.382. Space group *Pna*; *a* 11.22, *b* 19.76, *c* 7.55 Å. U.C. 4. Crystals prismatic with {110}, {010}, {011}, {211}, {210}, or {001}, {013}, {110}, {010}, {011}. Fig. 47. Imperfect 001 cleavage. D 1.21. M.P. 170°. The optic plane is 010; X = *a*. (–)2V = 9°50′ Na, 10°17′ Tl. N_X = 1.5202 Li, 1.5241 Na, 1.5291 Tl, N_Y = 1.8670 Na, 1.8848 Tl, N_Z = 1.8725 Na, 1.8897 Tl, $N_Z - N_X$ = 0.3484 Na. Ref: 119, 563.

1,3,5-Tri-(*p*-chlorophenyl)benzene [$(C_6H_4Cl)_3C_6H_3$] is orthorhombic with *a*:*b*:*c* = 0.866:1:0.672. Crystals {100} plates long ∥ *c* with {010}, {110}, {011}, etc. D 1.39. M.P. 238°. X = *c*, Y = *a*. (+)2V = 85°, r > v. N_X = 1.650, N_Y = 1.740, N_Z = 1.87, $N_Z - N_X$ = 0.22. Ref: 468a.

Curtisite ($C_{24}H_{18}$) is probably orthorhombic with perfect 001 and poor 100 cleavages. H < 2. D 1.236. M.P. > 350°. Soluble in hot benzene. The optic plane is 010; Z = *c*. (+)2V = 83.5°, r > v weak. N_X = 1.557, N_Y = 1.734, N_Z = 2.07, $N_Z - N_X$ = 0.513. Color greenish yellow with X = pale yellow to colorless, Y = yellow, Z = yellow, and X < Y < Z. Rare about hot springs. Ref: 389, 390.

Dibiphenylene-ethylene ($C_{26}H_{16}$) is orthorhombic with a 17.22, b 36.9, c 8.23 Å. U.C. 12. D 1.26. Crystals acicular. X $= c$. (–)2V $=$?, $N_X = 1.55$, $N_Y > 1.7$, $N_Z > 1.7$, $N_Z - N_X > 0.15$. Pleochroic with X $=$ yellow, Y and Z $=$ red.

Ref: 456a.

Class 2. Hydroxy compounds.

l-2-Isopropyl-5-methylcyclohexanol or l-menthol has at least four crystal phases. The α-phase (I) is stable from 0° to 42.5°. The

$$\left[CH_3 \cdot CH \begin{array}{c} CH_2 \cdot CHOH \\ \diagdown \\ CH_2 \cdot CH_2 \end{array} CH \cdot CH(CH_3)_2 \right]$$

other phases are monotropic with respect to it and fuse at 35.5° (β), 33.5° (γ), and 31.5° (δ). l-α-menthol is hexagonal with $c/a = 1.635$. a 11.82, c 19.32 Å. U.C. 8. Crystals prismatic needles with prismatic cleavage. D 0.884. Uniaxial negative with $N_O = 1.497$, $N_E = 1.476$, $N_O - N_E = 0.021$ Na (Wright); $N_O = 1.496$, $N_E = 1.474$, $N_O - N_E = 0.022$ Na (Merwin). The fused substance has N $= 1.458$ Na at 25°. β-Menthol (II) forms radial spherulites with birefringence between 0.001 and 0.002 and N $= 1.486$. Elongation is positive γ-Menthol (III) forms radial spherulites with birefringence about 0.006, and negative elongation. δ-Menthol (IV) forms radial spherulites with birefringence between 0.001 and 0.002 and negative elongation. Ref: 392.

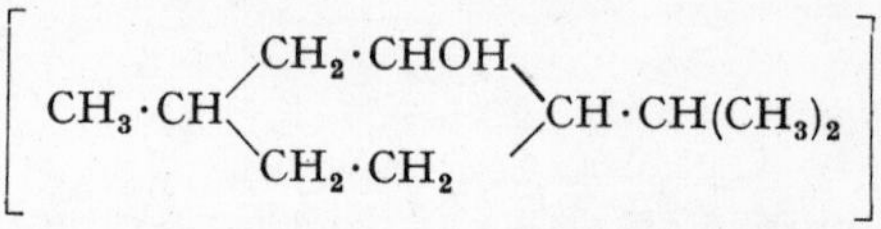

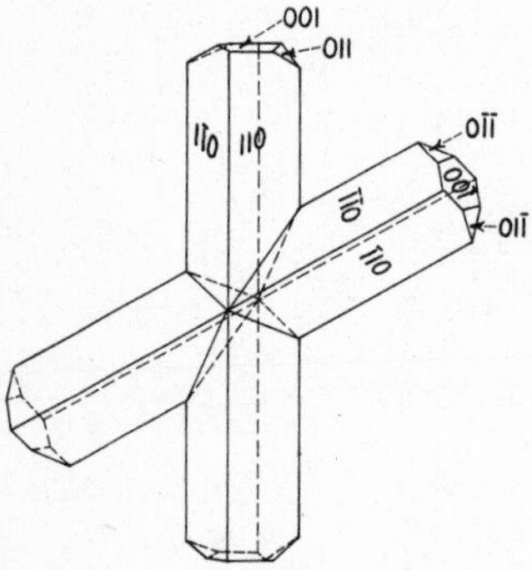

Fig. 48.
d-Bornyl methylene ether.

Menthylxanthic anhydride $[(C_{10}H_{19}O) \cdot CS \cdot S \cdot CS \cdot (OC_{10}H_{19})]$ is orthorhombic disphenoidal with[1] $a:b:c = 0.615:1:0.425$. Crystals have {100}, {010}, {101}, {110}, etc. M.P. 148°–149°. The optic plane is 001; X $= a$. (–)2V $= 83°48'$ Li, 85°6′ Na, 86°37′ Tl. $N_X = 1.5143$ Li, 1.5257 Na, 1.5302 Tl, $N_Y = 1.5919$ Li, 1.5967 Na, 1.6003 Tl, $N_Z = 1.6523$ Li, 1.6652 Na, 1.6720 Tl, $N_Z - N_X = 0.1395$ Na. Ref: 117.

1,3,3-Trimethylbicyclo(2,2,1)heptan-2-ol or 2,6,6-trimethyl-2,5-endomethylene-1-cyclohexanol or α-fenchyl alcohol ($C_{10}H_{17}OH$) is hexagonal, probably rhombohedral, with $c/a = 0.93$. Crystals {0001} tablets with {10$\bar{1}$0}, {20$\bar{2}$5}, etc. M.P. 49°. Uniaxial positive with $N_O = 1.525$, $N_E = 1.525$, $N_E - N_O =$ very weak. (α) $= -5.36°$ (c $= 6.56$ per cent in alcohol). Ref: 261.

d-Bornyl methylene ether $[CH_2(O \cdot C_{10}H_{17})_2]$ is orthorhombic disphenoidal with $a:b:c = 0.913:1:0.565$. Crystals prismatic with {110}, {001}, {011}; twinning on 031. Fig. 48. No distinct cleavage. M.P. 167°–168°. The optic plane is 010; Z $= c$. (+)2V $= 75°44'$ Na, r $>$ v. $N_X = 1.5343$ Li, 1.5375 Na, 1.5401 Tl, $N_Y = 1.5390$ Li, 1.5422 Na, 1.5449 Tl, $N_Z = 1.5459$ Li, 1.5493 Na, 1.5520 Tl, $N_Z - N_X = 0.0118$ Na. Ref: 117.

---

[1] $a\,b\,c$ changed to $a\,c\,b$ to make $b > a > c$.

Methyl *l*-bornylxanthate $[C_{10}H_{17}\cdot O\cdot CS\cdot S\cdot CH_3]$ is orthorhombic disphenoidal with[1] $a:b:c = 0.688:1:0.477$. Crystals domatic or {001} tablets or equant with {101}, {001}, {102}, {110}. M.P. 56° – 57°. The optic plane is 001; $X = c$. (–)2V = 29°18′ Li, 33°24′ Na. $N_Y = 1.638$ Li, 1.646 Na. Ref: 117.

Ethyl (*d* or *l*)-bornylxanthate $[C_{10}H_{17}\cdot O\cdot CS\cdot S\cdot C_2H_5]$ is orthorhombic disphenoidal with $a:b:c = 0.684:1:0.480$. Crystals short domatic with {011}, {102}, {001}, {110}, etc. M.P. 52° – 53°. The optic plane is 001. (–)2V = 32°9′ Na, 2E = 41°23′ Li, 51°16′ Na, 60°36′ Tl. $N_X = 1.556$, $N_Y = 1.562$, $N_Z = 1.648$, $N_Z - N_X = 0.092$ Na. Ref: 117.

Bicyclo-(0,4,4)-decane peroxide or decahydronaphthalene peroxide or decaline peroxide $(C_{10}H_{17}OOH)$ is monoclinic in needles with D 1.15. M.P. 96.5°. Extinction angle 20°. (+)2V = 12°, $N_X = 1.550$, $N_Y \approx N_X$, $N_Z = 1.570$, $N_Z - N_X = 0.020$. Ref: 502.

trans-4-Cyclohexylcyclohexanol $(C_{12}H_{22}O)$ is monoclinic. Crystals acicular with X || elongation. (–)2V = 90° (probably varying through 90°), r > v. $N_X = 1.542$, $N_Y = 1.555$, $N_Z = 1.568$, $N_Z - N_X = 0.026$. Ref: 527b.

cis-4-Cyclohexylcyclohexanol $(C_{12}H_{22}O)$ is monoclinic. Crystals acicular with Y || elongation. (+)2V ≈ 70 – 75°, r > v. $N_X = 1.534$ (±.004), $N_Y = 1.549$, $N_Z = 1.572$, $N_Z - N_X = 0.038$. Ref: 527b.

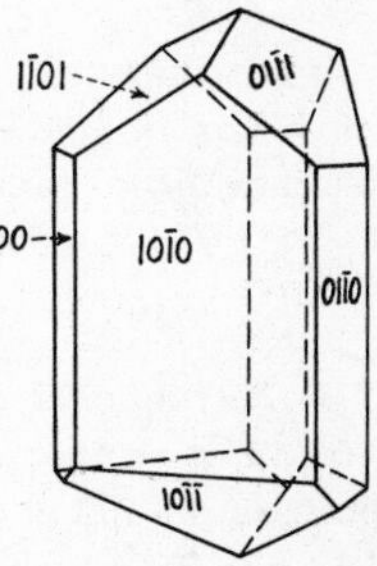

Fig. 49. Guajol.

Champaca oil or guajol or champacol $(C_{15}H_{25}OH)$ is trigonal tetartohedral hemimorphic with $c/a = 0.550$. Crystals hexagonal prismatic with {10$\bar{1}$0}, {10$\bar{1}$1}, etc. Fig. 49. Perfect 10$\bar{1}$0 cleavage. M.P. 93°. Uniaxial positive with $N_O = 1.5449$, $N_E = 1.5480$, $N_E - N_O = 0.0031$ Na. Ref: 117.

Partheniol $(C_{15}H_{26}O)$ is orthorhombic in acicular crystals with X || elongation. M.P. 131°. $N_X = 1.538$, $N_Y = ?$, $N_Z = 1.590$, $N_Z - N_X = 0.052$. Ref: 612a.

Phenol or carbolic acid $[C_6H_5(OH)]$ is orthorhombic with 110: 1$\bar{1}$0 = 64° *ca.* Crystals thin prisms with {010}. M.P. 43° and very volatile. The optic plane is 010; acute bisectrix = *a*. $N_1 = 1.61$, $N_2 = 1.65$, $N_2 - N_1 = 0.04$. 2V = biaxial, r < v strong. Ref: 34, 35, 118.

Phenoxybenzene, phenyl ether, or diphenyl ether $(C_6H_5\cdot O\cdot C_6H_5)$ is orthorhombic with $a:b:c = 0.361:1:0.273$. Crystals {010} tablets elongated along *c*. M.P. = 28°. The optic plane is 001; $X = b$. (–)2V = 82°0′. $N_X = 1.617$, $N_Y = 1.658$, $N_Z = 1.691$, $N_Z - N_X = 0.074$ D. Ref: 382.

Tetrakis(phenoxymethyl)methane or pentaerythritol tetraphenyl ether $[C(CH_2OC_6H_5)_4]$ is tetragonal pyramidal with $c/a = 0.684$. Space group *I*4; *a* 12.32, *c* 8.43 Å. U.C. 2. Crystals show {110}, {101}. D 1.145. M.P. 113°. No

[1] *a b c* changed to *c a b* to make $b > a > c$.

observed cleavage. Uniaxial positive with $N_O = 1.593$ (Hg yellow), 1.597 (Hg green), 1.621 (Hg blue), $N_E = 1.599$ (Hg yellow), 1.603 (Hg green), 1.626 (Hg blue), $N_E - N_O = 0.006$ (Hg yellow). Ref: 25, 326, 327.

Tetrakis(4-chlorophenoxymethyl)methane or pentaerythritol tetrakis (*p*-chlorophenyl) ether [$C(CH_2OC_6H_4Cl)_4$] is monoclinic sphenoidal with $a:b:c = 0.677:1:0.651$, $\beta = 98°32'$. Crystals show {001}, {110}, {1$\bar{1}$0}, {011}, {100}, etc. D 1.360. M.P. 142°. The optic plane and Z are normal to 010; X $\wedge$ c = small. (-)2V = 80° calc. $N_X = 1.607$, $N_Y = 1.630$, $N_Z = 1.646$, $N_Z - N_X = 0.039$ Na. Ref: 327.

2,4-Dichlorophenol ($C_6H_3Cl_2OH$) forms fibers or six-sided needles. M.P. 45°. Easily soluble in alcohol, slightly in water. Indices: N_1 (|| length) = 1.514, N_2 (|| width) > 1.70, $N_2 - N_1 > 0.186$. Ref: 529.

2,4-Dichlorophenoxy-acetic acid ($C_6H_3Cl_2O \cdot CH_2CO_2H$) is monoclinic in equant and tabular crystals showing {110}, {101}, {10$\bar{1}$}. Inclined extinction. Y = b. (-)2E = 96°, 2V = 52°, $N_X = 1.480$, $N_Y = 1.645$, $N_Z = 1.700$ calc., $N_Z - N_X = 0.220$. Ref: 529.

o-Nitrophenol ($C_6H_4NO_2OH$) is monoclinic prismatic with $a:b:c = 0.893:1:0.477$, $\beta = 103°34'$. Crystals prismatic with good 010 cleavage. D 1.49. M.P. 45°. The optic plane is normal to 010; the acute bisectrix $\wedge$ c = - 5°. (-?)2V = ?, $N_X < 1.47$, $N_Y > 1.78$, N_Z = ?, $N_Z - N_X > 0.31$. Pleochroic with X = pale green, Y = green, Z = ? Ref: 118, 444.

m-Nitrophenol ($C_6H_4NO_2OH$) is monoclinic prismatic with $a:b:c = 0.922:1:0.153$, $\beta = 120°21'$. Crystals {001} tablets with {110}, {120}, etc. Twinning common on 100 or 001. Perfect 110, good 120, and poor 010 cleavages. D 1.49. M.P. 96° (93°). The optic plane is normal to 010; extinction on 110 at 1.5° to c. (+)2V = 60°, $N_1 = 1.502$, $N_2 = 1.691$. Abnormal interference colors (lavender and fawn). Ref: 118, 444.

p-Nitrophenol ($C_6H_4NO_2OH$) is dimorphous; one phase stable above 63° is monoclinic prismatic with $a:b:c = 1.342:1:0.693$, $\beta = 106°52'$. Crystals equant or {101} tablets. Perfect 111 cleavage. D 1.48. M.P. 113°. Elongated plates have an angle of 77°, X $\wedge$ elongation = 21°. (+)2V = 60° - 75°, $N_1 = 1.484$, $N_2 > 1.78$, $N_2 - N_1 > 0.296$. A metastable phase (inverting at 63°) is also monoclinic prismatic with $a:b:c = 1.384:1:0.340$, $\beta = 106°55'$. Crystals prismatic or {001} tablets with {110}, {010}, etc. Distinct 001 cleavage (?). D 1.495. M.P. below 113°. The optic plane is 010; the acute bisectrix $\wedge$ c = – 22° Na. Cleavage parallel to elongation, which is negative. Extinction angle 30.5° on plates having an angle of 40°. (+ ?)2V = ?, $N_Z - N_X$ = strong. Interference colors bright purple, blue, green, and gold. Ref: 118, 444.

α-Isodypnopinacoline ($C_{32}H_{26}O$) is orthorhombic with $a:b:c = 0.621:1:1.403$. Habit pyramidal. Perfect 001 cleavage. M.P. 131°. Y = a, Z = c. (+)2V = ?, $N_Y = 1.78$, $N_Z = 1.798$. (∴ $N_X < 1.762$ and $N_Z - N_X < 0.036$ – A.N.W.) Ref: 568a.

2,4,6-Trinitrophenol or Picric Acid and Derivatives

2,4,6-Trinitrophenol or picric acid [$C_6H_2(NO_2)_3OH$] is orthorhombic pyramidal with $a:b:c = 0.485:1:0.507$. Space group *Pca*; *a* 9.25, *b* 19.08, *c* 9.68 Å. U.C. 8. Crystals {010} plates elongated along *c* or equant with {010}, {110}, {111}, {120}, {001}, etc. Very imperfect 010 and 120 cleavages. D 1.767. M.P. 122°. The optic plane is 100; Z = *c*. (+)2V = 82°19′ Li, 82°43′ Na. $N_X = 1.68$ *ca.*, $N_Y = 1.71$ *ca.*, $N_Z = 1.742$, $N_Z - N_X = 0.06$ *ca.* Color yellow.
Ref: 118, 243, 347, 421, 557.

Ammonium picrate [$C_6H_2(NO_2)_3(O \cdot NH_4)$] is orthorhombic with $a:b:c = 0.680:1:0.360$. Crystals {100} or {010} tablets with {110}, {121}, {211}, etc. Fig. 50. Distinct 100 cleavage. M.P. 240°. The optic plane is 100 for $\lambda > 541$ and 010 for $\lambda < 541$; X = *c*. (-)2V = 41°+ (668), 29° D, 0° (541), 17° (528). $N_X = 1.599$ (668), 1.508+ D, 1.522 (528), $N_Y = 1.816$ (668), 1.872 D, 1.944 (528), $N_Z = 1.880$ (668), 1.908 D, 1.961 (528), $N_Z - N_X = 0.400$ D. For $\lambda = 5461$: (-)2V = 13°, $N_X = 1.515$, $N_Y = 1.926$, $N_Z = 1.934$, $N_Z - N_X = 0.419$. Color yellow with blue schiller color on {010} and {110}. "Red modification" is essentially the same, but Y has a red tint indicating oriented colored inclusions, possibly picramide.
Ref: 118, 243, 557.

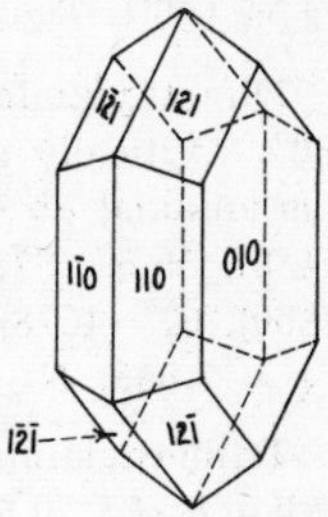

Fig. 50. Ammonium picrate.

Potassium picrate [$C_6H_2(NO_2)_3(OK)$] is orthorhombic with $a:b:c = 0.697:1:0.373$. Crystals thin prismatic with {110}, {100}, {010}, {011}, {121}, etc; also {010} tablets. 100 cleavage. D 1.85. The optic plane is 100 for red and yellow and 010 for blue. X = *c*. (-)2V = 44°37′ (He red), 33°34′ (He yellow), $N_X = 1.5155$ (He red), 1.5272 (He yellow), $N_Y = 1.8352$ (He red), 1.9026 (He yellow), 2.0464 (He green), $N_Z = 1.9118$ (He red), 1.9523 (He yellow), $N_Z - N_X = 0.4251$ (He yellow).
Ref: 118.

Thallous picrate [$C_6H_2(NO_2)_3(OTl)$] is monoclinic sphenoidal with $a:b:c = 2.112:1:2.335$, $\beta = 100°58'$. Crystals {100} tablets or prismatic with {110}, {1̄10}, {100}, {101}, {001}, etc. D 3.16 or 3.04. No distinct cleavage. The optic plane is 010. $N_Y = 1.827$ Na. Color red.
Ref: 118.

2-Hydroxyethylamine picrate or 2-aminoethanol picrate [$H_2N \cdot CH_2 \cdot CH_2OH \cdot C_6H_2(NO_2)_3OH$] is monoclinic in compact yellow prisms and thin plates. M.P. 159° - 160°. The optic plane and X are normal to 010. Horizontal dispersion of 11.5° from 4600 to 6234. (+)2H (in cedar oil) = 77° (4600), 66° (5780), 64° (6908), $N_X = 1.620$, $N_Y = 1.688$, $N_Z = 1.925$, $N_Z - N_X = 0.305$. (+)2V = 62° (5461).
Ref: 39a.

Guanylurea picrate or carbamylguanidine picrate [$C_2H_6ON_4C_6H_2(NO_2)_3OH$] is monoclinic in yellow prismatic needles with X = *b*. Z ∧ *c* = 22° (5461). Strong crossed dispersion. (-)2E = 89° (4710), 54° (5050), 71° (5780). $N_X = 1.447$, $N_Y = 1.90$, $N_Z = 1.97$, $N_Z - N_X = 0.523$. 2V = 35° calc.
Ref: 39a.

Guanidine picrate [$NH:C(NH_2)_2OC_6H_2(NO_2)_3$] is orthorhombic (?). Decomposes at 315°. Axial dispersion: (-)2H = 0° (about 7750), 21.5° (6908), 47.5° (5780), 58° (5461), 96° (4916). For λ = 5461: (-)2V = 44°, N_X = 1.422, N_Y = 1.998, N_Z = 2.18 ± 01, $N_Z - N_X$ = 0.76. Ref: 557.

Dicyanodiamide picrate {$NH_2C(NH)NHCNC_6H_2(NO_2)_3OH$} is orthorhombic. Crystals columnar with 100 cleavage. Color yellow-orange. X = *c*, Y = *b*. (+)2E > 170°, 2V = 76° calc; strong dispersion, N_X = 1.660, N_Y = 1.72, N_Z = 1.83, $N_Z - N_X$ = 0.17. Ref: 529, 563a.

Monomethylamine picrate [$CH_3NH_2OC_6H_2(NO_2)_3$] is orthorhombic dipyramidal with *a*:*b*:*c*[1] = 0.493:1:0.427. Crystals {010} tablets. D 1.687. M.P. 211°. Optically negative. Axial dispersion: 2H = 38° (6908), 42° (6234), 47.5° (5780), 53° (5461), 72° (4800). For λ = 5461: (-)2V = 42°, N_X = 1.473, N_Y = 1.878, N_Z = 1.987, $N_Z - N_X$ = 0.514. Color yellow. Ref: 118, 557.

Dimethylamine picrate [$(CH_3)_2NHOC_6H_2(NO_2)_3$] is orthorhombic (?). M.P. 160°. Optically positive above λ = 4820 and negative below λ = 4820; further it is uniaxial at λ = 4620. Axial dispersion: (+)2H over Z = 44° (6908), 47.5° (6438), 55.5° (5780), 63° (5461), 80° (5086), 95° (4916). (-)2H over X = 111° (4800), 67° (4678), 38.50° (4640), 0° (4629), 45° (4560). For 5461: (+)2V = 56°, N_X = 1.648, N_Y = 1.689, N_Z = 1.855, $N_Z - N_X$ = 0.207. Ref: 557.

Trimethylamine picrate [$(CH_3)_3NOC_6H_2(NO_2)_3$] is orthorhombic dipyramidal with *a*:*b*:*c*[2] = 0.520:1:0.469. M.P. 213.5°. No good cleavage. Axial dispersion: (-)2H = 31° (6438), 29° (5461), 24.5° (5086), 16.5° (4800), 0° (4670), 14° (4678). For λ = 5461: (-)2V = 30° calc. N_X = 1.457, N_Y = 1.790, N_Z = 1.815, $N_Z - N_X$ = 0.358. Ref: 557.

Tetramethylammonium picrate [$(CH_3)_4NOC_6H_2(NO_2)_3$] is probably monoclinic since prisms (of 52°35′) show inclined extinction. Decomposes above 300°. (-)2H = 51° (6908). 45.5° (5780), 38° (5461), 0° (5120), 38.5° (4916). The optic plane for λ > 500 is at right angles to its position for λ < 500. For λ = 5461: (-)2V = 32°, N_X = 1.450, N_Y = 1.789, N_Z = 1.822, $N_Z - N_X$ = 0.372. Ref: 118, 557.

Monoethylamine picrate [$C_2H_5NH_2OC_6H_2(NO_2)_3$] is monoclinic prismatic with *a*:*b*:*c* = 2.277:1:1.535, β = 92°27′. No good cleavage. D 1.61. M.P. 170°. Axial dispersion: (-)2H = 34° (6908), 44.5° (5780), 50° (5461), 65° (4916), 70° (4850). For λ = 5461: (-)2V = 40°, N_X = 1.447, N_Y = 1.900, N_Z = 1.994, $N_Z - N_X$ = 0.547. Ref: 557.

Diethylamine picrate [$(C_2H_5)_2NHOC_6H_2(NO_2)_3$] is monoclinic. M.P. 74°. Z = *b*. Optically positive above λ = 4660 and negative below λ = 4660. Axial dispersion: 2H over Z = 74° (6908), 77° (5780), 79° (5461), 84.5° (5086), 94.5° (4800), 2H over X = 99° (4550), 91° (4500). Also crossed dispersion. For λ = 5461: (+)2V = 72°, N_X = 1.558, N_Y = 1.640, N_Z = 1.825, $N_Z - N_X$ = 0.267. Ref: 557.

[1] *a b c* changed to *b c a* to make *b* > *a* > *c*.
[2] *a b c* changed to *b a c* to make *b* > *a* > *c*.

Triethylamine picrate $[(C_2H_5)_3NOC_6H_2(NO_2)_3]$ is orthorhombic with $a:b:c$[1] = 0.529:1:0.366. Crystals {010} tablets. Poor 100 cleavage. M.P. 173°. Axial dispersion: (-)2H = 20° (6908), 21.5° (5780), 22° (5461), 25.5° (5086), 28.5° (4650). For $\lambda = 5461$: (-)2V = 19°, $N_X = 1.467$, $N_Y = 1.735$, $N_Z = 1.745$, $N_Z - N_X = 0.278$. Ref: 557.

Tetraethylammonium picrate $[(C_2H_5)_4NOC_6H_2(NO_2)_3]$ is monoclinic. M.P. 261.5°. X = *b*. Strong crossed dispersion such that if Z is taken as 0° for λ = 6908, it is at 5° for 6438, 14° for 5780, 21° for 5461, 31° for 4916. Axial dispersion: (-)2H = 51° (6908), 52° (6438), 59.5° (5780), 66° (5461), 88° (5086). For λ = 5461: (-)2V = 56°, N_X = 1.525, N_Y = 1.774, N_Z = 1.868, $N_Z - N_X$ = 0.343. Ref: 557.

n-Propylamine picrate $[C_3H_7NH_2OC_6H_2(NO_2)_3]$ is monoclinic. M.P. 138°. The optic plane and X are normal to 010; there is very strong crossed dispersion; assuming Z at 0° for λ = 6908, it is at 2° for 6438, 6° for 5780, 13° for 5461, 34° for 5165, 63° for 4916 and 75° for 4700; axial dispersion: (-)2H = 47° (6908), 45° (6438), 40° (5780), 35° (5461), 30° (minimum) (5165), 37° (4916), 46° (4800), 56.5° (4700). For λ = 5461: (-)2V = 30°, N_X = 1.455, N_Y = 1.790, N_Z = 1.828, $N_Z - N_X$ = 0.373. Ref: 557.

Di-*n*-propylamine picrate $[(C_3H_7)_2NHOC_6H_2(NO_2)_3]$ is orthorhombic (?). M.P. 97.5°. Axial dispersion: (-)2H = 38.5° (6908), 37.5° (5780), 35° (5461), 28° (5086), 18° (4916), 0° (4840). For λ = 5461: (-)2V = 30°, r > v marked, N_X = 1.478, N_Y = 1.751, N_Z = 1.781, $N_Z - N_X$ = 0.203. Ref: 557.

Tri-*n*-propylamine picrate $[(C_3H_7)_3NOC_6H_2(NO_2)_3]$ is orthorhombic (?). M.P. 115.5°. Axial dispersion: (-)2H = 0° (8000), 6.5° (6908), 11° (6438), 16.5° (5780), 18.5° (5461), 24° (5086), 31.5° (4820). For λ = 5461: (-)2V = 17° r < v, N_X = 1.455, N_Y = 1.674, N_Z = 1.677, $N_Z - N_X$ = 0.222. Ref: 557.

Isopropylamine picrate $[C_3H_7NH_2OC_6H_2(NO_2)_3]$ is monoclinic. M.P. 150°. The optic plane and X are normal to 010; there is very strong crossed dispersion; assuming Z at 0° for λ = 6908, it is at 5° for 6438, 28° for 5780, 49° for 5461, 65° for 5086, 69° for 4800; Axial dispersion: (-)2H = 44° (6908), 30.5° (6438), 25°, (minimum at 5850), 28.5° (5461), 44° (5086), 53.5° (4916), 62.5° (4800). For λ = 5461: (-)2V = 24°, N_X = 1.451, N_Y = 1.806, N_Z = 1.831, $N_Z - N_X$ = 0.380. Ref: 557.

Di-isopropylamine picrate $[(C_3H_7)_2NHOC_6H_2(NO_2)_3]$ is dimorphous. The low temperature phase (II) is monoclinic (?). M.P. 147.5°. X = *b*; crossed dispersion, so that if Z is at 0° for 6908, it is at 1° for 6438, 4° for 5780, 8° for 5461, 16° for 5086 and 19° for 4916. Axial dispersion: (-)2H = 51.5° (6908), 52° (5780), 53° (5461), 56° (5086), 58.5° (4916). For λ = 5461: (-)2V = 45°, N_X = 1.476, N_Y = 1.759, N_Z = 1.833, $N_Z - N_X$ = 0.357. The high temperature phase (I) is also monoclinic, but has Z = *b* with horizontal dispersion such that if X is at 0° for λ = 6908, it is at 1° for 5708, 2° for 5461, 5.5° for 5086 and 10° for 4800; axial dispersion: (-)2H (in cedar oil) = 28.5° (6908), 33.5° (6438), 41° (5780), 46° (5461), 58.5° (4916). Ref: 557.

[1] *a b c* changed to *b c a* to make *b* > *a* > *c*.

n-Butylamine picrate [$C_4H_9NH_2OC_6H_2(NO_2)_3$] is monoclinic. M.P. 145.5°. The optic plane and X are normal to 010; there is strong crossed dispersion so that if Z is at 0° for $\lambda = 6908$, it is at 1° for 5708, 3° for 5461, 9° for 5086, 37° for 4830, 54° for 4800 and 67° for 4700. Axial dispersion: (-)2H = 54.5° (6908), 49.5° (5780), 46° (5461), 39° (5086), 27° (4800), 23.5° (minimum–4830), 37° (4700). For $\lambda = 5461$: (-)2V = 40°, $N_X = 1.455$, $N_Y = 1.753$, $N_Z = 1.810$, $N_Z - N_X = 0.355$. Ref: 557.

Di-*n*-butylamine picrate [$(C_4H_9)_2NHOC_6H_2(NO_2)_3$] is monoclinic (?) M.P. 64.5°. X = *b*; strong crossed dispersion so that if Z is taken at 0° for $\lambda = 6908$, it is at 2° for 5780, 3° for 5461, 5° for 5086, 11° for 4800, 28° for 4650, 48° for 4600, 74° for 4500. Axial dispersion: (-)2H = 65° (6908), 60.5° (5780), 58° (5461), 44° (4800), 32.5° (4600), 44° (4500). For $\lambda = 5461$: (-)2V = 52°, $N_X = 1.480$, $N_Y = 1.680$, $N_Z = 1.743$, $N_Z - N_X = 0.263$. Ref: 557.

Tri-*n*-butylamine picrate [$(C_4H_9)_3NOC_6H_2(NO_2)_3$] is monoclinic (?). M.P. 107°. The optic plane is 010; weak dispersion; if Z is taken as 0° for $\lambda = 6908$, it is at 0° for 5780, 0.8° for 4916 and 1.7° for 4678. (-)2H = 55° (5780), 53° (4800). For $\lambda = 5461$: (-)2V = 51°, $N_X = 1.473$, $N_Y = 1.641$, $N_Z = 1.690$, $N_Z - N_X = 0.217$. Ref: 557.

Di-*sec*-butylamine picrate [$(C_4H_9)_2NHOC_6H_2(NO_2)_3$] is orthorhombic (?). M.P. 111°. Axial dispersion: (-)2H = 67.5° (6908), 71.5° (5780), 72° (5461), 74.5° (5086), 78.5° (4916). For $\lambda = 5461$: (-)2V = 62° $r < v$, $N_X = 1.474$, $N_Y = 1.711$, $N_Z = 1.827$, $N_Z - N_X = 0.353$. Ref: 557.

Isobutylamine picrate [$C_4H_9NH_2OC_6H_2(NO_2)_3$] is monoclinic. M.P. 151°. X = *b*; strong crossed dispersion so that if Z is taken at 0° for $\lambda = 6908$, it is at 2° for 6438, 6° for 5780, 13° for 5461, 32° for 5200, 55° for 5086, 68° for 4916, 74° for 4800, 80° for 4600. Axial dispersion: (-)2H = 47.5° (6908), 38.5° (5780), 31.5° (5461), 26° (minimum – 5220), 29° (5086), 38° (4900), 61° (4700). For $\lambda = 5461$: (-)2V = 26°, $N_X = 1.470$, $N_Y = 1.821$, $N_Z = 1.848$, $N_Z - N_X = 0.378$. Ref: 557.

Di-isobutylamine picrate [$(C_4H_9)_2NHOC_6H_2(NO_2)_3$] is polymorphous. One phase (I) is monoclinic (?). M.P. 119° X = *b*? Axial dispersion: (-)2H = 35° (6908), 46° (5780), 52° (5461), 64° (5086), 75.5° (4916), 91° (4800). For $\lambda = 5461$: (-)2V = 44°, $N_X = 1.510$, $N_Y = 1.770$, $N_Z = 1.829$, $N_Z - N_X = 0.319$. Another phase (II) is monoclinic, but Z = *b* and the horizontal dispersion is 26° from $\lambda = 691$ to $\lambda = 509$, while the axial dispersion in the same range is 15° with $r > v$. A third phase (III) is uniaxial negative. Ref: 557.

Ethylenediamine picrate [$(CH_2NH_2)_2OC_6H_2(NO_2)_3$] is orthorhombic (?). Decomposes at 246 – 248°. Axial dispersion: (-)2H = 40.5° (6908), 37° (6438), 26.5° (5780), 6.5° (5461), 0° (5435), 12° (5380), 27.5° (5200), 35.5° (5086), 49° (4916) 82° (4650). For $\lambda = 5461$: (-)2V = 5°, $N_X = 1.470$, $N_Y = 1.916$, $N_Z = 1.919$ calc. $N_Z - N_X = 0.449$. Ref: 557.

Diethylenetriamine picrate [$(CH_4NH_2)_2NHOC_6H_2(NO_2)_3$] is orthorhombic (?). Decomposes at 225 – 227°. Axial dispersion: (-)2H = 36.5° (6908), 28° (5780), 20°

(5461), 0° (5210), 19.5° (5086), 33° (4916), 53° (4700). For $\lambda = 5461$: (-)2V = 16°, $N_X = 1.480$, $N_Y = 1.858$, $N_Z = 1.871$, $N_Z - N_X = 0.391$. Ref: 557.

Triethylenetetramine picrate $[(C_2H_4)_3(NH_2)_2(NH)_2OC_6H_2(NO_2)_3]$ is orthorhombic (?). Decomposes at 247 - 248°. Axial dispersion: (-)2H = 24.5° (6908), 22° (6438), 8° (5780), 0° (5645), 17.5° (5461), 41.5° (4916), 69° (4600). For $\lambda =$ 5461: (-)2V = 14°, $N_X = 1.505$, $N_Y = 1.865$, $N_Z = 1.872$, $N_Z - N_X = 0.367$. Ref: 557.

Hexamethylenetetramine picrate $[(CH_2)_6N_4OC_6H_2(NO_2)_3]$ is monoclinic. Decomposes at 187 - 189°. The optic plane is 010; inclined dispersion such that if Z is taken as 0° at 6908, it is at 0.5° at 5780, 1° at 5461, 5° at 4916, and 14.5° at 4678. Axial dispersion: (-)2H = 92.5° (6908), 90° (5780), 88° (5461), 78° (4916), 38° (4678). For $\lambda = 5461$: (-)2V = 71°, $N_X = 1.621$, $N_Y = 1.822$, $N_Z = 1.948$, $N_Z - N_X = 0.327$. Ref: 557.

Diethylaminoethanol picrate $[(C_2H_5)_2NC_2H_4OHOC_6H_2(NO_2)_3]$ is orthorhombic (?). M.P. 79°. Axial dispersion: (-)2H = 23.5° (6908), 19° (6438), 0° (5900), 9° (5780), 24° (5461), 46.5° (4916), 50.5° (4800). For $\lambda = 5461$: (-)2V = 20°, $N_X = 1.465$, $N_Y = 1.793$, $N_Z = 1.807$, $N_Z - N_X = 0.342$. A second phase has 2H = 31.5° (6908), 33.5° (5780), 34.5° (5461), 40° (4800). Ref: 557.

Diethanolamine picrate $[(C_2H_4OH)_2NHOC_6H_2(NO_2)_3]$ is monoclinic. M.P. 110°. The optic plane and X are normal to 010; crossed dispersion such that if Z is taken as 0° at 6908, it is at 2.5° for 5708, 4.5° for 5461, 13° for 5086, 35° for 4920, 62° for 4800. Axial dispersion: (-)2V = 59° (6908), 50.5° (5780) 45.5° (5461), 25° (4916), 28° (4900), 44° (4700). For $\lambda = 5461$: (-)2V = 38°, $N_X =$ 1.518, $N_Y = 1.787$, $N_Z = 1.833$, $N_Z - N_X = 0.315$. Ref: 557.

2,2′,2″-Trihydroxytriethylamine picrate or triethanolamine picrate $[(C_2H_4 \cdot OH)_3NOC_6H_2(NO_2)_3]$ is monoclinic. M.P. 128°. Z = *b*. Optically positive for $\lambda > 4900$ and negative for $\lambda < 4900$. Crossed dispersion such that if Z is taken as 0° for 6908, it is 0.5° for 5780, 1° for 5461, 6.5° for 4916 and 9° for 4800. Axial dispersion: 2H over Z = 77.5° (6908), 82,5° (5780), 86.5° (5461), 96° (5086), about 113° (4800); 2H over X = about 120° (5461), 111.5° (5086), 101° (4800), 80° (4540). For $\lambda = 5461$: (+)2V = 80°, $N_X = 1.575$, $N_Y = 1.651$, $N_Z = 1.783$, $N_Z - N_X = 0.208$. Ref: 557.

Hydroxyethylethylenediamine picrate $[(HOC_2H_4NHC_2H_4NH_2OC_6H_2(NO_2)_3]$ is orthorhombic (?). Decomposes at 224 - 227°. Axial dispersion: (-)2H = 63° (6908), 53.5° (5780), 46.5° (5461), 0° (5025), 32.5° (4916), 63.5° (4800). The optic plane for $\lambda > 5205$ is at right angles to its position for $\lambda < 5205$. For $\lambda = 5461$: (-)2V = 38°, $N_X = 1.575$, $N_Y = 1.837$, $N_Z = 1.879$, $N_Z - N_X = 0.304$. Ref: 557.

Germanium tetrakis(phenylmercaptide) or tetrakis(phenylmercapto) germanium $[Ge(SC_6H_5)_4]$ is orthorhombic with $a:b:c = 0.507:1:0.484$. Crystals {010} tablets with {110}, {001}, and {111}. M.P. 101.5°. The optic plane is 010; X = *c*. (-)2V = ?. $N_X = 1.728$ (Hg yellow), 1.7348 (Hg green), 1.7789 (Hg blue), $N_Y = 1.7753$ (Hg yellow), 1.7821 (Hg green), 1.8248 (Hg blue), $N_Z = ?$. Ref: 11.

Benzenesulfonylbenzene or phenyl sulfone or diphenyl sulfone ($C_6H_5 \cdot SO_2 \cdot C_6H_5$) is monoclinic with $a:b:c = 1.56:1:1.45$, $\beta = 98°17'$. Crystals {100} tablets with {011}, {001}, {$\bar{1}02$}. The optic plane is 010; $Z \wedge c = +50°50'$. (+)2V = 64°20'. $N_X = 1.606$, $N_Y = 1.632$, $N_Z = 1.703$, $N_Z - N_X = 0.097$ D. Ref: 382.

4,4'Dichlorodiphenylsulfone {$(C_6H_4Cl)_2SO_2$} is monoclinic with $a:b:c = 2.455:1:4.092$, $\beta = 90°31'$. $X = b$, $Z \wedge c = 17°$ in acute β. (+)2V = 65°48' $N_X = 1.603$, $N_Y = 1.653$, $N_Z = 1.785$, $N_Z - N_X = 0.182$ for $\lambda = 578$. Ref: 605b.

4,4'-Dibromodiphenylsulfone {$(C_6H_4Br)_2SO_2$} is monoclinic with $a:b:c = 2.459:1:4.118$, $\beta = 92°40'$. a 12.32, b 5.04, c 20.75 Å. U.C. 4. Crystals {100} needles along b. $X = b$, $Z \wedge c = 24°$ (21°) in acute β. Perfect 001 cleavage. (+)2V = 49°48' (56°). $N_X = 1.633$, $N_Y = 1.662$ (also given as 1.673), $N_Z = 1.817$, $N_Z - N_X = 0.184$ for $\lambda = 578$. Ref: 605b.

1,1-Diphenyl-3-(phenylsulfonyl)-2-propen-1-ol or 3-phenylsulfonyl-1,1-diphenyl-2-propen-1-ol [$(C_6H_5)_2C(OH) \cdot CH:CHSO_2C_6H_5$] is monoclinic with $a:b:c = 1.060:1:0.328$, $\beta = 99°5'$. Crystals show {010}, {100}, {110}, {011}, {101}. M.P. 193°. The optic plane and Z are normal to 010; $X \wedge c = 23°$. (+)2V = 88° calc. $N_X = 1.607$, $N_Y = 1.657$, $N_Z = 1.706$, $N_Z - N_X = 0.099$. Again $N_X = 1.608$, $N_Y = 1.656$, $N_Z = 1.710$, $N_Z - N_X = 0.102$. (2V is described as "medium"). Ref. 28.

2-Benzenesulfonylbutanoic acid or α-(phenylsulfonyl)butyric acid ($C_6H_5 \cdot SO_2 \cdot CO_2H$) is orthorhombic $a:b:c = 0.389:1:0.954$. Crystals show {001}, {110}, {010}, {111}, etc. Perfect 001 and imperfect 010 cleavages. M.P. 123° - 124°. The optic plane is 010; $X = a$. (-)2V = 46°45'. $N_X = 1.304$ calc. Na, $N_Y = 1.5975$, $N_Z = 1.6493$ Na, $N_Z - N_X = 0.345$ calc. Ref: 118.

Phenyldibromosulfide [$(C_6H_4Br)_2S$] is monoclinic with $a:b:c = 1.368:1:4.233$, $\beta = 96°$. a 8.02, b 5.86, c 24.81 Å. U.C. 4. The optic plane is 010; $Z \wedge c = -3°$. (+)2V = large, $N_X = 1.575$, $N_Y = 1.755$, $N_Z = 2.0$ *ca.*, $N_Z - N_X = 0.425$ *ca.* Ref: 606.

2-Nitro-diphenylsulfide ($C_{12}H_9NO_2S$) is monoclinic prismatic with $a:b:c = 1.045:1:1.005$, $\beta = 113°21'$. Space group $P2_1/a$. a 10.89, b 10.36, c 10.58 Å. U.C. 4. $Y = b$. (+)2V = 55° calc. $N_X = 1.616$, $N_Y = 1.693$, $N_Z = 1.970$, $N_Z - N_X = 0.354$. Ref: 605a.

Sodium dinitro-*o*-cresol [$NO_2(CH_3)C_6H_2NO_2ONa$] is orthorhombic. Crystals columnar with {100}, {010}, {001}, {110}. Color light orange. (-)2E = 95° - 100°, 2V = 50° - 55°. N_X (‖ length) = 1.528, $N_Y = 1.750$, $N_Z > 1.83$, $N_Z - N_X > 0.30$. Ref: 529.

Di-*p*-tolylselenium dibromide {$(CH_3) \cdot (C_6H_3)_2SeBr_2$} is orthorhombic with $a:b:c = 0.595:1:0.398$. a 8.65, b 14.56, c 5.81 Å. U.C. 2. Crystals short prisms or acicular. D 1.91. $X = c$, $Y = b$. (+)2V = 80°, r > v strong. $N_X = 1.715$, $N_Y = 1.83$, $N_Z = 2.05$, $N_Z - N_X = 0.335$. Ref: 553c.

4,6-Ammonium dinitro-*o*-cresol (monohydrate?) [$CH_3C_6H_2(NO_2)_2ONH_4 \cdot H_2O$] is orthorhombic with columnar habit. X parallel to elongation. (–)2E > 170°, 2V near 90°, r > v, $N_X = 1.580$, $N_Y = 1.73$, $N_Z > 1.80$, $N_Z - N_X > 0.220$. Color orange-yellow. Ref: 529.

Dibenzyl succinate ($C_6H_5CH_2OCO \cdot (CH_2)_2CO \cdot O \cdot CH_2 \cdot C_6H_5$) is orthorhombic with $a:b:c = 0.565:1:0.454$. *a* 10.35, *b* 18.32, *c* 8.32 Å. U.C. 4. Crystals {010} plates with 010 and 100 cleavages. M.P. 46°. D 1.256. X = *b*, Y = *c*. (–)2V = 42°, r < v weak. $N_X = 1.519$, $N_Y = 1.628$, $N_Z = 1.645$, $N_Z - N_X = 0.126$. Ref: 535c.

o-Nitrobenzyl alcohol ($C_6H_4NO_2CH_2OH$) forms plates with terminations inclined at 62°. M.P. 74°. X parallel to elongation. (–?) 2V = ?, $N_X = 1.477$, $N_Z = 1.72$, $N_Z - N_X = 0.243$. Color pale brown. Ref: 444.

p-Nitrobenzyl alcohol ($C_6H_4NO_2CH_2OH$) forms plates with terminations inclined at 75°. M.P. 93°. X′ ∧ elongation = 24°. Bluish green on one side and yellow on the other side of imperfect extinction due to strong dispersion. (–?)2V = ?, $N_X = 1.515$, $N_Z = 1.72$, $N_Z - N_X = 0.205$. Color pale yellow. Ref: 444.

Germanium tetrakis(*p*-tolylmercaptide) or tetrakis(*p*-tolylmercapto)germanium [$Ge(SC_6H_4CH_3)_4$] is orthorhombic with $a:b:c = 0.841:1:0.837$. Crystals elongated along *c* with {010}, {210}, {121}, {110}, etc. Perfect 010 cleavage. M.P. = 110° – 111°. The optic plane is 010; Z = *c*. $N_X = 1.720$ yellow, 1.726 green, 1.76 blue, $N_Y = 1.7638$ yellow, 1.7716 green, 1.8224 blue, $N_Z = ?$. Ref: 11.

2-Nitro-5-methyldiphenylsulfide ($C_{13}H_{11}NO_2S$) is monoclinic prismatic with $a:b:c = 2.113:1:1.714$, $\beta = 107°42'$. Space group $P2_1/a$. *a* 14.92, *b* 7.02, *c* 12.09 Å. U.C. 4. Y = *b*. (–)2V = 80° calc. $N_X = 1.669$, $N_Y = 1.752$, $N_Z = 1.808$, $N_Z - N_X = 0.139$ for $\lambda = 578$. Ref: 605a.

4-Nitro-methyldiphenylsulfide ($C_{13}H_{11}NO_2S$) is triclinic with[1] $a:b:c = 0.782:1:0.617$, $\alpha = 95°56'$, $\beta = 73°37'$, $\gamma = 67°1'$. Biaxial with $N_1 = 1.618$ ($\approx N_X$), $N_2 = 1.884$ ($\approx N_Z$), $N_2 - N_1 = 0.266$. Ref: 605a.

Silicon tetrakis(phenylmercaptide) or tetrakis(phenylmercapto) silicane [$Si(SC_6H_5)_4$] is orthorhombic with $a:b:c = 505:1:0.477$. Crystals show {110}, {001}, {010}, {111}. M.P. 114.5° – 115°. The optic plane is 010; X = *c*. (–)2E = 75° *ca.* 2V = 41° calc. $N_X = 1.6979$ D, 1.7038 (Hg green) calc., 1.7366 (Hg blue) calc., $N_Y = 1.7499$ D, 1.7558 (Hg green), 1.7918 (Hg blue), $N_Z = 1.757$ D, 1.763 (Hg green), 1.799 (Hg blue), $N_Z - N_X = 0.059$ D. Ref: 11.

bis(4-Nitrobenzyl)*trans*-2-methylbutenedioate or *p*-nitrobenzyl mesaconate [$O_2N \cdot C_6H_4 \cdot CH_2 \cdot O_2C \cdot CH{:}C(CH_3) \cdot CO_2 \cdot CH_2 \cdot C_6H_4 \cdot NO_2$] melts at 134°. It has parallel extinction and negative elongation. (+)2V = 60° calc. $N_X = 1.610$, $N_Y = 1.627$, $N_Z = 1.680$ (all ± 0.003), $N_Z - N_X = 0.070$. It forms rods and plates. Ref: 253.

[1] *a b c* changed to *b c a* to make *b* > *a* > *c*.

Gold dibenzylsulfonium chloride or aurodibenzylsulfonium chloride [$Au \cdot S(CH_2 \cdot C_6H_5)_2 \cdot Cl$] is ditetragonal pyramidal with $c/a = 0.867$. Crystals long prismatic with {110}, {100}, {111}, etc. Fig. 51. Perfect 110 and distinct 001 cleavage. Decomposes on solution. Uniaxial negative with $N_O = 1.7527$ Li, 1.7606 Na, 1.7738 Tl, $N_E = 1.6930$ Li, 1.7046 Na, 1.7166 Tl, $N_O - N_E = 0.0560$ Na. A stable phase is monoclinic with weak birefringence; the optic plane is 010 and the optic angle is near 90°. Ref: 119.

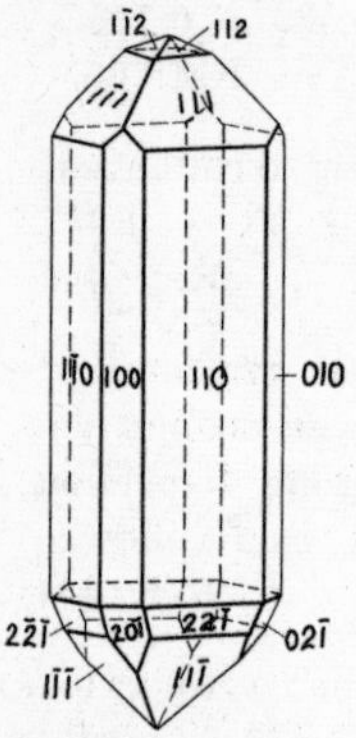

Fig. 51. Aurodibenzylsulfonium chloride.

S-Benzylisothiourea hydrochloride or *S*-benzylthiopseudourea hydrochloride [$NH_2 \cdot C(:NH) \cdot S \cdot CH_2 \cdot C_6H_5 \cdot HCl$] forms rods and fibers with M.P. 176°. Parallel extinction and positive elongation with $N_X = 1.631$, $N_Y = 1.683$, $N_Z = 1.689$, $N_Z - N_X = 0.058$. ∴ (−)2V = small. Ref 125.

Mesitol or hydroxymesitylene or 2,4-6-trimethylphenol [$(CH_3)_3C_6H_2OH$] is monoclinic. Crystals are acicular and may be in radial spherulites. M.P. 71°. Plates normal to X are elongated along Y; those normal to Z are elongated along X. (−)2V = 89°, r > v. $N_X = 1.532$, $N_Y = 1.62 \pm .01$, $N_Z = 1.68 \pm .01$, $N_Z - N_X = 0.15$ (for $\lambda = 5461$). Ref: 556a.

2-Isopropyl-5-methylphenol or 3-*p*-cymenol or thymol [$C_6H_3OH(CH_3) \cdot CH(CH_3)_2$] is trigonal rhombohedral with $c/a = 1.568$. Crystals show {10$\bar{1}$1}, {01$\bar{1}$2}, {0001}. Perfect 10$\bar{1}$1 cleavage. Uniaxial positive with $N_O = 1.5218$ Li. 1.5252 Na, 1.5305 Tl, $N_E = 1.602$ Li, 1.609 Na, 1.613 Tl, $N_E - N_O = 0.0838$ Na. Ref: 118.

2-Isopropyl-5-methylphenoxyethyldiethylamine hydrochloride ($C_{16}H_{27}ON \cdot HCl$) is orthorhombic (?). Crystals circular or rods. M.P. 121 – 122°. Z ‖ elongation. (+)2V = 70° calc. $N_X = 1.549$, $N_Y = 1.556$, $N_Z = 1.570$, $N_Z - N_X = 0.021$. Colorless. Ref: 477b.

trans-4-Phenylcyclohexanol ($C_{12}H_{16}O$) is probably monoclinic. Crystals have negative elongation. (+)2V ≈ 75 – 80°, r > v. $N_X = 1.549$, $N_Y = 1.595$, $N_Z = 1.688$, $N_Z - N_X = 0.139$. Ref: 527b.

cis-4-Phenylcyclohexanol ($C_{12}H_{16}O$) is probably hexagonal. Uniaxial negative with $N_O = 1.581$, $N_E = 1.550$, $N_O - N_E = 0.031$. Ref: 527b.

Axerophthol or vitamin A ($C_{20}H_{29}OH$) is monoclinic in rods with $\beta = 132°$. D 1.044. M.P. 62°. X ∧ c = 40°, Y = b. (+)2V = 50°, $N_X = 1.532$, $N_Y = 1.634$. $N_Z = 2.16$ *ca.* $N_Z - N_X = 0.63$ *ca.* Ref: 436b.

1-Hydroxynaphthalene or 1-naphthol or α-naphthol [$C_{10}H_7(OH)$] is monoclinic with $a:b:c = 2.748:1:2.772$, $\beta = 117°10'$. Crystals acicular or {001} plates with {100}, {201}, etc.; often twinned on 101 and elongated along b. Perfect 001 and imperfect 100 and 201 cleavages. M.P. 94°. The optic plane is normal to 010 and makes an angle of about 15° with c. The acute bisectrix is b. 2V = small. $N_1 = 1.66+$, $N_2 > 1.74$, $N_2 - N_1 = 0.08$. *ca.* Ref: 119, 239.

2-Hydroxynaphthalene or 2-naphthol or β-naphthol $[C_{10}H_7(OH)]$ is monoclinic with $a:b:c = 1.366:1:2.030$, $\beta = 119°48'$. a 8.14, b 5.92, c 18.2 Å. Crystals {001} tablets with {110}, {011}. Common twinning on 001. Perfect 001 cleavage. M.P. 122°. The optic plane is 010; an optic axis with strong dispersion is visible through 001 in the obtuse angle β. $N_X = 1.566$, $N_Y = 1.577$, $N_Z = 1.69$, $N_Z - N_X = 0.124$; $\therefore$ (+)2V = 30° *ca.* calc. Also $N_1 = 1.56$, $N_2 = 1.69$, $N_2 - N_1 = 0.13$, with "parallel extinction and negative elongation". Again $N_X = 1.523$, $N_Z = 1.733$, $N_Z - N_X = 0.210$; also $N_1 = 1.548$, $N_2 = 1.712$. β-Naphthol forms a continuous isomorphous series with naphthalene and also with naphthylamine.
Ref: 34, 35, 119, 239, 343c, 518, 553, 558.

1-Nitroso-2-naphthol or 1,2-naphthoquinone 1-monoxime or α-nitroso-β-naphthol $[C_{10}H_6(NO)(OH]$ is monoclinic with a prism angle $(110:1\bar{1}0)$ of 82° and a pyramid angle $(111:1\bar{1}1)$ of 72°10′. M.P. 110°. Bolland gives for "nitroso-β-naphthol" inclined extinction at 44° and $N_1 = 1.75$, $N_2 > 1.95$, $N_2 - N_1 > 0.20$.
Ref: 34, 35.

4,4-Dinitrodiphenyl with 4-hydroxydiphenyl $(O_2NC_6H_4C_6H_4NO_2)$ with $(C_6H_5C_6H_4OH)$ is monoclinic with $a:b:c = 2.12:1:1.177$, $\beta = 99°39'$, a 20.06, b 9.46, c 11.13 Å. U.C. 2. M.P. 230°. D 1.43. $X \wedge c = 4°$, $Y = b$. (+)2V = 45°, $N_X = 1.59$, $N_Y = 1.64$, $N_Z = 2.03$, $N_Z - N_X = 0.44$. Color yellow. Ref: 588b.

4,4-Dinitrodiphenyl with dihydroxydiphenyl $(O_2NC_6H_4C_6H_4NO_2)$ with $(OHC_6H_4C_6H_4OH)$ is monoclinic with $a:b:c = 1.072:1:0.606$, $\beta = 95°$. a 20.0, b 18.65, c 11.3 Å. U.C. 4. D 1.45. M.P. 250°. Z = b. (+)2V = 29°, $N_X = 1.62$, $N_Y = 1.63$, $N_Z = 1.99$, $N_Z - N_X = 0.37$. Color orange yellow. Ref: 588b.

β-Dimethylaminoethyl benzhydryl ether hydrochloride or benadryl $[C_{13}H_{10}\cdot(H)OCH_2CH_2N(CH_3)_2\cdot HCl]$ is orthorhombic (?) in columnar plates with lengthwise cleavage. X || length. Soluble in water and alcohol. Crystals usually give only flash interference figures. (-)2V = small, $N_X = 1.602$, $N_Y = 1.625$, $N_Z = 1.630$, $N_Z - N_X = 0.028$. Colorless. With $PtCl_4$ it forms X-shaped groups. Ref: 523.

2-Benzylphenoxy-N,N-dimethylethanolamine dihydrogen citrate $[C_{13}H_{11}OC\cdot(OH)CH_2N(CH_3)_2]$ forms rods and needles. M.P. 130°. Inclined extinction. (-)2V = 86° calc. $N_X = 1.556$, $N_Y = 1.585$, $N_Z = 1.610$, $N_Z - N_X = 0.054$.
Ref: 477d.

Triphenylmethanol or triphenylcarbinol $[(C_6H_5)_3COH]$ is trigonal with $c/a = 0.698$. Crystals rhombohedral with $\{10\bar{1}1\}$, $\{11\bar{2}0\}$, {0001}, or {0001} tablets. Distinct $11\bar{2}0$ and 0001 cleavages. D 1.188. M.P. 157°. But it is also monoclinic or triclinic with an extinction angle ($Z \wedge c$) of 6° and (+)2V = 50° *ca.*, $N_X = 1651$, $N_Y = 1.656$, $N_Z = 1.663$, $N_Z - N_X = 0.012$.
Ref: 119, 140, 397, 398.

Harrison red (made from toluidine red which is *o*-nitro-*p*-toluene-β-naphthol $(C_{17}H_{13}O_3N_3)$) is probably orthorhombic in grains and prisms with negative elongation and parallel extinction. $N_X = 1.60$ Na, $N_Y \approx 2.1$ Na, $N_Z = 2.25$ Li, 2.33 Na, $N_Z - N_X = 0.73$ Na $\therefore$ (-)2V = 70° calc. Strongly pleochroic with X = orange, Y = Z = deep red. Grains are practically opaque to green and blue but transmit some violet. Soluble in hot linseed oil. Ref: 556.

Methoxytriphenylmethane or methyl triphenylmethyl ether or triphenylmethyl methyl ether, or methyl trityl ether $[(C_6H_5)_3C\cdot O\cdot CH_3]$ is monoclinic or triclinic with $Z \wedge c = 22°$ and $(-)2V = 60°$, $r < v$. $N_X = 1.646$, $N_Y = 1.676$, $N_Z = 1.696$, $N_Z - N_X = 0.050$. Ref: 397, 398.

Ethoxytriphenylmethane or ethyl triphenylmethyl ether or triphenylmethyl ethyl ether or ethyl trityl ether $[(C_6H_5)_3C\cdot O\cdot CH_2CH_3]$ is monoclinic or triclinic with $Z \wedge c = 40°$ and $(+)2V = 60°$, $r < v$. $N_X = 1.626$, $N_Y = 1.636$, $N_Z = 1.676$, $N_Z - N_X = 0.050$. Ref: 397, 398.

Triphenylpropoxymethane or propyl triphenylmethyl ether or triphenylmethyl propyl ether or propyl trityl ether $[(C_6H_5)_3C\cdot O\cdot (CH_2)_2CH_3]$ is monoclinic or triclinic with $(-)2V = 55°$. $N_X = 1.648$, $N_Y = 1.658$, $N_Z = 1.666$, $N_Z - N_X = 0.018$. Ref: 397, 398.

Isopropoxytriphenylmethane or isopropyl triphenylmethyl ether or triphenylmethyl isopropyl ether $[(C_6H_5)_3C\cdot O\cdot CH(CH_3)_2]$ is monoclinic or triclinic with $Z \wedge c = 32°$ and $(+)2V = 60°$, $r > v$. $N_X = 1.636$, $N_Y = 1.641$, $N_Z = 1.686$, $N_Z - N_X = 0.050$. Ref: 397, 398.

(Benzyloxy)triphenylmethane or benzyl triphenylmethyl ether $[(C_6H_5)_3C\cdot O\cdot CH_2C_6H_5]$ is monoclinic or triclinic with an extinction angle $(Z \wedge c)$ of 64°. $(-)2V = 88°$, $r > v$. $N_X = 1.636$, $N_Y = 1.657$ calc., $N_Z = 1.676$, $N_Z - N_X = 0.040$. Ref: 398.

Triphenyl(2-phenylethoxy)methane or phenethyl triphenylmethyl ether or triphenylmethyl 2-phenylethyl ether $[(C_6H_5)_3C\cdot O(CH_2)_2C_6H_5]$ is biaxial with $Z \wedge c = 54°$, and $(-)2V = 80°$, $r < v$. $N_X = 1.640$, $N_Y = 1.660$, $N_Z = 1.682$, $N_Z - N_X = 0.042$. Ref: 397, 398.

Ethoxytris(4-methylphenyl)methane or ethyl tri-*p*-tolylmethyl ether $[(CH_3\cdot C_6H_4)_3C\cdot O\cdot C_2H_5]$ has $N_X = 1.58$, $N_Y = ?$ $N_Z = 1.646$, $N_Z - N_X = 0.066$. Ref: 398.

cis-1,4-Cyclohexanediol or hexahydrohydroquinone $(C_6H_{12}O_2)$ has three crystal phases. One is isometric, often octahedral, with $N = 1.517$ (a little greater). M.P. 90° *ca.* Another is tetragonal with prismatic cleavage. It is uniaxial and negative with $N_E > 1.517$ D. M.P. 90° *ca.* A third is triclinic in prisms often twinned on a prism face with which other prism faces make angles of 112° and 140°. The prismatic crystals have ± elongation and an extinction angle attaining 10°. The optic angle is very near 90°. $N_Y = 1.517$ *ca.* Ref: 105.

2,5,5-Trimethyl-1,3-cyclohexanediol is ditrigonal pyramidal with $c/a = 0.513$. M.P. 116 – 117°. Crystals long prismatic with $\{10\bar{1}0\}$, $\{11\bar{2}0\}$, $\{10\bar{1}1\}$, $\{40\bar{4}1\}$, etc.

$$\left[(CH_3)_2C\left\langle\begin{matrix}CH_2\cdot CHOH\\CH_2\cdot CHOH\end{matrix}\right\rangle CH\cdot CH_3\right]$$

Distinct $11\bar{2}0$ and $40\bar{4}1$ cleavages. H 2 – 3. Uniaxial negative with $N_O = 1.5034$, $N_E = 1.4843$, $N_O - N_E = 0.0191$ Na. Ref: 144.

1-Methyl-4-(1-hydroxyisopropyl)cyclohexanol or 1,8-*p*-menthanediol or terpinol or terpin $(C_{10}H_{20}O_2)$ is orthorhombic with $a:b:c = 0.789:1:0.822$.

Crystals pyramidal or {001} tablets with {111}, {011}, etc. Perfect 001 and imperfect 110 cleavages. The optic plane is 001; $Z = b$. (+)2V = 79°42′ (546). $N_X = 1.5209$ (546), $N_Y = 1.5292$, $N_Z = 1.5416$, $N_Z - N_X = 0.0207$. Again: $N_X = 1.512$, $N_Y = 1.517$, $N_Z = 1.522$, $N_Z - N_X = 0.010$. Ref: 282, 553c.

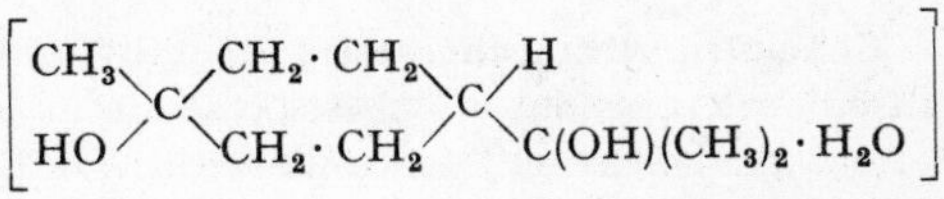

cis-Terpinol monohydrate or *cis*-terpin monohydrate is orthorhombic with $a:b:c = 0.807$: : 1 : 0.476. Crystals short prismatic with {110}, {011}, {111}, {010}. Fig. 52. Imperfect 110 cleavage. D 1.09. M.P. 117°. The optic plane is 010; $Z = a$. (+)2V = 77°37′ Li, 77°27′ Na, 77°18′ Tl. $N_X = 1.5024$ Li, 1.5049 Na, 1.5073 Tl, $N_Y = 1.5093$ Li, 1.5124 Na, 1.5148 Tl, $N_Z = 1.5211$ Li, 1.5243 Na, 1.5272 Tl, $N_Z - N_X = 0.0194$ Na. The natural substance is called "flagstaffite." Ref: 117, 379a.

$$\left[\begin{array}{c} CH_3 \\ \diagdown C \diagup \quad \diagup CH_2 \cdot CH_2 \diagdown \quad \diagup H \\ \qquad\qquad C \\ HO \diagup \quad \diagdown CH_2 \cdot CH_2 \diagup \quad \diagdown C(OH)(CH_3)_2 \cdot H_2O \end{array} \right]$$

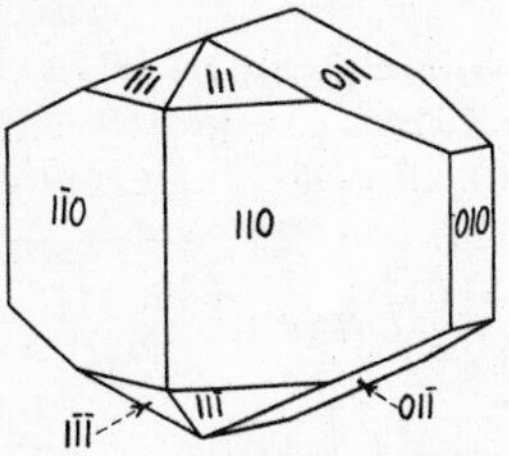

Fig. 52. *cis*-Terpin monohydrate.

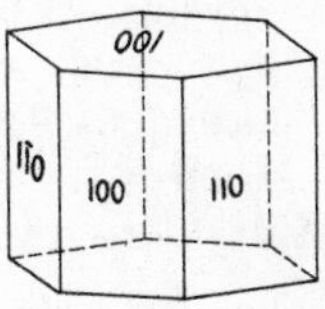

Fig. 53. Pyrocatechol.

1,2-Dihydroxybenzene or pyrocatechol or catechol [$C_6H_4(OH)_2$] is monoclinic with $a:b:c = 1.609:1:1.023$, $\beta = 95°15′$. Crystals {100} tablets or prismatic with {100}, {110}, {001}, etc. Fig. 53. Perfect 100 cleavage. D 1.37. M.P. 104°. The optic plane and X are normal to 010; $Z \wedge c = 6° - 7°$. (+)2V = 35°, r < v. $N_X = 1.5980$ C, 1.6044 D, 1.6204 F, $N_Y = 1.6073$ C, 1.6139 D, 1.6314 F, $N_Z = 1.7255$ C, 1.7336 D, 1.7536 F, $N_Z - N_X = 0.1292$ D. Ref: 118.

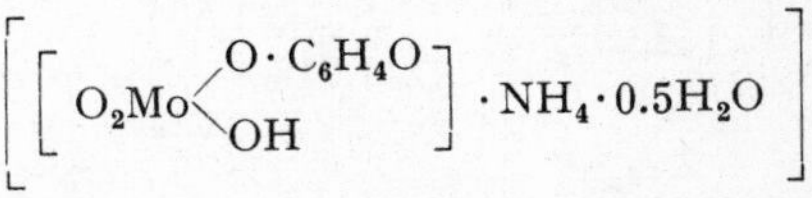

Ammonium pyrocatechol molybdate hemihydrate or ammonium catechol molybdate hemihydrate is orthorhombic with $a:b:c = 0.589:1:0.911$.

$$\left[O_2Mo \diagdown_{OH}^{O \cdot C_6H_4O} \right] \cdot NH_4 \cdot 0.5H_2O$$

Crystals {010} tablets or prisms with {110}, {010}, {111}, {001}, etc. Perfect 010 and distinct 001 cleavage. The optic plane is 001; $Z = b$. (+)2V = 81°38′, r < v, weak. $N_X = 1.631$ Li, 1.632 Na, $N_Y = 1.708$ Li, 1.709 Na, $N_Z = = 1.823$ calc. $N_Z - N_X = 0.191$; Color dark red with X = straw yellow, Y = deep brown-red, Z = brownish yellow. Ref: 21.

Tris(2-hydroxyphenyl) Arsenate or Tripyrocatechol Arsenate and Derivatives

Tripyrocatechol arsenate tetrahydrate [$O:As(O \cdot C_6H_4 \cdot O)_3H_3 \cdot 4H_2O$] is orthorhombic with $a:b:c = 0.958:1:0.988$. Crystals {100} tablets or equant with {100}, {010}, {001}, {110}, {111}, etc. Perfect 100 and very good 010 and 001 cleavages. M.P. 103°. The optic plane is 010; $Z = c$. (+)2V = 79°52′, r > v strong. $N_X = 1.563$, $N_Y = 1.582$, $N_Z = 1.610$, $N_Z - N_X = 0.047$. Ref: 21.

Chromium tripyrocatechol arsenate dodecahydrate $[[O:As(O \cdot C_6H_4 \cdot O)_3]_3 \cdot CrH_3 \cdot 12H_2O]$ is isometric in cubes and octahedrons with imperfect 100 cleavage. Common twinning on 111. Isotropic with N = 1.61 *ca*. Bluish green in transmitted light; iron gray to black and metallic in reflected light. Ref: 21.

Cobalt tripyrocatechol arsenate octahydrate $[[O:As(O \cdot C_6H_4 \cdot O)_3]_2CoH_4 \cdot 8H_2O]$ is isometric diploidal in cubes, octahedrons, dodecahedrons, and pyritohedrons. No observed cleavage. Isotropic with N = 1.595 *ca*. Color red-violet. Splinters in transmitted light peach-colored. Ref: 21.

Nickel tripyrocatechol arsenate octahydrate $[[O:As(O \cdot C_6H_4 \cdot O)_3]_2NiH_4 \cdot 8H_2O]$ is isometric in cubes, octahedrons, and dodecahedrons. Perfect 100 cleavage. Pale green in transmitted light and turquoise blue in reflected light. Isotropic with N = 1.602. Ref: 21.

Sodium dipyrocatechol nickel acid dodecahydrate $[[Ni(O \cdot C_6H_4 \cdot O)_2]Na_2 \cdot 12H_2O]$ is monoclinic with $a:b:c = 1.19:1:?$, $\beta = 102.5°$. Crystals {001} tablets with {110}. Perfect 001 and very good 100 and 010 cleavages. The optic plane and X are normal to 010; $Z \wedge c = -6.5°$. (-)2V = 84°24′, r < v distinct; crossed dispersion weak. $N_X = 1.482$, $N_Y = 1.547$, $N_Z = 1.638$, $N_Z - N_X = 0.156$. Color dark green with X = nearly colorless to bluish, Y = darker green, Z = ?. Ref: 21.

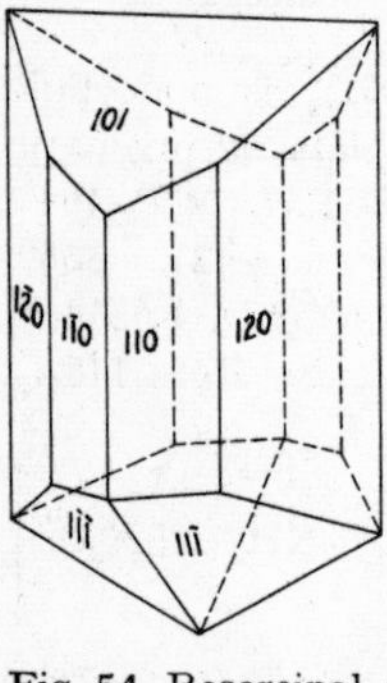

Fig. 54. Resorcinal.

o-Methoxyphenol or guaiacol $[C_6H_4(OH)(O \cdot CH_3)]$ is trigonal with $c/a = 0.993$. Crystals thick prisms with $\{10\bar{1}0\}$, $\{2\bar{1}\bar{1}0\}$, $\{11\bar{2}1\}$. Very plastic. M.P. 31° - 32°. Uniaxial positive with $N_O = 1.569$, $N_E = 1.666$, $N_E - N_O = 0.097$ Na. Ref: 118.

Potassium guaiacol sulfate dihydrate $[(C_6H_3(OH)OCH_3 \cdot SO_3K \cdot 2H_2O)]$ forms needles or plates with $N_1 = 1.527$, $N_2 = 1.565$, $N_3 = 1.626$, $N_3 - N_1 = 0.099$. Again: $N_X = 1.516$, $N_Y = 1.552$, $N_Z = 1.627$, $N_Z - N_X = 0.111$. ∴ (+)2V = moderate. Ref: 343c, 518, 524.

Guaiacol carbonate $[(C_7H_7O)_2CO_3]$ melts at 85 - 88° $N_1 = 1.540$, $N_2 = 1.695$, $N_2 - N_1 = 0.155$. Ref: 343c.

1,3-Dihydroxybenzene or resorcinol $[C_6H_4(OH)_2]$ is orthorhombic disphenoidal with $a:b:c = 0.933:1:0.527$. Space group *Pnn*; *a* 9.56, *b* 10.25, *c* 5.64 Å. U.C. 4. Crystals thick prismatic with {110}, {120}, {101}, $\{11\bar{1}\}$, etc. Fig. 54. Imperfect 110 cleavage. D 1.28. M.P. 110°. The optic plane is 001; X = *a*. (-)2V = 46°14′. $N_X = 1.5725$ C, 1.5781 D, 1.5901 F, $N_Y = 1.6132$ C, 1.6197 D, 1.6372 F, $N_Z = 1.6208$ C, 1.6273 D, 1.6449 F, $N_Z - N_X = 0.0492$ D. Also: $N_1 = 1.595$, $N_2 = 1.622$, $N_2 - N_1 = 0.027$. This substance inverts at 74° to β-resorcinol which is also orthorhombic disphenoidal with $a:b:c = 0.629:1:0.437$. Space group *Pna*; *a* 7.91, *b* 12.57, *c* 5.50 Å U.C. 4. Crystals acicular parallel to *c*. Often intergrown with the α-phase. M.P. 110°. D 1.327. Ref: 118, 143, 239, 419, 581.

2,4,6-Trinitro-1,3-benzenediol or 2,4,6-trinitroresorcinol $[C_6H(NO_2)_3(OH)_2]$ has two crystal phases. The stable form (I) melts at 177°. It is monoclinic in nearly equant crystals showing {100}, {001}, {010}, etc.; longer along *b*. The optic plane is 010; X ∧ *c* = 7°. 2V = very large. N_X = 1.57 *ca.*, N_Y > 1.70, N_Z = ? The unstable form (II) melts at 165.5°. It is ditrigonal pyramidal with *c*/*a* = 0.787. Space group *C*3*c*; *a* 12.7, *c* 10.0 Å. U.C. 6. Crystals often rhombohedral with {0001} and {10$\bar{1}$0}. Uniaxial negative with N_O > 1.70, N_E = 1.603 red, $N_O - N_E$ > 0.097. Ref: 288.

1-4-Dihydroxybenzene or hydroquinone $[C_6H_4(OH)_2]$ is rhombohedral with *c*/*a* = 0.255. Space group *C*$\bar{3}$; *a* 22.06, *c* 5.62 Å. U.C. 18. Crystals acicular to prismatic with {11$\bar{2}$0}, {10$\bar{1}$1}, {01$\bar{1}$2}, etc. D 1.33. M.P. 169° – 170°. Uniaxial negative with N_O = 1.6260 C, 1.6325 D, 1.6479 F, N_E = 1.6195 C, 1.6262 D, 1.6420 F, $N_O - N_E$ = 0.0063 D. Again N_O = 1.638, N_E = 1.636, $N_O - N_E$ = 0.002. Hydroquinone is also monoclinic (metastable), but the indices have not been measured. Ref: 118, 239, 432.

Hydroquinone methyl alcohol complex $\{3C_6H_4(OH)_2 \cdot CH_3OH\}$ is hexagonal with *c*/*a* = 0.3318. Crystals prismatic. D 1.35. M.P. 170°. Uniaxial negative with N_O = 1.630, N_E = 1.624, $N_O - N_E$ = 0.006. Ref: 568a.

Hydroquinone formic acid complex $\{3C_6H_4(OH)_2 \cdot HCO_2H\}$ is hexagonal with *c*/*a* = 0.6883. Crystals prismatic. D 1.367. M.P. 160°. Uniaxial positive with N_O = 1.613, N_E = 1.633, $N_E - N_O$ = 0.020. Ref: 568a.

Hydroquinone sulfur dioxide complex $\{3C_6H_4(OH)_2 \cdot SO_2\}$ is hexagonal with *c*/*a* = 0.7135. Crystals prismatic. D 1.44. M.P. 170°. Uniaxial positive with N_O = 1.629, N_E = 1.655, $N_E - N_O$ = 0.026. Ref: 568a.

Hydroquinone acetonitrile complex $\{3C_6H_4(OH)_2 \cdot CH_3CN\}$ is hexagonal with *c*/*a* = 0.7779. Crystals prismatic. D 1.33. M.P. 170°. Uniaxial positive with N_O = 1.606, N_E = 1.666, $N_E - N_O$ = 0.060. Ref: 568a.

Quinol hydrochloride $[3C_6H_4(OH)_2 \cdot HCl]$ is rhombohedral with *a* 16.58, *c* 5.47 Å. D 1.38. Uniaxial negative with N_O = 1.632, N_E = 1.623, $N_O - N_E$ = 0.009. Ref: 565a.

Quinol hydrogen sulfide $[3C_6H_4(OH)_2 \cdot H_2S]$ is rhombohedral with *a* 16.61, *c* 5.50 Å. D 1.34. Uniaxial negative with N_O = 1.651, N_E = 1.635, $N_O - N_E$ = 0.016. Ref: 565a.

Quinol acetylene $[3C_6H_4(OH)_2 \cdot C_2H_2]$ is rhombohedral with *a* 16.66, *c* 5.47 Å. D 1.31. Uniaxial negative with N_O = 1.632, N_E = 1.612, $N_O - N_E$ = 0.02. Ref: 565a.

Quinol methyl cyanide $[3C_6H_4(OH)_2 \cdot CH_3CN]$ is trigonal pyramidal with *a* 15.98, *c* 6.25 Å. D 1.33. Uniaxial positive with N_O = 1.606, N_E = 1.666, $N_E - N_O$ = 0.060. Ref: 565a.

Quinol hydrochloride sulfur dioxide $[3C_6H_4(OH)_2 \cdot HCl \cdot SO_2]$ is rhombohedral. Crystals hexagonal prisms. Uniaxial negative with N_O = 1.630, N_E = 1.629, $N_O - N_E$ = 0.001. Color yellow. Ref: 565a.

Allobetulin $[C_{30}H_{48}(OH_2)]$ is triclinic pedial with $a:b:c = 0.607:1:1.0375$, $\alpha = 90°11'$, $\beta = 95°6'$, $\gamma = 90°7'$. Crystals of varied habit, often triangular in aspect, with {010}, $\{\bar{1}\bar{1}0\}$, $\{1\bar{1}0\}$, $\{1\bar{2}0\}$, {001}, $\{00\bar{1}\}$, etc. Extinction (Z′) in 001 is at 4° to 010 and 35° to $1\bar{1}0$ and 27° to $\bar{1}\bar{1}0$. An optic axis at 6.5° to the normal to 001. $N_Y = 1.56$. Optic sign positive. Ref: 230.

Betulin diacetate $[C_{30}H_{48}(O_2C \cdot CH_3)_2]$ is orthorhombic disphenoidal with $a:b:c = 0.992:1:0.798$. Crystals short prismatic with {110}, {111}, (sphenoid), {010}, {001}, etc. The optic plane is 100; Z = *b*. (+)2V = ?., $N_X = 1.59$. Ref: 230.

1,2-Diacetoxy-1,2-diphenylethylene or α,α′-stilbenediol diacetate or α,α′-diacetoxy stilbene $[C_6H_5 \cdot C(O \cdot C_2H_3O):C(O \cdot C_2H_3O) \cdot C_6H_5]$ is monoclinic with $a:b:c = 2.828:1:3.242$, $\beta = 93°4'$. Crystals show {100}, $\{10\bar{1}\}$, {110}. {001}, {120}, etc. Figs 55, 56. Twinning on 001. Perfect 001 and distinct 010 cleavages. M.P. 118°. Z = *b*. $X \wedge c = +13°$, r < v. (-)2V = 81°39′ Na. $N_X = 1.551$, $N_Y = 1.617$, $N_Z = 1.719$, $N_Z - N_X = 0.168$ Na. Ref: 119.

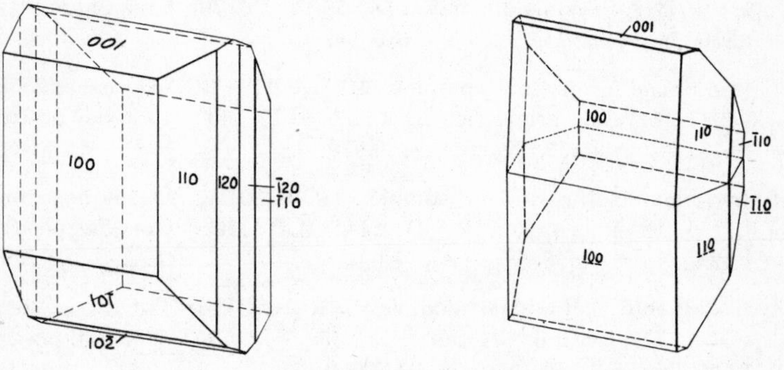

Figs. 55, 56. Diacetoxystilbene.

2,2-*bis*(4-Methoxyphenyl)propane $[(CH_3OC_6H_4)_2:C:(CH_3)_2]$ is orthorhombic with $a:b:c = 0.850:1:0.764$. Crystals show {110}, {101}, {010}, etc. D 1.15. M.P. 60.5°. (-)2V = 89°54.5′ Na. $N_Y = 1.6494$ Na. Ref: 119.

1,2,3-Trihydroxybenzene or pyrogallol $[C_6H_3(OH)_3]$ is triclinic (?). Crystals said to be pyrogallol gave angles: 110: $\bar{1}10$ = 84°0′, 110:001 = 54°40′, 110:010 = 20°0′, $1\bar{1}0$:001 = 84°0′. Cleavage on 001 and apparently on $1\bar{1}0$. Parallel extinction and positive elongation with $N_1 = 1.49$, $N_2 = 1.72$, $N_2 - N_1 = 0.23$. Also $N_1 = 1.502$, $N_2 = 1.710$ Ref: 34, 35, 119, 343c.

3,4,5-Tribromo-2,6-dimethoxyphenol or 4,5,6-tribromopyrogallol 1,3-dimethyl ether or 3,4,5-tribromo-1-hydroxy-2,6-dimethoxybenzene $[C_6Br_3(OCH_3)_2OH]$ is monoclinic with $a:b:c = 0.934:1:1.583$, $\beta = 94°13'$. Crystals {101} tablets elongated along *b*. D 2.293. The optic plane is 010. 2V = 48°. $N_X = 1.652$, $N_Y = 1.79$ *ca.*, N_Z = ? $N_Z - N_X$ = extreme. Ref: 145.

1,2,3-Trihydroxy-5-nitrobenzene hemihydrate or 5-nitrogallol hemihydrate [$C_6H_2(NO_2)(OH)_3 \cdot 0.5H_2O$] is monoclinic with $a:b:c = 0.394:1:0.180$, $\beta = 96°55'$. Crystals show {110}, {010}, {011}, {001}, etc. M.P. 195° (dec. 205°) (Barth). X nearly = c, so elongation is negative. (-)2V = small. $N_X = 1.3918$ red, 1.4048 Na, 1.4189 blue, $N_Y = 1.6380$ red, 1.6499 Na, 1.7078 blue (so N_Z must be only a little greater than 1.6499 Na, etc. – A.N.W.). $N_Z - N_X > 0.2451$ Na.
Ref: 145.

1,3,5-Trihydroxybenzene or phloroglucinol {$C_6H_3(OH)_3$} is orthorhombic with $a:b:c = 0.825:1:3.417$. Crystal columnar. M.P. 217°. Perfect 001 cleavage. X = a, Y = b. (+)2V = 65°, r < v weak. $N_X = 1.557$, $N_Y = 1.617$, $N_Z = 1.796$, $N_Z - N_X = 0.239$. Ref: 418a.

1,3,5-Trihydroxybenzene dihydrate or phloroglucinol dihydrate {$C_6H_5(OH)_3 \cdot 2H_2O$} is orthorhombic dipyramidal with $a:b:c = 0.838:1:1.691$. Space group *Pnnm*; a 6.79, b 8.10, c 13.70 Å. U.C. 4. Crystals {001} or {100} plates with {110} and {201}, elongated along b. Perfect 100 cleavage. D 1.39. M.P. 217°; 219°. The optic plane is 001; X = a. (-)2E = 62°58′ Li, 63°49′ Na, 64°34′ Tl. 2V = 36°26′ Na, calc. $N_X = 1.41$, $N_Y = 1.69$, $N_Z = 1.72$, $N_Z - N_X = 0.31$. Again (for a different phase?) for $\lambda = 546$: $N_X = 1.499$, $N_Y = 1.689$, $N_Z = 1.692$, $N_Z - N_X = 0.193$; for $\lambda = 589$: $N_X = 1.481$, $N_Y = 1.648$, $N_Z = 1.659$, $N_Z - N_X = 0.178$, ∴ (-)2V = 20° *ca.* and for $\lambda = 656$: $N_X = 1.464$, $N_Y = 1.607$, $N_Z = 1.629$, $N_Z - N_X = 0.165$, ∴ (-)2V = 40° *ca.* Color honey yellow with X = almost colorless, Y = brownish yellow, Z = clear yellow. When heated in air the crystals begin to lose water at 50° and X and Z exchange places.
Ref: 103, 413, 443b.

1,2,4-Trimethoxy-5-(1-propenyl)benzene or asaron [$C_6H_2(CH:CHCH_3)(OCH_3)_3$] is monoclinic with $a:b:c = 1.873:1:0.998$, $\beta = 106°13'$. Crystals show {110}, {010}, {100}, {001}, etc. M.P. 59° (67°?). D 1.165. Perfect 100 (?) cleavage. The optic plane is 010; the acute bisectrix makes an angle of -18° with c. $N_1 = 1.515$, $N_2 = 1.74$, $N_2 - N_1 = 0.225$. Ref: 34, 35, 118.

Amyrolin or sesquiterpene alcohol ($C_{14}H_{12}O_3$) is monoclinic with $a:b:c = 0.758:1:1.111$, $\beta = 103°5'$. Crystals equant or {100} tablets with {110}, {010}, {111}, {011}, etc. Imperfect 010 cleavage. H 1. D 1.35. M.P. 124°. The optic plane is 010; X ∧ c = -57°. (-)2V = 68°1′ D, 70°6′ (436). $N_X = 1.4589$ (691), 1.4645 D, 1.4778 (436); $N_Y = 1.7323$ (691), 1.7480 D, 1.8164 (436); $N_Z = 1.9138$ (691), 1.9458 D, 2.0986 (436); $N_Z - N_X = 0.4813$ D. Ref: 283.

bis(*p*-Methoxyphenyl)phenetylguanidine hydrochloride or di-*p*-anisyl phenetylguanidine hydrochloride ($C_{23}H_{25}O_3N_3 \cdot HCl$) is granular and acicular. M.P. 176°. Easily soluble in water or alcohol. $N_1 = 1.587$, $N_2 > 1.74$, $N_2 - N_1 > 0.153$.
Ref: 239.

1,2,3,5-Cyclohexanetetrol-5-carbonate ($C_7H_{12}O_6$) is monoclinic domatic with $a:b:c = 0.604:1:0.600$, $\beta = 131°25'$. Crystals basal plates with {110}, {010}, etc. M.P. 174°. The optic plane is 010; Z ∧ c = - 6°. (-)2V = 74.5°. $N_1 = 1.55$, $N_2 = 1.56$, $N_2 - N_1 = 0.01$. Ref: 35.

1,2,3,4-Tetramethoxybenzene or tetramethylapionol [$C_6H_2(OCH_3)_4$] is orthorhombic with $a:b:c = 0.945:1:1.076$. Crystals short domatic with {201}, {101}, {001}, {021}, {110}, etc. M.P. 89°. Glide planes are 110, on which pressure produces twinning. The optic plane is 100; Z = *c*. (+)2V = 49°13′. N_Y = 1.5439 Na. Ref: 118.

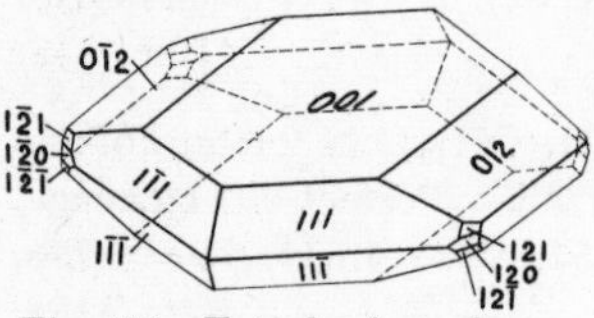

Fig. 57. Tetrahydroxybenzohydrol ethyl ether.

2,6,2′,5′-Tetrahydroxybenzohydrol ethyl ether [$C_6H_3(OH)_2CH(OC_2H_5)C_6H_3(OH)_2$(?)] is orthorhombic with $a:b:c = 0.596:1:0.709$. Crystals {001} tablets with {012}, {111}, {010}, {120}, etc. Fig. 57. D 1.26. M.P. 125°. The optic plane is 100; the acute bisectrix is parallel with *b*. 2V=79°11′. N_Y = 1.627 Na. Ref: 119.

l-1,2,3,4,5,6-Cyclohexanehexol or *l*-inositol {$C_6H_6(OH)_6$} is monoclinic with $a:b:c = 0.677:1:0.749$, $\beta = 106°36'$. Space group $P2_1$(?). *a* 6.17, *b* 9.11, *c* 6.83 Å. U.C. 2. Crystals colorless plates normal to X. D 1.567. M.P. 238° (Tanret); 242° (Clark); 253° (Cook). (–)2V = not large. N_X = 1.553 *ca.* N_Y = 1.562, N_Z = 1.566, $N_Z - N_X$ = 0.013 *ca.* Again: Y = *b*; Z ∧ *c* = 14°. (–)2V = 50°, N_X = 1.527, N_Y = 1.560 N_Z = 1.567, $N_Z - N_X$ = 0.040 (Cook).
Ref: 179, 436b, 617.

l-1,2,3,4,5,6-Cyclohexanehexol dihydrate or inositol dihydrate {$C_6H_6(OH)_6 \cdot 2H_2O$} is monoclinic in {010} plates with {110}, {101}, {023} and $\beta = 110°$. D 1.525. X ∧ *c* = 18°, Z = *b*. (+)2V = 34°, N_X = 1.522, N_Y = 1.526, N_Z = 1.564, $N_Z - N_X$ = 0.042. Ref: 436b.

l-Methoxycyclohexanepentol or quebrachitol or *l*-methylinositol [$C_6H_6(OH)_5(OCH_3)$] is monoclinic sphenoidal with $a:b:c = 0.923:1:1.21$, $\beta = 90°$ *ca.* Space group $P2_1$(?); *a* 6.60, *b* 7.15, *c* 8.65 Å. U.C. 2. It is in colorless rhombs and six-sided forms which melt at 192° - 193°. Z normal to plates. (+)2V = 70° calc. N_X = 1.546, N_Y = 1.552, N_Z = 1.572, all ± .003, $N_Z - N_X$ = 0.026.
Ref: 179, 566.

Benzenehexamethanol hexaacetate or hexa(acetoxymethyl)benzene [$C_6(CH_2O_2CCH_3)_6$] is monoclinic with $a:b:c = 1.956:1:?$, $\beta = 109°37'$. Crystals {001} plates with {110} and {100}. M.P. 163°. The optic plane is 010; one optic axis is nearly normal to 001. (+)2V = 70° calc. N_X = 1.5258 (Hg yellow), 1.5285 (Hg green), 1.543 (Hg blue); N_Y = 1.543 (Hg yellow), 1.545 (Hg green); N_Z = 1.5648 (Hg yellow), 1.5678 (Hg green), 1.586 (Hg blue); $N_Z - N_X$ = 0.0390 (Hg yellow). Ref: 12.

Hexa(methylmercaptomethyl)benzene [$C_6(CH_2SCH_3)_6$] is rhombohedral with $c/a = 0.321$. Crystals short prisms with an obtuse rhombohedron. M.P. 220° - 222°. Uniaxial negative with N_O = 1.826 (Hg green), N_E = 1.701, $N_O - N_E$ = 0.125. Ref: 13.

Class 3. Carbonyl compounds.

l-2-Isopropyl-5-methylcyclohexanone semicarbazone or 3-*p*-menthanone semicarbazone or *l*-menthone semicarbazone $[CH_3[(CH_3)_2CH]C_6H_8:N\cdot NH\cdot CONH_2]$ melts at 184°. It is biaxial (?) with $N_X = 1.528$, $N_Y = ?$, $N_Z = 1.590$, $N_Z - N_X = 0.062$. Ref: 378.

2,2,3,4,5,5,6,6,-Octachloro-3-cyclohexen-1-one or *β*-octachlorocyclohexenone (C_6Cl_8O) is orthorhombic with $a:b:c = 0.262:1:0.156$. Crystals short prismatic with {110}, {010}, {100}, {141}, etc. Perfect 010 and distinct 001 cleavages. D = 2.02. M.P. 90°. The optic plane is 010; Z = *a*. $N_X = 1.626$, $N_Y = 1.646$, $N_Z = 1.712$, $N_Z - N_X = 0.086$. ∴ (+)2V = 58° *ca.* Ref: 117.

2,2,3,4,5,5,6,6-Octachloro-3-cyclohexen-2-one or *γ*-octachlorocyclohexenone (C_6Cl_8O) is monoclinic with $a:b:c = 0.900:1:1.206$, $\beta = 123°26'$. Crystals with {110}, {010}, {100}, {120}, {001}, etc. D 2.06. M.P. 88° - 89°. The optic plane is 010; $X \wedge c = -93°$ *ca.* (-)2V = 37°38'. $N_X = 1.619$, $N_Y = 1.688$, $N_Z = 1.696$, $N_Z - N_X = 0.077$. Ref: 117.

β-1-Isopropyl-4-methylbicyclo(3.1.0)hexan-3-one semicarbazone or *β*-thujone semicarbazone or tanacetone semicarbazone ($C_{10}H_{16}:N\cdot NH\cdot CONH_2$) melts at 170°. It is biaxial (?) with $N_X = 1.5200$, $N_Y = ?$, $N_Z = 1.590$, $N_Z - N_X = 0.070$. Ref: 378.

Matico camphor ($C_{12}H_{20}O$) is hexagonal with $c/a = 0.5475$. Crystals prismatic. Uniaxial negative with $N_O = 1.5447$, $N_E = 1.5436$, $N_O - N_E = 0.0011$ Ref: 467, 568a.

d-3-Bromo-1,7,7-trimethylbicyclo-(2.2.1)heptan-2-one or *d*-*α*-bromocamphor ($C_{10}H_{15}OBr$) is orthorhombic with $a:b:c = 0.739:1:0.469$. Crystals short prismatic with {010}, {110}, {101}; no cleavage observed. D 1.484. M.P. 78°. The optic plane is 001; X = *a*. (-)2V = 69°10′ Na. $N_X = 1.5535$, $N_Y = 1.5787$, $N_Z = 1.5912$, $N_Z - N_X = 0.0377$ Na. Ref: 228.

d-3,3-Dibromo-1,7,7-trimethylbicyclo-(2.2.1)heptan-2-one or *d*-*α*,*α*-dibromocamphor ($C_{10}H_{14}OBr_2$) is orthorhombic disphenoidal with $a:b:c = 0.649:1:1.262$. Crystals short brachydomatic with {001}, {011}, {101}, {110}, etc. M.P. 61°. The optic plane is 100; X = *b*. (-)2V = 56°5′, r > v. $N_Y = 1.512$ Na. Ref: 117.

d-5-Isopropenyl-2-methyl-2-cyclohexen-1-one semicarbazone or △ - 6,8 (9)-*p*-menthadien-2-one semicarbazone, or *d*-carvone semicarbazone ($C_{11}H_{17}N_3O$) melts at 143°. (-)2V = 66° calc. $N_X = 1.490$, $N_Y = 1.645$, $N_Z = 1.710$, $N_Z - N_X = 0.220$. Ref: 378.

Benzaldehyde semicarbazone ($C_6H_5\cdot CH:N\cdot NHCONH_2$) melts at 217°. It is biaxial (?) with $N_X = 1.560$, $N_Y = 1.685$, $N_Z = ?$ Ref: 378.

o-Nitrobenzaldehyde ($C_6H_4NO_2CHO$) crystallizes from alcohol and benzene in greenish blades with indefinite ends. M.P. 114°. X parallel to elongation. (-?)2V = ?, $N_X = 1.511$, $N_2 > 1.74$. Ref: 444.

m-Nitrobenzaldehyde ($C_6H_4NO_2CHO$) is orthorhombic (?). Crystals very small needles or tablets. M.P. 58°. Optic plane parallel to elongation. (+)2V = ?, $N_1 = 1.495$, $N_2 = 1.74$. Colorless. Ref: 444.

p-Nitrobenzaldehyde ($C_6H_4NO_2CHO$) is orthorhombic pyramidal (?). Crystals acicular or tabular with unlike ends. Very strong rhombic dispersion so that the optic plane for red is at right angles to that for green and blue. (+)2V varying through 0°. $N_1 = 1.70$, $N_2 = 1.71$. Interference colors are abnormal yellows, blues, and purples. Ref: 444.

m-Nitrobenzylidene diacetate, 3-nitro-α,α-toluenediol diacetate, or 3-nitrobenzal diacetate [$NO_2C_6H_4CH(O_2C \cdot CH_3)_2$] is monoclinic with $a:b:c = 0.880:1:0.957$, $\beta = 116°56'$. Crystals prismatic with {110}, {001}, {011}, {111}. Good 110 cleavage. D 1.393. M.P. 67°. The optic plane is 010; an optic axis is nearly normal to 001 and X is in the obtuse angle β. (−)2V = 70° *ca.* calc. $N_X = 1.457$, $N_Y = 1.576$, $N_Z = 1.635$, $N_Z - N_X = 0.178$ D. Ref: 225.

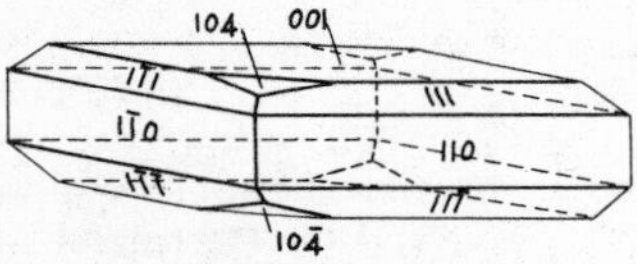

Fig. 58. Hexachloro-2-ketotetrahydronaphthalene.

Methyl *p*-tolyl ketone semicarbazone or *p*-methylacetophenone semicarbazone [$CH_3 \cdot C_6H_4 \cdot C(CH_3):[N \cdot NH(CO) \cdot NH_2] \cdot CH_3$] melts at 210°. $N_X = 1.445$, $N_Y = ?$, $N_Z = 1.645$, $N_Z - N_X = 0.200$. Ref: 378.

4-Phenyl-3-buten-2-one semicarbazone or benzylideneacetone semicarbazone [$CH_3 \cdot C:[N \cdot NH(CO)NH_2] \cdot CH:CH \cdot C_6H_5$] melts at 186°. (−)2V = 80° calc. $N_X = 1.450$, $N_Y = 1.618$, $N_Z > 1.736$, $N_Z - N_X > 0.286$. Ref: 378.

1,3-Diphenyl-2-propene-1-one semicarbazone or chalcone semicarbazone or α-benzylideneacetophenone semicarbazone or phenylstyrylketone semicarbazone [$C_6H_5 \cdot CH:CH \cdot C(C_6H_5):NNH \cdot CONH_2$] is probably orthorhombic. Six-sided {100} prisms lying on 010 have parallel extinction and negative elongation. For vibrations parallel to elongation (= *c*) $N_1 = 1.66$; for vibrations normal to elongation (= *a*) $N_2 = 1.75$; $N_2 - N_1 = 0.09$. Pleochroic with *a* = greenish yellow, *c* = colorless. The γ-form (M.P. 179 – 180°) is colorless. Ref: 132.

1,1,3,3,4,4-Hexachloro-3,4-dihydro-2(1)-naphthalenone or 1,1,3,3,4,4-hexachloro-2-keto-1,2,3,4-tetrahydronaphthalene [$CO \cdot CCl_2 \cdot C_6H_4 \cdot CCl_2 \cdot CCl_2$] is orthorhombic with $a:b:c = 0.493:1:0.683$. Crystals {001} tablets with {110}, {111}, etc; also prismatic. Fig. 58. No observed cleavage. M.P. 129°. The optic plane is 100; X = *c*. Birefringence negative for red, positive for yellow and green. 2V over X = 89°16′ Li, 91°6′ Na, 92°16′ Tl. $N_X = 1.6320$ Li, 1.6375 Na, 1.6429 Tl; $N_Y = 1.6395$ Li, 1.6430 Na, 1.6465 Tl; $N_Z = 1.6468$ Li, 1.6490 Na, 1.6504 Tl; $N_Z - N_X = 0.0115$ Na. Ref: 119.

1,1,4-Trichloro-2(1)-naphthalenone or 1,1,4-trichloro-1,2-dihydro-2-keto-naphthalene [$CO \cdot CCl_2 \cdot C_6H_4 \cdot CCl:CH$] is orthorhombic with $a:b:c = 0.490:1:3.006$. Crystals {001} tablets elongated parallel to *a* with {011}, {110}, {010}.

Fig. 59. No distinct cleavage. M.P. 86° - 87°. The optic plane is 100; Z = *c*. (+)2V = 57°6′ Na. N_Y = 1.5617 Na, $N_Z - N_X$ = rather strong. 2E = 96°30′ Li, 93°34′ Na, 89°24′ Tl. Ref: 119.

4-4′-Dichlorobenzophenone ($C_{13}H_8OCl_2$) is monoclinic with *a*:*b*:*c* = 1.237:1:4.039, β = 95°20′. *a* 7.72, *b* 6.17, *c* 24.92 Å. U.C. 4. Crystals {100} tablets long ‖ *b*. Y = *b*, Z ∧ *c* = 8° in obtuse β. (-)2V = 83°, calc. For λ = 578; N_X = 1.498, N_Y = 1.724, N_Z = 1.897, $N_Z - N_X$ = 0.399. Ref: 605b.

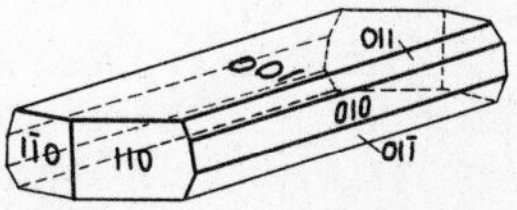

Fig. 59. Trichloro-1,2-dihydro-2-ketonapthalene.

p-Methylbenzophenone or phenyl *p*-tolyl ketone [$C_6H_5 \cdot CO \cdot C_6H_4(CH_3)$] has two phases. The stable phase is monoclinic with *a*:*b*:*c* = 1.012:1:0.412, β = 95°7′. Crystals {010} tablets or equant with {110}, {210}, {100}, {011}, {001}, etc. Figs. 60, 61. No distinct cleavage. M.P. 60°. The optic plane is 010 for red to green and normal thereto for blue and violet. X ∧ *c* = +37°. (-)2E = 49°11′ Li, 35°15′ Na, 6°55′ Tl, 49°32′ blue. The matastable phase is ditrigonal pyramidal with *c*/*a* = 1.225. Crystals show both trigonal prisms, {10$\bar{1}$0} and {1$\bar{1}$00}, etc. Fig. 62. M.P. 55°. Uniaxial negative with N_O = 1.7067 Li, 1.7170 Na, 1.7250 Tl; N_E = 1.5564 Li, 1.5629 Na, 1.5685 Tl; $N_O - N_E$ = 0.1541 Na. Ref: 119.

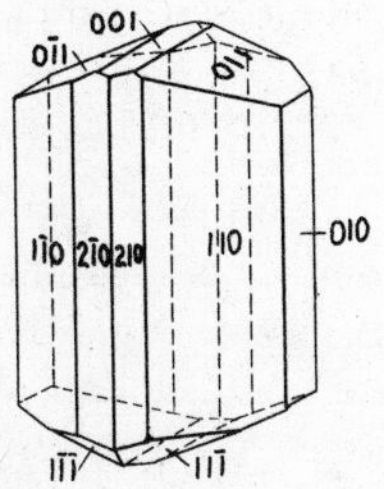

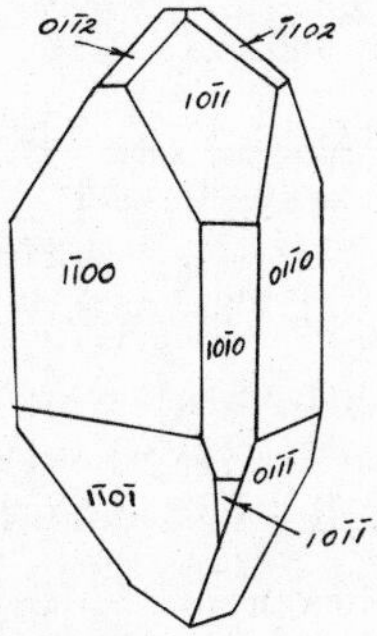

Figs. 60, 61. Phenyl-β-tolyl ketone.

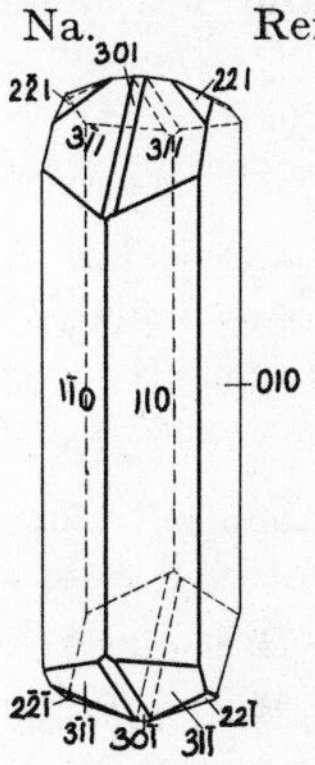

Fig. 62. Anthraquinone.

3-Phenyl-1-*p*-tolyl-2-propen-1-one or α-benzylidene 4-methyl acetophenone or 3′-methylchalcone or *m*-tolylstyrylketone [$C_6H_5 \cdot CH:CH \cdot CO \cdot C_6H_4(CH_3)$] is orthorhombic with *a*:*b*:*c* = 0.617:1:0.379. Crystals {010} tablets with vertical elongation and {110}, {001}, {100}, {211}. M.P. 77°. The optic plane is 001; Z = *b*. (+)2V = 40°31′ Li, 36°4′ Na, 32°12′ Tl. N_X = 1.6075 Li, 1.6206 Na, 1.6346 Tl; N_Y = 1.6341 Li, 1.6427 Na, 1.6529 Tl; N_Z = 1.8806 Li, 1.9087 Na, 1.9340 Tl; $N_Z - N_X$ = 0.2881 Na. (Int. Crit. Tables give N_Z = 1.648; typographical error?) Ref: 119, 152.

Cupric salt of 1-phenyl-1,3-butanedione, or copper benzoylacetonate ($C_{19}H_{18} \cdot O_4Cu$) is monoclinic prismatic with *a*:*b*:*c* = 1.742:1:0.424, β = 96°38′. Space group $P2_1/n$; *a* 18.19, *b* 10.44, *c* 4.43 Å. U.C. 2. Crystals long prisms with {100} and {110}. D 1.53. X ∧ ⊥ 001 = 21°. N_X = 1.57, N_Y = ?, N_Z > 1.78, $N_Z - N_X$ > 0.21. Ref: 64.

1,3-Indandione or 1,3-diketohydrindene [$C_6H_4(CO)_2CH_2$] is tetragonal with $c/a = 0.941$. Crystals prismatic with {100}, {101}, {121}, etc. D 1.37. Uniaxial positive with $N_O = 1.614$ (649), 1.620 (589), 1.650 (458); $N_E = ?$; $N_E - N_O =$ strong. Ref: 272.

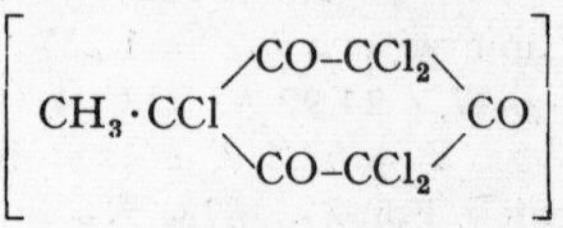

2,2,4,4,6-Pentachloro-6-methyl-1,3,5-cyclohex-anetrione is orthorhombic with $a:b:c = 0.949$: 1 : 0.577. Crystals {001} tablets with {110}, {111}, {011}, {010}. Good 001 cleavage. M.P. 50°.

$$CH_3 \cdot CCl \begin{array}{c} \diagup CO\text{-}CCl_2 \diagdown \\ CO \\ \diagdown CO\text{-}CCl_2 \diagup \end{array}$$

The optic plane is 100; Z = c. (+)2E = 45° *ca*. Parallel extinction and positive elongation with $N_1 = 1.57$, $N_2 = 1.68$, $N_2 - N_1 = 0.11$. (These indices are probably N_X and N_Y, but in that case N_Z must be extremely high. – A.N.W.) Ref: 34, 35, 117.

2-Nitro-1,3-diketohydrindene or 2-nitroindandion-1,3 ($C_9H_5O_4N$) is monoclinic with Y ∧ elongation = 10°. M.P. 128°. (–)2V = very large, with strong dispersion. $N_X = 1.678$, $N_Y = 1.770$ (?) $N_Z \gg 1.870$, $N_Z - N_X \gg 0.192$. Ref: 539a.

Glycine nitroindandionate ($C_{11}H_{10}O_6N_2$) is monoclinic in rods and needles with Z ∧ elongation = 10°. M.P. 224°. (+)2V = very large, r < v. $N_X = 1.636$, $N_Y = 1.717$, $N_Z > 1.870$, $N_Z - N_X > 0.254$. (From (+)2V, N_Y and N_X, N_Z is near 1.87 – A.N.W.). Color yellow. Ref: 539a.

dl-Alanine nitroindandionate ($C_{12}H_{12}O_6N_2$) is monoclinic. Crystals are parallelogram plates with Z ∧ elongation = 40°. M.P. 226°. (–)2V = very large, r < v. $N_X = 1.478$, $N_Y = 1.738$, $N_Z > 1.870$, $N_Z - N_X > 0.392$. (From (–)2V, N_Y and N_X, N_Z must be < 1.998 – A.N.W.). Ref: 539a.

d-Valine nitroindandionate ($C_{14}H_{16}O_6N_2$) is orthorhombic in rectangular plates with Z || elongation. M.P. 217°. (–)2V = very large, r < v. $N_X = 1.467$, $N_Y = 1.678$, $N_Z \gg 1.870$, $N_Z - N_X \gg 0.303$. Colorless. Ref: 539a.

d-Lysine dinitroindandionate hexahydrate ($C_{24}H_{24}O_{10}N_4 \cdot 6H_2O$) is ortho-rhombic in prisms and tablets with Z || elongation. M.P. 169°. (+)2V = 10°, calc., r > v. $N_X = 1.517$, $N_Y = 1.552$, $N_Z = 1.781$, $N_Z - N_X = 0.264$. Ref: 539a.

l-Leucine nitroindandionate ($C_{15}H_{18}O_6N_2$) is orthorhombic in rectangular plates with X || elongation. M.P. 190°. (–)2V = large, r > v. $N_X = 1.449$, $N_Y = 1.645$, $N_Z = 1.758$, $N_Z - N_X = 0.309$. (–)2V = 75° calc. Color yellow. Ref: 539a.

d-Isoleucine nitroindandionate ($C_{15}H_{18}O_6N_2$) is orthorhombic in needles with X || elongation. M.P. 198°. (–)2V = 75° calc. $N_X = 1.450$, $N_Y = 1.652$, $N_Z = 1.771$, $N_Z - N_X = 0.321$. Color yellow. Ref: 539a.

l-Aspartic acid nitroindandionate ($C_{13}H_{12}O_8N_2$) is orthorhombic. Crystals are needles and with Y || elongation. M.P. 224°. (+)2V = large, r > v. $N_X = 1.631$, $N_Y = 1.683$, $N_Z > 1.870$, $N_Z - N_X > 0.239$ (From (+)2V, N_Y and N_X, N_Z is near 1.87 – A.N.W.). Color yellow. Ref: 539a.

d-Glutamic acid nitroindandionate ($C_{14}H_{14}O_8N_2$) is orthorhombic in rectangular plates with X || elongation. M.P. 214°. (–)2V = large, r < v. $N_X = 1.449$, $N_Y = 1.689$, $N_Z > 1.870$, $N_Z - N_X > 0.421$. Color yellow.   Ref: 539a.

dl-Serine nitroindandionate ($C_{12}H_{12}O_7N_2$) is monoclinic in rods and needles with Z ∧ elongation = 5°. M.P. 170°. (+)2V = very large (82° calc.) r > v. $N_X = 1.705$, $N_Z = 1.802$, $N_Z - N_X = 0.176$. Color yellow.   Ref: 539a.

l-Cysteine nitroindandionate monohydrate ($C_{12}H_{12}O_6N_2S \cdot H_2O$) is orthorhombic. Crystals are rectangular tablets with Z || elongation. M.P. 152°. (–)2V = large, r < v. $N_X = 1.513$, $N_Y = 1.748$, $N_Z > 1.870$, $N_Z - N_X > 0.357$.   Ref: 539a.

d-Methionine nitroindandionate ($C_{14}H_{16}O_6N_2S$) is orthorhombic, in needles and thin plates with Z || elongation. M.P. 193°. (+)2V = ? r < v. $N_X = 1.622$, $N_Y = 1.667$, $N_Z = ?$, $N_Z - N_X = ?$ Ref: 539a.

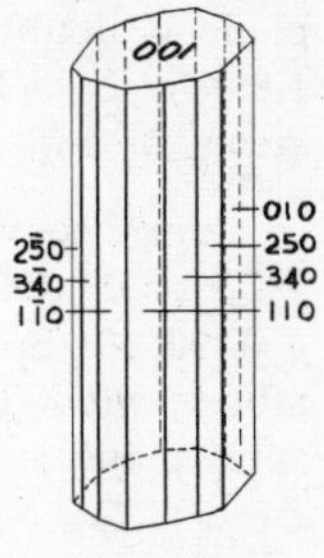

Fig. 63.
Anthraquinone.

Beryllium 3-benzoyl trimethylbicyclo(2.2.1)heptan-2-one or 3-benzoylcamphor beryllate $[[H_2C \cdot CH_2 \cdot CH \cdot C(CH_3)_2 \cdot C(CH_3) \cdot CO \cdot CH \cdot CO \cdot C_6H_5]_2Be]$ is tetragonal with $c/a = 1.732$. Crystals show {001}, {301}, {101}, etc. D 1.176. Uniaxial negative with $N_O = 1.66$, $N_E = 1.61$, $N_O - N_E = 0.05$. Ref: 46.

1,2-Diphenylethanedione or benzil ($C_6H_5 \cdot CO \cdot CO \cdot C_6H_5$) is trigonal trapezohedral with $c/a = 1.632$. Space group $C3_12$. a 8.15, c 13.46 Å. U.C. 3. Crystals prismatic. Perfect 0001 cleavage. D 1.23. M.P. 95°. Uniaxial positive with birefringence decreasing to zero at $\lambda = 4205$:

$\lambda = 6560$ (C)	5893 (D)	5780	5461	4860 (F)	4380	4205
$N_O = 1.648$	1.658	1.660	1.667	1.682	1.712	1.737
$N_E = 1.672$	1.679	1.680	1.684	1.695	1.718	1.737
$N_E - N_O = 0.024$	0.021	0.020	0.017	0.013	0.006	0.000

Benzil may show optic anomalies. Thermal expansion along c 9.5 times, and along a 5 times that of platinum. No piezoelectric properties. A plate 1 mm. thick rotates the plane of polarization 25° (Na).   Ref: 119, 415, 425.

1,5-Diphenyl-1,5-pentanedione dioxime or 1,3-dibenzoylpropane dioxime $[C_6H_5 \cdot C:NOH \cdot (CH_2)_3 \cdot C:NOH \cdot C_6H_5]$ is tetragonal with $c/a = 0.848$. Crystals {001} tablets with {101}. M.P. 165° – 166°. Uniaxial negative with $N_O = 1.698$ Na, $N_E = 1.597$, $N_O - N_E = 0.101$.   Ref: 289.

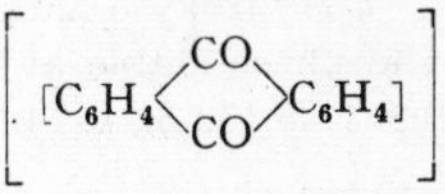

Anthraquinone is dimorphous; one phase (I) is orthorhombic dipyramidal with $a:b:c = 0.801:1:0.161$. Space group $Pmmn$; a 19.7, b 24.6, c 3.95 Å. U.C. 8. Crystals short prismatic. Figs. 62, 63. Poor 100 and 001 cleavages. D 1.43. M.P. 273°. The optic plane is 100; X = c. (+)2V = small, $\left[C_6H_4 {\Large \langle} {}^{CO}_{CO} {\Large \rangle} C_6H_4 \right]$

$N_X' = 1.57$, $N_Y = 1.75$, $N_Z' = 1.9$ *ca*, $N_Z' - N_X' = 0.3$ *ca*. Absorption X > Z. Colorless. The natural substance has been called *hoelite*. A second phase (II) is monoclinic with $a:b:c = 3.982:1:1.990$, $\beta = 102°43'$. *a* 15.85, *b* 3.98, *c* 7.92. For $\lambda = 589$, $N_X = 1.506$, $N_Y = 1.698$, $N_Z = 1.816$, $N_Z - N_X = 0.310$, ∴(-)2V = 75°. Ref: 119, 264, 443b, 477, 590.

2,4-Dioximino-5-cyclohexene-1,3-dione monohydrate or 5-cyclohexene-1,2,3,4-tetrone 1,3-dioxime monohydrate or 2.4-dinitrosoresorcinol monohydrate [$C_6H_2O_2(NOH)_2 \cdot H_2O$] is orthorhombic with $a:b:c = 0.9(?):1:0.613$. Crystals thin rhombic plates. Perfect 001 cleavage. Explodes at 162° - 163°. The optic plane is doubtless 100: X = *c*. (-)2V = small (?). $N_X = 1.44$, $N_Y = ?$, $N_Z = 1.89(?)$, $N_Z - N_X = 0.45(?)$. Strongly pleochroic with X = pale yellow or green, Y and Z = tobacco brown. Ref: 108.

Cupric salt of 2-hydroxybenzaldehyde oxime or copper disalicylaldoxime [$[C_6H_4(OH)CH:NO]_2Cu$] is monoclinic prismatic with $a:b:c = 4.602:1:1.310$, $\beta = 98°13'$. Space group $P2_1/n$; *a* 27.61, *b* 6.00, *c* 7.86 Å. U.C. 4. Crystals {100} tablets with {011}, {111}, and {11$\bar{1}$} formed from chloroform. D 1.72. The optic plane is 010; Z nearly normal to 100. (+)2V = near 90°. $N_X = 1.55$, $N_Y = 1.73$, $N_Z > 1.91$, $N_Z - N_X > 0.36$. Ref: 64.

Anisaldazine or dianisalhydrazine ($C_{16}H_{16}O_2N_2$) in liquid crystals at 165° has $N_O = 1.539$, $N_E = 1.840$, $N_E - N_O = 0.301$. Color yellow. Ref: 566a.

4-Methoxybenzaldehyde semicarbazone or anisaldehyde semicarbazone [$CH_3O \cdot C_6H_4 \cdot CH \cdot N \cdot NH(CO)NH_2$] melts at 210°. (+)2V = 86°40'. $N_X = 1.653$, $N_Y = 1.692$, $N_Z > 1.736$, $N_Z - N_X > 0.083$. Ref: 378.

Benzoin [$C_6H_5CH(OH)COC_6H_5$] is monoclinic prismatic with $a:b:c = 3.440:1:1.891$, $\beta = 106°51'$. Space group probably $P2_1a$. *a* 18.75, *b* 5.72, *c* 10.46 Å, $\beta = 105°51'$. U.C. 4. Crystals elongated tabular. M.P. 132°. (+) 2 V = 70° - 80°, $N_Y = 1.695$. Ref: 529, 571.

d-3-Benzoyl-1,7,7-trimethylbicyclo(2.2.1)-2-hepten-2-ol or *d*-hydroxy-benzoylcamphor or 3-benzoylcamphor enol ($C_{17}H_{20}O_2$) is orthorhombic disphenoidal with $a:b:c = 0.973:1:0.655$. Crystals show {100}, {101}, {111}, {110}, etc. M.P. 89°. The optic plane is 100; X = *c*. (-)2V = 60° *ca.*, r < v strong. $N_X = 1.65$, $N_Y = 1.69$, $N_Z = 1.70$, $N_Z - N_X = 0.05$ Na. Strong dispersion produces abnormal interference colors, especially in sections nearly normal to an optic axis. Ref: 118, 337.

2-Ethyl-2-chloro-3-ethoxy-3-phenylhydrindone ($C_{19}H_{19}O_2Cl$) is orthorhombic[1] with $a:b:c = 0.918:1:0.737$. M.P. 186°. Turns yellow in light. (+)2V = 65°30'. $N_X = 1.596$, $N_Y = 1.622$, $N_Z = 1.685$, $N_Z - N_X = 0.086$. Ref: 473a.

4-Hydroxy-3-methoxybenzaldehyde or vanillin has four crystal phases. The phase stable at room temperature is orthorhombic with $a:b:c = 0.964:1:0.561$. *a* 13.53, *b* 14.04, *c* 7.88 Å. U.C. 8. X = *c*, Y = *b*, Z = *a*. (-)2V = 75°

[1] *a b c* changed to *b c a* to make $b > a > c$.

calc., r < v very strong. $N_X = 1.551$, $N_Y = 1.694$, $N_Z = 1.80$, $N_Z - N_X = 0.249$. Another phase is monoclinic with $a:b:c = 1.794:1:3.946$, $\beta = 119°29'$. Crystals {001} tablets with {10$\bar{1}$}, {110}, {11$\bar{2}$}, often twinned on 10$\bar{1}$. Perfect 001 cleavage. M.P. 81°. The optic plane is normal to 010 and nearly normal to 10$\bar{1}$. $N_1 = 1.55$, $N_2 = 1.74$, $N_2 - N_1 = 0.19$. Ref: 239, 553b.

4-Hydroxy-3-methoxy benzaldehyde semicarbazone, or vanillin semicarbazone [$CH_3O \cdot C_6H_3(OH) \cdot CH:N \cdot NH(CO)NH_2$] melts at 230°. It is biaxial (?) with $N_X = 1.692$. Ref: 378.

3-Ethoxy-4-hydroxybenzaldehyde semicarbazone or ethylprotocatechu aldehyde semicarbazone [$C_2H_5O(HO)C_6H_3 \cdot CH:N \cdot NH \cdot CO \cdot NH_2$] melts at 175°. (–)2V = 15° calc. $N_X = 1.445$, $N_Y = ?$, $N_Z = 1.736$, $N_Z - N_X = 0.291$. An intermediate index, 1.690, occurs frequently: is it N_Y? Ref: 378.

2-Hydroxy-3-methyl-1,4-naphthoquinone or phthiocol ($C_{11}H_8O_3$) is monoclinic in prismatic rods with an angle of 78° and $\beta = 118°$. D 1.344. M.P. 106°. $X \wedge c = 23°$, $Y = b$. (–)2V = 36°, $N_X = 1.461$, $N_Y = 1.802$, $N_Z = 1.86$, $N_Z - N_X = 0.399$. Ref: 436b.

Potassium nitranilate or potassium salt of 2,5-dihydroxy-3,6-dinitrobenzoquinone [$C_6(NO_2)_2(OH)_2O_2$] has two phases: one (I) is monoclinic in needles or {100} or {010} plates. Good pyramidal cleavage. The optic plane is 010; $Z \wedge c = 42°$. An optic axis is visible through 100. (–)2V = moderate, r < v. $N_X = 1.468$, N_Y and $N_Z > 1.743$, $N_Z - N_X > 0.275$. Color yellow to brown with X = clear yellow, Y and Z = yellow to golden. A second phase (II) is also monoclinic with $N_X = 1.50$ *ca.* N_Z and N_Y much greater. Yellow, weakly pleochroic. Ref: 131.

3-Hydroxy-1-phenyl-3-*p*-tolyl-2-propen-1-one or α-*p*-toluylacetophenone enol or β-hydroxy-4-methylchalcone [$CH_3 \cdot C_6H_4 \cdot C(OH):CH \cdot CO \cdot C_6H_5$] is orthorhombic[1] with $a:b:c = 0.793:1:0.652$. Crystals {010} tablets with {011}, {100}, {212}, etc. D 1.22. Cleavage parallel to 100. The optic plane is 001; Z = *b*.

λ=	710	646.5	601	523.5	479	438
(+)2V=	22.6°	27.2°	31.8°	41.4°	48.8°	60°
N_X=	1.6355	1.6381	1.6426	1.6566	1.6708	1.6895
N_Y=	1.6440	1.6519	1.6619	1.6958	1.7323	1.8045
N_Z=	1.9320	1.9512	1.9768	2.0781	2.1666	2.3590
$N_Z - N_X$=	0.2965	0.3131	0.3342	0.4215	0.4958	0,6695

This substance has a dispersion (for N_Z) which is extraordinary; $N_F - N_C$ for $N_X = 0.0290$, for $N_Y = 0.0750$, for $N_Z = 0.2035$. Ref: 281.

---

[1] *b* and *c* interchanged to make *b* > *a* > *c*.

3-Hydroxy-1,3-diphenyl-2-propen-1-one or β-hydroxychalcone or β-dibenzoylmethane enol is orthorhombic[1] with $a:b:c = 0.892:1:0.717$. Crystals {010} tablets with {011}, {100}, etc. M.P. 77.5°. Imperfect 010 cleavage. The optic plane is 001 for $\lambda < 526.5$ and 100 for $\lambda > 526.5$; Z = b.

$$\left[\begin{matrix} C_6H_5 \cdot \underset{OH}{\dot{C}}:CH \cdot \underset{\ddot{O}}{C} \cdot C_6H_5 \end{matrix}\right]$$

λ=	720	660	580	526.5	480	430
+)2V=	42.5°	38.3°	28.0°	0°	32.4°	58.8°
N_X=	1.6401	1.6746	1.6672	1.6913	1.7031	1.7268
N_Y=	1.6697	1.6731	1.6817	1.6913	1.7264	1.8252
N_Z=	1.9185	1.9343	1.9746	2.0242	2.0989	2.2997
$N_Z - N_X$=	0.2784	0.2867	0.3074	0.3329	0.3958	0.5729

The dispersion in this substance is: $N_F - N_C$ for $N_X = 0.0530$, for $N_Y = 0.0477$, for $N_Z = 0.1511$. Ref: 281.

3-Dodecyl-2,5-dihydroxy-1,4-benzoquinone or embelin or embelic acid ($C_{18}H_{28}O_4$) has parallel extinction and negative elongation with $N_1 = 1.64$, $N_2 = 1.69$, $N_2 - N_1 = 0.05$. Ref: 34, 35.

Alizarin or 1,2-dioxyanthraquinone {$C_{14}H_6O_2(OH)_2$} is orthorhombic prismatic with $a:b:c = 0.271:1:0.048$. Space group *Cmma*; *a* 21.0, *b* 77.4, *c* 3.75 Å. U.C. 24. Crystals acicular with {130}, {110}, {010}. Distinct 001 cleavage. H = 2. D 1.54. Vitreous luster. The optic plane is 010; X = *c* (elongation). (-)2V = moderate to large, $N_X = 1.55$ *ca.* $N_Y > 1.80$, N_Z = ?, $N_Z - N_X > 0.25$. Pleochroic with X = yellow, Y and Z = deep reddish orange to red, and X < Y < Z. Ref: 560.

Tetrakis(hydroxymethyl)cyclopentanone ($C_9H_{16}O_5$) is orthorhombic with $a:b:c = 0.687:1:1.328$. Basal cleavage. $N_X = 1.528$, $N_Y = 1.545$, N_Z = ?. Ref: 537a.

3(4-Hydroxyphenyl)-1-(2,4,6-trihydroxyphenyl)-1-propanone or phloretin [$HO \cdot C_6H_4 \cdot CH_2 \cdot CH_2 \cdot CO \cdot C_6H_3 \cdot (OH)_3$] melts at 255°. It has inclined extinction at 41° with $N_1 = 1.515$, $N_2 > 1.95$, $N_2 - N_1 > 0.435$. Ref: 34, 35.

Purpurin or 1,2,4-trioxyanthraquinone [$C_{12}H_5(CO)_2(OH)_3$] is orthorhombic with $a:b:c = 0.398:1:0.332$. *a* 8.0, *b* 20.3, *c* 6.73 Å. U.C. 4. Crystals tiny prismatic needles. D 1.56. X = *c* (elongation). (-)2V = ?, $N_X = 1.54$ *ca.*, $N_Y < N_Z$ very high, $N_Z - N_X$ = very strong. Pleochroic in orange and red with X <Y and Z. Ref: 560.

1,8-Dioxyanthraquinone or chrysazine {$C_{12}H_5(CO)_2(OH)_2$} is tetragonal with $c/a = 0.368$. *a* 5.73, *c* 31.2 Å. U.C. 4. Crystals {001} tablets which may

---

[1] *b* and *c* interchanged to make $b > a > c$.

have low pyramid faces. D = 1.54. Uniaxial positive or (+)2V = 0° - 20°; twinning common in four parts. N_O = 1.787, N_E = 1.945, $N_E - N_O$ = 0.163. Color orange. Ref: 560.

1,7-*bis*(4-Hydroxy-3-methoxyphenyl)-1,6-heptadiene-3,5-dione or curcumin [$[(CH_3\cdot O)(HO)C_6H_3\cdot CH:CH\cdot CO]_2CH_2$] is orthorhombic with a prism angle of about 80° and brachydome angle of about 96°. M.P. 183°. It has N_1 = 1.52, N_2 > 1.95, $N_2 - N_1$ > 0.43, with parallel extinction and negative elongation. Ref: 34, 35, 118.

Class. 4. Carboxylic Acids

Subclass A. Monocarboxylic Acids

β-Dibromomethylcyclohexyl-4-acetic acid {$CH_3C_6H_9BrCHBrCOOH$} is tetragonal with *c*/*a* = 1.452. Crystals prismatic. D 1.83. Uniaxial negative with N_O = 1.612, N_E = 1.585, $N_O - N_E$ = 0.027. Ref: 568a.

Tetrahydro-*d*-pimaric acid ($C_{20}H_{34}O_2$) is orthorhombic with *a*:*b*:*c* = 0.710:1:1.923. Crystals brachydomatic with {011}, {101}, {110}, {100}, {001}. The optic plane is 100; Z = *c*. (+)2V = 25°, r < v. N_X = 1.538, N_Y = 1.540, N_Z = 1.574, $N_Z - N_X$ = 0.036 Na. Ref: 287.

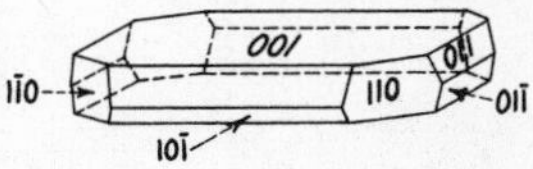

Fig. 64. Benzoic acid.

Benzoic acid ($C_6H_5\cdot CO_2H$) is monoclinic prismatic with *a*:*b*:*c* = 1.051: 1:4.208, *β* = 97°5′. Space group $P2_1c$; *a* 5.44, *b* 5.18, *c* 21.8. U.C. 4. Crystals {001} tablets with {101}, {10$\bar{1}$}, {110}, etc. Fig. 64. Perfect 001 cleavage. D 1.32. M.P. 121.4°. The optic plane is 010; Z ∧ *c* = - 35.5°. 2V = 62°37′. N_Y = 1.6176. Intense inclined dispersion. Also for *λ* = 587.6: (+)2V = 64°24′, N_X = 1.5815, N_Y = 1.6120, N_Z = 1.6975, $N_Z - N_X$ = 0.1160; for *λ* = 501.6: N_X = 1.5941, N_Y = 1.6246, N_Z = 1.7113, $N_Z - N_X$ = 0.1172. Also N_X = 1.610, N_Y = 1.617, N_Z = 1.64. Ref: 118, 138, 343c, 419, 518.

Lithium benzoate ($C_6H_5CO_2Li$) forms thin flakes with N_X = 1.585, N_Z = 1.640, $N_Z - N_X$ = 0.055. Ref: 524.

Sodium benzoate monohydrate ($C_6H_5\cdot CO_2Na\cdot H_2O$) forms prisms which darken in air and lose water at 120° C; soluble in water. It has N_1 = 1.490, N_2 = 1.680, $N_2 - N_1$ = 0.19. Colorless. Ref: 518.

1,2-Dibenzoxy-1,2-diphenylethene, α,α′-stilbenediol dibenzoate or 1,2-dihydroxy-1,2-diphenylethylene dibenzoate [$C_6H_5\cdot C(O\cdot CO\cdot C_6H_5):C(O\cdot CO\cdot C_6H_5)\cdot C_6H_5$] is monoclinic sphenoidal with *a*:*b*:*c* = 0.968:1:0.841, *β* = 100°34.5′. Crystals thick {001} tablets or prismatic with {001}, {110}, {100}, {11$\bar{1}$}, etc. Figs. 65, 66. Perfect 100 and distinct 001 cleavages. Twinning on *c* and also on 100. M.P. 158°. The optic plane and Z are normal to 010; X ∧ *c* = - 54.5° Na, r < v. (+)2V = 85°58′ Na. N_X = 1.604 Na, N_Y = 1.654, N_Z = 1.718, $N_Z - N_X$ = 0.114 Na. Ref: 119.

1-Dimethylamino-2-(dimethylaminomethyl)-2-butanol benzoate dihydrochloride or alypine ($C_{16}H_{26}O_2N_2 \cdot 2HCl$) forms a crystalline powder, easily soluble in water, often containing six-sided prisms. M.P. 173°. $N_1 = 1.504$, $N_2 = 1.603$, $N_2 - N_1 = 0.099$. Again: (-)2V = ?, $N_X = 1.509$, $N_Y = 1.602$. Ref: 123, 239.

4-Dimethylamino-2-methyl-2-butanol benzoate hydrochloride or (2-dimethylaminoethyl)dimethylcarbinyl benzoate hydrochloride [$(CH_3)_2 \cdot N \cdot (CH_2)_2 \cdot CO(CH_3)_2 \cdot CO \cdot C_6H_5 \cdot HCl$] is monoclinic with $\beta = 105 - 110°$. Crystals prismatic or {100} tablets with {110}, {010}, {001}, {011}, etc. Good 100 cleavage. The optic plane is 010; $Z \wedge a = + 20°$, so $X \wedge c = - 35°$ to $- 40°$. (-)2V = 7°10′. $N_X = 1.520$, $N_Y = 1.595$, $N_Z = 1.597$, $N_Z - N_X = 0.077$. Colorless. Ref: 50.

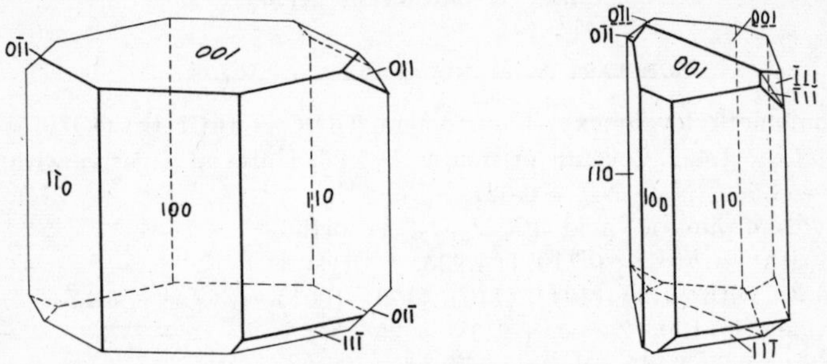

Figs. 65, 66. 1,2-Dibenzoxy-1,2-diphenylethene.

1-Dimethylamino-2-methyl-2-butanol benzoate hydrochloride or dimethylaminomethylmethylcarbinyl benzoate hydrochloride or stovaine [$(CH_3)_2N \cdot CH_2C(CH_3) \cdot (C_2H_5) \cdot O \cdot CO \cdot C_6H_5 \cdot HCl$] is monoclinic. Crystals prismatic or {010} tablets. Distinct 001, 100, and 010 cleavages. M.P. 175°. Negative elongation; $X \wedge c = 21°$. (-)2V = 34°24′. $N_X = 1.525$, $N_Y = 1.620$, $N_Z = 1.630$, $N_Z - N_X = 0.105$. (Checked a year later by E. F. Williams: $N_X = 1.528$, $N_Y = 1.620$, $N_Z = 1.628$, $N_Z - N_X = 0.100$.) Again $N_X = 1.514$, N_Y = ? $N_Z = 1.647$, $N_Z - N_X = 0.133$. Colorless. Ref: 50, 123, 239.

1-Dimethylamino-2-methyl-2-propanol benzoate hydrochloride or dimethylamino-*tert*-butyl benzoate hydrochloride [$(CH_3)_2 \cdot N \cdot CH_2 \cdot C(CH_3)_2 \cdot O \cdot CO \cdot C_6H_5 \cdot HCl$] is monoclinic with $\beta = 88°$ *ca.* Crystals usually prismatic or in {100} tablets. Distinct 100 cleavage. M.P. 202°. The optic plane is 010; $X \wedge c = + 19°$. (-)2V = 52°40′. $N_X = 1.504$, $N_Y = 1.605$, $N_Z = 1.635$, $N_Z - N_X = 0.131$. (Checked a year later by E. F. Williams: $N_X = 1.512$, $N_Y = 1.615$, $N_Z = 1.635$, $N_Z - N_X = 0.123$). Colorless. Ref: 50.

5-Dimethylamino-2-methyl-2-pentanol benzoate hydrochloride or (3-dimethylaminopropyl)dimethylcarbinyl benzoate hydrochloride [$(CH_3)_2N \cdot (CH_2)_3 \cdot CO(CH_3)_2 \cdot CO \cdot C_6H_5 \cdot HCl$] is monoclinic with β about 105 - 110°. Crystals prismatic equant with {110}, {011}, {100}, {010}, etc. The optic plane is 010; $Z \wedge a = 12°$. (+)2V = 58° calc. $N_X = 1.534$, $N_Y = 1.543$, $N_Z = 1.572$, $N_Z - N_X = 0.038$. (Checked a year later by E. F. Williams: $N_X = 1.533$, $N_Y = 1.543$, $N_Z = 1.570$, $N_Z - N_X = 0,037$.). Colorless. Ref: 50, 377.

Benzoyl peroxide $[(C_6H_5 \cdot CO)_2O_2]$ is orthorhombic with $a:b:c = 0.629:1:0.659$. Crystals show {110}, {001}, {111}, {011}, etc. No distinct cleavage. M.P. 103.5°. The optic plane is 100; Z = *b*. (+)2V = 4° *ca.* $N_X = 1.545$, $N_Y = 1.546$, $N_Z = 1.837$, $N_Z - N_X = 0.292$. Ref: 119.

Benzamide $(C_6H_5 \cdot CONH_2)$ is monoclinic with $a:b:c = 4.378:1:4.452$, $\beta = 90°38'$. Crystals often {100} plates with twinning on 100 to pseudoorthorhombic forms. Perfect 100 and distinct $10\bar{1}$ cleavages. D 1.34. M.P. 128°. The optic plane is 010; a bisectrix makes an angle of – 40° with *c*. (+)2V = 87°, r < v. $N_X = 1.541$, $N_Y = 1.666$, $N_Z = 1.830$, $N_Z - N_X = 0.289$. Also triclinic with 2V = 41°. Ref: 118, 377c.

2-Benzoylaminoethanoic acid, or *N*-benzoylglycine or hippuric acid $[C_6H_5 \cdot CO \cdot NH(CH_2 \cdot CO_2H)]$ is orthorhombic sphenoidal with $a:b:c = 0.839:1:0.862$. Crystals {100} tablets or pyramidal or prismatic with {110}, {100}, {101}, {011}, {001}, {102}, {012}, etc. Fig. 67. Distinct 001 and imperfect 110 cleavages. D 1.31. M.P. 187.5°. The optic plane is 001. (+)2V = 66°6′ Li, 65°49.5′ Na, 65°22′ Tl. $N_X = 1.5348$ Na, $N_Y = 1.5921$, $N_Z = 1.7598$, $N_Z - N_X = 0.2250$. Ref: 118, 165.

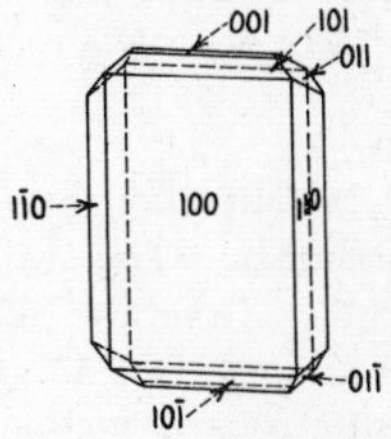

Fig. 67.
Hippuric acid.

4-(Benzoylmethylamino)butanoic acid or γ-*N*-methylbenzamidobutyric acid $[C_6H_5 \cdot CO \cdot N(CH_3)(CH_2)_3 \cdot CO_2H]$ is monoclinic with $a:b:c = 1.114:1:1.738$, $\beta = 100°31'$. Crystals {001} tablets with {100}, {011}, {1$\bar{1}\bar{1}$}. Perfect 001 and good 100 cleavages. Twinning on 001. M.P. 78° - 79°. The optic plane is 010; $Z \wedge a = +30°$. (+)2V = 56.5° Na, r < v strong. $N_X = 1.537$ Na, $N_Y = 1.569$, $N_Z = 1.648$, $N_Z - N_X = 0.111$. Ref: 263.

N-Ethoxybenzamidine or *O*-ethylbenzamidoxime or benzamidoxime ethyl ether $[C_6H_5 \cdot C(NH_2):N(O \cdot C_2H_5)]$ is orthorhombic with $a:b:c = 0.694:1:0.979$. Crystals {001} tablets with {111}, {101}, etc. Very perfect 001 cleavage. M.P. 67°. The optic plane is 001; the acute bisectrix is normal to 100. 2V = 83°21′ Na, r > v. $N_Y = 1.656$ Na. Ref: 118.

syn-Methyl benzohydroxamate benzoate or α-(*syn*)dibenzhydroxamic acid methyl ether $[C_6H_5 \cdot C(O \cdot CH_3):N \cdot O \cdot CO \cdot C_6H_5]$ is orthorhombic with $a:b:c = 0.971:1:?$. Crystals {110} prisms with {010}. M.P. 53° - 54°. The optic plane is 100; X = *c*. (-)2V = 70°10′, r < v. $N_Y = 1.674$ Na. Ref: 119.

o-Chlorobenzoic acid $(C_6H_4Cl \cdot CO_2H)$ is monoclinic with $a:b:c = 1.893:1:6.168$, $\beta = 96°12'$. Crystals {001} plates elongated along *b* with {100} and small {111}. Very perfect 001 and perfect 100 cleavages. D 1.54. M.P. 137°. (Steinmetz); 142° (Fels). The optic plane is normal to 010 and nearly bisects the angle β; X = *b*. $Y \wedge c = 2°$. (-)2V = 60° calc. $N_X = 1.446$, $N_Y = 1.686$, $N_Z = 1.766$, $N_Z - N_X = 0.320$. Ref: 84, 118, 304, 398.

p-Chlorobenzoic acid $(C_6H_4Cl \cdot CO_2H)$ is triclinic with $a:b:c = 0.484:1:0.251$, $\alpha = 95°40'$, $\beta = 122°48'$, $\gamma = 69°9'$. Crystals columnar with {100}, {010}, {001},

{1$\bar{1}$0}, {$\bar{1}$11}, etc. or {010} plates with {100}, {1$\bar{1}$0}, {$\bar{1}$01}, {$\bar{1}$11}, etc. Often twinned. D 1.54. M.P. 235°. Very perfect 010 and 001 and perfect 100 cleavages. The obtuse bisectrix is nearly normal to 010; the optic plane is inclined 6° to the *a* axis and 10° to a normal to 010 toward 100. (-)2V = 45°30′. N_X = 1.446, N_Y = 1.676, N_Z = 1.726, $N_Z - N_X$ = 0.280. Ref: 118, 397, 398.

o-Nitrobenzoic acid [$C_6H_4(NO_2) \cdot CO_2H$] is triclinic with *a*:*b*:*c* = 0.536:1: 0.358, α = 131°11′, β = 109°37′, γ = 61°54′. Crystals vary in habit being equant or {010} plates or {001} tablets. Perfect 100, 010, and 001 cleavages. D 1.575. M.P. 147°. Z ∧ *c* = 86°. (-)2V = 60°, r < v. N_X = 1.616, N_Y = 1.706, N_Z = 1.756, $N_Z - N_X$ = 0.140. Again: (+)2V = ?, N_1 = 1.643, N_2 = 1.78. Ref: 118, 397, 398, 444.

m-Nitrobenzoic acid ($C_6H_4NO_2 \cdot COOH$) has three phases, all monoclinic prismatic. The stable phase (I) (M.P. 142°) has *a*:*b*:*c* = 0.966:1:1.233, β = 91° 11.5′. Crystals {001} tablets or plates with many other faces. Distinct 001 cleavage. D 1.53. The optic plane is 010. X or Z ∧ *c* = 50° in obtuse β. An optic axis is visible through 001. N_1 = 1.651, N_2 = 1.6575 (Young). Another phase (with *a*:*b*:*c* = 0.765:1:0.350, β = 93°57′) has the optic plane parallel with 010; and an optic axis visible through 100. No good cleavage. (+)2V = 60° *ca.* N_X = 1.557, N_Y = 1.76 *ca.* (Davies). Abnormal purple and greenish interference colors. Ref: 118, 397, 398, 444.

p-Nitrobenzoic acid [$C_6H_4(NO_2) \cdot CO_2H$] is monoclinic with *a*:*b*:*c* = 2.562: 1:4.231, β = 96°38′. Crystals {001} plates elongated along *a* (Steinmetz) or *b* (Davies). Very perfect 001 and distinct 100 cleavages. D 1.61. M.P. 238°. The optic plane is 010; an optic axis with very strong dispersion is visible through 001; it lies in the acute angle β at about 45° to *c*. (-)2V = 60°, r < v. N_X = 1.656, N_Y = 1.706, N_Z = 1.726, $N_Z - N_X$ = 0.070; Y ∧ *c* = 2° (Young.). (+)2V = 60°, N_1 = 1.651, N_2 = 1.6575 (Davies). Ref: 118, 397, 398, 444.

5-Isopropyl-2-methylcyclohexyl *o*-nitrobenzoate or menthyl *o*-nitrobenzoate or *o*-nitrobenzoic acid menthyl ester [$C_6H_4(NO_2) \cdot CO_2(C_1 H_{19})$] is orthorhombic disphenoidal with.[1] *a*:*b*:*c* = 0.686:1:0.585. Crystals elongated parallel to *c* with {010}, {110}, {101}, {111}. Perfect 010 cleavage. M.P. 62° - 64°. The optic plane is 100; X = *c*. (-)2V = 30°32′ Na, r < v very strong. N_X = 1.4927 Li, 1.4966 Na, 1.5003 Tl; N_Y = 1.5203 Na; N_Z = 1.5659 Li, 1.5722 Na, 1.5781 Tl; $N_Z - N_X$ = 0.0756 Na. Weakly pleochroic with X = clear-brown, Y = brown, Z = dark brown. Ref: 118.

5-Isopropyl-2-methylcyclohexyl *p*-nitrobenzoate or menthyl *p*-nitrobenzoate [$C_6H_4(NO_2 \cdot CO_2)(C_{10}H_{19})$] is orthorhombic disphenoidal with *a*:*b*:*c* = 0.466:1: 0.434. Crystals (from alcohol) prismatic with {110}, {010}, {011}, {012}, etc. Perfect 010 cleavage. M.P. 61° - 63°. The optic plane is 001; X = *a*. (-)2V = 17°54.5′ Na, r > v very strong. N_X = 1.472 Na; N_Y = 1.6071 Li, 1.6151 Na; N_Z = 1.6192 Na; $N_Z - N_X$ = 0.1472 Na. Ref: 118.

---

[1] *a b c* changed to *b a c* to make *b* > *a* > *c*.

Methyl 3,5-dinitrobenzoate $[(NO_2)_2C_6H_3CO_2CH_3]$ is probably monoclinic in plates {010 ?} with extinction (Y) at 45° to elongation. M.P. 108°. For $\lambda = 546$: (-)2V = 40°, $N_X = 1.382$, $N_Y = 1.780$, $N_Z = 1.837$ calc., $N_Z - N_X = 0.455$. Ref: 38.

Ethyl 3,5-dinitrobenzoate $[(NO_2)_2C_6H_3 \cdot CO_2 \cdot CH_2 \cdot CH_3]$ is probably monoclinic with extinction parallel to acicular elongation along *b* of ± sign. M.P. 93°. For $\lambda = 546$: (+)2V = 45°, $N_X = 1.560$, $N_Y = 1.576$, $N_Z = 1.69$ calc. $N_Z - N_X = 0.13$ calc. Ref: 38.

Propyl 3,5-dinitrobenzoate $[(NO_2)C_6H_3 \cdot CO_2 \cdot CH_2 \cdot CH_2 \cdot CH_3]$ is probably monoclinic in needles elongated along *b* with parallel extinction and ± elongation. M.P. 74°. For $\lambda = 546$: (-)2E = large, $N_X = 1.486$, $N_Y = 1.603$, N_Z = ?, $N_Z - N_X$ = strong. $\therefore 1.72 > N_Z > 1.62$ and $0.234 > N_Z - N_X > 0.134$. Ref: 38.

Isopropyl 3,5-dinitrobenzoate $[(NO_2)_2C_6H_3 \cdot CO_2 \cdot CH(CH_3)_2]$ is probably monoclinic in needles elongated along *b* with parallel extinction and ± elongation. M.P. 123°. For $\lambda = 546$: (-)2V = 67°, N_X = ?, $N_Y = 1.609$, N_Z = ?, $N_Z - N_X$ = strong. Ref: 38.

Butyl 3,5-dinitrobenzoate $[(NO_2)_2C_6H_3 \cdot CO_2 \cdot CH_2 \cdot CH_2 \cdot CH_2 \cdot CH_3]$ is probably monoclinic with extinction parallel to acicular and platy elongation along *b* of ± sign. M.P. 64°. For $\lambda = 546$: (-)2V = 59°, $N_X = 1.488$ calc., $N_Y = 1.621$, $N_Z = 1.665$, $N_Z - N_X = 0.177$ calc. Ref: 38.

Isobutyl 3,5-dinitrobenzoate $[(NO_2)_2C_6H_3 \cdot CO_2 \cdot CH_2 \cdot CH_3 \cdot (CH_3)_2]$ is probably monoclinic with extinction parallel to acicular and platy elongation along *b* of ± sign. M.P. = 87°. For $\lambda = 546$: (+)2V = 10°, $N_X = 1.558$, $N_Y = 1.558$, N_Z = ?, $N_Z - N_X$ = medium. Ref: 38.

sec-Butyl 3,5-dinitrobenzoate or 2-butyl 3,5-dinitrobenzoate $[(NO_2)_2C_6H_3 \cdot CO_2 \cdot CH(CH_3) \cdot CH_2 \cdot CH_3]$ is probably orthorhombic in plates with parallel extinction and ± elongation. M.P. 76°. For $\lambda = 546$: (-)2V = 70°, $N_X = 1.486$, $N_Y = 1.578$, $N_Z = 1.624$ calc., $N_Z - N_X = 0.138$ calc. Ref: 38.

2-Methyl-2-propyl 3,5-dinitrobenzoate or *tert*-butyl 3,5-dinitrobenzoate $[(NO_2)_2C_6H_3CO_2 \cdot C(CH_3)_3]$ is probably orthorhombic in plates with parallel extinction and ± elongation. M.P. 142°. For $\lambda = 546$: (-)2E = large, $N_X = 1.484$, $N_Y = 1.585$, N_Z = ?, $N_Z - N_X$ = strong; $\therefore 1.68 > N_Z > 1.60$ and $0.196 > N_Z - N_X > 0.116$. Ref: 38.

2-Methyl-2-butyl 3,5-dinitrobenzoate, or *tert*-amyl-3,5-dinitrobenzoate $[(NO_2)_2C_6H_3 \cdot CO_2 \cdot C(CH_3)_2 \cdot CH_2 \cdot CH_3]$ is probably monoclinic in plates with elongation along *b*, parallel extinction and ± elongation. M.P. 116°°. For $\lambda = 546$: (-)2E = large, $N_X = 1.491$, $N_Y = 1.588$, N_Z = ? $N_Z - N_X$ = strong; $\therefore 1.685 > N_Z > 1.60$ and $0.194 > N_Z - N_X > 0.110$. Ref: 38.

Phenyl 3,5-dinitrobenzoate $[(NO_2)_2 \cdot C_6H_3 \cdot CO_2C_6H_5]$ forms rods with parallel extinction and negative elongation. M.P. 145.8°. 2V = biaxial. $N_X = 1.505$, $N_Y = 1.690$, $N_Z > 1.740$, $N_Z - N_X > 0.235$. Ref: 271.

2-Methylphenyl 3,5-dinitrobenzoate, or *o*-tolyl 3,5-dinitrobenzoate [$(CH_3 \cdot C_6H_4 \cdot O_2C \cdot C_6H_3(NO_2)_2$] forms plates. M.P. 138.4°. 2V = biaxial. $N_X = 1.490$, $N_Y = ?$, $N_Z > 1.720$, $N_Z - N_X > 0.230$. Ref: 271.

3-Methylphenyl 3,5-dinitrobenzoate or *m*-tolyl 3,5-dinitrobenzoate or *m*-cresol 3,5-dinitrobenzoate [$(CH_3 \cdot C_6H_4 \cdot O_2C \cdot C_6H_3(NO_2)_2$] forms plates with parallel extinction and negative elongation. M.P. 165.4°. (-)2V = 45° *ca.* calc., $N_X = 1.475$, $N_Y = 1.700$, $N_Z = 1.740$, $N_Z - N_X = 0.265$. Ref: 271.

4-Methylphenyl 3,5-dinitrobenzoate, or *p*-tolyl 3,5-dinitrobenzoate [$(CH_3 \cdot C_6H_4 \cdot O_2C \cdot C_6H_3(NO_2)_2$] forms plates. M.P. 188.6°. 2V = biaxial. $N_X = 1.500$, $N_Y = ?$, $N_Z = 1.740$, $N_Z - N_X = 0.240$. Ref: 271.

3,5-Dimethylphenyl 3,5-dinitrobenzoate or 3,5-xylyl 3,5-dinitrobenzoate [$(CH_3)_2C_6H_3 \cdot O_2C \cdot C_6H_3(NO_2)_2$] forms rods with parallel extinction and negative elongation. M.P. 195.4°. 2V = biaxial. $N_X = 1.485$, $N_Y = 1.650$, $N_Z > 1.740$, $N_Z - N_X > 0.255$. Ref: 271.

2,4-Dimethylphenyl 3,5-dinitrobenzoate or 2,4-xylyl 3,5-dinitrobenzoate [$(CH_3)_2C_6H_3 \cdot O_2C \cdot C_6H_3(NO_2)_2$] forms rods and plates with parallel extinction and negative elongation. M.P. 164.6°. 2V = biaxial. $N_X = 1.517$, $N_Y = 1.645$, $N_Z > 1.690$, $N_Z - N_X > 0.173$. Ref: 271.

3,4-Dimethylphenyl 3,5-dinitrobenzoate or 3,4-xylyl 3,5-dinitrobenzoate [$(CH_3)_2C_6H_3 \cdot O_2C \cdot C_6H_3(NO_2)_2$] forms rods and needles with parallel extinction and negative elongation. M.P. 181.6°. 2V = biaxial. $N_X = 1.508$, $N_Y = 1.670$, $N_Z > 1.740$, $N_Z - N_X > 0.232$. Ref: 271.

2,5-Dimethylphenyl 3,5-dinitrobenzoate or 2,5-xylyl 3,5-dinitrobenzoate [$(CH_3)_2 \cdot C_6H_3 \cdot O_2C \cdot C_6H_3(NO_2)_2$] forms needles with parallel extinction and negative elongation. M.P. 137.2°. 2V = 90° *ca.* $N_X = 1.487$, $N_Y = 1.665$, $N_Z = 1.740$, $N_Z - N_X = 0.253$. (Indices and 2V are inconsistent-A.N.W.). Ref: 271.

2,6-Dimethylphenyl 3,5-dinitrobenbenzoate or 2,6-xylyl 3,5-dinitrobenzoate [$(CH_3)_2 \cdot C_6H_3 \cdot O_2C \cdot C_6H_3(NO_2)_2$] forms rods and plates with parallel extinction and negative elongation. M.P. 158.8°. 2V = biaxial. $N_X = 1.512$, $N_Y = 1.670$, $N_Z > 1.740$, $N_Z - N_X > 0.228$. Ref: 271.

2-Isopropyl-5-methylphenyl 3,5-dinitrobenzoate or thymyl 3,5-dinitrobenzoate [$[(CH_3)_2CH] \cdot (CH_3) \cdot C_6H_3 \cdot O_2C \cdot C_6H_3(NO_2)_2$] forms needles with parallel extinction and negative elongation. M.P. = 103.2°. (-)2V = 80° *ca.* calc. $N_X = 1.480$, $N_Y = 1.625$, $N_Z = 1.705$, $N_Z - N_X = 0.225$. Ref: 271.

p-Cyclohexylphenyl 3,5-dinitrobenzoate [$C_6H_{11} \cdot C_6H_4 \cdot O_2C \cdot C_6H_3(NO_2)_2$] forms needles with parallel extinction and ± elongation. M.P. 168°. (-)2V = 80° calc. $N_X = 1.515$, $N_Y = 1.625$, $N_Z = 1.702$, $N_Z - N_X = 0.187$. Color brownish white. Ref: 271.

l-Naphthyl 3,5-dinitrobenzoate, or α-naphthyl 3,5-dinitrobenzoate [$(C_{10}H_7 \cdot O_2C \cdot C_6H_3(NO_2)_2$] forms needles with parallel extinction and negative elongation.

M.P. $217.4°$. $(+)2V$ = biaxial. $N_X = 1.490$, $N_Y = 1.615$, $N_Z > 1.740$, $N_Z - N_X > 0.250$.   Ref: 271.

2-Naphthyl 3,5-dinitrobenzoate or β-naphthyl 3,5-dinitrobenzoate $[C_{10}H_7 \cdot O_2C \cdot C_6H_3(NO_2)_2]$ forms needles with parallel extinction and negative elongation. M.P. $210.2°$. $(+)2V$ = biaxial. $N_X = 1.475$, $N_Y = 1.740$. $N_Z > 1.740$, $N_Z - N_X > 0.265$.   Ref: 271.

2-Methoxyphenyl 3,5-dinitrobenzoate or guaiacol 3,5-dinitrobenzoate $[CH_3O \cdot C_6H_4 \cdot O_2C \cdot C_6H_3(NO_2)_2]$ forms needles which fuse at $141.2°$ and are biaxial with $N_X = 1.530$, $N_Y =$?, $N_Z > 1.740$, $N_Z - N_X > 0.210$.   Ref: 271.

2-Methoxy-4-methylphenyl 3,5-dinitrobenzoate or creosol 3,5-dinitrobenzoate $[CH_3O(CH_3) \cdot C_6H_3 \cdot O_2C \cdot C_6H_3(NO_2)_2]$ forms rods and needles with parallel extinction and positive elongation. M.P. $170°$. $(+)2V$ = $55°$ ca. calc. $N_X = 1.550$, $N_Y = 1.570$, $N_Z = 1.640$, $N_Z - N_X = 0.090$.   Ref: 271.

2-Methoxy-4-propylphenyl 3,5-dinitrobenzoate $[CH_3 \cdot CH_2 \cdot CH_2(CH_3O)C_6H_3 \cdot O_2C \cdot C_6H_3(NO_2)_2]$ forms needles with parallel extinction and positive elongation. M.P. $116.2°$. $2V$ = biaxial. $N_X = 1.520$, $N_Y =$?, $N_Z = 1.650$, $N_Z - N_X = 0.130$.   Ref: 271.

Diethylene glycol-3,5-dinitrobenzoate $\{[C_6H_3(NO_2)_2CO_2C_2H_4]_2O\}$ is probably orthorhombic. Crystals long tablets with N_1 (parallel to length = 1.557, N_2 (normal to length) = 1.674, $N_2 - N_1 = 0.117$.   Ref: 529.

Benzoyl disulphide $(C_6H_5 \cdot CO \cdot S \cdot S \cdot CO \cdot C_6H_5)$ is monoclinic with $a:b:c = 0.751:1:1.024$, $\beta = 107°10'$. Crystals $\{001\}$ tablets with $\{111\}$, $\{11\bar{1}\}$, $\{010\}$, $\{100\}$, etc. The optic plane is 010; $Z \wedge c = +18°$. $2V = 84° - 85°$ (calc. from extinction angle on $11\bar{1}$); $2V = 80°45'$ (calc. from position of optic axis and Z). $N_Y = 1.702$.   Ref: 385.

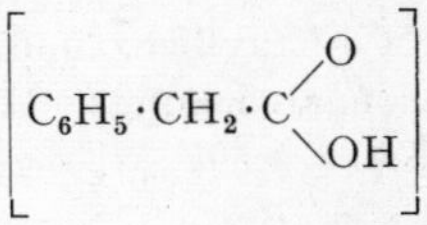

Phenylacetic acid or α-toluic acid is monoclinic with $a:b:c = 2.88:1:2.04$, $\beta = 102°$. a 14.36, b 4.98, c 10.17 Å. U.C. 4. D 1.23. M.P. $76°$. $Y \wedge c = 5°$ in acute β. $(+)2V = 39°$, $r < v$ weak. $N_X = 1.558$, $N_Y = 1.569$, $N_Z = 1.671$, $N_Z - N_X = 0.113$.

$$\left[C_6H_5 \cdot CH_2 \cdot C \diagup{\begin{matrix} O \\ OH \end{matrix}} \right]$$

Ref: 474a.

Methyl phenylacetamidoacetate or methyl phenaceturate $[C_6H_5 \cdot CH_2 \cdot CO \cdot NH[CH_2 \cdot CO_2(CH_3)]]$ is orthorhombic with $a:b:c = 0.816:1:0.785$. Crystals have $\{010\}$, $\{110\}$, $\{120\}$, $\{011\}$, $\{001\}$. M.P. = $86.5°$. The optic plane is 010; $Z = a$. $N_X = 1.5467$ Na, $N_Y =$?, $N_Z = 1.6130$, $N_Z - N_X = 0.0663$. Ref: 118.

Ethyl phenylacetamidoacetate or ethyl phenaceturate $[C_6H_5 \cdot CH_2 \cdot CO \cdot NH \cdot CH_2 \cdot CO_2(C_2H_5)]$ is orthorhombic with $a:b:c = 0.820:1:0.778$. Crystals prismatic with $\{110\}$, $\{010\}$, $\{011\}$, $\{001\}$. Perfect 010 and distinct 110 cleavage. M.P. $79°$. The optic plane is 010; $2H$ (in almond oil) = $44°41'$ Na, $r > v$. $N_X = 1.5639$, $N_Y = 1.6277$, $N_Z =$? $2V = 40°23'$ calc. (Probably optically negative; if so, $N_Z = 1.6357$ calc. and $N_Z - N_X = 0.0718$ calc. - A.N.W.).   Ref: 118.

α-(4-Bromophenyl)acetonitrile or *p*-bromo-α-tolunitrile or *p*-bromo-benzyl cyanide [$C_6H_4Br \cdot CH_2(CN)$] is tetragonal with $c/a = 1.488$. Crystals show {111}, {001}. Perfect 001 and distinct 110 and 100 cleavages. M.P. 47°. D 1.52. Uniaxial negative with $N_O = 1.643$ red, 1.646 yellow; $N_E = 1.639$ red, 1.642 yellow: $N_O - N_E = 0.004$ yellow. Optically biaxial sections frequently found. Ref: 118.

o-Toluamide [$CH_3 \cdot C_6H_4 \cdot CONH_2$] is triclinic (?) in tablets with good cleavage. Plates show an uncentered obtuse bisectrix interference figure. M.P. 41.2°. (-)2V = 44°, $N_X = 1.470$, $N_Y = 1.715$, $N_Z = 1.761$, $N_Z - N_X = 0.291$. Ref: 377c.

m-Toluamide [$CH_3 \cdot C_6H_4 \cdot CONH_2$] is monoclinic in prismatic crystals. M.P. 93.7°. The optic plane is 010; extinction angle to *c* attains 43°. (-)2V = 20°. $N_X = 1.468$, $N_Y = 1.737$, $N_Z = 1.752$, $N_Z - N_X = 0.284$. Ref: 377c.

p-Toluamide [$CH_3 \cdot C_6H_4 \cdot CONH_2$] is monoclinic in square plates with good rectangular cleavage. M.P. 159.6°. The optic plane and Z are normal to 010. (-)2V = 36°. $N_X = 1.510$, $N_Y = 1.708$, $N_Z = 1.734$, $N_Z - N_X = 0.224$. Ref: 377c.

Methyl ether of 4-methylbenzohydroxamic acid or methyl ether of *p*-toluhydroxamic acid [$C_6H_4(CH_3) \cdot C(OH)(:NOCH_3)$] is monoclinic with $a:b:c = 3.245:1:2.541$, $\beta = 100°58'$. Crystals thick rectangular {100} tablets with {001}, {10$\bar{1}$}, {110}, etc. Perfect 100 cleavage. The optic plane and X are normal to 010; $Z \wedge c = -31.5°$ red, $-30°$ Na. (-)2H (in olive oil) = 72°57′ Li, 72°24′ Na, 70°4′ blue. $N_X = 1.566$ red, 1.5787 Na, 1.626 blue. Ref: 118.

2,6-Dimethylbenzamide or 2,6-xylamide [$(CH_3)_2 \cdot C_6H_3 \cdot CONH_2$] is monoclinic in long rectangular plates with M.P. 137.3°. The optic plane is 010; $X \wedge c = 8° \pm$. (+)2V = 61°. $N_X = 1.565$, $N_Y = 1.591$, $N_Z = 1.673$, $N_Z - N_X = 0.108$. Ref: 377c.

o-Ethylbenzamide ($C_2H_5 \cdot C_6H_4 \cdot CONH_2$) is monoclinic in rectangular crystals elongated along *b*. M.P. 153°. The optic plane is 010. (+)2V = 71°. $N_X = 1.547$, $N_Y = 1.592$, $N_Z = 1.693$, $N_Z - N_X = 0.146$. Ref: 377c.

p-Ethylbenzamide ($C_2H_5 \cdot C_6H_4 \cdot CONH_2$) is monoclinic in tabular crystals elongated along *b*. M.P. 164.2°. The optic plane is 010. The obtuse bisectrix is normal to the tablet faces. (-)2V = 72°. $N_X = 1.505$, $N_Y = 1.638$, $N_Z = 1.726$, $N_Z - N_X = 0.221$. Ref: 377c.

p-Butylbenzamide ($C_4H_9C_6H_4CONH_2$) is monoclinic in prisms elongated along *c*. M.P. 121.5°. The optic plane is 010; $X \wedge c = 40°$. (+)2V = 56°. $N_X = 1.547$, $N_Y = 1.577$, $N_Z = 1.700$, $N_Z - N_X = 0.153$. Ref: 377c.

p-*sec*-Butylbenzamide ($C_4H_9 \cdot C_6H_4 \cdot CONH_2$) is monoclinic in needles and long rectangular plates. M.P. 117.2° from H_2O and 128.4° from petroleum ether. (-)2V = 86°. $N_X = 1.49$, $N_Y = 1.596$, $N_Z = 1.72$, $N_Z - N_X = 0.23$. Ref: 377c.

p-Isobutylbenzamide ($C_4H_9 \cdot C_6H_4 \cdot CONH_2$) is monoclinic in thin {010} laminae or long prisms along *c*. M.P. 151.2°. The optic plane is 010; $X \wedge c = 37° \pm$. (-)2V = 79°. $N_X = 1.464$, $N_Y = 1.605$, $N_Z = 1.724$, $N_Z - N_X = 0.260$. Ref: 377c.

p-Propylbenzamide ($C_3H_7 \cdot C_6H_4 \cdot CONH_2$) is monoclinic in rectangular crystals. M.P. 128.4°. Perfect 010 cleavage. The optic plane is 010; $X \wedge c = 40° \pm$. (-)2V = 33°. $N_X = 1.562$, $N_Y = 1.674$, $N_Z = 1.689$, $N_Z - N_X = 0.163$. Ref: 377c.

4-Isopropyl-3-nitrobenzoic acid or 3-nitrocumic acid [$C_6H_3(NO_2)CO_2H) \cdot CH(CH_3)_2$] is monoclinic with $a:b:c = 1.550:1:1.255$, $\beta = 99°54'$. Crystals varied with {001}, {110}, {011}, {010}, {11$\bar{1}$}, etc. Fig. 68. Perfect 001 and imperfect 10$\bar{1}$ cleavage. M.P. 156° - 157°. The optic plane is 010; $X \wedge c = +14°11'$. (-)2V = 36°58′ Na, r > v. $N_Y = 1.6812$ Na. Pleochroism distinct with X = sulphur yellow, Y = grayish yellow, Z = colorless. Ref: 118.

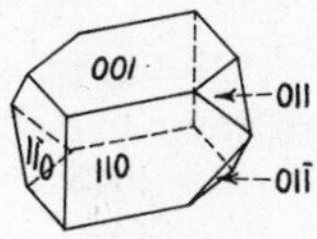

Fig. 68.
Nitrocumic acid.

2-Cyano-1,3-dimethylbenzene or 2,6-xylonitrile [$(CH_3)_2 C_6H_3 \cdot CN$] is monoclinic in long rectangular crystals. M.P. 89.5°. X = *a*, Y = *b*, Z = *c* (?). (-)2V = 20°. $N_X = 1.454$, $N_Y = 1.737$, $N_Z = 1.748$, $N_Z - N_X = 0.294$. Ref: 377c.

2,6-Dimethyl-4-*tert*-butylbenzoic anhydride or 4-*tert*-butyl-2,6-xylic anhydride [$(CH_3)_3CC_6H_2(CH_3)_2CO \cdot O \cdot COC_6H_2(CH_3)_2C(CH_3)_3$] is monoclinic with $a:b:c = 1.262:1:1.238$, $\beta = 121°6'$. Crystals thick {001} tablets with {100}, {$\bar{1}$01}, {110}, {$\bar{1}$12}, etc. Distinct 010 and imperfect $\bar{1}$01 and $\bar{2}$01 cleavages. The optic plane is 010; $Z \wedge c = -47°$. ($X \wedge a = +16°$). (-)2V = 80°. $N_X = 1.50$, $N_Y = 1.59$, $N_Z = 1.66$, $N_Z - N_X = 0.16$. Ref: 302a.

trans-3-Phenylpropenoic acid or *trans*-cinnamic acid [$C_6H_5 \cdot CH{:}CH \cdot CO_2H$] has at least two phases. The stable phase (I) is monoclinic with $a:b:c = 0.863:1:0.314$, $\beta = 96°49'$. Crystals show {010}, {110}, {011}, etc. Perfect 010 and good 011 cleavages. D 1.246. M.P. 135°. The optic plane and X are normal to 010; $Z \wedge c = -58°$. $2H_O = 149°48'$ Li, 159°6′ Na, 167°15′ Tl. $N_1 = 1.61$, $N_2 > 1.74$, $N_2 - N_1 > 0.13$. Ref: 118, 239.

l-Abietic acid ($C_{20}H_{30}O_2$) is monoclinic sphenoidal with $a:b:c = 1.187:1:0.990$, $\beta = 112°19'$. Crystals prisms or {100} plates with {1$\bar{1}$0}, {11$\bar{1}$}, {001}. Imperfect 001 and 100 cleavages. M.P. 171° - 173°. $X \wedge c = -13°$; Y = *b*. (-)2V = 38° calc., r < v. $N_X = 1.510$, $N_Y = 1.578$, $N_Z = 1.618$, $N_Z - N_X = 0.108$. Also $N_X = 1.515$, $N_Y = 1.590$, $N_Z = 1.600$, $N_Z - N_X = 0.085$ D. Ref: 117, 152, 190.

Sodium abietate ($C_{20}H_{29}O_2Na$) is orthorhombic (?). Crystals acicular or bladed, long along *c*. Prismatic (?) cleavage. Y = *c*. (-)2V = 65° *ca.*, $N_X = 1.528 \pm \cdot 003$, $N_Y = 1.551 \pm \cdot 003$, $N_Z = 1.570 \pm \cdot 003$, $N_Z - N_X = 0.042$. Differs from sodium tetra-abietate in being soluble in water. Ref: 619.

Sodium acid *l*-abietate or sodium tetra-abietate ($C_{19}H_{29}CO_2Na \cdot 3C_{20}H_{30}O_2$) is orthorhombic dipyramidal in colorless rods and needles with parallel extinction and negative elongation. X = *c*. Y = *b*. M.P. 205° - 208°. (+)2V = 45° *ca.*, $N_X = 1.540 \pm \cdot 003$, $N_Y = 1.551 \pm \cdot 003$, $N_Z = 1.584 \pm \cdot 003$, $N_Z - N_X = 0.044$. Again: $N_X = 1.555$, $N_Y = 1.575$, $N_Z = 1.595$, $N_Z - N_X = 0.040$. [*a*] D = - 97°. Ref: 190, 619.

Methyl dihydroabietate ($C_{21}H_{34}O_2$) is monoclinic, probably hemimorphic, with *a*:*b*:*c* = 1.448:1:3.440, β = 103°7′. Crystals often skeletal {001} tablets with {100}, {$\bar{1}$01}, {101}, {111}, etc. Y = *b*; Z ∧ *c* = - 20°. (-)2V = 49° Na, r < v. $N_X = 1.527$ Na, $N_Y = 1.560$, $N_Z = 1.567$ calc. $N_Z - N_X = 0.040$. Ref: 261.

n-Butylamine *l*-abietate [$CH_3(CH_2)_3NH_2 \cdot C_{20}H_{30}O_2$] crystallizes in colorless plates which extinguish sharply. M.P. 164° - 169° with decomposition. $N_X = 1.553$, N_Y = ? $N_Z = 1.600$, $N_Z - N_X = 0.047$. [*a*]D = - 72.7°. Ref: 190.

Di-*n*-amylamine *l*-abietate [$\{CH_3(CH_2)_4\}_2NH \cdot C_{20}H_{30}O_2$] is probably orthorhombic in rods with parallel extinction and positive elongation. M.P. 141° - 142°. $N_X = 1.513$, N_Y = ?, $N_Z = 1.548$, $N_Z - N_X = 0.035$. [*a*]D = - 74.5°. Ref: 190.

Di-isoamylamine *l*-abietate [$\{(CH_3)_2CH(CH_2)_2\}_2NH \cdot C_{20}H_{30}O_2$] is probably orthorhombic in rods with parallel extinction and positive elongation. M.P. 139 - 141°. $N_X = 1.515$, N_Y = ?, $N_Z = 1.556$, $N_Z - N_X = 0.041$. [*a*]D = - 62.4. Ref: 190.

d-Pimaric acid ($C_{20}H_{30}O_2$) is orthorhombic disphenoidal with *a*:*b*:*c* = 0.716:1:1.895. Crystals {001} tablets elongated along *a* with {011}, {110}, {101}. M.P. 212°. Y = *a*; Z = *c*. (+)2V = 46°38′ Na, r > v weak. $N_X = 1.556$, $N_Y = 1.564$, $N_Z = 1.606$, $N_Z - N_X = 0.050$. Ref: 112, 189a, 261.

Ethyl *d*-pimarate ($C_{19}H_{29}CO_2C_2H_5$) is monoclinic with *a*:*b*:*c* = 0.820:1:1.813, β = 102°39′. Crystals {001} tablets with {$\bar{1}$01}, {101}, {100}, {121}, {$\bar{1}$21} etc. Good 001 cleavage. M.P.53°. Y = *b*; Z nearly normal to 001. (+)2V = 48°0′ Na, r < v strong. $N_X = 1.547$ Na, $N_Y = 1.568$, $N_Z = 1.689$ calc., $N_Z - N_X = 0.142$. [α] = 60.25° (c = 2 in alcohol). Ref: 261.

Chlorodihydro-*d*-pimaric acid ("dextropimaric acid hydrochloride") ($C_{20}H_{31}O_2Cl$) is monoclinic with *a*:*b*:*c* = 2.117:1:1.863, β = 100°1′. Crystals {001} plates or prisms with {110}, {100}, {001}, {$\bar{1}$01}. Good 100 cleavage. M.P. 184°. X is nearly normal to 100; Y = *b*. 2E = 100° *ca.* $N_Y = 1.554$; ∴ 2V = 60° *ca.* Ref: 336.

l-Pimaric acid or *l*-sapietic acid ($C_{20}H_{30}O_2$) is orthorhombic disphenoidal with *a*:*b*:*c* = 0.810:1:0.614. Crystals prismatic with {110}, {1$\bar{1}$0}, {001}, {111}, etc. M.P. 140 - 150°. X = *b*; Y = *a*. (-)2V = 62°3′ red, 61°45′ Na, 61°23′ blue. $N_Y = 1.5986$ red, 1.5998 Na, 1.6002 blue. Also: $N_X = 1.537$, $N_Y = 1.588$, $N_Z = 1.620$, $N_Z - N_X = 0.083$. Ref: 117, 189a

Sandaraco-pimaric acid ($C_{20}H_{30}O_2$) is orthorhombic disphenoidal with *a*:*b*:*c* = 0.680:1:1.959. Crystals {001} tablets elongated along *a* with {110}, {011}, {021}, etc. M.P. 173°. Y = *a*; Z = *c*. (+)2V = 43°11′ Na calc. N_X = 1.543 Na, N_Y = 1.551, N_Z = 1.605, $N_Z - N_X$ = 0.062. Ref: 18a.

Methyl sandaraco-pimarate ($C_{19}H_{29}CO_2CH_3$) is orthorhombic with *a*:*b*:*c* = 0.702:1:2.015. Crystals {001} tablets with {110}, {011}, {111}. M.P. 69°. Y = *a*; Z = *c*. (+)2V = 23°10′ Na. N_X = 1.556 Na, N_Y = 1.562, N_Z = 1.67 calc., $N_Z - N_X$ = 0.114. [α] = + 27.91° (c = 0.6 in methanol). Ref: 261

Dihydrosandaraco-pimaric acid ($C_{20}H_{32}O_2$) is orthorhombic with *a*:*b*:*c* = 0.736:1:1.940. Crystals {001} tablets with {100}, {110}, {011}, etc. M.P. 180°. Y = *a*; Z = *c*. (+)2V = 67°18′ Na. N_X = 1.534 Na, N_Y = 1.550, N_Z = 1.635 calc., $N_Z - N_X$ = 0.101. [α] = – 23.9° (c = 0.4 in alcohol). Ref: 261.

Parthenyl cinnamate ($C_{24}H_{32}O_2$) is tetragonal. Crystals are basal tablets and pyramids. M.P. 125 – 126°. Uniaxial positive with N_O = 1.550, N_E > 1.641 $N_E - N_O$ > 0.090. Soluble in high index liquids. Ref: 612a.

2,3-Dimethyl-3-*p*-tolylpropenoic acid or *p*,α,β-trimethylcinnamic acid [$CH_3 \cdot C_6H_4 \cdot C(CH_3) \cdot C(CH_3)CO_2H$] is orthorhombic with *a*:*b*:*c* = 0.786:1:1.223. Crystals pyramidal or elongated along *a* and flattened on 001. H 1 – 1.5. No cleavage. The optic plane is 100; X = *b*. (–)2V = ? N_X = ?, N_Y = 1.53, 1.85 > N_Z > 1.78. (N_X must be < 1.28. – A.N.W.). Ref: 286.

Ethyl 2,3,3-trimethyl-2-phenylcyclopentanecarboxylate is monoclinic sphenoidal with *a*:*b*:*c* = 1.372:1:2.429, β = 101°39′. Crystals show {001}, {110}, {101}, etc. Perfect 100 cleavage. M.P. 48° – 50°. The optic plane is 010; X ∧ *c* = + 50°. (–)2V = 65°20′, dispersion weak. N_X = 1.5101, N_Y = 1.5777, N_Z = 1.6083, $N_Z - N_X$ = 0.0982 Na. Ref: 118.

$$\left[\begin{array}{lr} C_6H_5C(CH_3)\cdot CH(CO_2\cdot C_2H_5)\cdot & CH_2 \\ \quad | & | \\ \quad C(CH_3)_2 & CH_2 \end{array}\right]$$

α-Naphthalene-acetic acid ($C_{10}H_7CH_2COOH$) is monoclinic prismatic. β = about 120°. Crystals {100} or {001} tablets long ‖ *b*. Perfect 100 and distinct 001 and 010 cleavages. Y = *b*; Z about normal to 001. (+)2V = 5° – 15°, N_X = 1.601 ±·002, N_Y = 1.604 ±·002, N_Z > 1.73, $N_Z - N_X$ = 0.15 (est. – A.N.W.). Ref: 619.

β-Naphthalene-acetic acid ($C_{10}H_7CH_2COOH$) seems to be dimorphous. One phase (I) shows rhombic plates (with angles of *ca.* 60° and 120°) normal to Z with (+)2V = 55° *ca.* N_X = 1.555 ±·003, $N_Z - N_X$ = moderate. Another phase (II) shows rhombic plates with angles of *ca.* 73° and 107° which give an optic axis at the edge of the field. (+ ?)2V = 80° *ca.*, N_X < 1.549, $N_Z - N_X$ = strong. Ref: 619.

Ethyl diphenylacetate [$(C_6H_5)_2 \cdot CH \cdot CO_2(C_2H_5)$] is orthorhombic pyramidal with *a*:*b*:*c* = 0.381:1:0.923. Crystals {001} tablets with {00$\bar{1}$}, {100}, {010}, etc. No distinct cleavage. D 1.186. M.P. 59°. The optic plane is 010; X = *c*. (–)2V = 62°40′ Li, 62°6′ Na, 61°4′ Tl. N_X = 1.599 Li, 1.603 Na, 1.607 Tl; N_Y = 1.606 Li, 1.610 Na, 1.613 Tl; N_Z = 1.625 Li, 1.629 Na, 1.632 Tl; $N_Z - N_X$ = 0.026 Na. Ref: 142.

SUBCLASS B. DICARBOXYLIC ACIDS AND DERIVATIVES

4-Bromo-2,2-dimethyl-1,3-cyclopentanedicarboxylic acid or *trans*-bromopyrocamphoric acid [$BrCH \cdot CH(CO_2H) \cdot C(CH_3)_2 \cdot CH(CO_2H) \cdot CH_2$] is triclinic with $a:b:c = ?:1:1.995$, $\alpha = 112°18'$, $\beta = 83°38'$, $\gamma = 116°27'$. Crystals {001} plates with {010}, {01$\bar{1}$}, {100}, often twinned on *a* or *b*. Very soft and flexible. Perfect 011 cleavage. M.P. 207° - 208°. Extinction in 001 at 17.5° to *a*. An optic axis seen in 001. N = 1.495 *ca.* $N_Z - N_X$ = rather strong. Ref: 117.

d-1,2,2-Trimethyl-1,3-cyclopentane dicarboxylic acid or *d*-camphoric acid [$C_5H_5 \cdot (CH_3)_3 \cdot (CO_2H)_2$] is monoclinic sphenoidal with $a:b:c = 0.653:1:0.548$, $\beta = 110°53.5'$. Crystals six-sided prisms with {110}, {001}, {010}, etc. Common twinning. Perfect 11$\bar{1}$ and 10$\bar{1}$ and good 010 cleavages. M.P. 187°. D 1.19. The optic plane and X are normal to 010; $Z \wedge c = -64°$. (+)2H = 70.5°, $r < v$. Also $N_1 = 1.47$, $N_2 = 1.48$, $N_3 = 1.533$, $N_3 - N_1 = 0.063$. Bolland gives for "camphersäure" (which one ?): parallel extinction and positive elongation with $N_1 = 1.485$, $N_2 = 1.525$, $N_2 - N_1 = 0.040$. Ref: 34, 35, 117, 343c.

1,2-Benzenedicarboxylic acid or phthalic acid [$C_6H_4(CO_2H)_2$] is monoclinic with $a:b:c = 0.708:1:1.345$, $\beta = 93°35'$. Crystals of varied habit being {001} tablets, prismatic equant, or {010} plates. Distinct 21$\bar{2}$ and indistinct 001 and 011 cleavages. D 1.59. M.P. 195°, with decomposition. The optic plane and Z are normal to 010; $X \wedge c = +44°30'$; an optic axis visible through 212. (-)2V = 30° - 32° *ca.* $N_X = 1.456$, $N_Y = 1.696$, $N_Z = 1.756$, $N_Z - N_X = 0.300$. Also $N_X = 1.463$, $N_Y = 1.76$, $N_Z = 1.79$, $N_Z - N_X = 0.327$. Again: $N_X = 1.461 - 1.465$, $N_Y = ?$, $N_Z > 1.75$. Again: (-)2V = 34° *ca.*, $N_X = 1.455$, $N_Y = 1.762$, $N_Z > 1.78$, $N_Z - N_X > 0.340$. Also: $N_X = 1.458$, $N_Y = 1.738$, $N_Z = ?$. (The data suggest that there are at least two phases - A.N.W.).
Ref: 100, 118, 396, 397, 398, 560, 599.

Potassium 1,2-benzenedicarboxylate or potassium phthalate [$C_6H_4(CO_2K)_2(H_2O\,?)$] forms flat tablets which are very soluble. 2V = 5°. $N_X = 1.487$, $N_Y = ?$, $N_Z = 1.6$, $N_Z - N_X = 0.113$. Ref: 396.

Dipotassium alcohol phthalate [$C_6H_4(CO_2K)_2 \cdot C_2H_5OH$] forms laths with $N_1 = 1.466$, $N_2 = 1.557$, $N_2 - N_1 = 0.091$. Ref: 597.

Cobalt 1,2-benzenedicarboxylate or cobalt phthalate [$C_6H_4(CO_2)_2Co(H_2O\,?)$] forms red prisms that turn lavender on loss of water. (-)2V = 72°. $N_X = 1.491$, $N_Y = 1.595$, $N_Z = 1.62$, $N_Z - N_X = 0.129$. Ref: 396.

Copper 1,2-benzenedicarboxylate or copper phthalate [$C_6H_4(CO_2)_2Cu(H_2O\,?)$] is monoclinic with extinction angle of 23°. $N_X = 1.530$, $N_Y = ?$, $N_Z = 1.780$, $N_Z - N_X = 0.250$. Blue and pleochroic. Ref: 396.

Nickel 1,2-benzenedicarboxylate or nickel phthalate [$C_6H_4(CO_2)_2Ni(H_2O\,?)$] is isometric with N = 1.605. Green crystals. Ref: 396.

Mercuric 1,2-benzenedicarboxylate or mercuric phthalate [$C_6H_4(CO_2)_2Hg(H_2O\,?)$] is orthorhombic in colorless prisms with parallel extinction. (+)2V = large. $N_X = 1.540$, $N_Y = ?$, $N_Z = 1.730$, $N_Z - N_X = 0.190$. Ref: 396.

Zinc 1,2-benzenedicarboxylate or zinc phthalate $[C_6H_4(CO_2)_2Zn(H_2O\ ?)]$ forms colorless prisms which are optically negative with $N_X = 1.59$. Ref: 396.

Strontium 1,2-benzenedicarboxylate or strontium phthalate $[C_6H_4(CO_2)_2Sr(H_2O\ ?)]$ is orthorhombic in colorless prisms with parallel extinction. $N_X = 1.571$, $N_Y = 1.58$, $N_Z = ?$. Ref: 396.

Ammonium acid phthalate or ammonium biphthalate $[(NH_4)O_2C \cdot C_6H_4 \cdot CO_2H]$ is orthorhombic with $a:b:c = 0.624:1:1.254$. Crystals {001} tablets with {011}, {111}. Distinct 001 cleavage. D 1.415. The optic plane is 001; X = *a*. (–)2V = 32°52′ Na. $N_X = 1.510$ Na, $N_Y = 1.658$, $N_Z = 1.673$, $N_Z - N_X = 0.163$. Ref: 118, 375.

Sodium acid phthalate or sodium biphthalate $(NaO_2C \cdot C_6H_4 \cdot CO_2H)$ is orthorhombic with $a:b:c = 0.726:1:1.420$. D 1.577. Crystals {001} tablets with {011}, {221}, {223}. Perfect 001 cleavage. The optic plane is 001; X = *a*. (–)2V = 20°34′ Na. $N_X = 1.485$ Na, $N_Y = 1.661$, $N_Z = 1.668$, $N_Z - N_X = 0.183$. Ref: 118, 375.

Potassium acid phthalate or potassium biphthalate $(KO_2C \cdot C_6H_4 \cdot CO_2H)$ is orthorhombic with $a:b:c = 0.671:1:1.383$. Crystals {001} tablets with {011}, {111}, etc. Perfect 001 cleavage. D 1.636. The optic plane is 010; X = *a*. (–)2V = 16°24′ Na. $N_X = 1.498$ Na, $N_Y = 1.659$, $N_Z = 1.663$, $N_Z - N_X = 0.165$. Ref: 118, 375.

Rubidium acid phthalate or rubidium biphthalate $[RbO_2C \cdot C_6H_4 \cdot CO_2H]$ is orthorhombic with $a:b:c = 0.658:1:1.299$. Crystals {001} tablets with {011}, {111}, {010}, etc. Perfect 001 cleavage. D 1.933. The optic plane is 001; X = *a*. (–)2V = 24°16′ Na. $N_X = 1.503$ Na, $N_Y = 652$, $N_Z = 1.660$, $N_Z - N_X = 0.157$. Ref: 118, 375.

Caesium acid phthalate or caesium biphthalate $[CsO_2C \cdot C_6H_4 \cdot CO_2H]$ is orthorhombic with $a:b:c = 0.609:1:1.186$. Crystals {001} tablets with {111}, {011}, {010}. Good 001 cleavage. D 2.178. The optic plane is 001; X = *a*. (–) 2 V = 37°52′ Na. $N_X = 1.530$ Na, $N_Y = 1.653$, $N_Z = 1.670$, $N_Z - N_X = 0.140$. Ref: 118, 375.

1,3,3-Trimethylbicyclo 2.2.1-heptan-2-ol acid phthalate or fenchyl acid phthalate $[CH_3C \cdot CH_2 \cdot CH_2 \cdot CH \cdot C(CH_3)_2 \cdot CH \cdot O_2C \cdot C_6H_4CO_2H]$ is orthorhombic with $a:b:c = 0.818:1:1.199$. Crystals {001} tablets elongated along *a* with {101}, {011}, etc. Good 001 and 100 cleavages. M.P. 146°. The optic plane is 100; X = *c*. 2 V = 45° Na, $r < v$ strong. $N_X = 1.52$ calc. Na, $N_Y = 1.566$, $N_Z = 1.613$ *ca.*, $N_Z - N_X = 0.09$. (The indices and 2 V are inconsistent; if 2 V, N_Z, and N_Y are correct and the sign is –, then $N_X = 1.29$. If 2 V, N_Z, and N_Y are correct and the sign is +, then $N_X = 1.548$ and $N_Z - N_X = 0.065$. – A.N.W.) Ref: 261.

6-Carboxy-2-nitrobenzoic acid methyl ester monohydrate or 3-nitrophthalic acid 2-methyl ester monohydrate $(C_6H_3 \cdot NO_2 \cdot CO_2H \cdot CO_2 \cdot CH_3 \cdot H_2O)$ is monoclinic in tabular and prismatic crystals with M.P. = 152° after three re-crystallizations from hot water. (–)2V = 10 – 20°. $N_X = 1.448$, $N_Y = 1.637$, $N_Z = 1.680$, $N_Z - N_X = 0.232$. Ref: 118, 214a, 219a.

6-Carboxy-2-nitrobenzoic acid ethyl ester or 3-nitrophthalic acid 2-ethyl ester[1] ($C_6H_3 \cdot NO_2 \cdot CO_2H \cdot CO_2 \cdot C_2H_5$) is monoclinic in tabular and prismatic crystals with M.P. = 156 – 157° after two recrystallizations from hot water. (–)2V = 15 – 25°. $N_X = 1.450$, $N_Y = 1.638$, $N_Z = 1.665$, $N_Z - N_X = 0.211$. Large crystals are pale green-yellow. Ref: 214a.

6-Carboxy-2-nitrobenzoic acid *n*-propyl ester or 3-nitrophthalic acid 2-*n*-propyl ester [$C_6H_3(NO_2)(CO_2H)(CO_2 \cdot C_3H_7)$] is monoclinic in rhombic plates with M.P. = 138 – 139° after nineteen recrystallizations from hot water. (–)2V = very large. $N_X = 1.536$, $N_Y = 1.601$, $N_Z = 1.611$, $N_Z - N_X = 0.075$. Ref: 214a.

6-Carboxy-2-nitrobenzoic acid isopropyl ester or 3-nitrophthalic acid 2-isopropyl ester [$C_6H_3(NO_2)(CO_2H)(CO_2 \cdot C_3H_7)_2$] is monoclinic in rhombic plates with M.P. = 152 – 153° after two recrystallizations from hot water. (–)2V = large. $N_X = 1.535$, $N_Y = 1.659$, $N_Z = 1.678$, $N_Z - N_X = 0.141$. Ref: 214a.

6-Carboxy-2-nitrobenzoic acid *n*-butyl ester or 3-nitrophthalic acid 2-*n*-butyl ester [$C_6H_3(NO_2)(CO_2H)(CO_2 \cdot C_4H_9)$] is monoclinic in rhombic plates with M.P. = 146 – 147° after ten recrystallizations from hot aqueous butyl alcohol, later hot water. (–)2V = large. $N_X = 1.531$, $N_Y = 1.589$, $N_Z = 1.630$, $N_Z - N_X = 0.099$. Ref: 214a.

6-Carboxy-2-nitrobenzoic acid isobutyl ester or 3-nitrophthalic acid 2-isobutyl ester [$C_6H_3(NO_2)(CO_2H)(CO_2 \cdot C_4H_9)$] is monoclinic in rhombic plates with M.P. = 180 – 181° after four recrystallizations from hot water and washing with benzene. (–)2V = very large. $N_X = 1.540$, $N_Y = 1.609$, $N_Z = 1.643$, $N_Z - N_X = 0.103$. Ref: 214a.

6-Carboxy-2-nitrobenzoic acid isoamyl ester or 3-nitrophthalic acid 2-isoamyl ester [$C_6H_3(NO_2)(CO_2H)(CO_2 \cdot C_5H_{11})$] is monoclinic in very thin rhombic plates with M.P. = 164 – 165° after recrystallization three times from hot water, twice from benzene, and three times from hot water. (–)2V = large. $N_X = 1.450$, $N_Y = 1.580$, $N_Z = 1.615$, $N_Z - N_X = 0.165$. Ref: 214a.

6-Carboxy-2-nitrobenzoic acid *n*-hexyl ester or 3-nitrophthalic acid 2-*n*-hexyl ester [$C_6H_3(NO_2)(CO_2H)(CO_2 \cdot C_6H_{13})$] is monoclinic in flaky plates with M.P. = 123 – 124° after several recrystallizations from carbon tetrachloride and hot water. (–)2V = large. $N_X = 1.528$, $N_Y = 1.601$, $N_Z = 1.629$, $N_Z - N_X = 0.101$. Ref: 214a.

6-Carboxy-2-nitrobenzoic acid benzyl ester or 3-nitrophthalic acid 2-benzyl ester [$C_6H_3(NO_2)(CO_2H)(CO_2 \cdot CH_2C_6H_5$] is monoclinic in rhombic plates with

[1] It is not known whether the following ten esters of nitrophthalic acid are hydrated or not.

M.P. = 174 – 175° after one recrystallization from ethanol and one from water. (+)2V = 83°. N_X = 1.586, N_Y = 1.636, N_Z = 1.739, $N_Z - N_X$ = 0.153. Ref: 214a.

2-Carboxy-4-nitrobenzoic acid methyl ester or 4-nitrophthalic acid 1-methyl ester [$C_6H_3(NO_2)(CO_2H)(CO_2 \cdot CH_3)$] is monoclinic or orthorhombic in six-sided thin plates with M.P. = 129° after recrystallization from several organic solvents and finally from water. (–)2V = large. N_X = 1.525, N_Y = 1.530, N_Z = 1.673, $N_Z - N_X$ = 0.148. (But indices require (+)2V = 15° *ca.* – A.N.W.). Ref: 214a.

2-Carboxy-4-nitrobenzoic acid ethyl ester or 4-nitrophthalic acid 1-ethyl ester [$C_6H_3(NO_2)(CO_2H)(CO_2 \cdot C_2H_5)$] is monoclinic in prismatic plates with M.P. = 127 – 128° after recrystallization from benzene and from water. (–)2V = 22.5°. N_X = 1.445, N_Y = 1.665, N_Z = 1.676, $N_Z - N_X$ = 0.231. Ref: 214a.

4-Nitrophthalimide {$NO_2 \cdot C_6H_3(CO_2)_2 \cdot NH$} is dimorphous; one phase (from alcohol is probably orthorhombic having Z || elongation. M.P. 198°. No good cleavage, but conchoidal fracture. (–)2V = 60°, N_Y = 1.703. A second phase (from fusion) has (–)2E = 33°. Color yellow. Ref: 530.

N-Ethyl-4-nitrophthalimide {$NO_2 \cdot C_6H_3(CO_2)_2 \cdot N \cdot C_2H_5$} is probably monoclinic, (or triclinic) crystals usually giving a slightly uncentered biaxial optic axis interference figure. M.P. 114°. No distinct cleavage, but conchoidal fracture. (–)2V = 85° – 90°, N_Y = 1.652. Color yellow. Ref: 530.

N-*n*-Propyl-4-nitrophthalimide {$NO_2 \cdot C_6H_3(CO_2)_2 \cdot N \cdot C_3H_7$} is biaxial. M.P. 102°. No cleavage, but conchoidal fracture. Crystals platy (without angular outlines) usually give a biaxial optic axis interference figure. (–)2V = 73°, N_Y = 1.635. Ref: 530.

N-*n*-Butyl-4-nitrophthalimide {$NO_2 \cdot C_6H_3(CO_2)_2N \cdot C_4H_9$} is dimorphous. One phase (from alcohol) is probably orthorhombic, having Z || elongation. Conchoidal fracture. M.P. 95 – 96°. Crystal plates often give a biaxial optic axis interference figure. (+)2V = 33 – 34°, N_Y = 1.623. A second phase (from fusion) often gives an uncentered optic axis interference figure. (–)2V = 80 – 85°. Ref: 530.

N-*n*-Amyl-4-nitrophthalimide {$NO_2 \cdot C_6H_3(CO_2)_2 \cdot N \cdot C_5H_{11}$} is probably orthorhombic, having Z || elongation. Conchoidal fracture. M.P. 95°. Plates give an optic axis interference figure. (–)2V = 66°, N_Y = 1.596. Ref: 530.

N-*n*-Hexyl-4-nitrophthalimide {$NO_2 \cdot C_6H_3(CO_2)_2 \cdot N \cdot C_6H_{13}$} is probably orthorhombic, with Z || elongation. Conchoidal fracture. M.P. 95°. (–)2V = 84°, N_Y = 1.590. Ref: 530.

N-*n*-Heptyl-4-nitrophthalimide {$NO_2 \cdot C_6H_3(CO_2)_2N \cdot C_7H_{15}$} is probably monoclinic having X ∧ elongation = 40° *ca.* Conchoidal fracture. M.P. 93°. (–?)2V = 85° – 90°, N_Y = 1.591. Ref: 530.

N-*n*-Octyl-4-nitrophthalimide {$NO_2 \cdot C_6H_3(CO_2)_2N \cdot C_8H_{17}$} is dimorphous; one phase (from alcohol) has no crystal boundaries, but much conchoidal fracture. M.P. 88°. (+)2V = 45 – 50°, N_Y = 1.580. Another phase (from fusion) has (+)2E = 120 – 125°. Ref: 530.

N-n-Nonyl-4-nitrophthalimide $\{NO_2 \cdot C_6H_3(CO_2)_2N \cdot C_9H_{19}\}$ is probably orthorhombic, crystals being bladed with Z || elongation. M.P. 89°. $(\pm)2V = 90°$ *ca*, $N_Y = 1.600$. Ref:530.

N-n-Decyl-4-nitrophthalimide $\{NO_2 \cdot C_6H_3(CO_2)_2N \cdot C_{10}H_{21}\}$ is platy with no angular outline. M.P. 88°. $(+?)2V = 88 - 90°$, $N_Y = 1.581$. Ref: 530.

N-Benzyl-4-nitrophthalimide $\{NO_2 \cdot C_6H_3(CO_2)_2N \cdot CH_2C_6H_5\}$ is probably dimorphous. One phase (from alcohol) is probably orthorhombic forming long plates with X || elongation and Y normal to the plates. No cleavage. M.P. 164°. $(+)2V = 72°$, $N_Y = 1.640$. Another phase (from fusion) seems to be optically negative. Ref: 530.

1,4-Benzenedicarboxylic acid or terephthalic acid $\{C_6H_4(CO_2H)_2\}$ is monoclinic or triclinic with $X \wedge c = 14°$ and $(-)2V = 63°30'$, $N_X = 1.436$, $N_Y = 1.616$, $N_Z = 1.706$, $N_Z - N_X = 0.270$. Ref: 397.

Subclass C. Tricarboxylic Acids and Derivatives

1,2,3-Benzenetricarboxylic acid or hemimellitic acid $[C_6H_3(CO_2H)_3]$ is triclinic with[1] $a:b:c = 0.587:1:0.363$, $\alpha = 122°18'$, $\beta = 92°22'$, $\gamma = 118°26'$. Crystals vertically elongated with {100}, {010}, {001}, {110}, etc. Good 010 and 201 cleavages. D 1.545. M.P. 191°. The optic plane is nearly normal to 010 and to 201; X is nearly normal to 201 and Z is nearly normal to 010; the angle between these cleavages is 87°50′. $(-)2V = 47°$, $r < v$. $N_X = 1.4316$, $N_Y = 1.6358$, $N_Z = 1.6744$ calc., $N_Z - N_X = 0.2428$. Ref: 1,2.

s-Trimesic acid ethyl ester $\{C_6H_3(CO_2C_2H_5)_3\}$ is hexagonal with $c/a = 1.825$. Crystals prismatic. Good 0001 cleavage. M.P. 134 – 135°. Uniaxial negative with $N_O = 1.69$, $N_E = 1.48$, $N_O - N_E = 0.21$. Ref: 568a.

Subclass F. Hexacarboxylic Acids and Derivatives

Aluminum benzenehexacarboxylate octadecahydrate or aluminum mellitate octadecahydrate $[Al_2C_6(CO_2)_6 \cdot 18H_2O]$ is tetragonal with $c/a = 0.745$. Crystals {111} pyramids. Indistinct 111 cleavage. H 2-2.5. D 1.6. Uniaxial negative with $N_O = 1.539$ D, $N_E = 1.511$, $N_O - N_E = 0.028$. Color honey yellow, reddish, white. The natural substance is called "mellite"; found in brown coal.
Ref: 118, 379a.

Subclass J. Hyroxycarboxylic Acids and Derivatives

2-Hydroxybenzoic acid or salicylic acid $[C_6H_4(OH) \cdot CO_2H]$ is monoclinic with $a:b:c = 1.030:1:0.434$, $\beta = 91°22'$. *a* 11.56, *b* 11.22, *c* 4.93 Å U.C. 4. Crystals acicular with {110}, {201}, {111}, etc. Perfect 110 and poor 001 cleavages. D 1.439. M.P. 156°. The optic plane is 010; $Z \wedge c = 42.5°$. An optic axis is at 23° to *c* for yellow and 28° for blue. $(-)2V = ?$, $N_X = 1.55$, $N_Y = ?$, $N_Z = 1.75$, $N_Z - N_X = 0.20$. Extinction at 28° to *c* (on 110?).
Ref: 34, 35, 118, 123, 343c, 419.

[1] *a* and *b* interchanged to make $b > a > c$.

Sodium 2-hydroxybenzoate or sodium salicylate [$C_6H_4(OH)\cdot CO_2Na$] has parallel extinction and positive elongation with $N_1 = 1.40$, $N_2 = 1.69$, $N_2 - N_1 = 0.29$. Also $N_X = 1.435$, $N_Y = ?$, $N_Z = 1.686$, $N_Z - N_X = 0.251$. Again $N_X = 1.421$, $N_Y = 1.445$, $N_Z = 1.678$, $N_Z - N_X = 0.257$. $\therefore (+)2V = 32°$ calc.
Ref: 34, 35, 343c, 518.

Ammonium 2-hydroxybenzoate hemihydrate or ammonium salicylate hemihydrate [$NH_4CO_2\cdot C_6H_4(OH)\cdot 0.5H_2O$] is monoclinic with $a:b:c = 0.762:1:0.593$, $\beta = 127°4'$. Crystals six-sided {010} tablets with {110}, {001}, {11$\bar{1}$}. Parallel extinction and positive elongation with $N_1 = 1.59$, $N_2 = 1.72$, $N_2 - N_1 = 0.13$.
Ref: 34, 35.

Strontium salicylate dihydrate [$(C_6H_4OHCO_2)_2Sr\cdot 2H_2O$] forms a white powder with $N_X = 1.485$, $N_Y = ?$, $N_Z = 1.693$, $N_Z - N_X = 0.208$. Ref: 524.

Hexamethylenetetramine salicylate [$(CH_2)_6N_4\cdot C_6H_4(OH)CO_2H$] is monoclinic with $a:b:c = 2.035:1:4.538$, $\beta = 110°43'$. Crystals often elongated along a. D 1.26. The optic plane is 010. (−)2V = 70° (red) calc. $N_X' = 1.530$ (red); 1.560 (blue), $N_Y = 1.6039$ (red), 1.6329 (blue); $N_Z = 1.700$ (red), $N_Z - N_X > 0.170$.
Ref: 220.

2-Acetoxybenzoic acid or aspirin or acetylsalicylic acid [$C_6H_4(CO_2H)(CH_3CO_2)$] is monoclinic prismatic with $a:b:c = 1.739:1:1.739$, $\beta = 95°42.5'$. Space group $P2_1/c$; a 11.37, b 6.54, c 11.37 Å. U.C. 4. Also given as $a:b:c = 1.712:1:1.681$, $\beta = 95°27'$. Crystals {001} tablets sometimes elongated along b or a, with {100}, {011}, {$\bar{2}$01}, etc. Perfect 001 and distinct 100 cleavage. H 1. M.P. 133.5°. D 1.35. The optic plane and Z are normal to 010; X $\wedge$ c = − 48°; 45° − 46°. $N_1 = 1.565$ often seen.

λ	(−)2V	N_X	N_Y	N_Z	$N_Z - N_X$	Author
		1.505	1.645	1.655	0.150	Keenan
	30°30′	1.502	1.640	1.652	0.150	Watanabe
576	15°46′	1.5042	1.6424	1.6554	0.1512	Nitta
546	16°14′	1.5066	1.6464	1.6604	0.1538	Nitta
436	18°31′	1.5216	1.6720	1.6914	0.1698	Nitta

Aspirin or acetylsalicylic acid is also orthorhombic with $a:b:c = 0.906:1:0.391$. Crystals show {110}, {201}, {111}, {311}. Perfect 110 cleavage. The optic plane is 001; X = a. (−)2V = ? It is also said to be trigonal.
Ref: 130, 152, 221a, 260, 344, 518, 562.

Phenyl 2-hydroxybenzoate or phenyl salicylate or salol [$C_6H_4(OH)\cdot CO\cdot O\cdot C_6H_5$] is orthorhombic with $a:b:c = 0.968:1:0.697$. Crystals {010} tablets with {100}, {111}, etc.; also {100} plates. No distinct cleavage. M.P.42°. The optic plane is 100; optic angle through 010 in oil = 92°30′, r > v. $N_1 = 1.50$, $N_2 > 1.66$, $N_2 - N_1 > 0.16$.
Ref: 119, 239.

Acetolsalicylate or salicetol [$HOC_6H_4CO_2CH_2COCH_3$] is monoclinic. Crystals (nearly) rectangular plates with cleavage parallel to elongation. Z $\wedge$ elongation = 43°. Y = *b*. (+)2V = 70°, r < v strong; also inclined dispersion. Soluble in alcohol and index liquids. N_X = about 1.52, N_Z = about 1.65. Ref: 123.

Ethyl 3,5-dichloro-2-hydroxybenzoate or ethyl 3,5-dichlorosalicylate [$C_6H_2Cl_2(OH)\cdot CO_2(C_2H_5)$] is orthorhombic with *a*:*b*:*c* = 0.940:1:0.427. Crystals {010} tablets with {001}, {120}, etc. No distinct cleavage. M.P. 57°. The optic plane is 010; X = *c*. N_X = 1.331 Li, 1.335 Na, 1.338 Tl; N_Y = 1.421 calc.; N_Z = 1.455 Li, 1.459 Na, 1.463 Tl; $N_Z - N_X$ = 0.124 Na. (-)2E = 111°12′ Li, 112°33′ Na, 111°38′ Tl. ∴ (-)2V = 72° Na. Ref: 118.

p-Methoxybenzoic acid or anisic acid [$C_6H_4(O\cdot CH_3)\cdot CO_2H$] is monoclinic with *a*:*b*:*c* = 1.550:1:0.362, β = 98°26′. Crystals long prisms with {110}, {100}, {010}, {001, {111}. No distinct cleavage. D 1.36 - 1.38. M.P.184°. The optic plane is 010; extinction in 010 at - 18° to *c*. 2E = 100°. "Parallel extinction and negative elongation," according to Bolland, with N_1 = 1.48, N_2 = 1.575, $N_2 - N_1$ = 0.095. Ref: 34, 35, 118,

Methyl *p*-hydroxybenzoate or methylparaben ($OH\cdot C_6H_4\cdot CO_2\cdot CH_3$) is orthorhombic (?). Crystals acicular to equant. M.P. 126 - 127°. Z || elongation. (-)2V = 36°, r > v very strong. N_X = 1.590, N_Y = 1.688, N_Z = 1.695, $N_Z - N_X$ = 0.105. Again: N_X = 1.540, N_Y = 1.689, N_Z = 1.700, $N_Z - N_X$ = 0.060. Ref: 433b, 524.

Ethyl *p*-hydroxybenzoate ($OH\cdot C_6H_4\cdot CO_2\cdot C_2H_5$) is orthorhombic. Crystals tabular to equant. M.P. 115 - 116°. Elongation ±. (-)2V = 64°, r < v rather strong. N_X = 1.423, N_Y = 1.648, N_Z = 1.768, $N_Z - N_X$ = 0.345. Ref: 433b.

n-Propyl *p*-hydroxybenzoate or propylparaben ($OH\cdot C_6H_4\cdot CO_2\cdot C_3H_7$) is orthorhombic (?). M.P. 96 - 97°. Crystals laths or feathery. Elongation +. (-)2V = 70°, r < v. N_X = 1.488, N_Y = 1.650, N_Z = 1.768, $N_Z - N_X$ = 0.280. Ref: 433b.

n-Butyl *p*-hydroxybenzoate ($OH\cdot C_6H_4\cdot CO_2\cdot C_4H_9$) is orthorhombic (?). M.P. 69 - 71°. Crystals large. Parallel extinction. (-)2V = 61°, r < v strong. N_X = 1.436, N_Y = 1.645, N_Z = 1.744, $N_Z - N_X$ = 0.308. Ref: 433b.

Benzyl *p*-hydroxybenzoate ($OH\cdot C_6H_4\cdot CO_2\cdot C_6H_5\cdot CH_2$) is orthorhombic. Elongation ±. (+)2V = 82°, r > v. N_X = 1.588, N_Y = 1.651, N_Z = 1.783, $N_Z - N_X$ = 0.195. Ref: 433b.

$$\left[C_6H_4(CH_3)\cdot C\begin{matrix}\nearrow N\cdot O\cdot CO\cdot C_6H_5\\ \searrow O\cdot CO\cdot C_6H_4(O\cdot CH_3)\end{matrix}\right]$$

p-Tolbenzanishydroxylamine or anisoyl-*p*-toluhydroxamic acid benzoate or anisic *p*-toluhydroxamic anhydride benzoate is monoclinic with *a*:*b*:*c* = 0.429:1:0.441, β = 98°11′. Crystals prismatic or {001} tablets with {110}, {010}, {11$\bar{1}$}, etc. Imperfect 100 cleavage. M.P. 142°. The optic plane is 010; Z $\wedge$ *c* = - 33°. (-)2V = 69°0′ Li, 68°32′ Na, 68°0′ Tl. N_Y = 1.6843 Li, 1.6944 Na, 1.7006 Tl. Ref: 119.

Benzanis-*p*-tolhydroxylamine or *p*-tol-uylbenzohydroxamic acid anisate or benzo-hydroxamic *p*-toluic anhydride anisate has two phases. The α-phase (I) is mono

$$C_6H_5 \cdot C \begin{cases} N \cdot O \cdot CO \cdot C_6H_4(O \cdot CH_3) \\ O \cdot CO \cdot C_6H_4(CH_3) \end{cases}$$

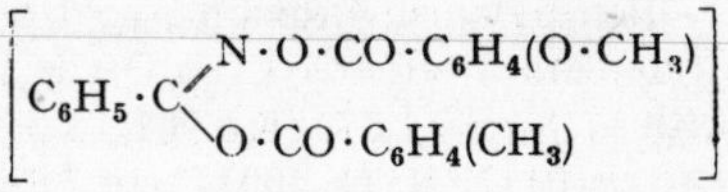

clinic with $a:b:c = 0.950:1:1.614$, $\beta = 94°21'$. Crystals {001} tablets with {111}, {11$\bar{1}$}, {010}, etc. Perfect 010 and imperfect 001 and 111 cleavages. M.P. 120 - 121°. The optic plane is nearly parallel to 001; Z nearly parallel to *a*. $(+)2V = 77°18'$ Li, 78° 59′ Na, 76°39′ Tl. $N_X = 1.5480$ Li, 1.5487 Na, 1.5525 Tl; $N_Y = 1.6322$ Li, 1.6382 Na, 1.6442 Tl; $N_Z = 1.7940$ Li, 1.8159 Na, 1.8307 Tl; $N_Z - N_X = 0.2667$ Na. The β-phase (II) is also monoclinic with $a:b:c = 1.453:1:1.267$, $\beta = 98°22'$. Crystals prismatic with {120}, {110}, {100}, {001}, etc. Perfect 010 and less distinct 100 cleavages. The optic plane is 010; Z ∧ *c* = + 30° *ca*. $(+)2V = 55°46'$ Li, 56°24′ Na, 56°59′ Tl. $N_Y = 1.6352$ Li, 1.6381 Na, 1.6465 Tl. Ref: 119.

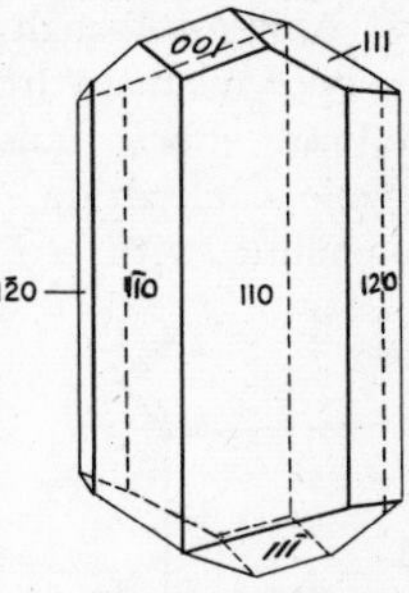

Fig. 69. *p*-Tolanishy-droxamic acid.

p-Tolanishydroxamic acid or *p*-toluhydroxamic acid anisate $[C_6H_4(CH_3) \cdot C(OH):N \cdot O \cdot CO \cdot C_6H_4(O \cdot CH_3)]$ is monoclinic with $a:b:c = 0.850:1:0.504$, $\beta = 107°41'$. Crystals incomplete prisms with {110}, {120}, {11$\bar{1}$}, {001}. Fig. 69. Imperfect 11$\bar{1}$ cleavage. M.P. 155°. The optic plane is 010; Z nearly normal to 001. $(+)2V = 63°49'$ Na. $N_Y = 1.579$ Na, $N_Z - N_X = $ strong. Ref: 119.

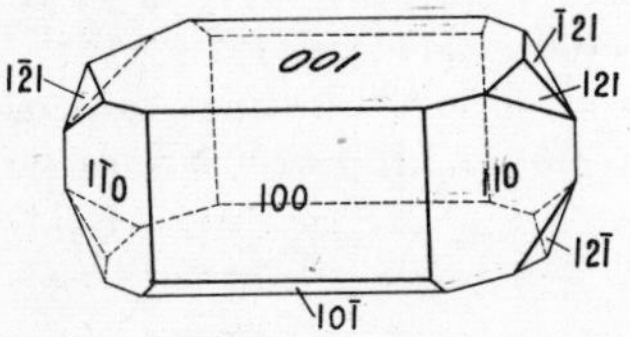

Fig. 70. Tolanisbenzhydroxylamine.

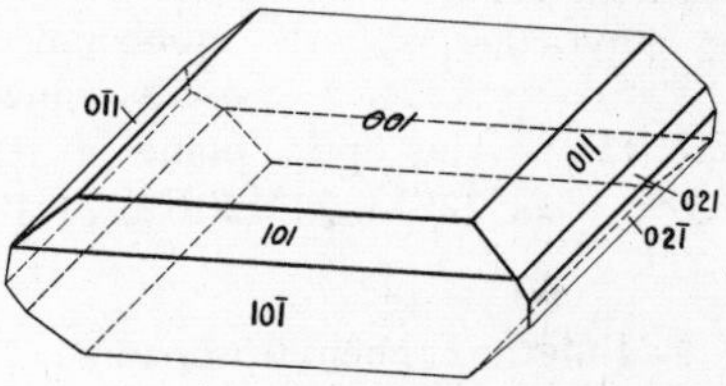

Fig. 71. Anis-*p*-tolhydroxamic acid.

p-Tolanisbenzhydroxylamine or benzoyl-*p*-toluhydroxamic acid ani-sate or benzoic *p*-toluhydroxamic an-hydride anisate is monoclinic with

$$C_6H_4(CH_3) \cdot C \begin{cases} N \cdot O \cdot CO \cdot C_6H_4(O \cdot CH_3) \\ O \cdot CO \cdot C_6H_5 \end{cases}$$

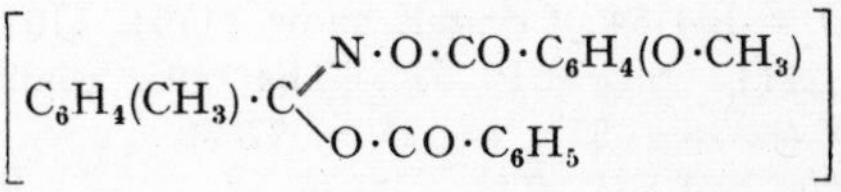

$a:b:c = 1.177:1:1.125$, $\beta = 100°30.5'$. Crystals {001} tablets with {100}, {110}, {10$\bar{1}$}, etc. Fig. 70. Imperfect 010 cleavage. M.P. 146°. The optic plane and X are normal to 010; Z ∧ *c* = − 62.5°. $(−)2V = 84°24'$ Li, 84°55′ Na, 85°31′ Tl. $N_Y = 1.6378$ Li, 1.6447 Na, 1.6509 Tl; $N_Z - N_X = $ strong. Ref: 119.

Anis-*p*-tolhydroxamic acid or anishydroxamic acid *p*-toluate $[C_6H_4(OCH_3) \cdot C(OH):N \cdot O \cdot CO \cdot C_6H_4(CH_3)]$ is monoclinic with $a:b:c = 0.405:1:0.976$, $\beta = 100°42'$. Crystals {001} tablets with {011}, {101}, {10$\bar{1}$}, etc. Fig. 71. Perfect 001 cleavage. M.P. 146. The optic plane is 010; Z ∧ *c* = + 49°. $(+)2V = 50°$ 4′ Li, 50° 10′ Na, 50°12′ Tl. $N_Y = 1.5542$ Li, 1.5607 Na, 1.5666 Tl; $N_Z - N_X = $ rather strong. Ref: 119.

Benzoylanishydroxamic acid ethyl ether or anisohydroxamic benzoic anhydride ethyl ether [$C_6H_4(O\cdot CH_3)\cdot C(:N\cdot O\cdot C_2H_5)\cdot O\cdot CO\cdot C_6H_5$] is monoclinic with $a:b:c = 1.372:1:0.901$, $\beta = 102°52.5'$. Crystals prismatic with {110}, {20$\bar{1}$}, {011}, {11$\bar{1}$}, {001}, etc. Fig. 72. M.P. 93 - 94°. Imperfect 001 cleavage. The optic plane and Z are normal to 010; X $\wedge$ c = + 1°. (+)2V = 73°5′ Li, 71°55′ Na, 70°45′ Tl. N_Y = 1.6234 Li, 1.6268 Na, 1.6304 Tl. Ref: 119.

Anis-*p*-tolbenzhydroxylamine or benzoylanishydroxamic acid *p*-toluate or anisohydroxamic benzoic anhydride *p*-toluate is [α-$C_6H_4(O\cdot CH_3)\cdot C\langle^{N\cdot O\cdot CO\cdot C_6H_4(CH_3)}_{O\cdot CO\cdot C_6H_5}$] monoclinic with $a:b:c = 2.157:1:0.907$, $\beta = 92°38'$. Crystals six-sided {001} tablets with {110}, {100}, {111}, etc. Fig. 73. Distinct 001 and imperfect 110 cleavages. M.P. 162°. The optic plane and X are normal to 010; Z $\wedge$ c = - 60° *ca.* (distinct dispersion). (+)2V = 64°56′ Li, 64°32.5′ Na, 64°12′ Tl. N_Y = 1.6255 Li, 1.6272 Na, 1.6282 Tl; $N_Z - N_X$ = strong. The β-phase (II) is also monoclinic with $a:b:c$ = 0.894:1:0.291 and M.P. 132°. Ref: 119.

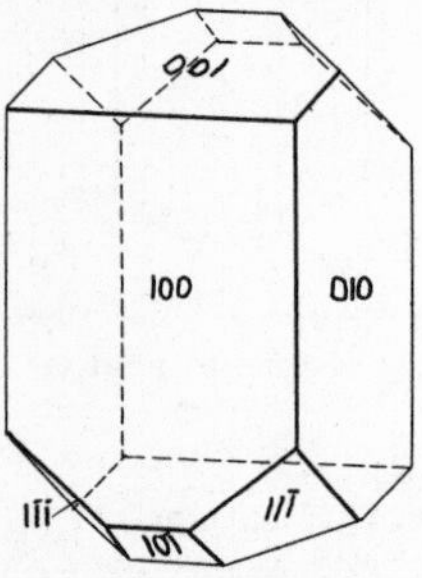

Fig. 72. Benzoylanishydroxamic acid ethyl ether.

Anisbenz-*p*-tolhydroxylamine or *p*-toluylanishydroxamic acid [$C_6H_4(O\cdot CH_3)C\langle^{NO\cdot CO\cdot C_6H_5}_{O\cdot CO\cdot C_6H_4(CH_3)}$] benzoate or anisohydroxamic *p*-toluic anhydride benzoate is monoclinic with $a:b:c = 1.670:1:1.977$, $\beta = 97°21'$. Crystals show {001}, {100}, {111}, {11$\bar{1}$}, etc. M.P. 133 - 134°. The optic plane is 010; Z $\wedge$ c = + 50.5° (distinct dispersion). (+)2V = 71°22′ Li, 71°12′ Na, 71°4′ Tl. N_Y = 1.6103 Li, 1.6200 Na, 1.6298 Tl. Ref: 119.

2-(4-Methoxyphenyl)propanoic acid or *p*-methoxyhydratropic acid [$CH_3OC_6H_4\cdot CH(CH_3)CO_2H$] is monoclinic with $a:b:c$=1.055:1:0.967, β = 104°34′. Crystals show {110}, {101}, {001}, {22$\bar{1}$}, etc. M.P. 57°. The optic plane is 010; Z $\wedge$ c = + 57°. (+)2V = 77°58′, r>v distinct. N_Y = 1.503. Ref: 118.

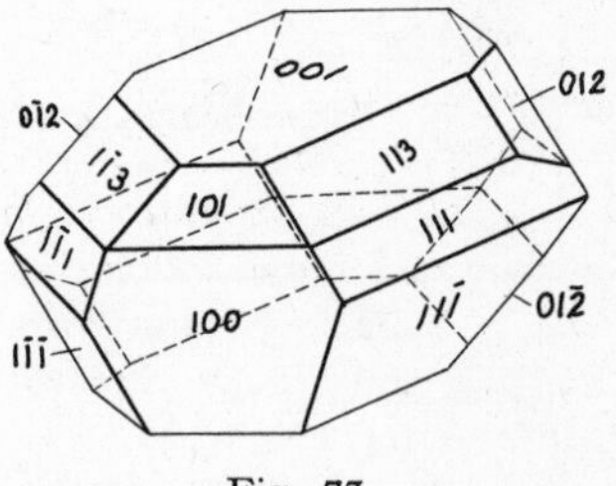

Fig. 73. Anis-*p*-tolbenzhydroxylamine.

3-(2-Hydroxyphenyl)propenoic acid or *o*-coumaric acid or *o*-hydroxycinnamic acid ($C_9H_8O_3$) has parallel extinction and negative elongation with N_1 = 1.56, N_2 > 1.95, $N_2 - N_1$ > 0.39. Ref: 34, 35.

Ethyl 3-(4 methoxyphenyl)propenoate or ethyl *p*-methoxycinnamate [$C_6H_4(O\cdot CH_3)\cdot CH:CH\cdot CO_2(C_2H_5)$] is monoclinic with $a:b:c = 1.375:1:0.888$, β = 93°34′. Crystals prismatic with {100}, {120}, {110}, {001}, etc. Perfect 110 cleavage. M.P. 52°. The optic plane is 010; extinction in 010 at - 49°10′ to c. N_Y = 1.545. Ref: 118.

Benzyl hydroxydiphenylacetate or benzyl benzilate $[(C_6H_5)_2C(OH)\cdot CO_2(CH_2\cdot C_6H_5)]$ is monoclinic with $a:b:c = 0.585:1:0.431$, $\beta = 121°52'$. Crystals {001} tablets with {010}, {110}, {120}, etc. Fig. 74. M.P. 75 – 76°. The optic plane and Z are normal to 010; X $\wedge$ c = – 104°. (–)2V = 73°26′ Li, 74°10′ Na, 74°52′ Tl. N_Y = 1.5922 Li, 1.6010 Na, 1.6081 Tl, $N_Z - N_X$ = weak. Ref: 119.

Bromoshikimilactone $(C_7H_9O_5Br)$ is hexagonal trapezohedral with c/a = 2.232. Crystals acicular with {10$\bar{1}$1}, {20$\bar{2}\bar{1}$}, {000$\bar{1}$}. Perfect 0001 cleavage. D 1.965. M.P. 235°. Uniaxial positive with N_O = 1.5840, N_E = 1.6262, $N_E - N_O$ = 0.0422 D. (α) = + 22°. Ref: 79, 117.

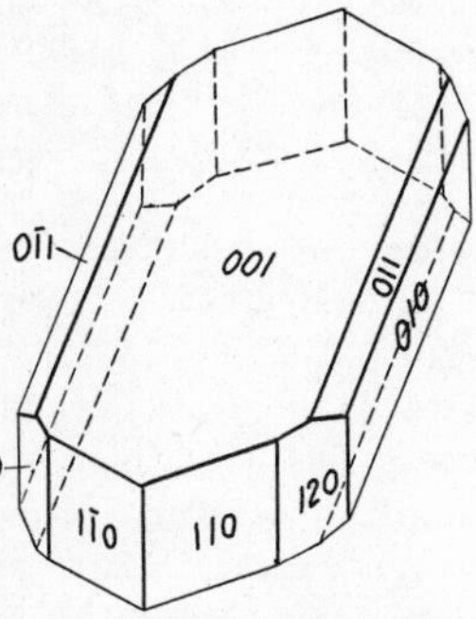

Fig. 74. Benzyl benzylate.

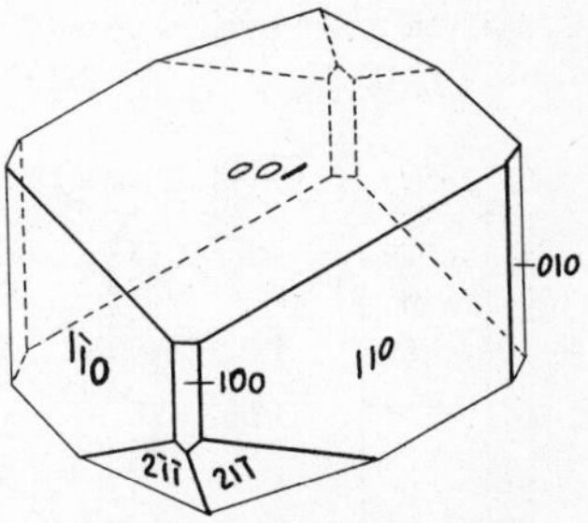

Fig. 75. Diphenyl-2,4-dihydroxyphenyl acetic acid.

1,2-Dibromo-3,4,6-trihydroxycyclohexane carboxylic acid or dibromotrihydroshikimic acid $[C_6H_6Br_2(OH)_3CO_2H]$ is orthorhombic disphenoidal with $a:b:c = 0.933:1:1.010$. Crystals sphenoidal with {111}, {001}, {1$\bar{1}$1}, {110}. M.P. 188° *ca.* The optic plane is 001. (+)2V = 76°43′. N_X = 1.6420, N_Y = 1.6618, N_Z = 1.6952, $N_Z - N_X$ = 0.0432 Na. (α) = – 58°. Ref: 79, 117.

(2,4-Dihydroxyphenyl)diphenylacetic acid or diphenyl(2,4-dihydroxyphenyl)-acetic acid $[(C_6H_5)_2C_6H_3(OH)_2C\cdot CO_2H]$ is monoclinic with $a:b:c = 1.114:1:1.812$, $\beta = 120°27'$. Crystals show {001}, {110}, {21$\bar{1}$}, {010}, etc. Fig. 75. No (distinct cleavage. D 1.29. The optic plane and X are normal to 010; Z $\wedge$ c = 7°. (–)2V = 77°18′. N_X = 1.5973, N_Y = 1.6587, N_Z = 1.6979, $N_Z - N_X$ = 0.1006. Ref: 119.

Ammonium 3,4,6-trihydroxy-1-cyclohexene-1-carboxylate or ammonium shikimate $[C_6H_6(OH)_3\cdot CO_2(NH_4)]$ is orthorhombic disphenoidal with $a:b:c = 0.827:1:1.759$. Crystals {001} tablets with {110}, {010}, etc. Perfect 010 cleavage. The optic plane is 001; X = a. (–)2V = 68°37′ Na. N_X = 1.4679 C, 1.4699 D, 1.4763 F; N_Y = 1.5811 C, 1.5865 D, 1.5947 F; N_Z = 1.6459 C, 1.6522 D, 1.6681 F; $N_Z - N_X$ = 0.1823 D. Ref: 79, 117.

3,4,5-Trihydroxybenzoic acid monohydrate or gallic acid monohydrate $[C_6H_2(OH)_3CO_2H\cdot H_2O]$ is monoclinic with $a:b:c = 1.217:1:0.841$, $\beta = 91°12'$. Crystals {100} plates, always twinned on 100, with {150}, {101}, {10$\bar{2}$}, etc. Imperfect 10$\bar{2}$ cleavage. The optic plane is 010; an optic axis (doubled by twinning) visible through 100. Parallel extinction and negative elongation with $N_1 = 1.49$, $N_2 = 1.69$, $N_2 - N_1 = 0.20$. Also $N_1 = 1.489$, $N_2 = 1.68$, $N_3 > 1.70$. Another phase is known. Ref: 34, 35, 118, 343c.

(2,3-Dimethoxyphenoxy)acetic acid or decarboxyrissic acid $[(CH_3O)_2C_6H_3OCH_2CO_2H]$ forms lath-like rods from benzene, often with six sides. The extinction is inclined, and the sign of elongation is negative. Interference figures often show one optic axis. (-)2V = 45° calc. $N_X = 1.508$, $N_Y = 1.655$, $N_Z = 1.685$, all ±·003, $N_Z - N_X = 0.179$. Ref: 184.

2-(Carboxymethyl)-4,5-dimethoxyphenoxy acetic acid or derric acid $[C_6H_2(OCH_3)_2(CH_2CO_2H)(OCH_2CO_2H)]$ is probably monoclinic. M.P. 168°. Positive elongation and inclined extinction. (+)2V = 70° calc. $N_X = 1.525$, $N_Y = 1.565$ $N_Z = 1.640$, $N_Z - N_X = 0.115$. Colorless. Ref: 173a.

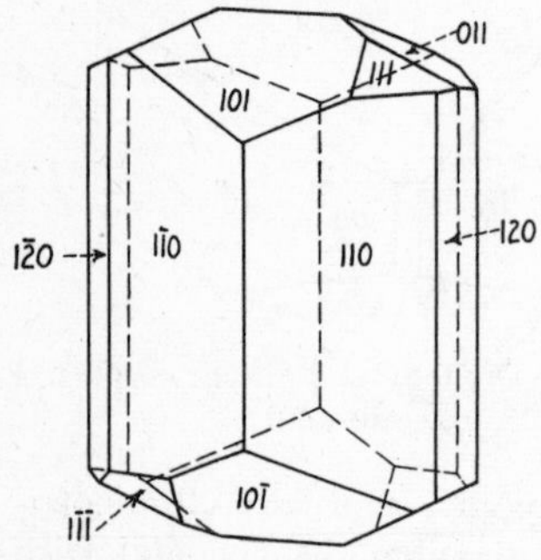

Fig. 76.
Ethyl tetra-acetylquinate.

1,3,4,5-Tetrahydroxycyclohexanecarboxylic acid or quinic acid $[C_6H_7(OH)_4CO_2H]$ is monoclinic with $a:b:c = 0.590:1:0.639$, $\beta = 131°32'$. Crystals of varied habit with {110}, {001}, {010}, {11̄1̄}, {011}, etc. Imperfect 001 cleavage. M.P. 162°. D 1.64. The optic plane is 010; an optic axis makes an angle of - 30° with *c*. Parallel extinction and negative elongation with $N_1 = 1.55$, $N_2 = 1.56$, $N_2 - N_1 = 0.01$. Ref: 34, 35, 117.

Ethyl 1,3,4,5-tetra-acetoxycyclohexanecarboxylate or ethyl quinate tetraacetate or ethyl tetra-acetylquinate $[C_6H_7(O_2CCH_3)_4(CO_2C_2H_5)]$ is orthorhombic disphenoidal with $a:b:c = 0.531:1:0.444$. Crystals short prismatic with {110}, {120}, {101}, {011}, {111}, etc. Fig. 76. Imperfect 001 and 120 cleavages. M.P. 135°. The optic plane is 100; X = *c*. (-)2V = 79°58′. $N_X = 1.4869$ Li, 1.4897 Na, 1.4931 Tl; $N_Y = 1.4967$ Li, 1.4995 Na, 1.5029 Tl; $N_Z = 1.5111$ Li, 1.5138 Na, 1.5172 Tl, $N_Z - N_X = 0.0241$ Na. Ref: 117.

2-(2,4-Dicarboxy-3-hydroxyphenoxy)-2,2-dimethylacetic acid or 4-(2-carboxyisopropoxy)-2-hydroxyisophthalic acid or nicouic acid $[C_6H_2(CO_2H)_2(OH)O \cdot C(CH_3)_2CO_2H]$ melts at 196° with decomposition. It has inclined extinction. $N_X = 1.455$, $N_Y = ?$, $N_Z > 1.740$, $N_Z - N_X > 0.285$. Colorless. Ref: 175.

Ouabain or acocantherin $(C_{29}H_{44}O_{12})$ is dimorphous. Phase I, crystallized from water, is probably tetragonal. Crystals usually rectangular plates. Uniaxial negative with $N_O = 1.525$, $N_E = 1.523$, $N_O - N_E = 0.002$. Phase II, crystallized from alcohol, is probably orthorhombic; crystals rectangular rods with Z ∥ elongation. (+)2V = 67° calc. $N_X = 1.533$, $N_Y = 1.547$, $N_Z = 1.580$, $N_Z - N_X = 0.047$. Ref: 523f.

Subclass K. Carbonyl Carboxylic Acids and Derivatives

Santonic acid ($C_{15}H_{20}O_4$) is orthorhombic disphenoidal[1] with $a:b:c = 0.639:1:0.612$. Crystals {010} plates with {110}, {101}, {011}, {001}, etc. Perfect 001 cleavage. Decomposes at 120°. The optic plane is 010; *a* is the acute bisectrix for blue with 2V = 87°40′; the optic angle for red is about 90°. Bolland gives $N_1 = 1.61$, $N_2 = 1.62$, $N_2 - N_1 = 0.01$, with parallel extinction and positive elongation. Ref: 34, 35, 119.

Methyl santonate ($C_{16}H_{22}O_4$) is orthorhombic disphenoidal[1] with $a:b:c = 0.938:1:0.501$. Crystals show {010}, {110}, {120}, {111}, {212}, etc. Perfect 010 cleavage. D 1.167. M.P. 86°. The optic plane is {010}; X = *a*. (-)2V = 74°24′ red, 75°21′ green, 76°14′ blue. $N_Y = 1.5236$ red, 1.5331 green. Ref: 119.

Ethyl santonate ($C_{17}H_{24}O_4$) is orthorhombic disphenoidal[1] with $a:b:c = 0.663:1:0.451$. Crystals show {010}, {110}, {011}, {120}, {101}, {111}. No distinct cleavage. D 1.15. M.P. 88 - 89°. The optic plane is 010; Z = *a*. (+)2V = 64°6′ red, 62°8′ green, 60°2′ blue. $N_X = 1.5288$ red, 1.5349 green, 1.5391 blue; $N_Y = 1.5334$ red, 1.5385 green, 1.5418 blue; $N_Z = 1.5455$ red (calc.); $N_Z - N_X = 0.0167$ red (calc.). Ref: 119.

Subclass L. Hydroxy Carbonyl Carboxylic Acids and Derivatives

6-Formyl-2,3-dimethoxybenzoic acid or 5,6-dimethoxyphthalaldehydic acid or 3,4-dimethoxybenzaldehyde-2-carboxylic acid or opianic acid [$C_6H_2(OCH_3)_2(CO_2H)(CHO)$] has parallel extinction and negative elongation with $N_1 = 1.51$, $N_2 = 1.66$, $N_2 - N_1 = 0.15$. Also reported doubtfully as (-)2V = ?, $N_X = 1.51$, N_Y = ?, $N_Z = 1.74$, $N_Z - N_X = 0.23$. Ref: 34, 35, 121a.

Class 6. Sulfonic Acids and Derivatives

Bismuth *m*-nitrobenzenesulfonate heptahydrate [$[C_6H_4(NO_2)\cdot SO_3]_3Bi\cdot 7H_2O$] is monoclinic with $a:b:c = 1.867:1:2.493$, $\beta = 93°8'$. Crystals elongated parallel to *b* with {100}, {001}, {302}, {301}, etc. Cleavage on 001. The optic plane is 010; $Z \wedge c = -93°$. (+)2V = 60° *ca.* $N_X = 1.537$, $N_Y = 1.6465$, $N_Z = 1.6805$, $N_Z - N_X = 0.1435$. Ref: 118.

Yttrium *m*-nitrobenzenesulfonate heptahydrate [$[C_6H_4(NO_2)\cdot SO_3]_3Y\cdot 7H_2O$] is monoclinic with $a:b:c = 1.867:1:2.493$, $\beta = 93°8'$. Crystals show {001}, {100}, {101}, {302}, {111}, etc. Lamellar twinning on 001. Cleavage on 001. The optic plane is 010; $Z \wedge c = -85°$. (+)2V = 50° *ca.* $N_X = 1.507$, $N_Y = 1.618$, $N_Z = 1.645$, $N_Z - N_X = 0.138$. Ref: 118.

Dibenzenesulfonyl trisulfide or *bis*(phenylsulfonyl) trisulfide or sulfobenzene trisulfide [$(C_6H_5SO_2)_2S_3$] is tetragonal trapezohedral with $c/a = 2.383$. Crystals pyramidal with {112}, {111}, {001}. M.P. 101 - 102°. Distinct rotation of the polarization plane. Uniaxial negative with $N_O = 1.7204$, $N_E = 1.7077$, $N_O - N_E = 0.0127$ Na. Ref: 119.

---

[1] *a b c* changed to *b c a* to make $b > a > c$.

Sodium *p*-toluenesulfonchloramide trihydrate or sodium *N*-chloro-*p*-toluenesulfonamide trihydrate or chloramine ($NaC_7H_7O_2NClS \cdot 3H_2O$) forms colorless prisms which explode at about 175 – 180° C. $N_X = 1.487$, $N_Y = 1.574$.
Ref: 343c.

Di-4-methylbenzenesulfonyl trisulfide or *bis*(*p*-tolylsulfonyl) trisulfide or *p*-sulfotoluene trisulfide $[[C_6H_4(CH_3) \cdot SO_2]_2S_3]$ is tetragonal (trapezohedral?) with $c/a = 2.691$. M.P. 180 – 182°. Uniaxial negative with $N_O = 1.7064$, $N_E = 1.6639$, $N_O - N_E = 0.0425$ Na.
Ref: 119.

Dicyanodiamide-*p*-toluene sulfonate $\{NH_2C(NH)NHCN \cdot C_6H_4CH_3HSO_3\}$ forms columnar to tabular crystals with curved sides. X ∧ elongation = 31° *ca.* (-)2E = 120°, 2V = 68° calc. $N_X = 1.547$, $N_Y = 1.582$, $N_Z = 1.598$, $N_Z - N_X = 0.051$.
Ref: 529, 563a.

Dicyanodiamide benzyl sulfonate $\{H_2NC(NH)NHCNC_6H_5CH_2HSO_3\}$ forms lamellar tablets with undulatory extinction. Z normal to tablet. (+)2V > 80°, $N_X = 1.485$, $N_Y = 1.590$, $N_Z = 1.715$ (calc. A.N.W.), $N_Z - N_X = 0.23$ (calc. A.N.W.).
Ref: 529.

S-Benzylisothiourea α-naphthalenesulfonate or benzylthiopseudourea salt of 1-naphthalenesulfonic acid $[NH_2 \cdot C(:NH) \cdot S \cdot CH_2 \cdot C_6H_5 \cdot C_{10}H_7SO_3H]$ forms rods with M.P.138°. Parallel extinction and ± elongation with $N_X = 1.611$, $N_Y = 1.672$, $N_Z = 1.680$, $N_Z - N_X = 0.069$. (-)2V = small.
Ref: 125.

S-Benzylisothiourea β-naphthalenesulfonate or benzylthiopseudourea salt of 2-naphthalenesulfonic acid $[NH_2 \cdot C(:NH) \cdot S \cdot CH_2 \cdot C_6H_5 \cdot C_{10}H_7SO_3H]$ forms rods with M.P. 193°. Parallel extinction and positive elongation with $N_X = 1.577$, $N_Y = 1.590$, $N_Z = 1.682$, $N_Z - N_X = 0.105$. (+)2V = small. (40° calc. – A.N.W.).
Ref: 125.

Ferrous 2-naphthalenesulfonate hexahydrate or ferrous β-naphthalene sulfonate hexahydrate $[Fe(C_{10}H_7SO_3)_2 \cdot 6H_2O]$ is biaxial in thin plates, sometimes showing a 140° termination. Stable in air. Loses its water at 150 – 160° and becomes brown. Plates normal to Y with parallel extinction. (+)2V = large. $N_X = 1.500$ D, N_Y = ?, $N_Z = 1.660$, $N_Z - N_X = 0.160$ D, all ±·005. Colorless.
Ref: 4.

1,5-Naphthalenedisulfonic acid tetrahydrate $[C_{10}H_6(SO_3)_2 \cdot H_2 \cdot 4H_2O]$ is monoclinic with $a:b:c = 0.794:1:1.252$, $\beta = 100°25.5'$. Crystals {001} tablets with {110}, {111}, etc. D 1.65. X = *b*; Z ∧ *c* = + 84°. (-)2V = 55°34′ Na calc. $N_X = 1.492$ Na, $N_Y = 1.675$, $N_Z = 1.739$, $N_Z - N_X = 0.247$. Ref: 374.

Ammonium 1,5-naphthalenedisulfonate $[C_{10}H_6(SO_3)_2 \cdot (NH_4)_2]$ is monoclinic with $a:b:c = 1.090:1:3.057$, $\beta = 96°51'$. Crystals {001} tablets with {111}, $\{11\bar{1}\}$, $\{10\bar{1}\}$. D 1.645. Z = *b*; X ∧ *c* = 73° to 80°. (-)2V = 49°40′ obs., 40°12′ calc., r < v. $N_X = 1.559$, $N_Y = 1.729$, $N_Z = 1.744$, $N_Z - N_X = 0.185$.
Ref: 374.

Barium 1,5-naphthalenedisulfonate monohydrate $[BaC_{10}H_6(SO_3)_2 \cdot H_2O]$ is orthorhombic with $a:b:c = 0.621:1:1.207$. Crystals show {001}, {111}, {221}, {010}. D 2.282. X = *b*; Z = *c*. (-)2V = 30° *ca.* obs., 40°22′ calc. $N_X = 1.614$ Na, $N_Y = 1.714$, $N_Z = 1.729$, $N_Z - N_X = 0.115$. Ref: 374.

Lithium 1,5-naphthalenedisulfonate dihydrate $[C_{10}H_6(SO_3)_2 \cdot Li_2 \cdot 2H_2O]$ is monoclinic with $a:b:c = 1.004:1:2.575$, $\beta = 97°24'$. Crystals {001} tablets with {111}, {11$\bar{1}$}, {012}, etc. D 1.664. X $\wedge$ *a* = 0° *ca.*; Z = *b*. (-)2V = 23° obs., 30° calc., r < v. $N_X = 1.507$, $N_Y = 1.638$, $N_Z = 1.698$, $N_Z - N_X = 0.191$. Ref: 374.

Sodium 1,5-naphthalenedisulfonate dihydrate $[C_{10}H_6(SO_3)_2 \cdot Na_2 \cdot 2H_2O]$ is monoclinic with $a:b:c = 0.965:1:2.642$, $\beta = 94°13.5'$. Crystals show {001}, {100}, {302}, {120}, elongated parallel to *b*. Twinning on 001. D 1.77. X = *b*; Z $\wedge$ *c* = 0° *ca.* (+)2V = 24.5° obs., 24°52′ calc., r > v. $N_X = 1.577$, $N_Y = 1.636$, $N_Z = 1.639$, $N_Z - N_X = 0.062$. Ref: 374.

Potassium 1,5-naphthalenedisulfonate dihydrate $[C_{10}H_6(SO_3)_2 \cdot K_2 \cdot 2H_2O]$ is monoclinic with $a:b:c = 0.930:1:2.554$, $\beta = 98°26'$. Crystals {001} tablets; with {111}, {11$\bar{1}$}, {11$\bar{3}$}, etc. Common twinning on 001. D 1.797. X $\wedge$ *c* = 78°; Z = *b*. (-)2V = 38°50′ calc., r < v. $N_X = 1.485$, $N_Y = 1.669$, $N_Z = 1.697$, $N_Z - N_X = 0.212$. Ref: 374.

Copper 1,5-naphthalenedisulfonate hexahydrate $[C_{10}H_6(SO_3)_2 \cdot Cu \cdot 6H_2O]$ is monoclinic with $a:b:c = 1.486:1:1.012$, $\beta = 93°17'$. Crystals {001} tablets with {111}, {11$\bar{1}$}, {110}, etc. Perfect 100 cleavage. D 1.783. X $\wedge$ *c* = 75° *ca.*; Y = *b*. (-)2V = 62°48′ calc., 61°39′ obs., r < v. $N_X = 1.541$ Na, $N_Y = 1.625$, $N_Z = 1.660$, $N_Z - N_X = 0.119$. Ref: 374.

Magnesium 1,5-naphthalenedisulfonate hexahydrate $[C_{10}H_6(SO_3)_2 \cdot Mg \cdot 6H_2O]$ is monoclinic with $a:b:c = 1.443:1:1.969$, $\beta = 92°17'$. Crystals {001} tablets with {111}, {11$\bar{1}$}, etc. Perfect 100 cleavage. D 1.635. X $\wedge$ *c* = - 73.5°; Y = *b*. Optic axis visible through 100 and also through 001. (-)2V = 52°20′ obs., r > v, 53°6′ calc. $N_X = 1.520$ Na, $N_Y = 1.613$, $N_Z = 1.639$, $N_Z - N_X = 0.119$. Ref: 374.

Zinc 1,5-naphthalenedisulfonate hexahydrate $[C_{10}H_6(SO_3)_2 \cdot Zn \cdot 6H_2O]$ is monoclinic with $a:b:c = 1.455:1:1.990$, $\beta = 92°14'$. Crystals {001} tablets with {111}, {11$\bar{1}$}, etc. Perfect 100 cleavage. D 1.793. X $\wedge$ *c* = 74 *ca.*; Y = *b*. (-)2V = 59°2′ calc., 58°18′ Na obs. $N_X = 1.531$ Na, $N_Y = 1.625$, $N_Z = 1.659$, $N_Z - N_X = 0.128$. Ref: 374.

Cobalt 1,5-naphthalenedisulfonate hexahydrate $[C_{10}H_6(SO_3)_2 \cdot Co \cdot 6H_2O]$ is monoclinic with $a:b:c = 1.450:1:1.986$, $\beta = 92°4'$. Crystals {001} tablets with {111}, {11$\bar{1}$}, {101}, {100}. Perfect 100 cleavage. D 1.771. X $\wedge$ *c* = - 72.5°; Y = *b*. An optic axis visible through 100 and also through 001. (-)2V = 60°31′ calc., 61°40′ obs., r < v. $N_X = 1.532$ Na, $N_Y = 1.628$, $N_Z = 1.655$, $N_Z - N_X = 0.133$. Pleochroic with X = dark red, Y = pink. Ref: 374.

Nickel 1,5-naphthalenedisulfonate hexahydrate [$C_{10}H_6(SO_3)_2 \cdot Ni \cdot 6H_2O$] is monoclinic with $a:b:c = 1.450:1:1.992$, $\beta = 92°1'$. Crystals {001} tablets with {111}, {11$\bar{1}$}, {101}, {100}. Perfect 100 cleavage. D 1.788. X $\wedge$ c = 74° *ca*; Y = *b*. (-)2V = 58°8′ calc., 59°56′ obs., r < v. N_X = 1.541 Na, N_Y = 1.636, N_Z = 1.669, $N_Z - N_X$ = 0.128. Ref: 374.

S-Benzylisothiourea 1,5-naphthalenedisulfonate or *S*-benzylthiopseudourea salt of 1,5-naphthalenedisulfonic acid {$(NH_2C(:NH)SCH_2C_6H_5) \cdot C_{10}H_6(SO_3H)_2$} forms fragments with M.P. 251°. (-)2V = small. N_X = 1.580, N_Y = 1.670, N_Z = 1.690, $N_Z - N_X$ = 0.110. Ref: 125.

1,6-Naphthalenedisulfonic acid tetrahydrate [$C_{10}H_6(SO_3)_2 \cdot H_2 \cdot 4H_2O$] is monoclinic with $a:b:c = 2.090:1:?$, $\beta = 101°49'$. Crystals {001} tablets with {100}, {110}. D 1.56. X = *b*; Z $\wedge$ c = 14° to 18°. (-)2V = 78°48′ calc. 79.5° obs. N_X = 1.460 Na, N_Y = 1.614, N_Z = 1.697, $N_Z - N_X$ = 0.237. Ref: 374.

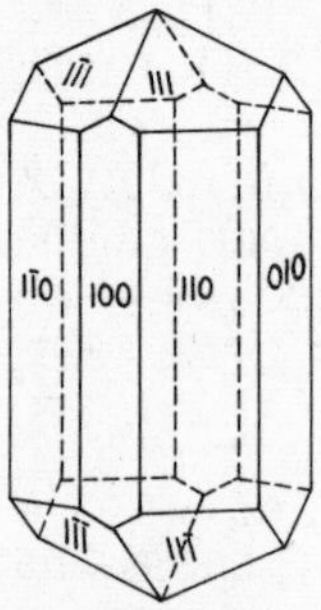

Fig. 77. Potassium-*p*-phenolsulfonate.

S-Benzylisothiourea 1,6-naphthalenedisulfonate or *S*-benzylthiopseudourea salt of 1,6-naphthalenedisulfonic acid [$[NH_2C(:NH)SCH_2C_6H_5]_2 \cdot C_{10}H_6(SO_3H)_2$] forms rods and fragments with M.P. 81°. Parallel extinction and positive elongation. (+)2V = small. N_X = 1.565, N_Y = 1.580, N_Z = 1.670, $N_Z - N_X$ = 0.105. Ref: 125.

S-Benzylisothiourea 2,6-naphthalenedisulfonate or *S*-benzylthiopseudourea salt of 2,6-naphthalenedisulfonic acid [$(NH_2C(:NH)SCH_2C_6H_5)_2C_{10}H_6(SO_3H)_2$] forms rods and needles with M.P. 256°. Essentially parallel extinction and positive elongation. (+)2V = small. N_X = 1.570, N_Y = 1.585, N_Z = 1.670, $N_Z - N_X$ = 0.100. Ref: 125.

S-Benzylisothiourea 2,7-naphthalenedisulfonate or *S*-benzylthiopseudourea salt of 2,7-naphthalenedisulfonic acid [$(NH_2C(:NH)SCH_2C_6H_5)_2C_{10}H_6(SO_3H)_2$] forms thin six-sided plates with M.P. 211 - 212°. (+)2E = 100°. N_X = 1.570, N_Y = ?, N_Z = 1.645, $N_Z - N_X$ = 0.075; $\therefore$ (+)2V = 57°44′, N_Y = 1.587. Ref: 125.

Potassium 4-hydroxybenzenesulfonate or potassium 1-phenol-4-sulfonate [$C_6H_4(OH) \cdot KSO_3$] is orthorhombic with $a:b:c = 0.880:1:1.004$. Crystals {001} plates with {110}, {111}. Fig. 78. No distinct cleavage. D 1.87. M.P. > 260°. Y = *c*; Z = *b*. (+)2V = 67°49′ Li, 68°15′ Na, 68°36′ Tl. N_X = 1.5672 C, 1.5714 D, 1.5834 F; N_Y = 1.6033 C, 1.6079 D, 1.6222 F; N_Z = 1.6879 C, 1.6942 D, 1.7114 F; $N_Z - N_X$ = 0.1228 D. Ref: 118.

Potassium 2-hydroxybenzenesulfonate dihydrate or potassium 1-phenol-2-sulfonate dihydrate [$C_6H_4(OH) \cdot KSO_3 \cdot 2H_2O$] is orthorhombic with $a:b:c$ = 0.780:1:0.462. Crystals prismatic with {110}, {010}, {100}, {111}. Fig. 77. Perfect 100 cleavage. D 1.73. Y = *a*; Z = *c*. (+)2V = 70° calc. N_X = 1.5228 C, 1.5265 D, 1.5362 F; N_Y = 1.5634 C, 1.5677 D, 1.5796 F; N_Z = 1.6410 C, 1.6467 D, 1.6636 F; $N_Z - N_X$ = 0.1202 D. Ref: 118.

Sodium 4-hydroxybenzenesulfonate dihydrate or sodium 1-phenol-4-sulfonate dihydrate ($C_6H_4OH \cdot SO_3Na \cdot 2H_2O$) is monoclinic with $a:b:c = 0.761:1:0.790$, $\beta = 94°37'$. Crystals prismatic with {111}, {11$\bar{1}$}, {100}, etc. Twinning on 100. Poor basal cleavage. Y = b, Z $\wedge$ c = + 9°. (+)2V = 70° r > v. $N_1 = 1.523$, $N_2 = 1.58$, $N_3 = 1.61$, $N_3 - N_1 = 0.087$. Ref: 118, 343c.

Potassium 4-hydroxy-1,3-benzene disulfonate monohydrate or potassium 1-phenol-2,4-disulfonate monohydrate [$K_2C_6H_3(OH) \cdot (SO_3)_2 \cdot H_2O$] is orthorhombic with $a:b:c = 0.685:1:0.513$. Crystals {001} tablets or short prismatic with {110}, {010}, {001}, etc. Very perfect 010 cleavage. X = a; Y = b. (-)2V = 65°30′ Li, 65°35′ Na, 64°40′ Tl. $N_X = 1.584$ Na calc. $N_Y = 1.602$ Li, 1.607 Na, 1.613 Tl; $N_Z = 1.662$ Li, 1.664 Na, 1.672 Tl. $N_Z - N_X = 0.080$ Na calc. Ref: 118.

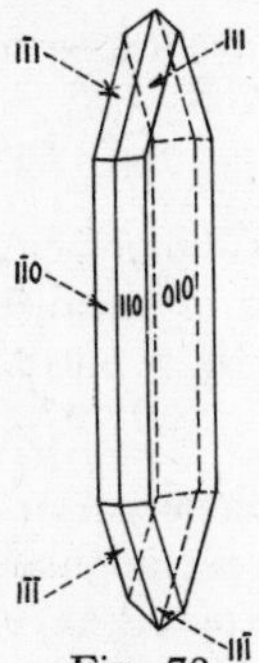

Fig. 78. Potassium-*o*-phenolsulfonate dihydrate.

Barium 4-hydroxy-1,3-benzenedisulfonate tetrahydrate or barium 1-phenol-2,4-disulfonate tetrahydrate [$BaC_6H_3(OH) \cdot (SO_3)_2 \cdot 4H_2O$] is monoclinic with $a:b:c = 1.654:1:1.340$, $\beta = 93°27'$. Crystals short prismatic with {110}, {001}, {101}, {100}, {10$\bar{1}$}. Fig. 79. Perfect 001 cleavage. X $\wedge$ c = 7° *ca.*; Z = b. (-)2V = 61°48′ Li, 61°58′ Na, 62°13′ Tl. $N_Y = 1.624$ Na, $N_Z - N_X$ = strong. Also: X $\wedge$ c = + 5°20′ Na, $N_Y = 1.604$ Li, 1.607 Na, 1.611 Tl. Ref: 118.

1-Benzoxy-4-naphthalenesulfonic acid or 1-naphthol-4-sulfonic acid benzoate [$C_6H_5CO_2 \cdot C_{10}H_6SO_3H$] forms rhombs with angles of 70.5° and 109.5°. Extinction at 30.6° to long edge. $N_1 = 1.460$, $N_2 = 1.654$, $N_2 - N_1 = 0.194$. Ref: 373.

2,4-Dinitro-1-naphthol-7-sulfonic acid salt of 5-guanido-2-aminopentanoic acid, or arginine flavianate [$H_2NC(:NH)NH(CH_2)_3CHNH_2CO_2H \cdot HO_3SC_6H_3CHOH:CNO_2CH:CNO_2$] forms thin plates with positive elongation and parallel extinction. $N_1 > 1.778$, probably about 1.80, N_2 = probably about 1.85. Ref: 65.

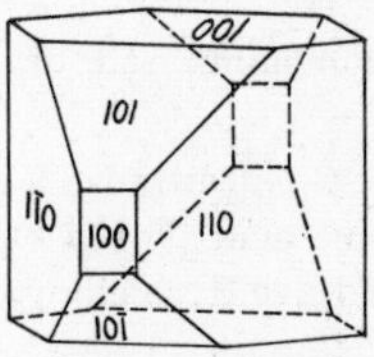

Fig. 79. Barium 1-phenol-2,4-disulfonate.

2,4-Dinitro-1-naphthol-7-sulfonic acid salt of 2.6-diaminohexanoic acid, or lysine flavianate [$H_2N(CH_2)_4CHNH_2CO_2H \cdot HO_3SC_6H_3CHOH:CNO_2CH:CNO_2$] forms rosettes of slender yellow needles with negative elongation and parallel extinction. $N_1 = 1.546$, $N_2 = 1.735$, $N_2 - N_1 = 0.189$. Ref: 65.

2,4-Dinitro-1-naphthol-7-sulfonic acid salt of 2-amino-4-methylpentanoic acid, or leucine flavianate [$(CH_3)_2CHCH_2CHNH_2CO_2H \cdot HO_3SC_6H_3CHOH:CNO_2CH:CNO_2$], forms slender yellow needles (in tiny rosettes) with positive elongation and parallel extinction. $N_1 = 1.60 \pm 0.01$, $N_2 = 1.651$, $N_2 - N_1 = 0.05$. Index liquids dissolve the crystals. Ref: 65.

2,4-Dinitro-1-naphthol-7-sulfonic acid salt of 3-methyl-2-aminopentanoic acid, or isoleucine flavianate [$CH_3CH_2CH(CH_3)CHNH_2CO_2H \cdot HO_3SC_6H_3CHOH$:$CNO_2CH$:$CNO_2$] forms rosettes and ropes of yellow needles with negative elongation and parallel extinction. $N_1 = 1.616$, $N_2 = 1.666$, $N_2 - N_1 = 0.050$. Ref: 65.

2,4-Dinitro-1-naphthol-7-sulfonic acid salt of 2-amino-4-(methylmercapto)-butanoic acid, or methionine flavianate [$CH_3S(CH_2)_2CHNH_2CO_2H \cdot HO_3SC_6H_3$ $CHOH$:CNO_2CH:CNO_2] forms sheaves and loose rosettes of yellow needles with negative elongation and parallel extinction. $N_1 = 1.635$, $N_2 = 1.683$, $N_2 - N_1 = 0.048$. Ref: 65.

2-Naphthol-6-sulfonic acid benzoate or 2-benzoxy-6-naphthalenesulfonic acid [$C_6H_5CO_2 \cdot C_{10}H_6SO_3H$] forms clusters of rectangular needles with parallel extinction and positive elongation. $N_1 = 1.628$, $N_2 = 1.646$, $N_2 - N_1 = 0.018$. Ref: 373.

2-Naphthol-3,6-disulfonic acid benzoate or 2-benzoxy-3,6-naphthalene disulfonic acid [$C_6H_5CO_2 \cdot C_{10}H_5(SO_3H)_2$] forms rosettes of plates or long rectangular rods. Both have parallel extinction and positive elongation, but the plates have $N_Z = 1.591$, $N_2 = 1.617$, $N_2 - N_1 = 0.026$, and the rods have $N_1 = 1.552$, $N_2 = 1.697$, $N_2 - N_1 = 0.145$. (Probably $N_X = 1.552$, $N_Y = 1.6$ *ca.*, $N_Z = 1.697$ $N_Z - N_X = 0.145$. - A.N.W.). Ref: 373.

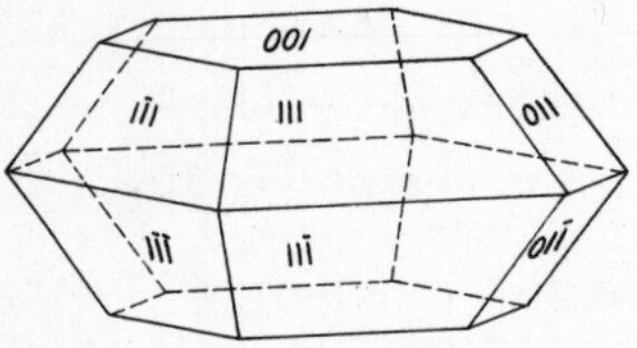

Fig. 80.
Ammonium salt of *o*-sulfobenzoic acid.

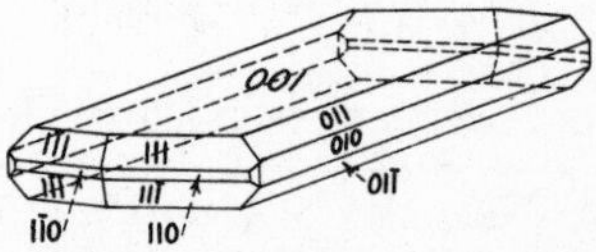

Fig. 81.
Potassium salt of *o*-sulfobenzoic acid.

2-Naphthol-6,8-disulfonic acid benzoate or 2-benzoxy-6,8-naphthalene disulfonic acid [$C_6H_5CO_2 \cdot C_{10}H_5(SO_3H)_2$] forms very long rods with parallel extinction and negative elongation. $N_1 = 1.547$, $N_2 = 1.681$, $N_2 - N_1 = 0.134$. Ref: 373.

β-Bromo-α-camphorsulfonyl chloride ($C_{10}H_{14}O_3ClBrS$) is orthorhombic with $a:b:c = 0.299:1:0.377$. Crystals {001} tablets with {110}, {011}, {010}. $Y = b$; $Z = c$. $(+)2V$ = large, $N_X = 1.55$, $N_Y = 1.56$, $N_Z = 1.58$, $N_Z - N_X = 0.03$. Ref: 47.

Ammonium salt of *o*-sulfobenzoic acid or ammonium 2-carboxybenzenesulfonate ($NH_4SO_3 \cdot C_6H_4 \cdot CO_2H$) is orthorhombic with $a:b:c = 0.668:1:1.207$. Crystals {001} tablets with {111}, {011}, etc. Fig. 80. D 1.52. M.P. > 250°. Perfect 001 and distinct 010 and 110 cleavages. $X = a$; $Y = b$. $(-)2E = 84°36'$ Li, $84°39'$ Na, $N_Y = 1.4958$ Na. $(-)2V = 53.5°$. Ref: 118.

Potassium salt of *o*-sulfobenzoic acid or potassium 2-carboxybenzenesulfonate ($KSO_3 \cdot C_6H_4 \cdot CO_2H$) is orthorhombic with $a:b:c = 0.685:1:1.231$. Crystals {001} tablets with {111}, {011}, etc. Fig. 81. Perfect 001 cleavage. D 1.70. X $= a$; Y $= b$. (-)2V = 42°38′ Na, r > v. $N_Y = 1.5930$. Ref: 118.

Class 9. Amines and Derivatives

Subclass A. Monoamines and Derivatives

Phenylamine hydrochloride or aniline hydrochloride ($C_6H_5NH_2 \cdot HCl$) is probably monoclinic. M.P. 198°. It has an extinction angle of 42°, and $N_X = 1.56$, $N_Y = 1.57$, $N_Z = 1.60$, $N_Z - N_X = 0.04$. (+)2V = 60° calc. Ref: 34, 35.

Phenylamine nitrate or aniline nitrate ($C_6H_5 \cdot NH_2 \cdot HNO_3$) is orthorhombic dipyramidal with $a:b:c = 0.572:1:0.626$. Crystals pyramidal or {010} tablets with perfect 010 cleavage. The optic plane is 100; X $= c$. (-)2V = ?, r < v. Rhombic {010} plates, (with an angle of 85°) are normal to the obtuse bisectrix, Z, and show symmetrical extinction. Indices measured on them are $N_X = 1.508 \pm .003$, $N_Y = 1.590 \pm .003$. Ref: 118, 599.

Phenylamine sulfate or aniline sulfate [$(C_6H_5NH_2)_2 \cdot H_2SO_4$] has extinction at 32° and $N_1 = 1.55$, $N_2 = 1.71$, $N_2 - N_1 = 0.16$. Ref: 34, 35.

Phenylamine *cis*-2-sulfo-ethene-1-carboxylate monohydrate or aniline *cis*-*β*-sulfoacrylate monohydrate ($C_3H_4O_5S \cdot C_6H_7N \cdot H_2O$) is orthorhombic pyramidal with $a:b:c = 0.913:1:0.691$. Crystals show {100}, {02$\bar{1}$}, {111}, {110}, {010}, etc. Loses water at 100° and decomposes at 156°. X $= a$; Y $= c$. (-)2V = ?. $N_X = 1.485$ Na, $N_Y = 1.596$, $N_Z = ?$. Ref: 9.

Phenylamine hexafluorogermanate or aniline hexafluorogermanate [$(C_6H_5NH_2)_2 \cdot H_2GeF_6$] is monoclinic in {110} prisms with {100} and {001}; $\beta = 95°$ *ca.* D 1.579. X(?) $\wedge$ $c = 80°$; Y $= b$. (-)2V = 35° *ca.*, r > v strong. $N_X = 1.471$, $N_Y = 1.532$, $N_Z = 1.541$, $N_Z - N_X = 0.070$. Ref: 68.

N-Methylaminobenzene hexafluorogermanate or *N*-monomethylaniline hexafluorogermanate [$(C_6H_5NHCH_3)_2 \cdot H_2GeF_6$] is probably orthorhombic in {110} prisms with {011}. 011:0$\bar{1}$1 = 100° *ca.* D 1.631. X $= a$; Y $= c$. (-)2V = 60° *ca.*, r > v strong. $N_X = 1.472$, $N_Y = 1.562$, $N_Z = 1.565$, $N_Z - N_X = 0.093$. (Indices inconsistent with 2V. - A.N.W.). Ref: 68.

Dimethylaminobenzene hexafluorogermanate or *N,N*-dimethylaniline hexafluorogermanate [$[C_6H_5N(CH_3)_2]_2H_2GeF_6$] is monoclinic. Crystals show {011}, {010}, {100}, {001}. $\beta = 150°$. D 1.548. Y $= b$. Extinction at 40° in 010. 2V = 90° *ca.* $N_X = 1.445$, $N_Y = 1.53 \pm \cdot 005$, $N_Z = 1.617$, $N_Z - N_X = 0.172$. Ref: 68.

N-Phenyl-2-naphthylamine ($C_{16}H_{13}N$) is orthorhombic with $a:b:c = 0.942:1:0.412$. *a* 17.45, *b* 18.25, *c* 7.52 Å. U.C. 8. Crystals short rods. D 1.237. M.P. 107 - 108°. X $= b$, Y $= c$. (-)2V = 65°, r < v. $N_X = 1.636$, $N_Y = 1.82$, $N_Z = 1.92$ calc., $N_Z - N_X = 0.284$. Ref: 553c.

Diphenylamine $[(C_6H_5)_2NH]$ is monoclinic in {001} plates with {110}, which show a bisectrix of large optic angle with strong inclined dispersion. It has parallel (?) extinction and negative elongation with $N_1 = 1.605$, $N_2 = 1.66$, $N_2 - N_1 = 0.055$. Ref: 33, 34, 35, 119.

Diphenylamine hydrochloride $[(C_6H_5)_2NH \cdot HCl]$ has parallel extinction and positive elongation with $N_1 = 1.545$, $N_2 = 1.72$, $N_2 - N_1 = 0.175$. Ref: 34.

2,4,6,2′,4′,6′-Hexanitrodiphenylamine (HND) $\{(NO_2)_3C_6H_2NHC_6H_2(NO_2)_3\}$ is orthorhombic with $a:b:c = 0.615:1:0.389$. a 11.75, b 19.10, c 7.43 Å. U.C. 4. Crystals massive or elongated along b. D 1.75. X = a, Y = b. (-)2V = 62°, $N_X = 1.75$, $N_Y = 1.80$, $N_Z = 1.82$, $N_Z - N_X = 0.07$. at 25° C. Crossed axial plane dispersion with double change of sign. Uniaxial at about 5500 Å. Ref: 553d.

3,3′,5-Trimethyl-2′-amino-5′-chlorobiphenyl $(C_{15}H_{16}NCl)$ is monoclinic with $a:b:c = 7.296:1:2.649$, $\beta = 104°16'$. a 37.63, b 5.16, c 13.66 Å. U.C. 8. (+)2V = 61°18′. $N_X = 1.6517$, $N_Y = 1.6734$, $N_Z = 1.7410$, $N_Z - N_X = 0.0893$. Ref: 542a.

Lithol fast yellow GG (or N,N′-methylene-*bis*-2-nitro-4-chloroaniline?) $[ClC_6H_3(NO_2)NHCH_2NHC_6H_3(NO_2)Cl]$ is orthorhombic (?). X ∥ length. $N_X = 1.564$, $N_Y = ?$, $N_Z = 1.96$, $N_Z - N_X = 0.396$. Pleochroic with X = light yellow, Z = bright yellow. Ref: 577.

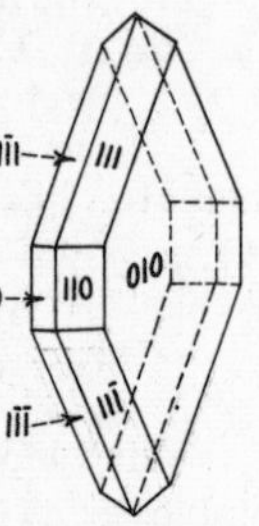

Fig. 82. Amylene nitrolaniline.

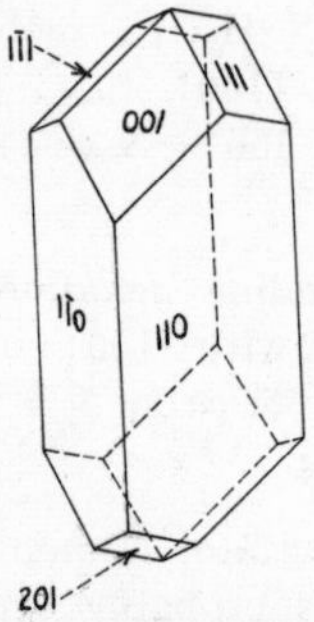

Fig. 83. Amylene nitrolaniline hydrochloride.

3-Anilino-3-methyl-2-butanone oxime or 2-methyl-2-phenylamino-3-oximino-butane or amylene nitrolaniline $[C_6H_5NHC(CH_3)_2C(:NOH)CH_3]$ is orthorhombic with $a:b:c = 0.798:1:0.730$. Crystals {010} plates with {111}, {110}, etc. Fig. 82. M.P. 140 - 141°. Y = a; Z = c. (+)2V = 88°4′ Li, 88°21′ Na, 88°39′ Tl. $N_Y = 1.5832$ Li, 1.5867 Na, 1.5902 Tl. Ref: 118.

3-Anilino-3-methyl-2-butanone oxime hydrochloride or 2-methyl-2-phenyl-amino-3-oximinobutane hydrochloride or amylene nitrolaniline hydrochloride $[(C_6H_5NHC(CH_3)_2C(:NOH)CH_3 \cdot HCl]$ is monoclinic with $a:b:c = 1.569:1:0.736$, $\beta = 133°48'$. Crystals short prismatic with {110}, {001}, {1̄11}, etc. Fig. 83. Twinning on 100. X = b; Z ∧ c = -96°. (+)2V = 75°30′ Li, 75°41′ Na, 76°5′ Tl. $N_Y = 1.5696$ Li, 1.5734 Na, 1.5763 Tl. Ref: 118.

Acetanilide or antifebrin $(C_6H_5NHCOCH_3)$ is orthorhombic with $a:b:c = 0.842:1:2.067$. Crystals of varied habit, {001} tablets or equant with {001}, {012}, {111}, {100}, {201}, {101}, etc. Perfect 001 and distinct 100 cleavages. D 1.219. M.P. 112°. Y = b; Z = c. (+)2V = 88°50′ Li, 88°36′ Na, 88°4′ Tl. $N_X = 1.506$, $N_Y = 1.516$, $N_Z = 1.627$ D, $N_Z - N_X = 0.121$. These indices are inconsistent with 2V. Also $N_X = 1.512$, $N_Y = 1.621$. Again: $N_X = 1.515$, $N_Y = 1.620$, $N_Z > 1.733$, $N_Z - N_X > 0.218$. Measures by Ray Wilcox give 2V = 88°, $N_X = 1.510$ calc., $N_Y = 1.620$, $N_Z = 1.730$, $N_Z - N_X = 0.22$; crystals show abnormal interference colors when cut normal to an optic axis.

Ref: 42, 118, 123, 239, 343c, 376, 518.

N-Methylacetanilide [$C_6H_5N(CH_3)(COCH_3)$] is orthorhombic with $a:b:c = 0.929:1:2.349$. Crystals {001} tablets with {101}, {012}, etc. Imperfect 001 cleavage. M.P. 101 - 104°. $Y = b$; $Z = c$. (+)2V = 51°41′ Na, r < v weak. $N_X = 1.5604$, $N_Y = 1.5761$, $N_Z = 1.6467$, $N_Z - N_X = 0.0863$ Na. Ref: 118.

Acetyldiphenylamine or *N,N*-diphenylacetamide [$C_6H_5N(COCH_3)C_6H_5$] is orthorhombic with $a:b:c = 0.786:1:1.098$. Distinct 001 cleavage. M.P. 103°. $Y = c$; $Z = a$. (+)2V = 49°24′ Li, 52°2′ Na, 52°28′ Tl. $N_X = 1.6206$ Na, $N_Y = 1.6285$, $N_Z = 1.6608$, $N_Z - N_X = 0.0402$. Ref: 119.

Oxanilide ($C_6H_5NHCOCONHC_6H_5$) forms tablets with M.P. 245°. N_1 (|| width) = 1.706, N_2 (|| length) = 1.72, $N_2 - N_1 = 0.014$. Ref: 598.

Acetoacetic anilide or acetoacetanilide I is orthorhombic pyramidal with $a:b:c = 0.573:1:0.450$. *a* 11.07, *b* 19. 31, *c* 8.68 Å. U.C. 8. D 1.23. M.P. 83°. Distinct 100 cleavage. $Y = b$; $Z = a$. (+)2V = 74°, r > v. $N_X = 1.556$, $N_Y = 1.603$, $N_Z = 1.697$, $N_Z - N_X = 0.141$. Three other forms are known. Ref: 535c.

$$\left[CH_3 \cdot \underset{\ddot{O}}{C} \cdot CH_2 \cdot \underset{\ddot{O}}{C} \cdot NH \cdot C_6H_5 \right]$$

Phenyloxaluric acid methylamide or *N*-methyl-N′phenylcarbamyloxamide ($CH_3NHCOCONHCONHC_6H_5$) has parallel extinction and negative elongation with $N_1 = 1.595$, $N_2 = 1.700$, $N_2 - N_1 = 0.105$. Ref: 93.

Ethyl phenyloxalurate ($C_6H_5NHCONHCOCO_2C_2H_5$) has two crystals phases. One (I) has parallel extinction and negative elongation. It is biaxial with $N_1 = 1.590$, $N_2 = 1.680$, $N_2 - N_1 = 0.090$. The other (II) has an extinction angle of 17° - 19° with $N_1 = 1.675$, $N_2 = 1.755$, $N_2 - N_1 = 0.080$. Ref: 93.

Phenylurea ($C_6H_5NHCONH_2$) is monoclinic with $a:b:c = 1.308:1:0.212$. $\beta = 94°7′$. Crystals {100} plates or prisms with {110}, {120}, {100}, {001}, {101}, etc. Perfect 100 cleavage. D 1.30. M.P. 147°. The optic plane and X are normal to 010; $Z \wedge c = +78°$ red, + 79° blue. (+)2V = 44°48′ Na, r > v. $N_1 = 1.602$, $N_2 = 1.627$, $N_2 - N_1 = 0.025$. {100} plates have parallel extinction and positive elongation. (Such plates must be elongated vertically and N_1 must be N_X, and N_2 must be near N_Y; therefore N_Z must be about 1.72. - A.N.W.).

Ref: 118, 248.

N-Methyl-*N*′-phenylurea or α-methyl-β-phenylurea ($C_6H_5NHCONHCH_3$) forms square plates with parallel extinction. $N_1 = 1.513$, $N_2 = 1.636$, $N_2 - N_1 = 0.123$. Ref: 248.

N,N′-Diphenylurea or carbanilide ($C_6H_5NHCONHC_6H_5$) is orthorhombic with $a:b:c = 0.861:1:1.117$. Crystals elongated along *a* with {001}, {011}, {100}, etc. Fig. 84. Perfect 010 and 011 and distinct 100 cleavages. D 1.24. M.P. 235°. $X = c$; $Y = a$. (-)2H (in α-bromonaphthalene) = 56°30′ Na, r > v strong. $N_X = 1.583$, $N_Z = 1.74$?. $N_Z - N_X = 0.157$. Parallel extinction and negative elongation; positive elongation with "$N_X = 1.620$". Again: $Y = c$, $Z = a$. (+)2V = 50°, r > v strong. $N_X = 1.581$, $N_Y = 1.624$, $N_Z = 1.818$ calc., $N_Z - N_X = 0.237$ calc.   Ref: 93, 119, 248, 553b.

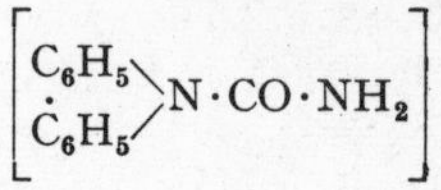

unsym.-Diphenylurea is orthorhombic with $a:b:c = 0.818:1:0.809$. M.P. 186° D 1.276. $Y = c$, $Z = a$. (+) 2V = 38°, r < v strong. $N_X = 1.645$, $N_Y = 1.651$, $N_Z = 1.703$, $N_Z - N_X = 0.058$.   Ref: 553b.

$$\begin{array}{c} C_6H_5 \\ \diagdown \\ N \cdot CO \cdot NH_2 \\ \diagup \\ C_6H_5 \end{array}$$

N'-Phenyl-N-carbethoxyurea, or ethyl γ-phenylallophanate ($C_6H_5NHCONH$ $CO_2C_2H_5$) forms thin plates with symmetrical extinction and positive elongation. 2V = biaxial. $N_1 = 1.445 +$, $N_2 = 1.610$, $N_2 = 1.610$, $N_2 - N_1 = 0.165$.
                                                                        Ref: 94.

ω-Phenylbiuret ($C_8H_9O_2N_3$) forms thin rectangular plates with X parallel with elongation. Uniaxial negative with $N_O = 1.665$, $N_E = 1.645$, $N_O - N_E = 0.020$.
                                                Ref: 94.

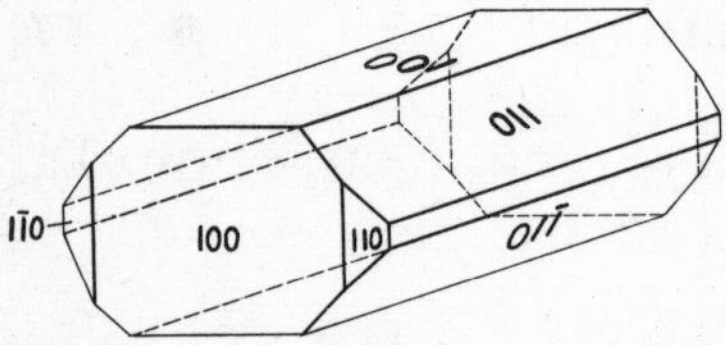

Fig. 84. *N,N′*-Diphenyl urea.

Phenylbiuret ($C_8H_9O_2N_3$) also forms short prisms with M.P. 190° and extinction at 32° – 34°, and $N_X = 1.532$, $N_Z = 1.649 +$, $N_Z - N_X = 0.117 +$. It also forms long needles with M.P. 196 – 198° (with decomposition) and extinction at 32° – 33° and $N_X = 1.559$, $N_Z = 1.73 +$, $N_Z - N_X = 0.171 +$.   Ref: 92.

1-Methyl-5-phenylbiuret ($C_6H_5NHCONHCONHCH_3$) forms six-sided plates with M.P. 133°. They have symmetrical extinction and positive elongation. Uniaxial positive with $N_O = 1.595$, $N_E = 1.671$, $N_O - N_E = 0.076$.   Ref: 94.

3-Methyl-1-phenylbiuret [$NH_2CON(CH_3)CONHC_6H_5$] forms rectangular plates with parallel extinction and negative elongation. M.P. 183°. $N_1 < 1.445$, $N_2 = 1.725$, $N_2 - N_1 > 0.280$.   Ref: 94.

N-Methyl-N-phenylcarbamylglycine or β-methyl-△-phenylhydantoic acid [$C_6H_5NHCON(CH_3)CH_2CO_2H$] forms platy crystals with symmetrical extinction and negative elongation. M.P. 150°. $N_1 = 1.530$, $N_2 = 1.625$, $N_2 - N_1 = 0.095$.   Ref: 95.

1,5-Diphenylbiuret ($C_6H_5NHCONHCONHC_6H_5$) forms plates with parallel extinction and negative elongation. (+)2V = large. $N_X = 1.591$, $N_Y = 1.650$, $N_Z > 1.755$, $N_Z - N_X > 0.164$.   Ref: 94, 248.

Diethyl (phenylureido)malonate [$C_6H_5NHCONHCH(CO_2C_2H_5)_2$] forms needles with parallel extinction and negative elongation. M.P. 112 – 114°. $N_1 = 1.550$, $N_2 = 1.610$, $N_2 - N_1 = 0.060$.   Ref: 95.

N,N'-Dimethyl-α-(phenylureido)malonamide [$C_6H_5NHCONHCH(CONHCH_3)_2$] forms thin six-sided plates with symmetrical extinction and ± elongation. M.P. 225°. 2V = biaxial. $N_Y = 1.598$. Ref: 95.

Phenylguanidine carbonate [$[C_6H_5NHC(NH)NH_2]_2 \cdot H_2CO_3$] is monoclinic prismatic. Crystals equant with {001}, {110}. Y near *c*. (-)2E = 38°, 2V = 22°, $N_X = 1.573$, $N_Y = 1.663$, $N_Z = 1.665$, $N_Z - N_X = 0.092$. Ref: 529.

Phenylbiguanide {$H_2NC(NH)NHC(NH)NHC_6H_5$} is monoclinic in tablets. D 1.25 - 1.30. (+)2E = 57°, 2V = 34°, $N_X = 1.600$, $N_Y = 1.620$, $N_X = 1.91$ calc., $N_Z - N_X = 0.31$ calc. Ref: 529.

Phenylbiguanide hydrochloride {$H_2NC(NH)NHC(NH)NHC_6H_5 \cdot HCl$} is monoclinic (?). Crystals tabular. D 1.35 - 1.40. (-)2E > 160°. 2V = 70 - 80°. N_Y (|| length) = 1.657. N_2 (= N_Z?) (|| width) = 1.750. Ref: 529.

N-Methyl-*N'*-phenylthiourea ($CH_3 \cdot NH \cdot CS \cdot NH \cdot C_6H_5$) forms tabular crystals with parallel extinction. M.P. 112 - 113°. (+)2V = 88°. $N_X = 1.662$, $N_Y = 1.695$, $N_Z = 1.730$, $N_Z - N_X = 0.068$. Ref: 377b.

N-Ethyl-*N'*-phenylthiourea ($C_2H_5 \cdot NH \cdot CS \cdot NH \cdot C_6H_5$) forms tabular crystals with parallel extinction. M.P. 101 - 102°. (+)2V = 82°. $N_X = 1.650$, $N_Y = 1.680$, $N_Z = 1.720$, $N_Z - N_X = 0.070$. Ref: 377b.

N-Phenyl-*N'*-propylthiourea ($C_6H_5 \cdot NH \cdot CS \cdot NH \cdot C_3H_7$) forms needles with parallel extinction. M.P. 64°. (+)2V = 56°. $N_X = 1.690$, $N_Y = 1.700$, $N_Z = 1.735$, $N_Z - N_X = 0.045$. Ref: 377b.

N-Butyl-*N'*-phenylthiourea ($C_4H_9 \cdot NH \cdot CS \cdot NH \cdot C_6H_5$) forms rhombic plates with symmetrical extinction. M.P. 63°. (+)2V = 37°. $N_X = 1.590$, $N_Y = 1.603$, $N_Z = 1.775$ (est.), $N_Z - N_X = 0.185$ (est.). Ref: 377b.

N-Amyl-*N'*-phenylthiourea ($C_5H_{11} \cdot NH \cdot CS \cdot NH \cdot C_6H_5$) forms rhombic plates with symmetrical extinction. M.P. 68 - 69°. (+)2V = 20°. $N_X = 1.620$, $N_Y = 1.630$, $N_Z = 1.76$ (est.), $N_Z - N_X = 0.140$ (est.). Ref: 377b.

N-i-Amyl-*N'*-phenylthiourea or *N*-isoamyl-*N'*-phenylthiourea ($C_5H_{11} \cdot NH \cdot CS \cdot NH \cdot C_6H_5$) forms tabular crystals with symmetrical extinction. M.P. 101 - 102°. (-?)2V = large. $N_X = 1.620$, $N_Y = 1.700$, N_Z = ?. Ref: 377b.

Phenylisoguanylurea hydrochloride {$(NH_2CN)_2C_6H_4OH \cdot HCl$} is tabular. N_1 (|| length) = 1.621, N_2 (||width) = 1.680, $N_2 - N_1 = 0.059$. Incomplete extinction due to strong dispersion. Ref: 529.

Diethylhydrazone of phenylisocyanate [$C_6H_5N{:}C{:}N \cdot N(C_2H_5)_2$] is apparently monoclinic with M.P. 125°. (+)2V = small, r > v marked. $N_X = 1.515 \pm .005$, $N_Y = 1.535 \pm .005$, $1.740 > N_Z > 1.635$ (nearer 1.740), $N_Z - N_X = 0.2$ *ca.* Ref: 342.

Phenylaminoethanoic acid hydrochloride or *N*-phenylglycine hydrochloride, or anilinoacetic acid hydrochloride [$C_6H_5NH(CH_2CO_2H) \cdot HCl$] is orthorhombic with $a{:}b{:}c = 0.682{:}1{:}1.025$. Crystals short prismatic with {110}, {010}, {001}, {111}, etc. Very perfect 010 and imperfect 001 cleavages. The optic plane is 010; X = *a*. (-)2V = 18°25′ Li, 18°9′ Na. N_X = 1.548 Na calc., N_Y = 1.6709 Li, 1.6767 Na; N_Z = 1.6747 Li, 1.6799 Na, $N_Z - N_X$ = 0.132 Na calc. Ref: 118.

Ethylmethylphenylbetaine monohydrate $[C_6H_5N(CH_3)(C_2H_5)CH_2CO \cdot H_2O]$ is probably orthorhombic in acicular groups. M.P. 175.5°. Parallel extinction and negative elongation. (+)2V = ?, N_X = 1.549 ± .003, N_Y = 1.585, N_Z = ?. Ref: 122, 476.

Ethylmethylphenylbetaine dihydrate $[C_6H_5N(CH_3)(C_2H_5)CH_2CO \cdot 2H_2O]$ is monoclinic in {001} plates elongated along *b*. M.P. 79.5°, resolidifying promptly and freezing again at about 100°. Crystals tabular with angles of 75°40′ and 97°32′. Two cleavages (001 and 100 ?). The optic plane is 010. (+)2V = very small, r > v marked. N_X = 1.549 ± .003, N_Y < 1.585, N_Z = ?. Ref: 122, 476.

Methylphenylpropylbetaine monohydrate $[C_6H_5N(CH_3)(C_3H_7)CH_2CO \cdot H_2O]$ is probably orthorhombic in elongated plates. M.P. 172°. Parallel extinction and ± elongation. The optic plane is normal to the elongation and Z is normal to the plates. (+)2V = ?. N_X = 1.555 ± .003, N_Y = 1.595, N_Z = ? Ref: 122, 476.

Methylphenylpropylbetaine dihydrate $[C_6H_5N(CH_3)(C_3H_7)CH_2CO \cdot 2H_2O]$ is prismatic with Z normal to plates. (+)2V = very small. N_X < 1.555, N_Y < 1.595, N_Z = ?, $N_Z - N_X$ = probably very strong. Ref: 122, 476.

N-Phenylbenzenesulfonamide or benzenesulfonanilide $(C_6H_5SO_2NHC_6H_5)$ is tetragonal with *c*/*a* = 1.204. Crystals pyramidal with {111}, {221}, etc. Perfect 001 cleavage. M.P. 110°. Uniaxial positive with N_O = 1.5999, N_E = 1.6486, $N_E - N_O$ = 0.0487 Na. Ref: 119.

p-(2,2-Dimethylpropyl)benzenesulfonanilide or *p*-neopentylbenzenesulfonanilide $[(CH_3)_3CCH_2C_6H_4SO_2NHC_6H_5]$ is monoclinic with *a*:*b*:*c* = 0.687:1:0.754, β = 113°17′. Crystals equant or {001} tablets with {011}, {111}, {110}, etc. M.P.137°. X ∧ *c* = - 42°; Z = *b*. (-)2V = 73°29′. N_X = 1.545 D, N_Y = 1.590 *ca.*, N_Z = 1.628, $N_Z - N_X$ = 0.083. Ref: 402.

Trimethyl(*p*-phenylsulfamylbenzyl)silicane or trimethylbenzylsilicon-*p*-sulfonanilide $[(CH_3)_3SiCH_2C_6H_4SO_2NHC_6H_5]$ is monoclinic with *a*:*b*:*c* = 0.697:1:0.770, β = 113°38′. Crystals {001} tablets with {111}, {011}, {110}, etc. M.P. 125°. X ∧ *c* = - 41° *ca.*; Z = *b*. (-)2V = 61°18′. N_X = 1.541 D, N_Y = 1.601 *ca.*, N_Z = 1.632, $N_Z - N_X$ = 0.091. This compound seems to form mix-crystals with the preceding (in all proportions ?). Ref: 402.

3-Methyl-3-*N*-nitrosoanilino-2-butanone oxime or methyl(α-phenylnitrosaminoisopropyl) ketoxime or nitroso-amylene nitrolaniline $[C_6H_5N(NO)C(CH_3)_2C(:NOH)CH_3]$ is orthorhombic with *a* : *b* : *c* = 0.888 : 1 : 0.683. Crystals thick

{010} tablets with {100}, {101}, {110}, {111}. Fig. 85. Perfect 100 cleavage. M.P. 127° - 128°. Y = *b*; Z = *c*. (+)2V = 83°58′ Li, 82°51′ Na, 81°53′ Tl. N_Y = 1.5659 Li, 1.5669 Na, 1.5686 Tl. Ref: 118.

N,N′-(or α,β-)or *s*-Diphenylthiourea ($C_6H_5 \cdot NH \cdot CS \cdot NH \cdot C_6H_5$) is orthorhombic dipyramidal with *a*:*b*:*c* = 0.745:1:1.326. Crystals show {001}, {110}, {111} in rhombic plates with symmetrical extinction. Perfect 001 and distinct 010 cleavages. D 1.318. M.P. 153°. Y = *a*; Z = *c*. (+)2H = 95°40′ Na, 95°7′ Tl (in bitter almond oil). N_X = 1.645, N_Y = 1.720. Again: (+)2V = 65° ± 4°, r > v, N_X = 1.642, N_Y = 1.716 (∴ N_Z = 1.89 calc., $N_Z - N_X$ = 0.17 *ca.* - A.N.W.). Ref: 119, 377b, 529.

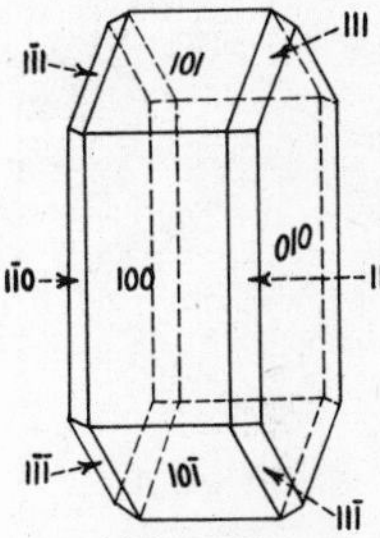

Fig. 85. Nitrosoamylene nitrolaniline.

N-(*o*-Chlorophenyl)-*N′*-phenylthiourea ($C_6H_4Cl \cdot NH \cdot CS \cdot NH \cdot C_6H_5$) forms needles with parallel extinction. M.P. 158°. 2V = 29°. N_Y = 1.72. Ref: 377b.

N,N′-(or α,β-) or *s*-Di-*p*-tolythiourea [$C_6H_4(CH_3) \cdot NH \cdot CS \cdot NH \cdot C_6H_4 \cdot CH_3$] is orthorhombic with *a*:*b*:*c* = 0.839:1:0.617. Crystals prismatic with {110}, {111}, and {100}. No good cleavage. M.P. 178°. Y = *c*; Z = *b*. (+)2V = 43°. N_X = 1.675, N_Y = 1.685, N_Z = 1.74 (est.), $N_Z - N_X$ = 0.085 (est.) Also possibly monoclinic (with inclined extinction in some crystals). Ref: 119, 377b.

N-(4-Bromophenyl)acetamide or acet-*p*-bromoanilide or *p*-bromoacetanilide ($CH_3CONHC_6H_4Br$) has three crystal phases. The stable form (I) is monoclinic with *a*:*b*:*c* = 0.781:1:0.722, β = 117°13′. Crystals equant or {010} tablets with {100}, {011}, {101}, {110}, {120}, {001}, etc. Twinning on 100. Perfect 101 and poor 100 cleavages. D 1.72. M.P. 165.4 - 167.5°. Y = *b*; Z ∧ *c* = + 35°; X nearly ⊥ 101. (+)2V = 86°, r > v moderate. $2H_a$ = 97°. N_X = 1.497, N_Y = 1.663, N_Z = 1.945, $N_Z - N_X$ = 0.448 for λ = 546.1. A metastable form (II), which is probably orthorhombic, has elongation along Y (if the plate is normal to Z) or along Z (if the plate is normal to X). (+)2V = 71°, r > v moderate. N_X = 1.610, N_Y = 1.678, N_Z = 1.805, $N_Z - N_X$ = 0.195 for λ = 546.1. Another metastable phase (III) has elongation along Y, if the plate is normal to X or Z, or along X, the plate being normal to ?. (-)2V = 85°. N_Y = 1.68 ± 0.01 $N_Z - N_X$ = very strong. Ref: 41.

N-(4-Bromophenyl)propanamide or *p*-bromopropionanilide or propion-*p*-bromoanilide ($C_2H_5CONHC_6H_4Br$) has two crystal phases. The stable phase (I) is orthorhombic with *a*:*b*:*c* = 0.447:1:0.895. Crystals show {100}, {010}, {110}, {011}. Perfect 100 cleavage. M.P. 149°. Y = *c*; Z = *a*. (+)2V = 78°, r > v strong. N_X = 1.590, N_Y = 1.653, N_Z = 1.755, $N_Z - N$ = 0.165 for λ = 546.1. A metastable phase (II) has (+)2V = 72°, N_X = 1.653, N_Y = 1.660, N_Z = 1.674 calc., $N_Z - N_X$ = 0.021 calc., for λ = 546.1. The metastable phase of propion-*p*-bromanilide intercrystallizes freely with one phase of *p*-bromoacetanilide at high temperature. Mix-crystals are obtained by quenching. The optic angle and melting point variations in the series are shown in Fig. 86. The optic angle passes through 0°, and the optic plane changes from one position to a position normal thereto at about 87 per cent acetic bromanilide (for light with $\lambda = 546{:}1$).

Ref: 41.

N-(4-Bromophenyl)butanamide or *p*-bromobutyranilide or butyr-*p*-bromoanilide [$CH_3(CH_2)_2CONHC_6H_4Br$] forms long narrow rectangular crystals from alcohol. If elongation is along *c* the optic plane and Z are normal to 010; X (or Y) $\wedge$ $c = 20° - 40°$. For $\lambda = 5461$ Å: (+)2V = 88°, r > v weak; $N_X = 1.478$, $N_Y = 1.615$, $N_Z = 1.783$ (all $\pm$ .003), $N_Z - N_X = 0.305$. Ref: 41.

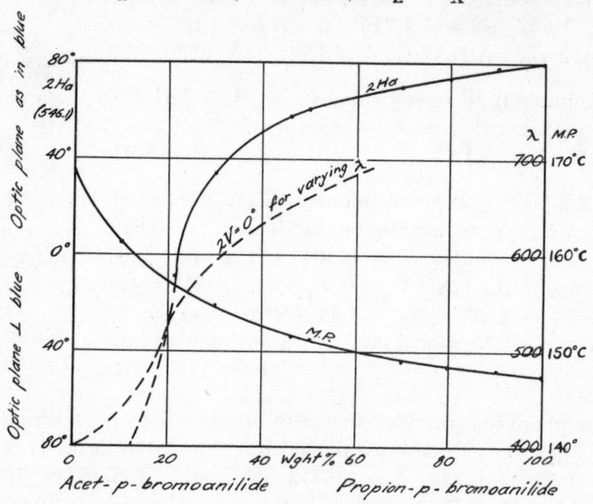

Fig. 86. Optic angle and melting point in the acet- and propion-*p*-anilide series. See Bryant: Jour. Am. Chem. Soc. 60, 1394 (1938).

N-(4-Bromophenyl)-2-methylpropanamide or *p*-bromoisobutyranilide or isobutyr-*p*-bromoanilide [$(CH_3)_2CHCONHC_6H_4Br$] forms large rectangular crystals (from alcohol) with $\pm$ elongation and parallel extinction. For $\lambda = 5461$ Å: (+)2V = 73°, r > v weak; $N_X = 1.520 \pm .003$, $N_Y = 1.588 \pm .003$, $N_Z = 1.750 \pm .005$, $N_Z - N_X = 0.23$.

Ref: 41.

N-(4-Bromophenyl)-2,2,2-trimethylethanamide or *p*-bromopivalanilide or trimethylacet-*p*-bromoanilide [$(CH_3)_3CCONHC_6H_4Br$] forms long rectangular plates from alcohol and needles from acetone. Plates normal to Z have elongation parallel to X and plates normal to X have elongation parallel to Y. For $\lambda = 5461$ Å: (+)2V = 50°, r > v; $N_X = 1.570$, $N_Y = 1.590$, $N_Z = 1.708$ (all $\pm$.003), $N_Z - N_X = 0.138$.

Ref: 41.

N-(4-Bromophenyl)-2-ketopropanamide or *p*-bromopyruvanilide or pyruv-*p*-bromoanilide ($CH_3COCONHC_6H_4Br$) forms rectangular plates from alcohol and needles from acetone. Sections normal to Z have elongation parallel to X and sections normal to X have elongation parallel to Y. For $\lambda = 5461$ Å: (+)2V = 63°, r > v; $N_X = 1.535$, $N_Y = 1.608$, (both $\pm$ .003). $N_Z > 1.85$, $N_Z - N_X > 0.31$.

Ref: 41.

N-(4-Bromophenyl)-2-methoxyethanamide, or *p*-bromo-α-methoxyacetanilide or methoxyacet-*p*-bromoanilide ($CH_3OCH_2CONHC_6H_4Br$) forms acicular crystals from alcohol and acetone. Plates normal to Z and also those normal to X have elongation parallel to Y. For $\lambda = 5461$ Å: (+)2V = 85°, r > v; $N_X = 1.503 \pm .003$, $N_Y = 1.620 \pm .003$, $N_Z = 1.83 \pm .01$, $N_Z - N_X = 0.33$. Ref: 41.

dl-*N*-(4-Bromophenyl)-2-methylbutanamide or *p*-bromo-α-methylbutyranilide or *dl*-methylethylacet-*p*-bromoanilide [$C_2H_5(CH_3)CHCONHC_6H_4Br$] has two phases; the stable phase (I)forms small rectangular plates from alcohol, benzene, and acetone. In plates normal to Z the elongation is parallel to X, and in plates normal to X the elongation is parallel to Z. For $\lambda = 5461$ Å: (+)2V = 61°, r < v strong, with inclined dispersion. $N_X = 1.578 \pm .003$, $N_Y = 1.602 \pm .003$, $N_Z = 1.66 \pm .01$, $N_Z - N_X = 0.08$. $2H_a = 64.5°$. The mestastable phase (II) is optically positive with $2H_a = 82°$, r > v strong, with inclined dispersion; plates normal to Z have elongation parallel to Y. Ref: 41.

N-(4-Bromophenyl)pentanamide or *p*-bromovaleranilide or valer-*p*-bromoanilide [$CH_3(CH_2)_3CONHC_6H_4Br$] has two phases; the stable phase (I) forms fine needles from alcohol and benzene or rectangular plates from acetone. Plates normal to Bx_a have extinction (X) at 50 - 75° from the elongation and plates normal to Bx_0 have elongation parallel to Y. For $\lambda = 5461$ Å: (+ ?)2V = 85°, r > v weak; $N_X = 1.482$, $N_Y = 1.617$, $N_Z = 1.773$, (all ± .003), $N_Z - N_X = 0.291$, $2H_a = 92° \pm 3°$. The metastable phase (II) has elongation along Y in plates normal to Bx_a. (+)$2H_a = 66.5°$. $N_Z - N_X$ strong. Ref: 41.

N-(4-Bromophenyl)-2-methylpropenamide, or *p*-bromomethacrylanilide or methacryl-*p*-bromoanilide [$CH_2{:}C(CH_3)CONHC_6H_4Br$] has two phases. The stable phase forms rectangular plates from alcohol and needles from benzene and acetone. For $\lambda = 5461$ Å: (+)2V = 81°, r > v; $N_X = 1.526$, $N_Y = 1.656$, (± .003), $N_Z > 1.85$, $N_Z - N_X > 0.324$. $2H_a = 91°$. The metastable phase has strong positive birefringence with $2H_a = 82.5°$, r > v; sections normal to Z have elongation parallel to Y. Ref: 41.

N-(4-Bromophenyl)-3-methylbutanamide or *p*-bromoisovaleranilide or isovaler-*p*-bromoanilide [$(CH_3)_2CHCH_2CONHC_6H_4Br$] has two phases; the stable phase (I) forms small rectangular plates and prisms from alcohol, larger plates from acetone. In plates normal to Bx_a Y makes an angle of 25° to 40° with the elongation; in plates normal to Bx_0 the elongation is normal to Z. For $\lambda = 5461$ Å: (+ ?)2V = 88°, r > v weak; $N_X = 1.488$, $N_Y = 1.615$, $N_Z = 1.777$ (all ± .003), $N_Z - N_X = 0.289$. $2H_a = 95.5°$. The metastable phase (II) has (+)$2H_a = 71°$, r > v; $N_Z - N_X$ = strong; in plates normal to Bx_a Y is at 12° to the elongation. Ref: 41.

m-Nitroaniline [$C_6H_4(NO_2)NH_2$] is orthorhombic pyramidal with $a{:}b{:}c = 0.745{:}1{:}0.764$. Space group *Pca*; *a*[1] 6.48, *b* 19.23, *c* 5.06 Å. U.C. 4. M.P. 110°. D 1.40. Crystals short prisms with parallel extinction and negative elongation. Perfect 010 cleavage. X = *c*; Y = *a*. (-)2V = small. $N_X = 1.687$, $N_Y = 1.72 - 1.74$, $N_Z > 1.78$, $N_Z - N_X > 0.10$. Color yellow, weakly pleochroic with X > Z. Ref: 118, 128, 489.

[1] *a b c* changed to *b a c* to make *b* > *a*.

p-Nitroaniline [$C_6H_4(NO_2)NH_2$] is monoclinic with $a:b:c = 2.520:1:1.422$, $\beta = 126°11'$. M.P. 147°. D 1.437. Perfect 001 cleavage. The optic plane is 010; (+?)2V = about 80°. $N_X' = 1.556$, $N_Y > 1.78$, $N_Z = ?$. Color yellow, not pleochroic.
Ref: 118, 128.

o-Nitroacetanilide [$C_6H_4(NO_2)NH \cdot CO \cdot CH_3$] is monoclinic with $a:b:c = 0.894:1:1.920$, $\beta = 96°9'$. Yellow plates elongated along *b*. D 1.419. M.P. 94°. The optic plane is 010. (+)2E = 26.5° (4358), 15.5° (4650), 29° (5780), 35.5° (6908). 2V = 16° (5461), $N_X = 1.626$, $N_Y = 1.629$, $N_Z = 1.800$, $N_Z - N_X = 0.214$ (5461). Optic plane is 010 for red to green and normal thereto for blue and violet.
Ref: 39a, 118, 157a.

2,4,6-Trinitrodiphenylamine or picrylaniline [$C_6H_2(NO_2)_3NHC_6H_5$] is monoclinic prismatic with $a:b:c = 1.49:1:2.13$, $\beta = 115°33'$. Space group $P2_1/c$; *a* 11.3, *b* 7.62, *c* 16.2 Å. U.C. 8. Needles parallel to *c* or columns elongated along *b*. D 1.54. M.P. 179°. The optic plane is 010; X $\wedge$ *c* = − 66°37′. (−)2V = 86°35′. $N_X = 1.549$, $N_Y = 1.800$, $N_Z = 2.168$, $N_Z - N_X = 0.619$ D. Color scarlet red.
Ref: 382, 622.

N-Picryl-*p*-iodaniline [$IC_6H_4NHC_6H_2(NO_2)_3$] is trimorphous; phase I (red) is monoclinic with $\beta = 113°$; space group $P2_1/c$, *a* 14.15, *b* 5.85, *c* 18.30 Å. U.C. 4. D 2.01. M.P. 191°. X = *b*, Z $\wedge$ *c* = 48° in obtuse β. (+)2V = 81°, $N_X = 1.620$, $N_Y = 1.750$, $N_Z = 1.99$ calc. $N_Z - N_X = 0.37$ calc. Phase (II) (yellow) is also monoclinic with $\beta = 98°30'$; space group $P2_1/a$, *a* 13.45, *b* 5.15, *c* 20.65 Å. U.C. 4. D 2.00. M.P. 18°. X = *b*, Z $\wedge$ *c* = 32° in obtuse β. (+)2V = 55°30′, $N_X = 1.680$, $N_Y = 1.740$, $N_Z = 2.02$ calc. $N_Z - N_X = 0.34$ calc. Phase III (orange) is orthorhombic with[1] $a:b:c = 0.549:1:0.228$. Space group $P2_12_12_1$. U.C. 4. Crystals acicular along *c*. D 1.98. M.P. 181°, Y = *a*, Z = *b*. (+)2V = 38°50′, $N_X = 1.699$, $N_Y = 1.743$, $N_Z = 2.3$, calc. $N_Z - N_X = 0.601$ calc. Ref: 475a.

2,3,4,6-Tetranitroaniline [$C_6H(NO_2)_4NH_2$] is monoclinic or triclinic. D 1.89. M.P. 170°. (−)2E = at least 120°. $N_X = 1.650$, $N_Y = 1.760$, $N_Z = 1.870$, $N_Z - N_X = 0.220$.
Ref: 152.

2-Methylphenylamine hydrobromide or *o*-toluidine hydrobromide [$C_6H_4(CH_3)NH_2 \cdot HBr$] is orthorhombic with $a:b:c = 0.914:1:0.308$. Crystals {100} tablets or short prisms with {110}, {100}, {001}, etc. Perfect 100 cleavage. X = *b*; Y = *c*. (−)2V = 82°37′ Na, r > v rather strong. $N_Y = 1.6669$ Na.
Ref: 118.

dl-Phenylisopropylamine sulfate or *dl*-amphetamine sulfate or benzedrine sulfate ($C_9H_{13}N \cdot H_2SO_4$) forms irregular particles, but X || elongations. $N_X = 1.520$. When treated with gold chloride very thin quadratic plates form which are biaxial with (−)2V = small.
Ref: 523d.

d-Phenylisopropylamine sulfate or *d*-amphetamine sulfate or dexedrine sulfate ($C_9H_{13}N \cdot H_2SO_4$) forms plates with 6 – 8 sides and X || elongation. (+)2V = small, $N_X = 1.505$, $N_Y = 1.545$, $N_Z = 1.608$, $N_Z - N_X = 0.103$. (indices

[1] *a* and *b* interchanged to make *b* > *a* > *c*.

and small 2V inconsistent - A.N.W.) Z normal to plates. When treated with gold chloride short prisms and needles form rapidly; they have parallel extinction. Ref: 523d.

N-(2-Methylphenyl)ethanamide or *o*-acetotoluide [$C_6H_4(CH_3)NH(COCH_3)$] is orthorhombic[1] with $a:b:c = 0.417:1:0.148$. Crystals acicular to equant with {110}, {101}, {010}, {001}, {100}. D 1.17. M.P. 110°. The optic plane is 100; $Z = b$. (+)2V = 58°28′. $N_X = 1.556$, $N_Y = 1.587$, $N_Z = 1.700$, $N_Z - N_X = 0.144$ Na. Ref: 118.

N-(2-Methylphenyl)benzamide or *o*-benzotoluide or *N*-benzoyl-*o*-toluidine [$C_6H_5CONHC_6H_4(CH_3)$] is orthorhombic[1] with $a:b:c = 0.541:1:0.152$. Crystals thin prisms with {110}, {010}, {011}, {001}. Perfect 010 and distinct 001 cleavages. D 1.21. M.P. 143°. $Y = b$; $Z = c$. (+)2V = 87°33′ Na. $N_X = 1.621$, $N_Y = 1.654$, $N_Z = 1.691$, $N_Z - N_X = 0.070$ Na. Ref: 119.

N,N′-Di-*o*-tolylthiourea ($C_6H_4CH_3 \cdot NH \cdot CS \cdot NH \cdot C_6H_4CH_3$) forms needles with parallel extinction. M.P. 158°. (+)2V = 66°. $N_X = 1.655$, $N_Y = 1.663$, $N_Z = 1.725$, $N_Z - N_X = 0.070$. Ref: 373b.

N′-(Phenyl)-*N′*-(benzyl)-*N,N*-dimethylethylenediamine hydrochloride or antergan hydrochloride [$(CH_3)_2NC_2H_4N(C_6H_5CH_2)C_6H_5 \cdot HCl$] forms short prisms. M.P.200°. (+)2V = 70° calc. $N_X = 1.587$, $N_Y = 1.635$, $N_Z = 1.734$, $N_Z - N_X = 0.147$. Ref: 477d.

Di-*o*-tolylguanidine {$CH_3C_6H_4NHC(NH)NHC_6H_4CH_3$} is orthorhombic in tabular crystals. M.P. 179°. X parallel to length. (+)2V = 79°, 2E > 170°, $N_X = 1.6375 \pm .0005$, $N_Y = 1.6873 \pm 0.0005$, $N_X = 1.77$, $N_Z - N_X = 0.14$. Ref: 584.

o-Tolylbiguanide hydrochloride ($C_9H_{13}N_3 \cdot HCl$) is probably monoclinic in columnar to tabular crystals. M.P. 227° C. (-)2V = 45°, $N_X = 1.573$, $N_Y = 1.666$, $N_Z = 1.686$, $N_Z - N_X = 0.113$. Colorless. Ref: 405a.

Di-*o*-tolylguanidine zinc chloride {$CH_3C_6H_4NHC(NH)NHC_6H_4CH_3 \cdot ZnCl_2$} is granular. (+)2E = 113°, 2V = 61°, $N_X = 1.595$, $N_Y = 1.631$, $N_Z = 1.752$, $N_Z - N_X = 0.157$. Ref: 584.

N-Phenyl-*N′*-*o*-tolylthiourea ($C_6H_5 \cdot NH \cdot CS \cdot NH \cdot C_6H_4 \cdot CH_3$) forms needles with parallel extinction. M.P. 138°. (+)2V = 35°. $N_X = 1.655$, $N_Y = 1.663$, $N_Z = 1.74$ (est.), $N_Z - N_X = 0.085$ (est.). Ref: 377b.

N-(3-Methylphenyl)benzamide or *m*-benzotoluide or *N*-benzoyl-*m*-toluidine [$C_6H_5CONHC_6H_4(CH_3)$] is monoclinic with $a:b:c = 0.530:1:0.367$, $\beta = 91°9′$. Crystals prismatic with {110}, {010}, {011}, or {210}, {310}, {320}, etc. D 1.17. M.P. 125°. $X = b$. The optic plane is normal to 010 and extinction in 010 is at 50°. (-)2V = 22°36′ Na. $N_X = 1.586$, $N_Y = 1.668$, $N_Z = 1.680$, $N_Z - N_X = 0.094$ Na. Ref: 119.

[1] *a* and *b* interchanged to make $b > a > c$.

Diethyl(4-methylphenyl)amine hydrobromide or *N,N*-diethyl-*p*-toluidine hydrobromide $[C_6H_4(CH_3)N(C_2H_5)_2 \cdot HBr]$ is monoclinic with $a:b:c = 0.958:1:1.161$, $\beta = 99°20.5'$. M.P. 158 – 159°. The optic plane is normal to 010; extinction at + 1° to *c* in 010. (+)2V = 69°41.5'. $N_Y = 1.5715$ Na. Ref: 118.

Diethyl(4-methylphenyl)amine chloroplatinate or *N,N*-diethyl-*p*-toluidine chloroplatinate $[C_6H_4(CH_3)N(C_2H_5)_2 \cdot 2H_2PtCl_6]$ is orthorhombic with $a:b:c = 0.888:1:0.755$. Crystals short prisms with {110}, {101}, {011}, {100}, {101}. Fig. 87. Imperfect 001 cleavage. Y = *a*; Z = *b*. (+)2V = 63°35' Li, 63°0' Na, 62°30' Tl. N_Y = 1.6310 Li, 1.6362 Na, 1.6406 Tl. Color carmine to yellowish red. Ref: 118.

4'-Methyl-2,4,6-trinitrodiphenylamine or *N*-picryl-*p*-toluidine $[C_6H_2(NO_2)_3NHC_6H_4(CH_3)]$ is dimorphous; one phase (I) is monoclinic prismatic with $a:b:c = 2.53:1:2.72$, $\beta = 114°8'$. Space group $P2_1/c$; *a* 14.9, *b* 5.94, *c* 16.3 Å. U.C. 4. Crystals acicular along *b*. D 1.543. Y = *b*; Z ∧ *c* = + 30°23'. (+)2V = 83°45'. $N_X = 1.580$, $N_Y = 1.747$, $N_Z = 2.052$, $N_Z - N_X = 0.472$ D. For $\lambda = 670$:

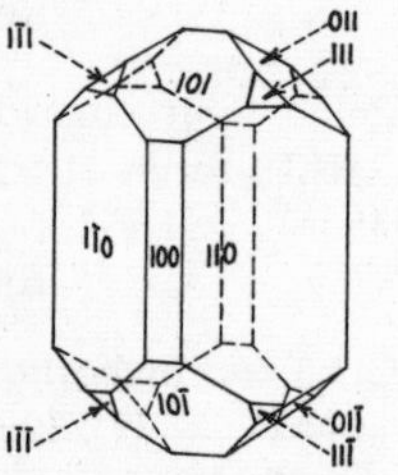

Fig. 87. Diethyltoluidine chloroplatinate.

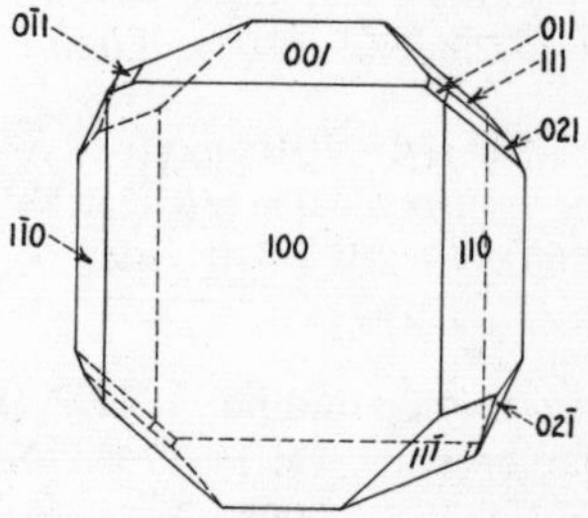

Fig. 88. *p*-Acetotoluidine.

(+)2V = 84°30'; $N_X = 1.560$, $N_Y = 1.719$, $N_Z = 1.998$, $N_Z - N_X = 0.438$. Color yellow. A second phase (II) is monoclinic prismatic with $a:b:c = 0.74:1:0.37$, $\beta = 103°$. Space group $P2_1/c$; *a* 12.9, *b* 17.5, *c* 6.04 Å. U.C. 4. Crystals acicular along *c*. D 1.532. X = *b*; Y ∧ *c* = – 7°. (–)2V = 85°30'. $N_X = 1.557$, $N_Y = 1.769$. $N_Z = 2.041$, $N_Z - N_X = 0.484$ ($\lambda = 670$). Color red. Ref: 382.

N-(4-Methylphenyl)ethanamide, or *p*-acetotoluide $[C_6H_4(CH_3)NH(COCH_3)]$ is monoclinic with $a:b:c = 1.218:1:0.787$, $\beta = 106°7'$, Crystals {100} tablets or short prisms with {110}, {100}, {010}, {001}, {111̄}, etc. Fig. 88. Perfect 001 and distinct 100 cleavages. D 1.21. Y = *b*; Z ∧ *c* = – 15.5°. (+)2V = 88°30'. $N_X = 1.495$, $N_Y = 1.625$, $N_Z = 1.807$, $N_Z - N_X = 0.312$ Na. Another phase (II) is metastable; it is orthorhombic with $a:b:c = 0.652:1:0.329$. Crystals prismatic with {010}, {100}, {001}, etc. X = *a*; Y = *b*. (–)2H = 84° red, r < v. Ref: 118.

N-(4-Methylphenyl)benzamide or *p*-benzotoluide or *N*-benzoyl-*p*-toluidine $[C_6H_5CONHC_6H_4(CH_3)]$ is orthorhombic[1] with $a:b:c = 0.371:1:0.349$. Crystals

[1] *a b c* changed to *b c a* to make *b* > *a* > *c*.

show {010}, {041}, {021}, {111}, etc. Imperfect 001 cleavage. D 1.20. M.P. 157°. Y = *a*; Z = *c*. (+)2V = 73°43′ Na. N_X = 1.587, N_Y = 1.646, N_Z = 1.769, $N_Z - N_X$ = 0.182 Na. Ref: 119.

N-Phenyl-*N′*-*p*-tolylthiourea ($C_6H_5 \cdot NH \cdot CS \cdot NH \cdot C_6H_4CH_3$) forms rods with parallel extinction. M.P. 139° - 140°. (+)2V = 63°. N_X = 1.610, N_Y = 1.675, N_Z = 1.8 (est.), $N_Z - N_X$ = 0.190 (est.). Ref: 377b.

N,N′-Dibenzylurea ($C_6H_5CH_2NHCONHCH_2C_6H_5$) is orthorhombic (?) in needles with parallel extinction and positive elongation. Large optic angle. N_X' = 1.5952, N_Z = 1.658 ± .003, $N_Z - N_X'$ = 0.063 *ca.* Ref: 529.

4-Methyl-3,5-dinitrophenylamine or 3,5-dinitro-*p*-toluidine [$(C_6H_2(NO_2)_2(CH_3)(NH_2)$] is orthorhombic with *a*:*b*:*c* = 0.997:1:0.518. Crystals brachydomatic with {011}, {021}, {001}, {110}, {201}. Perfect 110 cleavage. M.P. 69 - 71°. The optic plane is 010 for red and 100 for yellow, green and blue; X = *c*. (-)2H = 8°1′ Li, 12°13′ Na, 20°52′ Tl. N_Y = 1.476 *ca.* Ref: 5.

Indium sulfate benzylamine sulfate hexahydrate [$(C_6H_5CH_2NH_2)_2 \cdot H_2SO_4$ $In_2(SO_4)_36H_2O$] is monoclinic in prisms with multiple twinning and positive elongation. M.P. above 300°. (-)2V = moderate. N_X < 1.484, N_Y = 1.552, N_Z = 1.580, $N_Z - N_X$ > 0.096. Ref: 76.

N-*β*-Hydroxyethyl-*N′*-phenylthiourea ($C_2H_4OH \cdot NH \cdot CS \cdot NH \cdot C_6H_5$) forms needles with parallel extinction. M.P. 138°. (-?)2V = ?, N_X = 1.675, N_Y = 1.692, N_Z = ?. Ref: 377b.

d-Desoxyephedrine hydrochloride ($C_{10}H_{15}N \cdot HCl$) forms irregular units. (+)2V = not large. N_X = 1.530, N_Y= 1.537, N_Z = 1.615, $N_Z - N_X$ = 0.085. Ref: 523e.

dl-Desoxyephedrine hydrochloride ($C_{10}H_{15}N \cdot HCl$) forms plates with X || elongation. N_Z > 1.734. Ref: 523e.

d-Desoxyephedrine with chloro-auric acid ($C_{10}H_{15}N$ with $AuCl_2$ acid) forms yellow rods and needles with square ends and X || elongation. N_X = 1.580, N_Y = ?, $N_Z \gg$ 1.734, $N_Z - N_X \gg$ 0.154. Ref: 523e.

Vonedrine hydrochloride ($C_{10}H_{15}N \cdot HCl$) forms rods with X || elongation. N_X = 1.577, N_Y = ?, N_Z = 1.603, $N_Z - N_X$ = 0.026. With chloroauric acid yellow prisms are formed, probably monoclinic, with inclined extinction, and N_X = 1.603, N_Z = 1.734, $N_Z - N_X$ = 0.131. Ref: 523e.

3,5-Dimethylphenylamine or 3,5-xylidine [$C_6H_3(CH_3)_2NH_2$] is probably monoclinic in {010} plates with vertical elongation. X ∧ *c* = 12°; Y = *b*. N_X = 1.45, N_Y = ?, N_Z = 1.69, $N_Z - N_X$ = 0.24. Ref: 124.

N-(3,5-Dimethylphenyl)ethanamide or 3.5-acetoxylide [$(CH_3)_2C_6H_3NHCO$ CH_3] is probably monoclinic in {010} plates with irregular borders. M.P. 139.6° - 140.2°. The extinction angle to a prominent edge is 12°. In converging light no distinct interference figure is seen, suggesting that Y = *b*. Negative elongation. N_X = 1.45, N_Y = ?, N_Z = 1.69, $N_Z - N_X$ = 0.24. (Apparently the same as the preceding-A.N.W.). Ref: 353.

4-Isopropylphenylamine or cumidine [$(CH_3)_2CHC_6H_4NH_2$] melts at 63°. $N_1 = 1.62$, $N_2 = 1.95$, $N_2 - N_1 = 0.33$, with parallel extinction and negative elongation. Ref: 34, 35.

1-Naphthylamine 1-naphthalenesulfonate or α-naphthylamine α-naphthalenesulfonate ($C_{10}H_7NH_2 \cdot C_{10}H_7SO_3H$) is probably orthorhombic in plates with parallel extinction. The plates are normal to Y. M.P. 232°. $N_X = 1.552$ D, $N_Y = ?$, $N_Z = 1.795$, $N_Z - M_X = 0.243$ D, all ± .005. Ref: 4.

1-Naphthylamine 2-naphthalenesulfonate or α-naphthylamine 2-naphthalenesulfonate [$(C_{10}H_7NH_2 \cdot C_{10}H_7SO_3H)$] is probably orthorhombic in needles with parallel extinction and positive elongation. M.P. 240 - 242°. (+)2V = 80° calc. $N_X = 1.600$ D, $N_Y = 1.650$, $N_Z = 1.725$, $N_Z - N_X = 0.125$ D, all ± .005. Ref: 4.

1-Naphthylamine 1,5-naphthalenedisulfonate or α-naphthylamine 1,5-naphthalenedisulfonate [$(C_{10}H_7NH_2)_2 \cdot C_{10}H_6(SO_3H)_2$] is probably monoclinic in irregular plates normal to Y with inclined extinction. $N_X = 1.600$ D, $N_Y = ?$, $N_Z = 1.795$, $N_Z - N_X = 0.195$ D, all ± .005. Ref: 4.

1-Naphthylamine 1,6-naphthalenedisulfonate or α-naphthylamine1,6-naphthalenedisulfonate [$(C_{10}H_7NH_2)_2 \cdot C_{10}H_6(SO_3H)_2$] is probably monoclinic in rods or needles with extinction at 17° and negative elongation. Rods often lie normal to Y. Decomposes at 265° - 267°. (-)2V = large. $N_X = 1.583$ D, $N_Y = 1.730$, $N_Z = 1.770$, $N_Z - N_X = 0.187$ D, all ± .005. Ref: 4.

1-Naphthylamine 2,6-naphthalenedisulfonate or α-naphthylamine2,6-naphthalenedisulfonate [$(C_{10}H_7NH_2)_2 \cdot C_{10}H_6(SO_3H)_2$] is biaxial in grains or rods with inclined extinction. Stable to 280°. (-)2V = large. $N_X = 1.583$ D, $N_Y = 1.640$ $N_Z = 1.690$, $N_Z - N_X = 0.107$ D, all ± .005. Ref: 4.

1-Naphthylamine 2,7-naphthalenedisulfonate or α-naphthylamine 2,7-naphthalenedisulfonate [$(C_{10}H_7NH_2)_2 \cdot C_{10}H_6(SO_3H)_2$] is probably orthorhombic in rods with parallel extinction and negative elongation. (+)2V = 55° calc. $N_X = 1.560$ D, $N_Y = 1.650$, $N_Z = 1.675$, $N_Z - N_X = 0.115$ D, all ± .005. Ref: 4

2-Naphthylamine 1-naphthalenesulfonate or β-naphthylamine 1-naphthalenesulfonate ($C_{10}H_7NH_2 \cdot C_{10}H_7SO_3H$) is probably orthorhombic in needles or diamond-shaped plates with 125° termination, parallel extinction, and positive elongation. The salt blackens at 202° and melts at 211°. (+)2V = 48° *ca.* $N_X = 1.620$, $N_Y = 1.670$, $N_Z > 1.850$, $N_Z - N_X > 0.23$, all ± .005. Ref: 4.

2-Naphthylamine 2-naphthalenesulfonate or β-naphthylamine β-naphthalenesulfonate [$(C_{10}H_7NH_2 \cdot C_{10}H_7SO_3H)$] forms plates or rods with wavy structure. M.P. 276 - 279°. $N_X = 1.640$ D, $N_Y = ?$, $N_Z = 1.730$, $N_Z - N_X = 0.090$, all ± .005. Ref: 4.

2-Naphthylamine 1,5-naphthalenedisulfonate or β-naphthylamine 1,5-naphthalenedisulfonate [$(C_{10}H_7NH_2)_2 \cdot C_{10}H_6(SO_3H)_2$] forms plates of irregular outline normal to Z. It is stable to 280°. (+)2V = 40° calc. $N_X = 1.631$ D, $N_Y = 1.647$, $N_Z = 1.755$, $N_Z - N_X = 0.124$ D, all ± .005. Ref: 4.

An acid salt [probably $C_{10}H_7NH_2 \cdot C_{10}H_6(SO_3H)_2$] closely related to the preceding (and formed with it) occurs in plates normal to Z and has (+)2V = large, $N_X = 1.550$ D, $N_Y = 1.700$, $N_Z > 1.850$, $N_Z - N_X > 0.300$ D, all ± .005. Ref: 4.

2-Naphthylamine-1,6-naphthalenedisulfonate or β-naphthylamine 1,6-naphthalenedisulfonate [$(C_{10}H_7NH_2)_2 \cdot C_{10}H_6(SO_3H)_2$] is probably orthorhombic in flat needles with parallel extinction and negative elongation. Stable to 280°. (–)2V = large. $N_X = 1.550$ D, $N_Y = 1.700$, $N_Z = 1.755$, $N_Z - N_X = 0.205$, all ± .005. Ref: 4.

2-Naphthylamine 2,6-naphthalenedisulfonate or β-naphthylamine 2,6-naphthalenedisulfonate [$(C_{10}H_7NH_2)_2 \cdot C_{10}H_6(SO_3H)_2$] is probably monoclinic in plates (or needles) normal to Z with extinction at 40° and ± elongation. Stable to 280°. (+)2V = 40° *ca.* $N_X = 1.610$ D, $N_Y = 1.634$, $N_Z = 1.830$, $N_Z - N_X = 0.220$ D, all ± .005. Ref: 4.

2-Naphthylamine 2,7-naphthalenedisulfonate or β-naphthylamine 2,7-naphthalenedisulfonate [$(C_{10}H_7NH_2)_2 \cdot C_{10}H_6(SO_3H)_2$] is probably monoclinic in plates or rods, sometimes showing a 130° termination, and normal to Z. Often twinned. Stable to 280°. N_X is often shown lengthwise on the twins, but crosswise on the rods with parallel extinction; N_Y is lengthwise on the latter. Extinction at 8° to the twinning plane. Elongation ±. (–)2V = large. $N_X = 1.530$ D, $N_Y = 1.700$, $N_Z = 1.740$, $N_Z - N_X = 0.210$, all ± .005. Ref: 4.

N-Ethyl-1, 6, 8-trinitro-2-naphthylamine or 1, 6, 8-trinitro-2-ethylaminonaphthalene [$C_{10}H_4(NO_2)_3(NHC_2H_5)$] is monoclinic with $a:b:c = 2.291:1:1.103$, $\beta = 106°29'$. Crystals often elongated along *b* with {001}, {100}, {11$\bar{1}$}, {110}, etc. Distinct 010 cleavage. The optic plane and Z are normal to 010; X ∧ *c* = + 63.5°. (+)2V = 81°22′. $N_X = 1.5177$, $N_Y = 1.854$, $N_Z = 2.316$ D, $N_Z - N_X = 0.7983$. Strongly pleochroic with Y′ (in 001) = orange-yellow, X = yellowish green. Ref: 314.

2-Aminodiphenyl or 2-phenylaniline ($C_6H_5C_6H_4NH_2$) crystallizes from alcohol solution. M.P. 49°. (–?)2V = ?, $N_Y = 1.674 \pm .005$. Ref: 584.

N,N-Dichloro-α-methylbenzohydrylamine or *N,N*-dichloromethyldiphenylcarbinamine or methyldiphenylmethyldichloramine [$(C_6H_5)_2(CH_3)CNCl_2$] is monoclinic with $a:b:c = 0.402:1:0.365$, $\beta = 112°44'$. Crystals often skeletal and vertically striated or acicular. Perfect 010 and imperfect 001 cleavages. X ∧ *c* = – 74°; Z = *b*. (+) 2V= 68° *ca.* $N_X = 1.64$ *ca.* (1.66?), $N_Y = 1.68$, $N_Z = 1.74$ *ca.* (1.727?), $N_Z - N_X = 0.10$ (or less; 0.067?). Ref: 89.

Subclass B. Diamines and Derivatives

Rhodium *l*-1,2-cyclohexanediamine trichloride trihydrate [$Rh(l\text{-}C_6H_{10}(NH_2)_2)Cl_3 \cdot 3H_2O$] is dihexagonal pyramidal with $c/a = 2.673$. Crystals hexagonal pyramids with {10$\bar{1}$3}, {10$\bar{1}\bar{3}$}, {0001}, and {000$\bar{1}$}. No good cleavage. Uniaxial negative with $N_O = 1.606 \pm .002$, N_E = ?. Ref: 156a.

α-*dl*-Tri-1,2-cyclohexanediamine cobaltic chlorate trihydrate [Co(*dl*-C_6H_{10} $(NH_2)_2)_3(ClO_3)_3 \cdot 3H_2O$] is hexagonal with $c/a = 0.765$. Crystals show {10$\bar{1}$0} and {10$\bar{1}$1}. D 1.47. Uniaxial negative with $1.580 > N_O > 1.566$. The β-form is monoclinic. Ref: 331.

dl-Tri-1,2-cyclohexanediamine cobaltic perchlorate trihydrate [Co(*dl*-C_6H_{10} $(NH_2)_2)_3(ClO_4)_3 \cdot 3H_2O$] is hexagonal with $c/a = 0.764$. Crystals show {10$\bar{1}$0} and and {10$\bar{1}$1}. D 1.55. Uniaxial negative with $N_O = 1.563$, $N_E = ?$. Ref: 331.

dl-Tri-1,2-cyclohexanediamine cobaltic nitrate trihydrate [Co(*dl*-$C_6H_{10}(NH_2)_2)_3$ $(NO_3)_3 \cdot 3H_2O$] is hexagonal with $c/a = 0.783$. Crystals show {10$\bar{1}$0} and {10$\bar{1}$1}. No good cleavage. Uniaxial negative with $N_O = 1.5830$ Na, 1.5863 Hg green; $N_E = 1.5744$ Na, 1.5783 Hg green; $N_O - N_E = 0.0086$ Na. Ref: 331.

2-Aminomethylcyclopentylamine picrate ($C_6H_{14}N_2 \cdot C_6H_3O_7N_3$) is monoclinic. Crystals acicular prisms. M.P. 258°. Elongation is parallel to Y in plates normal to Z and parallel to Z in plates normal to X. (-)2V = 54°, r > v, with strong crossed dispersion. $N_X = 1.599$, $N_Y = 1.850$, $N_Z = 1.950$, $N_Z - N_X = 0.331$ (for $\lambda = 5461$). Ref: 556a.

Hexa(dimethylamino)benzene [$C_6(N(CH_3)_2)_6$] is monoclinic with $a:b:c = 1.946:1:1.263$, $\beta = 104°43'$. Crystals show {100}, {111}, {$\bar{1}$11}, {001}. The optic plane is 010. (+)2V = 70° calc. $N_X = 1.553$, $N_Y = 1.574$, $N_Z = 1.612$, $N_Z - N_X = 0.059$. Ref: 330.

Cyclotrimethylenetrinitramine or cyclonite or RDX ($C_3H_6O_6N_6$) is orthorhombic with $a:b:c = 0.881:1:0.813$. *a* 11.61, *b* 13.18, *c* 10.72 Å. U.C. 8. Crystals varied, but often {001} plates. D 1.82. Decomposes at 205°. X = *c*, Y = *a*. (-)2V = 53°22′, r > v. $N_X = 1.5775$, $N_Y = 1.5966$, $N_Z = 1.6015$, $N_Z - N_X = 0.024$ for $\lambda = 5893$. Ref: 553b.

Cyclotetramethylene tetranitramine or HMX ($C_4H_8O_8N_8$) is polymorphous. Phase I is monoclinic sphenoidal with $\beta = 103°$ and 101 ∧ 10$\bar{1}$ = 83°. D 1.96. Y = *b*; Z ∧ *c* = 30° in acute β. (+)2V = 20°, r > v weak. $N_X = 1.589$, $N_Y = 1.594$, $N_Z = 1.73$, $N_Z - N_X = 0.141$. Phase II is orthorhombic with 110 ∧ $\bar{1}$10 = 116° and 101 ∧ $\bar{1}$01 = 43°. D 1.87. Y = *b* (red); Y = *c* (blue). (+)2V = 10° to 30° (red), = 8° to 30° (blue). $N_X = 1.561$ to 1.565, $N_Y = 1.562$ to 1.566, $N_Z = 1.72$ to 1.74, $N_Z - N_X \approx 0.17$. Phase III is monoclinic with $\beta = 120°$. Crystals usually show {001}, {110}, and {100}. D 1.82. X ∧ *c* = 42° in obtuse β; Y = *b*. (+)2V = 75°, r < v strong. $N_X = 1.537$, $N_Y = 1.585$, $N_Z = 1.666$, $N_Z - N_X = 0.129$. Phase IV is hexagonal in rods and needles. M.P. 279°. D 1.78. Uniaxial negative. $N_O = 1.607$, $N_E = 1.566$, $N_O - N_E = 0.041$. Ref: 551a, 553b.

Subclass G. Hydroxyamines and Derivatives

o-Aminophenol ($H_2N \cdot C_6H_4OH$) is orthorhombic with $a:b:c = 0.367:1:0.398$. Space group *Pbca*; *a* 7.85, *b* 19.74, *c* 7.25 Å. U.C. 8. Crystals {010} tablets with {111}, {121}, {100}, etc. D 1.28. M.P. 173°. X = *c*, Y = *a*. Z = *b*. (+)2V = 39°, r > v very weak. $N_X = 1.618$, $N_Y = 1.632$, $N_Z = 1.774$, $N_Z - N_X = 0.158$. Ref: 553a.

p-(2-Aminopropyl)phenol hydrobromide or paredrine hydrobromide ($C_9H_{13}ON \cdot HBr$) forms irregular units. (-)2V = 70° calc., $N_X = 1.560$, $N_Y = 1.680$, $N_Z = 1.734$, $N_Z - N_X = 0.174$. Ref: 523e.

2-Amino-4,6-dinitrophenol or picramic acid [$C_6H_2(NO_2)_2(NH_2)OH$] has parallel extinction. M.P. 168°. (+)2V = small. $N_X = 1.505$, $N_Y = 1.54$, $N_Z > 1.95$, $N_Z - N_X > 0.445$. Ref: 34, 35.

Benzalaminophenol ($C_6H_5CH:N \cdot C_6H_4OH$) is monoclinic with $a:b:c = 0.839:1:0.434$, $\beta = 119°$. Crystals usually equant or long ‖ a with {010}, {001}, and {110}. Twinning on 100. D 1.30. M.P. 183°, X ∧ c = 3° (blue), 5° (yellow) in obtuse β. Y = b. (+)2V = 63°, r < very strong. $N_X = 1.698$, $N_Y = 1.736$, $N_Z = 1.84$, $N_Z - N_X = 0.142$. Crystals are light yellow with X < Y < Z. Ref: 553a.

1-Amino-4-hydroxybenzene or *p*-aminophenol [$C_6H_4(OH)NH_2$] is orthorhombic with $a:b:c = 0.785:1:0.721$. Crystals show {100}, {010}, {110}, {011}. Perfect 100 cleavage. M.P. 184°. X = a; Y = c. (-)2E = 47°37′ Na, r > v. $N_1 = 1.58$, $N_2 = 1.66$, $N_2 - N_1 = 0.08$. Caspari from X-ray studies reported two phases, both unlike the one first described. Ref: 34, 35.

1-Amino-4-hydroxybenzene hydrochloride or *p*-aminophenol hydrochloride [$C_6H_4(OH)NH_2 \cdot HCl$] has parallel extinction and positive elongation with $N_1 = 1.545$, $N_2 = 1.72$, $N_2 - N_1 = 0.175$. Ref: 34.

Citrophen or *p*-phenetidine citrate ($C_6H_4(OC_2H_5)NH_2 \cdot C_3H_4(OH)(CO_2H)_3$] is biaxial with M.P. 186°. $N_1 = 1.55$, $N_2 = 1.661$ (?), $N_2 - N_1 = 0.111$ (?). Ref: 239.

1-Acetamido-4-ethoxybenzene or *p*-acetophenetidine or phenacetin [$C_6H_4(OC_2H_5)NHCOCH_3$] is polymorphous; one phase (I) is monoclinic with M.P. 134.5° and $N_X = 1.518$, $N_Y = 1.574$, $N_Z > 1.733$, $N_Z - N_X > 0.215$, ∴ (+)2V = not large. Again (+)2V = 63°, r < v; $N_Y = 1.574$. A metastable phase (II) is also monoclinic with M.P. 128 – 129°. Y makes an angle of 7° with the elongation and X = b. If the elongation is along c, twinning may occur on 001 with an angle of 80° between the parts. (-)2V = 70° *ca.*, $N_X = 1.473$, $N_Y = 1.627$, $N_Z > 1.70$ and < 1.74, $N_Z - N_X > 0.227$ and < 0.267. Also $N_1 = 1.54$, $N_2 = 1.58$, $N_3 = 1.59$. Ref: 34, 87, 123, 343c, 518.

p-Methylaminophenol sulfate or metol ($2C_7H_9ON \cdot H_2SO_4$) is monoclinic with $a:b:c = 3.180:1:2.512$; $\beta = 92°40'$. Crystals long ‖ b with {100}, {001}, {101}, etc. D 1.42. M.P. about 250°. X = c *ca.*, Y = b; (-)2V = 81°, r > v. $N_X = 1.508$, $N_Y = 1.607$, $N_Z = 1.694$, $N_Z - N_X = 0.186$. Ref: 436a.

4-Ethoxyphenylcarbamide or dulcine ($H_2NCONHC_6H_4OC_2H_5$) is orthorhombic (?). Crystals long rectangular or irregular with X ‖ length. (+)2V = 46°; $N_X = 1.585$, $N_Y = 1,589$, $N_Z = 1.610$ calc., $N_Z - N_X = 0.025$ (calc.). Ref: 123.

Neostigmine bromide or prostigmine bromide ($C_{12}H_{19}N_2O_2Br$) is soluble in water. It has M.P. = 167° C. and $N_X = 1.560$, $N_Y = 1.658$, $N_Z = 1.675$, $N_Z - N_X = 0.115$, ∴ (-)2V = 45° *ca.* Colorless. Ref: 518.

Neostigmine methyl sulfate or prostigmine methyl sulfate ($C_{13}H_{22}N_2O_2SO_4$) is soluble in water. It has M.P. = 142 - 145°. and $N_X = 1.519$, $N_Y = 1.525$, $N_Z = 1.580$, $N_Z - N_X = 0.061$, $\therefore$ (+)2V = 35° *ca.* Colorless. Ref: 518.

4-Acetamidophenyl 2-hydroxybenzoate or 4-acetamidophenyl salicylate or salophen [$C_6H_4(OH)CO_2C_6H_4(NHCOCH_3)$] forms four-sided acute-angled crystals and needles. Easily soluble in alcohol; nearly wholly insoluble in cold water. M.P. 187°. $N_1=1.572$, $N_2=1.681$, $N_2 - N_1=0.109$. Colorless. Ref: 239, 240.

N,N'-bis(4-Ethoxyphenyl)acetamidine hydrochloride or phenacaine or holocaine [$C_2H_5OC_6H_4NHC(CH_3){:}NC_6H_4OC_2H_5 \cdot HCl$] is monoclinic usually in long rhombic plates or needles. M.P. 189°. Easily soluble in alcohol. If c is || elongation, Z = b and X $\wedge$ c = 40°. (+)2V = 80°. $N_X = 1.520$ calc., $N_Y = 1.602$, $N_Z = 1.725$, $N_Z - N_X = 0.205$ calc. Again: $N_X = 1.523$, $N_Y = 1.600$, N_Z slightly less than 1.74, $N_Z - N_X$ slightly less than 0.22. $\therefore$ (+)2V = 75° calc. Again $N_X = 1.518$, $N_Y = 1.603$, $N_Z = 1.733$, $N_Z - N_X = 0.215$. Ref: 123, 239, 518.

Ethyl *N*-acetyl-*N*-(4-hydroxyphenyl)carbamate or acetyl-*p*-hydroxyphenylurethan or neurodine [$HOC_6H_4(CH_3CO)NCO_2C_2H_5$] has parallel extinction and negative elongation with $N_1 = 1.55$, $N_2 = 1.61$, $N_2 - N_1 = 0.06$. Ref: 34.

Ethyl *N*-acetyl-*N*-(4-ethoxyphenyl)carbamate or (4-ethoxyphenyl)-acetylurethan or thermodine [$(C_2H_5O_2C)N(COCH_3)C_6H_4OC_2H_5$] melts at 86°. It has $N_1 = 1.54$, $N_2 = 1.69$, $N_2 - N_1 = 0.15$. Ref: 34.

N-(4-Ethoxyphenyl)-2-hydroxypropanamide or *N*-lactyl-*p*-phenetide or lactophenine [$C_6H_4(OC_2H_5)NHCOCHOHCH_3$] is monoclinic in {100} tablets with {011}, {110}, and {010}. 011 $\wedge$ $0\bar{1}1$ = 104°; β = 100° *ca.* Easily soluble in alcohol. M.P. 118 - 120°. Crystals obtained by sublimation at about 105° under 12 mm. Hg of pressure and at 3 - 5 mm. distance. X = b; Y $\wedge$ c = - 8°. (+)2V = rather small. $N_X = 1.492$, $N_Y = 1.532$, $N_Z > 1.70$, $N_Z - N_X > 0.208$. Mayrhofer measured two indices: $N_1 = 1.49$, $N_2 = 1.534$.
Ref: 206, 239, 343c.

2-(3,5-Dichloro-4-hydroxyphenyl)ethylamine or 3,5-dichlorotyramine [$C_6H_2Cl_2(OH)(CH_2)_2NH_2$] is monoclinic with $a{:}b{:}c = 0.879{:}1{:}0.902$, β = 101°2′. Crystals {100} plates with {110}, {111}, {011}. X $\wedge$ c = small; Y = b. (+)2V = 87°44′ Na. $N_X = 1.568$, $N_Y = 1.623$, $N_Z = 1.668$ calc., $N_Z - N_X = 0.100$.
Ref: 400, 403.

dl-1-Phenyl-2-aminoethanol sulfate or α-(aminomethyl)benzyl alcohol sulfate [$C_6H_5CH(OH)CH_2NH_2 \cdot H_2SO_4$] is apparently orthorhombic. (+)2V = medium. $N_X = 1.561$, $N_Y = 1.581$ $N_Z > 1.61$ calc., $N_Z - N_X > 0.05$ calc. Ref: 341.

Ephedrinephenylthiocarbamide [$C_6H_5CHOHCH(CH_3)NCH_3C({:}S)(NHC_6H_5)$] is orthorhombic sphenoidal with $a{:}b{:}c = 0.817{:}1{:}0.428$. Crystals prismatic with {110}, {101}, {100}, {111}. Fig. 89. Perfect 100 and 010 and distinct 001 cleavages. M.P. 115° (with decomposition). Y = b; Z = a. (+)2V = 66°25′, r < v very weak. The remarkably low indices recorded are: $N_X = 1.2696$ Na, $N_Y = 1.2876$, $N_Z = 1.3332$, $N_Z - N_X = 0.0636$. Ref: 119.

l-2-Methylamino-1-phenyl-1-propanol hydrochloride or α-(1-methylaminoethyl)benzyl alcohol hydrochloride or *l*-ephedrine hydrochloride [$C_6H_5CH(OH)CH(NHCH_3)CH_3 \cdot HCl$] is monoclinic sphenoidal with $a:b:c = 2.066:1:1.192$, $\beta = 102°6'$. Space group $P2_1$; *a* 12.64, *b* 6.15, *c* 7.34 Å. U.C. 2. Crystals long {100} tablets often twinned on 100. Perfect 100 and 001 cleavages. M.P. 216 – 220° Soluble in water and alcohol. Y = *b*; Z nearly normal to 100. (-)2E = large, r < v. 2V = 70° calc. $N_X = 1.530$, $N_Y = 1.603$, $N_Z = 1.638$, all ± .002, $N_Z - N_X = 0.108$. Also $N_1 = 1.602$, $N_2 = 1.624$, $N_3 = 1.640$. Ref: 269, 343c, 473, 523e.

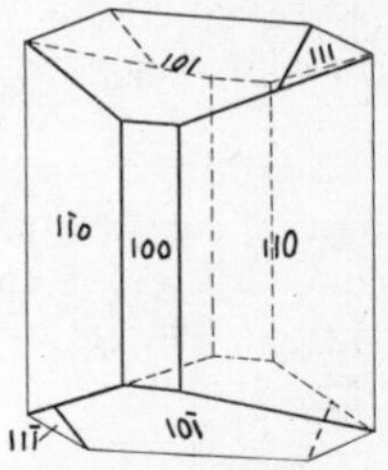

Fig. 89. Ephedrine-phenylthiocarbamide.

1-Phenyl-2-methylcinnamylaminopropanol-1 or *N*-cinnamyl-*l*-ephedrine [$C_6H_5CHOHCHCH_3NCH_3(CH)_2C_6H_5$] forms needles and rods with X parallel to elongation. M.P. 85.6 – 85.7°. $N_X = 1.582$, $N_Y = ?$, $N_Z = 1.733$, $N_Z - N_X = 0.151$. Ref: 614.

1-Phenyl-2-methylcinnamylaminopropanol-1- hydrochloride or *N*-cinnamyl-*l*-ephedrine hydrochloride [$C_6H_5CHOHCHCH_3NCH_3(CH)_2C_6H_5 \cdot HCl$] forms irregular plates with M.P. 180.5 – 182°. $N_X = 1.550$, $N_Y = ?$, $N_Z = 1.733$, $N_Z - N_X = 0.183$. Ref: 614.

l-2-Methylamino-1-phenyl-1-propanol sulfate or *l*-ephedrine sulfate [$(C_{10}H_{15}ON)_2 \cdot H_2SO_4$] forms elongated crystals, probably orthorhombic, easily soluble in water or hot alcohol. Parallel extinction with the optic plane normal to the elongation. (+)2E = large. $N_X = 1.540 \pm .001$, $N_Y = 1.565 \pm .002$, N_Z doubtless > 1.59, $N_Z - N_X > 0.05$. Again: $N_X = 1.540$, $N_Y = 1.565$, $N_Z = 1.587$, $N_Z - N_X = 0.047$. Ref: 269, 523e, 523h.

dl-2-Methylamino-1-phenyl-1-propanol hydrochloride or *dl*-ephedrine hydrochloride ($C_6H_5CHOHCHNHCH_3CH_3 \cdot HCl$) is monoclinic prismatic with $a:b:c = 1.887:1:1.894$, $\beta = 118°24'$. Space group $P2_1c$; *a* 13.27, *b* 7.04, *c* 13.44 Å. U.C. 4. Perfect 100 and $\bar{1}01$ cleavages. D 1.231. X = *b*. Z nearly normal to 100. (-)2E = 120° *ca*. $N_X = 1.57$, $N_Y = 1.61$. Again: (-)2V = 70° calc. $N_X = 1.570$, $N_Y = 1.608$, $N_Z = 1.630$, $N_Z - N_X = 0.060$. Also: $N_X = 1.530$, $N_Y = 1.603$, $N_Z = 1.638$, $N_Z - N_X = 0.108$. Ref: 472, 523e, 523h.

Isodrine sulfate or *dl*-1-(*p*-hydroxyhenyl)-2-methylaminopropane sulfate {[$HOC_6H_4CH_2CH(CH_3)NHCH_3]_2 \cdot H_2SO_4$} is monoclinic. Crystals often six-sided plates with symmetrical extinction or rods with X ∧ elongation = 13°. (+)2V = 65° calc., $N_X = 1.516$, $N_Y = 1.552$, $N_Z = 1.645$, $N_Z - N_X = 0.129$. Ref: 617c.

1-Phenyl-2-methylcinnamylaminopropanol-1 or *N*-cinnamyl-*dl*-ephedrine ($C_6H_5CHOHCHCH_3NCH_3CH_2CH$) forms needles and rods with X parallel to elongation. M.P. 66.7 – 67.7°. $N_X = 1.570$, $N_Y = ?$, $N_Z = 1.733$, $N_Z - N_X = 0.163$. Ref: 614.

β-(4-Methylbenzhydryl)-N,N-dimetylethanolamine hydrochloride [$(CH_3)_2NCH_2CHOH \cdot C \cdot (CH_3)(C_6H_5)_2 \cdot HCl$] forms rectangular plates and fragments.

M.P. 147°. Extinction inclined; ± elongation. (-)2E = small, N_X = 1.562, N_Y = 1.606, N_Z = 1.610, $N_Z - N_X$ = 0.048. 2V = 32° calc. Ref: 477d.

2-Amino-1,2-diphenylethanol hydrochloride or diphenylethanolamine hydrochloride [$C_6H_5CH(OH)CH(NH_2)C_6H_5 \cdot HCl$] is hexagonal or trigonal with *c/a* = 1.732 (metastable). Crystals show {10$\bar{1}$0}, {11$\bar{2}$0}, etc. Twinning cruciform at 60°. Uniaxial negative with N_O = ? N_E = 1.63. Ref: 119.

3-Hydroxy-4-methoxybenzylamine hydrochloride or vanillylamine hydrochloride or α-aminocreosol hydrochloride [$(HO)(CH_3O)C_6H_3CH_2NH_2 \cdot HCl$] is monoclinic (?) in rods with extinction reaching 35°. Elongation usually negative. (-)2V = 39° *ca.*, r < v. N_X = 1.510, N_Y = 1.705, N_Z = 1.735, $N_Z - N_X$ = 0.225 D, all ± .005. Ref: 369.

3,4-Dimethoxybenzylamine hydrochloride or veratrylamine hydrochloride [$(CH_3O)_2C_6H_3CH_2NH_2 \cdot HCl$] is monoclinic in rods and plates with extinction reaching 40°. The optic plane is normal to the plates and an optic axis is nearly normal thereto. (-)2V = 35° *ca.*, r < v weak. N_X = 1.505, N_Y = 1.670, N_Z = 1.700, $N_Z - N_X$ = 0.195 D, all ± .005. Ref: 369.

N-(4-Hydroxy-3-methoxybenzyl)ethanamide or *N*-vanillylacetamide [$(HO)(CH_3O)C_6H_3CH_2NHCOCH_3$] is monoclinic in rods with extinction reaching 30°. M.P. 84 - 85°. The optic plane is parallel to the elongation. (+)2V = 62° *ca*, distinct axial dispersion. N_X = 1.550, N_Y = 1.585, N_Z = 1.685, $N_Z - N_X$ = 0.135, all ± .005. Ref: 370.

N-(4-Hydroxy-3-methoxybenzyl)propanamide or *N*-vanillylpropionamide [$(HO)(CH_3O)C_6H_3CH_2NHCOCH_2CH_3$] is orthorhombic in rods with parallel extinction. M.P. 108 - 110°. (-)2V = 56° *ca.*, distinct axial dispersion. N_X = 1.495, N_Y = 1.635, N_Z = 1.680, $N_Z - N_X$ = 0.185, all ± .005. Ref: 370.

N-(4-Hydroxy-3-methoxybenzyl)butanamide or *N*-vanillylbutyramide [$(HO)(CH_3O)C_6H_3CH_2NHCO(CH_2)_2CH_3$] is probably triclinic in rods and grains with extinction reaching 45°. M.P. 68 - 70°. (+)2V = large, distinct dispersion. N_X = 1.515, N_Y = 1.580, N_Z = 1.655, $N_Z - N_X$ = 0.140, all ± .005. Ref: 370.

N-(4-Hydroxy-3-methoxybenzyl)-2-methylpropanamide or *N*-vanillylisobutyramide [$(HO)(CH_3O)C_6H_3CH_2NHCOCH(CH_3)_2$] is orthorhombic in rectangular plates and pyramids. M.P. 118 - 120°. Symmetrical extinction. (-)2V = 11° *ca.*, distinct axial dispersion. N_X = 1.465, N_Y = 1.633, N_Z = 1.635, $N_Z - N_X$ = 0.170, all ± .005. Ref: 370.

N-(4-Hydroxy-3-methoxybenzyl)heptanamide or *N*-vanillylenanthamide [$(HO)(CH_3O)C_6H_3CH_2NHCO(CH_2)_5CH_3$] is probably monoclinic with usually inclined extinction. M.P. 59 - 61°. (-)2V = 62° *ca.*, distinct axial dispersion. N_X = 1.515, N_Y = 1.595, N_Z = 1.625, $N_Z - N_X$ = 0.110, all ± .005. Ref: 370.

N-(4-Hydroxy-3-methoxybenzyl)octanamide or *N*-vanillylcaprylamide [(HO)$(CH_3O)C_6H_3CH_2NHCO(CH_2)_6CH_3$] is orthorhombic (?) in needles with parallel extinction and negative elongation. M.P. 41 - 43°. $N_X = 1.56$, $N_Y = ?$, $N_Z = 1.57$, $N_Z - N_X = 0.01$. Ref: 370.

N-(4-Hydroxy-3-methoxybenzyl) nonenamide or *N*-vanillylpelargonamide $[(HO)(CH_3O)C_6H_3CH_2NHCO(CH_2)_7CH_3]$ is like the preceding except that M.P. is 47 - 52°. $N_X = 1.57$, $N_Y = ?$, $N_Z = 1.59$, $N_Z - N_X = 0.02$. Ref: 370.

N-(4-Hydroxy-3-methoxybenzyl) decanamide or *N*-vanillylcapramide or *N*-vanillyldecanamide $[(HO)(CH_3O)C_6H_3CH_2NHCO(CH_2)_8CH_3]$ is probably orthorhombic in plates and needles with parallel extinction and ± elongation. M.P. 59 - 60°. (+)2V = small. $N_X = 1.545$, $N_Y = 1.555$, $N_Z = 1.620$, $N_Z - N_X = 0.075$, all ± .005. Ref: 370.

N-(4-Hydroxy-3-methoxybenzyl) undecanamide or *N*-vanillylundecanamide $[(HO)(CH_3O)C_6H_3CH_2NHCO(CH_2)_9CH_3]$ is apparently triclinic in irregular plates with inclined extinction. M.P. 54 - 56°. (+)2V = 64° *ca.*, distinct dispersion. $N_X = 1.515$, $N_Y = 1.540$, $N_Z = 1.615$, $N_Z - N_X = 0.100$, all ± .005. Ref: 370.

N-(4-Hydroxy-3-methoxybenzyl) dodecanamide or *N*-vanillylauramide or *N*-vanillyldodecanamide $[(HO)(CH_3O)C_6H_3CH_2NHCO(CH_2)_{10}CH_3]$ is probably monoclinic in plates with extinction reaching 30° and negative elongation. M.P. 60 - 61°. (+)2V = moderate. $N_X = 1.52$, $N_Y = 1.54$, $N_Z = 1.60$, $N_Z - N_X = 0.08$, all ± .01. Ref: 370.

N-(4-Hydroxy-3-methoxybenzyl)-2-butenamide or N-vanillylcrotonamide $[(HO)(CH_3O)C_6H_3CH_2NHCOCH{:}CHCH_3]$ is probably orthorhombic in rods and irregular bodies with parallel extinction. M.P. 119 - 120°. (+)2V = large, distinct axial dispersion. $N_X = 1.515$, $N_Y = 1.605$, $N_Z = 1.735$, $N_Z - N_X = 0.220$, all ± .005. Ref: 370.

N-(4-Hydroxy-3-methoxybenzyl)-8-methyl-6-nonenamide or 8-methyl-*N*-vanillyl-6-nonenamide or capsaicin $[(HO)(CH_3O)C_6H_3CH_2NHCO(CH_2)_4CH{:}CH\,CH(CH_3)_2]$ is probably monoclinic. M.P. 64°. Rectangular plates have parallel extinction, but others have an extinction angle reaching 20°. (+)2V = 30° *ca.* $r < v$ strong. $N_X = 1.520$ D, $N_Y = 1.540$, $N_Z = 1.580$, $N_Z - N_X = 0.060$, all ± .005. Ref: 369, 371.

N-(3,4-Dimethoxybenzyl)-8-methyl-6-nonenamide or 8-methyl-*N*-veratryl-6-nonenamide or capsaicin methyl ether or methylcapsaicin $[(CH_3O)_2C_6H_3CH_2\,NHCO(CH_2)_4CH{:}CHCH(CH_3)_2]$ is probably monoclinic in clustered needles. M.P. 77 - 78°. Extinction reaches 45°. $N_X = 1.55$, $N_Y = 1.58$, $N_Z = 1.60$, $N_Z - N_X = 0.05$ D, all ± .01. ∴ probably (-)2V = large. Ref: 369, 371.

N-(4-Hydroxy-3-methoxybenzyl)-8-methylnonanamide or η-methyl-*N*-vanillylpelargonamide or hydrogenated capsaicin $[(HO)(CH_3O)C_6H_3CH_2NHCO(CH_2)_6\,CH(CH_3)_2]$ is biaxial with $N_X = 1.510$, $N_Y = 1.520$, $N_Z = 1.555$, $N_Z - N_X = 0.045$; ∴ (+)2V = 55° calc. Ref: 371.

N-(4-Hydroxy-3-methoxybenzyl)-10-undecenamide or *N*-vanillylundecenamide $[(HO)(CH_3O)C_6H_3CH_2NHCO(CH_2)_8CH:CH_2]$ is probably orthorhombic in splintery masses and small needles with parallel extinction and negative elongation. M.P. 53 – 55°. (+)2V = very large. $N_X = 1.55$, $N_Y = 1.60$, $N_Z = 1.63$, $N_Z - N_X = 0.08$, all ± .01. Optic sign and indices inconsistent-A.N.W.)
Ref: 370.

N-(4-Hydroxy-3-methoxybenzyl)benzamide or *N*-vanillylbenzamide $[(HO)(CH_3O)C_6H_3CH_2NHCOC_6H_5]$ is probably orthorhombic in needles and rods with parallel extinction and positive elongation. M.P. 140 – 142°. (–)2V = 48° *ca.*, distinct axial dispersion. $N_X = 1.590$, $N_Y = 1.675$, $N_Z = 1.695$, $N_Z - N_X = 0.105$, all ± .005.
Ref: 370.

Oxedrine tartrate or *dl*-1-(*p*-hydroxyphenyl)-2-methylaminoethanol tartrate or sympathol or synephrine tartrate $\{[HOC_6H_4CHOHCH_2NHCH_3]_2 \cdot C_4H_6O_6\}$ is triclinic. Crystals are rods with Z ∧ elongation usually 30 – 32°. Often show an uncentered optic axis figure. (+)2V = large, $N_X = 1.517$, $N_Y = 1.59$, *ca.*, $N_Z = 1.689$, $N_Z - N_X = 0.172$. $N_1 = 1.625$ often seen with extinction at 30 – 32°.
Ref: 617c.

3,4,5-Trimethoxyphenethylamine sulfate or mescaline sulfate (dihydrate?) $[[(CH_3O)_3C_6H_2(CH_2)_2NH_2]_2 \cdot H_2SO_4]$ is biaxial with 2V near 90°. $N_X = 1.575$, $N_Y = 1.59$, $N_Z = 1.605$, $N_Z - N_X = 0.030$.
Ref: 34, 35.

Supriphen hydrochloride or *dl*-1-(*p*-hydroxyphenyl)-2-methylaminopropanol hydrochloride $\{HOC_6H_4CHOH \cdot CH(CH_3)CHNHCH_3 \cdot HCl\}$ is orthorhombic. Crystals rectangular rods with Y along elongation. (–)2V = 80° calc., $N_X = 1.507$, $N_Y = 1.604$, $N_Z = 1.668$, $N_Z - N_X = 0.161$.
Ref: 617c.

3,4-Dihydroxy-α-(methylaminomethyl)benzyl alcohol or adrenalin or epinephrine $\{(HO)_2C_6H_3CHOH \cdot CH_2NHCH_3\}$ forms colorless or light brown crystals or powder, darkening on exposure to air. $N_1 = 1.555$, $N_2 = 1.733$, $N_2 - N_1 = 0.178$.
Ref: 518.

Subclass H. Carbonyl Amines and Derivatives

3-Isopropyl-6-methyl-6-methylamino-2-cyclohexen-1-one oxime or 1-methylamino-Δ^3-2-*p*-menthenone or terpinene nitrolmethylamine $[C_{10}H_{15}(:NOH)NH(CH_3)]$ is monoclinic with $a:b:c = 0.882:1:0.429$, $\beta = 109°5'$. Crystals short prismatic with {110}, {001}, etc. Distinct 100 and imperfect 001 cleavages. M.P. 141°. The optic plane is normal to 010. The acute bisectrix makes an angle of – 31° Na with *c*. 2V = 55°20′. $N_Y = 1.5744$ Na.
Ref: 117.

6-Ethylamino-3-isopropyl-6-methyl-2-cyclohexen-1-one oxime or 1-ethylamino-Δ^3-2-*p*-menthenone or terpinene nitrolethylamine $[C_{10}H_{15}(:NOH)NH(C_2H_5)]$ is monoclinic with $a:b:c = 1.062:1:0.447$, $\beta = 108°11'$. Crystals short prismatic with {110}, {100}, {001}, etc. Fig. 90. Perfect 100 and imperfect 001 cleavages. M.P. 130 – 131°. The optic plane is normal to 010. The acute bisectrix makes an angle of – 26° with *c*. 2V = 70°53′, r < v. $N_Y = 1.5536$ Na. Ref: 117.

6-Dimethylamino-$\triangle^{6, 8(9)}$-2-*p*-menthadienone perchlorate or 6-dimethylaminocarvone perchlorate [$H_2C:C(CH_3)CHCH_2CN(CH_3)_2:C(CH_3)COCH_2 \cdot HClO_4$] is orthorhombic with $a:b:c = 0.785:1:0.596$. Crystals show {011}, {101}, {100}, {001}, {120}, etc. Perfect 100 and good 110 cleavages. Y = *c*; Z = *a*. (+)2V = 85.5°, r < v weak. $N_X = 1.507$, $N_Y = 1.536$, $N_Z = 1.570$, $N_Z - N_X = 0.063$. Colorless. [α] = – 40.1° (in water). Ref: 121a.

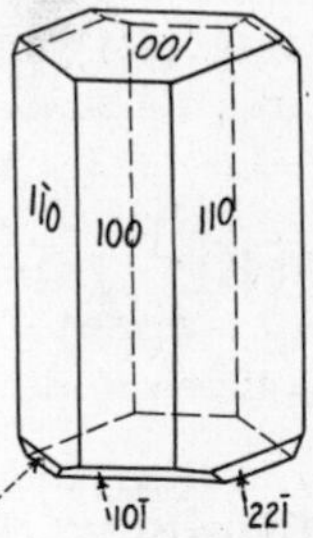

Fig. 90. Terpinene nitrolethylamine.

6-Dimethylamino-1-hydroxy-$\triangle^{8(9)}$-2-*p*-menthenone perchlorate or 1-hydroxy-6-dimethylaminodihydrocarvone perchlorate [$H_2CC(CH_3)CH_2CHN(CH_3)_2COH(CH_3)COCH_2 \cdot HClO_4$] is monoclinic sphenoidal with $a:b:c = 0.893:1:0.877$, $\beta = 91°50'$. Crystals short columns along *b* with {001}, {100}, {011}, {121}, {1$\bar{1}$0}, etc. Perfect 001 and good 100 cleavages. The optic plane and X are normal to 101 and Z = *a* nearly. (-)2V = 39°. $N_X = 1.510$, $N_Y = 1.526$, $N_Z = 1.528$, $N_Z - N_X = 0.018$. Colorless. [α] = + 9.86° (in water). Ref: 121a.

1-Dimethylamino-6-hydroxy-$\triangle^{8(9)}$-2-*p*-menthenone perchlorate or 1-dimethylamino-6-hydroxydihydrocarvone perchlorate [$H_2CC(CH_3)CHCH_2CHOHC(CH_3)(N(CH_3)_2)COCH_2 \cdot HClO_4$] is monoclinic with $a:b:c = 1.03:1:0.726$, $\beta = 90°56'$. It forms fine needles elongated along *b* with {201}, {100}, {$\bar{1}$01}, {$\bar{2}$01}, {101}, etc. No cleavage found. Z = *b*. (-)2V = 72°18′, r < v strong. $N_X = 1.513$, $N_Y = 1.528$, $N_Z = 1.536$, $N_Z - N_X = 0.023$. Colorless. [α] = – 12.78° (in water). Ref: 121a.

1-Salicylaminoanthraquinone [$C_6H_4(CO)_2C_6H_3NHCOC_6H_4OH$] is orthorhombic (?). Crystals prismatic. M.P. 273° C. Z || length. (-)2V = (?), with strong axial dispersion. $N_X = 1.704$, $N_Y = (?)$, $N_Z = 1.915$, $N_Z - N_X - 0.211$. Very little pleochroism in light yellow. Called helio fast yellow 6GL. Ref: 543, 576.

4,4-Diphenyl-6-dimethylamino-3-heptanone hydrochloride or methadon hydrochloride or dolophine or amidone ($C_{21}H_{27}ON \cdot HCl$) is monoclinic domatic with $\beta = 106°$. M.P. 236° (or 241°, corrected). Soluble in water. Y = *b*. Z nearly = *c*. (-)2V = 52°, r > v. $N_X = 1.5713$, $N_Y = 1.6232$, $N_Z = 1.6360$, $N_Z - N_X = 0.0647$. Colorless. Ref: 459a.

2,7-*bis*(1-Anthraquinonylamino)anthraquinone or 2,7-di-α-anthraquinonyldiaminoanthraquinone ($C_{42}H_{22}O_6N_2$) is monoclinic (?). X ∧ length = 80°. $N_X = 1.522$, $N_Y = ?$, $N_Z = 2.14$, $N_Z - N_X = 0.618$. Called indanthrene red R. Pleochroic with X = light yellow, Z = dark red. Ref: 577.

Subclass J. Hydroxy Carbonyl Amines and Derivatives

3,4-Dihydroxy-α-methylaminoacetophenone hydrochloride monohydrate or adrenaline hydrochloride monohydrate or methylaminoacetopyrocatechol hydrochloride monohydrate [$C_6H_3(OH)_2COCH_2NH(CH_3) \cdot HCl \cdot H_2O$] has two phases. One (I) is orthorhombic(pyramidal?) with $a:b:c = 0.680:1:2.337$. Crystals {001} tablets with {121}, {012}, {111}. Good 010 cleavage. D 1.394.

M.P. 240° with decomposition. X = *a*; Y = *b*. (-)2V = 89°44′ Na. N_X = 1.5166 Na, N_Y = 1.6255, N_Z = 1.7605, $N_Z - N_X$ = 0.2439, all ± .0002. Later measures gave: N_X = 1.5010 (λ = 640), 1.5043 D, 1.514 (λ = 500); N_Y = 1.6039 (λ = 640), 1.6108 D, 1.6232 (λ = 500); N_Z = 1.753 (λ = 640), 1.757 D, 1.794 (λ = 500); $N_Z - N_X$ = 0.2527 D. The other phase (II) (more stable) is monoclinic with *a*:*b*:*c* = 1.508:1:0.697, β = 95°17′. Crystals short prismatic with {110}, {101}, {$\bar{1}$01}, 100, etc. Twinning with *c* as twinning axis and 010 as composition face. No cleavage observed. D 1.393. M.P. 240° with decomposition X $\wedge$ *c* = + 0°8′ ± 3′; Y = *b*. (-)2V = 73°44′ Na. N_X = 1.5049 Na, N_Y = 1.6444, N_Z = 1.7294, $N_Z - N_X$ = 0.2375. Later measures gave N_X = 1.5003 (λ = 640), 1.5031 D, 1.5108 (λ = 500); N_Y = 1.6414 (λ = 640), 1.6473 D, 1.6639 (λ = 500); N_Z = 1.7380 (λ = 640), 1.7480 D, 1.7750 (λ = 500); $N_Z - N_X$ = 0.2449 D. Indices are different on different crystals; reason not known. Ref: 81, 82.

1-Benzamido-(or 1-benzoylamino)-4-hydroxyanthraquinone $\{C_6H_4(CO)_2C_6H_2(OH)NHCOC_6H_5\}$ is orthorhombic (?). Crystals tabular and short columnar. Z || length. N_X = 1.915, N_Y = (?), N_Z = 2.135, $N_Z - N_X$ = 0.22. Weakly pleochroic in red. Called helio fast pink RL; also algol pink R or vat pink B. Ref: 543, 576, 577.

Subclass K. Amino Carboxylic Acids and Derivatives

o-Aminobenzoic acid or anthranilic acid $(NH_2 \cdot C_6H_4 \cdot CO_2H)$ has three crystal phases. M.P. 145°. Phase I is orthorhombic with *a*:*b*:*c* = 0.838:1:0.724. Crystals {100} plates or rods along *c*. D 1.41. X = *b*; Y = *c*. (-)2V = 39°, r > v. N_X = 1.500, N_Y = 1.74, N_Z = 1.77, $N_Z - N_X$ = 0.27. Pleochroic with X = colorless, Y and Z = red. Phase II is orthorhombic with *a*:*b*:*c* = 0.727:1:0.447. Crystals rods or needles long || *c* with {100}, {010} and {111}. D 1.37. X = *b*, Y = *c*. (-)2V = 46°, r > v. 2E = 85° red, 78.5° yellow, 73° blue. N_X = 1.560, N_Y = 1.73, N_Z = 1.76, $N_Z - N_X$ = 0.20. Phase III is monoclinic with polar interfacial angles of 64° and 123°. Crystals rods elongated along *c*. X = *b*, Y $\wedge$ *c* = 33°. (-)2V = 73°, r > v with strong crossed dispersion. 2V = 75° red and 68° blue. N_X=1.562, N_Y=1.707, N_Z=1.78 calc. $N_Z - N_X$=0.22 calc. Ref: 118, 553a.

Ammonium *o*-aminobenzoate hydrochloride or ammonium anthranilate hydrochloride $\{C_6H_4(CO_2NH_4)(NH_2) \cdot HCl\}$ is monoclinic with *a*:*b*:*c* = 0.457:1:1.436, β = 104°26′. Crystals {010} tablets with {110}, {011}, {102}, etc. Distinct 010 and fair 001 and 100 cleavages. Other cleavages reported are: 102, 103, 104, $\bar{1}$03, $\bar{1}$04. M.P. 202 - 203°. D 1.174. X $\wedge$ *c* = + 49°; Z = *b*. (-)2V = 32°4′, r < v; horizontal dispersion visible. N_X = 1.536, N_Y = 1.653, N_Z = 1.664 calc., $N_Z - N_X$ = 0.128. Colorless. Ref: 121.

Guanidine anthranilate $\{NH_2C(NH)NH_2 \cdot NH_2C_6H_4CO_2H\}$ forms columnar crystals with N_1 (||length) = 1.514, N_2 (|| width) = 1.648, $N_2 - N_1$ = 0.134. Ref: 468.

Biguanide anthranilate $\{NH_2C(NH)NHC(NH)NH_2 \cdot CO_2HC_6H_4NH_2\}$ forms elongated tablets with N_1 (|| length) = 1.626, N_2 (|| width) = 1.723, $N_2 - N_1$ = 0.097. Ref: 468.

Guanylurea anthranilate $\{NH_2C(NH)NHCONH_2 \cdot NH_2C_6H_4 \cdot CO_2H\}$ forms columnar crystals with N_1 (|| length) = 1.535, N_2 (|| width) = 1.697, $N_2 - N_1$ = 0.162. Ref: 468.

Ethyl *p*-aminobenzoate or benzocaine or anästhesin $[NH_2C_6H_4 \cdot CO_2 \cdot C_2H_5]$ forms rectangular plates with Z parallel to the elongation M.P. 90°. Soluble in index liquids. Biaxial; probably optically positive. $N_1 = 1.535$, $N_2 = 1.565$, $N_3 > 1.70$, $N_3 - N_1 > 0.165$. Again: $N_X = 1.52$ *ca.*, $N_Z > 1.74$, $N_Z - N_X > 0.22$. Ref: 123, 343c.

2-Diethylaminoethyl *p*-aminobenzoate hydrochloride or procaine hydrochloride or novacaine hydrochloride $\{H_2NC_6H_4CO_2CH_2CH_2N(C_2H_5)_2HCl\}$ forms six sided plates or needles. M.P. 156°. Plates normal to Z with Y parallel to elongation. Plates do not extinguish sharply indicating strong absorption in a monoclinic or triclinic crystal. (+)2E = 60° (2V = 37° calc.), $N_X = 1.570$, $N_Y = 1.580$, $N_Z > 1.734$, $N_Z - N_X > 0.164$. Again: $N_X = 1.540$, $N_Y = 1.556$, $N_Z > 1.690$, $N_Z - N_X > 0.150$. Ref: 239, 343c, 518, 522.

2-Diethylaminoethyl *p*-aminobenzoate borate or procaine borate or borocaine or novocaine borate $\{(C_2H_5)_2NCH_2CH_2O_2CC_6H_4NH_2 \cdot 5HBO_2\}$ forms small tabular crystals, apparently monoclinic. M.P. 165 - 166°. (+)2V = 20° calc., r > v. $N_X = 1.497$, $N_Y = 1.502$, $N_Z = 1.602$, all ± 0.002, $N_Z - N_X = 0.105$. Ref: 340.

Mono-*n*-amylaminoethyl-*p*-aminobenzoate hydrochloride or amylcaine hydrochloride $(C_{14}H_{22}O_2N_2 \cdot HCl)$ is dimorphous. One phase (M.P. 153.5°) is orthorhombic (?) in rectangular long plates with Z parallel to the elongation. (+)2V = large, $N_X = 1.510$, $N_Y = 1.582$, $N_Z > 1.655$, $N_Z - N_X > 0.145$. A second phase (M.P. 176°) is hexagonal. Crystals prismatic rods with X parallel to the elongation. Uniaxial negative with $N_O = 1.582$, $N_E = 1.573$, $N_O - N_E = 0.009$. Colorless. Ref: 536.

γ-Dibutylaminopropyl-*p*-aminobenzoate-N-sulfate or *p*-aminobenzoyl-γ-dibutylaminopropanol sulfate or butacaine sulfate or butyn $\{(C_{18}H_{30}N_2O_2)_2 \cdot H_2SO_4\}$ is probably monoclinic. Crystals acicular often in spherulites. M.P. 103° C. Soluble in alcohol. Some needles {100} show parallel and some {010} show inclined extinction with negative elongation. Extinction is not sharp. Z probably = *b*, (+)2V = 45° calc. $N_X = 1.550$, $N_Y = 1.570$, $N_Z = 1.680$, $N_Z - N_X = 0.130$. Ref: 522.

4-Butylamidobenzoyl-β-dimethylaminoethanol hydrochloride or tetracaine hydrochloride $\{C_4H_9NH \cdot C_6H_4 \cdot CO_2(CH_2)_2N(CH_3)_2 \cdot HCl\}$ is soluble in water. It has M.P. 147 - 150° C and $N_1 = 1.488$, $N_2 = 1.733$, $N_3 > 1.733$, $N_3 - N_1 > 0.245$. Colorless. Ref: 518.

2-α(*p*-Aminophenyl)acetamidoethanoic acid or *N*-(*p*-amino-α-toluyl) glycine or *p*-aminophenaceturic acid $[C_6H_4(NH_2)CH_2CONH(CH_2CO_2H)]$ is monoclinic with $a:b:c = 0.668:1:?$, $\beta = 118°46'$. Crystals tiny {110} prisms with {001}. 001 cleavage. X ∧ *c* = small; Z = *b*. (-)2E = 102.5°, r < v. $N_X = 1.544$ red, 1.548 yellow, 1.556 blue; $N_Y = 1.69$ calc.; $N_Z = 1.721$ red, 1.726 yellow, 1.744 blue; $N_Z - N_X = 0.178$ yellow. (-)2V = 55° calc. Ref: 118.

4,4′-Dicyanodibenzylamine or α,α′-iminodi-*p*-tolunitrile or *bis* (*p*-cyanobenzyl)-amine [$C_6H_4(CN)CH_2NHCH_2C_6H_4(CN)$] is triclinic with $a:b:c = 0.397:1:0.751$, $\alpha = 111°56'$, $\beta = 135°39'$, $\gamma = 76°29'$. Crystals {001} tablets elongated parallel to *a* with {010}, {100}, {011}, {10$\bar{1}$}. M.P. 105 - 106°. The optic plane is nearly parallel with 001; extinction in 001 is at 22° to the edge of 010 and at 54° to the edge of 100. The acute bisectrix makes an angle of - 35.8° with *a*. Extremely strong birefringence. 2V = 69°39′ Na. $N_Y = 1.6023$ Na. Ref: 119.

2-Amino-3-phenylpropanoic acid or β-phenylalanine [$C_6H_5CH_2CH(NH_2)CO_2H$] is biaxial with M.P. 283°. (+)2V = 40° *ca.* calc. $N_X = 1.600$, $N_Y = 1.610$, $N_Z = 1.675$, $N_Z - N_X = 0.075$. Apparently inclined extinction. Ref: 169.

Copper β-phenylalanine salt [$Cu(O_2C \cdot CHNH_2CH_2C_6H_5)_2$] forms needles somewhat resembling spearheads with parallel extinction and negative elongation. $N_1 = 1.599$, $N_2 = 1.612$, $N_2 - N_1 = 0.013$. Ref: 66.

Propyl-*n*-(*p*-phenylbenzalamino)-α-ethylcinnamate [$C_6H_5C_6H_4CH:N(C_6H_4CH):C(C_2H_5)CO_2C_3H_7$] forms liquid crystals of three phases. Phase I (between 70° and 100°) is uniaxial positive with (at 71.4°) $N_O = 1.5271$, $N_E = 1.9200$, $N_E - N_O = 0.3909$. Phase II (between 100° and 117°) has (at 110°) $N_O = 1.5269$, N_E = ?. Phase III (between 119° and 133°) has (at 125°) $N_O = 1.5623$, N_E = ?. The liquid at 132° has N = 1.6325. Ref: 218.

Ethyl-*p*-(*p*-ethoxybenzalamino)-α-methylcinnamate ($C_2H_5OC_6H_4CH:NC_6H_4CH:CCH_3CO_2C_2H_5$) forms liquid crystals of two phases. Phase I (between 45° and 75°) at 48° is uniaxial positive with $N_O = 1.5155$, $N_E = 1.8853$, $N_E - N_O = 0.3698$. Phase II (between 80° and 119°) at 98° is uniaxial positive with $N_O = 1.5347$, $N_E = 1.8045$, $N_E - N_O = 0.2698$. M.P. about 120° Ref: 447, 548.

Ethyl-*p*-(*p*-ethoxybenzalamino)-α-ethylcinnamate ($C_2H_5OC_6H_4CH:NC_6H_4CH:CC_2H_5CO_2C_2H_5$) forms liquid crystals of two phases. Phase I (between 27° and 30°) at 28° is uniaxial positive with $N_O = 1.5288$ D, $N_E = 1.9075$, $N_E - N_O = 0.3787$. Phase II (between 30° and 56°) at 40° has $N_O = 1.5487$ D, N_E = ?. M.P. about 58°. Ref: 447, 548.

Amyl-*p*-cyanbenzalaminocinnamate ($CNC_6H_4C:HNC_6H_4CH:CHCO_2C_5H_{11}$) forms liquid crystals (between 75° and 95°) which are uniaxial positive with (at 80° for $\lambda = 592$) $N_O = 1.680$, $N_E = 1.5506$, $N_O - N_E = 0.1294$. Another phase was observed. Ref: 601.

Subclass L. Amino Hydroxy Carboxylic Acids and Derivatives

Methyl 3-amino-4-hydroxybenzoate or orthocaine or orthoform [$C_6H_3(NH_2)(OH)CO_2CH_3$] is acicular in rectangular and six-sided forms. M.P. 141 - 143°. Soluble in alcohol. (+)2V = small. $N_X = 1.515$, $N_Y = 1.523$, $N_Z = 1.582 - 1.587$, $N_Z - N_X = 0.070$ *ca.* Published data are conflicting as to "orthoform", and Kofler reports that it is tetragonal in short prisms with {110}, {100}, {111}, {001}. M.P. 142°. Formed by sublimation at 100° to 130°. Uniaxial negative with $N_O = 1.658$, $N_E = 1.622$, $N_O - N_E = 0.036$. Haas gives $N_1 = 1.598$,

N_2 = 1.657. Is it possible that these data belong to the "old" orthoform - that is, methyl 4-amino-3-hydroxybenzoate, which melts at 120°, and perhaps N_1 = 1.598 to its hydrate? Ref: 123, 206, 211a, 239.

Methyl 3-amino-4-hydroxybenzoate hydrate or orthocaine hydrate or orthoform hydrate [$C_6H_3(OH)(NH_2)CO_2CH_3 \cdot nH_2O$] is pseudotetragonal and monoclinic; it is obtained from solution in water-alcohol mixture. It melts with loss of water and becomes cloudy at 52° - 60°. N_1 = 1.515, N_2 = 1.523, $N_2 - N_1$ = 0.008. Ref: 206, 211a.

2-Amino-3-(4-hydroxyphenyl)-propanoic acid salt of 2,4-dinitro-1-naphthol-7-sulfonic acid, or tyrosine flavianate [$HOC_6H_4CH_2CH(NH_2)CO_2H \cdot HO_3SC_6H_3 \cdot COH{:}CNO_2 \cdot CH{:}CNO_2$] forms bright-yellow prisms which tend to form spherical clusters. Negative elongation and parallel extinction. N_1 = 1.493, N_2 = 1.778, $N_2 - N_1$ = 0.285. Ref: 65.

l-2-Amino-3-[4-hydroxyphenyl] propanoic acid or *l*-tyrosine [$HOC_6H_4CH_2CH(NH_2)CO_2H$] is biaxial in needles and rods with D 1.456. M.P. 295°. (+)2V = 65° *ca.* calc. N_X = 1.550, N_Y = 1.600, N_Z = 1.680, $N_Z - N_X$ = 0.130. Needles have parallel extinction and positive elongation. Ref: 169.

dl-2-Amino-3-(3-chloro-4-hydroxyphenyl)propanoic acid or *dl*-(mono)chlorotyrosine [$C_6H_3Cl(OH)CH_2CH(NH_2)CO_2H$] is orthorhombic with 010:110 = 68°23′, 110:1$\bar{1}$0 = 43°14′, 010:011 = 68°37′, 011:0$\bar{1}$1 = 42°47′. Crystals {010} tablets with {110} and {011}. X = *a*; Y = *b*. (-)2V = 30°, r < v. N_X = 1.485, N_Y = 1.617, N_Z = 1.628, $N_Z - N_X$ = 0.143. Ref: 400, 403.

dl-2-Amino-3-(3,5-d chloro-4-hydroxyphenyl)propanoic acid or *dl*-dichlorotyrosine [$C_6H_2Cl_2(OH)CH_2CHNH_2CO_2H$] is orthorhombic with 110:1$\bar{1}$0 = 90°16′, 001:101 = 70°13′, 101:10$\bar{1}$ = 39°41′. Crystals {001} tablets with {110}, {101}, {011}. Y = *a*. (-)2E = 44°40′, r < v weak. N_Z = 1.692, $N_Z - N_X$ = strong. Ref: 400, 403.

2,4-Dinitro-1-naphthol-7-sulfonic acid salt of 2-amino-3-(3,5-dichloro-4-hydroxyphenyl)propanoic acid[1], or dichlorotyrosine flavianate [$(HO)Cl_2C_6H_2CH_2CHNH_2CO_2H \cdot HO_3SC_6H_3 \cdot COH{:}CNO_2 \cdot CH{:}CNO_2$] forms loose rosettes of yellow crystals with negative elongation and parallel extinction. N_1 = 1.458, 1.778 > N_2 > 1.74, about 1.75, 0.320 > $N_2 - N_1$ > 0.282. Ref: 65.

l-2-Amino-3-(3,5-dichloro-4-hydroxyphenyl)propanoic acid or *l*-dichlorotyrosine [$C_6H_2Cl_2(OH)CH_2CHNH_2CO_2H$] is orthorhombic with 110:1$\bar{1}$0 = 44°21′, 010:011 = 68°18′, 011:0$\bar{1}$1 = 43°19′. Crystals equant. Y = *b*. (-)2V = 30°20′, r < v. N_Z = 1.628, $N_Z - N_X$ = strong. Ref: 400, 403.

dl-2-Amino-3-(?-bromo-4-hydroxyphenyl)propanoic acid or *dl*-bromotyrosine ($C_9H_{10}O_3NBr$) is orthorhombic with 010:110 = 68°24′, 110:1$\bar{1}$0 = 43°15′,

[1] Positions of the chlorine atoms are not specified, but these seem most probable. Apparently a derivative of *l*-tyrosine.

010:011 = 68°18′, 011:0$\bar{1}$1 = 43°26′. Crystals columnar with {110}, {010}, {011}. X = *a*; Y = *b*. (-)2E = 68°36′. N_Z = 1.632. Ref: 401.

2,4-Dinitro-1-naphthol-7-sulfonic acid salt of 2-amino-3-(4-hydroxy-3,5-di-iodophenyl)propanoic acid,[1] or di-iodotyrosine flavianate [$HOI_2C_6H_2CH_2CHNH_2CO_2H \cdot HO_3SC_6H_3 \cdot COH:CNO_2 \cdot CH:CNO_2$] forms small loose rosettes of yellow crystals with negative elongation and parallel extinction. N_1 = 1.495, N_2 = 1.720 $N_2 - N_1$ = 0.225. Ref: 65.

3,5-Di-iodo-*l*-tyrosine nitroindandionate ($C_{18}H_{14}O_7N_2I_2$) is orthorhombic in thin plates and radiating needles with X || elongation. M.P. 231°. (+)2V = very large, $r \ll v$. N_X = 1.766, N_Y = 1.786, N_Z > 1.870, $N_Z - N_X$ > 0.102. (From indices 2V cannot be more than 50° *ca.* - A.N.W.). Ref: 539a.

Sodium *dl*-thyroxine pentahydrate ($NaC_{15}H_{10}I_4NO_4 \cdot 5H_2O$) is triclinic with *a* 15.81, *b* 9.53, *c* 8.33 Å and α = 94.8°, β = 84.1°, γ = 95.5°. U.C. 2. D 2.381. Z nearly parallel with 23$\bar{2}$. (+)2V = 67°, N_X = 1.65, N_Y = 1.69, N_Z = 1.79, $N_Z - N_X$ = 0.14. Ref: 505a.

2-Methylbutyl 3-[4-(4-cyanobenzalamino)phenyl] propenoate or *p*-cyanobenzylideneaminocinnamate of active amyl alcohol [$N:CC_6H_4CH:NC_6H_4CH:CHCO_2CH_2CH(CH_3)CH_2CH_3$] as "liquid crystals" at 80° is uniaxial negative with N_O = 1.652 (702), 1.680 (592), 1.733 (496); N_E = 1.534 (702), 1.549 (592), 1.575 (496); $N_O - N_E$ = 0.131 (592). Solid crystals have: N_E = 1.697 (702), 1.721 (592), 1.765 (496). Ref: 309.

Subclass P. Amino Sulfonic Acids and Derivatives

Sodium 4-aminobenzenesulfonate dihydrate or sodium sulfanilate dihydrate ($H_2NC_6H_4SO_3Na \cdot 2H_2O$) is orthorhombic with *a*:*b*:*c* = 0.789:1:0.793. Crystals {001} tablets with {111}. Fig. 91. No distinct cleavage. Y = *b*; Z = *c*. (+)2V = 65°40′ Li, 65°22′ Na, 65°4′ Tl. N_X = 1.5312 Li, 1.5362 Na, 1.5411 Tl, N_Y = 1.5611 Li, 1.5667 Na, 1.5722 Tl, N_Z = 1.6405 Li, 1.6490 Na, 1.6573 Tl; $N_Z - N_X$ = 0.1128 Na. Ref: 118.

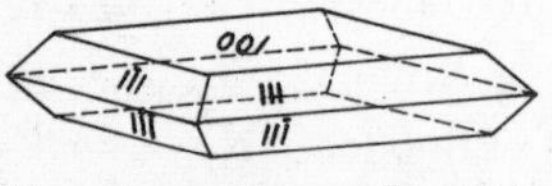

Fig. 91. Sodium sulfanilate dihydrate.

p-Aminobenzenesulfonamide or sulfanilamide ($C_6H_4NH_2SO_2NH_2$) has four crystal phases. Phase I, obtained from solution at 70 - 110° C. is monoclinic (domatic ?). It may be obtained from other phases by heating[2] to *ca.* 125°. Crystals are rhomboid {001} plates with angles of 62° and 118°. Y = *b*, Z $\wedge$ *c* = 40°. (+)2V = near 90°, N_X = 1.500 ± .003, N_Y = 1.674 ± .003, N_Z = 1.840 ± .005, $N_Z - N_X$ = 0.340. Phase II crystallizes from aqueous solution at *ca.* 30 - 50°. Large crystals can be obtained by crystallizing from methanol. It is monoclinic prismatic. Crystals {001} plates with {100} and the prism faces.

[1] Positions of the iodine atoms are not specified, but these seem most probable. Apparently a derivative of *l*-tyrosine.

[2] Phase II begins to invert at about 98° under some conditions.

$Y = b$, $Z \wedge c = 78°$ (or $X \wedge c = 12°$). (+)2V = 85°, $N_X = 1.550 \pm .003$, $N_Y = 1.674 \pm .003$, $N_Z = 1.820 \pm .005$, $N_Z - N_X = 0.270$. Phase III crystallizes from aqueous solution at *ca.* 30 – 50°. It is orthorhombic dipyramidal with $a:b:c = 0.951:1:0.287$. Crystals {001} plates with {100} and prism faces (at an angle of 105°). $Y = b$, $Z = c$. (+)2V = 71°, $N_X = 1.548 \pm .003$, $N_Y = 1.623 \pm .003$, $N_Z = 1.810 \pm .005$, $N_Z - N_X = 0.262$. Phase IV crystallizes from aqueous solution at *ca.* 25°. It is orthorhombic dipyramidal. Crystals {001} plates with {100} and prism faces (at an angle of 68°). $Y = a$, $Z = c$. (+)2V = 24°, $N_X = 1.606 \pm .003$, $N_Y = 1.615 \pm .003$, $N_Z = 1.820 \pm .005$, $N_Z - N_X = 0.214$. Ref: 518, 619.

p-Aminobenzenesulfonamide monohydrate or *p*-anilinesulfonamide monohydrate or sulfanilamide monohydrate ($C_6H_4NH_2SO_2NH_2 \cdot H_2O$) is orthorhombic dipyramidal. It crystallizes at abont 4° C. and dehydrates at *ca.* 25° C. Crystals are rhombic {001} plates with angles of 102° and 78°. $Y = a$, $Z = c$. (+)2V = 89°, $N_X = 1.517 \pm .003$, $N_Y = 1.636 \pm .003$, $N_Z = 1.735 \pm .005$, $N_Z - N_X = 0.218$. Again: $N_X = 1.505$, $N_Y = 1.639$, $N_Z > 1.85$, $N_Z - N_X > 0.345$. With $AgNO_3$ it forms rectangular plates in radial aggregates with notched ends. These show anomalous blue and purple interference colors; they have X || elongation, $N_X = 1.590$, $N_Y = ?$, $N_Z = 1.734$, $N_Z - N_X = 0.144$. Ref: 523b, 617a, 619.

Benzylidene sulfanilamide ($C_{13}H_{12}O_2N_2S$) is monoclinic. M.P. 188°. Elongation ±. (+)2V = ?, r > v. $N_X = 1.494$, $N_Y = 1.676$, $N_Z > 1.703$ (also > 1.85, since the optic sign is plus. – A.N.W.), $N_Z - N_X > 0.36$. Ref: 617a.

o-Chlorobenzylidene sulfanilamide ($C_{13}H_{11}O_2ClN_2S$) is monoclinic. M.P. 180°. Elongation negative. (+)2V = ?, r > v. $N_X = 1.514$, $N_Y \approx 1.703$, $N_Z > 1.73$ (also > 1.89, since the optic sign is +. – A.N.W.), $N_Z - N_X > 0.38$. Ref: 617a.

p-Chlorobenzylidene sulfanilamide ($C_{13}H_{11}O_2ClN_2S$) is monoclinic. M.P. 186°. Elongation ±. (+)2V = ?, r > v. $N_X = 1.486$, $N_Y = 1.655$, $N_Z > 1.703$ (also > 1.82, since the optic sign is +. – A.N.W.), $N_Z - N_X > 0.334$. Ref: 617a.

o-Nitrobenzylidene sulfanilamide ($C_{13}H_{11}O_4N_3S$) is orthorhombic. M.P. 183°. Elongation negative. (–)2V = ?, $N_X = 1.476$, $N_Y = 1.690$, $N_Z > 1.703$ (also < 1.904, since the optic sign is –. – A.N.W.), $N_Z - N_X > 0.227$. Ref: 617a.

p-Nitrobenzylidene sulfanilamide ($C_{13}H_{11}O_4N_3S$) is orthorhombic. M.P. 175°. Elongation negative. (–)2V = ?, $N_X = 1.524$, N_Y slightly > 1.703, $N_Z > 1.703$ (also < 1.88, since the optic sign is –. – A.N.W.), $N_Z - N_X > 0.179$. Ref: 617a.

m-Nitrobenzylidene sulfanilamide ($C_{13}H_{11}O_4N_3S$) is orthorhombic. M.P. 170°. Elongation positive. (–)2V = ?, $N_X = 1.574$, $N_Y = 1.676$, $N_Z > 1.703$ (also < 1.770, since the optic sign is –. – A.N.W.), $N_Z - N_X > 0.129$. Ref: 617a.

o-Hydroxybenzylidene sulfanilamide ($C_{13}H_{12}O_3N_2S$) is monoclinic. M.P. 211°. Elongation negative. (+)2V = ?, $N_X = 1.482$, $N_Y = 1.680$, $N_Z > 1.703$ (also > 1.88, since the optic sign is +. – A.N.W.), $N_Z - N_X > 0.40$. Ref: 617a.

p-Hydroxybenzylidene sulfanilamide ($C_{13}H_{12}O_3N_2S$) is monoclinic. M.P. 204°. Elongation negative. (+)2V = ?, $N_X = 1.512$, $N_Y = 1.666$, $N_Z > 1.703$ (also > 1.82, since the optic sign is +. – A.N.W.), $N_Z - N_X > 0.308$. Ref: 617a.

p-Methoxybenzylidene sulfanilamide ($C_{14}H_{14}O_3N_2S$) is monoclinic. M.P. 200°. Elongation positive. (+)2V = ?, r > v. $N_X = 1.498$, $N_Y = 1.645$, $N_Z > 1.703$ (also > 1.79, since the optic sign is +. – A.N.W.), $N_Z - N_X > 0.294$. Ref: 617a.

2,4-Dimethoxybenzylidene sulfanilamide ($C_{15}H_{16}O_4N_2S$) is monoclinic. M.P. 197°. Elongation negative. (+)2V < 80° calc., r < v. $N_X = 1.655$, $N_Y = 1.674$, $N_Z > 1.703$, $N_Z - N_X > 0.048$. Ref: 617a.

3-4-Dimethoxybenzylidene sulfanilamide ($C_{15}H_{16}O_4N_2S$) is monoclinic. M.P. 193°. Elongation positive. (+)2V < 85° calc., r < v. $N_X = 1.521$, $N_Y = 1.605$, $N_Z > 1.703$ $N_Z - N_X > 0.182$. Ref: 617a.

m-Methylbenzylidene sulfanilamide ($C_{14}H_{14}O_2N_2S$) is monoclinic. M.P. 201°. Elongation negative. (+)2V = ?, $N_X = 1.492$, $N_Y = 1.661$, $N_Z > 1.703$ (also > 1.83, since the optic sign is +. – A.N.W.), $N_Z - N_X > 0.338$. Ref: 617a.

Cinnamylidene sulfanilamide ($C_{15}H_{15}O_2N_2S$) is monoclinic. M.P. 216°. Elongation negative. (+)2V = ?, $N_X = 1.528$, N_Y slightly > 1.703, $N_Z > 1.703$ (also > 1.88, since the optic sign is +. – A.N.W.), $N_Z - N_X > 0.35$. Ref: 617a.

Acetysulfanilamide ($NH_2C_6H_4NHCOCH_3$) is tetragonal with $c/a = 0.509$. Crystals prismatic with perfect 100 cleavage. M.P. 182 – 184°. Uniaxial negative with $N_O = 1.697$, $N_E = 1.503$, $N_O - N_E = 0.194$. Ref: 572a.

N-Butyrylsulfanilamide ($NH_2C_6H_4SO_2NHCOC_3H_7$) is monoclinic prismatic with $\beta = ca.\ 93°$. Crystals rhombic-shaped with {100} prisms and domes. X = *b*, Z ∧ *c* = 27° (Z ∧ *c* = 60°) (+)2E = 67°, 2V = 41°, $N_X = 1.572 \pm .003$, $N_Y = 1.588 \pm .005$, $N_Z = 1.712 \pm .005$, $N_Z - N_X = 0.140$. Ref: 619.

N-Isobutyrylsulfanilamide ($NH_2C_6H_4SO_2NHCOC_3H_7$) is monoclinic prismatic. Crystals equant or prisms along *c*. Y = *b*, Z ∧ *c* = 26° in obtuse β. (+)2V = 75 - 80° (est.), $N_X = 1.561 \pm .003$, $N_Y = 1.605 \pm .003$, $N_Z = 1.670 \pm .003$, $N_Z - N_X = 0.109$. Ref: 619.

N-Isovalerylsulfanilamide ($C_4H_9CONHSO_2C_6H_4NH_2$) is monoclinic prismatic with $\beta = 93°$. Crystals prismatic ‖ *c* with {010} and domes. X ∧ *c* = 22° in acute β; Y = *b*. (–?)2V = large, $N_X = 1.567 \pm .005$, $N_Y = 1.633 \pm .005$, $N_Z = 1.688 \pm .005$, $N_Z - N_X = 0.121$. Ref: 619.

N'-Guanylsulfanilamide or sulfaguanidine [$NH_2C(NH)NHSO_2 \cdot C_6H_4NH_2$] forms a colorless powder with (+)2V = 85° calc., $N_X = 1.606$, $N_Y = 1.663$, $N_Z = 1.734$, $N_Z - N_X = 0.128$. Grains often show one optic axis interference figure. With HNO_3 it forms rods having Z ‖ elongation (or nearly so) and $N_X = 1.578$, N_Y = ?, $N_Z = 1.663$, $N_Z - N_X = 0.085$. Ref: 523b.

N-Sulfanilylguanidine monohydrate or sulfaguanidine monohydrate [$NH_2C(NH)NHSO_2C_6H_4NH_2 \cdot H_2O$] is monoclinic prismatic. Crystals {100} tablets with acute ends. Cleavage parallel to *b* = elongation. Y = *b*, Z ∧ *c* = *ca.* 78°, or X ∧ *c* = *ca.* 12° in obtuse β. (+)2V = 84° ± 5°, r > v. $N_X = 1.603 \pm .005$, $N_Y = 1.648 \pm .003$, $N_Z = 1.720 \pm .005$, $N_Z - N_X = 0.117$. Again: Z ∧ *c* = 17°, $N_X = 1.586$, $N_Y = 1.649$, $N_Z = 1.731$, $N_Z - N_X = 0.145$. Ref: 434a, 619.

N[4]-Acetylsulfanilylguanidine monohydrate $\{CH_3CONHC_6H_4SO_2NC(NH_2)_2H_2O\}$ is orthorhombic disphenoidal. Crystals {001} tablets with {100}, {010}, etc. Perfect 100 and 010 cleavages. X = *b*, Y = *a*. (-)2V = 75° est. $N_X = 1.565 \pm .005$ $N_Y = 1.695 \pm .005$, N_Z = ?, ($N_Z - N_X = 0.2$ est. A.N.W.). Ref: 619.

N[4]-(2-Hydroxybenzylidene)sulfaguanidine ($C_{14}H_{14}O_3N_4S$) is orthorhombic in lamellar crystals with M.P. 225°. Y parallel elongation. (+)2V = large. $N_X = 1.561$, $N_Y = 1.668$, $N_Z > 1.86$, $N_Z - N_X > 0.299$. Color yellow, with no pleochroism. Ref: 434a.

N[4]-(2-Hydroxy-3-methoxybenzylidene)sulfaguanidine ($C_{15}H_{16}O_4N_4S$) is monoclinic in tabular crystals with M.P. 226°, ± elongation (Y = *b*) and Z ∧ *c* = 58°. (+)2V = small, r > v = weak. $N_X = 1.577$, $N_Y = 1.614$, $N_Z > 1.86$, $N_Z - N_X > 0.283$. Color orange, with X < Y < Z. Ref: 434a.

Sulfacetamide ($C_8H_{10}O_3N_2S$) is orthorhombic in pyramidal crystals with M.P. 184°, and symmetrical extinction. (+)2V = 21° (or less) with no dispersion. $N_X = 1.559$, $N_Y = 1.564$, $N_Z = 1.727$, $N_Z - N_X = 0.168$. Colorless. Ref: 434a.

N[4]-(2-Hydroxybenzylidene)sulfacetamide ($C_{15}H_{14}O_4N_2S$) is monoclinic. Needles have ± elongation and a maximum extinction angle of 12°. M.P. 213. (+)2V = very large, r > v very great. $N_X = 1.491$, $N_Y = 1.689$, $N_Z > 1.86$, $N_Z - N_X > 0.369$. Color orange, with X < Y < Z. Ref: 434a.

N[4]-(2-Hydroxy-3-methoxybenzylidene)sulfacetamide ($C_{16}H_{16}O_5N_2S$) is orthorhombic in needles along *c* with Y = *c*. M.P. 231°. (+)2V = very large, r > v. $N_X = 1.507$, $N_Y = 1.682$, $N_Z > 1.86$, $N_Z - N_X > 0.353$. Strong red to yellow with X < Y < Z. Ref: 434a.

β-Naphthylamine-1-sulfonic acid or tobias acid ($C_{10}H_6NH_2SO_3H$) is orthorhombic. Crystals prismatic often showing optic axis figures. Y parallel to the elongation. (+)2V = 59°, $N_X = 1.645$, $N_Y = 1.691$, $N_Z = 1.88$ (calc. from N_X, N_Y and 2V), $N_Z - N_X = 0.23$ calc. Ref: 543.

β-Naphthylamine-1-sulfonic acid monohydrate or tobias acid monohydrate ($C_{10}H_6NH_2SO_3H \cdot H_2O$) is orthorhombic (?). Crystals rhombic plates with symmetrical extinction. Y = *a*. (-)2V = ?, $N_X = 1.543$, $N_Y = 1.758$, N_Z = ?. Ref: 543.

β-Naphthylamine-1-sodium sulfonate or 2-aminonaphthalene-1-sodium sulfonate or sodium tobiasate ($C_{10}H_6NH_2SO_3Na$) forms six-sided plates with symmetrical and oblique extinctions (monoclinic?). 2V = nearly 90°, $N_1 = 1.626$, $N_2 = 1.666$, $N_2 - N_1 = 0.040$. Ref: 543.

2-Benzamido-1-naphthalene sulfonic acid ($C_6H_5CONHC_{10}H_6SO_3H$) forms clusters of rods with parallel extinction and negative elongation. $N_1 = 1.632$, $N_2 = 1.703$, $N_2 - N_1 = 0.071$. Ref: 373.

Sodium 4-amino-1-naphthalenesulfonate tetrahydrate or sodium 1-naphthylamine-4-sulfonate tetrahydrate or sodium naphthionate tetrahydrate [$NaSO_3$

$C_{10}H_6(NH_2) \cdot 4H_2O]$ is monoclinic with $a:b:c = 0.826:1:0.954$, $\beta = 98°41'$. Crystals show {001}, {110}, {11$\bar{1}$}. Distinct 001 and 110 cleavages. The optic plane is 010; Z $\wedge$ c = + 3,5°. (+)2V = 69°25′ Li, 69°10′ Na, 68°46′ Tl. N_X = 1.5660 Li, 1.5731 Na, 1.5800 Tl; N_Y = 1.5906 Li, 1.5987 Na, 1.6067 Tl; N_Z = 1.6460 Li, 1.6570 Na, 1.6657 Tl; $N_Z - N_X$ = 0.0839 Na. A metastable phase is orthorhombic. Ref: 119.

cis-Nitroaquodiethylamine cobaltinaphthionate trihydrate $[[Co(C_2H_5)_2(H_2O)(NO_2)][SO_3C_{10}H_6NH_2]_2 \cdot 3H_2O]$ has two crystal phases. The *d*- and *l*-forms are orthorhombic in plates and rods with parallel extinction, and (+)2V = 30.5°. N_X = 1.653, N_Y = 1.661, N_Z = 1.736, $N_Z - N_X$ = 0.083. The inactive form is also orthorhombic in plates and rods with parallel extinction, and (+)2V = 37°, N_X = 1.659, N_Y = 1.665, N_Z = 1.739, $N_Z - N_X$ = 0.080. Ref: 244.

4-Benzamido-1-naphthalenesulfonic acid ($C_6H_5CONHC_{10}H_6SO_3H$) forms diamond-shaped crystals with symmetrical extinction bisecting angles of 76° and 104°. For direction bisecting 104°, N_1 = 1.537; at 90°, N_2 = 1.653, $N_2 - N_1$ = 0.116. Ref: 373.

5-Benzamido-1-naphthalenesulfonic acid ($C_6H_5CONHC_{10}H_6SO_3H$) forms large oval plates changing to aggregates with parallel extinction and negative elongation. N_1 = 1.576, N_2 = 1.633, $N_2 - N_1$ = 0.057. Ref: 373.

5-Benzamido-2-naphthalenesulfonic acid ($C_6H_5CONHC_{10}H_6SO_3H$) forms rectangular plates with parallel extinction and positive elongation. N_1 = 1.628, N_2 = 1.646, $N_2 - N_1$ = 0.018. Ref: 373.

6-Benzamido-2-naphthalenesulfonic acid ($C_6H_5CONHC_{10}H_6SO_3H$) is dimorphous. One phase (I) forms bayonet-shaped crystals which change in several hours (to a day) to the second phase. The former phase has parallel extinction and negative elongation. N_1 = 1.612, $N_2 \geqslant$ 1.71, $N_2 - N_1 \geqslant$ 0.098. The second phase (II) forms rectangular plates with parallel extinction and positive elongation. Biaxial interference figure common. N_1 = 1.545, N_2 = 1.620, $N_2 - N_1$ = 0.075. Ref: 373.

8-Benzamido-2-naphthalenesulfonic acid ($C_6H_5CONHC_{10}H_6SO_3H$) forms rosettes of plates with parallel extinction and negative elongation. N_1 = 1.606, N_2 = 1.685, $N_2 - N_1$ = 0.079. Ref: 373.

7-Benzamido-1,3-naphthalenedisulfonic acid $[C_6H_5CONHC_{10}H_5(SO_3H)_2]$ forms hair-like tufts with parallel extinction and negative elongation. N_1 = 1.510, N_2 = 1.691, $N_2 - N_1$ = 0.181. Ref: 373.

Subclass Q. Amino Hydroxy Sulfonic Acids and Derivatives

6-Benzamido-1-naphthol-3-sulfonic acid benzoate or 7-benzamido-4-benzoxy-2-naphthalenesulfonic acid $[(C_6H_5CONH)(C_6H_5CO_2)C_{10}H_5 \cdot SO_3H]$ forms long flexible needles with parallel extinction and positive elongation. N_1 = 1.629, N_2 = 1.696, $N_2 - N_1$ = 0.067. Ref: 373.

7-Benzamido-1-naphthol-3-sulfonic acid benzoate or 6-benzamido-4-benzoxy-2-naphthalenesulfonic acid $[(C_6H_5CONH)(C_6H_5CO_2)C_{10}H_5 \cdot SO_3H]$ slowly forms spherulites of needles with parallel extinction and negative elongation. $N_1 = 1.624$, $N_2 > 1.71$, $N_2 - N_1 > 0.086$. Ref: 373.

8-Benzamido-1-naphthol-5-sulfonic acid benzoate or 4-benzamido-5-benzoxy-1-naphthalenesulfonic acid $[(C_6H_5CONH)(C_6H_5CO_2)C_{10}H_5 \cdot SO_3H]$ slowly forms needles with parallel extinction and negative elongation. $N_1 = 1.662$, $N_2 = 1.684$, $N_2 - N_1 = 0.022$. Ref: 373.

8-Benzamido-1-naphthol-3,6-disulfonic acid benzoate or 4-benzamido-5-benzoxy-2,7-naphthalenedisulfonic acid $[(C_6H_5CONH)(C_6H_5CO_2)C_{10}H_4 \cdot (SO_3H)_2]$ forms long needles with extinction (X′) at 17° to elongation. $N_1 = 1.592$, $N_2 = 1.694$, $N_2 - N_1 = 0.102$. Ref: 373.

Subclass R. Amino Carbonyl Sulfonic Acids and Derivatives

p-(*p*-Aminobenzoyl)benzenesulfonic acid or 4′-aminobenzophenone-4-sulfonic acid. $(H_2NC_6H_4COC_6H_4 \cdot SO_3H)$ is monoclinic with $a:b:c = 2.53:1:?$, $\beta = 98°$ *ca.* Crystals show {001} tablets with {110}. Distinct 100 cleavage. The optic plane is 010; $Z \wedge c = +6°$ *ca.* (-)2V = ?. $N_X \geqslant 1.64$, $N_Y \leqslant 1.74$, $N_Z > 1.74$, $N_Z - N_X < 0.20$. Ref: 22.

Barium *p*-(*p*-aminobenzoyl)benzenesulfonate or barium 4′-aminobenzophenone -4-sulfonate $[(H_2NC_6H_4COC_6H_4SO_3)_2Ba]$ is monoclinic with $\beta = 96.5°$. Crystals {010} plates elongated parallel to *c* with {100} and {001}. Twinning on 100. Distinct 100 and also other cleavages. The optic plane is 010; $Z \wedge c = +6°$ *ca.* $N_X = 1.523$, $N_Y = ?$, $N_Z > 1.74$, $N_Z - N_X > 0.217$. Color yellowish green, with X = colorless or pale greenish, Y = ?, Z = yellowish green. Ref: 22.

Class 10. Hydroxylamines and Derivatives

1,7,7-Trimethyl-3-(phenylhydroxylaminomethylene)bicyclo-[2.2.1] heptan-2-one, or methylenecamphor-phenylhydroxylamine $(C_{17}H_{21}O_2N)$ is monoclinic[1] with $a:b:c = 0.997:1:1.065$, $\beta = 103°50'$. Crystals elongated along *b* with {001}, {100}, {101}, {130}, etc. M.P. 206 - 208°. Good 100 and poor 101 cleavages. The optic plane is 010; X nearly normal to 100. (-)2V = 63°30′. $N_Y = 1.598$. Ref: 285.

Class 11. Hydrazines and Derivatives

β-Acetylphenylhydrazine I or hydracetin $(CH_3 \cdot CO \cdot NH \cdot NH \cdot C_6H_5)$ is orthorhombic with $a:b:c = 0.444:1:0.355$. *a* 9.55, *b* 21.54, *c* 7.64 Å. U.C. 8. Crystals {010} plates. Good 010 cleavage. D 1.28. M.P. 128 - 129°. Y = *a*; Z = *b*. (+)2V = 48°, $N_X = 1.585$, $N_Y = 1.609$, $N_Z = 1.75$, $N_Z - N_X = 0.165$. Ref: 620a.

[1] The constants given are for the substance obtained by the oxidation of methylenecamphor hydroxylamine with $K_3Fe(CN)_6$.

Methylphenylketonemethylphenylhydrazone or acetophenone methylphenylhydrazone [$C_6H_5C(CH_3):N \cdot N \cdot (CH_3) \cdot C_6H_5$] is monoclinic with $a:b:c = 1.336:1:1.167$, $\beta = 103°44'$. Crystals {001} or {100} tablets with {110}, {111}. Fig. 92. No distinct cleavage. M.P. = 124°. The optic plane is 010; a bisectrix is nearly normal to 100. 2V = large. $N_Y = 1.536$ Na, $N_Z < 1.66$, $N_Z - N_X$ = very strong. Ref: 119.

1,2-Diacetyl-1,2-diphenylhydrazine or N,N′-diacetylhydrazobenzene [$C_6H_5N(COCH_3)N(COCH_3) \cdot C_6H_5$] is orthorhombic with $a:b:c = 0.673:1:0.561$ Crystals equant with {110}, {011}. Fig. 93. No distinct cleavage. M.P. 105° C. X = *a*; Y = *b*. (–)2V = 88°45′ Na. $N_X = 1.6116$ Na, $N_Y = 1.6465$, $N_Z = 1.662$, $N_Z - N_X = 0.0504$. Ref: 119.

1,5-Diphenyl carbohydrazide (or *sym.*-diphenylcarbazide) ($C_6H_5NHNHCONHNHC_6H_5$) is orthorhombic with $a:b:c = 0.328:1:0.222$. *a* 8.44, *b* 25.72, *c* 5.72 Å. U.C. 4. M.P. 174 – 175°. D 1.31. Crystals acicular or platy. X = *a*, Y = *c*. (–)2V = 83°, r > v moderate. $N_X = 1.610$, $N_Y = 1.677$, $N_Z = 1.74$ $N_Z - N_X = 0.13$. Ref: 620a.

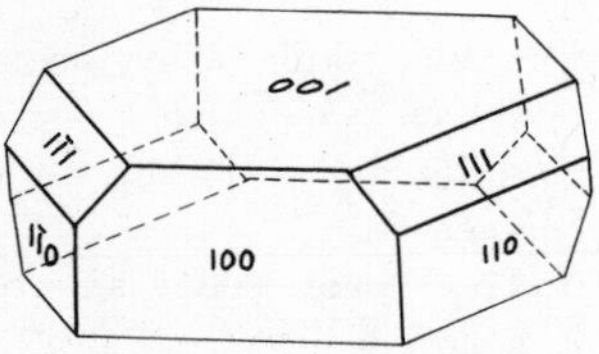

Fig. 92. Acetophenone methylphenylhydrazone.

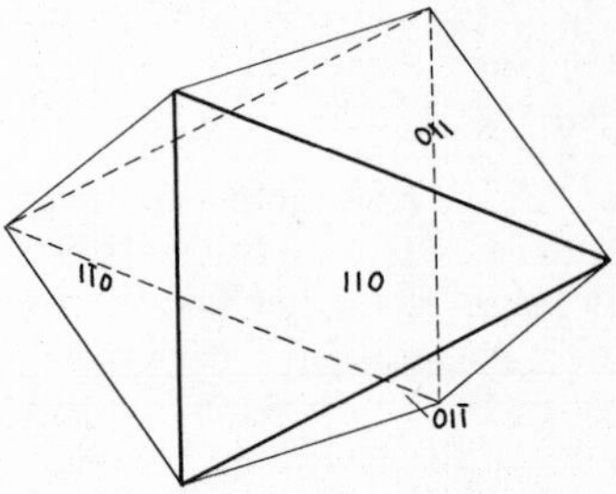

Fig. 93. Diacetylhydrazobenzene.

Ethyl 2-phenylhydrazonopropanoate or ethyl ester phenylhydrazone of pyruvic acid [$C_6H_5 \cdot NH \cdot N:C(CH_3)(CO_2 \cdot C_2H_5)$] is monoclinic with $a:b:c = 1.681:1:0.910$, $\beta = 92°57'$. Crystals prismatic with {210}, {100}, {111}, {11$\bar{1}$}, etc. No distinct cleavage. M.P. 118 – 120°. X $\wedge$ *c* = + 47°4′ Na (larger for red); Z = *b*. (–)2V = 67°54′ Na, r < v. $N_X = 1.4867$, $N_Y = 1.7258$, $N_Z = 1.8802$, $N_Z - N_X = 0.3935$ yellow. Ref: 118.

2-Ketopropanedioic acid phenylhydrazone or 2-phenylhydrazonopropanedioic acid or mesoxalic acid phenylhydrazone [$C_6H_5NHN:C(CO_2H)_2$] forms fine needles which melt at 165°. They have parallel extinction and negative elongation with $N_1 = 1.450$, $N_2 > 1.800$, $N_2 - N_1 > 0.350$. Ref: 93.

2-Ketopropanedioic acid monomethylamide phenylhydrazone or 2-methylcarbamyl-2-phenylhydrazonoethanoic acid or N-methyl mesoxalamic acid hydrazone [$C_6H_5 \cdot NH \cdot N:C(CO_2H) \cdot CO \cdot NH \cdot CH_3$] forms six-sided plates with symmetrical extinction and positive elongation. M.P. 167°. 2V = large. $N_1 = 1.600$, $N_2 = 1.715$, $N_2 - N_1 = 0.115$. Ref: 93.

Benzaldehyde 4-nitrophenylhydrazone [$C_6H_5CH:N\cdot NH\cdot C_6H_4\cdot NO_2$] has two crystal phases. The stable phase (I) is monoclinic. M.P. 261 – 262°. Crystals elongated on *c*. The optic plane and Z are normal to 010. 2V = large. N_X = ?, N_Y = 1.70 *ca.*, N_Z > 1.74. The unstable phase (II) melts at 234 – 236° and is probably monoclinic with an extinction angle of 20°. The optic plane is across the elongation. Indices unknown. Ref: 88.

2,4-Dinitrophenylhydrazine hydrochloride [$(NO_2)_2C_6H_3NHNH_2\cdot HCl$] is probably orthorhombic. M.P. 198 – 200°. Plates normal to Z have Y || elongation. (+)2V = 31°, r > v, with crossed axial plane dispersion; uniaxial at 4740 Å. N_X = 1.700, N_Y = 1.715, N_Z = 1.752 calc. $N_Z - N_X$ = 0.52 (for λ = 5461). Ref: 556a.

Formaldehyde 2,4-dinitrophenylhydrazone {$(O_2N)_2C_6H_3\cdot NH\cdot N:CH_2$} is triclinic with *a*:*b*:*c* = 0.961:1:0.406, α = 94°, β = 95°, γ = 87°; *a* 10.00, *b* 10.41, *c* 4.23 Å. U.C. 2. Crystals {010} tablets; a cleavage makes an angle of 52° with *c* in 010; crystals also prismatic, with inclined extinction. D 1.592. M.P. 166°. For λ = 5461: (-)2E = 130°, 2V = 57°, N_Y = 1.901, $N_Z - N_X$ = very strong. Limits of transmission bands for X are 508 – 670, for Y 510 – 670, for Z 500 – 670. Color yellow. Crystals from fusion have (-)2E = 86° (546), 92° (578). Also described as monoclinic in plates with X ∧ *c* = 37°, Y = *b*. Ref: 38, 435, 530.

Acetaldehyde 2,4-dinitrophenylhydrazone {$(O_2N)_2\cdot C_6H_3\cdot NH\cdot N:CH(CH_3)$} has two phases. The stable form (I) is monoclinic in {001} tabular crystals with {011}, {110}, {100}, usually elongated along *a*. M.P. 168°. X′ ∧ *a* = 4° ± 1°, measured on 011; Y = *b*. Z is nearly normal to 001. (-)2V = 38° (546), 42.5° (680) with strong inclined dispersion. For λ = 680: N_X = 1.540, N_Y = 1.866, N_Z = 1.938, $N_Z - N_X$ = 0.398, all ± .005. For λ = 546: N_X = 1.560, N_Y = 1.969, N_Z = 2.040, $N_Z - N_X$ = 0.480, all ± .005. Pleochroic with X = greenish yellow, Y = orange-yellow. Limits of transmission bands are, for X, 510 – 650, for Z, 520 – 670. The metastable phase (II) is also monoclinic in {001} tablets with {110}, {100}, and a pyramid, usually elongated along *a*. Also may be prismatic, vertically elongated. M.P. 157°. The optic plane is 010 for λ = 535 and normal thereto (with Z = *b*) for red. X is nearly normal to 001; X ∧ *c* = 48°. (-)2E = 45° (691), 35° (589), 8° (546), 23° (535). Uniaxial at λ = about 544. Also (-)2V = 23° (680), 4° ± 1° (546). For λ 680: N_X = 1.410, N_Y = 1.938, N_Z = 1.96, $N_Z - N_X$ = 0.55. For λ 546: N_X = 1.412, N_Y = 2.078, N_Z = 2.078, $N_Z - N_X$ = 0.666. Pleochroic with X = greenish yellow, Y and Z = orange-yellow. Limits of transmission bands are, for X: 518 – 670, for Y: 533 – 660, for Z: 533 – 680. Two other phases are known, one being tetragonal and the other orthorhombic. Ref: 39, 435, 530.

Acetaldehyde 2,4-dinitrophenylhydrazone forms a continuous series of mix-crystals with propionaldehyde 2,4-dinitrophenylhydrazone, but the series is interrupted by a change of phase at about 80% propionaldehyde. Variations in the apparent optic axial angle (2H) with change of composition are shown in Fig. 94 for four different wave lengths; the variations in the melting point are also shown. Propionaldehyde 2,4-dinitrophenylhydrazone also forms mix-crystals in all proportions with acetone 2,4-dinitrophenylhydrazone, but these belong to three different phases. Ref: 556a.

Propionaldehyde 2,4-dinitrophenylhydrazone $\{(O_2N)_2C_6H_3 \cdot NH \cdot N{:}CH(CH_2)_2CH_3\}$ is dimorphous. One phase (I) is probably monoclinic, in prisms. M.P. 156°. Z = *b*; X ∧ elongation = 54°. For green (546). (-)2V = 24° (2E = 44°), $N_X = 1.426$, $N_Y = 1.917$, $N_Z = 1.959$, $N_Z - N_X = 0.533$; for $\lambda = 680$, 2E = 58°.

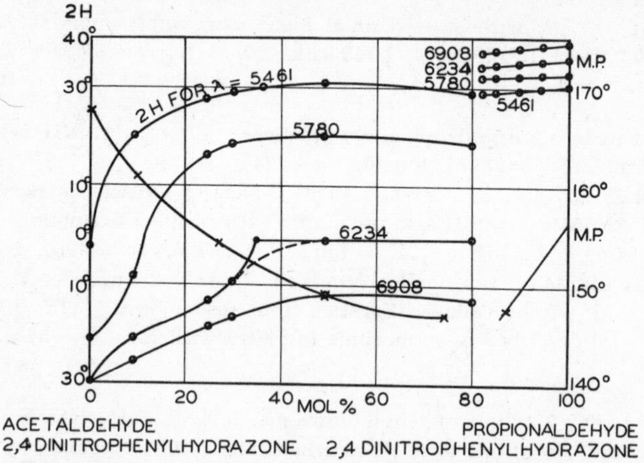

Fig. 94. Optic angle variations in the acetaldehyde-2,4-dinitrophenylhydrazone-to propionaldehyde-2,4-dinitrophenylhydrazone series.

Another phase (II) is probably monoclinic having Y = *b* below $\lambda = 624$ and Z = *b* above that; X ∧ *c* = 38° and (-)2E = 40° (546), 26° (577), 0° (624), 17° (681). Limits of transmission bands are, for X, 515 – 650, for Y and Z, 530 – 680. Color red-orange. Crystals from fusion are orthorhombic with X = *c*, Y = *a*. Crystals show (001), (010), (110). (-)2E = 49° (546), 57° (577). Ref: 38, 530.

Butyraldehyde 2,4-dinitrophenylhydrazone $\{(O_2N)_2C_6H_3 \cdot NH \cdot N{:}CHCH_2CH_2CH_3\}$ is trimorphous; one phase (I) is orthorhombic with *a*:*b*:*c* = 0.274:1:0.302. *a* 4.90, *b* 17.9, *c* 5.40 Å. Crystals prismatic, with parallel or symmetrical extinction and negative elongation. D 1.3. M.P. 123°. X = *c*; Y = *b*. (-)2V = 40°, (2E = 80°). $N_X = 1.426$, $N_Y = 1.869$, $N_Z = 1.965$, $N_Z - N_X = 0.539$ for $\lambda = 546$. For $\lambda = 680$, 2E = 88°. Limits of transmission bands are, for X, 520 – 660, for Y and Z, 540 – 660. Color yellow. Another phase has an orange color and a third an amber color, but these have not been measured optically. Ref: 38, 435, 530.

Isobutyraldehyde 2,4-dinitrophenylhydrazone $\{(O_2N)_2C_6H_3 \cdot NH \cdot N{:}CH \cdot CH(CH_3)_2\}$ is dimorphous; one phase (I), from fusion, is orthorhombic, crystals having {001}, {110}, and {010}, and a prism angle of 48°. M.P. 187°. X = *c*;

Y = *b*. For $\lambda = 546$: (-)2E = 78° (Bryant), 86° (Kirkpatrick). $N_X = 1.426$, $N_Y = 1.906$, $N_Z = 2.002$, $N_Z - N_X = 0.576$. 2V = 42°. For $\lambda = 577$; 2E = 90° (Kirkpatrick). For $\lambda = 680$: 2E = 87° (Bryant). Color yellow. Limits of transmission bands about 520 to 660. Ref: 38, 530.

Class 12. Azo Compounds

trans-Azobenzene or diphenyldi-imide ($C_6H_5 \cdot N:N \cdot C_6H_5$) is monoclinic prismatic with $a:b:c = 2.114:1:2.676$, $\beta = 114°26'$. Space group $P2_1/a$. *a* 12.20, *b* 5.77, *c* 15.40 Å. U.C. 4. Crystals {001} tablets with {110}, {100}, etc. D 1.22. M.P. 68°. X = *b*, Z ∧ *a* = 7° in obtuse β. (+)2V = 27° (red), 36° D, 49° (blue); 2E = 48° (red), 64° D, 88° (blue) with strong horizontal dispersion. $N_X = 1.706$, $N_Y = 1.720$, $N_Z = 1.85$, $N_Z - N_X = 0.144$. Ref: 552a.

2-Ethoxyazobenzene or 2-phenylazophenetole or azobenzene-*o*-phenetole or benzolazo-*o*-phenetole [$C_6H_5N:NC_6H_4(OC_2H_5)$] is monoclinic with $a:b:c = 1.509:1:2.851$, $\beta = 95°2'$. Crystals show {001}, {100}, {111}, etc. Imperfect 001 cleavage. M.P. 43 - 44°. X ∧ *c* = + 39°; Z = *b*. (-)2V = 76°22′ Li, 68° Na. $N_X = 1.507$ Li; $N_Y = 1.710$ Li, 1.7146 Na; $N_Z = 1.886$ Li; $N_Z - N_X = 0.379$ Li. Pleochroic with X = blood red, Y = orange-yellow, Z = purple red. Ref: 119.

α-(4-Chloro-2-nitrophenylazo)acetoacetanilide or *p*-chloro-*o*-nitrobenzene-azo-acetoacetic anilide {$ClC_6H_3(NO_2)N:NCH(COCH_3)CONHC_6H_4C_6H_5$} is orthorhombic (?) with good 110 cleavage; parallel and symmetrical extinction. X ∥ length. (-)2V = (?), $N_X = 1.46$, N_Y = (?), $N_Z = 1.90$, $N_Z - N_X = 0.44$. Weakly pleochroic with X = pale yellow, Z = bright yellow. Called Hansa yellow 10G (pigment). Ref: 543, 576.

α-(4-Methyl-2-nitrophenylazo)acetoacetanilide or *o*-nitro-*p*-toluene-aceton-acetic-anilide {$CH_3C_6H_3(NO_2)N:NCH(COCH_3)CONHC_6H_5$} is monoclinic (?) in fine yellow needles with X ∧ *c* = 18°. (-)2V = (?). $N_X = 1.45$, N_Y = (?), $N_Z = 2.13$, $N_Z - N_X = 0.68$. Again X ∧ length = 25°, $N_X = 1.468$, $N_Z = 2.13$. Pleochroic with X = light yellow, Z = dark yellow. Called Hansa yellow G (pigment). Ref: 543, 576, 577.

Hansa yellow GSA (formula ?) is monoclinic (?). Crystals prismatic; also acicular. X ∧ *c* = 45°. Biaxial. $N_X = 1.455$, N_Y = ?, $N_Z = 2.20$, $N_Z - N_X = 0.745$. Weakly pleochroic from lemon (X) to yellow (Z). Ref: 543, 576.

Hansa yellow GR (formula ?) is monoclinic (?). Crystals acicular with prismatic cleavage; units ∥ X often show nearly rectangular twinning giving nearly simultaneous extinction. Some grains are rhombs with $N_X' > 1.46$ and strong absorption ∥ Z′. X ∧ *c* = 43°. (-)2V = rather large, $N_X = 1.46$, N_Y = (?), $N_Z = 2.20$, $N_Z - N_X = 0.74$. Pleochroic with X = lemon, Z = dark orange. Ref: 543, 576.

Hansa yellow 3R (formula ?) is monoclinic (?). Crystals acicular; rarely rhombic. Needles often lie ⊥ Y. X ∧ *c* = 5°. (-)2V = large, $N_X = 1.465$,

N_Y = (?), N_Z = 2.07, $N_Z - N_X$ = 0.605. Strongly pleochroic with X = lemon, Z = orange red. This pigment may contain another substance with slight pleochroism, X ∧ *c* = 43°, N_X = 1.465, N_Y = ?, N_Z = 2.23, $N_Z - N_X$ = 0.765. Ref: 543, 576.

1-(4-Nitrophenylazo)-2-naphthol or *p*-nitrobenzene-azo-β-naphthol {$NO_2C_6H_4N{:}NC_{10}H_6OH$} is monoclinic (?). Crystals acicular; rarely ⊥ X; usually show N_X' = 1.485. X ∧ *c* = 8 - 10°. 2V = (?), N_X = 1.455, N_Y = (?), N_Z = 2.5, $N_Z - N_X$ = 1.045. Strongly pleochroic with X = light yellow, Z = dark red. Called pigment tener red B. (Commonly known as para red).

Ref: 543, 576.

1-(2,4-Dinitrophenylazo)-2-naphthol or 2,4-dinitroanilineazo-β-naphthol {$NO_2C_6H_3(NO_2)N{:}NC_{10}H_6OH$} is orthorhombic (?). Crystals long needles with X ∥ length. N_X = 1.49, N_Y = (?), N_Z = 2.33, $N_Z - N_X$ = 0.84. Pleochroic with X = yellow, Z = dark orange. Called lithol fast orange RN.

Ref: 543, 576, 577.

1-(2-Choro-4-nitrophenylazo)-2-naphthol or *o*-chloronitrobenzene-azo-naphthol {$NO_2C_6H_3(Cl)N{:}NC_{10}H_6OH$ (?)} is orthorhombic (?) Crystals long needles with X ∥ length. N_X = 1.505, N_Y = ?, N_Z = 2.37, $N_Z - N_X$ = 0.865. Pleochroic with X = yellow-orange Z = orange-red. Called fast red R.

Ref: 543, 576, 577.

1-(4-Methyl-2-nitrophenylazo)-2-naphthol or *o*-nitro-*p*-toluene-azo-β-naphthol {$CH_3C_6H_3(NO_2)N{:}NC_{10}H_6OH$} is monoclinic(?). Crystals long needles lying ⊥ Y. X ∧ *c* = 10°. (–)2V = (?). N_X = 1.52, N_Y = (?), N_Z = 2.45, $N_Z - N_X$ = 0.93. Also said to have X ∥ length and N_X = 1.52, N_Z = 2.52, $N_Z - N_X$ = 1.00. Pleochroic with X = orange-red, Z = dark red. Called lithol fast scarlet NRN or toluidine red or lithol fast ruby. Ref: 543, 576, 577.

1-(1-Naphthylazo)-2-naphthol or α-naphthalene-azo-β-naphthol ($C_{10}H_6N{:}NC_{10}H_6OH$) is monoclinic(?). M.P. 220. Crystals tiny needles with X ∧ length = 4 - 5°. N_X = 1.47, N_Y = (?), N_Z = 2.26, $N_Z - N_X$ = 0.79. Very strong pleochroism with X = lemon yellow, Z = dark red. Called autol red RLP. Apparently the same compound forms tablets (another phase?) which have Z ∥ length and N_X = 2.0, N_Y = (?), N_Z = 2.53, $N_Z - N_X$ = 0.53. Pleochroism not great with X = red, Z = dark red. Called naphthylamine Bordeaux.

Ref: 543, 576.

4-(4-Sulfophenylazo)-1-naphthol or *p*-sulfobenzene-azo-α-naphthol {$HSO_3C_6H_4N{:}NC_{10}H_6OH$} is orthorhombic(?). Crystals acicular with Z ∥ length. N_X = 1.580, N_Y = (?), N_Z = 1.750, $N_Z - N_X$ = 0.170. Weakly pleochroic in light yellow hues. Called orange 2B. Are these properties of the sodium salt?

Ref: 543, 576.

6-Sulfo-4-chloro-azo-β-naphthol (?) {$ClC_6H_3HSO_3N{:}NC_{10}H_6(OH)COOH$?} forms tiny needles with Z ∥ length. N_X = 2.06, N_Y = (?), N_Z = 2.23, $N_Z - N_X$ = 0.17. Insignificant pleochroism. Called lithol ruby GK. Ref: 543, 576.

1-(4-Nitro-2-sulfophenylazo)-2-naphthol or *o*-sulfo-*p*-nitrobenzene-azo-β-naphthol $\{NO_2C_6H_3(HSO_3)N:NC_{10}H_6OH\}$ is monoclinic (?) with Z ∧ length = 18° (?). Crystals varied. (+)2V = (?). $N_X = 2.06$, N_Y = (?); $N_Z = 2.67$, $N_Z - N_X = 0.61$. Insignificant pleochroism. Called lake red P. Ref: 543, 576.

1-(2,4-Dinitro-6-sulfophenylazo)-2-hydroxy-3-naphthoic acid or 2-sulfo-4,6-dinitrobenzene-azo-β-hydroxynaphthoic acid $\{(NO_2)_2C_6H_2(HSO_3)N:NC_{10}H_5(OH)COOH\}$. Sample contained two kinds of crystals. One is orthorhombic (?) in long needles with Z ∥ length; $N_X = 1.745$, N_Y = (?), $N_Z = 2.32$, $N_Z - N_X = 0.575$; strongly pleochroic with X = yellow, Z = dark red. The other is also acicular with $N_X = 1.92$, N_Y = (?), $N_Z = 2.32$, $N_Z - N_X = 0.40$. (Probably crystals in two positions with $N_X = 1.745$, $N_Y = 1.92$, $N_Z = 2.32$ and (+)2V = mod. - A.N.W.). Weakly pleochroic from light to dark red. Called Hansa ruby G. Ref: 543, 576.

1-(4-Chloro-3-methyl-6-sulfophenylazo)-2-naphthol or 6-sulfo-4-chloro-3-toluene-azo-β-naphthol $\{Cl(CH_3)C_6H_2(HSO_3)N:NC_{10}H_6OH\}$ forms basal plates which are uniaxial negative with $N_O = 2.06$, $N_O - N_E$ = weak. The sample contained about 10% of other crystals which are nearly rectangular, but have strongly inclined extinction and have $N_X = 1.783$ and $N_Z > 2.14$, $N_Z - N_X > 0.36$. Strongly pleochroic from yellow to red. Called lake red C. Ref: 543, 576.

Sodium salt of 1-(4-chloro-3-methyl-6-sulphophenyl)-2-hydroxy-3-naphthoic acid or sodium salt of 6-sulfo-4-chloro-3-toluene-azo-β-hydroxynaphthoic acid $\{Cl(CH_3)C_6H_2NaSO_3N:NC_{10}H_5(OH)COOH\}$ is orthorhombic (?). Crystals rectangular plates with X ∥ length. $N_X = 2.06$, N_Y = (?), $N_Z = 2.23$, $N_Z - N_X = 0.17$. Insignificant pleochroism. Called lithol red GG. Ref: 543, 576

1-(1-Sulfo-2-naphthylazo)-2-naphthol or 1-sulfo-β-naphthol $\{C_{10}H_6(HSO_3)N:NC_{10}H_6OH\}$ is monoclinic (?) with parallel extinction on {100} and X ∧ length = 18°. Crystals acicular. (–)2V = (?), $N_X = 1.90$, N_Y = ?, $N_Z = 2.14$, $N_Z - N_X = 0.24$. Almost no pleochroism. Called lithol red R. (Described by Riskin as isometric!) Ref: 543, 576.

1-(1-Sulfo-2-naphthylazo)-2-hydroxy-3-naphthoic acid or 1-sulfo-β-naphthalene-azo-β-hydroxynaphthoic acid $\{HSO_3C_{10}H_6N:NC_{10}H_6(OH)COOH\}$ forms tiny needles with Z ∥ length. $N_X = 2.06$, N_Y = ?, $N_Z = 2.35$, $N_Z - N_X = 0.29$. Insignificant pleochroism. Called Lake Bordeaux BN. Ref: 543, 576.

1-(1-Naphthylazo)-2-naphthol-6-sulfonate or α-naphthalene-azo-naphthol-6-sulfonic acid $(C_{10}H_7N:NC_{10}H_5OH \cdot HSO_3)$ is monoclinic (?). Crystals acicular with Z nearly ∥ length. $N_X = 1.56$, N_Y = ?, $N_Z = 2.26$, $N_Z - N_X = 0.70$. Strongly pleochroic with X = light orange, Z = dark red. Called Lake Bordeaux BK. Are these properties of the sodium salt? Ref: 543, 576.

1-(Phenylazo)-2-naphthol-6,8-disulfonate or benzene-azo-β-naphthol-6,8-disulfonic acid $\{C_6H_5N:NC_{10}H_4OH(HSO_3)_2\}$ has X ∥ length. $N_X = 1.73$, N_Y = (?), $N_Z = 2.00$, $N_Z - N_X = 0.27$. Pleochroic with X = bright red, Z = dark red. Called fast light orange G. Are these properties of the sodium salt? Ref: 543, 576.

Disodium 1-phenylazo-2-naphthol-6,8-disulfonate or sodium salt of benzene-azo-β-naphthol-6,8-disulfonic acid $\{C_6H_5N:NC_{10}H_4(OH)(NaSO_3)_2\}$ is orthorhombic (?). X || length. $N_X = 1.514$, $N_Y = ?$, $N_Z = 1.87$, $N_Z - N_X = 0.356$. Pleochroism weak with X $\leqslant$ Z (in orange). Called orange GG. Ref: 577.

1-(1-Naphthylazo)-2-naphthol-6,8-disulfonate or α-naphthylene-azo-β-naphthol-6,8-disulfonic acid $\{C_{10}H_7N:NC_{10}H_4(OH)(HSO_3)_2\}$ is monoclinic (?). Crystals tabular of varied shape, but all are normal to Y. Z $\wedge$ length = 19°. (+)2V = (?), $N_X = 1.495$, $N_Y = ?$, $N_Z = 2.29$, $N_Z - N_X = 0.895$. Strongly pleochroic with X = light yellow, Z = dark red. Called crystal crimson 6R. Are these properties of the sodium salt? Ref: 543, 576.

p-Aminoazobenzene or aniline yellow S $(C_{12}H_{11}N_3)$ is monoclinic with $a:b:c = 2.442:1:2.530$, $\beta = 98°11'$. Space group $P2_1/n$. *a* 13.69, *b* 5.604, *c* 14.18 Å. U.C. 4. Crystals long || *c* with {110}, {100}, {001}, etc. D 1.20. M.P. 125°. X = *b*, Y nearly = *c*. (+)2V = 85°, r > v. $N_X = 1.675$, $N_Y = 1.81$, $N_Z = 2.02$, $N_Z - N_X = 0.345$. Ref: 552a.

Sodium salt of 4-(3-sulfophenylazo)diphenylamine or sodium salt of *m*-sulfobenzene-azo-diphenylamine $\{NaSO_3C_6H_4N:NC_6H_4NHC_6H_4\}$ is orthorhombic (?). X || length. $N_X = 1.485$, $N_Y = ?$, $N_Z = 1.80$, $N_Z - N_X = 0.315$. Pleochroic with X = light yellow, Z = yellow. Called metanil yellow. Ref: 577.

Permanent ruby PhB-ASH (formula ?) forms tablets with Z || length. $N_X = 2.0$, $N_Y = ?$, $N_Z = 2.55$, $N_Z - N_X = 0.55$. Pleochroism not great with X = red, Z = dark red. Ref: 543, 576.

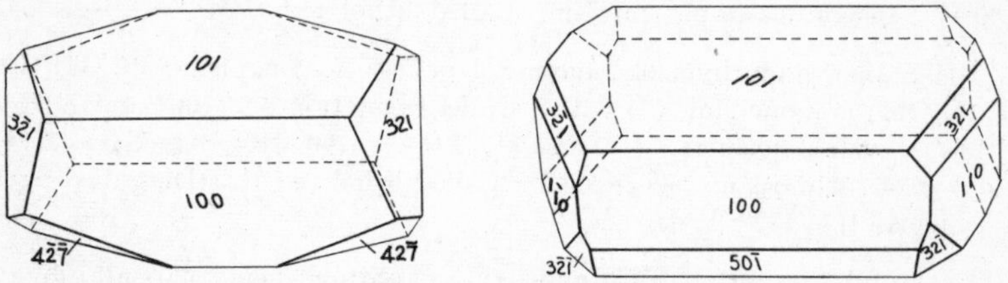

Figs. 95, 96. Diethylaniline azaline.

4′-Dimethylaminoazobenzene-4-sulfonic acid or *p*-(*p*-dimethylaminophenyl-azo)benzenesulfonic acid or helianthin or methyl orange $[(CH_3)_2NC_6H_4N:NC_6H_4\cdot SO_3H]$ has two modifications, the quinoid and the benzoid. The former (I) is monoclinic sphenoidal in {001} lamellae with {110}, {100} and {010}. D 1.468. X = *b*; Z $\wedge$ *c* = 47°. (+)2V = 35°, r > v. $N_X = 1.55$, $N_Y = 1.60 - 1.61$, $N_Z > 2.4$, $N_Z - N_X > 0.8$. Pleochroic with X = orange-red and Y = brownish red. The second (II) is probably monoclinic in {001} lamellae with {110} and {010}. D 1.473. X = *b*; Z $\wedge$ *c* = 68°. (+)2V = 63°, r > v. $N_X = 1.48$, $N_Y = 1.60 - 1.61$, $N_Z > 2.1$, $N_Z - N_X > 0.6$. Pleochroic with X = clear yellow, Y = dark yellow. Ref: 276.

4,4′-*bis*(Diethylamino)azobenzene, *p,p*′-azobis N,N-diethylaniline or *p,p*′-azodiethylaniline, or diethylaniline azyline $[C_6H_4[N(C_2H_5)_2]N:NC_6H_4[N(C_2H_5)_2]]$

is monoclinic with $a:b:c = 1:0.711:0.949$, $\beta = 98°30'$. Crystals domatic with {101}, {100}, {321}, {110}, etc. Figs 95, 96. D 1.11. M.P. 170°. No optic axis visible through 101, 100, or 010. $N_Y = 1.507$, $N_Z - N_X$ = weak. Color reddish brown with bluish black schiller; pleochroic with b = clear yellow; normal thereto dark brown. Ref. 119.

2,4-Diaminoazobenzene or 4-phenylazo-*m*-phenylenediamine or chrysoidine [$C_6H_5N:NC_6H_3(NH_2)_2$] has parallel extinction and positive elongation with $N_1 = 1.68$, $N_2 > 1.95$, $N_2 - N_1 > 0.27$. Ref: 34, 35.

Class 14. Azoxy Compounds

4,4′-Dimethoxyazoxybenzene or *p,p′*-azoxydianisole [$(CH_3OC_6H_4)_2ON_2$] is monoclinic prismatic with $a:b:c = 1.988:1:2.590$, $\beta = 108°20'$. Space group $P2/c$; a 16.0, b 8.08, c 20.5 Å. U.C. 8. Crystals show {001}, {100}, {012}, {11$\bar{1}$}. D 1.35. M.P. 115° to anisotropic liquid, which becomes isotropic at 134°. X = b; Z ∧ 001 = 41°, Z is normal to $\bar{1}$01. (+)2V = 14° D. At ordinary temperature the crystals have:

λ	N_X	N_Y	N_Z	$N_Y - N_X$	Authority
650	1.559	1.568	2.148	0.589	Chatelain
589	1.564	1.572	2.198	0.634	Zadoc-Kahn
589	1.565	1.573	2.212	0.647	Chatelain
546	1.569	1.578	2.266	0.697	Zadoc-Kahn
546	1.570	1.580	2.275	0.705	Chatelain

At higher temperature the "liquid crystals" and liquid have:

Anisotropic			Isotropic	
Temperature = 105°	125°	132°	137°	150°
λ = 650 N_O = 1.540	1.546	1.560	N = 1.626	1.616
N_E = 1.874	1.820	1.773		
λ = 546 N_O = 1.560	1.565	1.580	N = 1.655	1.644
N_E = 1.912	1.852	1.803		
λ = 436 N_O = 1.662	1.676	1.692	N = 1.788	1.774
N_E = 2.180	2.096	2.028		

Ref: 54, 399, 624.

4,4′-Diethoxyazoxybenzene or *p,p′*-azoxydiphenetole [$(C_2H_5OC_6H_4)_2ON_2$] is monoclinic domatic with $a:b:c = 2.93:1:3.23$, $\beta = 94°20'$. Space group Cc; a 15.9, b 5.42, c 17.5 Å. U.C. 4. Crystals show {001}, {100}, {101}, and {211}. Good 100 cleavage. D 1.25. M.P. 136.9°. Y = b; Z ∧ 001 = 59.5°; Z is nearly normal to (102). An optic axis is at 6° with a normal to 001. Dispersion verv weak. (+)2V = 49°30′ D.

λ	N_X	N_Y	N_Z	$N_Z - N_X$
650	1.510	1.575	2.036	0.526
589	1.517	1.584	2.093	0.576
546	1.521	1.587	2.139	0.618
492	1.529	1.599	2.254	0.725

Crystals strongly absorb violet light vibrating in direction of Z. For the liquid:

Anisotropic			Isotropic
Temperature = 135°	155°	165°	185°
$\lambda = 650$ $N_O = 1.507$	1.516	1.528	N = 1.588
$N_E = 1.815$	1.777	1.726	
$\lambda = 546$ $N_O = 1.531$	1.540	1.549	N = 1.603
$N_E = 1.862$	1.816	1.765	
$\lambda = 436$ $N_O = 1.592$	1.610	1.628	N = 1.720
$N_E = 2.135$	2.040	1.975	

Ref: 51, 52, 53, 416.

Ethyl azoxy-α-methylcinnamate [$C_2H_5CO_2CCH_3$:$CHC_6H_4NONC_6H_4CH$:$CCH_3CO_2C_2H_5$] forms liquid crystals of two phases. Phase I (between 78° and 133°) is uniaxial positive with (at 80°) $N_O = 1.5128$ D, $N_E = 1.9328$, $N_E - N_O = 0.420$. Phase II (between 133° and 138°) has (at 135°) $N_O = 1.5531$, $N_E = ?$. Ref: 218.

Class 25. Carbon-Arsenic Compounds

Triphenylarsine [$(C_6H_5)_3As$] is triclinic pinacoidal with[1] a:b:c = 0.878:1:0.795, $\alpha = 99°51'$, $\beta = 80°2'$, $\gamma = 128°28'$. M.P. 58 - 59°. Space group $P\bar{1}$. a 19.43, b 17.72, c 11.14 Å. U.C. 8. Crystals acicular or tabular. The optic plane makes an angle of 66 - 68° with 010. (-)2V = 20 - 30°, $N_X' = 1.661$, $N_Z' = 1.755$, $N_Z' - N_X' = 0.094$.
Ref: 616.

Tri-*o*-phenylenediarsine [$(C_6H_4)_3As_2$] is monoclinic with a:b:c = 1.589:1:?, $\beta = 123°15'$. Crystals {100} tablets or prisms with {110}, {001}. M.P. 296°. The optic plane and Z are normal to 010; X is in the obtuse angle β. Very strong dispersion prevents extinction in white light. (-)2V = large ?. $N_Y = 1.790$ *ca.*
Ref: 149.

Class 27. Carbon-Bismuth Compounds

Triphenylbismuthine [$(C_6H_5)_3Bi$] is monoclinic prismatic with a:b:c = 2.307:1:1.164, $\beta = 109°34'$. Space group $C2/c$; a 26.74, b 5.78, c 20.44 Å. U.C. 8. Crystals are plates and needles. The optic plane and X are normal to 010; Z nearly = a. (+)2V = 66°, $N_X = 1.753$, $N_Y = 1.782$ calc., $N_Z = 1.85$, $N_Z - N_X = 0.097$.
Ref: 616.

[1] b and c interchanged to make $b > a > c$.

Triphenylbismuthine dichloride $[(C_6H_5)_3BiCl_2]$ is orthorhombic disphenoidal with $a:b:c = 0.774:1:0.409$. Crystals prismatic or domatic with {110}, {011}, {010}, {1$\bar{1}$1}, etc. Often pseudopyramidal. Cleavage on 100 and 001. M.P. 141°. The optic plane is 100 for red to green and 001 for green to violet. Z = *b*. (+)2E = 49°56′ Li, 36°18′ Na, 13°52′ Tl, and 69°18′ (in 001) for $\lambda = 436$. (+)2V = 20° Na, calc. $N_X = 1.733$ Na, 1.7495 (Hg green), 1.785 (Hg violet); $N_Y =$ 1.734 Na, 1.745 (Hg green), 1.7885 (Hg violet); $N_Z = 1.795$ Na, 1.803 (Hg green), 1.848 (Hg violet); $N_Z - N_X = 0.060$ Na. The colorless crystals show crossed dispersion. Ref: 37, 114, 115.

Class 28. Carbon-Antimony Compounds.

Triphenylstibine $[(C_6H_5)_3Sb]$ is triclinic pinacoidal with $a:b:c = 0.697:1:0.889$, $\alpha = 100°38'$, $\beta = 103°37'$, $\gamma = 75°25'$. Space group $P\bar{1}$; *a* 15.22, *b* 21.87, *c* 19.43 Å. U.C. 16. Crystals {001} tablets elongated along *a*; also needles. M.P. 48°. D 1.5. The optic plane in 001 makes an angle of 8° with *b* in the obtuse angle between *b* and *a*. It is nearly parallel with 001; X ∧ *a* = + 5°. $N_X = 1.700$, $N_Y = ?$, $N_Z = 1.829$, $N_Z - N_X = 0.129$. Ref: 119, 616.

Class 35. Carbon-Mercury Compounds

Phenylmercuric acetate $(CH_3COOHg \cdot C_6H_5)$ is biaxial. (+)2E = 125° - 135°. 2V = 60 - 70°, $N_X = 1.540$, $N_Y = 1.683$, $N_Z = 2.0$ (*ca.* - A.N.W.), $N_Z - N_X = 0.46$ (*ca.* - A.N.W.). Ref: 529.

III. HETEROCYCLIC COMPOUNDS

1. Compounds with one Oxygen in the Cycle

Class 1. Compounds with no Functional Group

3,3-*bis*(Iodomethyl)oxetone $(C_5H_8OI_2)$ is triclinic with $a:b:c = 0.863:1:0.692$. $\alpha = 85°1'$, $\beta = 66°56'$, $\gamma = 82°51'$. Extinction at 3° from *c* in acute β on 010, and at 27° from *b* in acute α on 100. X nearly ‖ *b*. (-)2E = 30°, $N_Z = 1.783$ for $\lambda = 578$ mμ Ref: 605b.

3,4-Dimethylthiacyclopentene 1-dioxide or 3,4-dimethyl-3-butenylene sulfone or 2,5-dihydro-3,4-dimethylthiophene 1-dioxide $[\overline{SO_2CH_2C(CH_3):C(CH_3)CH_2}]$ is orthorhombic with $a:b:c = 0.981:1:1.598$. Crystals {001} tablets with {101}, {011}, {010}, {111}. M.P. 135°. X = *b*; Y = *c*. (-)2V = 40° calc. $N_X = 1.4940$ (578), 1.4954 (546), 1.5037 (436); $N_Y = 1.5767$ (578), 1.5794 (546), 1.5928 (436); $N_Z = 1.5892$ (578), 1.5915 (546), 1.6043 (436); $N_Z - N_X = 0.0952$ (578). Ref: 325.

Class 2. Hydroxy Compounds

cis-3,4-Dihydroxy-3,4-dimethylthiacyclopentane 1-dioxide hemihydrate or *cis*-tetrahydro-3,4-dimethyl-3,4-thiophenediol 1-dioxide hemihydrate or 2,3-dihydroxy-2,3-dimethylbutylene sulfone hemihydrate [$SO_2CH_2C(OH)(CH_3)C(OH)(CH_3)CH_2 \cdot 0.5H_2O$] is monoclinic with $a:b:c = 2.666:1:1.465$, $\beta = 110°26'$. Crystals {110}, prisms with {100}, {111}, and {$\bar{1}01$}. Perfect 100 cleavage. M.P. 122°. X is nearly normal to 100; Z = *b*. (-)2V = 65° calc. $N_X = 1.5202$ Na, $N_Y = 1.5486$, $N_Z = 1.560$, $N_Z - N_X = 0.0398$. Ref: 329.

Hematoxylin trihydrate ($C_{16}H_{14}O_6 \cdot 3H_2O$) is monoclinic with $a:b:c = 1.528:1:1.033$, $\beta = 109°48'$. Crystals columnar along *b* with {100}, {001}, {110}, {$\bar{1}01$}, etc. The acute bisectrix of a small optic angle is *b*. Bolland gives for hematoxylin (with $3H_2O$?) parallel extinction and positive elongation with $N_1 = 1.64$, $N_2 = 1.69$, $N_2 - N_1 = 0.05$. (Therefore the optic sign is positive and $N_X = 1.64$, *ca.*, N_Y near 1.64, $N_Z = 1.69$, $N_Z - N_X = 0.05$. - A.N.W.). Ref: 35.

Class 3. Carbonyl Compounds

Furfurylidene sulfanilamide ($C_{11}H_{10}O_3N_2S$) is monoclinic. M.P. 196°. Elongation positive. (+)2V = ?, r > v. $N_X = 1.493$, $N_Y = 1.651$, $N_Z > 1.703$ (also > 1.80, since the optic sign is +. - A.N.W.), $N_Z - N_X > 0.307$. Ref: 617a.

3,(2-Hydroxyphenyl)-2-propenoic acid lactone or coumarin or *o*-coumaric acid lactone [$C_6H_4CH:CHCO\text{–}O$] is orthorhombic pyramidal with $a:b:c$[1] = 0.513:1:0.366. Space group *Pca*; *a* 7.92, *b* 15.44, *c* 5.66 Å. Crystals rectangular {010} plates. M.P. 67°. The optic plane is 001; Z = *a*. (+)2V = ?, $N_1 = 1.56$ *ca.*, $N_2 > 1.66$, $N_2 - N_1 > 0.10$. Two other crystals phases are known. Ref: 239, 602.

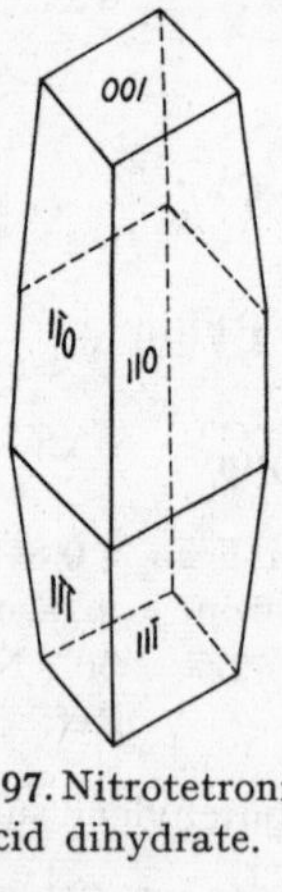

Fig. 97. Nitrotetronic acid dihydrate.

Phthalic anhydride {$C_6H_4(CO)_2O$} is orthorhombic with $a:b:c = 0.558:1:0.419$. *a* 7.90, *b* 14.16, *c* 5.94 Å. U.C 4. Crystals equant or acicular with 110 cleavages. M.P. 128°. D 1.48. X = *a*, Y = *c*. (-)2V = 70°, r < v strong. $N_X = 1.514$, $N_Y = 1.685$, $N_Z = 1.782$, $N_Z - N_X = 0.268$. Ref: 527, 620a.

2,4-Dihydroxy-3-nitrofuran or Nitrotetronic Acid and its Salts

Nitrotetronic acid dihydrate [$COH:CH \cdot O \cdot COH:CNO_2 \cdot 2H_2O$] is monoclinic with $a:b:c = 1.164:1:1.933$, $\beta = 129°1'$. Crystals prismatic with {110}, {$\bar{1}11$}, {001}. Fig. 97. Very perfect 001 cleavage. D 1.68. Decomposes at 184°. The optic plane is 010; extinction angle (in 110 ?) = 16° to *c*. $N_X = 1.367$, $N_Y = 1.409$, $N_Z = 1.536$ *ca.*, $N_Z - N_X = 0.169$ Na, ∴ (+)2V = 60°. Ref: 117.

[1] *a b c* changed to *b a c* to make $b > a > c$.

Calcium nitrotetronate hydrate [$(C_4H_2O_3NO_2)_2Ca \cdot nH_2O$] is monoclinic with $a:b:c = 2.733:1:?$, $\beta = 91°25'$. Crystals thick {001} tablets with {100}, {110}, {210}. Fig. 98. Distinct 110 cleavage. D 1.75. X $\perp$ 100 *ca.*, Z = *b*. (-)2V = 32°36', calc. $N_X = 1.462$, $N_Y = 1.643$, $N_Z = 1.722$, $N_Z - N_X = 0.260$ Na. Ref: 117.

Strontium nitrotetronate hydrate [$(C_4H_2O_3NO_2)_2Sr \cdot nH_2O$] is monoclinic with $a:b:c = 2.836:1:?$, $\beta = 90°42'$. Crystals like calcium nitrotetronate. Distinct 110 cleavage. D 2.04. X almost normal to 100; Z = *b*. (-)2V = 30°23' calc. $N_X = 1.453$, $N_Y = 1.637$, $N_Z = 1.707$ *ca.*, $N_Z - N_X = 0.254$ Na. Ref: 117.

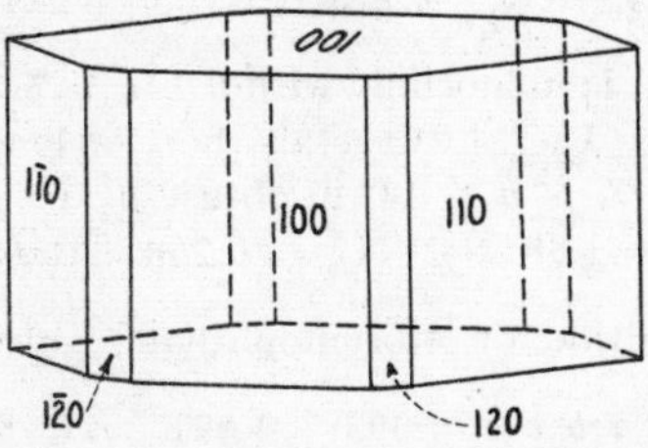

Fig. 98. Calcium nitrotetronate hydrate.

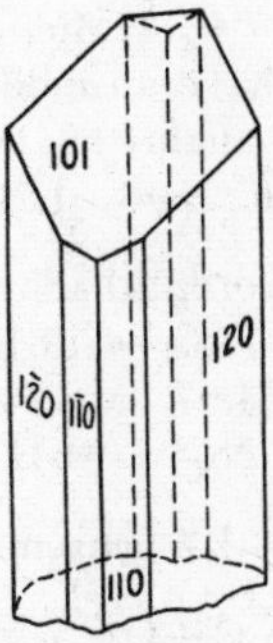

Fig. 99. Succinic acid anhydride.

Butanedioic anhydride or succinic anhydride ($\overline{CH_2CO \cdot O \cdot COCH_2}$) is orthorhombic with $a:b:c = 0.595:1:0.462$. Crystals short prismatic with {010}, {110}, {120}, {101}, {011}, etc. Fig. 99. Perfect 101 cleavage. D 1.50. M.P. 120°. Y = *c*; Z = *b*. (+)2V = 63°40' (576). $N_Y = 1.4957$ (576). Also $N_1 = 1.502$, $N_2 = 1.609$, $N_2 - N_1 = 0.107$. Ref: 117, 239, 303.

2-Butenedioic anhydride or maleic. anhydride ($\overline{CH:CHCHO \cdot O \cdot CO}$) is orthorhombic with $a:b:c = 0.641:1:0.481$ Crystals from chloroform show {101}, {110}, {120}, {010}. No distinct cleavage. M.P. 53°. Y = *c*; Z = *b*. (+)2V = 54°44' Li, 54°33' Na, 52°17' blue. $N_X = 1.4397$ Li, 1.4429 Na, 1.4519 blue; $N_Y = 1.4745$ Li, 1.4781 Na, 1.4866 blue; $N_Z = 1.6313$ Li, 1.6384 Na, 1.6584 blue; $N_Z - N_X = 0.1955$ Na. Ref: 117, 254.

2-Chloro-3-methyl-2-butenedioic anhydride or chlorocitraconic anhydride [$\overline{O \cdot COCCl:C(CH_3)CO}$] is orthorhombic with $a:b:c = 0.642:1:0.408$. Crystals {010} tablets with {001}, {101}, {210}, {111}. Perfect 010 cleavage. Y = *b*; Z = *c*. (+)2V = 63°34' red, 46°24' blue. $N_Y = 1.547$, $N_Z - N_X$ = strong. Ref: 117.

1,3-Dihydro-1-keto-3-oximinoisobenzofuran or phthaloxime or phthalic anhydride monoxime [$\overline{C_6H_4CO \cdot O \cdot C}:NOH$] is monoclinic in needles elongated along *b*. Parallel extinction and negative elongation. $N_X = 1.522$, $N_Z - N_X$ = about 0.300. Ref: 265.

4-Fluoro-1,2-benzenedicarboxylic anhydride or 4-fluorophthalic anhydride [$FC_6H_3CO \cdot O \cdot CO$] is triclinic in needles forming pseudohexagonal twins. M.P. 147 - 148°. Extinction nearly parallel on 100 and at + 38° on 010. (-)2V = 3 - 5°, r > v strong. $N_X = 1.400$, $N_Y = 1.74$, $N_Z = 1.74$, $N_Z - N_X = 0.34$. Ref: 297.

4-Chloro-1,2-benzenedicarboxylic anhydride or 4-chlorophthalic anhydride [$ClC_6H_3CO \cdot O \cdot CO$] is triclinic in needles with three pairs of faces with interfacial angles of 23°4′, 47°46′, and 109°8′. Needles lying so as to have nearly parallel extinction have an index near N_X for light vibrating normal to the elongation. Extinction angles on the three faces are 3°, 9°, and 14°. (-)2V = 55 - 60°. $N_X = 1.500$, $N_Y = 1.700$, $N_Z = 1.775$, $N_Z - N_X = 0.275$. Ref: 297.

Tetrachlorophthalic anhydride ($C_8O_3Cl_4$) is monoclinic with $a:b:c = 3.104:1:2.116$, $\beta = 132°$. *a* 18.10, *b* 5.83, *c* 12.34 Å. U.C. 4. Crystals short or long rods along *b*. D 1.97. M.P. 255 - 257°. Y = *b*; Z ∧ *a* = 14° in obtuse *β*. (+)2V = 87°, r < v. $N_X = 1.612$, $N_Y = 1.737$, $N_Z = 1.88$, $N_Z - N_X = 0.268$. Ref: 553c.

4-Bromo-1,2-benzenedicarboxylic anhydride or 4-bromophthalic anhydride [$BrC_6H_3CO \cdot O \cdot CO$] is monoclinic with $a:b:c = 1.095:1:1.091$, $\beta = 59°35'$. Crystals are {010} plates elongated along *c* with {110}, {101}, {041}. X ∧ *c* = - 15° to - 16°; Z = *b*. 2V = 90° *ca*. $N_X = 1.545$, $N_Y = 1.700$, $N_Z = 1.85$ calc., $N_Z - N_X = 0.31$. Ref: 297.

4-Iodo-1,2-benzenedicarboxylic anhydride or 4-iodophthalic anhydride [$IC_6H_3CO \cdot O \cdot CO$] is monoclinic with $a:b:c = 1.123:1:1.139$, $\beta = 106°31'$. Crystals are {010} plates elongated along *c*, with {110}, {101}, {$\bar{1}01$}, {012}. X ∧ *c* = small; Z = *b*. (-)2V = 60 - 70°. $N_X = 1.555$, $N_Y = 1.77$, $N_Z = 1.86$ calc., $N_Z - N_X = 0.31$ *ca*. calc. Ref: 297.

2,3-Diphenyl-2-butenedioic anhydride or diphenylmaleic anhydride [$COC(C_6H_5):C(C_6H_5)CO \cdot O$] is orthorhombic with $a:b:c = 0.518:1:0.702$. Crystals short prisms or domatic with {110}, {111}, {011}, {021}, {010}, etc. Figs. 100, 101. D 1.34. M.P. 155°. No distinct cleavage. Y = *a*; Z = *c*. (+)2V = small. $N_X = 1.505$ Li, 1.511 Na, 1.517 Tl; $N_Y = 1.505$ Li, 1.5115 Na, 1.518 *ca*. Tl; $N_Z = 1.811$ Li, 1.836 Na, 1.865 Tl; $N_Z - N_X = 0.325$ Na. A metastable phase (II) is monoclinic with $a:b:c = 2.562:1:2.328$. D 1.35. M.P. 146°. Ref: 119.

Tetrahydro-4-hydroxy-2-isopropyl-5-keto-3,3-dimethylfuran or α-hydroxy-γ-isopropyl-*β*,*β*-dimethylbutyrolactone [$(CH_3)_2CHCHC(CH_3)_2CH(OH)CO \cdot O$] is orthorhombic disphenoidal with $a:b:c = 0.752:1:0.816$. Crystals prismatic with {110}, {010}, {011}, {112}, etc. M.P. 92.5°. Perfect 100, distinct 010, and imperfect 110 cleavages. X = *a*; Y = *c*. (-)2V = 57°16′ Na, r > v moderate. $N_Y = 1.5130$ red, 1.5157 yellow, 1.5196 blue. Ref: 117.

Hydrosantonide $[(CH_3)_2C_{13}H_{13}O(:O)OH]$ is orthorhombic disphenoidal[1] with $a:b:c = 0.841:1:0.646$. Crystals brachydomatic with {011}, {110}, {100}, etc. M.P. 155°. $Y = b$; $Z = c$. $(+)2V = 55°50'$ red, $54°52'$ blue. $N_Y = 1.5585$ red, 1.5616 blue.   Ref: 119.

2,3,4-Trihydroxypentanoic acid 1,4-lactone or methyltetronic acid lactone or α,β-dihydroxy-γ-methylbutyrolactone $[CH_3\overline{CHCH(OH)CH(OH)CO\cdot O}]$ is biaxial with M.P. 123°. $N_X = 1.500$, $N_Y = 1.515$, $N_Z = 1.535$, $N_Z - N_X = 0.035$. $\therefore (+)2V = 80°$ $ca.$ $[\alpha]$ in water $= -44.7°$.   Ref: 367.

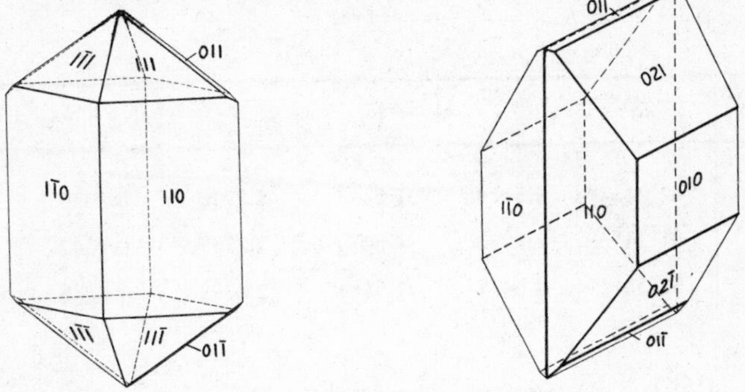

Figs. 100, 101. Diphenylmaleic anhydride.

2,3,5-Trimethyl-L-lyxono-1,4-lactone forms long monoclinic needles with $c = 4.42$ Å. $X \wedge c = 20°$ $ca.$ $N_X < 1.47$, $N_Z - N_X = $ fairly strong.   Ref: 60.

$$\left[\begin{array}{l} \quad\text{H}\quad\text{O}\ \text{OCH}_3\ \text{OCH}_3 \\ \text{HC}\!-\!\overset{|}{\text{C}}\!-\!\overset{|}{\text{C}}\!-\!\overset{}{\qquad}\overset{|}{\text{C}}\!-\!\!-\!\!-\text{C:O} \\ \quad\dot{\text{O}}\text{CH}_3\text{H H}\quad\ \text{H} \end{array}\right]$$

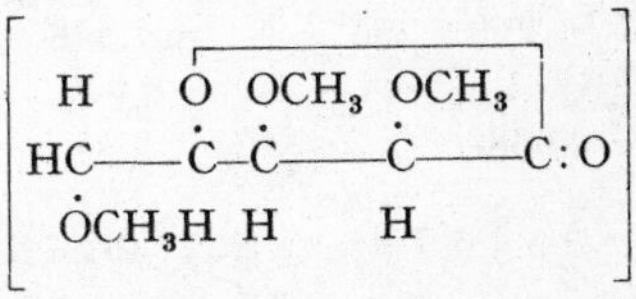

2,3,4-Trimethyl-D-xylono-1,5-lactone forms flattened needles with $c = 4.60$ Å. $X = c$. $(+)2V =$? $N_X = 1.465$.   Ref: 60.

$$\left[\begin{array}{l} \qquad\quad\text{CH}_3\quad\ \text{CH}_3 \\ \quad\text{O}\quad\text{O}\ \ \text{H}\quad\text{O} \\ \text{HC}\!-\!\text{C}\!-\!\text{C}\!-\!\text{C}\!-\!\text{C:O} \\ \quad\text{H}\quad\text{H}\ \ \text{O}\quad\text{H} \\ \qquad\qquad\quad\text{CH}_3 \end{array}\right]$$

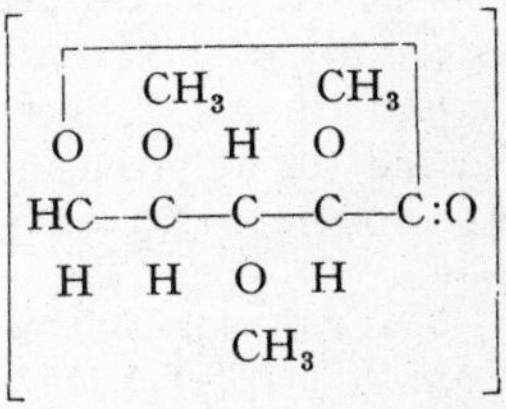

Rhamnono-1,4-lactone is orthorhombic with $a:b:c = 0.777:1:0.348$. No cleavage observed. Parallel extinction and negative elongation. $X = c$; $Y = b$. $(-)2E = 80°44'$ (650); $76°30'$ (480). $(-)2V = 50°$ (650) calc. $N_X = 1.497$, $N_Y = 1.525$, $N_Z = 1.532$, $N_Z - N_X = 0.035$ Na. $[\alpha] = +40°$.

$$\left[\begin{array}{l} \quad\ \text{H}\ \ \text{H}\ \text{OH OH} \\ \text{H}_3\text{C}\!-\!\text{C}\!-\!\text{C}\!-\!\text{C}\!-\!\text{C}\!-\!\text{C:O} \\ \quad\ \dot{\text{O}}\text{H}\dot{\text{O}}\ \ \text{H}\ \ \text{H} \end{array}\right]$$

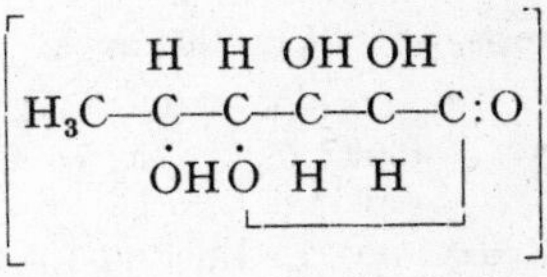

Ref: 387.

---

[1] a and b interchanged to make $b > a > c$.

Rhamnono-1,5-lactone is orthorhombic disphenoidal with $a:b:c = 0.687:1:1.259$. No cleavage observed. $Y = c$; $Z = a$. $(+)2V = 82°10'$ (650), $82°12'$ (480). $N_X = 1.514$, $N_Y = 1.546$, $N_Z = 1.592$, $N_Z - N_X = 0.078$ Na. $[\alpha] = +98°$.
Ref: 388.

$$\left[\begin{array}{c} \text{H} \quad \text{H} \quad \text{OH OH} \\ H_3C-C-C-\overset{\cdot}{C}-\overset{\cdot}{C}-C:O \\ \overset{\cdot}{O} \quad \overset{\cdot}{O}H\,H \quad H \end{array}\right]$$

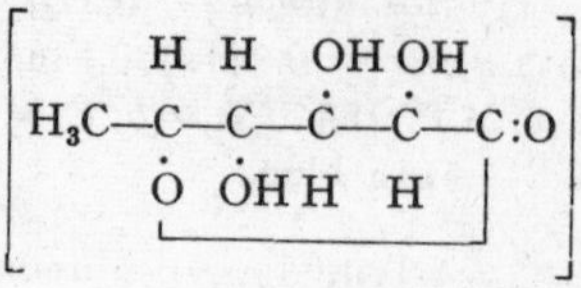

2-Methoxy-6-(p-methoxystyryl)-1,4-pyrone or yangonin [$H_3COC_6H_4CH:CH\overline{C:CHCHCOCH:C}(OCH_3)\cdot O$] is monoclinic with $a:b:c = 1.592:1:0.982$, $\beta = 94°19'$. Crystals prisms with {110}, {001}, {120}, {$\bar{1}11$}, {$\bar{2}01$}, etc. D 1.325. M.P. 152°. $X = b$; $Z \wedge c = 43°$ (average).

λ	$(+)2V$	N_X	N_Y	N_Z	$N_Z - N_X$	$Z \wedge c$
577	$62°23'$	1.5174	1.6383	2.2270	0.7096	$43°33'$
546	$61°24'$	1.5215	1.6476	2.2757	0.7542	$55°9'$
436	$56°33'$	1.5437	1.6841	2.8793	1.3356	

Ref: 154.

Phenolphthalein [$(C_6H_4OH)_2\overline{CC_6H_4CO\cdot O}$] is triclinic in crystals with {100}, {010}, {110}, {111}, etc.; often twinned on 010. $100 \wedge 010 = 71°18'$; $111 \wedge 010 = 70°51.5'$; $111 \wedge 100 = 30°29'$. Distinct 100 and imperfect 010 cleavages. M.P. 250 – 253°. $N_1 = 1.648$, $N_2 = 1.663$, $N_2 - N_1 = 0.015$. Also $N_1 = 1.635$, $N_2 = 1.675$, $N_2 - N_1 = 0.040$. Again $N_1 = 1.63$, $N_2 = 1.65$, $N_3 = 1.668$, $N_3 - N_1 = 0.038$.
Ref: 119, 239, 343c, 518.

2,3,4,5-Tetrahydroxy-2-methylpentanoic acid 1,4-lactone or saccharinic acid lactone [$\overline{O\cdot COC(CH_3)OH\cdot CHOHCHCH_2}OH$] is orthorhombic disphenoidal with $a:b:c = 0.684:1:0.737$. Crystals prismatic with {110}, {011}, {021}, etc. Perfect 010 and distinct 001 cleavages. M.P. 160°. The optic plane is 001 for red and 100 for green and blue; uniaxial for yellow. $(-)2V = $ small. $N_X = 1.615$, $N_Y = 1.69$ ca., $N_Z = 1.69$ ca., $N_Z - N_X = 0.075$.
Ref: 117, 239.

5-Ketorhamnolactone is orthorhombic with $a:b:c = 0.727:1:1.179$. Crystals brachydomatic with {011}, {021}, {110}, etc. Distinct 010 and imperfect 011 cleavages. M.P. 196°. $X = c$; $Y = a$. $(-)2V = 63°$. $N_X = 1.516$ calc., $N_Y = 1.570$, $N_Z = 1.598$ Na, $N_Z - N_X = 0.082$ calc. $[\alpha] = -24.7°$.

$$\left[\begin{array}{c} \overset{\cdot}{O} \quad \text{H} \quad \text{H} \\ H_3C-CO-\overset{\cdot}{C}-C-C-C:O \\ \text{H} \quad \overset{\cdot}{O}H\overset{\cdot}{O}H \end{array}\right]$$

Ref: 263.

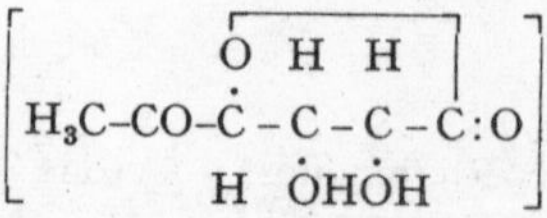

D- or L-Glucono-1,4-lactone or gluconic γ-lactone is biaxial in irregular grains. $(+)2V = $ large. $N_X = 1.517$, $N_Y = 1.544$, $N_Z = 1.577$, $N_Z - N_X = 0.060$, all $\pm .003$.
Ref: 192.

$$\left[\begin{array}{c} \text{H} \quad \text{H} \quad \text{H} \quad \text{OHH} \\ HOC-C-C-\overset{\cdot}{C}-C-C:O \\ \text{H} \quad \overset{\cdot}{O}H\overset{\cdot}{O} \quad \text{H} \quad \overset{\cdot}{O}H \end{array}\right]$$

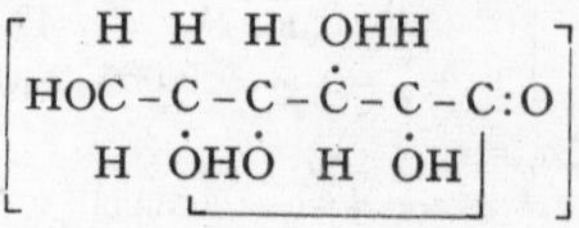

Glucuronolactone or glucurone ($C_6H_{11}O_6$) is monoclinic sphenoidal with $a:b:c = 0.908:1:0.888$, $\beta = 93°16'$. a 6.81, b 7.50, c 6.64 Å. U.C. 2. $\bar{1}01$ and 001 cleavages. D 1.75. (-)2V = 60°, $N_X = 1.548$, $N_Y = 1.578$, $N_Z = 1.588$, $N_Z - N_X = 0.040$. Ref: 527a.

Quercetin dihydrate or 3,3′,4′,5,7 pentahydroxyflavone dihydrate [$C_{15}H_{10}O_7 \cdot 2H_2O$] is a glucone of rutin. It forms yellow spindleshaped crystals. X || elongation. $N_X = 1.555$, $N_Y = 1.734$, $N_Z > 1.734$, $N_Z - N_X > 0.179$. Ref: 523c.

Quercitrin dihydrate [$C_{21}H_{20}O_{11} \cdot 2H_2O$] is a glycoside from the innerbark of black oak. It is orange-yellow in color. Crystals are thin plates. Uniaxial positive with $N_O = 1.508$, $N_E > 1.734$, $N_E - N_O > 0.226$. Ref: 523c.

Rutin dihydrate [$C_{27}H_{30}O_{16} \cdot 2H_2O$] crystallizes from alcohol in rods with X parallel to elongation. $N_X = 1.508$, N_Y (?) = 1.734 (often found), $N_Z > 1.734$, $N_Z - N_X > 0.226$. Ref: 523c.

Genistein or 4′,5,7-trihydroxyisoflavone ($C_{15}H_{10}O_5$) forms broad rectangular and six-sided rods with parallel extinction and negative elongation. M.P. 296°. $N_X = 1.530$, N_Y probably about 1.645, $N_Z > 1.733$, $N_Z - N_X > 0.203$. Often shows abnormal interference colors. Ref: 343.

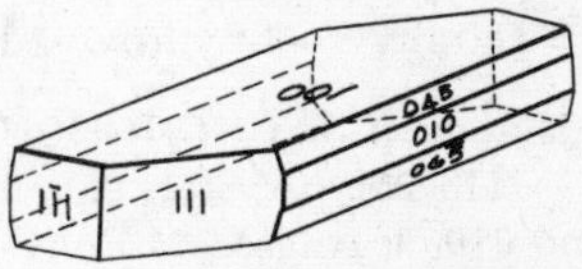

Fig. 102. Barium methyluvinate tetrahydrate.

Genistein triacetate [$C_{15}H_7O_5(CHCO)_3$] shows needles and boat-shaped forms. The needles show parallel extinction and negative elongation. The boat-shaped crystals show abnormal blue and purple interference colors. M.P. 200°. (+)2V = 55° calc. $N_X = 1.508$, $N_Y = 1.556$, $N_Z > 1.733$, $N_Z - N_X > 0.225$. Ref: 343.

Genistin or 4′,5,7-trihydroxyisoflavone glucoside ($C_{21}H_{20}O_{10}$) forms thin rectangular pale-yellow plates with parallel extinction and positive elongation. M.P. 256°. $N_X = 1.580$, N_Y = ?, $N_Z = 1.650$, $N_Z - N_X = 0.070$. [α] = - 28°. Ref: 343.

Genistin hexaacetate [$C_{21}H_{14}O_{10} \cdot (CH_3CO)_6$] forms fine long prisms with parallel extinction and positive elongation; the slender prisms tend to twist into spiral forms. M.P. 188°. (-)2V = 75° calc. $N_X = 1.520$, $N_Y = 1.556$, $N_Z = 1.577$, $N_Z - N_X = 0.057$. Ref: 343.

Class 4. Carboxylic Acids and Derivatives

Barium 2,5-dimethyl-3-furancarboxylate tetrahydrate or barium methyluvinate tetrahydrate [[$\overline{CH:C(CH_3) \cdot O \cdot C(CH_3):C}\cdot CO_2]_2Ba \cdot 4H_2O$] is orthorhombic pyramidal with $a:b:c = 0.999:1:4.371$. Crystals {001} tablets elongated parallel to a with {111}, {045}, {010}, etc. Fig. 102. Perfect 001 and imperfect 100 and 010 cleavages. Y = a; the acute bisectrix is parallel to b. 2V = 88°12′, N_Y = 1.5057 Na. Ref: 119.

Dixanthyl urea [$CO(NH_2)_2(C_{13}H_8O)_2$] forms elongated plates terminated by a face at 73° ± 3° to the length. X′ parallel to elongation. $N_X' = 1.614 \pm .003$, $N_Z' = 1.745 \pm .005$. Are these plates elongated along *b* of a monoclinic crystal? Ref: 599.

Dixanthyl biguanide {$C_{13}H_9ONHC(NH)NHC(NH)NH \cdot C_{13}H_9O$} forms thin tablets with N_1 (|| length) = 1.505, N_2 (⊥ width) = 1.590, $N_2 - N_1 = 0.090$. Ref: 529.

Dixanthyl thiourea [$CS(NH_2)_2(C_{13}H_8O)]_2$ forms laths or plates elongated along *c* and terminated by a low dome or pyramid with an angle of 142° ± 2°. X′ is parallel to the elongation and $N_X' = 1.705 \pm .003$ and $N_Z' = 1.750$, varying with the position of the lath. Optically positive. Ref: 599.

Furfurylhydrophenanthraquinone ($C_{18}H_{12}O_3$) ie tetragonal with *c* = 0.347. Crystals prismatic. M.P. 193°. Uniaxial positive with $N_O = 1.6603$. Pleochroic with O = reddish yellow and E = greenish yellow. Ref: 568a.

Tetrahydro-4-hydroxy-2-keto-5-phenylfuran or β-hydroxy-γ-phenylbutyro-γ-lactone [$C_6H_5\overline{CHCHOHCH_2CO \cdot O}$] is monoclinic with $a:b:c = 2.257:1:3.097$, $\beta = 113°26'$. Crystals equant with {001}, {110}, {$3\bar{5}\bar{5}$}, {100}, etc. Perfect 100 and 010 cleavages. M.P. 94°. X ∧ *c* = −96°; Y = *b*. 2H = 14°58′ Li, 13°48°′ Na, 12°21′ Tl, nearly 0° for blue. (−)2V = 12°38′ Na. $N_X = 1.5026$ Li, 1.5049 Na, 1.5075 Tl; $N_Y = 1.6514$ calc., $N_Z = 1.6539$ Na, 1.6596 Tl; $N_Z - N_X = 0.131$ Na.[1] Ref: 118, 224.

l-Tetrahydro-5,6,6-trimethylpyran-2,5-dicarboxylic acid monohydrate or *l*-cineolic acid monohydrate [$(CH_3)_2\overline{COCH(CO_2H)CH_2 \cdot CH_2C}(CO_2H)CH_3 \cdot H_2O$] is orthorhombic disphenoidal with $a:b:c = 0.982:1:1.477$. Crystals with {100}, {011}, {110}, {010} etc. Perfect 001 cleavage. X = *c*; Y = *b*. (−)2V = 25.5°. $N_X = 1.4798$, $N_Y = 1.5009$ calc., $N_Z = 1.5020$, $N_Z - N_X = 0.0222$ Na. Ref: 117.

4,5-Dihydro-5-keto-3-furancarboxylic acid; tautomeric with 5-hydroxy-3-furancarboxylic acid; or aconic acid [$\overline{CH_2CO \cdot O \cdot CH:C}CO_2H$] is orthorhombic with $a:b:c = 0.582:1:0.495$. Crystals show {110} and {111}, sometimes with {100}, {001}, etc. Very perfect 001 cleavage. M.P. 164°. X = *b*; Y = *a*. Obtuse optic angle in oil = 97°0′ Li, 97°20′ Na, 97°31′ Tl. $N_X = 1.3848$ Li, 1.3855 Na, 1.3878 Tl; N_Y = ?; $N_Z = 1.5286$ Li, 1.5300 Na, 1.5332 Tl; $N_Z - N_X = 0.1445$ Na. Ref: 117.

4-Acetyl-2,5-dimethyl-3-furancarboxylic acid or dehydrodiacetyllevulinic acid [$(CH_3)\overline{C:C(COCH_3)C(CO_2H):C(CH_3) \cdot O}$] is monoclinic with $a:b:c = 1.590:1:0.877$, $\beta = 110°19'$. Crystals prismatic with {110}, {100}, {001}, {010}, etc.

[1] If I understand Linck's description correctly, the indices he gives as β′ and γ must be N_Z and N_Y respectively. Also N_Y, calculated from 2H (with N = 1.5146) and 2V, is 1.6514 (therefore the optic sign is negative. – A.N.W.).

M.P. 152°. Perfect 001 cleavage. X = *b*; Z $\wedge$ *c* = −5°, r > v. Both optic axes visible through 001. (+)2V = 75° *ca.* N_X = 1.5256, N_Y = 1.5800, N_Z = 1.6866, $N_Z - N_X$ = 0.1610 Na. Ref: 117.

2,3-Dimethyl-7-oxabicyclo [2.2.1] heptane-2,3-dicarboxylic anhydride or 3,6-endoxy-1,2-dimethyl-1,2-cyclohexanedicarboxylic anhydride or cantharidin ($C_{10}H_{12}O_4$) is orthorhombic with *a*:*b*:*c* = 0.883:1:0.539. Crystals brachydomatic with {011}, {010}, {100}, {101}, {111}, etc. Perfect 010 and distinct 100 cleavages. Y = *c*; the acute bisectrix is *b*. (−?)2V = 89°7′ Na, r > v. N_X = 1.504, N_Y = 1.54, N_Z = 1.573, $N_Z - N_X$ = 0.069. Also has negative elongation and parallel extinction with 2V = 70°, N_1 = 1.52, N_2 = 1.56, $N_2 - N_1$ = 0.04. Again N_1 = 1.505, N_2 = 1.54. Kofler notes strong dispersion with N_X = 1.509, N_Y = 1.542, N_Z = 1.579, $N_Z - N_X$ = 0.070 (∴ (+)2V = 87°) for Lifa filter 200c. Cantharidin vapor is a dangerous irritant to the skin and especially the mucous membrane (*e. g.*, the eyes and nose). It sublimes to fine crystals at about 110°., 12 mm. Hg, 3 − 5 mm. distance. Ref: 196, 206, 239, 339.

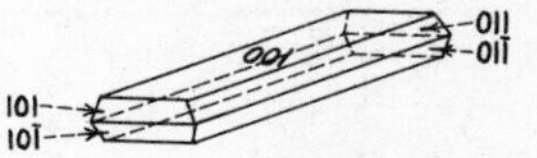

Fig. 103.
Bromophenylparaconic acid.

2-Bromotetrahydro-5-keto-2-phenyl-3-furancarboxylic acid or γ-bromo-γ-phenylbutyrolactone or bromophenylparaconic acid [$CH_2CO \cdot O \cdot C(C_6H_5)BrCH CO_2H$] is orthorhombic with *a*:*b*:*c* = 0.654:1:0.622. Crystals {001} tablets elongated parallel to *a* with {011}, {101}. Fig. 103. Imperfect 100 cleavage. M.P. 99°. Y = *b*; the acute bisectrix is *a*. 2V = 58°50′ Na, r > v. N_Y = 1.4692. Ref: 118.

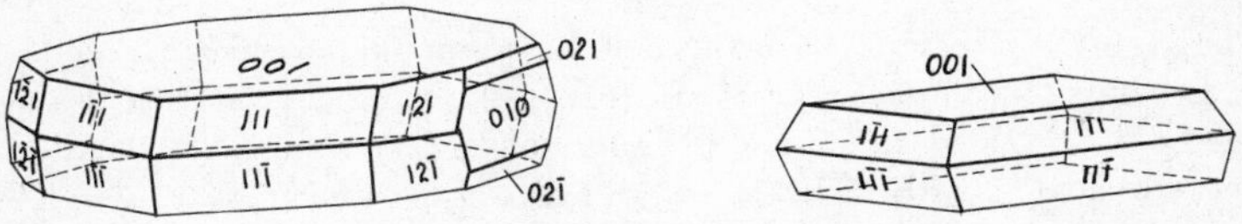

Figs. 104, 105. Pulvinic acid ethyl alcoholate.

2-(Carboxyphenylmethylene)tetrahydro-3,5-diketo-4-phenylfuran ethyl alcoholate or 4.5-dihydro-3,5-diketo-α,4-diphenyl-$\Delta^{2(3)}$-furanacetic acid ethyl alcoholate or pulvinic acid ethyl alcoholate [$C_6H_5C(CO_2H):C \cdot O \cdot COCH(C_6H_5)CO \cdot C_2H_5OH$] is orthorhombic with *a*:*b*:*c* = 0.756:1:1.717. Crystals {001} tablets with {111}, {010}, {121}, etc. Figs. 104, 105. Perfect 001, distinct 010, and imperfect 100 cleavages. Y = *a*; a bisectrix is parallel with *b*. 2V = 61°6′ Na. N_Y = 1.6578 Na. Color yellow with *a* and *c* = lively yellow, *b* = pale greenish yellow. Ref: 119.

2-(Carbomethoxyphenylmethylene)tetrahydro-3,5-diketo-4-phenylfuran or methyl 4,5-dihydro-3,5-diketo-α,4-diphenyl-$\Delta^{2(3)}$-furanacetate or methyl pulvinate or vulpinic acid [$C_6H_5C(CO_2CH_3):C \cdot O \cdot COCH(C_6H_5)CO$] is monoclinic with *a*:*b*:*c* = 3.521:1:1.994, β = 110°43′. Crystals equant or prismatic or {100} tablets with {110}, {100}, {$\bar{1}$01}, {001}, etc. Figs. 106, 107. Perfect 001 cleavage.

M.P.148°. Y = *b*; X near *c*; extinction in 110 at 17°20′ to *c*. (–)2V = ?. N_X = 1.5178 Na, N_Y = ?, N_Z = 1.8564, $N_Z - N_X$ = 0.2386 Na. Color dark yellow with weak pleochroism. Ref: 119.

Tetrahydro-5-keto-2,3-furandicarboxylic acid or lactoisocitric acid [$O \cdot CH(CO_2H)CH(CO_2H)CH_2CO$] forms irregular fragments which melt at 160 – 161°. (+)2V = 80° *ca.* calc. N_X = 1.487, N_Y = 1.505, N_Z = 1.600, all ± .003, $N_Z - N_X$ = 0.113. Ref: 189.

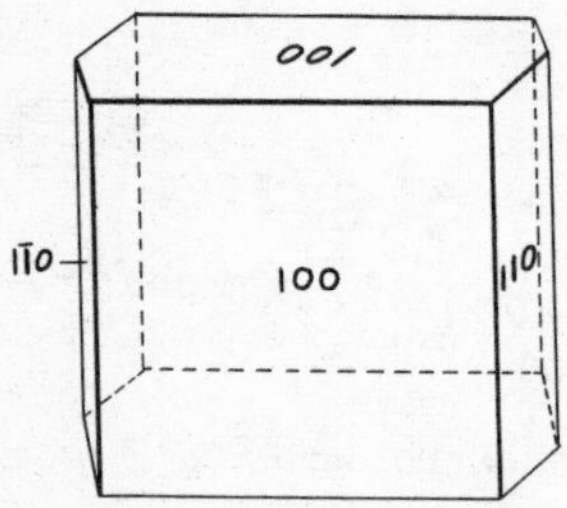

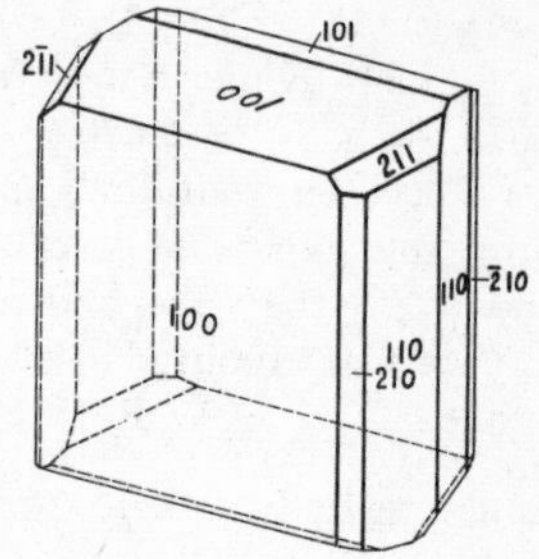

Figs. 106, 107. Vulpinic acid.

3-Hydroxy-4-keto-1,4-pyran-2,6-dicarboxylic acid trihydrate or *β*-hydroxy-pyrone-*α*,*α*′-dicarboxylic acid trihydrate or meconic acid trihydrate [$O \cdot C(CO_2H):C(OH)COCH:C(CO_2H) \cdot 3H_2O$] is orthorhombic pyramidal with *a*:*b*:*c* = 0.613:1:0.900. Crystals {100} plates with {110}, {010}, {011}, etc. Perfect 001 cleavage. X = *c*; Y = *b*. (–)2E = 48°55′ Na. Birefringence very strong. Bolland gives for "meconic acid" (with $3H_2O$?) N_1 = 1.39, N_2 = 1.665, $N_2 - N_1$ = 0.275, with parallel extinction and negative elongation. Gaubert gives N_X = 1.45 *ca.* and $N_Z - N_X$ > 0.30. Ref: 34, 35, 100, 119.

4-Cyano-3-ethyl-2,4-dihydroxy-2-methylpentanoic 1,4-lactone or 2-cyano-3-ethyltetrahydro-4-hydroxy-5-keto-2,4-dimethylfuran or *γ*-cyano-*β*-ethyl-*α*-hydroxy-*α*-methyl-*γ*-valerolactone or *γ*-cyano-*β*-ethyl-*α*-hydroxy-*α*,*γ*-dimethylbutyrolactone [$O \cdot C(CH_3)(CN)CH(C_2H_5)C(OH)(CH_3)CO$] is orthorhombic with *a*:*b*:*c* = 0.876:1:0.810. Crystals thick columnar with {100}, {010}, {001}, {011}, {210}. Perfect 100 and 001 cleavages. M.P. 109°. Y = *c*. The acute bisectrix is *b*. 2V = 50°33′. N_Y = 1.4780 Na. Ref: 117;

2-Acetoxy-2-(carboxymethyl)butanedioic anhydride, or acetate of anhydrocitric acid or citric acid 1,2-anhydride acetate [$CH_2(CO_2H)C(O_2CCH_3)CO \cdot O \cdot COCH_2$] is orthorhombic with *a*:*b*:*c* = 0.686:1:1.002. Crystals prismatic with {010}, {110}, {001}, etc. Perfect 001 and distinct 010 cleavages. M.P. 121°. X=*c*. Y = *a*. (–)2V = 71°2′, dispersion very weak. N_Y = 1.4920 Na. Ref: 117.

N′-Phenyl-N′-(2-thenylmethyl)-N-dimethylethylenediamine hydrochloride or diatrin hydrochloride ($C_{15}H_{20}N_2S \cdot HCl$) forms irregular crystals often showing an optic axis. M.P. 186 – 187°. (–)2V = 85° calc. $N_X = 1.604$, $N_Y = 1.675$, $N_Z = 1.733$, $N_Z - N_X = 0.129$. Colorless. Ref: 477b.

3-Di-(*n*-butyl)aminomethyl-4,5,6-trihydroxyphenylphthalide hydrochloride or anthallan hydrochloride [$(C_4H_9)_2NCH_2C_8H_5O_5 \cdot HCl$] forms rods and fragments. M.P. 80°. X || elongation. (–)2V = 65° calc. $N_X = 1.505$, $N_Y = 1.585$, $N_Z = 1.617$, $N_Z - N_X = 0.112$. Ref: 477d.

2. Compounds with two Oxygen Atoms in the Cycle

Class 1. Compounds with no Functional Groups

Phenoxselenine {$SeO(C_6H_4)_2$} is orthorhombic with $a:b:c$ = ?:1:2.579. Crystals prismatic. D 1.70. X = *c*, Y = *a*. (+)2V = 81°, $N_X = 1.66$, $N_Y = 1.74$, $N_Z = 1.87$, $N_Z - N_X = 0.21$. Ref: 568a.

Class 2. Hydroxy Compounds

2,5-Dimethoxy-2,5-dimethyl-1,4-dioxane or *bis*-methoxyacetol [$CH_2O \cdot C(CH_3)(OCH_3)CH_2 \cdot O \cdot C(CH_3)(OCH_3)$] is monoclinic with $a:b:c$ = 1.773:1:2.009., β = 95°47′. Crystals {001} tablets with {100}, {111}, etc. Common twinning on 001 (?). No distinct cleavage. M.P. 127°. The optic plane is normal to 010; r > v. $N_Y = 1.55$ *ca.* Ref: 117.

1-Allyl-2,5-dimethoxy-3,4-methylenedioxybenzene or 4,7-dimethoxy-5-(2-propenyl)-1,3-benzodioxole or apiole [$O \cdot CH_2O \cdot C_6H(OCH_3)_2CH_2CH:CH_2$] is biaxial with D 1.015, M.P. 29.5°. $N_X = 1.583$, $N_Y = 1.73$, N_Z = ?. Ref: 152.

Class 3. Carbonyl Compounds

3,4-Methylenedioxybenzaldehyde semicarbazone or 5-formyl-1,3-benzodioxole semicarbazone or piperonal semicarbazone or heliotropin semicarbazone [$O \cdot CH_2 \cdot O \cdot C_6H_3CH:NNHCONH_2$] melts at 234°. It is biaxial (?) with $N_X = 1.580$, N_Y = ?, $N_Z = 1.725$, $N_Z - N_X = 0.145$. Ref: 378.

Xanthotoxin ($C_{12}H_8O_4$) is dimorphous. One phase (I) (from ethyl or benzyl alcohol) is orthorhombic with $a:b:c$ = 0.818:1:0.307. *a* 12.95, *b* 15.83, *c* 4.86 Å. U.C. 4. Crystals rods or needles along *c*. Excellent 010 and 100 cleavages. D 1.45. M.P. 148°. X = *a*; Y = *c*. (–)2V = 43°, r > v strong. $N_X = 1.698$, $N_Y = 1.734$, $N_Z = 1.742$, $N_Z - N_X = 0.044$. Ref: 535b.

2,7-Dioxaspiro [4.4] nonane-1,6-dione or *bis*(2-hydroxyethyl)malonic acid
dilactone or *bis-γ*-butyrolactone-α,α spiran $[CH_2CH_2 \cdot O \cdot COCCO \cdot O \cdot CH_2CH_2]$
is rhombohedral with $c/a = 2.092$. Crystals {0001} tablets with {$10\overline{1}1$}. No
distinct cleavage. D 1.54. M.P. 109 – 110°. Uniaxial positive with $N_O = 1.552$,
$N_E = 1.588$, $N_E - N_O = 0.036$.   Ref: 27.

3,8-Dimethyl-2,7-dioxaspiro [4.4] nonane-1,6-dione or *bis*(2-hydroxypropyl)-
malonic acid dilactone or *bis-γ*-valerolactone-α,α-spiran $[CH_2CH(CH_3) \cdot O \cdot COCCO$
$\cdot O \cdot CH(CH_3)CH_2]$ is tetragonal with $c/a = 1.71$. Crystals equant or {001}
tablets with {101}, {201}, etc. Imperfect 100 cleavage. D 1.32. M.P. 105 - 106°.
Uniaxial positive with $N_O = 1.494$, $N_E = 1.571$, $N_E - N_O = 0.077$. Also biaxial
with an angle in oil ($N = 1.494$) of 8° to 15°, in basal plates showing twinning.
                                                                     Ref: 27.

2,3,4,5-Tetrahydroxy-2-methylhexanedioic acid 1,4,3,6-dilactone or α-methyltetrahydroxyadipic acid I dilactone $[O \cdot COCH(OH)CHCHC(OH)(CH_3)CO \cdot O]$ is
orthorhombic probably disphenoidal with $a:b:c = 0.642:1:1.259$. Crystals {001}
tablets with {101}, {011}, {110}, etc.; also acicular along *a*. Imperfect 001
cleavage. M.P. 195 – 196°. $X = b$; $Y = a$. $(-)2V = 11°$ Na, r > v very strong.
$N_X = 1.511$ Na, $N_Y = 1.536$, $N_Z = 1.536$, $N_Z - N_X = 0.025$.   Ref: 263.

2,3,4,5-Tetrahydroxy-2-methylhexanedioic acid 1,4,3,6-dilactone hemihydrate
or α-methyltetrahydroxyadipic acid II dilactone hemihydrate $[O \cdot COCH$
$(OH)CHCHC(CH_3)(OH)CO \cdot O \cdot O.5H_2O]$ is tetragonal,   probably pyramidal,
with $c/a = 2.214$. Crystals thick {001} tablets with {111}, {221}, etc. M.P. 166 –
167°. Uniaxial negative with $N_O = 1.547$ Na, $N_E = 1.502$, $N_O - N_E = 0.045$.
                                                                     Ref: 263.

2,3,5,6-Diacetone-*D,L*-
galactitol or α-diacetone-
dulcitol forms brilliant

$$\left[\begin{array}{cccc} O \cdot C(CH_3)_2 - O & & O \cdot C(CH_3)_2 \cdot O & \\ | & | & | & | \\ H_2C \!\!-\!\!-\!\!-\!\! HC \cdot CHCH\!\!-\!\!C\!\!-\!\!-\!\!-\!\! HC \cdot CH_2OH \end{array} \right]$$

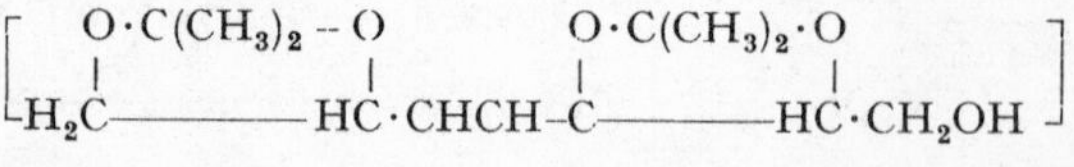

prisms which melt at 138 – 140°. $(+)2V = 40°$ *ca.* calc. $N_X = 1.503$, $N_Y =$
1.507, $N_Z - 1.538$, $N_Z - N_X = 0.035$.   Ref: 125a.

2,3,4,5 - Diacetonedulcitol
or β-diacetonedulcitol forms
long prisms which melt at

$$\left[\begin{array}{ccc} O \cdot C(CH_3)_2 - O & O \cdot C(CH_3)_2 - O & \\ | & | & | & | \\ H_2COH - CH & HC - CH & HC \cdot CH_2OH \end{array} \right]$$

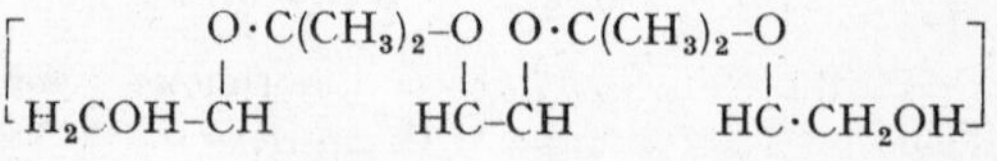

111°. $(-)2V = 30°$ *ca.* $N_X = 1.478$, $N_Y = 1.510$, $N_Z = 1.518$, $N_Z - N_X = 0.040$.
                                                                     Ref: 125a.

6. Compounds with six Oxygen Atoms in the Cycle

Class 1. Compounds with no Functional Group

Triacetrone-*D*-mannitol $[C_6H_8O_6(C_3H_6)_3]$ is monoclinic sphenoidal with $a:b:c = 2.830:1:1.731$, $\beta = 102°47'$. Crystals elongated along b with {001}, {101}, {100}, {10$\bar{1}$}, {110}. Perfect 001 cleavage. M.P. 70°. X = b; Z $\wedge$ c = - 26.9°. (+)2V = 76°42′ Li, 77°4′ Na, 77°24′ Tl. N_Y = 1.4987 Li, 1.4998 Na, 1.5017 Tl. Ref: 117.

9. Compounds with one Nitrogen Atom in the Cycle

Class 1. Compounds Containing no Functional Group

Coniine hydrochloride or 2-propylpiperidine hydrochloride $(C_8H_{17}N \cdot HCl)$ is orthorhombic disphenoidal with $a:b:c = 0.866:1:0.411$. M.P. 220°. The optic plane is 100 for red and 001 for green. 2E = 25.5° at 680, 10.5° at 620, 0° at 616, 16° at 600 and 25.5° at 580. No indices measured. Ref: 504.

Quinuclidinium hydrochloride $(C_7H_{13}N \cdot HCl)$ is monoclinic (or orthorhombic ?). Crystals rhombic {001} platelets. (+)2V = 50°, N_X = 1.5640, N_Y = 1.5686, N_Z = 1.5902, $N_Z - N_X$ = 0.0262. Ref: 411a.

Quinuclidium hydrobromide $(C_7H_{13}N \cdot HBr)$ is tetragonal with a = 9.52 and c = 9.57 Å. U.C. 4. Crystals {001} plates. Uniaxial positive with N_O = 1.5680 N_E = 1.5890, $N_E - N_O$ = 0.021. Ref: 411a.

Azine or Pyridine Salts

Pyridine nitrate $(C_5H_5N \cdot HNO_3)$ has parallel extinction and negative elongation with N_1 = 1.47, N_2 = 1.68, $N_2 - N_1$ = 0.21. Ref: 34, 35.

Pyridinium sulfamate $[C_5H_5N \cdot H_2NSO_3H]$ is probably monoclinic. Crystals are elongated plates and prisms. M.P. 117°. A section normal to X shows Z parallel with the elongation and one normal to Z has X $\wedge$ elongation = 28° ± 3°. Therefore, probably, Z = b and X $\wedge$ c = 28°. (-)2V = 49°, N_X = 1.487, N_Y = 1.630, N_Z = 1.665, $N_Z - N_X$ = 0.178 (for λ = 5461). Ref: 556a.

Pyridine citrate $(C_5H_5N \cdot C_6H_8O_7)$ has parallel extinction and negative elongation with N_1 = 1.545, N_2 = 1.62, $N_2 - N_1$ = 0.075. Ref: 34, 35.

Amminopyridinonitrochloroplatinum $(NH_3NO_2C_5H_5NPtCl)$ forms a yellow powder. X $\wedge$ elongation = 17°. N_X = 1.595, N_Y = 1.740, $N_Z \geqslant$ 1.780, $N_Z - N_X \geqslant$ 0.185, ∴ (-)2V = 55° *ca.* Ref: 418aa.

trans-Pyridinoamminodinitroplatinum $[C_5H_5NNH_3Pt(NO_2)_2]$ forms long white crystals with parallel extinction. (-)2V = 78°, N_X = 1.624, N_Y = 1.696, N_Z = 1.750, $N_Z - N_X$ = 0.126. Ref: 418aa.

cis-Pyridenebutylenedichloroplatinum $(C_4H_8C_5H_5NPtCl_2)$ is biaxial with (-)2V=78°, N_X=1.700, N_Y = 1.756, N_Z=1.80, $N_Z - N_X$=0.100. Ref: 418aa.

cis-Pyridineethylenedichloroplatinum ($C_5H_5NC_2H_4PtCl_2$) is probably orthorhombic, having parallel extinction. Crystals are greenish yellow needles. (+)2V = 28°, $N_X = 1.682$, $N_Y = 1.704$, $N_Z = 1.97$, $N_Z - N_X = 0.288$. Ref: 418aa.

trans-Pyrideneethylenedichloroplatinum ($C_5H_5NC_2H_4PtCl_2$) is probably orthorhombic having parallel extinction. Crystals are light yellow needles. $N_X = 1.608$, N_Y = ?, $N_Z = 1.785$, $N_Z - N_X = 0.177$. Ref: 418aa.

Tribromocarbonylplatinum pyridinium monohydrate ($C_5H_5NHPtCOBr_3 \cdot H_2O$) is tetragonal with $c/a = 0.914$. Crystals are orange needles. Uniaxial negative with $N_O > 1.785$, $N_E = 1.580$, $N_O - N_E > 0.205$. Apparently isomorphous with platinum trichlorocarbonylpyridinium monohydrate. Ref: 418aa.

cis-Di(monochloropyridene)dichloroplatinum [$(C_5H_4ClN)_2PtCl_2$] is orthorhombic with common twinning of platelets. $N_X = 1.661$, $N_Y = 1.706$, $N_Z > 1.82$, $N_Z - N_X > 0.16$, ∴ (+)2V < 65°. Ref: 418aa.

cis-Difluoropyridinodichloroplatinum [$(FC_5H_4N)_2PtCl_2$] forms a dendritic powder with inclined extinction. (-)2V = 50°, $N_X = 1.652$, $N_Y = 1.716$, $N_Z = 1.734$, $N_Z - N_X = 0.082$. Color yellow. Ref: 418aa.

trans-Dipyridinodichloroplatinum [$(C_5H_5N)_2PtCl_2$] forms yellow dendrites. $N_X = 1.578$, $N_Y = 1.770$, $N_Z > 1.780$, $N_Z - N_X > 0.202$. ∴ probably (-)2V > 20°. Ref: 418aa.

cis-Dipyridinodichloroplatinum [$(C_5H_5N)_2PtCl_2$] forms yellow dendrites with $N_1 = 1.620$, $N_2 = 1.780$, $N_2 - N_1 = 0.160$. Ref: 418aa.

Pyridine picrate [$C_5NH_5OC_6H_2(NO_2)_3$] has two phases. Both are monoclinic. One (I) has M.P. = 167 - 168°. X = *b*. Crossed dispersion such that if Z is taken as 0° at 6908, it is at 5° for 5780, 9° for 5461, 20° for 5086, 30° for 4916 and 45° for 4695. Axial dispersion: (-)2H = 69.5° (6908), 65.5° (5780), 64° (5461), 62° (minimum at 5086), 64.5° (4916), 71° (4800). For $\lambda = 5461$; (-)2V = 50°, $N_X = 1.549$, $N_Y = 1.893$, $N_Z = 1.997$, $N_Z - N_X = 0.448$. The other phase has X = *b*, (-)2H = 74.5° (6908), 75° (5780), 76° (5461), 74.5° (4800). It also has crossed dispersion - if Z is taken as 0° at 6908 it is at 1° at 5780, 2° at 5461, and 5° at 4916. Indices not reported. Ref: 557.

Pyridinebetaine monohydrate ($C_5H_5\overline{NCH_2CO \cdot O} \cdot H_2O$) is monoclinic with $a:b:c = 0.993:1:0.794$, $\beta = 92°32.5'$. Crystals {10$\bar{1}$} tablets with {110} and {101} or pseudo-octahedral with the same forms. X ∧ *c* = - 12°45'; Y = *b*. (-)2V = 25°58' Li, 25°16' Na, 24°30' Tl. $N_X = 1.5233$ Na, $N_Y = 1.6385$, $N_Z = 1.6450$, $N_Z - N_X = 0.1217$ Na. Ref: 119.

Pyridinebetaine hydrochloride [$C_5H_5N(Cl) \cdot CH_2CO_2H$] is monoclinic with $a:b:c = 1.128:1:0.893$, $\beta = 107°18.5'$. Crystals {001} tablets with {111}, {11$\bar{1}$}, etc., or with {120}, {111}, {11$\bar{1}$}, {100}. {110}. Perfect 100 cleavage. X = *b*; Z ∧ *c* = + 9°27'. (+)2V = 52°3', r < v. $N_X = 1.5290$ Na, $N_Y = 1.5568$, $N_Z = 1.6925$, $N_Z - N_X = 0.1635$ Na. Ref: 119.

Dipyridinebetaine hydrochloride monohydrate $[(C_5H_5N \cdot C_2H_2O_2)_2 \cdot HCl \cdot H_2O]$ is orthorhombic with $a:b:c = 0.839:1:0.650$. Crystals show {100}, {110}, {130}, {103}, {012}. Imperfect 100 cleavage. $Y = c$; $Z = a$. $(+)2V = 83°52'$ Na, $r < v$ weak. $N_X = 1.5374$ Na, $N_Y = 1.6083$, $N_Z = 1.7115$, $N_Z - N_X = 0.1741$ Na. Ref: 119.

Dipyridinebetaine hydrobromide monohydrate $[(C_5H_5N \cdot C_2H_2O_2)_2 \cdot HBr \cdot H_2O]$ is orthorhombic with $a:b:c = 0.843:1:0.658$. Crystals show {100}, {130}, {110}, {103}, {012}. Imperfect 100 cleavage. $Y = c$; $Z = b$. $(+)2V = 87°30'$, weak dispersion. $N_X = 1.5404$ Na, $N_Y = 1.6177$, $N_Z = 1.7171$, $N_Z - N_X = 0.1767$ Na. Ref: 119.

Chromium chloride dipyridine hydrochloride complex $\{Cr(C_5H_5N)_2 \cdot (HCl)_2 Cl_3 \cdot 8H_2O\}$ is monoclinic in needles with prismatic cleavage. Extinction angle $(X \wedge c)$ in needles varies from 0° to 30°. $(-)2V = 40°$ calc. $N_X = 1.550$, $N_Y = 1.720$, $N_Z = 1.740$, (all $\pm$ 0.003), $N_Z - N_X = 0.190$. Clearly pleochroic with X = very faint yellow gray, Y = green gray, Z = pinkish. Ref: 377a.

Chromium chloride dipyridine hydrobromide complex $\{Cr(C_5H_5N)_2 \cdot (HBr)_2 Cl_3 \cdot 8H_2O\}$ is tetragonal in needles with prismatic cleavage. Parallel extinction and negative elongation. Uniaxial negative with $N_O = 1.700$, $N_E = 1.575$ (both $\pm$ 0.003). $N_O - N_E = 0.125$. Clearly pleochroic with O = greenish to brown, E = pink to reddish and O > E. Ref: 377a.

Chromium chloride diquinoline hydrochloride complex $\{Cr(C_9H_7N)_2 \cdot (HCl)_2 Cl_3 \cdot 8H_2O\}$ is orthorhombic in needles or plates with longitudinal pinacoidal cleavage. Parallel extinction and positive elongation. $(-)2V = 40°$ calc. $N_Z = 1.537$, $N_Y = 1.710$, $N_X = 1.737$ (all $\pm$ 0.003), $N_Z - N_X = 0.200$. Color greenish with X = colorless (yellow tint), Y = light green to greenish yellow, Z = green to light green. Ref: 377a.

Chromium chloride diquinoline hydrobromide complex $\{Cr(C_9H_7N)_2 \cdot (HBr)_2 Cl_3 \cdot 8H_2O\}$ is tetragonal in plates and prisms with prismatic cleavage. Parallel extinction. Strongly pleochroic with O = dark green, E = light green. Uniaxial negative with $N_O = 1.647$, $N_E = 1.600$, $N_O - N_E = 0.047$. Ref: 377a.

Chromium chloride tetraquinoline hydrochloride complex $\{Cr(C_9H_7N)_2 \cdot (HCl)_2Cl_3 \cdot 8H_2O\}$ is monoclinic in thick prisms with poor longitudinal cleavage. $X \wedge c = 3°$. $(-)2V$ = large. $N_X = 1.540$, $N_Y = 1.700$, $N_Z = 1.735$ (all $\neq$ 0.003) $N_Z - N_X = 0.195$, $\therefore$ $(-)2V = 50°$ calc. Pale green with X = yellowish to colorless, Y and Z = yellow green to green. Ref: 377a.

1,3,3-Trimethyl-2-methyleneindoline hydriodide $[C_6H_4N(CH_3)C(:CH_2)C(CH_3)_2 \cdot HI]$ is orthorhombic with $a:b:c = 0.738:1:0.441$. Crystals prismatic with {120}, {111}, {110}, etc. Distinct 010 cleavage. M.P. 253°. $X = b$; $Y = c$. $(-)2E = 57°16'$ red, $64°12'$ green. $(-)2V = 23°48'$ red. $N_X = 1.567$ calc., $N_Y = 1.6483$, $N_Z = 1.6526$ red, $N_Z - N_X = 0.086$ calc. Ref: 119.

Quinoline-hydroquinone $\{(C_9H_7N)_2 \cdot nC_6H_6O_2\}$ has parallel extinction and negative elongation with $N_1 = 1.555$, $N_2 > 1.95$, $N_2 - N_1 > 0.395$. Ref: 34, 35.

Quinaldiniodoethylate ($C_6H_4C_3H_4CH_3NC_2H_5I$) is monoclinic sphenoidal with $a:b:c = 0.652:1:0.45$, $\beta = 94°44'$. Space group $P2/m$; a 10.3, b 16.0, c 7.21 Å. Crystals acicular with good 001 cleavage. D 1.66. Y = b; Z ∧ c = − 78°. (−)2V = 66.5°, r < v strong. N_Y slightly greater than 1.785, $N_Z - N_X$ = "strong". Pleochroic with X = clear greenish yellow, Y = dark brownish yellow, Z = distinct brownish yellow. Ref: 559.

α,α′- or 2,2′-Dipyridyl or 2,2′-bipyridine ($C_{10}H_8N_2$) is monoclinic prismatic. M.P. 69.5°. The optic plane is 010 for red and normal thereto for violet (Z = b). Y nearly parallel to elongation in red. (−)2H = 38° (3650), 0° (4150), 20° (4358), 44° (5780), 50° (6908). $N_X = 1.63$, $N_Y = 1.77$, $N_Z = 1.79$ (all ± .02) for 5461, $N_Z - N_X = 0.16$. Ref: 39a.

1-Piperidine-3,4-diphenylbutene-3 hydrochloride [$C_5H_{11}NC_{16}H_{15} \cdot HCl$] forms plates with a pearly luster. M.P. 240 − 244°. (+)2V = 72° calc. $N_X = 1.620$, $N_Y = 1.636$, $N_Z = 1.667$, $N_Z - N_X = 0.047$. Ref: 477d.

Carbazole or dibenzopyrrole ($C_6H_4N:C_6H_4$) melts at 244.8°. It has $N_1 = 1.60$, $N_2 = 1.75$, $N_2 - N_1 = 0.15$. Ref: 34, 35.

1(10-Acridyl)-dimethylaminoethane hydrochloride [$(CH_3)_2NC_2H_4C_{13}H_9N$] forms brownish thin plates with X ∥ elongation. M.P. 207°. $N_X = 1.617$, N_Y perhaps $= 1.636$, $N_Z > 1.733$, $N_Z - N_X > 0.116$. (If $N_Y = 1.636$, (+)2V < 45°). Ref: 477d.

9-Phenylacridine sulfate or 9-phenyl-2,3,5,6-dibenzopyridine acid sulfate [$C_6H_4 \cdot N \cdot C_6H_4 \cdot C \cdot C_6H_5 \cdot H_2SO_4$] has two phases; one (I) is monoclinic with $a:b:c = 2.398:1:2.141$, $\beta = 98°5'$. Crystals show {100}, {110}, {001}, etc. Perfect 100 and distinct 001 and 010 cleavages. D 1.43. Y = b; Z ∧ c = − 78.5° Na. (+)2V = 67° Na. $N_X = 1.70$ Na, $N_Y = 1.73$, $N_Z = 1.78$, $N_Z - N_X = 0.08$. N_Y and 2V have a maximum (1.80 for N_Y) at $\lambda = 492$. Color red; thin plates yellow with distinct pleochroism. The other phase (II) is triclinic with $a:b:c = 0.907:1:0.739$, $\alpha = 118°10'$, $\beta = 114°32'$, $\gamma = 59°42'$. Crystals show {010} (dominant), {100}, {001}, etc. Distinct 110 cleavage. D 1.45. An optic axis is nearly normal to 110. The optic angle shows a minimum for $\lambda = 501$. Dispersion of the optic plane is extremely strong, giving a variation of about 60° in the extinction position in 110 with one extreme position for $\lambda = 501$. Also extreme dispersion of the bisectrices. {010} plates show a diagonal division into four sectors, of which those on 100 are green and those on 001 are red. (−)2V = 42° Na. $N_X = 1.16$ calc. Na, $N_Y = 1.72$, $N_Z = 1.80$, $N_Z - N_X = 0.64$ calc. (These calculated values are improbable – A.N.W.). Color green. Ref: 119.

Class 2. Hydroxy Compounds

4-Benzoxy-2,2,6-trimethylpiperidine hydrochloride or 2,2,6-trimethyl-4-piperidol benzoate hydrochloride or β-eucaine hydrochloride [$C_6H_5CO_2CHCH_2CH(CH_3)NHC(CH_3)_2CH_2 \cdot HCl$] forms spherulitic masses or rectangular crystals. M.P. 268° with decomposition. Good cleavage normal to elongation. X parallel to elongation. (–)2V = 28°, N_X = 1.506, N_Y = 1.585, N_Z = 1.645. $N_Z - N_X$ = 0.139. (2V and indices are inconsistent – 2V probably greater – A.N.W.). Colorless. Ref: 123, 239, 518.

Pseudotropine ($C_8H_{15}ON$) is orthorhombic with *a*:*b*:*c* = 0.888:1:0.760, *a* 9.36, *b* 10.55, *c* 8.02 Å. U.C. 4. Crystals equant, prismatic or acicular. Excellent 110, good 100 and poor 010 cleavages. D 1.18. M.P. 118°. X = *a*, Y = *c*. (± ?)2V = 90° calc., Dispersion over X: r > v. N_X = 1.549, N_Y = 1.566, N_Z = 1.583, $N_Z - N_X$ = 0.034. Ref: 435a.

Eucatropine hydrochloride ($C_{17}H_{25}O_3N \cdot HCl$) is soluble in water. M.P. 183 – 184° C. N_1 = 1.560, N_2 = 1.610, $N_2 - N_1$ = 0.050. Colorless. Ref: 518.

5-Hydroxy-6-methyl-3,4-pyridinedicarbinol hydrochloride or pyridoxin hydrochloride or vitamin B_6 hydrochloride or vitamin H hydrochloride ($C_8H_{11}O_3N \cdot HCl$) is triclinic. Crystals equant with {100}, {001}, {010}, {110}, {101} and {111}. M.P. = 210°. D 1.434. (–)2V = 33°, N_X = 1.480, N_Y = 1.706, N_Z = 1.734, $N_Z - N_X$ = 0.254. Ref: 436b.

Class 3. Carbonyl Compounds

∈-Caprolactam or cyclohexanonisoxime ($C_6H_{11}ON$) is monoclinic; crystals are acicular and radial aggregates of plates. M.P. 68°. Plates normal to Z have X parallel with elongation. (+)2V = 86°, r > v, with horizontal dispersion; ∴ X = *b*. N_X = 1.497, N_Y = 1.534, N_Z = 1.585, $N_Z - N_X$ = 0.088 (for λ = 5641). Ref: 556a.

2-Ketotetrahydroquinoline or 3,4-dihydro-2(1)-quinolone or hydrocarbostyril ($C_6H_4NHCOCH_2CH_2$) is orthorhombic with *a*:*b*:*c* = 0.598:1:0.604. Crystals prismatic with {110}, {011}, {001}. Perfect 001 cleavage. M.P. 163°. X = *c*; Y = *a*. (–)2V = 60° *ca.* N_X = 1.4792 Na, 1.4821 Tl; N_Y = 1.7095 Na; N_Z = 1.8102 Na, 1.8258 Tl, $N_Z - N_X$ = 0.3310 Na. Ref: 119.

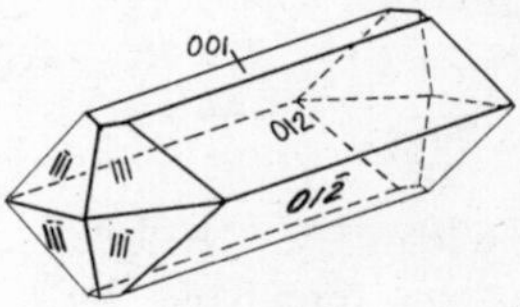

Fig. 108.
7-Isopropylhydrocarbosteril.

2,3-Dihydro-2-keto-3,3-dimethylindole or 2-keto-3,3-dimethylindoline or 3,3-dimethyloxindole [$C_6H_4NHCOC(CH_3)_2$] is orthorhombic with *a*:*b*:*c* = 0.852:1:0.721. Crystals prismatic or brachydomatic with {110}, {011}, {100}, {010}. Perfect 100 and 010 and imperfect 001 cleavages. M.P. 152 – 153°. X = *a*; Y = *c*. (–)2V = 46°3′ red, 46°39′ yellow, 47°22′ blue. N_Y = 1.652 red, 1.657 yellow, 1.677 blue; $N_Z - N_X$ = strong. Ref: 119.

1,2,3,4-Tetrahydro-7-isopropyl-2-ketoquinoline or 7-isopropylhydrocarbostyril [$(CH_3)_2CHC_6H_3NHCOCH_2CH_2$] is orthorhombic with *a*:*b*:*c* = 0.880:1:1.645. Crystals {001} tablets or brachydomatic with {012}, {111}, {001}. Fig. 108. M.P. 134°. The optic plane is 010; the acute bisectrix is *a*. 2V = 63°16.5′ Li, 64°51′ Na. N_Y = 1.6204 Na. Ref: 119.

2,3-Dihydro-2-keto-3,3,5-triphenyl-1-propylpyrrole or 3,5,5-triphenyl-1-pro-pyl-2(3)-pyrrolone [(C$_3$H$_7$)NC(C$_6$H$_5$):CHC(C$_6$H$_5$)$_2$CO] is orthorhombic (α-phase, I) with $a:b:c = 0.649:1:0.765$. Crystals short prisms with {110}, {011}, {012}, {010}, {101}, etc. Perfect 011 cleavage. M.P. 104 – 105°. Y $= a$; Z $= c$. (+)2V $= 68°50'$, r > v weak. N$_Y$ = 1.6377 Na. The β-phase (II) is monoclinic with the optic plane and Z normal to 010; X ∧ ⊥ 100 $= 10°$ ca. (–)2E $= 76°25'$ Na, r > v strong.   Ref: 119.

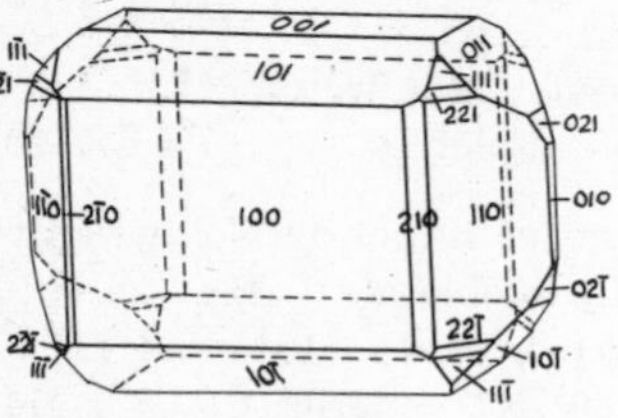

Fig. 109.
Bromomethyltriphenylpyrrolone.

?-Bromo-2,3-dihydro-2-keto-1-methyl-3,5,5-triphenylpyrrole or ?-bromo-1-methyl-3,5,5-triphenyl-2(3)-pyrrolone (C$_{23}$H$_{18}$ONBr) is monoclinic with $a:b:c = 1.655:1:1.043$, β $= 91°31'$. Crystals {100} tablets with {001}, {101}, {10$\bar{1}$}, {110}, {011}, etc. Fig. 109. Perfect 100 cleavage. M.P. 153°. X $= b$; Z nearly normal to 10$\bar{1}$. (+)2V $= 70°15'$, r < v weak. N$_Y$ = 1.5264 Na.   Ref: 119.

2-Methoxy-6-chloroacridone is monoclinic (?) with X parallel to elongation. Crystals usually show no centered interference figures. N$_X$ = 1.550, N$_Y$ > 1.732, N$_Z$ = ?, N$_Z$ – N$_X$ > 0.184.
$$\left[ClC_6H_3 \underset{NH}{\overset{CO}{<}} \! > C_6H_3OCH \right]$$
Ref: 526.

Tetrahydro-2,5-diketopyrrole or 2,5-pyrrolidinedione or butanimide or succinimide (CH$_2$CONHCOCH$_2$) is orthorhombic with $a:b:c = 0.781:1:1.328$. a 7.50, b 9.60, c 12.75 Å. U.C. 8. Crystals pyramidal. M.P. 125°. N$_1$ = 1.54, N$_2$ = 1.62, N$_2$ – N$_1$ = 0.08.   Ref: 34, 35, 117, 628.

Tetrahydro-1-iodo-2,5-diketopyrrole or N-iodobutanimide or N-iodosuccini-mide [CH$_2$CON(I)COCH$_2$] is tetragonal pyramidal with $c/a = 2.471$. Crystals prisms terminated by pyramids. Common twinning on 001. Rather distinct 102 cleavage. D 2.408. Uniaxial negative with N$_O$ = 1.6903 C, 1.6965 D, 1.7129 F; N$_E$ = 1.6652 C, 1.6726 D, 1.6909 F, N$_O$ – N$_E$ = 0.0239 D. Ref: 117, 335.

1-Ethyl-3,3,5-triphenyl-2(3)-pyrrolone {(C$_2$H$_5$)NCOC(C$_6$H$_5$)$_2$CH:C(C$_6$H$_5$)} has two phases. The monoclinic crystals have $a:b:c = 1.690:1:1.958$, β $= 93°6'$; they show {100}, {001}, {111}, {$\bar{1}$11}, etc.; nearly equant. Perfect 100 cleavage. M.P. 130°. The optic plane is 010 for part of the spectrum and normal thereto for the other part, the optic angle passing through 0° for $\lambda = 579$ at 20°, for $\lambda = 568$ at 30°. The dispersion of the optic axes is enormous, as in brookite. X ∧ ⊥ 100 $= 27°$ in the obtuse angle β. (–)2V $=$ small and rapidly varying with wave length and temperature. For $\lambda = 546$ at 25°: N$_X$ = 1.658, N$_Y$ = 1.712, N$_Z$ = 1.713, (all ± 0.003). N$_Z$ – N$_X$ = 0.055. The other phase is triclinic.   Ref: 37, 40.

2,3-Dihydro-2,3-diketoindole or 2,3-indoledione or isatin (C$_6$H$_4$NHCOCO) is monoclinic prismatic with $a:b:c = 0.425:1:0.502$, β $= 94°42'$. Space group

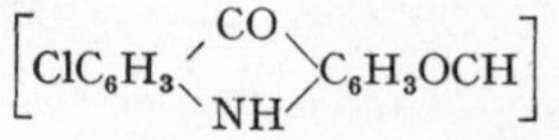

$P2_1/c$; a 6.19, b 14.55, c 7.19 Å. U.C. 4. Crystals {110} prisms with {010} ended by {011} or {10$\bar{2}$}. Good 10$\bar{2}$ cleavage. D 1.51. M.P. 200 - 201°. The optic plane is 010; X $\wedge$ c = + 63° (normal to 10$\bar{2}$). (-)2E = 100° *ca.* 2V = 50° calc. $N_X = 1.46 \pm .005$, $N_Y = 1.80 \pm .03$, $N_Z = 1.90 \pm .03$, $N_Z - N_X = 0.44$ Na. Color brownish red with orange-yellow and brownish-red colors seen in 010.
Ref: 61, 441.

α-1-Methylisatin {$C_6H_4N(CH_3)COCO$} is orthorhombic with[1] $a:b:c = 0.432:1:0.225$. a 13.62, b 31,51, c 7.09 Å. U.C. 16. D 1.40 (obs.); 1.41 (X-rays). X = c; Y = a. (-)2V = 45° calc. $N_X = 1.52$, $N_Y = 1.74$, $N_Z = 1.78$, all ± .01, $N_Z - N_X = 0.26$. Red and pleochroic. Ref: 61, 441.

β-1-Methylisatin {$C_6H_4N(CH_3)COCO$} is orthorhombic with[2] $a:b:c = 0.317:1:0.251$. a 10.60, b 33.45, c 8.39 Å. U.C. 16. Crystals {010} plates elongated along c with {100} and {101}. D 1.40 (obs.); 1.43 (X-rays). X = c; Y = a. (-)2V = 45° calc. $N_X = 1.56$, $N_Y = 1.71$, $N_Z = 1.74$, all ± .01, $N_Z - N_X = 0.18$. Yellow and pleochroic. Ref: 61, 441,.

o-Methylisatin {$C_6H_4N{:}C(OCH_3)CO$} is monoclinic prismatic with $a:b:c = 2.523:1:1.355$, $\beta = 101°$. Space group $P2_1/m$. a 15.99, b 6.14, c 8.32 Å. U.C. 4. Crystals columnar with {001}, {20$\bar{1}$}, and smaller {100} and {210}. D 1.37 (obs.); 1.38 (X-rays). X $\wedge$ c = 90° ±; Z = b. (+)2V = 85° calc. $N_X = 1.51 \pm .01$, $N_Y = 1.639 \pm .002$, $N_Z = 1.81 \pm .01$. $N_Z - N_X = 0.30$. Color red. Ref: 61.

N-Benzyl-2-hydroxylbutanimide or *N*-benzylmalimide {$C_6H_5CH_2NCOCH(OH)CH_2CO$} is orthorhombic with $a:b:c = 0.586:1:0.225$. Crystals prismatic with {110}, {120}, {011}. No distinct cleavage. M.P. 105°. X = c; Y = b. (-)2V = 62 - 66°. $N_X = 1.5163$ Na, 1.5219 Tl; $N_Y = 1.6121$ Na, 1.6181 Tl; $N_Z = 1.6338$ Na, 1.6588 Tl; $N_Z - N_X = 0.1175$ Na. Ref: 20, 118.

N′-(4-Fluorobenzyl)-N′-(2-pyridyl)-N,N-dimethylethylenediamine hydrochloride or *p*-fluorobenzyl D.P.E. hydrochloride [$(CH_3)_2NC_2H_4N(CH_2C_6H_4F)C_5H_4N \cdot HCl$] forms rods and plates, probably orthorhombic. M.P. 162°. (+)2E = large, $N_X = 1.585$, $N_Y = 1.600$, $N_Z = 1.668$, $N_Z - N_X = 0.083$. 2V = 50° calc.
Ref: 477d.

N′-(2-Pyridyl)-N-(3-phenyl)-N,N-dimethylethylenediamine hydrochloride or thenfanil hydrochloride [$(CH_3)_2NC_2H_4N(C_6H_5)(C_5H_4N) \cdot HCl$] forms square plates and prisms. M.P. 151°. 2V = large, $N_X = 1.590$, $N_Y = ?$, $N_Z = 1.680$, $N_Z - N_X = 0.90$. Ref: 477d.

Phthalimide {$C_6H_4(CO)_2NH$} is monoclinic prismatic in {100} laths with {110} {230}, etc. D 1.47. M.P. 233 - 235°. X $\wedge$ c = 74°; Z = b. (+)2V = 25° calc. $N_X = 1.501$, $N_Y = 1.519$, $N_Z = 1.755$, $N_Z - N_X = 0.254$. Found in burning coal heaps at Kladno, Bohemia. Ref: 586.

---

[1] *a b c* changed to *b c a* to make $b > a > c$.

[2] *a b c* changed to *b c a* to make $b > a > c$.

Class 4. Carboxylic Acids and Derivatives

l-Proline nitroindandionate ($C_{14}H_{14}O_6N_2$) is orthorhombic in thin rectangular plates with X || elongation. M.P. 228°. (+)2V = very large, r > v. $N_X = 1.524$, $N_Y = 1.678$, $N_Z > 1.870$, $N_Z - N_X > 0.346$. (From indices, 2V = 85° *ca.* – A.N.W.). Colorless. Ref: 539a.

l-Hydroxyproline nitroindandionate ($C_{14}H_{14}O_7N_2$) is orthorhombic; crystals prismatic with X || elongation. M.P. 241°. (+)2V = 85° calc., r < v. $N_X = 1.461$, $N_Y = 1.621$, $N_Z = 1.802$, $N_Z - N_X = 0.341$. Ref: 539a.

Derivatives of 2-Pyridinecarboxylic Acid or Picolinic Acid

α-Cupric picolinate $\{Cu(O_2CC_5H_4N)_2\}$ is triclinic in crystals like the dihydrate. M.P. 298°. $N_X \leqslant 1.54$, $N_Y = ?$, $N_Z \geqslant 1.76$, $N_Z - N_X \geqslant 0.22$. Color lavender blue. Ref: 63.

α-Cupric picolinate dihydrate $\{Cu(O_2CC_5H_4N)_2 \cdot 2H_2O\}$ is triclinic with $a:b:c = 0.726:1:0.474$, $\alpha = ?$, $\beta = ?$, $\gamma = 71°20'$. Space group $P\bar{1}$. *a* 7.80, *b* 10.75, *c* 5.10 Å. U.C. 1. Crystals thin six-sided plates. D 1.71. $N_X < 1.50$, $N_Y = ?$, $N_Z > 1.76$, $N_Z - N_X > 0.26$. Color blue. Ref: 63.

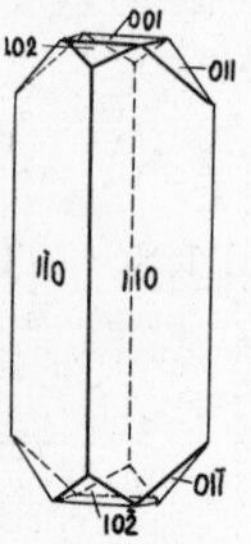

Fig. 110. Picolinic acid hydrochloride.

β-Cupric picolinate dihydrate $[Cu(O_2CC_5H_4N)_2 \cdot 2H_2O]$ is orthorhombic (?); acicular with parallel extinction and $N_X \leqslant 1.56$, $N_Y = ?$, $N_Z \geqslant 1.78$, $N_Z - N_X \geqslant 0.20$. Color blue. Ref: 63.

Argentic picolinate or silver picolinate $[Ag(O_2CC_5H_4N)_2]$ is triclinic and isomorphous with anhydrous α-cupric picolinate. Thin needles. $N_X \leqslant 1.50$, $N_Y = ?$, $N_Z \geqslant 1.76$, $N_Z - N_X \geqslant 0.26$. Ref: 63.

Picolinic acid hydrochloride or pyridinecarboxylic acid hydrochloride ($HO_2CC_5H_4N \cdot HCl$) is orthorhombic with $a:b:c = 0.562:1:0.962$. Crystals prismatic with {110}, {011}, {001}, etc. Fig. 110. Perfect 001 cleavage. X = *c*; Y = *b*. (–)2V = 40°56′ Li, 41°16′ Na, 41°54′ Tl. $N_X = 1.4438$ Li, 1.4482 Na, 1.4513 Tl; $N_Y = 1.6947$ Li, 1.7050 Na, 1.7131 Tl; $N_Z = 1.7411$ Li, 1.7540 Na, 1.7642 Tl; $N_Z - N_X = 0.3058$ Na. Ref: 119.

4-Phenyl-piperidine-4-carboxylic acid ethyl ester hydrochloride or ethyl-1-methyl-4-phenylpiperidine-4-carboxylatehydrochloride or demerol hydrochloride or N-phenylhexahydroisonicotinic acid ethyl ester hydrochloride or isonipecaine hydrochloride ($C_{12}H_{15}O_2N$ ethyl ester·HCl) forms six-sided elongated prisms with Z parallel to elongation. (+ ?)2V near 90° (calc.), $N_X = 1.545$, $N_Y = 1.581$, $N_Z = 1.618$, $N_Z - N_X = 0.073$. This compound in solution reacts with potassium iodide to form fine colorless rods with ± elongation and parallel to inclined extinction (∴ monoclinic with Y near *c*). (+)2V = 80° calc. $N_X = 1.605$, $N_Y = 1.625$, $N_Z = 1.653$, $N_Z - N_X = 0.048$. The same compound reacts with sodium nitroprusside $\{Na_2Fe(NO)(CN)_5\}$ to produce bladed crystals with a

shingle-like surface. The crystals have inclined extinction and negative elongation. (+ ?)2V near 90°, $N_X = 1.550$, $N_Y = 1.582$, $N_Z = 1.615$, $N_Z - N_X = 0.065$.
Ref: 521.

2-Phenyl-quinoline-4-carboxylic acid or phenylcinchoninic acid or cinchophen or atophan $\{C_6H_4 \cdot N:C(C_6H_5)CH:C(CO_2H)\}$ is dimorphous; one phase (I) is orthorhombic in needles and rectangular crystals. Insoluble in water; soluble in alkalies. M.P. 213°. Z || elongation. (+)2V < 45° calc., $N_X = 1.545$, $N_Y = 1.575$, $N_Z > 1.734$, $N_Z - N_X > 0.189$. Again: $N_X = 1.492$, $1.741 > N_Z > 1.730$. Another phase (II) is triclinic. M.P. 196 – 197°. $N_X = 1.545$, $N_Y = 1.590$, $N_Z = 1.630$, $N_Z - N_X = 0.085$; ∴ (–)2V = large. Color yellow.
Ref: 239, 343c, 524, 534, 617b.

4-Hydroxy-1,2,2,6,6-pentamethyl-4-piperidinecarboxylic acid or 4-hydroxy-1,2,2,6,6-pentamethylisonipecotic acid $\{HO_2CC(OH)CH_2C(CH_3)_2N(CH_3)C(CH_3)_2CH_2\}$ is orthorhombic with $a:b:c = 0.912:1:0.939$. Crystals show {111}, {110}, etc. Perfect 010 and distinct 001 cleavages. X = *b*; Y = *a*. (–)2V = 82°45′ Li, 82°31′ Na, 82°14′ Tl. $N_X = 1.5270$ Li, 1.5329 Na, 1.5409 Tl; $N_Y = 1.5412$ Li, 1.5459 Na, 1.5512 Tl; $N_Z = 1.5524$ Li, 1.5562 Na, 1.5591 Tl, $N_Z - N_X = 0.0233$ Na.
Ref: 119.

Pethidine with nitric acid ($C_{15}H_{21}O_2N$ with HNO_3) gives rods or rhombs which are monoclinic. Elongation negative. (+)2V = moderate. $N_X = 1.572$, $N_Y > 1.575$ and < 1.582, $N_Z = 1.590$, $N_Z - N_X = 0.018$. $N_1 = 1.575$ (|| length) and $N_2 = 1.585$ are common.
Ref: 617b.

Cinchophen with nitric acid ($C_{16}H_{11}O_2N$ with HNO_3) forms small needles with Z ≈ || elongation. $N_1 = 1.492$ (⊥ elongation) common, N_Y = ?, $N_Z > 1.730$ and < 1.741.
Ref: 617b.

Class 5. Sulfonic Acids and Derivatives

Pyridine-2-sulfonic acid ($C_5H_4N \cdot SO_3H$) is trimorphous. Phase I crystallizes from fusion at 248 – 250°, but inverts very quickly to phase II which forms very small bladed crystals. These also invert quickly to the stable phase III, which is orthorhombic with $a:b:c = 0.629:1:0.519$. D 1.71. Y = *a*, Z = *c*. (–)2V = 83°, r < v, $N_X = 1.530$, $N_Y = 1.650$, $N_Z = 1.76$, $N_Z - N_X = 0.23$.
Ref: 468a.

Pyridine-3-sulfonic acid ($C_5H_4N \cdot SO_3H$) is orthorhombic with $a:b:c = 0.757:1:0.478$. Crystals rods long || *c* with {310}, {010}, {111}, etc. D 1.72. M.P. 356 – 357°. Y = *a*, Z = *c*. (–)2V = 67°, r > v weak. $N_X = 1.534$, $N_Y = 1.670$, $N_Z = 1.74$, $N_Z - N_X = 0.206$.
Ref: 468a.

Class 6. Amines and Derivatives

trans-(Aminopyridino)pyridinodichloroplatinum $[(C_5H_4NH_2N)(C_5H_5N)PtCl_2]$ forms a greenish yellow powder. $N_X = 1.595$, $N_Y = 1.754$, $N_Z > 1.780$, $N_Z - N_X > 0.185$, ∴ (– ?)2V > 42°.
Ref: 418aa.

Pyribenzamine hydrochloride or *N'*-pyridyl-*N'*-benzyl-N-dimethylethylene-diamine hydrochloride $\{NC_5H_4N(CH_2C_6H_5)CH_2CH_2N(CH_3)_2 \cdot HCl\}$ forms rectangular colorless plates and prisms. Soluble in water. (-)2V = 80° calc., N_X = 1.580, N_Y = 1.655, N_Z = 1.705, $N_Z - N_X$ = 0.125. With $PtCl_4$ it forms radial groups.
Ref: 523.

2-Sulfanilamidopyridine or sulfapyridine $(NH_2C_6H_4 \cdot SO_2NH \cdot C_5NH_4)$ has five crystal phases. Phase I stable at room temperature; soluble in acetone; it is monoclinic in equant crystals, or tabular and elongated along *b*. M.P. 191 - 193°. Y = *b*; Z ∧ *c* = 39°; dispersion causes a blue-violet color at extinction. Elongation ± along *b*; also reported as negative. (+)2V = 88°, r > v very strong, N_X = 1.670, N_Y = 1.736, N_Z = 1.813, $N_Z - N_X$ = 0.143; again: (-?)2V = 90°, N_X = 1.673, N_Z = 1.770, $N_Z - N_X$ = 0.097. Also N_X = 1.680, N_Y = 1.733, N_Z > 1.733. Colorless or pale yellow, slowly darkening in light. Phase II crystallizes from a propyl alcohol solution at about 80° C. It is monoclinic in laths elongated along *b*. X ∧ *c* = 38°; Y = *b*. 2V = 36°, r< v with inclined dispersions. Crystals often give an optic axis interference figure inclined toward the obtuse bisectrix. N_X = 1.585, N_Y = 1.722, N_Z = 1.739, $N_Z - N_X$ = 0.154. Phase III crystallizes from a butyl, isobutyl, or amyl alcohol solution cooled to about 35°; inverts easily to phase I. Phase III crystals are orthorhombic in {100} plates elongated along *b*. M.P. 177°. X = *a*. Y = *b*. (+)2V = very large, r < v strong. Crystals often give a centered obtuse bisectrix interference figure. N_X = 1.68 (est.) N_Y = 1.697, N_Z = 1.721, $N_Z - N_X$ = 0.04 (est.). Phase IV crystallizes from a hot alcohol solution. Crystals are monoclinic and lamellar, elongated along *b*, Z ∧ *c* = 44°; Y = *b*, (+)2V = 74°, r > v. N_X = 1.625, N_Y = 1.693, N_Z = 1.835, $N_Z - N_X$ = 0.210. Phase V has not been obtained in pure state. Crystals are triclinic (?), equant. They often give an uncentered interference figure. (-)2V = very small, r > v strong, with anomalous dispersion. N_X = ?, N_Y = 1.745, N_Z = 1.761. (N_X probably below 1.6 - from (-)2V, N_Y and N_Z - A.N.W.). A solution of sulfapyridine forms yellow rods or blades in X-shaped aggregates when cooled with $AuCl_3$. Ref: 434, 518, 523b, 572a.

Sodium sulfanilamidopyridine or sodium sulfapyridine $(C_{11}H_{10}N_3O_2SNa)$ is orthorhombic; crystals are prisms and laths. Colorless. X = *c*. (+)2V = large, N_X = 1.590, N_Y = 1.660, N_Z = 1.728, $N_Z - N_X$ = 0.138. Again N_1 = 1.590, N_2 = 1.700.
Ref: 518, 572a.

Acetylsulfanilamidopyridine or acetylsulfapyridine $(C_{13}H_{13}N_3O_3S)$ is triclinic and pseudomonoclinic. Crystals {100} plates with {010}, {111}, etc. An optic axis nearly normal to 100. (-?)2V = very large, with extreme dispersion and ultra-blue interference colors. N_X = 1.640, N_Y = 1.70, N_Z > 1.770, $N_Z - N_X$ > 0.110.
Ref: 572a.

N^4-(2-Hydroxybenzylidene)sulfapyridine $(C_{18}H_{15}O_3N_3S)$ is monoclinic with M.P. 241°. Crystals lamellar with ± elongation. X ∧ *c* = 43°, Z = *b*. (+)2V = large, r > v. N_X = 1.619, N_Y = 1.750, N_Z > 1.86, $N_Z - N_X$ > 0.251. Color yellow, with no pleochroism.
Ref: 434a.

N^4-(2-Hydroxy-3-methoxybenzylidene)sulfapyridine ($C_{19}H_{17}O_4N_3S$) is monoclinic in tabular crystals with M.P. 204°. Z ∧ elongation = 21°. (-)2V = very large. $N_X = 1.542$, $N_Y = 1.750$, $N_Z > 1.86$, $N_Z - N_X > 0.318$. Color brick red. Ref: 434a.

3-Aminoquinoline {$C_6H_4N:CHC(NH_2):CH$} in its stable phase is orthorhombic disphenoidal with[1] $a:b:c = 0.612:1:0.604$. Crystals show {010}, {110}, {100}, {111}, {101}, etc. Distinct 100 cleavage. M.P. 94°. X = a; Y = c. (-)2V = 21° Li, 23.5° Na, 26° Tl. $N_X = 1.535$, $N_Y = 1.873$, $N_Z = 1.893$, $N_Z - N_X = 0.358$. The metastable phase is monoclinic. Ref: 119.

1-(4-Chlorophenyl)-1-(2-pyridyl)-3-N,N-dimethylpropylamine maleate or chlorotrimeton maleate [$(C_5H_4N)(C_6H_4Cl)C_3H_5N(CH_3)_2 \cdot C_4H_4O_4$] forms fragments and prisms. M.P. 130°. $N_X = 1.553$, N_Y probably = 1.668, $N_Z = 1.734$, $N_Z - N_X = 0.181$. ∴ probably (+)2V = 75°. Ref: 477d.

Atabrine or mepacrine or quinacrine (dihydrate?) ($C_{23}H_{30}ClNO_3 \cdot 2H_2O$?) Crystals prismatic with sharp extinction and no centered interference figure. $N_X = 1.500$, $N_Z > 1.733$, (but namy fragments give $N_Z' = 1.733$. Color yellow. Ref: 516.

Atabrine (or mepacrine or quinacrine) dihydrochloride dihydrate ($C_{23}H_{30}ClNO_3 \cdot 2HCl \cdot 2H_2O$) is soluble in water. Crystals rhombic with $N_1 = 1.522$, $N_2 = 1.733$, $N_3 > 1.733$, $N_3 - N_1 > 0.211$. Color yellow. Ref: 516, 518.

2-Amino-3-(3-indolyl) propanoic acid or α-amino-3-indolepropionic acid or tryptophan {$C_6H_4NHCH:C(CH_2CHNH_2CO_2H)$} is biaxial in very thin plates and rhombs. Biaxial interference figures frequently seen. (+)2V = ?, $N_X = 1.625$, N_Y = ?, $N_Z = 1.635$, $N_Z - N_X = 0.010$ Na. Ref: 169.

l-2-Amino-3-(3-indolyl)propanoic acid salt of 2,4-dinitro-1-naphthol-7-sulfonic acid or *l*-tryptophan flavianate {$C_6H_4NHCH:C(CH_2CHNH_2CO_2H) \cdot HO_3S C_6H_3COH:CNO_2CH:CNO_2$} forms rosettes of short yellow needles with negative elongation and parallel extinction. $N_1 = 1.493$, $N_2 = 1.778$, $N_2 - N_1 = 0.285$. Ref: 65.

N,N-Dimethyl-N′-(2-pyridyl)-N′-(2-thenyl)ethylenediamine or histadyl ($C_{13}H_{17}N_3S$) often forms six-sided plates. (-)2V > 80° calc. $N_X = 1.588$, $N_Y = 1.654$, $N_Z > 1.695$ and < 1.734, $N_Z - N_X > 0.107$ and < 0.146. Ref: 477a.

N,N-Dimethyl-N′-(2-pyridyl)-N′-(5-chloro-2-thenyl)ethylenediamine hydrochloride or chlorothen hydrochloride ($C_{13}H_{16}N_3SCl \cdot HCl$) often forms rectangular units (monoclinic?) M.P. 106 – 108°. (+)2V < 80° calc. $N_X = 1.533$, $N_Y = 1.625$, $N_Z > 1.734$, $N_Z - N_X > 0.181$. Ref: 477a.

---

[1] *a b c* changed to *b a c* to make $b > a > c$.

N,N-Dimethyl-N'-(2-pyridyl)-N'-(-5chloro-2-thenyl)ethylenediamine citrate or chlorothen citrate or tagathen ($C_{13}H_{16}N_3SCl\cdot C_6H_8O_7$) often forms tiny plates with rhombic outline. M.P. 116 – 118°. (+)2V = 70° calc. $N_X = 1.583$, $N_Y = 1.603$, $N_Z = 1.645$, $N_Z - N_X = 0.062$. Ref: 477a.

N,N-Dimethyl-N'-(2-pyridyl)-N'-(5-bromo-2-thenyl)ethylenediamine or bromothen ($C_{13}H_{16}N_3SBr$) forms rod-like crystals with inclined extinction and positive elongation. M.P. 124 – 126°. (+)2V = 70° calc., $N_X = 1.617$, $N_Y = 1.654$, $N_Z = 1.734$, $N_Z - N_X = 0.117$. Ref: 477a.

10. Compounds with two Nitrogen Atoms in the Cycle

Class 1. Compounds containing no Functional Group

Piperazine picrate $[(C_4N_2H_{10}OC_6H_2(NO_2)_3]$ is monoclinic. Decomposes above 300°. X = b. Axial dispersion: (–)2H = 64.5° (6908), 61° (5780), 60.5° (5461), 53° (4916), 49° (minimum – 4750), 53° (4600). Crossed dispersion such that if Z is taken as 0° at 6908, it is at 3° for 5780, 6° for 5461, 16° for 4916, 35° for 4700. For $\lambda = 5461$: (–)2V = 50°, $N_X = 1.526$, $N_Y = 1.832$, $N_Z = 1.913$, $N_Z - N_X = 0.387$. Ref: 557.

Chlorocyclizine N-methyl-N'-(4-chlorobenzhydryl)piperazine dihydrochloride or perazil dihydrochloride $[(C_6H_5)(C_6H_4Cl)CH\cdot(CH_3)C_4H_4N_2\cdot 2HCl]$ has a variable habit with Z ‖ elongation. M.P. 214°. (–)2V = small. $N_X = 1.610$, $N_Y = 1.660$, $N_Z = 1.665$, $N_Z - N_X = 0.055$. 2V = 32° calc. Ref: 477d.

Chlorocyclizine N-methyl-N'-(4-chlorobenzhydryl)piperazine monohydrochloride or diparalene monohydrochloride $[(C_6H_5)(C_6H_4Cl)CH\cdot(CH_3)C_4H_4N_2\cdot HCl]$ forms thin plates and irregular fragments. M.P. 217°. (+)2V = 76° – 5°. $N_X = 1.590$, $N_Y = 1.610$, $N_Z = 1.665$, $N_Z - N_X = 0.075$. Ref: 477d.

2-Methyl-4,5-dihydro-1,3-diazole d-tartrate or 2-methyl-2-imidazoline d-tartrate or lysidine d-tartrate [CH₃C:NCH₂CH₂NH·C₄H₄O₆] is monoclinic hemimorphic with $a:b:c = 0.459:1:0.293$, $\beta = 116°55'$. Crystals prismatic with {110}, {1̄10}, {100}, {010}, {001}, etc. Cleavage on 001. X ∧ c = + 30°; Y = b. (–)2V = 80°44' Li, 80°1' Na, 79°46' Tl. $N_Y = 1.5189$ Li, 1.5217 Na, 1.5255 Tl. Ref: 119.

Benzazoline hydrochloride or 2-benzyl-imidazoline(4,5) hydrochloride is probably monoclinic. Crystals lamellar, four- or six-sided; extinction usually unsymmetrical, with dispersion. (+)2V = 45° calc., $N_X = 1.586$, $N_Y = 1.604$, $N_Z = 1.703$, $N_Z - N_X = 0.117$.

$$\begin{bmatrix} N—C-CH_2C_6H_5 \\ | \quad\quad \rangle NH\cdot HCl \\ CH_2-CH_2 \end{bmatrix}$$

Ref: 617c.

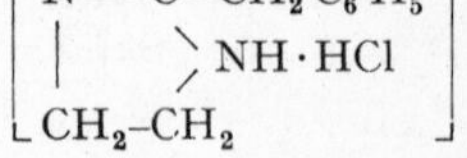

Naphthazoline nitrate or 2-(1-naphthylmethyl)-imidazoline-(4,5)nitrate is probably monoclinic. Acute bisectrix, centered or nearly so, observed on plates. (+)2V < 70° calc., $N_X = 1.560$, $N_Y = 1.619$, $N_Z > 1.740$, $N_Z - N_X > 0.180$.

$$\begin{bmatrix} N \quad C-CH_2C_{10}H_7 \\ | \quad\quad \rangle NH\cdot HNO_3 \\ CH_2\cdot CH_2 \end{bmatrix}$$

Ref: 617c.

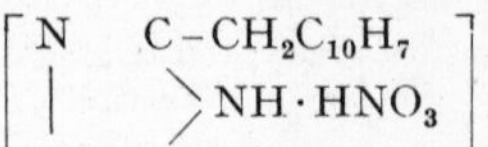

4-5-Dihydro-5-isopropyl-4,4-dimethyl-1,2-diazole hydrochloride or 5-isopropyl-4,4-dimethyl-2-pyrazoline hydrochloride [$(CH_3)_2$CCH:NNHCH(C_3H_7)·HCl] is monoclinic with $a:b:c = 1.393:1:0.844$, $\beta = 90°47'$. Crystals show {100}, {010}, {111}, etc., commonly twinned on 100; also lamellar twinning on 001, 10$\bar{1}$, or 101. Perfect 010, distinct 100, and imperfect 101 and 10$\bar{1}$ cleavages. M.P. 149°. X $\wedge$ c = -21°; Y = b. (-)2V = 56°, r > v. N_X = 1.553 red, 1.561 yellow, 1.570 blue; N_Y = 1.555 red, 1.563 yellow, 1.570 blue; N_Z = 1.568 red, 1.576 yellow, 1.586 blue; $N_Z - N_X$ = 0.015 yellow. (Indices and optic sign inconsistent - A.N.W.). Ref: 119.

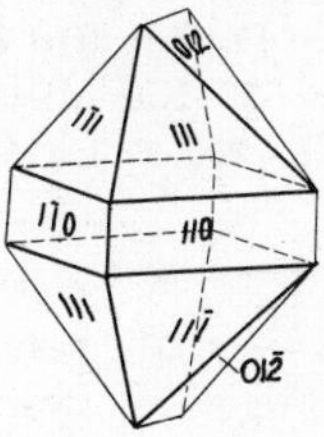

Fig. 111.
Benzimidazole.

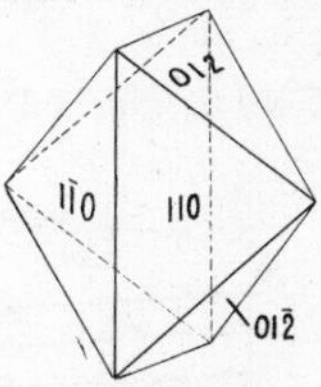

Fig. 112.
Benzimidazole.

N′-Phenyl-N′-benzylaminomethyl-imidazoline hydrochloride or anthistine hydrochloride ($C_{17}H_{19}N_2$·HCl) is orthorhombic? Crystals rod-shaped, Y parallel with elongation and Z usually normal. M.P. 234°. (+)2V = not large, N_X = 1.638, N_Y = 1.650, N_Z > 1.688 and < 1.733, $N_Z - N_X$ > 0.050 and < 0.095. Ref: 477b.

4,5-Benzo-1,3-diazole or benzimidazole [C_6H_4N:CHNH] is orthorhombic with $a:b:c = 0.982:1:1.961$. Crystals show {111}, {110}, {012}. Figs. 111, 112. Perfect 001 cleavage. M.P. 167°. Y = c; Z = b. (+)2V = 86°45′ Na, r < v. N_X = 1.6088 Na, N_Y = 1.6122, N_Z = 1.6161, $N_Z - N_X$ = 0.0073 Na. Ref: 119.

Benzimidazole (C_6H_4N:CHNH) (doubtless another phase) is monoclinic. Crystals tabular. Elongation along a. X = b, Z $\wedge$ c = 38°. (-)2V = 82°, r > v. N_X = 1.579, N_Y = 1.662, N_Z = 1.735, $N_Z - N_X$ = 0.156. Ref: 418a.

1,2,3,4-Tetrahydro-1,4,5-triphenyl-1,4-diazine or 1,2,3,4-tetrahydro-1,4,5-triphenyl pyrazine [CH_2N(C_6H_5)C(C_6H_5):CHN(C_6H_5)CH_2] is orthorhombic with $a:b:c = 0.766:1:1.862$. Crystals brachydomatic with {011}, {001}, {021}, etc. Perfect 001 cleavage. M.P. 130 - 131°. Y = a; Z = c. (+)2V = 66°4′ Na. N_X = 1.6255 calc. N_Y = 1.7252, N_Z = 1.9817 Na, $N_Z - N_X$ = 0.3562 calc. Ref: 119.

3,5-Diphenyl-1,2-diazole or 3,5-diphenylpyrazole [CH:C(C_6H_5)NHN:C(C_6H_5)] is monoclinic with $a:b:c = 0.987:1:1.161$, $\beta = 123°45'$. Crystals pseudobipyramidal with {110}, {11$\bar{1}$}, and {001}. M.P. 199° - 200°. The optic plane is normal to 010; the acute bisectrix makes an angle of + 44° with c. 2V = 43.5°. N_Y = 1.481 Na. Ref: 119.

3-Methyl-1,5-diphenyl-1,2-diazole or 3-methyl-1,5-diphenylpyrazole [CH:C(C_6H_5)N(C_6H_5)N:C(CH_3)] is monoclinic with $a:b:c = 2.640:1:3.103$, β =

90°36′. Crystals {001} tablets with {110}, {100}, {10$\bar{1}$}, etc. Fig. 113. Perfect 100 and distinct 010 cleavages. M.P. 63°. The optic plane is 010; the acute bisectrix makes an angle of about − 7° with *c*. 2V = 68°22′. N_Y = 1.4883 Na. Ref: 119.

1,1-Diallyl-2-phenyl-4,5-benzo-1,3-diazolium iodide or 1,1-diallyl-2-phenylbenzimidazolium iodide [$C_6H_4N(C_3H_5)_2(I)C(C_6H_5):N$] is monoclinic with *a*:*b*:*c* = 0.840:1:0.615, β = 92°49.5′. Crystals equant with {110}, {101}, {11$\bar{1}$}, {10$\bar{1}$}, {010}, etc. Fig. 114. Perfect 010 cleavage. Decomposes and fuses at 212°. X = *b*; Z $\wedge$ *c* = − 38°52′ Na (distinct dispersion). (+)2V = 86°25.5′ Li, 85°40.5′ Na, 84°47′ Tl. N_Y = 1.6963 Li, 1.6974 Na, 1.6979 Tl. Ref: 119.

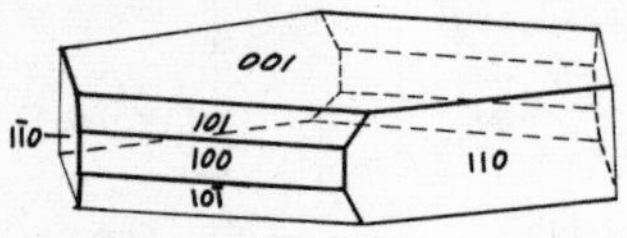

Fig. 113.
3-Methyl-1,5-diphenylpyrazole.

1,6-Dimethyl-2-(1-methyl-4(1)-quinolylidene-methyl)quinolinium iodide or [1-methylquinolin-(4)] [1,6-dimethylquinolin-(2)] methinecyanine iodide or pinaverdol ($C_{22}H_{21}N_2I$) is monoclinic with *a*:*b*:*c* = 1.101:1:1.605, β = 91°40′. Crystals prisms with {110}, {101}, {$\bar{1}$01}, etc. Also may be domatic. 010 faces reflect light of brass yellow color; faces near 001 are bronze violet in reflected light. Pyramids and domes are metallic green in color. Also pleochroic in transmitted light. X $\wedge$ *c* = + 5°. N_X = 1.58, N_Y > 1.75, N_Z = 2.0 (est.), $N_Z - N_X$ = 0.42 (est.) Ref: 360.

2,4,5-Triphenyl-4,5-dihydro-1,3-diazole or 2,4,5-Triphenyl-2-imidazoline or Amarine and its Salts

Amarine hydrochloride [$NHCH(C_6H_5)CH(C_6H_5)N:C(C_6H_5)\cdot HCl$] is rhombohedral with *c*/*a* = 0.422. Crystals show {10$\bar{1}$1}, {11$\bar{2}$0}, {10$\bar{1}$0}, etc. No distinct cleavage. M.P. 302°. Uniaxial positive with N_O = 1.6139 Li, 1.6230 Na, 1.6282 Tl; N_E = 1.6928 Li, 1.7471 Na, 1.7583 Tl; $N_E - N_O$ = 0.1241 Na. (N_E for Li apparently incorrect – A.N.W.). Ref: 119.

Amarine hydrobromide [$NHCH(C_6H_5)CH(C_6H_5)N:C(C_6H_5)\cdot HBr$] is rhombohedral with *c*/*a* = 0.417. Crystals show {10$\bar{1}$1}, {11$\bar{2}$0}, {10$\bar{1}$0}, etc. No distinct cleavage. M.P. 288°. Uniaxial positive with N_O = 1.6278 Li, 1.6303 Na, 1.6385 Tl; N_E = 1.7512 Li, 1.7566 Na, 1.7721 Tl; $N_E - N_O$ = 0.1263 Na. Ref: 119.

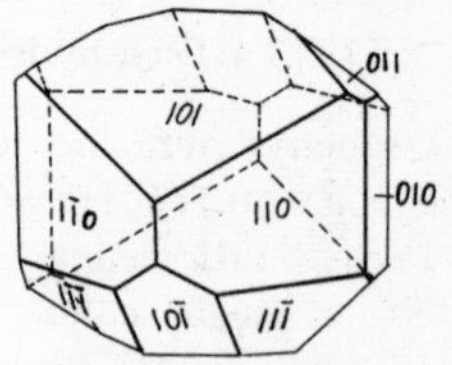

Fig. 114. Diallylphenylbenzimidazolium iodide.

Class 2. Hydroxy Compounds

5-Methoxy-3-methyl-1-phenyl-1,2-diazole 2-methiodide or 5-methoxy-3-methyl-1-phenylpyrazole 2-methiodide [$CH:C(OCH_3)N(C_6H_5)NI(CH_3):C(CH_3)$] is monoclinic with *a*:*b*:*c* = 0.890:1:0.615, β = 93° *ca.* Crystals short prismatic with {110}, {100}, {010}, {011}. Fig. 115. Perfect 110 cleavage. D 1.58. Decomposes at 130°. X $\wedge$ c = – 73° *ca.*; Y = b. (–)2V = 72° *ca.* Na, N_X = 1.617, N_Y = 1.650, N_Z = 1.710, $N_Z - N_X$ = 0.093. Ref: 119.

5-Ethoxy-3-methyl-1-phenyl-1,2-diazole 2-methiodide or 5-ethoxy-3-methyl-1-phenylpyrazole 2-methiodide [$CH:C(OC_2H_5)N(C_6H_5)NI(CH_3):C(CH_3)$] has two phases. One (I) is monoclinic with $a:b:c$ = 1.346:1:1.127, β = 122°24′. Crystals show {10$\bar{1}$}, {001}, {011}, {100}, etc. Twinning on 10$\bar{1}$. Perfect 100 and distinct 010 cleavages. D 1.58. Decomposes at 113 – 116°. X $\wedge$ c = – 8.5°; Z = b. (–)2E = 88° *ca.* N_X = 1.534 *ca.* The other phase (II) is also monoclinic with $a:b:c$ = 1.142:1:0.927, β = 119°33′. Crystals {001} tablets elongated parallel to b with {100}, {20$\bar{1}$}, {041}, {110}, etc. Distinct 10$\bar{1}$ cleavage. D 1.51. The optic plane is 010; Z $\wedge$ c = – 84.5°. (+)2V = 74°45′ Na. N_Y = 1.6295 Na. Ref: 119.

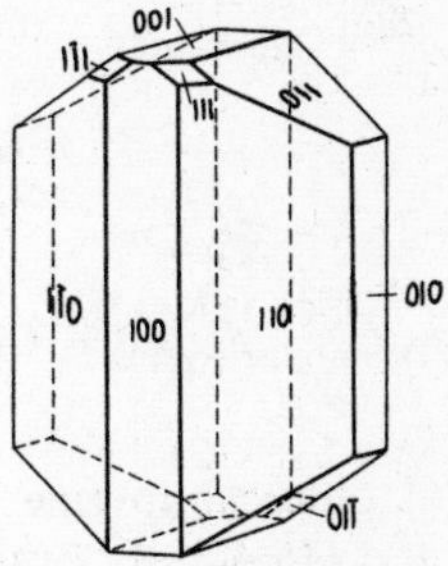

Fig. 115. 1-Phenyl-3-methyl-5-methoxy-pyrazole-2-methiodide.

2-Methoxyphenazine ($C_{13}H_{12}O_2N$) is monoclinic with $a:b:c$ = 1.008:1:0.799, β = 124°46′. Crystals equant with {110}, {001}, {100}, etc. Extinction on 010 at 61° to c. 2V = 74°, r < v. N = 1.73 – 1.74, $N_Z - N_X$ = ?. Ref: 550.

[5-Ethylquinuclidyl-(2)]-[6-ethoxy-quinolyl-(4)-carbinol] hydrochloride or ethylhydrocupreine hydrochloride [$NC_7H_{11}(C_2H_5)CH(OH)C_9H_5(OC_2H_5)N \cdot HCl$] forms colorless or faintly yellow crystals with M.P. 252 – 254°. N_X = 1.513, N_Y = ?, N_Z = 1.619, $N_Z - N_X$ = 0.106. Ref: 524.

Class 3. Carbonyl Compounds

Ethyleneurea or 2-imidazolidone ($NHCH_2CH_2NHCO$) is dimorphous. One phase, I, (unstable at room temperature), is uniaxial positive; it inverts to phase II at 80°. Phase II is biaxial with (+)2V = 47° calc., N_X = 1.537, N_Y = 1.563, N_Z = 1.694, $N_Z - N_X$ = 0.157. Ref: 589a.

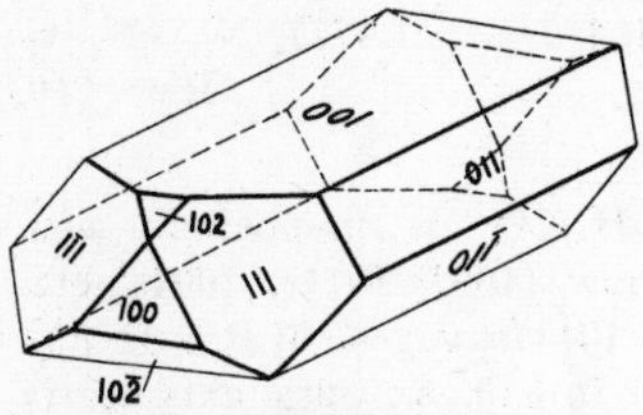

Fig. 116. 1-Phenyl-3-methyl-5-pyrazolone.

Ethyleneurea hemihydrate or 2-imidazolidone hemihydrate [$NHCH_2CH_2NHCO \cdot 0.5H_2O$] melts at 130°. Uniaxial positive with N_O = 1.521, N_E > 1.56, $N_E - N_O$ > 0.039. Ref: 589a.

4,5-Dihydro-5-keto-3-methyl-1-phenyl-1,2-diazole or 3-methyl-1-phenyl-5-pyrazolone [$CH_2CON(C_6H_5)N:C(CH_3)$] is monoclinic with $a:b:c$= 0.922:1:1.420, β = 95°4′. Crystals {001} tablets elongated parallel to a with {011}, {111}, {100}, {10$\bar{2}$}, etc. Fig. 116. Perfect 10$\bar{2}$ and distinct 100 cleavages. M.P. 127°. The optic plane and acute bisectrix are normal to 010 and much dispersed. Extinction at + 76° *ca.* to c in 010. 2V = 42°34′. N_Y =1.637 Na. Color yellowish. Ref: 119.

2,3-Dihydro-3-keto-1,5-dimethyl-2-phenyl-1,2-diazole or 1,5-Dimethyl-2-phenyl-3-pyrazolone or Antipyrine: its Salts and Derivatives

Antipyrine [$C_6H_5NN(CH_3)C(CH_3):CHCO$] is monoclinic with $a:b:c = 2.400:1:2.272$, $\beta = 117°9'$. Crystals {001} tablets with {100}, {011}, {11$\bar{1}$}; also prismatic or {100} tablets. Perfect 10$\bar{1}$ and distinct 010 cleavages. M.P. 113°. X $\wedge$ c = + 43°; Y = b. (-)2V = 53°42′ Li, 54°20′ Na, 55°30′ Tl. $N_X = 1.5697$ Na, $N_Y = 1.6935$, $N_Z = 1.7324$, $N_Z - N_X = 0.1627$ Na. Also $N_X = 1.570$, $N_Y = 1.576$, $N_Z > 1.686$, $N_Z - N_X > 0.116$. Very soluble in index liquids. Ref: 119, 123, 224a, 240.

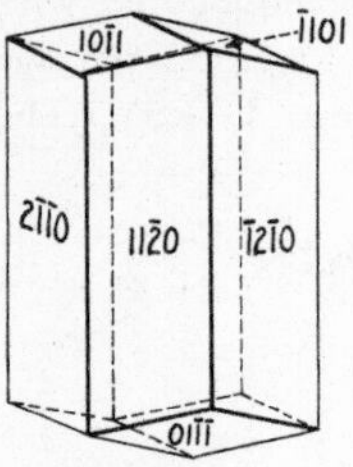

Fig. 117.
Bromoantipyrine.

Salipyrine or antipyrine salicylate [$C_{11}H_{12}N_2O$[$C_6H_4(OH)CO_2H$]] forms six-sided crystals and crystal fragments or needles or blades. M.P. 91 - 92°. $N_1 = 1.533$, $N_2 = 1.720$, $N_2 - N_1 = 0.187$. Also $N_1 = 1.56$, $N_2 = 1.65$, $N_3 = 1.71$, $N_3 - N_1 = 0.15$. Ref: 239, 343c.

Antipyrine acetylsalicylate or acetopyrine [$C_{11}H_{12}N_2O \cdot CH_3CO_2C_6H_4CO_2H$] is granular with M.P. 63 - 65°. Colorless. $N_1 = 1.534$, $N_2 = 1.709$, $N_2 - N_1 = 0.175$. Ref: 239.

Chloroantipyrine ($C_{11}H_{11}N_2ClO$) is monoclinic with $a:b:c = 2.853:1:0.973$, $\beta = 116°45'$. Crystals show {001}, {100}, {111}, etc. M.P. 129°. An optic axis is about normal to 001. (-)2V = 55° calc. $N_X = 1.501$, $N_Y = 1.680$ *ca.*, $N_Z = 1.733$ *ca.*, $N_Z - N_X = 0.232$ Na. Ref: 76a.

4-Bromoantipyrine [$BrC:C(CH_3)N(CH_3)N(C_6H_5)CO$] is rhombohedral with $c/a = 0.295$. Crystals short prismatic with {11$\bar{2}$0}, {10$\bar{1}$1}, etc. Fig. 117. Perfect 0001 cleavage. M.P. 117°. Uniaxial negative with $N_O = 1.5808$, $N_E = 1.4931$, $N_O - N_E = 0.877$ Na. Ref: 119.

4-Iodoantipyrine [$IC:C(CH_3)N(CH_3)N(C_6H_5)CO$] is rhombohedral with $c/a = 0.294$. Crystals short prismatic with {11$\bar{2}$0}, {10$\bar{1}$0}, {10$\bar{1}$1}, etc. Perfect 0001 cleavage. Uniaxial negative with $N_O = 1.6464$, $N_E = 1.4777$, $N_O - N_E = 0.1687$ Na. Ref: 119.

4-Methylantipyrine [$CH_3C:C(CH_3)N(CH_3)N(C_6H_5)CO$] is monoclinic with $a:b:c = 3.850:1:3.075$, $\beta = 120°56'$. Crystals show {100}, {011}, {001}, etc. Fig. 118. Perfect 001 and 100 and distinct 011 and 10$\bar{1}$ cleavages. M.P. 82–83°. The optic plane is 010; extinction at + 47° *ca.* to c in 010. An optic axis nearly normal to 100; another visible through 10$\bar{1}$. 2V = 86° *ca.* $N_Y = 1.6584$ Na. Ref: 119, 224a.

4-Ethylantipyrine [$C_2H_5C:C(CH_3)N(CH_3)N(C_6H_5)CO$] is monoclinic with $a:b:c = 0.809:1:0.441$, $\beta = 121°52'$. Crystals short prisms with {110}, {100}, {001}, {011}, etc. Fig. 119. Perfect 001 and distinct 100 cleavages. M.P. 68°.

The optic plane is 010; the acute bisectrix makes an angle of about $-40°$ with c; an optic axis is visible through 100. $2V = 30°$ *ca.* Na. $N_Y = 1.548$ Na.
Ref: 119.

Sodium picrolonate ($C_{10}H_7O_5N_4Na$) forms yellow needles with parallel extinction and negative elongation. $N_X = 1.616$, $N_Y = ?$, $N_Z > 1.734$, $N_Z - N_X > 0.118$.
Ref: 451a.

Potassium picrolonate ($C_{10}H_7O_5N_4K$) forms yellow needles with inclined extinction and negative elongation. $N_X = 1.505$, $N_i = 1.519$, $N_Z > 1.734$, $N_Z - N_X > 0.229$, ∴ probably $(+)2V$ = small.
Ref: 451a.

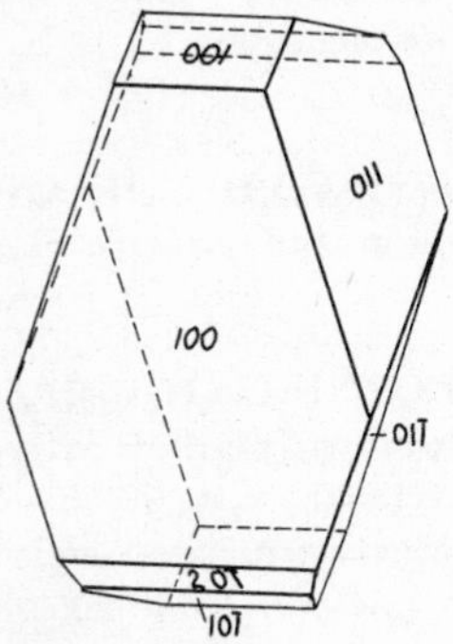

Fig. 118. Methylantipyrine.

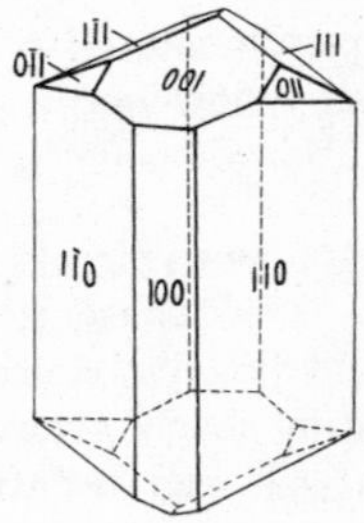

Fig. 119. Ethylantipyrine.

Ammonium picrolonate ($C_{10}H_7O_5N_4NH_4$) forms yellow rods (many bifurcated) with parallel extinction and positive elongation. $N_X = 1.644$, $N_i = 1.734$, $N_Z > 1.734$, $N_Z - N_X > 0.090$.
Ref: 452.

Strontium picrolonate $\{(C_{10}H_7O_5N_4)_2Sr(+H_2O\,?)\}$ forms tabular prisms with inclined extinction and negative elongation. $N_X = 1.448$, $N_Y = ?$, $N_Z > 1.734$, $N_Z - N_X > 0.286$.
Ref: 452.

Zinc picrolonate $\{(C_{10}H_7O_5N_4)_2Zn\}$ forms yellow needles and rods with parallel extinction and positive elongation. $N_X = 1.650$, $N_Y = ?$, $N_Z > 1.734$, $N_Z - N_X > 0.084$.
Ref: 452.

Copper picrolonate $\{(C_{10}H_7O_5N_4Cu)\}$ forms yellow needles and rods with parallel extinction and positive elongation. $N_X = 1.734$, $N_Y > 1.734$. $N_Z = ?$.
Ref: 452.

Alanine picrolonate $[H_2NCH(CH_3)CO_2H \cdot C_{10}H_8O_5N_4]$ forms long, yellow, pointed needles with parallel extinction and negative elongation. $N_1 = 1.575$, $N_2 = 1.580$, $N_2 - N_1 = 0.005$.
Ref: 73a.

Arginine picrolonate $[H_2NC(NH)NH(CH_2)_3CHNH_2CO_2H \cdot C_{10}H_8O_5N_4(H_2O\,?)]$ is polymorphous. One phase (I) is in fine needles, almost colorless to yellowish brown, with parallel extinction and positive elongation. $N_1 = 1.580$, $N_2 = 1.716$,

$N_2 - N_1 = 0.136$. A second phase (II) is in yellow-brown isotropic needles with $N = 1.578$. A third phase (III) is in light yellow needles which form slowly; they are anisotropic with parallel extinction and positive elongation. Ref: 73a.

Aspartic acid picrolonate ($HO_2CCHNH_2CH_2CO_2H \cdot C_{10}H_8O_5N_4$) is dimorphous. One phase (I) is in coarse yellow needles somewhat soluble in water. They have parallel extinction and positive elongation. $1.527 > N_1 > 1.512$; $N_2 < 1.527$. A second phase (II) is in fine yellowish-brown needles with parallel extinction and negative elongation. $N_2 > N_1 > 1.74$. Ref: 73a.

Cysteine picrolonate ($HSCH_2CHNH_2CO_2H \cdot C_{10}H_8O_5N_4$) forms yellowish-brown needles with parallel extinction and negative elongation. $N_2 > N_1 > 1.74$. Ref: 73a.

Cystine picrolonate ($HO_2CCHNH_2CH_2S_2CH_2CHNH_2CO_2H \cdot C_{10}H_8O_5N_4$) forms fine brownish-yellow needles with parallel extinction and positive elongation. $N_1 = 1.548$, $N_2 = 1.600$, $N_2 - N_1 = 0.052$. Ref: 73a.

Dibromotyrosine picrolonate ($HOC_6H_2Br_2CH_2CHNH_2CO_2H \cdot C_{10}H_8O_5N_4$) is dimorphous. One phase (I) is in fine yellowish-brown needles with parallel extinction and positive elongation. $1.616 > N_1 > 1.549$, $N_2 > 1.740$. Another phase (II) is in nearly colorless needles with obliquely truncated ends, having extinction at 44° and negative elongation $N_1 < 1.549$, $N_2 > 1.580$. Ref: 73a.

Dichlorotyrosine picrolonate ($HOC_6H_2Cl_2CH_2CHNH_2CO_2H \cdot C_{10}H_8O_5N_4$) forms an oil, then a granular aggregate, and then fibers with parallel extinction and positive elongation. $1.633 > N_1 > 1.618$, $1.740 > N_2 > 1.698$. Ref: 73a.

Glutamic acid picrolonate [$HO_2CCHNH_2(CH_2)_2CO_2H \cdot C_{10}H_8O_5N_4$] forms columnar crystals with parallel extinction and negative elongation. $N_1 = 1.574$, $N_2 = 1.596$, $N_2 - N_1 = 0.022$. Ref: 73a.

Glycine picrolonate ($C_2H_5NO_2 \cdot C_{10}H_8O_5N_4$) forms dense rosettes of yellowish-brown needles which have parallel extinction and positive elongation. $N_1 = 1.531$, $N_2 = 1.616$, $N_2 - N_1 = 0.085$. Ref: 73a.

Histidine picrolonate ($C_6H_9O_2N_3 \cdot C_{10}H_8O_5N_4$) forms yellowish-brown rosettes of needles with parallel extinction and positive elongation. $N_1 = 1.557$, $N_2 = 1.616$, $N_2 - N_1 = 0.059$. Ref: 73a.

Hydroxyproline picrolonate ($C_5H_9O_5N \cdot C_{10}H_8O_5N_4$) forms fine needles with pointed ends which have parallel extinction and positive elongation. $N_1 = 1.493$, $N_2 = 1.658$, $N_2 - N_1 = 0.165$. Ref: 73a.

Hydroxyvaline picrolonate [$(CH_3)_2COHCHNH_2CO_2H \cdot C_{10}H_8O_5N_4$] forms an oil, then on agitation coarse yellowish-brown needles with parallel extinction and positive elongation (slowly soluble in immersion liquids). $N_1 = 1.54$ *ca.*, $N_2 = 1.56$ *ca.*, $N_2 - N_1 = 0.02$ *ca.* Ref: 73a.

Isoleucine picrolonate [$CH_3CH_2CH(CH_3)CH(NH_2)CO_2H \cdot C_{10}H_8O_5N_4$] forms yellow needles with parallel extinction and positive elongation. $N_1 = 1.520$, $N_2 = 1.610$, $N_2 - N_1 = 0.090$. Ref: 73a.

Isoserine picrolonate [$H_2NCH_2CHOHCO_2H \cdot C_{10}H_8O_5N_4$] is polymorphous. One phase (I) exhibits six-sided columns with nearly square ends. They have parallel extinction and positive elongation. $N_1 = 1.70$ *ca.*, $N_2 > 1.740$, $N_2 - N_1 > 0.04$. A second phase (II) is in tiny brown needles with parallel extinction and positive elongation. $N_1 = 1.520$, $N_Z = 1.608$, $N_2 - N_1 = 0.088$. A third phase (III) forms short brown needles with parallel extinction and positive elongation. $N_1 = 1.529$, $N_Z = 1.660$, $N_2 - N_1 = 0.131$. Ref: 73a.

Leucine picrolonate [$(CH_3)_2CHCH_2CHNH_2CO_2H \cdot C_{10}H_8O_5N_4$] forms an oil, then, on agitation, long yellow needles with parallel extinction and positive elongation. $N_1 = 1.527$, $N_2 = 1.617$, $N_2 - N_1 = 0.090$. Ref: 73a.

Lysine picrolonate [$H_2N(CH_2)_4CHNH_2CO_2H \cdot C_{10}H_8O_5N_4$] forms reddish brown crystals (in rosettes) with parallel extinction and positive elongation. $N_1 = 1.520$, $N_2 = 1.645$, $N_2 - N_1 = 0.125$. Ref: 73a.

Methionine picrolonate [$CH_3S(CH_2)_2CHNH_2CO_2H \cdot C_{10}H_8O_5N_4$] forms a yellow oil and (slowly) groups of coarse, dark, pointed crystals with parallel extinction and positive elongation. $N_1 = 1.494$, $N_2 = 1.62$ *ca.*, $N_2 - N_1 = 0.126$ *ca.* Ref: 73a.

Norleucine picrolonate [$CH_3(CH_2)_3CHNH_2CO_2H \cdot C_{10}H_8O_5N_4$] forms crystals very slowly which are coarse and banded. They have parallel extinction and negative elongation; slowly soluble in immersion liquids. $N_1 > 1.658$, $N_2 < 1.740$. Ref: 73a.

Norvaline picrolonate [$CH_3(CH_2)_2CHNH_2CO_2H \cdot C_{10}H_8O_5N_4$] is dimorphous. One phase is in bundles of yellowish-brown needles with parallel extinction and positive elongation. Indices not measured. The other (II) is in coarse acicular crystals with parallel extinction and negative elongation. $N_1 = 1.684$, $N_2 > 1.74$, $N_2 - N_1 > 0.056$. Ref: 73a.

Phenylalanine picrolonate [$C_9H_{11}O_2N \cdot C_{10}H_8O_5N_4$] is dimorphous. One phase (I) shows brown needles with parallel extinction. The other phase (II) forms yellow six-sided plates with inclined extinction from dilute solutions. M.P. 238°. $N_2 > N_1 > 1.74$. Ref: 73a.

Proline picrolonate [$C_5H_9O_2N \cdot C_{10}H_8O_5N_4$] forms yellowish-brown needles with parallel extinction and negative elongation. $N_1 = 1.530$, $N_2 = 1.605$, $N_2 - N_1 = 0.075$. Ref: 73a.

Serine picrolonate [$HOCH_2CHNH_2CO_2H \cdot C_{10}H_8O_5N_4$] is dimorphous. One phase (I) shows long yellow-brown needles with extinction at 35° to 40° and positive elongation. $N_1 = 1.530$, $N_2 = 1.567$, $N_2 - N_1 = 0.037$. A second phase (II) forms light yellow needles with parallel extinction and negative elongation; soluble in immersion liquids. Ref: 73a.

Tryptophan picrolonate [$C_{11}H_{12}O_2N_2 \cdot C_{10}H_8O_5N_4$] forms a solid isotropic (isometric ?) mass with N = 1.712. It also forms orange red needles with M.P. 204°. Ref: 73a.

Tyrosine picrolonate [$C_6H_4OHCH_2CHNH_2CO_2H \cdot C_{10}H_8O_5N_4$] forms dark poined needles with a twisted appearance, which have extinction at 35° to 37° and positive elongation. $N_1 = 1.529$, $N_2 = 1.596$, $N_2 - N_1 = 0.067$. Ref: 73a.

Valine picrolonate [$(CH_3)_2CHCHNH_2CO_2H \cdot C_{10}H_8O_5N_4$] forms long yellowish-brown needles with parallel extinction and negative elongation. $N_1 = 1.549$, $N_2 > 1.740$, $N_2 - N_1 > 0.191$. Ref: 73a.

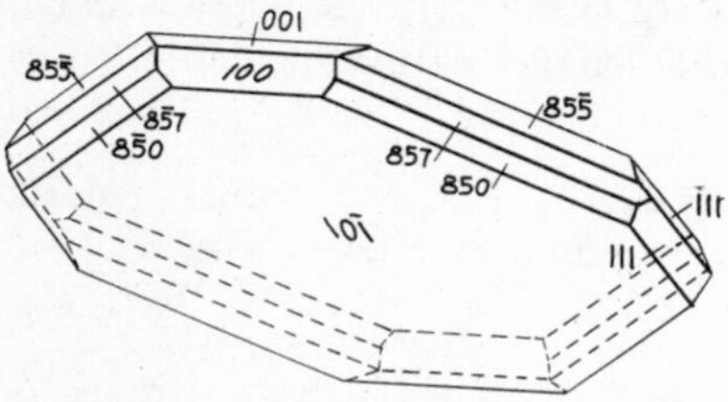

Fig. 120.
3,4,4-Trimethyl-1-phenyl-5-pyrazolone.

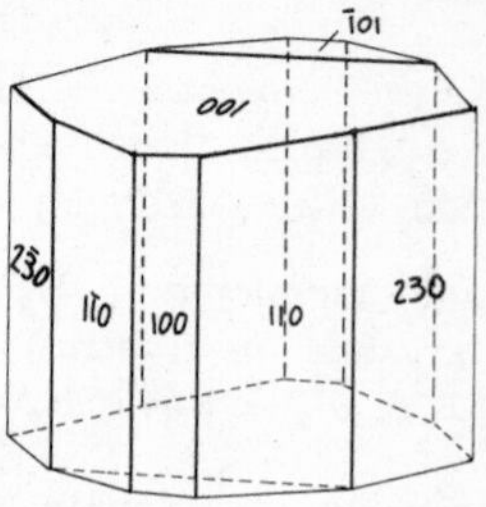

Fig. 121.
5-Methyl-2-phenyl-1-propyl-3-pyrazolone

4,5-Dihydro-5-keto-3,4,4-trimethyl-1-phenyl-1,2-diazole or 3,4,4-trimethyl-1-phenyl-5-pyrazolone [$(CH_3)_2CCON(C_6H_5)N\!:\!C(CH_3)$] is monoclinic with $a:b:c$ = 1.826:1:1.359, β = 101°24′. Crystals {10$\bar{1}$} plates with small {001}, {100}, etc. Fig. 120. Cleavage on 201. M.P. 55 - 56°. The optic plane is normal to 010; extinction at -65° to c in 010. 2V = 74°2′ Na. N_Y = 1.5384 Na. Ref: 119.

2,3-Dihydro-3-keto-5-methyl-2-phenyl-1-propyl-1,2-diazole or 5-methyl-2-phenyl-1-propyl-3-pyrazolone [$CH\!:\!C(CH_3)N(C_3H_7)N(C_6H_5)CO$] is monoclinic with $a:b:c$ = 0.976:1:0.142, β = 97°36′. Crystals short prismatic with {230}, {110}, {001}, {100}, etc. Fig. 121. Distinct 001 and 010 cleavages. M.P. 93°. The optic plane and acute bisectrix are normal to 010 and at - 70° *ca.* to c. 2V = 52°50′ Na. N_Y = 1.6020 Na. Ref: 119.

Decarboxyl-monomethyl Ciba yellow ($C_{23}H_{16}ON_2$) is monoclinic prismatic with $a:b:c$ = 2.869:1:1.326, β = 122°51′. a 23.22, b 8.09, c 10.73 Å. D 1.307. M.P. 168°. Crystals columnar with twinning on $\bar{2}$01. 010 cleavage. Y = b, Z $\wedge$ c = 16°. (-)2V = 56°. $N_X = 1.564$, $N_Y = 1.871$, $N_Z = 1.991$, $N_Z - N_X = 0.427$. Pleochroic with X = pale gray yellow, Y = ?, Z′ = darker yellow. Ref: 494a.

Tetrahydro-2,4-diketo-3-methyl-1-phenyl-1,3-diazole or 3-methyl-1-phenylhydantoin [$CH_2CON(CH_3)CONC_6H_5$] forms acicular crystals with M.P. 110°. Extinction is parallel and elongation is positive. $N_1 = 1.515$, $N_2 = 1.665$, $N_2 - N_1 = 0.150$. Ref: 95.

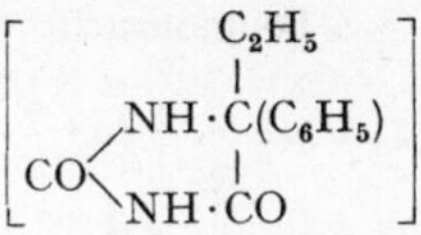

dl-5-Ethyl-5-phenylhydantoin or nirvanol forms needles and plates with cleavage normal to length. M.P. $199 - 200°$. Soluble in some index liquids. $(-)2V = 62°$, N_X notably less than 1.630, N_Y and N_Z between 1.630 and 1.645.

$$\begin{bmatrix} & & C_2H_5 \\ & & | \\ & NH \cdot C(C_6H_5) \\ CO & & | \\ & NH \cdot CO \end{bmatrix}$$

Ref: 123.

Diphenylhydantoin $[(C_6H_5)_2\overline{NHCONHCOCH}_2]$ forms colorless rods and needles with X ‖ elongation. Biaxial. $N_X = 1.600$, $N_Y = ?$, $N_Z = 1.635$, $N_Z - N_X = 0.035$.

Ref: 523g.

3-Methyl-6,5-phenylethylhydantoin or mesantoin $(C_{12}H_{14}O_2N_2)$ forms thin, colorless rhombs or plates. Z ‖ elongation. $(-)2E = 50° \pm 5°$, $N_X = 1.570$, $N_Y = 1.600$, $N_Z = 1.605$, $N_Z - N_X = 0.035$. $2V = 33°$ calc. Ref: 523g.

d-1-Acetyl-5-methyl-2-thiohydantoin or d-1-acetyl-2-thio-5-methylhydantoin $[\overline{CH_3CONCSNHCOCH}(CH_3)]$ is prismatic, at times six-sided. M.P. $161 - 162°$. 2E = rather large. $N_X = 1.485$, $N_Y = 1.685 \pm .003$, $N_Z > 1.733$, $N_Z - N_X > 0.248$. Probably optically negative. $[\alpha] = 118.5°$ in one per cent solution in alcohol. Ref: 183.

2,5-Piperazinedione $(C_4H_6O_2N_2)$ is monoclinic in tabular crystals, often twinned. Elongation along c. Y $\wedge$ $c = 7°$. $Z = b$. $(-)2V = 32°$, r < v. $N_X = 1.460$, $N_Y = 1.675$, $N_Z = 1.696$, $N_Z - N_X = 0.236$. Ref: 418a.

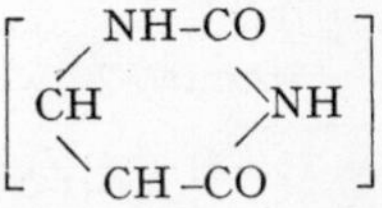

2,6-Dihydroxypyrimidine or uracil or isocytosine is monoclinic with $a:b:c = 0.921 : 1 : 0.293$, $\beta = 113°$. Crystals equant with $\{\bar{3}01\}$, $\{100\}$, $\{010\}$, $\{110\}$; $\bar{3}01$ cleavage. D 1.62. X $\wedge$ $c = 27.5°$ in acute β; X normal to cleavage.

$$\begin{bmatrix} & NH-CO \\ CH & \diagup \quad NH \\ & CH-CO \end{bmatrix}$$

Elongation $\pm$. $Z = b$. $(-)2V = 76°$, r < v weak. $N_X = 1.441$, $N_Y = 1.700$, $N_Z = 1.87$ ($\pm .05$), $N_Z - N_X = 0.43$. Again: $(+)2V = 80°$ calc., $N_X = 1.497$; $N_Y = 1.642$, $N_Z = 1.845$, $N_Z - N_X = 0.348$. Also: $(-)2V =$ large, $N_X = 1.416$, $N_Y = 1.688$, $N_Z = 1.85$, $N_Z - N_X > 0.434$. Is uracil trimorphous?

Ref: 134, 418a, 468b.

Sodium salt of 2-ethoxy-4-hydroxypyrimidine $[(C_2H_5O)\overline{C : NC(ONa) : CHCH : N}]$ is very soluble in water and alcohol and is very hygroscopic. M.P. $225°$ (dec.). $(-)2V = 80°$ calc. $N_X = 1.489$, $N_Y = 1.584$, $N_Z = 1.650$, $N_Z - N_X = 0.161$.

Ref: 134.

2-Ethoxy-4-hydroxypyrimidine $[\overline{N : C(OH)CH : CHN : C}(OC_2H_5)]$ is biaxial. M.P. $127.5 - 129°$. $(-)2V = 75°$ calc. $N_X = 1.486$, $N_Y = 1.618$, $N_Z = 1.697$, $N_Z - N_X = 0.211$.

Ref: 134.

5-Chlorouracil $(C_4H_3O_2N_2Cl)$ is monoclinic. Crystals columnar. Elongation ‖ b. $Y = b$. $Z \wedge c = 39°$. $(-)2V =$ large, r > v. $N_X = 1.424$, $N_Y = 1.754$, $N_Z > 1.85$, $N_Z - N_X > 0.426$.

Ref: 418a.

5-Bromouracil ($C_4H_3O_2N_2Br$) is monoclinic. Crystals columnar. Y = *b*, Z ∧ *c* = 40°. (–)2V = large, r > v. $N_X = 1.448$, $N_Y = 1.761$, $N_Z > 1.85$, $N_Z - N_X > 0.402$. Ref: 418a.

5-Iodouracil ($C_4H_3O_2N_2I$) is orthorhombic. Crystals lamellar. Elongation along *c*. X = *b*, Y = *c*. (+)2V = medium, r > v. $N_X = 1.667$, $N_Y = 1.727$, $N_Z > 1.85$, $N_Z - N_X > 0.188$. Ref: 418a.

5-Nitrouracil ($C_4H_3O_4N_3$) is monoclinic. Crystals columnar. X = *b*, Y ∧ *c* = 14°. (+)2V = large, r > v with horizontal dispersion. $N_X = 1.542$, $N_Y = 1.659$, $N_Z > 1.85$, $N_Z - N_X > 0.308$. Ref: 418a.

2-Thiouracil [SCNHCONHCHCH] forms tablets with (–)2E > 170°, 2V = 88 – 90°, $N_X = 1.567$, $N_Y = 1.805$, $N_Z > 1.81$. ($N_Z = 2.2$ calc., $N_Z - N_X = 0.64$ calc. – A.N.W.). Ref: 529.

4-Ethoxy-2-hydroxypyrimidine [N:C(OC_2H_5)CH:CHN:C(OH)] forms large prisms with M.P. 167 – 167.5°., insoluble in CCl_4 and soluble in water, ethyl acetate, acetone, and hot benzene. (–)2V = 51° calc. $N_X = 1.445$, $N_Y = 1.652$, $N_Z = 1.699$, $N_Z - N_X = 0.254$. Ref: 134.

Sodium salt of 4-ethoxy-2-hydroxypyrimidine [C(ONa):NCH:CHC(OC_2H_5):N] is soluble in water and alcohol. M.P. 305°. (–)2V = 74° calc. $N_X = 1.483$, $N_Y = 1.572$, $N_Z = 1.621$, $N_Z - N_X = 0.138$. Ref: 134.

4-Amino-2-hydroxypyrimidine picrate or cytosine picrate [NH_2C:NC(OH): NCH:CH·$C_6H_3O_7N_3$] is monoclinic in bladed crystals vertically elongated and twinned on (100?). Basal cleavage. β = 133° *ca*. X′ ∧ *c* = 34 – 48°. $N_1 = 1.50$, $N_2 > 1.80$, $N_2 - N_1 > 0.30$. Golden yellow color. Ref: 90.

Thymine ($C_5H_6O_2N_2$) is monoclinic in equant crystals. M.P. 326°. X ∧ *c* = 27°; Z = *b*. (–)2V = 14°, r > v, with horizontal dispersion. $N_X = 1.414$, $N_Y = 1.726$, $N_Z = 1.736$, $N_Z - N_X = 0.322$. Again: $N_Z = 1.729$. Ref: 418a.

4-Amino-2-hydroxy-5-methylpyrimidine picrate or 5-methylcytosine picrate [N:C(NH_2)C(CH_3):CHN:C(OH)·$C_6H_3O_7N_3$] is orthorhombic in lath-like crystals with parallel extinction and negative elongation. $N_X = 1.44$, N_Y = ?, $N_Z > 1.80$, $N_Z - N_X > 0.36$. Color in mass golden yellow. Ref: 90.

2-Thio-5-iodouracil ($C_4H_3ON_2SI$) is orthorhombic. Crystals tabular or columnar. X = *c*, Y = *b*(?). Elongation ±. (+)2V = small, r < v strong. $N_X = 1.697$, $N_Y = 1.76$, $N_Z > 1.85$, $N_Z - N_X > 0.153$. Ref: 418a.

1,3,6,8-Tetramethyldipyrrolo [*a,d*] pyrazine-5,10-dione or 1,2,4,5-di(2,4-dimethylpyrrolo)-3,6-diketohexahydro-1,4-diazine or 2,4,2′,4′-tetramethylpyrocoll

[HC:C(CH_3)NCOC = C(CH_3)
C(CH_3) : CCONC(CH_3):CH]

is orthorhombic disphenoidal with

$a:b:c = 0.788:1:0.946$. Crystals prismatic with {110}, {010}, {111}, {1$\bar{1}$1}, etc. Perfect 001 cleavage. M.P. 272 - 272.5°. X = c; Y = a. (-)2E = 44°56′ red, 46°20′ yellow, 54°25′ blue. N_X = 1.4676 red, 1.4707 yellow, 1.4746 green. Color orangeyellow with weak pleochroism, a nearly equals b = orange yellow, c = pale yellow. Ref: 119.

Highest yellow U ($C_{23}H_{12}O_2N_2$) is monoclinic domatic with a = 12.235, b = 16.43, c = 3.93 Å. Crystals laths with 010 and $\bar{1}\bar{1}0$ cleavages. D 1.488. M.P. 287°. X ∧ c = 4°, Y = b. (-)2V = 65°. N_X = 1.632, N_Y = 1.972, N_Z = 2.191, $N_Z - N_X$ = 0.559. Pleochroic with X = clear yellow, Y = clear yellow, Z = full golden yellow. Ref: 494a.

Indigo yellow 3G Ciba ($C_{22}H_{12}O_2N_2$) is monoclinic prismatic with $a:b:c$ = 4.512:1:3.63, β = 116°37′. a 21.475, b 4.76, c 17.28 Å. U.C. 4. Crystals acicular. D 1.457. M.P. 275°. X = b, Y ∧ c = 14°. (+)2V = 60°. N_X = 1.762, N_Y = 1.836, N_Z = 2.141, $N_Z - N_X$ = 0.379. Pleochroic with X = clear yellow, Y = citron yellow, Z = brownish yellow. Ref: 494a.

Tetrahydro-2,4,5-triketo-1,3-diazole or imidazoletrione oxalylurea or parabanic acid [CO·NH·CO·CO·NH] is monoclinic with $a:b:c$ = 1.301:1:0.616, β = 92°54.5′. Crystals {100} tablets with {010}, {101}. etc., or equant. Distinct 010 and poor 100 cleavages. M.P. 243°. Parallel extinction and negative elongation with N_1 = 1.43, N_2 = 1.55, $N_2 - N_1$ = 0.12. Ref: 34, 35, 117.

Barbituric acid {$CO(CO \cdot NH)_2CH_2$} is monoclinic. Crystals columnar along c. Y ∧ c = 11°. Z = b. (-)2V = 31°, r < v. N_X = 1.409, N_Y = 1.696, N_Z = 1.727, $N_Z - N_X$ = 0.318. Ref: 418a.

Barbituric acid dihydrate {$CO(CO \cdot NH)_2CH_2 \cdot 2H_2O$} is orthorhombic with $a:b:c$ = 0.698:1:1.411. Crystals columnar. X = a, Y = b. (-)2V = 14°, r < v. N_X = 1.391, N_Y = 1.642, N_Z = 1.647, $N_Z - N_X$ = 0.256. Ref: 418a.

Dilituric acid or 5-nitrobarbituric acid or nitromalonylurea ($NH \cdot CO \cdot NH \cdot CO \cdot CHNO_2 \cdot CO \cdot 3H_2O$) is monoclinic with an extinction angle of 31°, but forms plates having negative elongation and usually parallel extinction (probably {001} plates elongated along b). (-)2V = 60°, or more (calc.), r < v, N_X = 1.388, N_Y = 1.684, N_Z > 1.785, $N_Z - N_X$ > 0.397. Crystals often tabular showing the obtuse (?) bisectrix and N_Y and N_X. Ref: 567.

Dilituric acid trihydrate or 5-nitrobarbituric acid trihydrate or nitromalonylurea trihydrate ($C_4H_3O_5N_3 \cdot 3H_2O$) forms small plates which decompose at 181 - 183°. Biaxial with a large optic angle and probably negative since N_X < 1.408, N_Y = 1.678, N_Z > 1.781 and $N_Z - N_X$ > 0.373. Ref: 539b.

Ammonium diliturate ($NH \cdot CO \cdot NH \cdot CO \cdot CHNO_2 \cdot CO \cdot NH_3$) is monoclinic with an extinction angle of 44° (variable). (-)2V > 20° calc., r < v, N_X = 1.427, N_Y = 1.772, N_Z > 1.785, $N_Z - N_X$ > 0.358. Crystals equant and variable in position. Y ∧ elongation = 44°. Ref: 567.

Hydroxylamine diliturate ($NH \cdot CO \cdot NH \cdot CO \cdot CHNO_2 \cdot CO \cdot NH_2OH$) is monoclinic in tablets normal to Y with X ∧ elongation = 25°. (-)2V = 25° calc. $N_X = 1.487$, $N_Y = 1.748$, $N_Z = 1.763$, $N_Z - N_X = 0.276$. Crystals usually give N_Z and N_X. Ref: 567.

Hydrazine diliturate ($NH \cdot CO \cdot NH \cdot CO \cdot CHNO_2 \cdot CO \cdot NH_2 \cdot NH_2$) is monoclinic; columnar with X ∧ elongation = 26° and Z normal to plates. (-)2V = 37°, r < v. $N_X = 1.458$, $N_Y = 1.748$, $N_Z = 1.783$, $N_Z - N_X = 0.325$. Crystals usually normal to the obtuse bisectrix and give N_X and N_Y. Ref: 567.

Methylamine diliturate $\{NH \cdot CO \cdot NH \cdot CO \cdot CHNO_2 \cdot CO \cdot NH_2 \cdot CH_3\}$ is monoclinic, usually in plates with parallel extinction (*b*) but the extinction angle (X ∧ *c*) is 31°. (-)2V > 60° calc. r < v. $N_X = 1.462$, $N_Y = 1.696$, $N_Z > 1.785$, $N_Z - N_X > 0.359$. Crystals usually give N_Y. Ref: 567.

Ethylamine diliturate $\{NH \cdot CO \cdot NH \cdot CO \cdot CHNO_2 \cdot CO \cdot NH_2 \cdot C_2H_5\}$ is monoclinic in lath-shaped crystals with X parallel to usual elongation (*b*), but an extinction angle (Y ∧ *c*) of 43°. (-)2V > 45°, r < v. $N_X = 1.458$, $N_Y = 1.734$, $N_Z > 1.785$, $N_Z - N_X > 0.326$. Crystals usually give N_Y. Ref: 567.

n-Propylamine diliturate $\{NH \cdot CO \cdot NH \cdot CO \cdot CHNO_2 \cdot CO \cdot NH_2C_3H_7\}$ is orthorhombic in plates normal to Y with X parallel to elongation. (+)2V = 40° calc., r < v. $N_X = 1.606$, $N_Y = 1.619$, $N_Z = 1.701$, $N_Z - N_X = 0.095$. Crystals usually give N_Z and N_X. Ref: 567.

Isopropylamine diliturate $\{NH \cdot CO \cdot NH \cdot CO \cdot CHNO_2 \cdot CO \cdot NH_2 \cdot CH(CH_3)_2\}$ is monoclinic in plates with Y ∧ elongation = 43°. (-)2V = 60° calc., r < v. $N_X = 1.447$, $N_Y = 1.701$, $N_Z = 1.782$, $N_Z - N_X = 0.335$. Crystals usually give N_Y. Ref: 567.

n-Butylamine diliturate $\{NH \cdot CO \cdot NH \cdot CO \cdot CHNO_2 \cdot CO \cdot NH_2 \cdot C_4H_9\}$ is monoclinic in tabular crystals usually with parallel extinction (100 tablets ?), but the extinction may reach 43°. The optic plane is probably 010, and elongation positive. (-)2V = 60° calc., r < v. $N_X = 1.476$, $N_Y = 1.704$, $N_Z = 1.783$, $N_Z - N_X = 0.307$. Crystals usually give N_Y. Ref: 567.

2-Aminobutane diliturate $\{NH \cdot CO \cdot NH \cdot CO \cdot CHNO_2 \cdot CO \cdot CH_3 \cdot CHNH_2C_3H_7\}$ is orthorhombic in needles with Z parallel with elongation and Y normal to usual position. (-)2V = 25° calc., r > v. $N_X = 1.452$, $N_Y = 1.650$, $N_Z = 1.662$, $N_Z - N_X = 0.210$. Crystals acicular usually showing the optic normal interference figure and the indices N_X and N_Z. Ref: 567.

Isobutylamine diliturate $\{NH \cdot CO \cdot NH \cdot CO \cdot CHNO_2 \cdot CO \cdot NH_2 \cdot CH_2 \cdot CH(CH_3)_2\}$ is monoclinic and foliated normal to Z. (-)2V = ?, $N_X = 1.470$, $N_Y = 1.706$, N_Z = ?. X ∧ elongation = 41°, but a common extinction angle is 14°. Ref: 567.

n-Amylamine diliturate {NH·CO·NH·CO·CHNO$_2$·CO·NH$_2$·(CH)$_3$·CH(CH)$_2$ NH$_2$} is orthorhombic in rectangular plates normal to Y with Z parallel to elongation. (+)2V = 55° calc., r < v. $N_X = 1.596$, $N_Y = 1.614$, $N_Z = 1.679$, $N_Z - N_X = 0.083$. Ref: 567.

Isoamylamine diliturate {NH·CO·NH·CO·CHNO$_2$·CO·(CH$_3$)$_2$CH(CH$_2$)$_2$ NH$_2$} is monoclinic in needles with Y ∧ elongation = 6° (−)2V = 45° calc., r < v. $N_X = 1.456$, $N_Y = 1.644$, $N_Z = 1.672$, $N_Z - N_X = 0.216$. Crystals acicular, usually showing N_Z and N_X. Ref: 567.

Cyclohexylamine diliturate {NH·CO·NH·CO·CHNO$_2$·CO·NH$_2$·C$_6$H$_{11}$} is monoclinic in needles with ± elongation and usually parallel extinction; but extinction angle (Z ∧ *c*) is 29°. (−)2V = 57° calc., r < v. $N_X = 1.483$, $N_Y = 1.648$, $N_Z = 1.697$, $N_Z - N_X = 0.214$. Needles usually normal to obtuse bisectrix, showing N_X and N_Y. Ref: 567.

n-Heptylamine diliturate {NH·CO·NH·CO·CHNO$_2$·CO·NH$_2$·C$_7$H$_{15}$} is orthorhombic in thin plates with X parallel to elongation and Y normal to plates. (+)2V = 73° calc., r < v. $N_Y = 1.592$, $N_Y = 1.616$, $N_Z > 1.660$, $N_Z - N_X = 0.068$. Crystals usually give N_X and N_Z. Ref: 567.

2-Amino-*n*-octane diliturate {NH·CO·NH·CO·CHNO$_2$·CO·CH$_3$·CHNH$_2$·C$_6$H$_{13}$} is monoclinic with an extinction angle (Y ∧ *c*) of 30°. Poor cleavage; massive. Elongation ±. (−)2V = 30° calc., r > v. $N_X = 1.469$, $N_Y = 1.635$, $N_Z = 1.647$, $N_Z - N_X = 0.178$. Crystals foliated, usually showing the obtuse bisectrix and an extinction angle of 6° and the indices N_X and N_Y. Ref: 567.

Ethylenediamine diliturate {NH·CO·NH·CO·CHNO$_2$·CO·NH$_2$·(CH$_2$)$_2$·NH$_2$} is monoclinic in tablets with negative elongation and an extinction angle of 44°. (−)2V = ?, r < v. $N_X = 1.454$, $N_Y > 1.785$, N_Z = ?, $N_Z - N_X > 0.331$. Crystals usually give N_Z or N_Y. Ref: 567.

Diethylenetriamine diliturate {NH·CO·NH·CO·CHNO$_2$·CO·NH·C$_2$H$_4$·NH ·C$_2$H$_4$·NH$_2$} is monoclinic and lamellar with Y parallel to elongation, but an extinction angle of 26°. Two good cleavages. (−)2V = 10° calc., r < v. $N_X = 1.446$, $N_Y = 1.731$, $N_Z = 1.736$, $N_Z - N_X = 0.290$. Crystals usually give N_X and N_Z. Ref: 567.

Propylenediamine diliturate {NH·CO·NH·CO·CHNO$_2$·CO·NH$_2$CH$_2$·CHNH$_2$ ·CH$_3$} is monoclinic in thin plates normal to Z with Y ∧ elongation = 28°. (−)2V = ?, r < v, $N_X = 1.452$, $N_Y > 1.785$, N_Z = ?, $N_Z - N_X > 0.333$. Crystals usually give N_X and N_Y. Ref: 567.

2-4-Diaminobutane diliturate {NH·CO·NH·CO·CHNO$_2$·CO·CH$_3$·(CHNH$_2$)$_2$ ·CH$_3$} is monoclinic in plates or fibers. Y is normal to plates. Extinction angle

(X ∧ elongation) is 39°. (–)2V > 30° calc., r < v. $N_X = 1.455$, $N_Y = 1.761$, $N_Z = 1.785$, $N_Z - N_X > 0.330$. Plates and needles usually give N_X and N_Z.
Ref: 567.

Ethanolamine diliturate $\{NH \cdot CO \cdot NH \cdot CO \cdot CHNO_2 \cdot CO \cdot NH_2 \cdot CH_2 \cdot CH_2OH\}$ is monoclinic in lath-shaped crystals with X ∧ elongation = 39°. (–)2V = 37° calc., r < v. $N_X = 1.458$, $N_Y = 1.744$, $N_Z = 1.777$, $N_Z - N_X = 0.319$. Crystals usually give N_Y.
Ref: 567.

Glycine diliturate monohydrate ($C_6H_8O_7N_4 \cdot H_2O$) is monoclinic in rhombic plates which decompose at 294°. X ∧ elongation = 40°. (–)2V = very large (70° calc.), r < v, $N_X = 1.449$, $N_Y = 1.677$, $N_Z = 1.782$, $N_Z - N_X = 0.333$.
Ref: 539b.

dl-Alanine diliturate monohydrate ($C_7H_{10}O_7H_4 \cdot H_2O$) is monoclinic in rods and plates which decompose at 240°. Z ∧ elongation = 5°. (+)2V = large, (74° calc.), r > v. $N_X = 1.532$, $N_Y = 1.605$, $N_Z = 1.736$, $N_Z - N_X = 0.204$.
Ref: 539b.

dl-Valine diliturate dihydrate ($C_9H_{14}O_7N_4 \cdot 2H_2O$) is dimorphous. One phase (I) from dilute solutions is monoclinic in plates which decompose at 201°. X ∧ elongation = 15°. (–)2V = small (15° calc.), r < v. $N_X = 1.439$, $N_Y = 1.646$, $N_Z = 1.652$, $N_Z - N_X = 0.213$. Another phase (II) forms plates with X ∧ elongation = 45°. (–)2V = 82 calc. $N_X = 1.568$, $N_Y = 1.627$, $N_Z = 1.671$, $N_Z - N_X = 0.103$.
Ref: 539a.

d-Lysine di-diliturate tetrahydrate ($C_{14}H_{20}O_{12}N_8 \cdot 4H_2O$) is monoclinic in rhombic plates which decompose at 307°. X ∧ elongation = 30°. (–)2V = small (30° calc.), r < v. $N_X = 1.473$, $N_Y = 1.699$, $N_Z = 1.717$, $N_Z - N_X = 0.244$.
Ref: 539b.

l-Leucine diliturate trihydrate ($C_{10}H_{16}O_7N_4 \cdot 3H_2O$) is orthorhombic in thin plates and rods which decompose at 221°. X || elongation, (–)2V = very small (21° calc.), r < v. $N_X = 1.444$, $N_Y = 1.717$, $N_Z = 1.731$, $N_Z - N_X = 0.287$.
Ref: 539b.

d-Isoleucine diliturate trihydrate ($C_{10}H_{16}O_7N_4 \cdot 3H_2O$) is monoclinic in rhombic plates and long rods, which decompose at 257°. X ∧ elongation = 30°. (–)2V = small (35° calc.) r < v. $N_X = 1.441$, $N_Y = 1.592$, $N_Z = 1.609$, $N_Z - N_X = 0.168$.
Ref: 539b.

l-Aspartic acid diliturate trihydrate ($C_8H_{10}O_9N_4 \cdot 3H_2O$) is monoclinic in long rods which decompose at 207°. X ∧ elongation = 45°. (–)2V = small (35° calc.) r < v. $N_X = 1.433$, $N_Y = 1.636$, $N_Z = 1.656$, $N_Z - N_X = 0.223$.
Ref: 539b.

d-Glutamic acid diliturate hemipentahydrate ($C_9H_{12}O_9N_4 \cdot 2.5H_2O$) is orthorhombic in thin rectangular plates which decompose at 228°. X || elongation. (–)2V = small with great dispersion. 2V = 62° calc. $N_X = 1.532$, $N_Y = 1.621$, $N_Z = 1.653$, $N_Z - N_X = 0.121$.
Ref: 539b.

dl-Serine diliturate sesquihydrate ($C_7H_{10}O_8N_4 \cdot 1.5H_2O$) is orthorhombic in thin plates which decompose at 212°. X || elongation. (−)2V = very small (15° calc.), r < v. $N_X = 1.452$, $N_Y = 1.694$, $N_Z = 1.701$, $N_Z - N_X = 0.249$. Ref: 539b.

l-Cysteine diliturate ($C_7H_{10}O_7N_4S$) is orthorhombic in needles, which decompose at 166°. Z || elongation. (−)2V = small (52° calc.) r < v. $N_X = 1.449$, $N_Y = 1.682$, $N_Z = 1.737$, $N_Z - N_X = 0.288$. Ref: 539b.

l-Cystine di-diliturate trihydrate ($C_{14}H_{18}O_{14}N_8S_2 \cdot 3H_2O$) is orthorhombic in rectangular plates and rods which decompose at 202°. Y || elongation. (−)2V = small (37° calc.), r > v. $N_X = 1.631$, $N_Y = 1.724$, $N_Z = 1.738$, $N_Z - N_X = 0.107$. Ref: 539b.

dl-Methionine diliturate dihydrate ($C_9H_{14}O_7N_4S \cdot 2H_2O$) is orthorhombic in rectangular plates which decompose at 180°. X || elongation. $N_X = 1.527$, $N_Y = 1.683$, N_Z = ?. Ref: 539b.

α-Methylhydroxylamine diliturate ($NH \cdot CO \cdot NH \cdot CO \cdot CHNO_2 \cdot CO \cdot NH_2OCH_3$) is monoclinic usually in plates with Y ∧ elongation = 38°. (−)2V > 55° calc., r < v. $N_X = 1.416$, $N_Y = 1.702$, $N_Z > 1.785$, $N_Z - N_X > 0.369$. Lamellar plates are normal to an optic axis. Crystals usually give N_Y. Ref: 567.

Aniline diliturate {$NH \cdot CO \cdot NH \cdot CO \cdot CHNO_2 \cdot CO \cdot NH_2 \cdot C_6H_5$} is dimorphous; one phase is orthorhombic in {100?} tablets elongated along *c* with X = *c*, Z = *a*. Good 001 and 010 cleavages. (−)2V > 44° calc., r < v. $N_X = 1.447$, $N_Y = 1.738$, $N_Z > 1.785$, $N_Z - N_X > 0.338$. The second phase is monoclinic in {100?} tablets elongated along *b* with X = *b*, Y ∧ *c* = 16°. (−)2V = 82° calc., r < v. $N_X = 1.535$, $N_Y = 1.659$, $N_Z = 1.772$, $N_Z - N_X = 0.237$. Ref: 567a.

o-Chloroaniline diliturate {$NH \cdot CO \cdot NH \cdot CO \cdot CHNO_2 \cdot CO \cdot NH_2 \cdot C_6H_4 \cdot Cl$} is monoclinic in {100} tablets elongated along *c* with X ∧ *c* = 34°, Y = *b*. (+)2V = 88° calc., r > v. $N_X = 1.532$, $N_Y = 1.657$, $N_Z = 1.789$, $N_Z - N_X = 0.257$. Ref: 567a.

m-Chloroaniline diliturate {$NH \cdot CO \cdot NH \cdot CO \cdot CHNO_2 \cdot CO \cdot NH_2 \cdot C_6H_4 \cdot Cl$} is orthorhombic in {001?} tablets with a prism angle of 118°, elongated along *a*; X = *b*, Z = *a*. (−)2V > 17° calc., r > v. $N_X = 1.554$, $N_Y = 1.777$, $N_Z > 1.785$, $N_Z - N_X > 0.231$. Abnormal blue or purple interference color at extinction position. Ref: 567a.

p-Chloroaniline diliturate {$NH \cdot CO \cdot NH \cdot CO \cdot CHNO_2 \cdot CO \cdot NH_2 \cdot C_6H_4 \cdot Cl$} is monoclinic in {010} tablets with an angle β of 125°, elongated along *c*. Y ∧ *c*. = 22°, Z = *b*. (+)2V < 85° calc., r > v. $N_X = 1.575$, $N_Y = 1.670$, $N_Z > 1.785$, $N_Z - N_X > 0.210$. Ref: 567a.

2,4-Dichloroaniline diliturate {NH·CO·NH·CO·CHNO$_2$·CO·NH$_2$·C$_6$H$_3$·Cl$_2$} is monoclinic in {010} plates with crystal angles of 120° and 140°, elongated along *c*. Y ∧ *c* = 24°, Z = *b*. (+)2V < 80° calc., r < v. $N_X = 1.572$, $N_Y = 1.660$, $N_Z > 1.785$, $N_Z - N_X > 0.213$. Ref: 567a.

2,5-Dichloroaniline diliturate {NH·CO·NH·CO·CHNO$_2$·CO·NH$_2$·C$_6$H$_3$·Cl$_2$} is triclinic in {010 ?} tablets with crystal angles of 97°, 120°, and 130°, elongated along *c* with Y ∧ *c* = 28°. (+)2V < 90° calc., r < v. $N_X = 1.532$, $N_Y = 1.700$, $N_Z > 1.785$, $N_Z - N_X > 0.253$. (+ sign requires that $N_Z > 1.86$ and $N_Z - N_X > 0.34$ – A.N.W.). Ref: 567a.

o-Nitroaniline diliturate {NH·CO·NH·CO·CHNO$_2$·CO·NH$_2$·C$_6$H$_4$·NO$_2$} is monoclinic in {100 ?} tablets with a crystal angle of 125°, and X ∧ *c* = 33°; Y = *b*. (–)2V > 67° calc., r < v. $N_X = 1.540$, $N_Y = 1.714$, $N_Z > 1.785$, $N_Z - N_X > 0.245$. Ref: 567a.

m-Nitroaniline diliturate {NH·CO·NH·CO·CHNO$_2$·CO·NH$_2$·C$_6$H$_4$·NO$_2$} is dimorphous. One phase (I) (from ethanol) is orthorhombic in (100 ?) laths with a crystal angle of 120° and Y = *b*, Z = c. (–)2V > 45° calc., r > v. $N_X = 1.562$, $N_Y = 1.750$ D. (1.762 in white light), $N_Z > 1.785$, $N_Z - N_X > 0.223$; Another phase (II) (from water) is triclinic in (010 ?) tablets with a crystal angle of 120°, a common extinction angle of 3°, but a maximum angle, Z′ ∧ *c* = 28°. (+)2V = 87° calc., r < v. $N_X = 1.522$, $N_Y = 1.650$, $N_Z = 1.786$, $N_Z - N_X = 0.264$. Ref: 567a.

p-Nitroaniline diliturate {NH·CO·NH·CO·CHNO$_2$·CO·NH$_2$·C$_6$H$_4$·NO$_2$} is triclinic in (010 ?) tablets with crystal angles of 98° and 135°, usual extinction angle of 17° and X ∧ *c* = 36°. (+)2V < 88° calc., r < v. $N_X = 1.615$, $N_Y = 1.698$, $N_Z > 1.785$, $N_Z - N_X > 0.170$. Color yellow. Crystals slowly decompose and become colorless with lower refringence and smaller optic angle. Ref: 567a.

3-Nitro-4-chloroaniline diliturate {NH·CO·NH·CO·CHNO$_2$·CO·NH$_2$·Cl·C$_6$H$_3$·NO$_2$} is triclinic in equant crystals with an angle of 98°, a usual extinction angle of 16° and X′ ∧ *c* = 25°. (+)2V < 80° calc., r < v. $N_X = 1.605$, $N_Y = 1.680$, $N_Z = 1.785$, $N_Z - N_X > 0.180$. Ref: 567a.

o-Bromoaniline {diliturate {NH·CO·NH·CO·CHNO$_2$·CO·NH$_2$·C$_6$H$_4$·Br} is monoclinic in {100} tablets with angles of 90°, 119°, and 128°, elongated along *c*; X ∧ *c* = 35°, Y = *b*. (+)2V = 70° calc., r > v. $N_X = 1.580$, $N_Y = 1.647$, $N_Z = 1.788$, $N_Z - N_X = 0.208$. Usual crystals show no good extinction being nearly normal to an optic axis. Ref: 567a.

m-Bromoaniline diliturate {NH·CO·NH·CO·CHNO$_2$·CO·NH$_2$·C$_6$H$_4$·Br} is monoclinic in prismatic crystals elongated along *c* with X ∧ *c* = 16°, Z = *b*, (–)2V = 55° calc., r < v. $N_X = 1.525$, $N_Y = 1.708$, $N_Z = 1.735$, $N_Z - N_X =$

0.210. When crystals are lightly crushed plates are produced inclined to the acute bisectrix. Ref: 567a.

p-Bromoaniline diliturate {NH·CO·NH·CO·CHNO$_2$·CO·NH$_2$·C$_6$H$_4$·Br} is dimorphous; one phase (I) is monoclinic in rectangular {100} tablets elongated along *c* with X ∧ *c* = 18°, Y = *b*; (+)2V < 90°, calc. r > v. N_X = 1.456, N_Y = 1.749, N_Z > 1.785, $N_Z - N_X$ > 0.329. (The + sign requires that N_Z > 2.041). A second phase (II) is monoclinic in diamond-shaped {010} tablets elongated along *c* with Y ∧ *c* = 21°, Z = *b*. (+)2V < 88° calc., r > v. N_X = 1.597, N_Y = 1.688, N_Z > 1.785, $N_Z - N_X$ > 0.188. Ref: 567a.

p-Iodoaniline diliturate [NH·CO·NH·CO·CHNO$_2$·CO·NH$_2$·C$_6$H$_4$·I] is monoclinic in {100} tablets elongated along *c* with X ∧ *c* = 9°, Y = *b*. (+)2V < 90° calc., r < v. N_X = 1.500, N_Y = 1.751, N_Z > 1.785, $N_Z - N_X$ > 0.285. (The + sign requires that N_Z > 2.00 and $N_Z - N_X$ > 0.50! – A.N.W.). Ref: 567a.

d-Phenylisopropylamine diliturate or *d*-amphetamine diliturate or dexedrine diliturate ($C_9H_{13}N \cdot C_4H_3O_5N_3$) is orthorhombic. Crystals tabular with ± elongation and Z normal to plates. (–)2V = 55° calc., r < v. N_X = 1.471, N_Y = 1.653, N_Z = 1.704, $N_Z - N_X$ = 0.233. Ref: 566a.

dl-Phenylisopropylamine diliturate or *dl*-amphetamine diliturate or benzedrine diliturate ($C_9H_{13}N \cdot C_4H_3O_5N_3$) is orthorhombic. Crystals acicular with ± elongation. (–)2V = 55° calc., r < v. N_X = 1.470, N_Y = 1.645, N_Z = 1.698, $N_Z - N_X$ = 0.228. Ref: 566a.

o-Toluidine diliturate {NH·CO·NH·CO·CHNO$_2$·CO·NH$_2$·C$_6$H$_4$·CH$_3$} is monoclinic in (100 ?) tablets with X ∧ *c* = 38°, Y = *b*, (+)2V = 75° calc., r > v. N_X = 1.552, N_Y = 1.632, N_Z = 1.766, $N_Z - N_X$ = 0.214. Usual crystals show no good extinction being nearly normal to an optic axis. Ref: 567a.

m-Toluidine diliturate {NH·CO·NH·CO·CHNO$_2$·CO·NH$_2$·C$_6$H$_4$·CH$_3$} is triclinic in (010 ?) tablets with crystal angles of 98° and 140° and a usual extinction angle of about 10°, but a maximum extinction angle of 42°. (+)2V < 84° calc., r > v. N_X = 1.567, N_Y = 1.675, N_Z > 1.785, $N_Z - N_X$ > 0.218. Abnormal blue or purple interference color at the extinction position. Ref: 567a.

p-Toluidine diliturate {NH·CO·NH·CO·CHNO$_2$·CO·NH$_2$·C$_6$H$_4$·CH$_3$} is monoclinic in {010} tablets with *β* = 83° and Y ∧ *c* = 24°, Z = *b*. (+)2V = 45° calc., r > v. N_X = 1.670, N_Y = 1.680, N_Z = 1.734, $N_Z - N_X$ = 0.064. Ref: 567a.

3-Bromo-4-aminotoluene diliturate {NH·CO·NH·CO·CHNO$_2$·CO·NH$_2$Br·C$_6$H$_3$·CH$_3$} is monoclinic in {100 ?} tablets with angles of 116° and 120°, elongated along *c*; X ∧ *c* = 19°; Y = *b*. (+)2V < 88° calc., r > v. N_X = 1.578, N_Y = 1.679, N_Z > 1.785, $N_Z - N_X$ > 0.207. Ref: 567a.

Benzylamine diliturate {NH·CO·NH·CO·CHNO$_2$·CO·NH$_2$·CH$_2$·C$_6$H$_5$} is orthorhombic in rectangular plates normal to Y with X parallel to elongation. (-)2V > 25° calc., r < v. $N_X = 1.448$, $N_Y = 1.766$, $N_Z > 1.785$, $N_Z - N_X > 0.338$. Crystals tabular giving N_Z and N_X. Ref: 567.

2-Amino-1,3-dimethylbenzene diliturate {NH·CO·NH·CO·CHNO$_2$·CO·NH$_2$ C$_6$H$_3$·(CH$_3$)$_2$} is monoclinic in {010} plates elongated along *c* with X ∧ *c* = 20°, Z = *b*. (+)2V < 83° calc., r > v. $N_X = 1.583$, $N_Y = 1.670$, $N_Z > 1.785$, $N_Z - N_X > 0.115$. Ref: 567a.

2-Amino-1,4-dimethylbenzene diliturate {NH·CO·NH·CO·CHNO$_2$·CO·NH$_2$ ·C$_6$H$_3$·(CH$_3$)$_2$} is monoclinic in {010} plates elongated along *c* with X ∧ *c* = 28°, Z = *b*. (+)2V = 87° calc., r > v. $N_X = 1.572$, $N_Y = 1.657$, $N_Z = 1.752$, $N_Z - N_X = 0.180$. Crystal masses of very thin fragments may show gray interference colors. Ref: 567a.

4-Amino-1,3-dimethylbenzene diliturate {NH·CO·NH·CO·CHNO$_2$·CO·NH$_2$ ·C$_6$H$_3$·(CH$_3$)$_2$} is orthorhombic in {010} plates elongated along *c* with X = *c*, Z = *b*. (-)2V > 82°, r < v. $N_X = 1.522$, $N_Y = 1.671$, $N_Z > 1.785$, $N_Z - N_X > 0.263$. Ref: 567a.

5-Amino-1,3-dimethylbenzene diliturate {NH·CO·NH·CO·CHNO$_2$·CO·NH$_2$ C$_6$H$_3$(CH$_3$)$_2$} is monoclinic in {010} lamellae normal to Z with Y ∧ *c* = 39°. (-)2V = 85° calc., r > v. $N_X = 1.543$, $N_Y = 1.642$, $N_Z = 1.723$, $N_Z - N_X = 0.180$. Crystals in masses with vivid interference colors. Ref: 567a.

α-Naphthylamine diliturate {NH·CO·NH·CO·CHNO$_2$·CO·C$_{10}$H$_7$·NH$_2$} is dimorphous. One phase (I) is monoclinic in {010} lamellae elongated along *c* with X ∧ *c* = 14°, Z = *b*. (+)2V < 70° calc., r < v. $N_X = 1.635$, $N_Y = 1.684$, $N_Z > 1.785$, $N_Z - N_X > 0.150$. The second phase (II) is triclinic in {100?} plates elongated along *c* with a maximum extinction angle, X′ ∧ *c* = 44°. (-)2V > 10° calc., r < v. $N_X = 1.650$, $N_Y = 1.783$, $N_Z > 1.785$, $N_Z - N_X > 0.135$. Ref: 567a.

β-Naphthylamine diliturate {NH·CO·NH·CO·CHNO$_2$·CO·C$_{10}$H$_7$·NH$_2$} is orthorhombic in {100?} tablets with a crystal angle of 127°, elongated along *c*. X = *c*, Y = *b*. (-)2V > 35° calc., r < v. $N_X = 1.650$, $N_Y = 1.758$, $N_Z > 1.785$, $N_Z - N_X > 0.135$. Ref: 567a.

o-Aminodiphenyl diliturate {NH·CO·NH·CO·CHNO$_2$·CO·NH$_2$·C$_6$H$_4$·C$_6$H$_5$} is orthorhombic in long {100} laths with X = *c*, Y = *a*. (-)2V > 25°, calc., r > v. $N_X = 1.461$, $N_Y = 1.768$ D, ($N_Y = 1.774$ in white light), $N_Z > 1.785$, $N_Z - N_X > 0.324$. Ref: 567a.

p-Aminodiphenyl diliturate $\{\overline{NH \cdot CO \cdot NH \cdot CO \cdot CHNO_2 \cdot CO} \cdot NH_2 \cdot C_6H_4 \cdot C_6H_5\}$ is monoclinic in {010} laths with $X \wedge c = 12°$, $Z = b$. (+)2V < 62° calc., r > v. $N_X = 1.603$, $N_Y = 1.653$, $N_Z > 1.785$, $N_Z - N_X > 0.182$. Ref: 567a.

o-Phenylenediamine diliturate $\{\overline{NH \cdot CO \cdot NH \cdot CO \cdot CHNO_2 \cdot CO} \cdot (NH_2)_2 \cdot C_6H_4\}$ is triclinic in {100?} laths elongated along *c* with a usual extinction angle of 6° and $X' \wedge c = 18°$. (-)2V = 35° calc., r < v. $N_X = 1.438$, $N_Y = 1.737$, $N_Z = 1.772$, $N_Z - N_X = 0.334$. Ref: 567a.

m-Phenylenediamine diliturate $\{\overline{NH \cdot CO \cdot NH \cdot CO \cdot CHNO_2 \cdot CO} \cdot NH_2 \cdot C_6H_4\}$ is triclinic in {010?} lamellae elongated along *c* with a usual extinction angle of 7° and $Y' \wedge c = 30°$. (-)2V > 74° calc., r < v. $N_X = 1.493$, $N_Y = 1.683$, $N_Z > 1.785$, $N_Z - N_X > 0.292$. Ref: 567a.

p-Phenylenediamine diliturate $\{\overline{NH \cdot CO \cdot NH \cdot CO \cdot CHNO_2 \cdot CO} \cdot NH_2 \cdot C_6H_4\}$ is monoclinic in {010} tablets with $\beta = 110°$, $X \wedge c = 25°$, $Z = b$. (-)2V > 60° calc., r < v. $N_X = 1.501$, $N_Y = 1.716$, $N_Z > 1.785$, $N_Z - N_X > 0.284$. Ref: 567a.

p-Aminodimethylaniline diliturate $\{\overline{NH \cdot CO \cdot NH \cdot CO \cdot CHNO_2 \cdot CO} \cdot NH_2 \cdot C_6H_4 \cdot N(CH_3)_2\}$ is monoclinic in {100} plates elongated along *c* with $Y = b$. $Z \wedge c = 42°$. (-)2V > 75°, calc., r < v. $N_X = 1.462$, $N_Y = 1.668$, $N_Z > 1.785$, $N_Z - N_X > 0.323$. {100} plates are nearly normal to an optic axis and show no good extinction. Ref: 567a.

p-Aminodiethylaniline diliturate $\{\overline{NH \cdot CO \cdot NH \cdot CO \cdot CHNO_2 \cdot CO} \cdot NH_2 \cdot C_6H_4 \cdot N(C_2H_5)_2\}$ is monoclinic in {100} plates with Y parallel to elongation along *b*. $X \wedge c = 22°$. (-)2V = 67° calc., r < v. $N_X = 1.455$, $N_Y = 1.659$, $N_Z = 1.744$, $N_Z - N_X = 0.289$. Ref: 567a.

2,4-Diaminotoluene diliturate $\{\overline{NH \cdot CO \cdot NH \cdot CO \cdot CHNO_2 \cdot CO} \cdot CH_3 \cdot C_6H_3 \cdot (NH_2)_2\}$ is triclinic in columns elongated along *c* with crystal angles of 103°, 115°, and 134°, and a maximum extinction angle ($Y \wedge c$) of 35°, (-)2V > 37° calc., r < v. $N_X = 1.470$, $N_Y = 1.751$, $N_Z > 1.785$, $N_Z - N_X > 0.315$. Ref: 567a.

2,5-Diaminotoluene diliturate $\{\overline{NH \cdot CO \cdot NH \cdot CO \cdot CHNO_2 \cdot CO} \cdot CH_3 \cdot C_6H_3 \cdot (NH_2)_2\}$ is monoclinic in {010} lamellae with crystal angles of 112° and 142°, elongated along *c* with $Y \wedge c = 17°$ (-)2V > 42° calc., r < v. $N_X = 1.513$, $N_Y = 1.749$, $N_Z > 1.785$, $N_Z - N_X > 0.272$. Many crystals are thin, oval-shaped. Ref: 567a.

o-Aminophenol diliturate $\{\overline{NH \cdot CO \cdot NH \cdot CO \cdot CHNO_2 \cdot CO} \cdot NH_2 \cdot C_6H_4 \cdot OH\}$ is monoclinic in lamellae elongated along *b* with $X = b$ and an extinction angle of

29°. (+)2V < 70°, calc., r > v. $N_X = 1.618$, $N_Y = 1.673$, $N_Z > 1.785$, $N_Z - N_X > 0.167$. Usual crystals show no good extinction, being nearly normal to an optic axis. Ref: 567a.

m-Aminophenol dilurate {$NH \cdot CONH \cdot CO \cdot CHNO_2CO \cdot NH_4 \cdot C_6H_4 \cdot OH$} is dimorphous; one phase (I) is monoclinic in tablets having an angle of 112° and elongated along *b* with Y = *b* and X ∧ *c* = 33°. (-)2V > 37°, r < v. $N_X = 1.480$, $N_Y = 1.750$, $N_Z > 1.785$, $N_Z - N_X > 0.305$. The other phase (II) is triclinic in tablets having an angle of 135°, and a maximum extinction angle of 26°. (-)2V > 72° calc., r < v. $N_X = 1.501$, $N_Y = 1.689$, $N_X > 1.785$, $N_Z - N_X = 0.284$. Ref: 567a.

p-Aminophenol dilurate {$NH \cdot CO \cdot NH \cdot CO \cdot CHNO_2 \cdot CO \cdot NH_2 \cdot C_6H_4 \cdot OH$} is triclinic in {010 ?} tablets with a maximum extinction angle of 22° and negative elongation. (-)2V > 60° calc., r < v. $N_X = 1.508$, $N_Y = 1.715$, $N_Z > 1.785$, $N_Z - N_X > 0.277$. Ref: 567a.

2-Amino-4-nitrophenol dilurate {$NH \cdot CO \cdot NH \cdot CO \cdot CHNO_2 \cdot CO \cdot NH_2 \cdot OH \cdot C_6H_3 \cdot NO_2$} is monoclinic in needles elongated along *b* with Y = *b*, and an extinction angle of 16°. (+)2V < 84° calc., with marked inclined dispersion. $N_X = 1.672$, $N_Y = 1.722$, $N_Z > 1.785$, $N_Z - N_X > 0.113$. Ref: 567a.

2,6-Dibromo-4-aminophenol dilurate {$NH \cdot CO \cdot NH \cdot CO \cdot CHNO_2 \cdot CO \cdot NH_2 \cdot OH \cdot C_6H_2Br_2$} is triclinic in {010 ?} tablets elongated along *c* with crystal angles of 108°, 130°, and 137°. Y ∧ *c* = 44°. (+)2V < 70° calc., r < v. $N_X = 1.590$, $N_Y = 1.653$, $N_Z = 1.785$, $N_Z - N_X = 0.195$. Ref: 567a.

2-Amino-5-hydroxyltoluene dilurate {$NH \cdot CO \cdot NH \cdot CO \cdot CHNO_2 \cdot CO \cdot NH_2 \cdot OH \cdot C_6H_3 \cdot CH_3$} is monoclinic in {100} tablets with X ∧ *c* = 7°, Y = *b*. (-)2V 85° calc., r < v. $N_X = 1.520$, $N_Y = 1.651$, $N_Z = 1.763$, $N_Z - N_X = 0.243$. Ref: 567a.

2,4-Diaminophenol dilurate {$NH \cdot CO \cdot NH \cdot CO \cdot CHNO_2 \cdot CO \cdot (NH_2)_2 \cdot C_6H_3 \cdot OH$} is dimorphous; one phase (I) is monoclinic in needles elongated along *c* with X = *b*, Y ∧ *c* = 17°. (-)2V > 66° calc., r < v. $N_X = 1.508$, $N_Y = 1.701$, $N_Z > 1.785$, $N_Z - N_X > 0.277$. The needles often give the acute bisectrix interference figure. The second phase (II) is triclinic in {010 ?} tablets with angles of 95° and 133° and a maximum extinction angle of 43° (seen in 010); the extinction angle in 100 is small. (-)2V > 69° calc., r < v. $N_X = 1.498$, $N_Y = 1.695$, $N_Z > 1.785$, $N_Z - N_X > 0.287$. Ref: 567a.

p-Hydroxy-α-methylphenylamine dilurate or paredrine dilurate ($C_9H_{13}ON \cdot C_4H_3O_5N_3$) is triclinic. Crystals tabular with Z′ ∧ elongation = 43°. (-)2V > 45° calc., r < v. $N_X = 1.450$, $N_Y = 1.731$, $N_Z > 1.785$, $N_Z - N_X > 0.330$. Ref: 566a.

dl-Phenylpropanolamine diliturate or propadrine diliturate ($C_9H_{14}ON \cdot C_4H_3O_5N_3$) is dimorphous. Phase I is orthorhombic. Crystals often lath-shaped with **X** || elongation and Z normal to plates. (-)2V = 40° calc. r < v. $N_X = 1.461$, $N_Y = 1.678$, $N_Z = 1.708$, $N_Z - N_X = 0.247$. Phase II is also orthorhombic. Crystals lamellar with cleavage parallel to X and to elongation. (-)2V = 35° calc., r < v. $N_X = 1.471$, $N_Y = 1.663$, $N_Z = 1.685$, $N_Z - N_X = 0.214$.
Ref: 566a.

Ephedrine diliturate ($C_{10}H_{15}ON \cdot C_4H_3O_5N_3$) is orthorhombic. Crystals often six-sided plates normal to Z, with X parallel to elongation. (-)2V = 70° calc., r > v. $N_X = 1.544$, $N_Y = 1.619$, $N_Z = 1.655$, $N_Z - N_X = 0.111$. Ref: 566a.

dl-Ephedrine diliturate or racephedrine ($C_{10}H_{15}ON \cdot C_4H_3O_5N_3$) is triclinic. Crystals often six-sided plates with Y′ ∧ elongation = 38°. (-)2V = 75° calc., r < v. $N_X = 1.537$, $N_Y = 1.662$, $N_Z = 1.731$, $N_Z - N_X = 0.194$. Large crystals are yellow.
Ref: 566a.

2-Aminocymene diliturate {$NH \cdot CO \cdot NH \cdot CO \cdot CHNO_2 \cdot CO \cdot CH(CH_3)_2 \cdot NH_2 \cdot C_6H_3 \cdot CH_3$} is orthorhombic in plates normal to Z with X parallel to elongation. (-)2V = 40° calc., r < v. $N_X = 1.508$, $N_Y = 1.648$, $N_Z = 1.679$, $N_Z - N_X = 0.171$. Color pink. Crystal angles 90° or, rarely 125°. Ref: 567a.

Benzidine diliturate {$NH \cdot CO \cdot NH \cdot CO \cdot CHNO_2 \cdot CO \cdot NH_2 \cdot (C_6H_4)_2NH_2$} is triclinic in {010 ?} laths with an angle of 120°, negative elongation, and a maximum extinction angle of 37°. (+)2V < 87° calc., r > v. $N_X = 1.571$, $N_Y = 1.684$, $N_Z > 1.785$, $N_Z - N_X > 0.214$. Crystals usually inclined to an optic axis and giving an extinction angle of 30°.
Ref: 567a.

Tolidine diliturate {$NH \cdot CO \cdot NH \cdot CO \cdot CHNO_2 \cdot CO \cdot NH_2 \cdot C_{12}H_6 \cdot CH_3$} is monoclinic in {010} lamellae with $\beta = 60°$ and an angle of 138°. Y ∧ *c* = 25°, Z = *b*. (+)2V < 80° calc., r < v. $N_X = 1.590$, $N_Y = 1.705$, $N_Z > 1.785$, $N_Z - N_X > 0.195$. (The + sign requires that $N_Z > 1.82$ and $N_Z - N_X > 0.23$).
Ref: 567a.

β-Phenylalanine diliturate dihydrate ($C_{13}H_{14}O_7N_4 \cdot 2H_2O$) is dimorphous. One phase (I) from dilute solutions is monoclinic in rods which decompose at 249°. Z ∧ elongation = 20°. (-)2V = small (32° calc.) r < v. $N_X = 1.479$, $N_Y = 1.777$, $N_Z = 1.805$, $N_Z - N_X = 0.326$, Another phase (II) from concentrated solutions is also monoclinic in rods and rhombic plates which decompose at 249°. X ∧ elongation = 10°. (-)2V = small (20° calc.), r < v. $N_Z = 1.441$, $N_Y = 1.695$, $N_X = 1.704$, $N_Z - N_X = 0.263$. Ref: 539b.

l-Tyrosine diliturate trihydrate ($C_{13}H_{14}O_8N_4 \cdot 3H_2O$) forms fine needles which decompose at 172°. $N_X = 1.468$, $N_Y = ?$, $N_Z = 1.701$, $N_Z - N_X = 0.233$.
Ref: 539b.

Sulfanilamide diliturate monohydrate ($C_{10}H_{11}O_7N_5S \cdot H_2O$) is monoclinic in tabular crystals which become opaque at 150° and melt at 270°. Elongation ±;

X = *b*; maximum extinction angle = 40°(?). (-)2V = 51°, r < v, with very strong crossed dispersion. $N_X = 1.561$, $N_Y = 1.724$, $N_Z = 1.769$, $N_Z - N_X = 0.208$. Color pink; not pleochroic. Ref: 434a.

Sulfacetimide diliturate sesquihydrate ($C_{12}H_{13}O_8N_5S \cdot 1.5H_2O$) forms lamellar crystals with M.P. 222°. (-)2V = large, $N_X = 1.399$, $N_Y = 1.659$, $N_Z = 1.754$, (?), $N_Z - N_X = 0.355$ (?). Ref: 434a.

Sulfaguanidine diliturate ($C_{11}H_{13}O_7N_7S$) is triclinic in equant crystals which decompose at 255°. Elongation +; extinction inclined. (+)2V = 87°, r > v. $N_X = 1.572$, $N_Y = 1.688$, $N_Z = 1.854$, $N_Z - N_X = 0.282$. Color buff, with no pleochroism. Ref: 434a.

Sulfapyridine diliturate monohydrate ($C_{15}H_{14}O_7N_6S \cdot H_2O$) is monoclinic in lamellar crystals which melt at 220°. Elongation ±; Y = *b*(?). $X \wedge c = 26°$. (-)2V = 24°, r > v. $N_X = 1.542$, $N_Y = 1.785$, $N_Z = 1.799$, $N_Z - N_X = 0.257$. Color yellow; not pleochroic. Ref: 434a.

l-Proline diliturate dihydrate ($C_9H_{12}O_7N_4 \cdot 2H_2O$) is orthorhombic in rectangular plates which decompose at 187°. X || elongation. (-)2V = 75° calc., r < v. $N_X = 1.533$, $N_Y = 1.611$, $N_Z = 1.657$, $N_Z - N_X = 0.124$. Ref: 539b.

l-Hydroxyproline diliturate hemipentahydrate ($C_9H_{12}O_8N_4 \cdot 2.5H_2O$) is orthorhombic in small rectangular plates which decompose at 115°. Z || elongation. (-)2V = 77° calc., r < v. $N_X = 1.532$, $N_Y = 1.602$, $N_Z = 1.645$, $N_Z - N_X = 0.113$. Ref: 539b.

dl-Tryptophane diliturate trihydrate ($C_{15}H_{15}O_7N_5 \cdot 3H_2O$) forms rectangular plates and rods which decompose at 191°. Elongation negative. $N_X = 1.462$, N_Y = ?, $N_Z = 1.693$. Ref: 539b.

Sulfadiazine diliturate dihydrate ($C_{14}H_{13}O_7N_7S \cdot 2H_2O$) is monoclinic in long crystals which melt at 210°. (-)2V = 15° to 60° (variable, N_Z also varying). $N_Y = 1.714$. Color yellow with no pleochroism. Ref: 434a.

Sulfamerazine diliturate monohydrate ($C_{15}H_{15}O_7N_7S \cdot H_2O$) is orthorhombic. Crystals columnar along *c*. X = *c*. (-)2V = 40°, r < v. $N_X = 1.506$, $N_Y = 1.720$, $N_Z = 1.755$, $N_Z - N_X = 0.249$. Color yellow; not pleochroic. Ref: 434a.

5,5-Diethylhexahydro-2,4,6-triketopyrimidine or 5,5-diethylbarbituric acid or barbital or veronal {$CONHCONHCOC(C_2H_5)_2$} is polymorphous. It is easily soluble in alcohol, ether, etc. The stable phase (I) is trigonal, the rhombohedral plane angle is 105°. M.P. 191°. Uniaxial positive with $N_O = 1.526$, $N_E = 1.570$, $N_E - N_O = 0.044$. Another phase (II) is monoclinic with many crystal faces {110}, {011}, {010}, etc. $Y \wedge c = 0°$ *ca.*; Z = *b*. (-)2V = 45° calc. $N_X = 1.437$, $N_Y = 1.558$, $N_Z = 1.580$, $N_Z - N_X = 0.143$. The third phase (III) is orthorhombic dipyramidal with $a:b:c = 0.491:1:0.688$. Space group *Cmcm*; *a* 7.11, *b* 14.4, *c* 9.7 Å. U.C. 4. Multiple twinning common. (-)2V = 36°, $N_X = 1.463$, $N_Y = 1.550$, $N_Z = 1.576$, $N_Z - N_X = 0.113$. A fourth phase has been reported. Ref: 86, 123, 206, 239, 343c, 490, 491a.

Medinal or sodium barbital or sodium veronal ($NaC_8H_{11}O_3N_2$) forms a powder easily soluble in water. M.P. 171°. (+)2V = 40° *ca.* calc. $N_X = 1.519$, $N_Y = 1.532$, $N_Z = 1.617$, $N_Z - N_X = 0.098$. Again: $N_X = 1.5121$, $N_Z = 1.615$. Colorless. Ref: 239, 343c, 518.

1,3-*bis*(*o*-Bromobenzyl)-5,5-diethylbarbituric acid or barbital-*o*-bromobenzyl [$CON(BrC_6H_4CH_2)CON(BrC_6H_4CH_2)COC(C_2H_5)_2$] is monoclinic in thick rods with M.P. 140 – 141°. Elongation positive with an extinction angle of 16°. (–)2V = 55° calc. $N_X = 1.556$, $N_Y = 1.640$, $N_Z = 1.663$, $N_Z - N_X = 0.107$. Colorless. Ref: 148.

1,3-*bis*(*m*-Bromobenzyl)-5,5-diethylbarbituric acid or barbital-*m*-bromobenzyl [$CON(BrC_6H_4CH_2)CON(BrC_6H_4CH_2)COC(C_2H_5)_2$] is monoclinic in thin plates with M.P. 90 – 91°. Elongation positive with an extinction angle of 30°. (–)2V = 40° calc. $N_X = 1.577$, $N_Y = 1.679$, $N_Z = 1.693$, $N_Z - N_X = 0.136$. Colorless. Ref: 148.

1,3-*bis*(*o*-Chlorobenzyl)-5,5-diethylbarbituric acid or barbital-*o*-chlorobenzyl [$CON(ClC_6H_4CH_2)CON(ClC_6H_4CH_2)COC(C_2H_5)_2$] is monoclinic in long rods with M.P. 124 – 127°. Elongation positive with an extinction angle of 20°. (–)2V = 60° calc. $N_X = 1.548$, $N_Y = 1.649$, $N_Z = 1.696$, $N_Z - N_X = 0.148$. Colorless. Ref: 148.

1,3-*bis*(*m*-Chlorobenzyl)-5,5-diethylbarbituric acid or barbital-*m*-chlorobenzyl [$CON(ClC_6H_4CH_2)CON(ClC_6H_4CH_2)COC(C_2H_5)_2$] is monoclinic in thin plates with M.P. 100.5 – 102°. Elongation positive with an extinction angle of 23°. (–)2V = 70° calc. $N_X = 1.538$, $N_Y = 1.640$, $N_Z = 1.690$, $N_Z - N_X = 0.152$. Colorless. Ref: 148.

5,5-Diethyl-1,3-*bis*(*m*-nitrobenzyl)barbituric acid or barbital-*m*-nitrobenzyl [$CON(NO_2C_6H_4CH_2)CON(NO_2C_6H_4CH_2)COC(C_2H_5)_2$] is monoclinic in long needles with M.P. 159 – 160°. Elongation negative with an extinction angle of 7°. (+)2V = 80° calc., r < v strong. $N_X = 1.487$, $N_Y = 1.626$, $N_Z = 1.715$, $N_Z - N_X = 0.228$. Color pale yellow. Ref: 148.

5,5-Diethyl-1,3-*bis*(*p*-nitrobenzyl)barbituric acid or barbital-*p*-nitrobenzyl [$CON(NO_2C_6H_4CH_2)CON(NO_2C_6H_4CH_2)COC(C_2H_5)_2$] is monoclinic in needles and rods with M.P. 192 – 193°. Elongation positive with an extinction angle of 14°. (±)2V = 90° *ca.* with strong dispersion. $N_X = 1.510$, $N_Y = 1.606$, $N_Z = 1.706$, $N_Z - N_X = 0.196$. Color pale yellow. Ref: 148.

5,5-Diethyl-1,3-diphenacylbarbituric acid or barbital phenacyl [$CON(C_6H_5COCH_2)CON(C_6H_5COCH_2)COC(C_2H_5)_2$] is monoclinic in flat rods and plates with M.P. 191 – 192°. Elongation positive with an extinction angle of 42°. (–)2V = 40° calc., r > v moderate. $N_X = 1.587$, $N_Y = 1.626$, $N_Z = 1.634$, $N_Z - N_X = 0.047$. Colorless. Ref: 148.

1,3-*bis*(*p*-Chlorobenzyl)-5,5-diethylbarbituric acid or barbital-*p*-chlorobenzyl $[CON(ClC_6H_4CH_2)CON(ClC_6H_4CH_2)COC(C_2H_5)_2]$ is monoclinic in flat rods and plates with M.P. 142 - 144°. Elongation negative with an extinction angle of 33°. (+)2V = 45° calc. $N_X = 1.545$, $N_Y = 1.563$, $N_Z = 1.664$, $N_Z - N_X = 0.119$. Colorless. Ref: 148.

1,3-*bis*(*p*-Bromobenzyl)-5,5-diethylbarbituric acid or barbital-*p*-bromobenzyl $[CON(BrC_6H_4CH_2)CON(BrC_6H_4CH_2)COC(C_2H_5)_2]$ is monoclinic in flat rods or plates with M.P. 146 - 147°. Elongation negative with an extinction angle of 4°. (+)2V = 30° calc. $N_X = 1.556$, $N_Y = 1.577$, $N_Z = 1.698$, $N_Z - N_X = 0.142$. Colorless. Ref: 148.

1,3-*bis*(*p*-Bromophenacyl)-5,5-diethylbarbituric acid or barbital-*p*-bromophenacyl $[CON(BrC_6H_4COCH_2)CON(BrC_6H_4COCH_2)COC(C_2H_5)_2]$ is monoclinic in rods with M.P. 191.5 - 193°. Elongation positive with an extinction angle of 32°. (-)2V = 45° calc. $N_X = 1.599$, $N_Y = 1.642$, $N_Z = 1.649$, $N_Z - N_X = 0.050$. Colorless. Ref: 148.

5,5-Diethyl-1,3-*bis*(*p*-iodobenzyl)barbituric acid or barbital-*p*-iodobenzyl $[CON(IC_6H_4CH_2)CON(IC_6H_4CH_2)COC(C_2H_5)_2]$ is monoclinic in rods and thick plates with M.P. 122 - 123°. Elongation negative with an extinction angle of 34°. (+)2V < 25° calc. $N_X = 1.531$, $N_Y = 1.642$, $N_Z > 1.74$, $N_Z - N_X > 0.21$. Colorless. Ref: 148.

5,5-Dipropylbarbituric acid or proponal or dipropylmalonylurea $[NHCOC(C_3H_7)_2CONHCO]$ is acicular oteen in groups. M.P. 145 - 146°. $N_1 = 1.493$, $N_2 = 1.536$, $N_2 - N_1 = 0.043$. Again: $N_1 = 1.507$, $N_2 = 1.536$, $N_2 - N_1 = 0.029$. Ref: 239.

5-Ethyl-5-isopropylbarbituric acid or ipral $[CONHCONHCOCC_2H_5[CH(CH_3)_2]]$ is monoclinic; crystals form rods. M.P. 200°. Sign of elongation positive; common extinction angle 32°. (-)2V = 73° calc. $N_X = 1.477$, $N_Y = 1.573$, $N_Z = 1.624$, $N_Z - N_X = 0.147$. Ref: 499b.

1,3-*bis*(*p*-Chlorobenzyl)-5-ethyl-5-isopropylbarbituric acid or *p*-chlorobenzyl ipral $[CON(ClC_6H_4CH_2)CON(ClC_6H_4CH_2)COC[C_2H_5CH(CH_3)_2]]$ is monoclinic in rods and plates. M.P. 145°. Sign of elongation negative; common extinction angle 7°. (+)2V = 42° calc. $N_X = 1.551$, $N_Y = 1.568$, $N_Z = 1.674$, $N_Z - N_X = 0.123$. Ref: 499b.

1,3-*bis*(*p*-Bromobenzyl)-5-ethyl-5-isopropylbarbituric acid or *p*-bromobenzyl ipral $[CON(BrC_6H_4CH_2)CON(BrC_6H_4CH_2)COC[C_2H_5CH(CH_3)_2]]$ is monoclinic; crystals form rods and plates; M.P. 151°. Sign of elongation negative; common extinction angle 6°. (+)2V = 40° calc. $N_X = 1.567$, $N_Y = 1.582$, $N_Z = 1.705$. $N_Z - N_X = 0.138$. Ref: 499b,

1,3-*bis*(*p*-Nitrobenzyl)-5-ethyl-5-isopropylbarbituric acid or *p* nitrobenzyl ipral $[CON(NO_2C_6H_4CH_2)CON(NO_2C_6H_4CH_2)COC[C_2H_5CH(CH_3)_2]]$ is monoclinic; crystals form thin plates. M.P. 157°. Sign of elongation negative; common extinction angle 35°. $N_X = 1.563$, $N_Y = ?$, $N_Z = 1.696$, $N_Z - N_X = 0.133$. No optic axis interference figure seen. Ref: 499b.

5-Ethyl-5-butylbarbituric acid or neonal $[CONHCONHCOC(C_2H_5)(C_4H_9)]$ is monoclinic. Crystals form needles. M.P. 127 - 128°. Sign of elongation negative; common extinction angle 26°. (-)2V = 72°, calc. $N_X = 1.456$, $N_Y = 1.520$, $N_Z = 1.552$, $N_Z - N_X = 0.096$. Ref: 499b.

1,3-*bis*(*p*-Chlorobenzyl)-5-ethyl-5-butylbarbituric acid or *p*-chlorobenzyl neonal $[CON(ClC_6H_4CH_2)CON(ClC_6H_4CH_2)COC(C_2H_5)(C_4H_9)]$ is monoclinic. Crystals form rods and plates. M.P. 95°. Sign of elongation ±, common extinction angle 40°. (-)2V = 70°, calc. $N_X = 1.516$, $N_Y = 1.640$, $N_Z = 1.699$, $N_Z - N_X = 0.183$. Ref: 499b.

1,3-*bis*(*p*-Bromobenzyl)-5-ethyl-5-butylbarbituric acid or *p*-bromobenzyl neonal $[CON(BrC_6H_4CH_2)CON(BrC_6H_4CH_2)COC(C_2H_5)(C_4H_9)]$ is monoclinic. Crystals form rods and plates. M.P. 99°. Sign of elongation ±; common extinction angle 40°. (-)2V = 70°, calc. $N_X = 1.519$, $N_Y = 1.644$, $N_Z = 1.705$, $N_Z - N_X = 0.186$. Ref: 499b.

1,3-*bis*(*p*-Nitrobenzyl)-5-ethyl-5-butylbarbituric acid or *p*-nitrobenzyl neonal $[CON(NO_2C_6H_4CH_2)CON(NO_2C_6H_4CH_2)COC(C_2H_5)(C_4H_9)]$ is monoclinic. Crystals are yellow needles and rods. M.P. 148°. Sign of elongation positive; common extinction angle 20°. (+)2V = 25°, calc., $r < v$. $N_X = 1.546$, $N_Y = 1.556$, $N_Z = 1.705$, $N_Z - N_X = 0.159$. Ref: 488b.

5-Ethyl-5-α-methylbutylbarbituric acid or pentobarbital $(C_{11}H_{18}O_3N_2)$ is monoclinic in colorless needles. M.P. 130°. Negative elongation. (-)2V = 80° calc. $N_X = 1.469$, $N_Y = 1.528$, $N_Z = 1.569$, $N_Z - N_X = 0.100$. Ref: 499a.

Sodium 5-ethyl-5(1-methylbutyl)barbiturate or nembutal or pentobarbital sodium $(C_{11}H_{17}O_3N_2Na)$ is colorless. It has $N_1 = 1.477$, $N_2 = 1.523$, $N_2 - N_1 = 0.046$. Ref: 518.

5-Ethyl-5-isoamylbarbituric acid or amytal $(C_{11}H_{18}O_3N_2)$ is monoclinic. Crystals colorless rods. M.P. 157°. Positive elongation. (-)2V = 65° calc., $N_X = 1.467$, $N_Y = 1.533$, $N_Z = 1.560$, $N_Z - N_X = 0.093$. Ref: 499a.

p-Chlorobenzyl-5-ethyl-5-isoamylbarbiturate or *p*-chlorobenzyl amytal $(C_{25}H_{28}O_3N_2Cl_2)$ is monoclinic in colorless rods and plates. M.P. 102°. ± elongation. (+)2V = 58° calc. $N_X = 1.539$, $N_Y = 1.574$, $N_Z = 1.694$, $N_Z - N_X = 0.155$. 0.155. Ref: 499a.

p-Bromobenzyl-5-ethyl-5-isoamylbarbiturate or *p*-bromobenzyl amytal ($C_{25}H_{28}O_3N_2Br_2$) is monoclinic. Crystals colorless rods and plates. M.P. 134°. ± elongation. (+)2V = 42° calc., r < v. $N_X = 1.559$, $N_Y = 1.573$, $N_Z = 1.662$, $N_Z - N_X = 0.103$. Ref: 499a.

p-Nitrobenzyl-5-ethyl-5-isoamylbarbiturate or *p*-nitrobenzyl amytal ($C_{25}H_{28}O_7N_4$) is monoclinic. Crystals are pale yellow plates. M.P. 172°. ± elongation. (-)2V = 38° calc., r < v. $N_X = 1.510$, $N_Y = 1.640$, $N_Z = 1.656$, $N_Z - N_X = 0.146$. Ref: 499a.

p-Chlorobenzyl-5-ethyl-5-α-methylbutyl barbiturate or *p*-chlorobenzyl pentobarbital ($C_{25}H_{28}O_3N_2Cl_2$) is monoclinic in colorless thick plates. M.P. 111°. ± elongation. (-)2V = 70° calc., $N_X = 1.523$, $N_Y = 1.631$, $N_Z = 1.680$, $N_Z - N_X = 0.157$. Ref: 499a.

p-Bromobenzyl-5-ethyl-5-α-methylbutylbarbiturate or *p*-bromobenzyl pentobarbital ($C_{25}H_{28}O_3N_2Br_2$) is monoclinic in colorless thick plates. M.P. 114°. ± elongation. (-)2V = 75° calc. $N_X = 1.527$, $N_Y = 1.638$, $N_Z = 1.702$, $N_Z - N_X = 0.175$. Ref: 499a.

p-Nitrobenzyl-5-ethyl-5-α-methylbutylbarbiturate or *p*-nitrobenzyl pentobarbital ($C_{25}H_{28}O_7N_4$) is monoclinic in pale yellow rods and plates. M.P. 151°. Positive elongation. $N_X = 1.548$, N_Y = ?, $N_Z = 1.696$, $N_Z - N_X = 0.148$. Ref: 499a.

5-Ethyl-5-(1-methylbutyl)thiobarbituric acid or pentothal ($C_{11}H_{18}O_2N_2S$) is monoclinic. Crystals lamellar. (-)2V = 40 - 45° est. r > v (?). $N_X = 1.534$, $N_Y = 1.634$, $N_Z = 1.65$ (calc. from N_X, N_Y and 2V), $N_Z - N_X = 0.116$ calc. Ref: 433a.

5-Ethyl-5-*n*-hexylbarbituric acid or ortal ($C_{12}H_{20}O_3N_2$) is monoclinic. Crystals acicular with Y ∧ elongation = 27° (but usually – elongation). (-)2V = 76° calc. $N_X = 1.473$, $N_Y = 1.519$, $N_Z = 1.549$, $N_Z - N_X = 0.076$. Ref: 433a.

5-Allyl-5-isopropylbarbituric acid or alurate ($C_{10}H_{14}O_3N_2$) is monoclinic in {010?} plates with 001(?) cleavage. M.P. 138°. Z ∧ elongation (*c*?) = + 47°. β = 80°. X = *b*; Y (nearly) normal to an orthodome. (-)2V = 70°. $N_X = 1.505$, $N_Y = 1.558$ calc. $N_Z = 1.584$, $N_Z - N_X = 0.079$. Again: $N_X = 1.489$, $N_Y = 1.566$. $N_Z = 1.603$, $N_Z - N_X = 0.114$. Ref: 123, 499b, 567c.

Benzyl-5-allyl-5-isopropyl barbiturate or benzyl alurate ($C_{24}H_{26}N_2O_3$) is monoclinic in plates and clusters which melt at 115°. (+)2V = 50° calc. $N_X = 1.577$, $N_Y = 1.592$, $N_Z = 1.660$, $N_Z - N_X = 0.087$. Ref: 567c.

o-Bromobenzyl-5-allyl-5-isopropyl barbiturate or *o*-bromobenzyl alurate ($C_{24}H_{24}N_2O_3Br_2$) is monoclinic in plates which melt at 85°. (-)2V = 61° calc. $N_X = 1.591$, $N_Y = 1.631$, $N_Z = 1.655$, $N_Z - N_X = 0.064$. Ref: 567c.

m-Bromobenzyl-5-allyl-5-isopropyl barbiturate or *m*-bromobenzyl alurate ($C_{24}H_{24}N_2O_3Br_2$) is monoclinic in rods which melt at 104°. (-)2V = 38° calc., r < v. $N_X = 1.542$, $N_Y = 1.655$, $N_Z = 1.669$, $N_Z - N_X = 0.127$. Ref: 567c.

p-Bromobenzyl-5-allyl-5-isopropyl barbiturate or *p*-bromobenzyl alurate ($C_{24}H_{24}N_2O_3Br_2$) is monoclinic in plates and rods which melt at 129°. (+)2V = 50° calc., r > v. $N_X = 1.561$, $N_Y = 1.581$, $N_Z = 1.674$, $N_Z - N_X = 0.113$. Ref: 567c.

o-Chlorobenzyl-5-allyl-5-isopropyl barbiturate or *o*-chlorobenzyl alurate ($C_{24}H_{24}N_2O_3Cl_2$) is monoclinic in plates and rods which melt at 74°. Color yellow. (-)2V = 74° calc., r > v. $N_X = 1.549$, $N_Y = 1.649$, $N_Z = 1.705$, $N_Z - N_X = 0.156$. Ref: 567c.

m-Chlorobenzyl-5-allyl-5-isopropyl barbiturate or *m*-chlorobenzyl alurate ($C_{24}H_{24}N_2O_3Cl_2$) is monoclinic in plates and rods which melt at 66°. (+)2V = 81° calc. $N_X = 1.537$, $N_Y = 1.587$, $N_Z = 1.655$, $N_Z - N_X = 0.118$. Ref: 567c.

p-Chlorobenzyl-5-allyl-5-isopropyl barbiturate or *p*-chlorobenzyl alurate ($C_{24}H_{24}N_2O_3Cl_2$) is monoclinic in rods and plates which melt at 131°. Color yellow. (+)2V = 51° calc., r < v. $N_X = 1.532$, $N_Y = 1.560$, $N_Z = 1.682$, $N_Z - N_X = 0.150$. Ref: 567c.

p-Nitrobenzyl-5-allyl-5-isopropylbarbiturate or *p*-nitrobenzyl alurate ($C_{24}H_{24}N_4O_7$) is monoclinic in plates and rods which melt at 191°. (+)2V = 66° calc. $N_X = 1.583$, $N_Y = 1.602$, $N_Z = 1.681$, $N_Z - N_X = 0.098$. Ref: 567c.

5-Allyl-5-isobutylbarbituric acid or sandoptal {$CONHCONHCOCCH_2CHCH_2(CH_2CHCH_3)_2$} is monoclinic in (010?) plates and rods with 001? cleavage and M.P. 138°. X = *b*; Z' ∧ elongation about 20°. (-)2V = 70°, r > v, with crossed dispersion. $N_X = 1.511$, $N_Y = 1.574$, $N_Z = 1.584$, $N_Z - N_X = 0.073$. Again: $N_X = 1.516$, $N_Z = 1.581$, $N_Z - N_X = 0.065$. Ref: 123, 499b.

1,3-*bis*(*p*-Nitrobenzyl)-5-allyl-5-isobutylbarbituric acid or *p*-nitrobenzyl sandoptal {$CON(NO_2C_6H_4CH_2)CON(NO_2C_6H_4CH_2)COCCH_2CHCH_2[CH_2CH(CH_3)_2]$} is monoclinic. Crystals form yellow rods and needles. M.P. 178°. Sign of elongation positive; common extinction angle 20°. (+)2V = 20° calc., r > v. $N_X = 1.553$, $N_Y = 1.559$, $N_Z = 1.710$, $N_Z - N_X = 0.157$. Ref: 499b.

1,3-*bis*(*p*-Chlorobenzyl)-5-allyl-5-isobutylbarbituric acid or *p*-chlorobenzyl sandoptal {$CON(ClC_6H_4CH_2)CON(ClC_6H_4CH_2)COC[CH_2CHCH_2CH_2CH(CH_3)_2]$} is monoclinic. Crystals are diamond-shaped plates. M.P. 122°. Sign of elongation ±; common extinction angle 12°. (+)2V = 45° calc. $N_X = 1.545$, $N_Y = 1.567$, $N_Z = 1.690$, $N_Z - N_X = 0.145$. Ref: 499b.

1,3-*bis*(*p*-Bromobenzyl)-5-allyl-5-isobutylbarbituric acid or *p*-bromobenzyl sandoptal {$CON(BrC_6H_4CH_2)CON(BrC_6H_4CH_2)COC[CH_2CHCH_2CH_2CH(CH_3)_2]$} is monoclinic. Crystals form diamond-shaped plates. M.P. 127°. Sign of elongation positive; common extinction angle 10°. (+)2V = 47° calc. $N_X = 1.548$, $N_Y = 1.574$, $N_Z = 1.706$, $N_Z - N_X = 0.158$. Ref: 499b.

5-Allyl-5-(1-methylbutyl)barbituric acid or seconal ($C_{12}H_{18}O_3N_2$) is monoclinic. Crystals lath-shaped, elongated along *b*. M.P. 97 - 99°. Z = *b*. (-)2V = 31° calc., r > v, with horizontal dispersion. $N_X = 1.487$, $N_Y = 1.557$, $N_Z = 1.563$, $N_Z - N_X = 0.076$. Ref: 433a.

5,5-Diallylbarbituric acid or dial is monoclinic in rhombs with symmetrical extinction, Z′ bisecting the acute angle. M.P. 173°. Negative elongation. (-)2V ≈ 90°, $N_X = 1.516$, $N_Z = 1.584$. Again: (-)2V = 85° calc., $N_X = 1.518$, $N_Y = 1.567$, $N_Z = 1.610$, $N_Z - N_X = 0.092$. Ref: 123, 499b.

$$\left[\begin{matrix} C_3H_5 \\ C_3H_5 \end{matrix} > C < \begin{matrix} CONH \\ CONH \end{matrix} > CO\right]$$

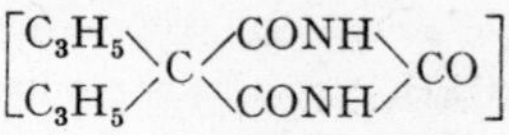

p-Chlorobenzyldiallylbarbiturate ($C_{24}H_{24}O_3N_2Cl_2$) is monoclinic in colorless flat rods. M.P. 125 - 134°. ± elongation. (+)2V < 40° calc., $N_X = 1.560$, $N_Y = 1.592$, $N_Z > 1.700$, $N_Z - N_X > 0.140$. Ref: 499b.

p-Bromobenzyldiallylbarbiturate ($C_{24}H_{24}O_3N_2Br_2$) is monoclinic in colorless rods and plates. M.P. 133°. Negative elongation. (+)2V < 45° calc., $N_X = 1.569$, $N_Y = 1.589$, $N_Z > 1.700$, $N_Z - N_X > 0.131$. Ref: 499b.

p-Nitrobenzyldiallylbarbiturate ($C_{24}H_{24}O_7N_4$) is monoclinic in pale yellow plates. M.P. 192°. Positive elongation. (-)2V = 55° calc., r < v. $N_X = 1.511$, $N_Y = 1.658$, $N_Z = 1.699$, $N_Z - N_X = 0.188$. Ref: 499b.

5-Isopropyl-5-*β*-bromoallylbarbituric acid or nostal [CONHCONHCOC[CH(CH$_3$)$_2$](CH$_2$CBrCH$_2$)] is monoclinic in plates. M.P. 178°. Sign of elongation ±; common extinction angle 36°. (-)2V = 70°, calc., r < v. $N_X = 1.524$, $N_Y = 1.598$, $N_Z = 1.633$, $N_Z - N_X = 0.109$. Ref: 499b.

1,3-*bis*(*p*-Nitrobenzyl)-5-isopropyl-5-*β*-bromoallylbarbituric acid or *p*-nitrobenzyl nostal [CON(NO$_2$C$_6$H$_4$CH$_2$)CON(NO$_2$C$_6$H$_4$CH$_2$)COC[CH(CH$_3$)$_2$](CH$_2$CBrCH$_2$)] is monoclinic. Crystals form yellow rods and plates. M.P. 204°. Sign of elongation positive; common extinction angle 20°. (+)2V = 20°, calc., r > v. $N_X = 1.587$, $N_Y = 1.593$, $N_Z = 1.725$, $N_Z - N_X = 0.138$. Ref: 499b.

1,3-*bis*(*p*-Bromobenzyl)-5-isopropyl-5-*β*-bromoallylbarbituric acid or *p*-bromobenzyl nostal [CON(BrC$_6$H$_4$CH$_2$)CON(BrC$_6$H$_4$CH$_2$)COC[CH(CH$_3$)$_2$](CH$_2$CBrCH$_2$)] is monoclinic. Crystals form thick plates. M.P. 146°. Sign of elongation positive; common extinction angle 12°. (+)2V = 20°, calc., r > v. $N_X = 1.606$, $N_Y = 1.611$ $N_Z = 1.720$, $N_Z - N_X = 0.114$. Ref: 499b.

5-*s*-Amyl-5-*β*-bromallylbarbituric acid or sigmodal ($C_{12}H_{17}O_3N_2Br$) is orthorhombic. Crystals lath-shaped. M.P. 158 - 159°. X = *a*, Y = *b*, Z = *c* (= elongation). (-)2V = 80° calc., r > v slight. $N_X = 1.519$, $N_Y = 1.583$, $N_Z = 1.634$, $N_Z - N_X = 0.115$. Ref: 433a.

1,3-*bis*(*p*-Chlorobenzyl)-5-isopropyl-5-*β*-chloroallylbarbituric acid or *p*-chlorobenzyl nostal [CON(ClC$_6$H$_4$CH$_2$)CON(ClC$_6$H$_4$CH$_2$)COC[CH(CH$_3$)$_2$](CH$_2$BrCH$_2$)] is monoclinic. Crystals form diamond-shaped plates. M.P. 141°. Sign of elongation positive; common extinction angle $20°$. $(+)2V = 25°$, calc. $N_X = 1.599$, $N_Y = 1.605$, $N_Z = 1.710$, $N_Z - N_X = 0.111$. Ref: 499b.

5-Ethyl-5-(1-methyl-1-butenyl)barbituric acid or delvinal ($C_{11}H_{16}O_3N_2$) is monoclinic. Crystals lamellar elongated along b. M.P. $168°$. $X = b$. $(+)2V = 61°$ calc. $r > v$. $N_X = 1.506$, $N_Y = 1.544$, $N_Z = 1.672$, $N_Z - N_X = 0.166$. Ref: 433a.

5-Allyl-5-cyclopentenylbarbituric acid or cyclopal ($C_{12}H_{14}O_3N_2$) is monoclinic. Crystals lath-shaped. M.P. $134 - 136°$. $X = b$; $Y \wedge c = 42°$. $(-)2V = 85°$ calc., $r < v$. $N_X = 1.520$, $N_Y = 1.575$, $N_Z = 1.626$, $N_Z - N_X = 0.106$. Ref: 433a.

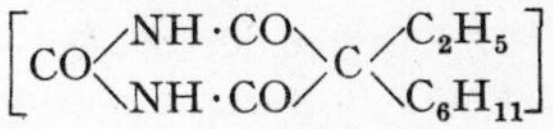

5-Cyclohexenyl-5-ethylbarbituric acid or phanodorn is monoclinic in crystals usually showing parallel or symmetrical extinction. M.P. $173°$.

$$\left[CO \underset{NH \cdot CO}{\overset{NH \cdot CO}{<}} C \underset{C_6H_{11}}{\overset{C_2H_5}{<}} \right]$$

$X = b$; $Y \wedge c$ ($=$ elongation) $= 28°$. $(+)2V = 68°$, $r > v$. $N_X = 1.526$, $N_{Y'} = 1.552$, $N_Z = 1.620$, $N_Z - N_X = 0.094$. Again: $N_X = 1.518$, $N_Y = 1.553$, $N_Z = 1.623$, $N_Z - N_X = 0.105$; also $N_X = 1.515$, $N_Y = 1.546$, $N_Z = 1.621$, $N_Z - N_X = 0.106$. Ref: 123, 433a, 499b, 567c.

o-Bromobenzyl-5-cyclohexenyl-5-ethylbarbiturate or o-bromobenzyl phanodorn ($C_{26}H_{26}N_2O_3Br_2$) is monoclinic in plates and rods which melt at $149°$. $(+)2V = 69°$ calc., $r > v$. $N_X = 1.588$, $N_Y = 1.608$, $N_Z = 1.651$, $N_Z - N_X = 0.063$. Ref: 567c.

m-Bromobenzyl-5-cyclohexenyl-5-ethylbarbiturate or m-bromobenzyl phanodorn ($C_{26}H_{26}N_2O_3Br_2$) is monoclinic in needles and rods which melt at $118°$. Color yellow. $(-)2V = 62°$ calc., $N_X = 1.596$, $N_Y = 1.654$, $N_Z = 1.675$, $N_Z - N_X = 0.079$. Ref: 567c.

p-Bromobenzyl-5-cyclohexenyl-5-ethylbarbiturate or p-bromobenzyl phanodorn ($C_{26}H_{26}N_2O_3Br_2$) is monoclinic in plates which melt at $132°$. $(+)2V = 82°$ calc. $N_X = 1.572$, $N_Y = 1.618$, $N_Z = 1.681$, $N_Z - N_X = 0.109$. Ref: 567c.

o-Chlorobenzyl-5-cyclohexenyl-5-ethylbarbiturate or o-chlorobenzyl phanodorn ($C_{26}H_{26}N_2O_3Cl_2$) is monoclinic in plates and clusters which met at $120°$. Color yellow. $(-)2V = 70°$ calc., $N_X = 1.564$, $N_Y = 1.623$, $N_Z = 1.651$, $N_Z - N_X = 0.087$. Ref: 567c.

m-Chlorobenzyl-5-cyclohexenyl-5-ethylbarbiturate or m-chlorobenzyl phanodorn ($C_{26}H_{26}N_2O_3Cl_2$) is monoclinic in plates and rods which melt at $102°$. $(+)2V = $?, $r > v$. $N_X = 1.585$, $N_Y = $?, $N_Z = 1.654$, $N_Z - N_X = 0.069$. Ref: 567c.

p-Chlorobenzyl-5-cyclohexenyl-5-ethylbarbiturate or p-chlorobenzyl phanodorn ($C_{26}H_{26}N_2O_3Cl_2$) is monoclinic in plates and rods which melt at $125°$. Color yellow. $(+)2V = 68°$ calc., $r < v$. $N_X = 1.566$, $N_Y = 1.600$, $N_Z = 1.679$, $N_Z - N_X = 0.113$. Ref: 567c.

p-Nitrobenzyl-5-cyclohexenyl-5-ethylbarbiturate or p-nitrobenzyl phanodorn ($C_{26}H_{26}N_4O_7$) is monoclinic in plates which melt at $194°$. Color pale yellow. $(-)2V = 88°$ calc., $r < v$. $N_X = 1.632$, $N_Y = 1.684$, $N_Z = 1.74$, $N_Z - N_X = 0.108$. Ref: 567c.

1,5-Dimethyl-5-Δ_1-cyclohexenylbarbituric acid or evipal ($C_{12}H_{16}N_2O_3$) is monoclinic in rods which melt at 144°. (-)2V = 71° calc., r > v. $N_X = 1.549$, $N_Y = 1.609$, $N_Z = 1.638$, $N_Z - N_X = 0.089$. Also orthorhombic with X = *b*, Y = *a*, Z = *c*. (-)2V = 64° calc., r > v. $N_X = 1.546$, $N_Y = 1.608$, $N_Z = 1.634$, $N_Z - N_X = 0.098$. Ref: 433a, 567c.

p-Nitrobenzyl-5-Δ_1-cyclohexenylbarbiturate or *p*-nitrobenzyl evipal ($C_{19}H_{21}N_3O_5$) is monoclinic in rods and plates which melt at 115°. (-)2V = 67° calc., r < v. $N_X = 1.551$, $N_Y = 1.621$, $N_Z = 1.650$, $N_Z - N_X = 0.099$. Ref: 567c.

5-Ethylhexahydro-2,4,6-triketo-5-phenylpyrimidine or 5-ethyl-5-phenyl-2,4,6(1,3,5)-pyrimidinetrione or luminal or 5-ethyl-5-phenyl barbituric acid or phenobarbital [$NHCOC(C_2H_5)(C_6H_5)CONHCO$] has three crystal phases. The stable phase (I) melts at 174°. Crystals can be obtained by sublimation at about 140° at 4 mm. distance and normal air pressure; they are rhomboidal with angles of 61° and a beveling plane at 94°. If these are taken as {010} plates, the longer edge may be {010} and the other {001}. Good 001 and 100 cleavages. $X \wedge c = +5°$; Z = *b*. Optic sign probably negative. 2V = ?, $N_X = 1.561$, $N_Y = 1.620$, N_Z = ? Also: $N_X = 1.559$, $N_Y = 1.623$. Again: $N_X = 1.557$, $N_Y = 1.620$, $N_Z = 1.667$, $N_Z - N_X = 0.110$; ∴ (-)2V = 80° *ca.* Also: $N_X = 1.560$, $N_Z = 1.612$, $N_Z - N_X = 0.052$. A metastable phase (II), which melts at 156° - 157°, forms long acicular crystals which are doubtless monoclinic needles resting on {100} or {010}. $Y \wedge c = -3°$ to $-5°$; Z = *b*. (-)2V = 70° calc. $N_X = 1.563$, $N_Y = 1.594$, $N_Z = 1.610$, $N_Z - N_X = 0.047$. Another metastable phase (III) melts at 166 - 167°. Crystals (often incomplete) are monoclinic hemimorphic, but are elongated along *b*. Y = *b*; Z nearly = *a*. (+)2V = medium, r > v. $N_X' = 1.595$, $N_Y = 1.607$, $N_Z = 1.637$, $N_Z - N_X > 0.042$. Ref: 123, 209, 343c, 518, 523g.

1,3-*bis*(*o*-Bromobenzyl)-5-ethyl-5-phenylbarbituric acid or phenobarbital-*o*-bromobenzyl [$CON(BrC_6H_4CH_2)CON(BrC_6H_4CH_2)COC(C_2H_5)(C_6H_5)$] is monoclinic in short rods with M.P. 113 - 116°. Elongation ± with an extinction angle of 36°. (+)2V = 40° calc., r > v moderate. $N_X = 1.605$, $N_Y = 1.620$, $N_Z = 1.720$, $N_Z - N_X = 0.115$. Colorless. Ref: 148.

1,3-*bis*(*m*-Bromobenzyl)-5-ethyl-5-phenylbarbituric acid or phenobarbital-*m*-bromobenzyl [$CON(BrC_6H_4CH_2)CON(BrC_6H_4CH_2)COC(C_2H_5)(C_6H_5)$] is monoclinic in thin plates with M.P. 130°. Elongation negative with an extinction angle of 7°. (-)2V = 60° calc., $N_X = 1.599$, $N_Y = 1.668$, $N_Z = 1.698$, $N_Z - N_X = 0.099$. Colorless. Ref: 148.

1,3-*bis*(*p*-Bromobenzyl)-5-ethyl-5-phenylbarbituric acid or phenobarbital-*p*-bromobenzyl [$CON(BrC_6H_4CH_2)CON(BrC_6H_4CH_2)COC(C_2H_5)C_6H_5)$] is monoclinic in thin plates, often twinned, with M.P. 117 - 118°. Elongation positive with an extinction angle of 9°. $N_X = 1.563$, N_Y = ?, $N_Z > 1.74$, $N_Z - N_X > 0.177$. Colorless. Ref: 148.

5-Ethyl-1,3-*bis*(*p*-nitrobenzyl)-5-phenylbarbituric acid, or phenobarbital-*p*-nitrobenzyl [$CON(NO_2C_6H_4CH_2)CON(NO_2C_6H_4CH_2)COC(C_2H_5)(C_6H_5)$] is monoclinic in rods and needles with M.P. 182.5 – 184°. Elongation positive with an extinction angle of 17°. (-)2V = 75° calc., r < v strong. $N_X = 1.534$, $N_Y = 1.666$, $N_Z = 1.74$, $N_Z - N_X = 0.206$. Color yellow. Ref: 148.

5-Ethyl-1-methyl-5-phenylbarbituric acid or mebaral ($C_{13}H_{14}O_3N_2$) is monoclinic. M.P. 179°. Crystals six-sided tablets with X || elongation and Y normal to plates. X = *b*. (-)2V = 65° calc., r < v with strong horizontal dispersion. $N_X = 1.594$, $N_Y = 1.610$, $N_Z = 1.651$, $N_Z - N_X = 0.057$. Ref: 433a.

1,3-*bis*(*p*-Bromophenacyl)-5-ethyl-5-phenylbarbituric acid or phenobarbital-*p*-bromophenacyl [$CON(BrC_6H_4COCH_2)CON(BrC_6H_4COCH_2)COC(C_2H_5)(C_6H_5)$] is monoclinic in rods and needles with M.P. 164 – 167°. Elongation negative with an extinction angle of 36°. (+)2V = 85° calc., r < v strong. $N_X = 1.599$, $N_Y = 1.656$, $N_Z = 1.703$, $N_Z - N_X = 0.104$. Colorless. Ref: 148.

1,3-*bis*(*p*-Chlorobenzyl)-5-ethyl-5-phenylbarbituric acid or phenobarbital-*p*-chlorobenzyl [$CON(ClC_6H_4CH_2)CON(ClC_6H_4CH_2)COC(C_2H_5)(C_6H_5)$] has two crystal phases, both monoclinic and colorless. One (I) forms thin plates with twinning and M. P. 111°. Elongation positive with an extinction angle of 8°. N_X = ?, $N_Y = 1.568$, $N_Z = 1.74$, $N_Z - N_X$ = ?. The other (II) forms thick plates with M.P. 113 – 114°. Elongation ±, with an extinction angle of 15°. (+)2V = 25° calc., $N_X = 1.585$, $N_Y = 1.593$, $N_Z = 1.730$, $N_Z - N_X = 0.145$. Ref: 148.

1,3-*bis*(*m*-Chlorobenzyl)-5-ethyl-5-phenylbarbituric acid or phenobarbital-*m*-chlorobenzyl [$CON(ClC_6H_4CH_2)CON(ClC_6H_4CH_2)COC(C_2H_5)(C_6H_5)$] is monoclinic in thin plates with M.P. 111°. Elongation negative with an extinction angle of 5°. (-)2V = 55° calc., $N_X = 1.580$, $N_Y = 1.660$, $N_Z = 1.681$, $N_Z - N_X$ = 0.101. Colorless. Ref: 148.

5-Ethyl-1,3-*bis*(*p*-iodobenzyl)-5-phenylbarbituric acid or phenobarbital-*p*-iodobenzyl [$CON(IC_6H_4CH_2(CON(IC_6H_4CH_2)COC(C_2H_5)(C_6H_5)$] is monoclinic in thick plates and rods with M.P. 127°. Elongation ± with an extinction angle of 34°. (-)2V = ?, $N_X = 1.580$, $N_Y = 1.730$; $1.88 > N_Z > 1.74$; $0.30 > N_Z - N_X > 0.16$. Colorless. Ref: 148.

5-Ethyl-1,3-*bis*(*m*-nitrobenzyl)-5-phenylbarbituric acid or phenobarbital-*m*-nitrobenzyl [$CON(NO_2C_6H_4CH_2)CON(NO_2C_6H_4CH_2)COC(C_2H_5)(C_6H_5)$] is monoclinic in flat rods and plates with M.P. 149.5 – 151°. Elongation positive with an extinction angle of 25°. (-)2V = 75° calc., r < v moderate. $N_X = 1.538$, $N_Y = 1.652$, $N_Z = 1.715$, $N_Z - N_X = 0.177$. Color pale yellow. Ref: 148.

5-Allyl-5-phenyl-barbituric acid or alphenal ($C_{13}H_{12}O_3N_2$) is orthorhombic (?). Crystals often six-sided plates. M.P. 158°. X = *c*, Y = *a*, Z = *b* (?). (+)2V = 67° calc., $N_X = 1.551$, $N_Y = 1.578$, $N_Z = 1.645$, $N_Z - N_X = 0.094$. Ref: 433a.

5,5-Dichloro-6-hydroxydihydrouracil ($C_4H_5O_3N_2Cl_2$) is monoclinic. Crystals columnar or tabular. X = *b*, Y $\wedge$ *c* = 14°. (+)2V = 77°, r < v with horizontal dispersion. $N_X = 1.504$, $N_Y = 1.554$, $N_Z = 1.648$, $N_Z - N_X = 0.144$.
Ref: 418a.

Class 4. Carboxylic Acids and Derivatives

Barium 3-methyl-1,2-diazole-5-carboxylate sesquihydrate or barium 3-methyl-5-pyrazolecarboxylate sesquihydrate [$(C_5H_5O_2N_2)_2Ba \cdot 1.5H_2O$] is triclinic with[1] *a*:*b*:*c* = 0.935:1:0.549, α = 149°0′, β = 39°10′, γ = 147°50′. Crystals {100} tablets with {010}, {001}, {110}, {$3\bar{2}0$}, {$\bar{1}01$}. Distinct 100 cleavage. D 1.90. The optic plane is nearly normal to 100. (–)2V = 56°24′ Na. $N_X = 1.454$ Na, $N_Y = 1.559$, $N_Z = 1.625$, $N_Z - N_X = 0.171$. Ref: 119.

1,2-Diazole-3,5-dicarboxylic acid monohydrate or 3,5-pyrazoledicarboxylic acid monohydrate [$CH{:}C(CO_2H)NHN{:}C(CO_2H)$] is monoclinic with *a*:*b*:*c* = 2.856:1:1.834, β = 93°27′. Crystals orthodomatic with {$10\bar{1}$}, {100}, {001}, {403}, {110}. D 1.63. The optic plane and Z are normal to 010; X nearly normal to 403. (–)2V = 77°. $N_X = 1.459$ Na, $N_Y = 1.555$, $N_Z = 1.582$, $N_Z - N_X = 0.123$.
Ref: 119.

Ethyl 4-*p*-cumyl-1,2,3,4-tetrahydro-2-keto-6-methyl-5-pyrimidinecarboxylate or β-cuminuraminocrotonic acid ethyl ester [$CH[C_6H_4CH(CH_3)_2]NHCONHC(CH_3){:}C(CO_2C_2H_5)$] is monoclinic with *a*:*b*:*c* = 1.351:1:1.427, β = 90°36′. Crystals {001} tablets with {221}, {$12\bar{1}$}, {100}, {$22\bar{1}$}, etc. No distinct cleavage. M.P. 164 – 165°. The optic plane is 010; an optic axis visible through 001. (+)2V = 44° *ca.* Na, r > v very strong. $N_X = 1.5723$ Na, $N_Y = 1.5873$, $N_Z = 1.6333$, $N_Z - N_X = 0.0610$ Na. Ref: 119.

Tetrahydro-2,5-diketo-1-methyl-1,3-diazole-4-carboxylic acid methylamide or 3-methyl-5-hydantoincarboxymethylamide [$CH_3NHCOCHNHCON(CH_3)CO$] is biaxial in six-sided and eight-sided plates with M.P. 235 – 237°. The extinction is symmetrical in eight-sided plates and at 14° to elongation in six-sided plates which have negative elongation. $N_X = 1.485$, $N_Y = 1.520$, $N_Z = 1.570+$, $N_Z - N_X = 0.085+$. (+)2V = ?. Ref: 96.

Tetrahydro-4-hydroxy-2,5-diketo-3-methyl-1,3-diazole-4-carboxylic acid 3-methylureide or 1-methyl-5-hydroxy-5-hydantoincarboxylic acid ω-methylureide [$CH_3NHCONHCOC(OH)N(CH_3)CONHCO$] is monoclinic with *a*:*b*:*c* = 0.797:1:1.218, β = 96°51′. Crystals show {011}, {$10\bar{1}$}, {001}. Perfect 010 cleavage. M.P. 201 – 203°. The optic plane and X are normal to 010; Z $\wedge$ *c* = + 2°. (+)2V = 40°2′ Li, 40°9′ Na, 40°14′ Tl. $N_X = 1.4911$ Li, 1.4949 Na, 1.5023 Tl; $N_Y = 1.5086$ Li, 1.5128 Na, 1.5206 Tl; $N_Z = 1.6648$ Li, 1.6716 Na, 1.6786 Tl; $N_Z - N_X = 0.1767$ Na. Ref: 117.

[1] *a* and *b* interchanged to make *b* > *a* > *c*.

Tetrahydro-2,5-diketo-1,3-dimethyl-1,3-diazole-4-carboxylic acid methylamide or 1,3-dimethyl-5-hydantoincarboxymethylamide [$CH_3NHCOCHN(CH_3)CON(CH_3)CO$] is biaxial and monoclinic (or triclinic), since extinction in needles varies from 0° to 41°. Elongation is positive. M.P. 179 - 180°. (+)2V = large. $N_X = 1.520$, $N_Y = 1.565$, $N_Z = 1.645$, $N_Z - N_X = 0.125$. Ref: 96.

Tetrahydro-2,5-diketo-1,3-diazole-4-ethanoic acid or malylureide acid or 5-hydantoinacetic acid or anhydroureidosuccinic acid [$HO_2CCH_2CHNHCONHCO$] is orthorhombic with $a:b:c = 0.907:1:0.800$. Crystals somewhat elongated along b with {101}, {011}, {100}, {010}, etc. 110 cleavage. The optic plane is 100; $Z = c$. (+)2V = 78°14′. $N_X = 1.5222$, $N_Y = 1.5919$, $N_Z = 1.7814$, $N_Z - N_X = 0.2592$ Na. Ref: 117.

Tetrahydro-2,5-diketo-1,3-diazole-4-ethanamide or malylureide acid amide or 5-hydantoinacetamide or anhydroureidosuccinic acid amide [$CONHCONHCHCH_2CONH_2$] is monoclinic with $a:b:c = 2.403:1:0.528$, $\beta = 109°6'$. Crystals prismatic with {110}, {100}, {001}, etc. The optic plane is 010; an optic axis visible through {001} and also through {100}. 2V = 79°35′ Na. $N_Y = 1.5503$. Ref: 117.

Tetrahydro-2,5-diketo-3-methyl-1-phenyl-1,3-diazole-4-carboxylic acid methylamide or 1-methyl-3-phenyl-5-hydantoincarboxymethylamide [$CH_3NHCOCHN(CH_3)CON(C_6H_5)CO$] forms fine needles with M.P. 164°. Z || elongation. (+)2V = large. $N_X = 1.555$, $N_Y = 1.585$, $N_Z = 1.627$, $N_Z - N_X = 0.072$. Ref: 95.

2,3-Dihydro-5-hydroxy-2-keto-1-phenyl-1,3-diazole-4-carboxylic acid methylamide or 3-phenyl-5-isohydantoincarboxymethylamide ($CH_3NHCOC:C(OH)N(C_6H_5)CONH$] forms needles with M.P. 249 - 250°. Rectangular plates have parallel extinction and negative elongation. 2V = large. $N_1 = 1.571$, $N_2 = 1.620$, $N_2 - N_1 = 0.049$. Ref: 93.

Tetrahydro-4-hydroxy-2,5-diketo-1-methyl-1,3-diazole-4-carboxylic acid methylamide or 5-hydroxy-3-methyl-5-hydantoincarboxymethylamide or isocaffuric acid [$NHC(OH)(CONHCH_3)CON(CH_3)CO$] has M.P. 194°. Extinction at 35° with positive elongation. 2V = biaxial. $N_X = ?$, $N_Y = ?$, $N_Z = 1.555$. Ref: 96.

Tetrahydro-4-hydroxy-2,5-diketo-1,3-dimethyl-1,3-diazole-4-carboxylic acid methylamide or 5-hydroxy-1,3-dimethyl-5-hydantoincarboxymethylamide or allocaffuric acid [$COC(OH)(CONHCH_3)N(CH_3)CON(CH_3)$] is biaxial in six-sided plates with M.P. 164 - 165°. Extinction symmetrical and elongation negative. 2V = large. $N_1 = 1.460$, $N_2 = 1.590(?)$, $N_2 - N_1 = 0.130(?)$. Ref: 96.

Tetrahydro-4-hydroxy-2,5-diketo-1-phenyl-1,3-diazole-4-carboxylic acid methylamide or 5-hydroxy-3-phenyl-5-hydantoincarboxymethylamide [NHC(OH)(CONHCH$_3$)CON(C$_6$H$_5$)CO] forms large thin rectangular plates with parallel extinction and negative elongation. 2V = large. $N_1 = 1.545$, $N_2 = 1.583$, $N_2 - N_1 = 0.038$. Ref: 93.

Tetrahydro-4-hydroxy-2,5-diketo-3-methyl-1-phenyl-1,3-diazole-4-carboxylic acid methylamide monohydrate or 5-hydroxy-3-methyl-1-phenyl-5-hydantoincarboxymethylamide monohydrate [N(CH$_3$)C(OH)(CONHCH$_3$)CON(C$_6$H$_5$)CO·H$_2$O] forms plates with parallel extinction and positive elongation. M.P. 196°. $N_1 = 1.510$, $N_2 = 1.620$, $N_2 - N_1 = 0.110$. Ref: 95.

Dimethyl tetrahydro-4,5-dihydroxy-2-keto-1,3-diazole-4,5-dicarboxylate or dimethyl 4,5-dihydroxy-2-keto-4,5-imidazolidinedicarboxylate or dimethyl ureindihydroxysuccinate [CONHC(OH)(CO$_2$CH$_3$)C(OH)(CO$_2$CH$_3$)NH] is orthorhombic with $a:b:c = 0.739:1:3.050$. Crystals show {110}, {001}, {010}, {108}. Perfect 001 cleavage. M.P. 180°. Y = b; Z = c. (+)2V = 72°15′ Na, 71°41′ Tl. $N_X = 1.4877$ Na, 1.4921 Tl; $N_Y = 1.5011$ Na, 1.5049 Tl; $N_Z = 1.5271$ Na, 1.5304 Tl; $N_Z - N_X = 0.0394$ Na. Ref: 117.

Diethyl tetrahydro-4,5-dihydroxy-2-keto-1,3-diazole-4,5-dicarboxylate or diethyl 4,5-dihydroxy-2-keto-4,5-imidazolidinedicarboxylate or diethyl ureindihydroxysuccinate [CONHC(OH)(CO$_2$C$_2$H$_5$)C(OH)(CO$_2$C$_2$H$_5$)NH] is orthorhombic with $a:b:c = 0.771:1:3.310$. Crystals show {010}, {001}, {111}, {011}, {104}. Perfect 001 cleavage. M.P. 165°. Y = b; Z = c. (+)2V = 83°45′ Li, 84°2′ Na, 84°23′ Tl. $N_X = 1.5352$ Li, 1.5366 Na, 1.5387 Tl; $N_Y = 1.5528$ Li, 1.5542 Na, 1.5566 Tl; $N_Z = 1.5756$ Li, 1.5767 Na, 1.5793 Tl; $N_Z - N_X = 0.0401$ Na. Ref: 117, 247.

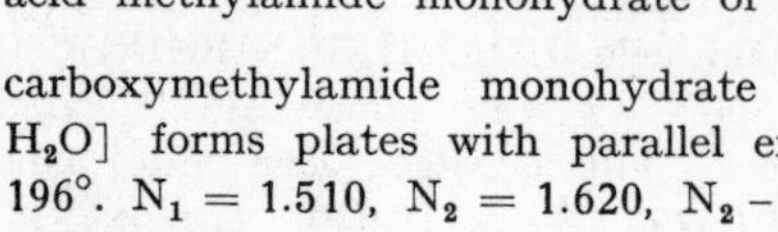

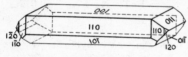

Fig. 122.
3-Methyl-4-pyrazolesulfonic acid.

Class 5. Sulfonic Acids and Derivatives

1,3-Diazole-4(or 5)-sulfonic acid or 4-(or 5)-pyraxolesulfonic acid or glyoxaline-4(or 5)-sulfonic acid [HO$_3$SC:CHNHCH:N] is tetragonal scalenohedral with $c/a = 0.839$. Space group $P42_1C$; a 11.08, c 9.22 Å. U.C. 8. Crystals equant with {110}, {001}, etc. Easy 110 and imperfect 001 cleavages. D 1.84. M.P. 307°. Uniaxial positive with $N_O = 1.551$ Na, $N_E = 1.625$, $N_E - N_O = 0.074$ Na. Ref: 116, 475.

3-Methyl-1,2-diazole-4-sulfonic acid or 3-methyl-4-pyrazolesulfonic acid [HO$_3$SC:CHNHN:C(CH$_3$)] is monoclinic with $a:b:c = 0.848:1:0.877$, $\beta = 93°10'$. Crystals {001} tablets elongated parallel to b with {100}, {10$\bar{1}$}, {011}, etc. Fig. 122. Perfect 010 and distinct 001 cleavages. M.P. 258°. X = b; extinction at −6.5° to c in 010. (−)2V = 53°. $N_X = 1.530$ Na, $N_Y = 1.605$, $N_Z = 1.658$, $N_Z - N_X = 0.128$. Ref: 119.

Class 7. Amines and Derivatives

Histamine monopicrate [HNCH:NC(CH$_2$CH$_2$NH$_2$):CH·C$_6$H$_2$(NO$_2$)$_3$OH] is monoclinic sphenoidal with $a:b:c = 1.222:1:1.227$, $\beta = 100°39'$. Crystals {001} tablets or large prisms. M.P. 233°. X = b; $Z \wedge c = 19°$ ($\lambda = 665.9$); 20° ($\lambda = 591.9$); 21° ($\lambda = 433$). For $\lambda = 665.9$: (+)2V = 78°12′, $N_X = 1.6851$, $N_Y = 1.7009$, $N_Z = 1.7532$, $N_Z - N_X = 0.0691$; for $\lambda = 591.9$: (+)2V = 73°42′, $N_X = 1.6922$, $N_Y = 1.7135$, $N_Z = 1.7535$, $N_Z - N_X = 0.0613$; for $\lambda = 433.0$: (+)2V = 70°40′, $N_X = 1.7122$, $N_Y = 1.7308$, $N_Z = 1.7568$, $N_Z - N_X = 0.0446$. Pleochroic with X = orange-yellow, Y = yellow, Z = green. Ref: 312.

N′-*p*-Methoxybenzyl-N′-2-pyrimidyl-N′-dimethylethylenediamine hydrochloride or neoheteramine hydrochloride ($C_{16}H_{22}OH_4$·HCl) is orthorhombic(?). Crystals plates with Z || elongation. M.P. 171 - 172° (–)2V = 45° calc. $N_X = 1.612$, $N_Y = 1.679$, $N_Z = 1.691$, $N_Z - N_X = 0.079$. Colorless. Ref: 477b.

2-Metanilamidopyrimidine (NH$_2$C$_6$H$_4$SO$_2$NHC$_4$N$_2$H$_3$) is probably monoclinic. Crystals tabular. Y = b. (+)2E = 118°, 2V = 62°, $N_X = 1.635$, $N_Y = 1.658$, $N_Z = 1.726$, $N_Z - N_X = 0.091$. Ref: 529.

N-Acetyl-2-metanilamidopyrimidine ($C_{12}H_{12}O_3N_4S$) is triclinic in thick tabular crystals. The obtuse bisectrix is about normal to plates. (–)2E = 180°, 2V = 74° calc., $N_X = 1.582$, $N_Y = 1.658$, $N_Z = 1.725$, $N_Z - N_X = 0.143$. Ref: 529.

4-Amino-2-hydroxypyrimidine hydrate or cytosine hydrate [N:C(OH)N:CHCH:C(NH$_2$)·H$_2$O] forms large plates with M.P. 308° (–)2V = 36° calc. $N_X = 1.445$, $N_Y = 1.747$, $N_Z = 1.782$, $N_Z - N_X = 0.337$. Ref: 134.

2-Sulfanilamidopyrimidine or sulfadiazine [NH$_2$C$_6$H$_4$SO$_2$NHCN$_2$(CH)$_3$] is monoclinic in crystals elongated along b. Two perfect pinacoidal cleavages at right angles (010 and 001 or 100). H = 1 - 2. M.P. 255°. Y || elongation (b); $Z \wedge c = 20°$ (?). (+)2V = 45 - 46°, $N_X = 1.680$, $N_Y = 1.695$, $N_Z = 1.788$, (all ± .002), $N_Z - N_X = 0.108$. Again: $Z \wedge c$ (or $Z \wedge a$?) = 30 - 35°, (+)2E > 160°, 2V = 77° calc. $N_X = 1.600$, $N_Y = 1.673$, $N_Z = 1.811 \pm .005$, $N_Z - N_X = 0.211$. Also: $Z \wedge c = 35°$, (+)2V = 76°, r > v. $N_X = 1.596$, $N_Y = 1.675$, $N_Z = 1.830$, $N_Z - N_X = 0.234$. Ref: 434a, 529, 618a.

N[4]-(2-Hydroxybenzylidene)sulfadiazine ($C_{17}H_{14}O_3N_4S$) is monoclinic in boat-shaped crystals with M.P. 245°. Elongation along b and Y = b; $Z \wedge c = 38°$. (+)2V = large, r > v weak. $N_X = 1.573$, $N_Y = 1.686$, $N_Z > 1.86$, $N_Z - N_X > 0.283$. Color yellow, with weak X < Y < Z. Ref: 434a.

N[4]-(2-Hydroxy-3-methoxybenzylidene)sulfadiazine ($C_{18}H_{16}O_4N_4S$) is monoclinic with M.P. 226° and ± elongation and "Y || c" and "$Z \wedge a = 40°$?" (+)2V = large, r > v. $N_X = 1.563$, $N_Y = 1.695$, $N_Z > 1.86$, $N_Z - N_X > 0.297$. Strong pleochroism, yellow to colorless, with X < Y < Z. Larger crystals brick red. Ref: 434a.

Metanilamido-5-chloropyrimidine or chlormetanilamide($NH_2C_6H_4SO_3NC_4N_2Cl$) is triclinic in elongated tablets with X ∧ length = 38°, (-)2E > 170°, 2V = 88 - 90°, $N_X = 1.612$, $N_Y = 1.678$, $N_Z = 1.740$, $N_Z - N_X = 0.128$. Ref: 529.

2-Sulfanilamido-5-chloropyrimidine ($NH_2C_6H_4SO_4NHC_4N_2H_2Cl$) forms columnar crystals with (+)2E > 140°, 2V = 65 - 75°, $N_Y = 1.685$. Ref: 529.

N-Acetyl-2-sulfanilamido-5-chloropyrimidine ($C_{12}H_{12}O_3N_4SCl$) forms spherulites. (-)2E > 175°, 2V = 65 - 75° *ca.* $N_Y = 1.658$. Ref: 529.

N′-(4-Methyl-2-pyrimidyl)sulfanilamide or sulfamethyldiazine or sulfamerazine ($NH_2C_6H_4SO_2NHC_4H_2N_2CH_3$) is orthorhombic dipyramidal. Crystals {001} plates long ∥ *b*. Perfect 001 (?) cleavage. X = *c*. Y = *a*. (-)2V = (55° calc.-A.N.W.). $N_X = 1.572 \pm .003$, $N_Y = 1.658 \pm .003$, $N_Z = 1.681 \pm .003$, $N_Z - N_X = 0.109$. Again $N_X = 1.587$, N_Y = ?, $N_Z = 1.675$, $N_Z - N_X = 0.088$. With picrolonic acid it forms spherulitic aggregates with X near elongation and $N_X = 1.572$, $N_Y = 1.733$, $N_Z > 1.733$, $N_Z - N_X > 0.161$. Ref: 523b, 619.

*N*⁴-Acetylsulfamethyldiazine {$CH_3CONHC_6H_4SO_2NHC_4N_2CH_3(H_2O\,?)$} is triclinic. (-)2V = 70° (calc.-A.N.W.), $N_X = 1.527 \pm .005$, $N_Y = 1.650 \pm .005$, $N_Z = 1.706 \pm .005$, $N_Z - N_X = 0.179$. Ref: 619.

N⁴-(2-Hydroxybenzylidene) sulfamerazine ($C_{18}H_{16}O_3N_4S$) is monoclinic in tabular crystals which turn from yellow to brick red at about 85° and melt at 225°. Y = *b*; Z ∧ elongation = 22°. (+)2V = large, r > v weak. $N_X = 1.553$, $N_Y = 1.679$, $N_Z > 1.86$, $N_Z - N_X > 0.307$. Pleochroic, colorless to yellow with X < Y < Z. Ref: 434a.

N⁴-(2-Hydroxy-3-methoxybenzylidene) sulfamerazine ($C_{19}H_{18}O_4N_4S$) is triclinic (?) in columnar crystals with M.P. 212° and - elongation. (+)2V = large, r > v. $N_X = 1.548$, $N_Y = 1.669$, $N_Z > 1.86$, $N_Z - N_X$ = > 0.312. Color brick red, with weak pleochroism and X < Y < Z. Ref: 434a.

2-Acetylsulfanilyl-4,6-dimethylpyrimidine {$CH_3CONH \cdot C_6H_4 \cdot SO_2NHC_4N_2H(CH_3)_2$} is orthorhombic dipyramidal forming {001} plates limited by prism faces whose acute angle is 41°. Prism faces striated. Perfect 010 cleavage. Y = *a*; Z = *c*. (-)2V = large, $N_X = 1.566$, $N_Y = 1.623$, $N_Z = 1.672$ (all ± .003). $N_Z - N_X = 0.106$. Ref: 619.

4-Dimethylamino-2,3-dihydro-3-keto-1,5-dimethyl-2-phenyl-1,2-diazole or pyramidone or aminopyrine or 4-dimethylaminoantipyrine [$C_6H_5NN(CH_3)C(CH_3):C[N(CH_3)_2]CO$] is triclinic with *a*:*b*:*c* = 0.409:1:0.597. U.C. 4. Easily soluble in alcohol. D 1.187. M.P. 108°. (-)2V = ?, $N_1 = 1.517$, $N_2 = 1.604$ *ca.*, $N_2 - N_1 = 0.087$ *ca.* Again: $N_X = 1.520$, N_Y = ?, $N_Z = 1.732$, $N_Z - N_X = 0.210$. (If $N_Y = 1.604$, 2V = 80°-A.N.W.) Ref: 239, 491, 518.

4-Dimethylamino-2,3-dihydro-3-keto-1,5-dimethyl-2-phenyl-1,2-diazole salicylate or pyramidone salicylate [$C_6H_5NN(CH_3)C(CH_3):C[N(CH_3)_2]COC_6H_4$

$(OH)(CO_2H)]$ is granular, easily soluble in ether. M.P. 69 - 76°. (+)2V = large. $N_X = 1.558$, $N_Y = 1.633$, N_Z slightly under 1.74, $N_Z - N_X < 0.18$. Colorless.
Ref: 239.

Tetrahydro-2,4-diketo-5-ureido-1,3-diazole or 5-ureidohydantoin or allantoin $[CONHCONHCHNHCONH_2]$ is monoclinic with $a:b:c = 1.559:1:1.435$, $\beta = 93°18'$. Crystals {001} or {100} tablets with {001}, {100}, {110}, {10$\bar{1}$}. Perfect 10$\bar{1}$ cleavage. M.P. 235°. The optic plane is 010; an optic axis is inclined about 60° to 001 in the obtuse angle β; another is nearly normal to 100; therefore 2V = 67° *ca.* $N_1 = 1.579$, $N_2 = 1.66$ –, $N_2 - N_1 = 0.081$ –. Six-sided plates with parallel extinction and negative elongation. Ref: 117, 248.

Hexahydro-2,4,6-triketo-5-[3-(2-propenyl)ureido]pyrimidine monohydrate or 9-allylpseudouric acid monohydrate $[CONHCONHCOCHNHCONHCH_2CH{:}CH_2 \cdot H_2O]$ is acicular with parallel extinction and negative elongation. Turns pink at 170°. M.P. 227 - 228° with decomposition. $N_1 = 1.591$, $N_2 = 1.69$, $N_2 - N_1 = 0.099$. Ref: 248.

Hexahydro-2,4,6-triketo-1,3-dimethyl-5-[3-(2-propenyl)ureido]pyrimidine or 9-allyl-1,3-dimethylpseudouric acid $[CON(CH_3)CON(CH_3)COCHNHCONHC_3H_5]$ forms octagonal plates with symmetrical extinction and negative elongation. M.P. 190°. $N_1 = 1.545$ +, $N_2 = 1.605$, $N_2 - N_1 = 0.060$ –. Ref: 95.

Hexahydro-2,4,6-triketo-5-(1-methyl-3-phenylureido)pyrimidine or 7-methyl-9-phenylpseudouric acid $[CONHCONHCOCHN(CH_3)CONH(C_6H_5)]$ forms needles with parallel extinction and positive elongation. M.P. 245 - 250° to a yellow liquid. $N_1 = 1.636$, $N_2 = 1.714$ +, $N_2 - N_1 = 0.078$ +. Ref: 248.

Hexahydro-2,4,6-triketo-1,3-dimethyl-5-(3-phenylureido)pyrimidine or 1,3-dimethyl-9-phenylpseudouric acid $[CON(CH_3)CON(CH_3)COCHNHCONHC_6H_5]$ forms plates which melt to a red liquid at 189 - 190°. Extinction at 25 - 37°. 2V = large. $N_1 = 1.525$, $N_2 = 1.647$, $N_2 - N_1 = 0.122$. Ref: 248.

Hexahydro-2,4,6-triketo-1,3-dimethyl-5-(3-phenylureido)pyrimidine monohydrate or 1,3-dimethyl-9-phenylpseudouric acid monohydrate $[CON(CH_3)CON(CH_3)COCHNHCONHC_6H_5 \cdot H_2O]$ forms needles which melt at about 190°. Parallel extinction and negative elongation. $N_1 = 1.583$, $1.800 > N_2 > 1.768$, $0.217 > N_2 - N_1 > 0.185$. Ref: 248.

Hexahydro-2,4,6-triketo-1-methyl-5-(1-methyl-3-phenylureido)pyrimidine or 1,7-dimethyl-9-phenylpseudouric acid $[CON(CH_3)CONHCOCHN(CH_3)CONHC_6H_5]$ forms six-sided plates with symmetrical extinction and negative elongation. M.P. 220° to orange red liquid. $N_1 = 1.555$, $N_2 = 1.695$, $N_2 - N_1 = 0.140$.
Ref: 93.

α-Amino-β-imidazyl-propionic acid or histidine (CHNCHCNHCH$_2$NH$_2$·CH·CO$_2$H) forms colorless plates with X || length. Biaxial. $N_X = 1.520$, $N_Y = ?$, $N_Z = 1.610$, $N_Z - N_X = 0.090$. Ref: 514.

l-Histidine dinitroindandionate ($C_{24}H_{19}O_{10}N_5$) is monoclinic in rectangular plates with X ∧ elongation = 15°. M.P. 269°. (-)2V = large, r < v. $N_X = 1.636$, $N_Y = 1.758$, $N_Z = ?$ $N_Z - N_X < 0.244$. (From (-)2V, N_Y and N_X, N_Z is < 1.88 – A.N.W.). Color tan. Ref: 539a.

2-Amino-3-[4-(1,3-diazolyl)]propanoic acid 2,4-dinitro-1-naphthol-7-sulfonate or histidine flavianate {HNCH:NC(CH$_2$CHNH$_2$CO$_2$H):CH·HO$_3$SC$_6$H$_3$CHOH:CNO$_2$CH:CNO$_2$} forms short yellow needles with extinction at 18° ± 1°. $N_1 = 1.546$, $N_2 = 1.735$, $N_2 - N_1 = 0.189$. Ref: 65.

l-Histidine di-diliturate trihydrate ($C_{14}H_{15}O_{12}N_9 \cdot 3H_2O$) is monoclinic in rods and needles which decompose at 302°. Z ∧ elongation = 25°. (-)2V = small (40° calc.), $N_X = 1.443$, $N_Y = 1.723$, $N_Z = 1.759$?, $N_Z - N_X = 0.316$. Ref: 539b.

3-[2-Mercapto-5-(1,3-diazolyl)]-2-trimethylaminopropanoic betaine or ergothioneine {NHCSNHCH:CCH$_2$CHCO·O·N(CH$_3$)$_3$} is monoclinic hemimorphic in plates and rods with extinction from 0° to 20°. M.P. 276°. (-)2V = 55° *ca.* calc., $N_X = 1.582$, $N_Y = 1.61$, $N_Z = 1.70$, $N_Z - N_X = 0.118$. Ref: 366a.

Ergothioneine hydrochloride dihydrate {NHCSNHCH:CCH$_2$CHCO·O·N(CH$_3$)$_3$·HCl·2H$_2$O} is orthorhombic disphenoidal with *a*:*b*:*c* = 0.883:1:1.159. Crystals six-sided {001} tablets with {110}, {011}, {101}, {111}. X = *b*; Y = *c*. (-)2V = 48°. $N_Y = 1.5622$. Ref: 119.

Fast yellow 4R {ClC$_6$H$_4$N:NC(COH)CNNC$_6$H$_5$} is monoclinic (?). Crystals prismatic, with steep pyramids. Rare grains with maximum pleochroism show crossed twinning. X ∧ *c* = 43°. Biaxial. $N_X = 1.465$, $N_Y = (?)$, $N_Z = 2.07$, $N_Z - N_X = 0.605$. Some grains with X′ darker than X have $N_X' = 1.49 (= N_Y ?)$. Strongly pleochroic with X = lemon, Z = orange red. Ref: 543, 576.

3-Methyl-4-phenylazo-1-(4-sulfophenylazo-5-pyrazolone or 4-benzene-azo-1-*p*-sulfobenzene-3-methyl-5-hydroxypyrazole {C$_6$H$_5$N:NCC(CH$_3$)NNC$_6$H$_5$(HSO$_3$)COH} is orthorhombic(?). Crystals acicular with X || length. $N_X = 1.465$, $N_Y = (?)$, $N_Z = 1.87$, $N_Z - N_X = 0.205$. Insignificant pleochroism in yellow hues. Called fast light acid yellow. Are these properties of the sodium salt? Ref: 543, 576.

11. Compounds with three Nitrogen Atoms in the Cycle

Class 1. Compounds containing no Functional Group

Hexahydro-1,3,5-trinitro-*s*-triazine or trimethylenetrinitramine $\{CH_2N(NO_2)CH_2N(NO_2)CH_2N(NO_2)\}$ is orthorhombic dipyramidal with $a:b:c = 0.878:1:0.815$. a 11.5, b 13.2, c 10.6 Å. U.C. 8. Crystals prismatic with {120}, {111}, {010}, {001}, etc. M.P. 202°. The optic plane is 100; X = c. (-)2V = 55°21′ (λ = 668), 53°22′ D, 48°4′ (λ = 486), N_X = 1.5725 (λ = 668), 1.5776 D, 1.5895 (λ = 486), N_Y = 1.5906 (λ = 668), 1.5972 D, 1.6113 (λ = 486), N_Z = 1.5957 (λ = 668), 1.6024 D, 1.6157 (λ = 486), $N_Z - N_X$ = 0.0248 D. Ref: 315, 499.

Hexahydro-2,4,6-trimethyl-*s*-triazine or acetaldehyde ammonia $\{NHCH(CH_3)NHCH(CH_3)NHCH(CH_3)\}$ is trigonal with c/a = 1.395. Space group probably $R3m$. a 8.19 Å. U.C. 6. Crystals usually cube-like rhombohedrons with {10$\bar{1}$1} cleavage. D 1.10. M.P. 95 – 99°. Uniaxial negative with N_O = 1.48, N_E = 1.46, $N_O - N_E$ = 0.02. Ref: 34, 35, 117, 481.

2,4,6-Trichloro-1,3,5-triazine or cyanuric chloride $\{C(Cl)NC(Cl)NC(Cl)N\}$ is monoclinic prismatic with $a:b:c = 1.018:1:1.501$, β = 96°10′. Crystals show {110}, {001}, {011}. Perfect $\bar{1}$01 cleavage. M.P. 146. D 1.32 *ca.* X nearly normal to $\bar{1}$01. Z = b. (-)2E = 28°, r < v weak. Again 2E = 27°, 2V = 15°, N_X = 1.440, N_Y = 1.470, N_Z = 1.745, $N_Z - N_X$ = 0.305. Ref: 117, 529.

4-(2,5-Dichlorophenylazo)-3-methyl-1-phenyl-5-pyrazolone or 2,5-dichlorobenzene-azo-4-(1-phenyl-3-methylpyrazolone $\{ClC_6H_3(Cl)N:NC(COH)CNNC_6H_5\}$ is monoclinic (?) Crystals acicular rarely lying ⊥ N_X; usually show N_i = 1.526. (-)2V = (?), N_X = 1.46, N_i = 1.526 (= N_Y ?), N_Z = 2.065, $N_Z - N_X$ = 0.605. Pleochroism distinct from yellow (X) to orange (Z ?). Some crystals show strong absorption with Z = almost black. Called Hansa yellow R (pigment). Ref: 543, 576.

Class 3. Carbonyl Compounds

3-Amino-1-phenyl-1,2,4-triazole hydrochloride monohydrate or 1-phenyl-3-iminotriazoline hydrochloride monohydrate $[C_6H_5NN:CNH_2N:CH \cdot HCl \cdot H_2O]$ or $[C_6H_5NNHC(:NH)N:CH \cdot HCl \cdot H_2O]$ is monoclinic with $a:b:c = 1.180:1:0.605$, β = 97°8′. Crystals show {010}, {110}, {011}, etc. Imperfect 100 cleavage. M.P. 187°. X = b; Z ∧ c = + 44° Na. (+)2V = ?, N_X = 1.4832, N_Y < 1.7761 < N_Z. (N_Z' in a prism 101:$\bar{1}$01 = 1.7761.) $N_Z - N_X$ > 0.2929. Ref: 119.

3-Amino-5-methyl-1-phenyl-1,2,4-triazole chloroplatinate or 3-imino-5-methyl-1-phenyl-1,2,4-triazoline chloroplatinate $[(C_6H_5NN:CNH_2N:CCH_3 \cdot HCl)_2 \cdot PtCl_4]$ is monoclinic with $a:b:c = 3.214:1:4.345$, $\beta = 118°20'$. Crystals {001} tablets with {10$\bar{1}$}, {100}, {110}, etc. Perfect 110 cleavage. Gradually becomes cloudy in air. M.P. 245°. The optic plane is 010; the obtuse bisectrix is nearly normal to 001. $N_Y = 1.6155$ Na. N_1 for a prism 001:$\bar{1}$00 = 1.7358. (Therefore the sign is probably +, and N_Z is not much more than 1.7358. – A.N.W.) Ref: 119.

Class 7. Amines and Derivatives

Potassium ammeline ($C_3H_4ON_5K$) is orthorhombic dipyramidal. Crystals prisms long || *c*. (–)2V = small, $N_X = 1.445 \pm .003$, $N_Y = 1.735 \pm .005$, $N_Z = 1.750 \pm .005$, $N_Z - N_X = 0.305$. Ref: 619.

Calcium ammelide dihydrate $\{(C_3H_3O_2N_4)_2Ca \cdot 2H_2O\}$ forms columns or needles. Loses all water at 150°. X normal to plates; Z parallel to elongation. (–)2V = 39°, 2E = 70°, $N_X = 1.442$, $N_Y = 1.712$, $N_Z = 1.742$, $N_Z - N_X = 0.300$. Colorless. Ref: 529.

Calcium ammeline pentahydrate $\{[C_3H_3N_3O(NH_2)_2]_2Ca \cdot 5H_2O\}$ is monoclinic (?). Crystals tabular. (–)2E = 170°, 2V = *ca.* 75 – 85°, $N_X = 1.498$, $N_Y = 1.626$, $N_Z > 1.7$, $N_Z - N_X > 0.30$. Ref: 529.

Guanidine ammelide $\{C(NH_2)NC(OH)NC(OH)N \cdot NH_2C(NH)NH_2\}$ is hexagonal in equant crystals with {10$\bar{1}$1}. Uniaxial negative with $N_O = 1.530$, $N_E = 1.690$, $N_E - N_O = 0.160$. Ref: 529.

2,4,6-Trihydroxy-1,3,5-triazine or cyanuric acid $\{HN \cdot COHN:COHN \cdot CO\}$ is monoclinic prismatic with $a:b:c = 1.172:1:1.341$, $\beta = 90°$ *ca.* Space group *C*2/*c*. *a* 7.90, *b* 6.74, *c* 9.04; U.C. 4. Crystals pseudorhombic prisms with 101 cleavage. M.P. 360°. D 1.768. Y = *b*; X nearly normal to 101, and Z to 10$\bar{1}$. (–)2E = 70°. 2H = 37°, r < v. $N_Y = 1.700$ for $\lambda = 5461$. Bolland describes "cyanuric acid" (with H_2O ?) as having parallel extinction and positive elongation with $N_1 = 1.43$, $N_2 = 1.70$, $N_2 - N_1 = 0.27$. Ref: 34, 35, 117, 556a, 618.

2,4,6-Trihydroxy-1,3,5-triazine dihydrate or cyanuric acid dihydrate $\{C(OH)NC(OH)NC(OH)N \cdot 2H_2O\}$ is monoclinic prismatic with $a:b:c = 1.369:1:1.850$, $\beta = 106°4'$. Crystals prismatic or {001} tablets. Perfect 101 and good 001 cleavages. M.P. 360°. Y = *b*; Z nearly = *c*. An optic axis visible through 001. (–)2E = 50°, 2V = 29°, $N_X = 1.370$, $N_Y = 1.705$, N_Z slightly > 1.73, $N_Z - N_X$ slightly > 0.36. Ref: 117, 529, 556a.

2,4,6-Triamino-1,3,5-triazine or melamine or cyanuramide $\{N:CNH_2N:CNH_2N:CNH_2\}$ is monoclinic prismatic with $a:b:c = 1.415:1:0.973$, $\beta = 112°2'$. Space group *P*2$_1$/*a*. *a* 10.54, *b* 7.45, *c* 7.25 Å. U.C. 4. Crystals {001} tablets with {110}, {011}. Also rhombic plates with an angle of about 70°. Good 001 and poor 110 cleavages. D 1.573. M.P. 250°. (361°–Mitchell.) The optic plane is 010; the plates give an optic axis on the edge of the field. $Z \wedge c = +24°$. $(-)2V = 72°$ calc. $N_X = 1.4876$ C, 1.4906 D, 1.4992 F; $N_Y = 1.7340$ C, 1.7429 D, 1.7656 F; $N_Z = 1.8608$ C, 1.8721 D, 1.9020 F; $N_Z - N_X = 0.3815$ D. Again: $(-)2V = 35°$, $r < v$ distinct, $N_X = 1.49$, $N_1 = 1.67$, $N_2 = 1.86$. Also for $\lambda = 5461$, $(-)2H = 37°$, $N_Y = 1.858$. Ref: 117, 143, 556a.

Melamine hydrochloride $\{C_3H_6N_6 \cdot HCl \cdot 0.5H_2O\ ?\}$ is monoclinic prismatic. Crystals {010} laths long ∥ *c*. Twinning on 100. Perfect 001 cleavage. $X \wedge c =$ *ca.* 27°, $Y = b$. $(-)2V = 47°$ calc., $N_X = 1.495 \pm .003$, $N_Y = 1.745 \pm .005$, $N_Z = 1.795 \pm .005$, $N_Z - N_X = 0.300$. Ref: 619.

Melamine sulfate $\{N{:}CNH_2N{:}CNH_2N{:}CNH_2 \cdot H_2SO_4\}$ is biaxial with $(-)2V = 20-25°$, $N_1 = 1.454$, $N_2 = 1.730$, $N_2 - N_1 = 0.276$. Ref: 468.

Dimelamine phthalate $\{C_8H_5O_4(C_3H_6N_6)_2\}$ is orthorhombic dipyramidal. Crystals are {100} plates, long ∥ *c*, with prism and pyramid faces. $X = c$, $Y = a$. $(-)2V < 60°$, $N_X = 1.490 \pm .003$, $N_Y = 1.725 \pm .005$, $N_Z = 1.745 \pm .005$, $N_Z - N_X = 0.255$. Other crystals (the monomer or a second phase) seem to be triclinic. They are plates with an angle of *ca.* 65°. $X' \wedge$ length $= 30°$. Z nearly normal to plate. $(+)2V =$ large (?), $N_1 = 1.460 \pm .003$, $N_2 = 1.685 \pm .003$, $N_2 - N_1 = 0.225$. Ref: 619.

2,4-Diamino-6-dimethylamine-1,3,5-triazine $\{(CH_3)_2NC_3N_3(NH_2)_2\}$ is hexagonal. Imperfect crystals. Uniaxial negative with $N_O = 1.688 \pm .003$, $N_E = 1.618 \pm .003$, $N_O - N_E = 0.070$. Ref: 619.

2-Amino-4,6-*bis*-methylamine-1,3,5-triazine or N^2N^4-dimethylmelamine $\{CH_3NHC_3N_3(NH_2)NHCH\}$ is hexagonal (?), granular. M.P. 210°. Uniaxial negative with $N_O = 1.683 \pm .003$, $N_E = 1.533 \pm .003$, $N_O - N_E = 0.150$. Ref: 619.

2-Amino-4,6-*bis*-dimethylamino-1,3,5-triazine $\{(CH_3)_2NC_3N_3(NH_2)N(CH_3)_2\}$ is orthorhombic dipyramidal. Crystals long prisms with {110} and {101}. M.P. 225 – 226°. $X = c$, $Y = b$. $(-)2E = 69°$, $2V = 40°$, $N_X = 1.549 \pm .003$, $N_Y = 1.675 \pm .003$, $N_Z = 1.685 \pm .003$, $N_Z - N_X = 0.136$. Ref: 619.

2,4,6-Trisdimethylamino-1,3,5-triazine or hexamethylmelamine $\{(CH_3)_2NC_3N_3[N(CH_3)_2]_2\}$ has dihexagonal dipyramidal symmetry. Crystals are long prisms with {0001}. Perfect basal cleavage. M.P. 171 – 172°. Uniaxial negative with $N_O = 1.692 \pm .003$, $N_E = 1.430 \pm .003$, $N_O - N_E = 0.262$. Ref: 619.

Butylmelamine $\{N{:}CNH_2N{:}CNH_2N{:}CNHC_4H_9\}$ forms tetragonal equant crystals. Uniaxial positive with $N_O = 1.567$, $N_E = 1.689$, $N_E - N_O = 0.122$. Ref: 529.

Monoguanylmelamine hydrochloride monohydrate $\{(NH_2CN)_4 \cdot HCl \cdot H_2O\}$ forms columnar crystals. N_1 (∥ length) $= 1.550$, N_2 (∥ width) $= 1.72$, $N_2 - N_1 = 0.17$. Ref: 529.

Monoguanylmelamine dihydrochloride hydrate $\{(NH_2CN)_4 \cdot (HCl)_2 \cdot nH_2O\}$ is probably monoclinic. Crystals columnar || *b*. Y (|| length) = *b*. (+)2E > 170°, 2V = 70 – 80°, N_X = 1.57 (*ca.* – A.N.W.), N_Y = 1.628, N_Z = 1.73, $N_Z - N_X$ = 0.16 (*ca.* – A.N.W.).
Ref: 529.

Diguanylmelamine monohydrate $\{(NH_2CH)_5 \cdot H_2O\}$ forms tablets with N_1 = 1.461, N_2 (|| width) > 1.80, N_3 (|| length) > 1.84, $N_3 - N_1$ > 0.38.
Ref: 529.

Phenyl-2,4,6-triamino-1,3,5-triazine or phenylcyanuramide or phenyl melamine $(C_9H_{10}O_6)$ is orthorhombic. Crystals prismatic. Z parallel *c* (elongation). M.P. 284°. (–)2E = 60°, 2V = 32°, N_X = 1.585, N_Y = 1.763, N_Z = 1.78 *ca.*, $N_Z - N_X$ = 0.200 *ca.*
Ref: 529.

Diphenylmelamine $\{(C_6H_5)_2NCNHNCNHNCNH_2\}$ forms columnar crystals. (–)2E = 65°, 2V = 34°. N_Y = 1.800.
Ref: 529.

Cyanuric triazide $\{N_3C{:}NC(N_3){:}NC(N_3){:}N\}$ is hexagonal with *c*/*a* = 1.464. Crystals prismatic, terminated by a single pyramid. Perfect 0001 cleavage. D 1.71. Uniaxial negative with extreme birefringence. N_O = 1.872, N_E = 1.381, $N_O - N_E$ = 0.491 for λ = 546; and N_O = 1.862, N_E = 1.378, $N_O - N_E$ = 0.484 for λ = 579.
Ref: 199, 311.

12. Compounds with four Nitrogen Atoms in the Cycle

Tetrazole (CH_2N_4) is triclinic with *a*:*b*:*c* = 0.915:1:0.687, α = 130°, β = 111°, γ = 63°. *a* 5.00, *b* 5.46, *c* 3.75 Å. U.C. 1. Crystals {001} plates with {010}, {100}, etc. D 1.41 (flotation); 1.63 (X-ray). M.P. 155.5°. X nearly normal to 001. Z′ ∧ *a* = 13° on 001. (–)2V = 51°, r < v weak. N_X = 1.388, N_Y = 1.595, N_Z = 1.660, $N_Z - N_X$ = 0.272.
Ref: 553c.

Metrazole or cardiazole or 6,7,8,9-tetrahydro-5-azepotetrazole or pentamethylenetetrazole $[CH_2(CH_2)_4C{:}NN{:}NN]$ is monoclinic with *a*:*b*:*c* = 1.817:1:1.569, β = 120°15′. Crystals {001} tablets or short prisms with {110}, {100}, {001}, {10$\bar{1}$}, etc. Twinning on 001. No distinct cleavage. The optic plane and Z are normal to 010; the acute bisectrix X is visible through 100. N_X = 1.617, N_Z = ?.
Ref: 305.

5-(4-Methoxyphenyl)tetrazole $[C[C_6H_4(OCH_3)]HN_4]$ is triclinic with[1] *a*:*b*:*c* = 0.835:1:0.725, α = 123°14′, β = 106°28′, γ = 95°8′. Crystals of varied habit with {110}, {100}, {$\bar{1}$10}, {01$\bar{1}$}, {001}, etc. Twinning common on 001 or normal to 100 or normal to 010. Perfect 001 cleavage. M.P. 228° (dec.). The optic plane is nearly normal to 100; X ∧ ⊥ 001 = 5°30′. Na (in air). (–)2V = 74°15′ red, 74°48′ yellow, 75°51′ blue. N_X = 1.5935 red, 1.5972 yellow, 1.6020 blue; N_Y = 1.6821 red, 1.6922 yellow, 1.7071 blue; N_Z = 1.7901 red, 1.8057 yellow, 1.8393 blue; $N_Z - N_X$ = 0.2085 yellow.
Ref: 119.

[1] *a* and *b* interchanged to make *b* > *a* > *c*.

1,2,3,6-Tetrahydro-2-keto-1,3,7-trimethyl-6,6-diphenylpurine or diphenyldesoxycaffeine [$CH_3NCH:NC:CC(C_6H_5)_2N(CH_3)CON(CH_3)$] is triclinic with $a:b:c = 0.748:1:0.709$, $\alpha = 83°34'$, $\beta = 109°17'$, $\gamma = 119°36'$. Crystals {100} tablets with {010}, {001}, {$\bar{1}$11}. No observed cleavage. D 1.475. M.P. 249 – 250°. Y′ ∧ *c* on 100 = 30°, Y′ ∧ *c* on 010 = 40°, Z′ ∧ *b* on 001 = 10°. (+)2V = 78°16′ Na, r<v. $N_X = 1.633$ Na, $N_Y = 1.664$, $N_Z = 1.709$, $N_Z - N_X = 0.076$ Na. Ref: 45.

1,2,3,6-Tetrahydro-2-keto-1,3,7,8-tetramethyl-6,6-diphenylpurine or 8-methyldiphenyldesoxycaffeine [$CH_3NC(CH_3):NC:CC(C_6H_5)_2N(CH_3)CON(CH_3)$] is monoclinic with $a:b:c = 1.753:1:1.713$, $\beta = 99°50'$. Crystals {100} tablets with {001}, {010}, {$\bar{1}$01}, {110}. Good 001 cleavage. D 1.452. M.P. 225°. The optic plane is 010; X ∧ *c* = – 45.5°, r > v. (-)2V = 65°8′, r > v. $N_X = 1.646$, $N_Y = 1.660$, $N_Z = 1.666$, $N_Z - N_X = 0.020$ Na. Color yellow with X and Z = white, Y = yellow. Ref: 45.

1,2,3,4-Tetrahydro-2-keto-1,3,7-trimethyl-6,6,8-triphenylpurine or 8-phenyldiphenyldesoxycaffeine [$CH_3NC(C_6H_5):NC:CC(C_6H_5)_2N(CH_3)CON(CH_3)$] is orthorhombic with $a:b:c = 0.371:1:0.443$. Crystals {010} tablets with {110}, {011}. Good 001 cleavage and easy 110 parting. D 1.451. M.P. 235°. Y = *a*; Z = *b*. (+)2V = 76°10′, r > v. $N_X = 1.630$ Na, $N_Y = 1.669$, $N_Z = 1.736$, $N_Z - N_X = 0.106$ Na. Ref: 45.

Hypoxanthine hydrochloride monohydrate ($C_5H_4ON_4 \cdot HCl \cdot H_2O$) is monoclinic. Crystals columnar. X ∧ *c* = 24°, Y = *b*. (-)2V = medium, r < v. $N_X = 1.456$, $N_Y = 1.748$, $N_Z > 1.85$, $N_Z - N_X > 0.394$. Ref: 418a.

Hypoxanthine nitrate sesquihydrate ($C_5H_4ON_4 \cdot HNO_3 \cdot 1.5H_2O$) is orthorhombic. Crystals columnar or tabular. Good 001 cleavage. X = *c*, Y = *b*. (-)2V=43°, r<v. $N_X = 1.385$, $N_Y = 1.720$, $N_Z = 1.797$, $N_Z - N_X = 0.412$. Ref: 418a.

Adenine hydrochloride hemihydrate ($C_5H_5N_5 \cdot HCl \cdot 0.5H_2O$) is monoclinic. Crystals lamellar. Elongation along *a*. Y = *b*, Z ∧ *c* = 20°. (+)2V = medium, $N_X = 1.626$, $N_Y = 1.669$, $N_Z = 1.85$, $N_Z - N_X = 0.224$. Ref: 418a.

Adenine sulfate dihydrate {$(C_5H_5N_5)_2 \cdot H_2SO_4 \cdot 2H_2O$} is monoclinic (very nearly orthorhombic). Crystals equant. Y nearly = *a*. Z = *b*. (-)2V = 64°, r < v, with horizontal dispersion. $N_X = 1.427$, $N_Y = 1.688$, $N_Z = 1.804$, $N_Z - N_X = 0.377$. Ref: 418a.

1,2,3,6-Tetrahydro-2,6-diketo-3,7-dimethylpurine, or theobromine, or 3,7-dimethylxanthine and its salts

Theobromine [$CH_3NCH:NC:CCONHCONCH_3$] is monoclinic with $\beta = 128°$. Lamellar twinning on 001. M.P. 357°. The optic plane is 010; X ∧ *c* = – 38° and Z = *c ca.* (Inconsistent). $N_X = 1.435$, N_Y little greater then 1.74, N_Z much greater than 1.74, $N_Z - N_X > 0.305$. (-)2V = 30°, r > v. Ref: 196, 205.

Theobromine hydrochloride [$CH_3NCH{:}NC{:}CCONHCONCH_3 \cdot HCl \cdot (H_2O\,?)$] is probably biaxial with parallel extinction and positive elongation. $N_1 = 1.72$, $N_2 = 1.75$, $N_2 - N_1 = 0.03$. Ref: 34, 35.

Theobromine salicylate [$CH_3NCN{:}NC{:}CCONHCONCH_3 \cdot C_6H_4(OH)(CO_2H)$] is probably biaxial with parallel extinction and negative elongation. $N_1 = 1.42$, $N_2 = 1.74$, $N_2 - N_1 = 0.32$. Ref: 34, 35.

Xanthine hydrochloride ($C_5H_4O_2N_4 \cdot HCl$) is orthorhombic. Crystals columnar or tabular. Good 001 cleavage. X = *c*, Y = *b*. (-)2V = 12°, r < v. $N_X = 1.426$, $N_Y = 1.772$, $N_Z = 1.778$, $N_Z - N_X = 0.352$. Ref: 418a.

Sodium xanthinate hemiheptahydrate ($C_5H_2O_2N_4Na_2 \cdot 3.5H_2O$) is monoclinic (?). Crystals columnar. X = *c* (?), Y = *b*. (-)2V = 41°. $N_X = 1.426$, $N_Y = 1.648$, $N_Z = 1.688$, $N_Z - N_X = 0.262$. Ref: 418a.

Guanine sulfate dihydrate {$(C_5H_5ON_5)_2 \cdot H_2SO_4 \cdot 2H_2O$} is monoclinic. Crystals columnar. Y = *b*, $Z \wedge c = 36°$. (-)2V = 47°, r < v. $N_X = 1.438$, $N_Y = 1.713$, $N_Z = 1.787$, $N_Z - N_X = 0.349$. Ref: 418a.

Guanine hydrochloride dihydrate ($C_5H_5ON_5 \cdot HCl \cdot 2H_2O$) is monoclinic. Crystals columnar. $X \wedge c = 32°$, Y = *b*. (+)2V = 49°. $N_X = 1.585$, $N_Y = 1.622$, $N_Z = 1.832$, $N_Z - N_X = 0.249$. Ref: 418a.

1,3-Dimethylxanthine monohydrate or theophylline monohydrate [$CO\langle^{NCH_3 \cdot CO \cdot C \cdot NH}_{NCH_3 \cdot C—N}\rangle CH \cdot H_2O$] is monoclinic with *a*:*b*:*c* = 1.071:1:?, β = 126° 35′. Crystals thin {010} tablets with {110}, {001}, etc. M.P. 270 - 274°. Weakly pleochroic in 010 from colorless to yellowish brown. $X \wedge c = -43°$, Z = *b*, $N_1 = 1.528$, $N_2 = 1.69$, $N_2 - N_1 = 0.162$. Again: $N_1 = 1.447$, $N_2 = 1.695$, $N_3 > 1.733$, $N_3 - N_1 > 0.286$. Ref: 117, 343c, 518.

1,2,3,6-Tetrahydro-2,6-diketo-1,3,7-trimethylpurine or 1,3,7-trimethylxanthine or caffeine and its salts

Caffeine [$CH_3NCH{:}NC{:}CCON(CH_3)CONCH_3$] is hexagonal in long prisms which become shorter by sublimation between 180° and 200°, but melt at 238° if heated rapidly. Uniaxial negative with $N_O = 1.70$ *ca.*, $N_E = 1.446$, $N_O - N_E = 0.254$ *ca.* Also $N_O = 1.707$, $N_E = 1.435$, $N_O - N_E = 0.272$. Crystals easily obtained by sublimation between 80° and 100° at reduced pressure and 5 mm. distance. Again: $N_X = 1.455$, $N_Y = 1.472$, $N_Z = 1.723$. Ref: 205, 343c, 518.

Caffeine monohydrate [$CH_3NCH{:}NC{:}CCON(CH_3)CONCH_3 \cdot H_2O$] is monoclinic. Crystals show {111}, {110}, {100}. Loses water at 70°. Needles have extinction at 32° and negative elongation. $X \wedge c = 32°$; Y = *b*. (-)2V = 30-35°.

$N_X = 1.421$, $N_Y = 1.661$ *ca.*, $N_Z = 1.689$ *ca.*, $N_Z - N_X = 0.268$ *ca.* (−)2V = rather small. Again: $N_1 = 1.54$, $N_2 = 1.66$. Ref: 196, 205, 239.

Caffeine hydrochloride [$CH_3NCH:NC:CCON(CH_3)CONCH_3 \cdot HCl$] has parallel extinction and negative elongation. $N_1 = 1.565$, $N_2 = 1.66$, $N_2 - N_1 = 0.095$. Ref: 34, 35.

Caffeine hydrobromide [$CH_3NCH:NC:CCON(CH_3)CONCH_3 \cdot HBr$] has parallel extinction and positive elongation. $N_1 = 1.55$, $N_2 = 1.70$, $N_2 - N_1 = 0.15$. Ref: 34, 35.

Caffeine sulfate [$CH_3NCH:NC:CCON(CH_3)CONCH_3 \cdot H_2SO_4$] is granular with $N_1 = 1.595$, $N_2 = 1.61$, $N_2 - N_1 = 0.015$. Ref: 34, 35.

2,2′,3,3′-Tetrahydro-3,3′-diketo-1,1′,5,5′-tetramethyl-2,2′-diphenyl-4,4′-*bis*-1,3-diazole or 4,4′-bisantipyrine [$OCN(C_6H_5)N(CH_3)C(CH_3):C \cdot C:C(CH_3)N(CH_3)N(C_6H_5)CO$] is monoclinic with $a:b:c = 3.904:1:1.510$, $\beta = 111°34'$. Crystals short prisms with {110}, {100}, {001}, {10$\bar{1}$}, etc. Fig. 123. Twinning on 100. Perfect 001 cleavage. M.P. 245°. The optic plane is 010; the acute bisectrix makes an angle of − 37° with *c*. 2V = 60°52′ Na. $N_Y = 1.5308$ Na. Ref: 119.

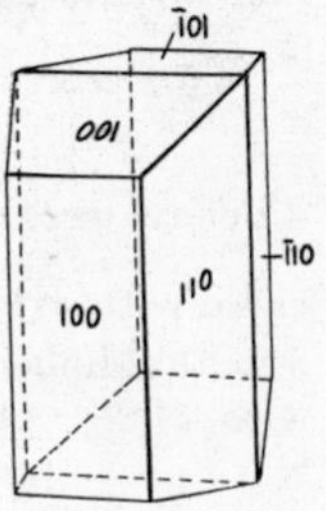

Fig. 123. Bisantipyrine.

bis[2,3-Dihydro-3-keto-1,5-dimethyl-2-phenyl-4-(1,2-diazolyl)]methane monohydrate or 4,4′-methylenediantipyrine monohydrate [$OCN(C_6H_5)N(CH_3)C(CH_3):CCH_2C:C(CH_3)N(CH_3)N(C_6H_5)CO \cdot H_2O$] is monoclinic with $a:b:c = 0.829:1:0.788$, $\beta = 93°16'$. Crystals {001} tablets with {111}, {11$\bar{1}$}, {110}, etc. The optic plane is 010; an optic axis visible through 001; the acute bisectrix makes an angle of − 56° with *c*. 2V = 76.5°, r < v weak. $N_Y = 1.649$ Na. Ref: 119.

2,6,8-Trihydroxypurine or uric acid [$N:COHNHC:CCOH:NCOH:N$] is orthorhombic with $a:b:c = 0.613:1:?$ Plates are {001} with {110}, etc. H = 2.5. D 1.89. The optic plane is 001 and X = *a*. $N_X = 1.573$, $N_Y = ?$, $N_Z = 1.830$, $N_Z - N_X = 0.257$. A dimorphous or hydrated form at low temperature has $N_X = 1.53$ and $N_Z = 1.73$. Crystals formed with dyestuffs have varying crystal habits and strong pleochroism. Ref: 36, 104, 117.

Sodium acid urate monohydrate ($C_5H_3O_3N_4Na \cdot H_2O$) is monoclinic (?). Crystals laths or needles with two perfect (and one poor ?) cleavages. Extinction parallel to one cleavage. Z ⊥ plates. (+)2V = ?, $N_X = 1.448$, $N_Y \approx 1.75$, $N_Z > 1.84$. (From indices and optic sign N_Z must be > 2.05 and $N_Z - N_X$ must be > 0.392 – A.N.W.) Ref: 573.

1,2,3,6-Tetrahydro-8-hydroxy-2,6-diketo-1,3,9-trimethylpurine or 1,3,9-trimethyluric acid [$N:COHN(CH_3)C:CCON(CH_3)CON(CH_3)$] is biaxial in six-sided plates with symmetrical extinction and positive elongation. $N_1 = 1.525$, $N_2 = 1.705$, $N_2 - N_1 = 0.180$. Ref: 96.

1,2,3,6,8,9-Hexahydro-2,6,8-triketo-1,3,7,9-tetramethylpurine or 1,3,7,9- tetramethyluric acid [$N(CH_3)CON(CH_3)C:CCON(CH_3)CON(CH_3)$] is monoclinic with $a:b:c = 1.789:1:1.914$, $\beta = 118°19'$. Crystals prismatic or orthodomatic with {110}, {001}, {10$\bar{1}$}, {100}, etc. Fig. 124. Perfect 001 and 110 cleavages. M.P. 228°. $X = b$; $Z \wedge c = +9.5°$. (+)2V = 75°41′ Li, 75°19′ Na, 74°43′ Tl. $N_X \pm 1.5320$ Li, 1.5384 Na, 1.5450 Tl; $N_Y = 1.6041$ Li, 1.6093 Na, 1.6158 Tl; $N_Z = 1.7496$ Li, 1.7539 Na, 1.7639 Tl; $N_Z - N_X = 0.2155$ Na. Described by Gatewood as platy or acicular with X parallel with elongation and $N_1 = 1.455$ (misprint for 1.545 ?), $N_2 = 1.710$. Ref: 96, 117.

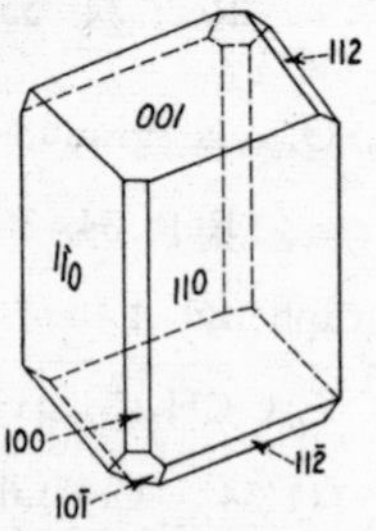

Fig. 124. Tetramethyluric acid.

9-Phenyluric acid dihydrate ($C_{11}H_8O_3N_4 \cdot 2H_2O$) has + sign of elongation and $N_X = 1.525$, $N_Z = 1.717$, $N_Z - N_X = 0.192$. Ref: 248.

4,5-Epoxyoctahydro-2,8-diketo-1,3,7-trimethyl-6,6-diphenylpurine or oxydiphenyldesoxycaffeine [$NHCON(CH_3)C \cdot CN(CH_3)CON(CH_3)C(C_6H_5)_2$] (with O bridge) is monoclinic with $a:b:c = 1.566:1:1.858$, $\beta = 114°30'$. Crystals obtained by oxidizing 8-methyldiphenyldesoxycaffeine with HNO_3. Crystals elongated parallel to c with {110}, {001}, {$\bar{1}$01}, {210}. Good 001 cleavage. D 1.473. M.P. 271°. $X \wedge c = +14°$; $Z = b$. (−)2V = 46°23′, r < v. $N_X = 1.608$, $N_Y = 1.663$, $N_Z = 1.674$, $N_Z - N_X = 0.066$ Na. Ref: 45.

9-Acetyl-4,5-epoxyoctahydro-2,8-diketo-1,3,7-trimethyl-6,6-diphenylpurine or acetyloxydiphenyldesoxycaffeine [$(CH_3CO)NCON(CH_3)C \cdot CN(CH_3)CON(CH_3)C(C_6H_5)_2$] (with O bridge) is monoclinic with $a:b:c = 2.248:1:1.852$, $\beta = 111°28'$. Crystals obtained by treating the preceding compound with acetylene. Crystals {100} tablets with {101}, {001}, {110}. No cleavage. D 1.454. M.P. 267 – 268°. $X \wedge c = 26°$; $Z = b$. (+)2V = 83°24′, r < v. $N_X = 1.560$, $N_Y = 1.603$, $N_Z = 1.649$, $N_Z - N_X = 0.089$ Na. Ref: 45.

3-Amino-1,5-diphenyl-1,2,4-triazole or 3-imino-1,5-diphenyl-1,2,4-triazoline [$C_6H_5NN:CNH_2N:CC_6H_5$] is monoclinic with $a:b:c = 0.882:1:0.772$, $\beta = 97°54'$. Crystals show {100}, {010}, {110}, {001}, {101}, etc. No true cleavage. M.P. 154°. The optic plane is 010; an optic axis visible through 100. Extinction at − 55°48′ Na with c in 010. $N_Y = 1.7339$ Na. Ref: 119.

2, 6, 8-Trihydroxy-9-(2-propenyl)purine or 9-allyluric acid $[CH_2: CHCH_2NC(OH): NC: CN: C(OH)N: COH]$ forms plates with symmetrical extinction and positive elongation. M.P. > 300°. Uniaxial negative with $N_O = 1.775 - 1.80$, $N_E = 1.75$, $N_O - N_E = 0.025 - 0.05$. Ref: 248.

1, 2, 3, 6-Tetrahydro-8-hydroxy-2, 6-diketo-1, 3-dimethyl-9-phenylpurine or 1, 3-dimethyl-9-phenyluric acid $[N: C(OH)N(C_6H_5)C: CON(CH_3)CON \cdot (CH_3)]$ forms six-sided and rectangular plates. M.P. > 300°. 2 V = large, $N_1 = 1.155 +$, $N_2 = 1.684 -$, $N_2 - N_1 = 0.529-$. Ref: 93, 248.

1, 2, 3, 6, 8, 9-Hexahydro-2, 6, 8-triketo-1, 3-dimethyl-9-phenylhexahydro-purine or 1,3-dimethyl-9-phenyluric acid (keto form) $[NHCON(C_6H_5)C{:}CCON(CH_3)CON(CH_3)]$ occurs as rectangular plates with parallel extinction and negative elongation. M.P. 249 - 250°. 2 V = large $N_1 = 1.571$, $N_2 = 1.620$, $N_2 - N_1 = 0.049$. Ref: 93.

1,2,3,6,8,9-Hexahydro-2,6,8-triketo-1,7-dimethyl-9-phenylpurine or 1,7-di-methyl-9-phenyluric acid $[(C_6H_5)NCON(CH_3)C{:}CNHCON(CH_3)CO]$ forms long rectangular or six-sided plates with symmetrical extinction and positive elonga-tion. M.P. > 280°. $N_1 = 1.540$, $N_2 > 1.755$, $N_2 - N_1 > 0.215$. Ref: 93.

1,2,3,6-Tetrahydro-8-hydroxy-2,6-diketo-1,3-dimethyl-9-(2-propenyl)purine or 9-allyl-1,3-dimethyluric acid $[CH_2{:}CHCH_2NCOH{:}NC{:}CN(CH_3)CON(CH)_3CO]$ forms rectangular plates with M.P. 280°. Parallel extinction and negative elongation. 2V = biaxial. $N_1 = 1.665$, $N_2 = 1.730$, $N_2 - N_1 = 0.065$. Ref: 95.

8,9-Dihydro-2,6-dihydroxy-8-keto-7-methyl-9-phenylpurine or 7-methyl-9-phenyluric acid $[CH_3NCON(C_6H_5)C{:}CCOH{:}NCOH{:}N]$ forms needles with parallel extinction and positive elongation. M.P. > 295°. $N_1 = 1.557$, $N_2 = 1.674 +$, $N_2 - N_1 = 0.117 +$. Ref: 248.

1,2,3,6,8,9-Hexahydro-2,6,8-triketo-1,3,7-trimethyl-9-phenylpurine or 1,3,7-trimethyl-9-phenyluric acid $[CH_3NCON(C_6H_5)C{:}CCON(CH_3)CON(CH_3)]$ forms thin plates with symmetrical extinction and negative elongation. M.P. 258–260°. Uniaxial negative (?) with $N_O = 1.670$, $N_E = 1.565$, $N_O - N_E = 0.105$. Ref: 95.

5,5′-Spirobihydantoin [NHCONHCOCCONHCONH] is monoclinic prismatic with $a{:}b{:}c = 0.531{:}1{:}0.818$, $\beta = 105°30'$. Space group $C2/c$; a 6.0, b 11.3, c 9.25 Å. U.C. 4. Six-sided plates have extinction at 25 - 26° and negative elongation. (+)2V = small, $N_X = 1.555$, $N_Z = 1.720$, $N_Z - N_X = 0.165$.

Again: $N_1 = 1.571$ *ca.*, $N_2 = 1.602$, $N_2 - N_1 = 0.031 +$, ($\therefore$ $N_Y = 1.58$ *ca.* - A.N.W.) Ref: 248, 568.

6,7-Dimethyl-9-(1-*d*-ribityl)isoalloxazine or lactoflavine or *d*-riboflavine or vitamin B_2 or vitamin G ($C_{17}H_{20}O_6N_4$) is dimorphous. Phase I is orthorhombic in prisms or rods. M.P. 275°. D 1.445. X || length. (+)2V = 82°, $N_X = 1.492$, $N_Y = 1.651$, $N_Z = 1.97$, $N_Z - N_X = 0.478$. Phase II is also orthorhombic in prisms or rods. Z || length. (+)2V = 50° calc. $N_X = 1.76$, $N_Y = 1.78$, $N_Z = 1.86$, $N_Z - N_X = 0.10$. Ref: 436b.

Aminotetrazole (CN_4HNH_2) is monoclinic prismatic. Crystals {100} tablets. Perfect 010 cleavage. X = *b*, Z $\wedge$ *c* = 23° *ca.* (-)2V = 18°, $N_X = 1.420 \pm .003$, $N_Y = 1.670 \pm .003$, $N_Z = 1.674 \pm .003$, $N_Z - N_X = 0.254$. Ref: 619.

Pentamethyleneaminotetrazole [$CH_2(CH_2)_4NHC:NN:NN$] is monoclinic with $a:b:c = 1.646:1:2.473$, $\beta = 84°37'$. Crystals thick {001} tablets elongated along *b* with {101}, {10$\bar{1}$}, {100}, etc. M.P. 91°. The optic plane is 010; one optic axis is visible through 001 (in the acute angle β) and another is visible through {101}, so 2V = 55° *ca.* $N_Y = 1.592$, $N_Z - N_X$ = strong. Ref: 305.

13. Compounds with one Nitrogen and one Oxygen[1] Atom in the Cycle

Morpholine picrate [$O(CH_2)_4NH_4OC_6H_2(NO_2)_3$] has two phases. One (I) is monoclinic with M.P. = 151.6°. X = *b*. Axial dispersion: (-)2H = 58° (6908), 54.5° (5780), 52° (5461), 37° (4916), 26° (minimum 4780), 46° (4600). Crossed dispersion such that if Z is taken as 0° at 6908, it is at 1.5° for 5780, 2° for 5461, 10° for 4916, 26° for 4800. For $\lambda = 5461$: (-)2V = 42°, $N_X = 1.504$, $N_Y = 1.852$, $N_Z = 1.926$, $N_Z - N_X = 0.422$. The second phase (II) is also monoclinic, with X = *b*. Axial dispersion: (-)2H = 45.5° (6908), 41° (5780), 40.5° (minimum at 5500), 51° (4916), 57° (4800). Crossed dispersion such that if Z is taken as 0° at 6908, it is at 2° for 6438, 9° for 5780, 19° for 5461, 47° for 4916 and 50° for 4800. Indices not reported. Ref: 557.

β-Morpholinoethyl benzhydryl ether hydrochloride or linadryl hydrochloride ($C_{19}H_{23}O_2N \cdot HCl$) is monoclinic (?). Crystals six-sided, elongated or irregular. M.P. 179 - 180°. Extinction parallel or inclined. (-)2V = 82° calc. $N_X = 1.577$, $N_Y = 1.631$, $N_Z = 1.672$, $N_Z - N_X = 0.095$. Ref: 477b.

2,3,5,6-Dibenzo-1,4-thiazine or thiodiphenylamine or phenothiazine [$SNH(C_6H_4)_2$] is orthorhombic with $a:b:c = 0.742:1:2.65$. Crystals tabular. D 1.34. M.P. 181 - 185°. X = *c*, Y = *a*. (+)2V = 81°, $N_X = 1.61$, $N_Y = 1.73$, $N_Z = 1.95$, $N_Z - N_X = 0.34$. Again: optically negative(?) with $N_X = 1.555$, $N_Y = 1.734$, $N_Z = 1.734$, $N_Z - N_X = 0.34$. Colorless or yellowish green, turning brown on exposure. Ref: 568a.

---

[1] Sulfur and selenium atoms are included here.

1,2-Dihydro-2-ketobenzisosulfonazole or *o*-benzosulfimide or saccharine is monoclinic prismatic with $a:b:c = 2.787:1:1.719$, $\beta = 93°51'$. Equant crystals with {100}, {011}, {10$\bar{1}$}, {001}, etc. Acicular crystals from sublimation. Twinning on (10$\bar{1}$). Perfect 100 cleavage. Soluble in water. M.P. 220°. The optic plane is 010; an optic axis almost normal to 10$\bar{1}$; extinction on 011 at 30° to *a* (-)2V = moderate (2E = 90 - 100°) $N_X = 1.535$, $N_Y = 1.690$, $N_Z > 1.733$, $N_Z - N_X > 0.198$. Again (-)2V = 88°, r < v; $N_Y = 1.671$.

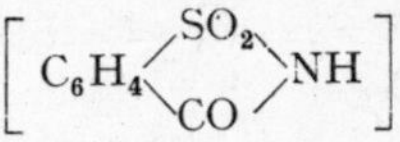

Ref: 118, 123, 239, 518.

5-(Bromomethyl)-4,5-dihydro-2-hydroxy-thiazole [$BrCH_2CHCH_2N:COHS$] is probably orthorhombic in flat rods with parallel extinction and negative elongation. (+)2V = large. $N_X = 1.530$, $N_Y = 1.650$, $N_Z = 1.830$, $N_Z - N_X = 0.300$, all ± 0.05. Ref: 361.

o-Sulfobenzoic acid imide sodium salt or *o*-benzoic acid sodium sulfimide or sodium salt of saccharin or soluble saccharin [$C_6H_4 \cdot SO_2 \cdot N(Na) \cdot CO$] is granular, easily soluble in water, and unstable in air. (+)2V = 30° *ca.* calc. $N_X = 1.455$, $N_Y = 1.471$, $N_Z = 1.646$, $N_Z - N_X = 0.191$. Also $N_1 = 1.470$, $N_2 = 1.665$.
Ref: 239, 343c.

Sodium *o*-benzosulfimide dihydrate or saccharine sodium dihydrate loses part of its water easily. It has $N_X = 1.560$, $N_Y = 1.642$, $N_Z = 1.733$, $N_Z - N_X = 0.173$. ∴ (+)2V = 87° *ca.* Colorless.

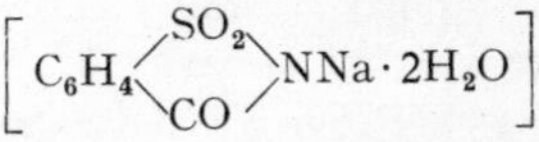

Ref: 518.

Cupric salt of *o*-sulfobenzoic acid imide hexahydrate or copper saccharin hexahydrate [$Cu(C_6H_4COSO_2N)_2 \cdot 6H_2O$] is monoclinic prismatic with $a:b:c = 0.513:1:0.448$, $\beta = 101°14'$. Space group $P2_1/c$; *a* 8.4, *b* 16.3, *c* 7.37 Å. U.C. 2. Crystals show {110}, {$\bar{1}$11}, {011}, {010}. D 1.809. $X \wedge c = +32°$; $Z = b$. (-)2V = 45°. $N_X = 1.491$, $N_Y = 1.700$, $N_Z = 1.746$, $N_Z - N_X = 0.255$.
Ref: 195.

Cupric salt of *o*-sulfobenzoic acid imide dipyridine dihydrate or copper pyridine disaccharin dihydrate [$Cu(C_6H_4COSO_2N)_2 \cdot 2C_5H_5N \cdot 2H_2O$] is orthorhombic with $a:b:c = 0.440:1:0.610$. Crystals {110} prisms with {001}, {010}, {011}, etc. No cleavage. D 1.509. $Y = b$; $Z = c$. (+)2V = large. N_X = ?, $N_Y = 1.6557$ (Hg blue); $N_Z = 1.6487$ (Hg yellow), 1.6530 (Hg green), 1.6782 (Hg blue). Pleochroic with X and Y = decided blue, Z = colorless. Ref: 24.

2-Mercaptobenzothiazole ($C_7H_5NS_2$) is monoclinic with $a:b:c = 2.655:1:1.335$, $\beta = 109°$. Crystals long ∥ *b* with {001}, {100}, etc. Cleavages ∥ 010 and 100. D 1.42. M.P. 181°. (-)2V = 50°, r > v with inclined dispersion. $Y = b$, $Z \wedge c = 6°$ in acute β. $N_X = 1.667$, $N_Y = 1.965$, $N_Z = 2.06$ calc., $N_Z - N_X = 0.4$ calc. (for $\lambda = 5461$). For white light: $N_X = 1.665$, $N_Y = 1.96$, $N_Z = 2.04$, $N_Z - N_X = 0.375$. Ref: 553a, 556a.

Benzothiazoleguanidine ($C_8H_{10}N_4S$) has three crystal phases. One phase (I) is orthorhombic in plates which may be considered {010}, elongated along *c*.

Y = *a*; Z = *b*. (+)2E = 100° *ca.*, r < v extreme. $N_X = 1.700$, $N_Y = 1.740$, $N_Z = 1.8+$ (est.), $N_Z - N_X = 0.100+$. Therefore (+)2V = 52° *ca.* calc. Another phase (II) is orthorhombic (or monoclinic ?) in prismatic crystals with parallel extinction and negative elongation. (-)2V = ?. $N_X = 1.525$, $N_Y = 1.745$, $N_Z = 1.8$ (est.), $N_Z - N_X = 0.275$ (est.). Phase III is monoclinic, elongated parallel to *b*. Y = *b*; Z is much inclined to the face normal to 010. (+)2E = 50° *ca.*, r < v. $N_X = 1.5$ *ca.*, $N_Y = 1.60$, $N_Z = 1.72$ *ca.*, $N_Z - N_X = 0.22$ *ca.* (+)2V = 30° *ca.* Ref: 298.

Benzothiazoleguanidine hydrochloride ($C_8H_{10}N_4S \cdot HCl$) is probably orthorhombic in needles with parallel extinction and negative elongation. (-)2V = large. $N_X = 1.590$, $N_Y = 1.765$, $N_Z = 1.82+$, $N_Z - N_X = 0.23+$. Ref: 298.

Benzothiazoleguanidine nitrate ($C_8H_{10}N_4S \cdot HNO_3$) is orthorhombic (?) in needles with parallel extinction. For vibrations parallel to needles N = 1.78 *ca.*; for vibrations normal thereto N = 1.53 *ca.* Ref: 298.

Phenylbiguanide mercaptobenzothiazole ($C_8H_{11}N_5 \cdot C_7H_5NS_2$) forms tabular colorless crystals. M.P. 171°. (+)2V = 45° calc., $N_X = 1.616$, $N_Y = 1.747$, $N_Z = 1.854$ calc., $N_Z - N_X = 0.238$ calc. Ref: 405a.

Benzoselenazoleguanidine ($C_8H_{10}N_4Se$) is probably monoclinic in prismatic or tabular crystals. The optic plane and X are parallel to the elongation; Z is inclined to a pinacoid. (+)2V = 30° *ca.*, r > v very strong. $N_X = 1.640$, $N_Y = 1.780$, $N_Z = 1.9$ (est.), $N_Z - N_X = 0.26$ (est.). Ref: 299.

Benzoselenazoleguanidine hydrochloride ($C_8H_{10}N_4Se \cdot HCl$) has two phases. At low temperature it is orthorhombic showing {110}, {001}, and {100} faces. M.P. 247 - 249°. X = *c*; Y = *b*. (-)2V = large, r > v. $N_X = 1.580$, $N_Y = 1.785$, $N_Z = 2.0$ (est.), $N_Z - N_X = 0.42$ D (est.). At high temperature it is monoclinic with an extinction angle of 15°, Z nearly normal to 001, and strong positive birefringence. Ref: 299.

Benzoselenazoleguanidine nitrate ($C_8H_{10}N_4Se \cdot HNO_3$) is monoclinic in prismatic crystals elongated along *c*. $\beta = 105°$ *ca.* M.P. 193 - 198°. $X \wedge c = 18°$; Z = *b*. (-)2V = 60°. $N_X = 1.460$, $N_Y = 1.81$, $N_Z = 1.87$, $N_Z - N_X = 0.41$. Ref: 299.

Benzoselenazoleguanidine sulfate ($C_8H_{10}N_4Se \cdot H_2SO_4$) is tetragonal, in thin rectangular plates which are uniaxial positive with M.P. 287 - 289°, and $N_O = 1.615 \pm .005$, $N_E = 1.83 \pm 0.1$, $N_E - N_O = 0.215$. Ref: 299.

Benzoselenazoleguanidine picrate [$C_8H_{10}N_4Se \cdot C_6H_2(NO_2)_3OH$] is probably monoclinic in acicular crystals with extinction from 0° to 18°. M.P. 267 - 270°. For lengthwise vibrations N = 1.495, for crosswise vibrations N = 1.9 *ca.* Color yellow with little or no pleochroism. Ref: 299.

Tetrahydro-2,4-diketo-3-phenylthiazole or 3-phenyl-2,4-thiazolidinedione [$\overline{CH_2CON(C_6H_5)COS}$] has two phases. At higher temperatures the stable phase (I) forms needles with parallel extinction and ± elongation. (-)2V = 80° *ca.*

$N_X = 1.570$, $N_Y = 1.696$, $N_Z = 1.779$, $N_Z - N_X = 0.209$. At room temperature the substance forms rectangular monoclinic blades elongated along *b* and flattened on 100. The angle β is 101.5°. Perfect 001 and poor 010 cleavages. The optic plane is 010; $X \wedge c = -41°$; $Y = b$. (-)2V = 83° *ca.* $N_X = 1.575$, $N_Y = 1.693$, $N_Z = 1.805$, $N_Z - N_X = 0.230$. Ref: 107.

5,5-Dimethyl-4-carboxylthiazolidine or penicillamine $\{(CH_3)_2CC(CO_2H)NHCH_2S\}$ is orthorhombic. Crystals columnar. M.P. 153 - 155°. Z || length. (+)2E < 10°. $N_X = 1.601$, $N_Y = 1.602$, $N_Z = 1.638$, $N_Z - N_X = 0.037$. Ref: 529.

Sulfathiazole or 2-sulfanilamidothiazole ($C_9H_9N_3O_2S_2$) is dimorphous. One phase (I) forms six-sided plates and prisms which melt at about 175° or invert at a lower temperature to the other phase which melts at about 200°. This phase (I) often shows the acute bisectrix interference figure. It has (+)2V = small, r > v. $N_X = 1.674$, $N_Y = 1.685$, $N_Z > 1.773$, $N_Z - N_X > 0.099$. Again $N_X = 1.678$, $N_Z = 1.763$, $N_Z - N_X = 0.085$. The second phase (II) forms rods with X normal to elongation and $N_X = 1.605$, $N_Y = 1.733$, $N_Z > 1.733$, $N_Z - N_X > 0.128$. With picrolonic acid this compound forms fine needles with X at an angle to elongation and $N_X = 1.582$, $N_Y = ?$, $N_Z > 1.733$, $N_Z - N_X > 0.151$. Ref: 120a, 475a, 518, 523a, 572a.

Sodium sulfathiazole or sodium 2-sulfanilamidothiazole ($C_9H_8N_3O_2S_2Na$) is monoclinic. Crystals laths with *c* lengthwise. $Z \wedge c = 12°$. (+)2V = ?, $N_X = 1.653$, $N_Y = 1.672$, $N_Z > 1.76$ and probably < 1.775, $N_Z - N_X > 0.107$ and probably > 0.122. Ref: 572a.

Sulfathiazole diliturate dihydrate ($C_{13}H_{12}O_7N_6S_2 \cdot 2H_2O$) is monoclinic in columnar crystals which decompose at 200°. Negative elongation and maximum extinction angle of 10° (?). (-)2V = 63°, r < v strong. $N_X = 1.565$, $N_Y = 1.716$, $N_Z = 1.785$, $N_Z - N_X = 0.220$. Color yellow, with no pleochroism. Ref: 434a.

Acetylsulfathiazole or acetyl-2-sulfanilamidothiazole ($C_{11}H_{11}N_3O_3S_2$) is orthorhombic. Crystals {010} laths with *c* lengthwise. $X = b$, $Y = c$, $Z = a$. (-)2V = small with strong dispersion and ultra-blue interference colors. (-)2V = small, $N_X = 1.645$, $N_Y = 1.763$, $N_Z = 1.770$, $N_Z - N_X = 0.125$. Ref: 572a.

Sulfasuxidine or *p*-2-thiazolylsulfamylsuccinanilic acid ($C_{13}H_{13}O_5N_3S_2$) has at least two phases. The high temperature phase (I) is triclinic. Massive crystals form above 35° and melt at about 180°; it inverts slowly to phase II at room temperature. (+)2V = about 80°, $N_X = 1.54$ *ca.*, $N_Y = 1.61$ *ca.*, $N_Z = 1.73$, $N_Z - N_X = 0.19$. Phase II is monoclinic with $a:b:c = 5.095:1:3.703$, $\beta = 127°$. *a* 26.39, *b* 5.17, *c* 19.61 Å. U.C. 4. Crystals long || *b* with {100}, {010}, {101}. D 1.53. Stable below 35°; melts at 125°, and resolidifies to phase I. $X = b$, $Y \wedge c = 41°$ in acute β. (-)2V = 58°, r < v strong. $N_X = 1.578$, $N_Y = 1.676$, $N_Z = 1.710$, $N_Z - N_X = 0.132$. Ref: 553a.

N^4-(2-Hydroxy-3-methoxybenzylidine)sulfathiazole ($C_{17}H_{15}O_4N_3S_2$) is orthorhombic in lamellar crystals long parallel to *c*. M.P. 199°. (+)2V = very large, r > v. $N_X = 1.632$, $N_Y = 1.734$, $N_Z > 1.86$, $N_Z - N_X > 0.228$. Color brick red, with strong pleochroism and X < Y < Z. Ref: 434a.

Thiamine hydrochloride monohydrate or aneurin monohydrate or vitamin B_1 or vitamin F ($C_{12}H_{17}ON_4SCl \cdot HCl \cdot H_2O$) is dimorphous. One phase is orthorhombic with profile angles of 117° and 126°. Crystals long plates and tablets. M.P. 245 - 248°. D 1.43. (+)2V = 61°, r > v strong. $N_X = 1.618$, $N_Y = 1.640$, $N_Z = 1.714$, $N_Z - N_X = 0.096$. Phase II is monoclinic with $a:b:c = 0.615:1:0.340$, $\beta = 113°55'$. Space group $P2_1a$. *a* 12.62, *b* 20.53, *c* 6.96 Å. U.C. 4. Crystals {010} tablets with {001}, etc. D 1.41. Y = *b*, $Z \wedge c = 20°$ in acute β. (+)2V = 87°, $N_X = 1.600$, $N_Y = 1.639$, $N_Z = 1.685$, $N_Z - N_X = 0.085$. Again $N_X = 1.606$, $N_Z = 1.689$. Ref: 436b, 552a, 560a.

N^4-(2-Hydroxybenzylidene)sulfathiazole ($C_{16}H_{13}O_3N_3S_2$) is monoclinic with M.P. 216°. Crystals tabular elongated along *b*. Y = *b*. $Z \wedge c = 31°$. (+)2V = large, r > v. $N_X = 1.601$, $N_Y = 1.735$, $N_Z > 1.86$, $N_Z - N_X > 0.259$. Color yellow, with X < Y < Z. Ref: 434a.

Dimethylaminoisopropylthiodiphenylamine hydrochloride or phenergan hydrochloride [$C_{12}H_8NSC(CH_3)_2N(CH_3)_2 \cdot HCl$] forms colorless rods and fragments. M.P. 204°. Z || elongation. (-?)2V = 73° calc. $N_X = 1.617$, $N_Y = 1.691$, $N_Z = 1.733$, all ± .002, $N_Z - N_X = 0.116$. Ref: 477c.

10-β-Dimethylaminoisopropylthiodiphenylamine hydrobromide or phenergan hydrobromide [$C_{12}H_8NSC(CH_3)_2N(CH_3)_2 \cdot HBr$] forms massive prisms. M.P. 211°. (+)2V = small, $N_X = 1.667$, $N_Y = 1.675$, $N_Z > 1.734$, $N_Z - N_X > 0.067$. 2V < 40° calc. Ref: 477d.

β-or 2-(1-Pyrrolidine)ethylthiodiphenylamine hydrochloride or pyrrolazote hydrochloride ($C_{12}H_8NSC_4H_8N \cdot HCl$) forms colorless prisms, easily broken. M.P. 198°. $N_X = 1.690 \pm .003$. N_Y = ?, $N_Z = 1.737$, $N_Z - N_X = 0.047$. Ref: 477c.

5-Bromo-5,6-dihydro-2-(1-piperidyl)-1,3,4-thiazine or 2-(1-piperidino)-5-bromo-5,6-dihydro-1,3-thiazine [$\overline{SCH_2CHBrCH_2N}:\overline{CN(CH_2)_4CH_2}$] is biaxial with $N_X = 1.625$, $N_Y = 1.685$, $N_Z = 1.745$, $N_Z - N_X = 0.120$. 2V = 90° *ca.* Ref: 361.

4,6,10-Triox-1-azatricyclo [$3 \cdot 3 \cdot 1 \cdot 1^{3,7}$] decane or trimorpholine ($C_6H_9O_3N$) is monoclinic with $a:b:c = 1.092:1:0.588$, $\beta = 115°43'$. Crystals {100} tablets with {001}, {120}, {$11\bar{1}$}, {111}, etc. Perfect 100 cleavage. Decomposes at 210 - 220°. The optic plane is 010; an optic axis visible through 001 and also through 100. (+)2V = 80°. $N_X = 1.5515$ Na, $N_Y = 1.5595$, $N_Z = 1.5779$, $N_Z - N_X = 0.0264$. Ref: 119.

Trimorpholine hydrochloride ($C_6H_9O_3N \cdot HCl$) is monoclinic with $a:b:c =$ 1.490:1:0.934, $\beta = 92°27.5'$. Crystals show only {100}, {110}, {011}. Perfect 100 cleavage. Decomposes at 255 - 260°. The optic plane is said to be 010 for blue, but normal to 010 for red. 2E given as 50 - 60° Na. Indices given as $N_X = 1.5653$ Na, $N_Y = 1.5669$, $N_Z = 1.5703$, whence $N_Z - N_X = 0.0071$. (But for these indices 2V must be about 87 - 88°; on the other hand, the optic angle must go through 0° to permit change in the position of the optic plane - A.N.W.) Ref: 119.

14. Compounds with two Nitrogen Atoms and one Oxygen Atom in the Cycle

Hexahydro-5-keto-3,3,7,7-tetramethyl-1,2,8-oxadiazocine or triacetonedihydroxylamine anhydride $\{(CH_3)_2\overline{CNH \cdot O \cdot NHC(CH_3)_2CH_2 \cdot CO \cdot C}H_2\}$ is triclinic with $a:b:c = 0.747:1:0.377$, $\alpha = 94°6'$, $\beta = 104°3'$, $\gamma = 85°31'$. Crystals short prismatic with {110}, {1$\bar{1}$0}, {001}, {11$\bar{1}$}, etc. Perfect 110 cleavage. M.P. 101 - 102°. Extinction at 16° to c on 1$\bar{1}$0; at 4° to c on 110; and at 5° to the edge 001:1$\bar{1}$0 on 001; an optic axis visible through 110. 2V = 57°57′ Li, 58°6′ Na, 58°15′ Tl, $N_Y = 1.5209$ Li, 1.5218 Na, 1.5228 Tl. Ref: 117.

IV. NATURAL PRODUCTS NOT ASSIGNED PLACES IN THE THREE PRECEDING GROUPS

1. Carotenoids

Dimethyl 4,8,12,16-tetramethyleicosa-2,4,6,8,10,12,14,16,18-nonaenedioate or dimethyl 3,7,11,15-tetramethyloctadeca-1,3,5,7,9,11,13,15,17-nonaene-1,18-dicarboxylate or bixin methyl ester $\{CH_3O_2CCH:[CHC(CH_3):CHCH]_4:CHCO_2CH_3\}$ is monoclinic with $a:b:c = 0.789:1:1.539$, $\beta = 120°54'$. Crystals {001} plates with {120}. Distinct 010 cleavage. Twinning on 001. $Y = b$; $Z \wedge c = +20°$. (+)2V = 66° ± 3°. $N_X = 1.44 \pm .01$, $N_Y = 1.649 \pm .002$, $N_Z = 1.63 \pm .18$ calc., $N_Z - N_X = 1.16 \pm 0.24$. Also $N_Y = 1.630$ ($\lambda = 650$), 1.649 D, 1.660 ($\lambda = 570$). The calculated birefringence seems incredibly high, but N_Z was found by observation to be decidedly higher than 2.36, and thin plates produce two images! Color is deep red with X = clear yellow, Y = orange, Z = dark red to black. Ref: 342a, 612.

2. Carbohydrates

D(–)-Ribose [$CH_2OH(CHOH)_3CHO$] is probably orthorhombic in rods and fragments. M.P. 95°. Parallel extinction and negative elongation. (+)2V = 80° *ca.* calc. $N_X = 1.533$, $N_Y = 1.549$, $N_Z = 1.570$, $N_Z - N_X = 0.037$, all ± .002. $[\alpha] = +23.7°$. Ref: 358.

α-*D*(-) or *L*(+)-Arabinose [$CH_2OH(CHOH)_3CHO$] is orthorhombic (?) in acicular crstals with sharp ends, often in groups. D 1.585. (-)2V = large. N_X = 1.551 D, N_Y = 1.567, N_Z = 1.571, $N_Z - N_X$ = 0.020 D. Extinction at small angle. [α] = 105.5° (equilibrium value). Ref: 117, 351.

β-*L*(+) or *D*(-)-Arabinose [$CH_2OH(CHOH)_3CHO$] is orthorhombic disphenoidal with $a:b:c$ = 0.335:1:0.249. Space group $P2_12_12_1$; *a* 6.51, *b* 19.43, *c* 4.85 Å. U.C. 4. Crystals show {120}, 101}, {100}, etc. D 1.625. Parallel extinction. X = *a*; Y = *c*. (-)2V = 48°. N_X = 1.553 (λ = 650), 1.555 D, 1.565 (λ = 450); N_Y = 1.571 (λ = 650), 1.573 D, 1.584 (λ = 450); N_Z = 1.574 (λ = 650), 1.577 D, 1.588 (λ = 450); $N_Z - N_X$ = 0.022 D. [α] = + 175° (initial) to + 105°. Ref: 117, 351, 439.

D- or *L*-Arabinose diphenylhydrazone [$CH_2OH(CHOH)_3CH:NN(C_6H_5)_2$] is orthorhombic in prisms with {110}, {010}, {011}, {100}, etc. Y = *c*; Z = *b*. Elongation ±. (+) 2V = 85° calc. N_X = 1.627, N_Y = 1.674, N_Z = 1.735, $N_Z - N_X$ = 0.108. Ref: 251.

Aldehydo-D-Arabinose hexa-acetate [$C_5H_6O_6(COCH_3)_6$] forms needles with M.P. 89.5°. Rod-like needles often six-sided. Parallel extinction and ± elongation. (+)2V = 80° calc. N_X = 1.455, N_Y = 1.472, N_Z = 1.495 (all ± .003), $N_Z - N_X$ = 0.040. [α] = - 28.1° (c. 1.33 chloroform.) Ref: 188.

2,3,4-Trimethyl-α-methyl-*D*-arabinopyranoside [$(C_8H_{16}O_5)$] (formerly known as β) is acicular, apparently orthorhombic. X = *c*. N_X = 1.475, N_Y = ?, $N_Z \geqslant 1.555$, $N_Z - N_X \geqslant 0.080$. Ref: 60.

Penta-acetyl-*D*-arabinose methyl hemiacetal [$C_{15}H_{23}O_{11}$] exists in two isomers. One melts at 76° and dissolves in ether or chloroform. Crystals often show the acute bisectrix and may be orthorhombic. (-)2E = 70° (± 5°), 2V = 45° calc. N_X = 1.448, N_Y = 1.500, N_Z = 1.510 (all ± 0.003), $N_Z - N_X$ = 0.062. [α] = - 26.9° in chloroform (c. 1.33). A second isomer melts at 68 - 70°. Crystals often show an optic axis or an unoriented figure. (+)2V = 60° calc. N_X = 1.455, N_Y = 1.464, N_Z = 1.490 (all ± .003), $N_Z - N_X$ = 0.035. [α] = - 34.7° in chloroform (c. 1.33). Ref: 188.

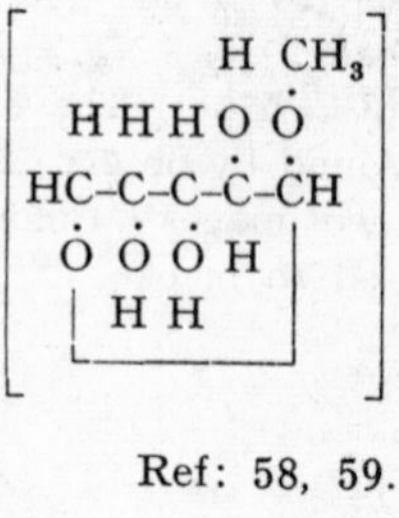

β-Methyl *L*-arabinopyranoside has two phases. One is orthorhombic disphenoidal with[1] $a:b:c$ = 0.468:1:0.353. Crystals {010} tablets elongated along *c*. D 1.44. The other is monoclinic sphenoidal with $a:b:c$ = 1.162:1:0.761, β = 115°35′. Space group $P2_1$; *a* 8.99, *b* 7.74, *c* 5.89 Å. U.C. 2. Crystals {100} plates elongated along *c* with {110}, {001}. Distinct 100 cleavage. D 1.47. M.P. 170°. Y nearly = *c*; Z = *b*. (+)2V = 71°, N_X = 1.524 Na, N_Y = 1.529, N_Z = 1.546, all ± .002, $N_Z - N_X$ = 0.022. Ref: 58, 59.

α-*D*(+)-Xylopyranose or xylose [$CH_2OH(CHOH)_3CHO$] is monoclinic, probably sphenoidal, with $a:b:c$ = 1.655:1:1.776, β = 117°5′. Crystals show

[1] *a* and *b* interchanged to make $b > a > c$.

{001}, {110}, {$\bar{1}$01}, etc. D 1.525. Small extinction angle and negative elongation. (-)2V = 32°. N_X = 1.515 (λ = 650), 1.517 D, 1.525 (λ = 450); N_Y = 1.542 (λ = 650), 1.544 D, 1.553 (λ = 450); N_Z = 1.543 + (λ = 650), 1.546 D, 1.555 (λ = 450); $N_Z - N_X$ = 0.029 D. (Keenan described L(-)"xylose" with (-)2E = 36° *ca.* N_X = 1.517, N_Y = 1.544, N_Z = 1.546, $N_Z - N_X$ = 0.029). [α] = - 92.0° (initial) to - 19.0°. (equilibrium). Ref: 351, 358.

2,3,4-Trimethyl-α-*D*-xylopyranose is monoclinic sphenoidal with $a:b:c$ = 1.044:1:0.800, β = 91°0′. Space group $P2_1$; *a* 8.68, *b* 8.31, *c* 6.65 Å. U.C. 2. Crystals often tabular on {110}. X = *b*. An optic axis is visible through 110. N_X = 1.48, N_Y = ?, N_Z = 1.555, $N_Z - N_X$ = 0.075. Ref: 60, 398a, 629.

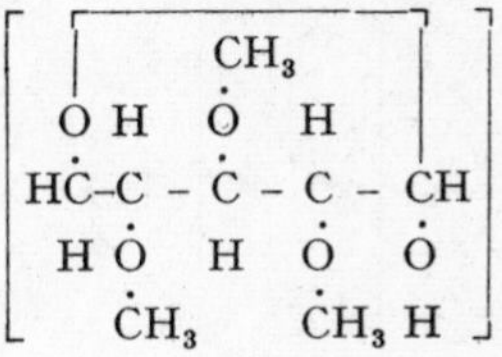

α-*D*-Methyl xylopyranoside is monoclinic sphenoidal with $a:b:c$ = 1.277:1:0.802, β = 111°36′. Crystals elongated parallel to *b* with {001}, {100}, {1$\bar{1}$1}, {021}, etc. D 1.41. M.P. 90 - 92°. X $\wedge$ *c* = + 30°; Y = *b*. (-)2V = 35°14′, r > v. N_Y = 1.5213 Li, 1.5236 Na, 1.5272 Tl. [α] = - 153.2°. Ref: 117.

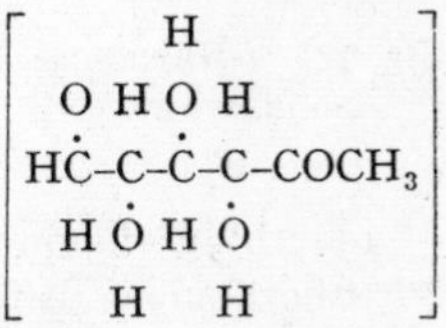

α-*D*(-)-Lyxose [$CH_2OH(CHOH)_3CHO$] is monoclinic with $a:b:c$ = 1.608: 1:1.828, β = 117°50′. Crystals short prisms (often six-sided) with {110}, {001}, {100}, {10$\bar{1}$}. No distinct cleavage. M.P. 101°. D 1.545. The optic plane and Z are normal to 010; acute negative bisectrix visible through 10$\bar{1}$. Extinction at a small angle. 2H (in oil with N = 1.50) = 85°45′. N_X = 1.530 (λ = 650), 1.532 D, 1.541 (λ = 450); N_Y = 1.538 + (λ = 650), 1.541 D, 1.550 (λ = 450); N_Z = 1.547 (λ = 650), 1.549 D, 1.559 (λ = 450); $N_Z - N_X$ = 0.017 D. (-)2V = 83° calc. Colorless. [α] = - 5.5° (initial) to + 13.9° (equilibrium). Ref: 117, 351.

2,3,4-Trimethyl-α-L-lyxopyranose is orthorhombic disphenoidal with[1] $a:b:c$ = 0.729:1:0.643. Space group $P2_12_12_1$; *a* 9.19, *b* 12.75, *c* 8.19 Å. U.C. 4. Crystals acicular along *b*. D 1.26. X is normal to *b* and parallel to (*a* or *c* ?). N_X = 1.48. Ref: 60.

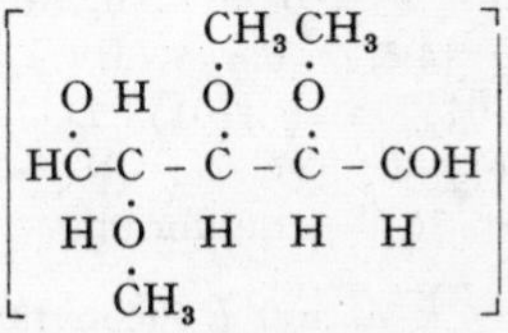

D- or *L*-Ribosazone or arabinosazone or araboketosazone [$CH_2OH(CHOH)_2$ $C(:NNHC_6H_5)CH:NNHC_6H_5$] is orthorhombic in needles with parallel extinction and negative elongation. M.P. 160°. 2V = ?. N_X = 1.765, N_Y = ?, N_Z = 1.870, $N_Z - N_X$ = 0.105. Abnormal interference colors. Also said to have positive elongation with Z = *c*, Y = *a*, in needles flattened on {100}. (+)2V = small. N_X = 1.760, N_Y = 1.765, N_Z = 1.800, $N_Z - N_X$ = 0.040. Abnormal green and yellow interference colors. Ref: 251, 386.

D- or *L*-Lyxosazone or xylosazone or xyloketosazone [$CH_2OH(CHOH)_2$ $C(:NNHC_6H_5)CH:NNHC_6H_5$] is orthorhombic in needles with parallel extinction

[1] *a b c* changed to *b a c* to make *b* > *a* > *c*.

and positive elongation. M.P. 160°. 2V = ?. $N_X = 1.745$, N_Y = ?, $N_Z = 1.860$, $N_Z - N_X = 0.115$. Characteristic green and yellow interference colors. Needles flattened on {100} have Z = *c* and Y = *a*. (+)2V = large. $N_X = 1.725$, $N_Y = 1.760$, $N_Z = 1.805$, $N_Z - N_X = 0.080$. Ref: 251, 386.

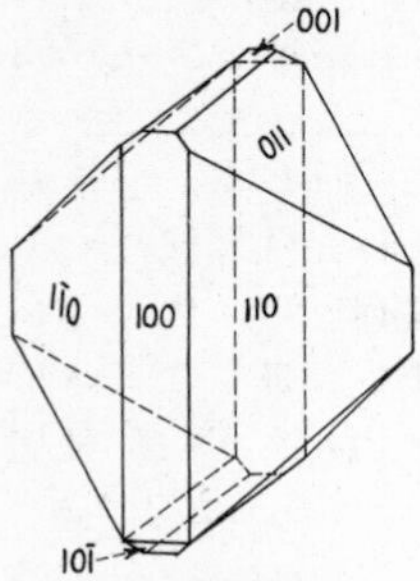

Fig. 125. *d*-Rhamnose monohydrate.

L(+)-Rhamnose monohydrate [$CH_3(CHOH)_4CHO \cdot H_2O$] is monoclinic sphenoidal with *a*:*b*:*c* = 0.9998:1:0.844, β = 95°25′. Space group $P2_1$; *a* 7.84, *b* 7.84, *c* 6.61 Å. U.C. 2. Crystals equant with {110}, {011}, {100}, {001}, {101̄} or clearly hemimorphic. Fig. 125. M.P. 93°. Distinct 101̄ and 100 cleavages. X ∧ *c* = + 83°26′ C, + 83°20′ D; Y = *b*. (-)2V = 58°59′ C, 58°5′ D, 55°42′ F. N_X = 1.5203 C, 1.5229 D, 1.5289 F; N_Y = 1.5284 C, 1.5311 D, 1.5372 F; N_Z = 1.5310 C, 1.5336 D, 1.5396 F, $N_Z - N_X$ = 0.0107 D. Optical rotation per mm. along optic axis A is - 12.9° and along B is - 5.4°. [α] = - 9.7° (equilibrium). Ref: 117, 383, 406.

α-Methyl *L*-rhamnopyranoside [$CH_3\overline{CH(CHOH)_3CH}OCH_3$] (ring closed through O) is orthorhombic disphenoidal with *a*:*b*:*c* = 0.621:1:0.564. Space group $P2_12_12_1$; *a* 8.26, *b* 13.31, *c* 7.54 Å. U.C. 4. Crystals equant with {110}, {010}, {101}, 021}, etc. Fig. 126. Imperfect 100 cleavage. M.P. 109°. X = *c*; Y = *b*. (-)2V = 37°31′ Li, 36°11′ Na 34°50′ Tl. N_X = 1.5337 Li, 1.5362 Na, 1.5392 Tl; N_Y = 1.5373Li, 1.5400 Na, 1.5429 Tl; N_Z = 1.5380 Li, 1.5407 Na, 1.5434 Tl; $N_Z - N_X$ = 0.0045 Na. [α] = + 62.5°. Ref: 117, 418a.

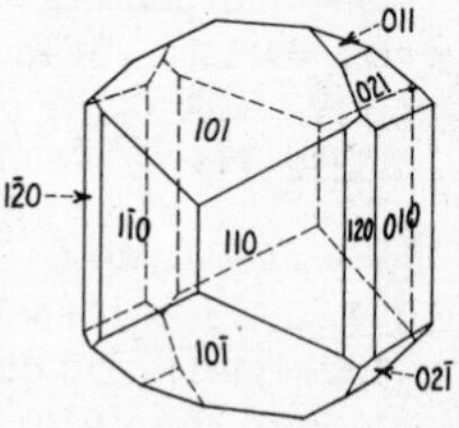

Fig. 126. *l*-Methyl-rhamnopyranoside.

α-*L*-Fucose is orthorhombic disphenoidal with *a*:*b*:*c*[1] = 0.531:1:0.461. Space group $P2_12_12$; *a* 7.6, *b* 14.3, *c* 6.6 Å. U.C. 4. Crystals columnar with {011} and {101}. D 1.49. $N_X = 1.537$, N_Y = ?, $N_Z = 1.557$, $N_Z - N_X = 0.020$. [α] = + 124.1° to + 76.4° (equilibrium). Ref: 59

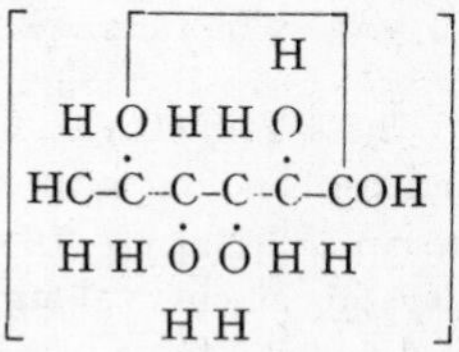

α-Methyl *L*-fucopyranoside is monoclinic sphenoidal with *a*:*b*:*c* = 1.277 : 1: 0.726, β = 102°36′. Space group $P2_1$; *a* 10.06, *b* 7.87, *c* 5.72 Å. U.C. 2. Crystals {100} tablets with {110}, {101̄}, {111} and {1̄1̄1}. Perfect 100 cleavage. D 1.31. M.P. 158°. Y apparently nearly = *c*; Z = *b*. (+ ?)2V = small ?. N_X = 1.488 ± .002, N_Y apparently = 1.49 *ca.*, $N_Z = 1.513$, $N_Z - N_X = 0.025$. Ref: 59.

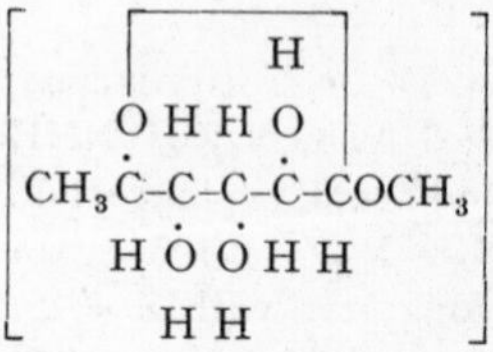

α-*D*(+)-Glucose or dextrose [$CH_2OH(CHOH)_4CHO$] is orthorhombic disphenoidal with *a*:*b*:*c* = 0.704:1:0.335. Space group $P2_12_12_1$; *a* 10.40, *b* 14.89,

[1] *a b c* changed to *b a c* to make *b* > *a* > *c*.

c 4.99 Å. U.C. 4. Crystals acicular with {110}, {111}, {010}, etc. D 1.544. M.P. 146°. Y = *a*; Z = *b*. R. C. Emmons gives (-)2V = 60° ± 12°, $N_X = 1.5285$, $N_Y = 1.5561$, $N_Z = 1.5653$, $N_Z - N_X = 0.0368$; X is normal to the face on which crystals commonly lie. Bryant reports M.P. 159°, and for $\lambda = 5461$: (-)2V = 50°, r < v, $N_X = 1.530$, $N_Y = 1.555$, $N_Z = 1.567$, $N_Z - N_X = 0.037$. Ref: 77, 117, 343c, 556a, 596.

D(+)-Glucose monohydrate or dextrose monohydrate [$CH_2OH(CHOH)_4CHO \cdot H_2O$] is monoclinic sphenoidal with *a*:*b*:*c* = 1.735 : 1 : 1.908, β = 97°59′. Space group $P2_1$; *a* 8.72, *b* 5.08, *c* 9.59 Å. U.C. 2. Crystals {001} tablets with {1$\bar{1}$0}, {101}, {10$\bar{1}$}. D 1.57. M.P. 83°. The optic plane and X are normal to 010; acute bisectrix Z nearly normal to 101. (+)2V = large. $N_X = 1.521$, N_Y = ?, $N_Z = 1.549$, $N_Z - N_X = 0.028$. Elongation along *b* negative with parallel extinction. R. C. Emmons gives (+)2V = 68° ± 8°, $N_X = 1.515$, $N_Y = 1.528$, $N_Z = 1.557$, all ± .001, $N_Z - N_X = 0.042$; average values: $N_X = 1.5153$, $N_Y = 1.528(5)$, $N_Z = 1.556(8)$, $N_Z - N_X = 0.0415$. Z ∧ 001 = 45° ± 10°. Often twinned on 001. Ref: 77, 117, 170, 251, 518, 596.

2,3,6-Trimethyl-α-D-glucopyranose is orthorhombic disphenoidal with[1] *a*:*b*:*c* = 0.582 : 1 : 0.234. Space group $P2_12_12$; *a* 11.90, *b* 20.45, *c* 4.79 Å. U.C. 4. Crystals acicular with {100}, {010}, and {001}. D 1.26. X = *c*. $N_X = 1.465$, N_Y = ?, $N_Z = 1.51$, $N_Z - N_X = 0.045$. Ref: 60.

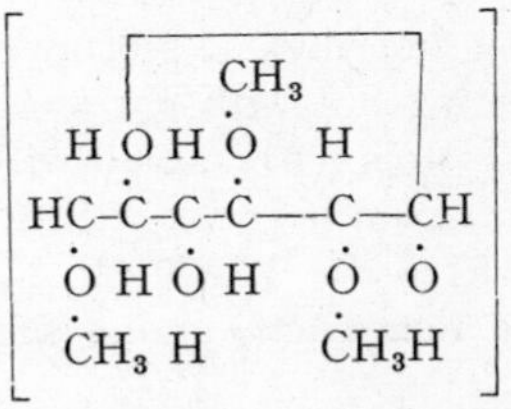

2,4,6-Trimethyl-β-methyl-*D*-glucopyranoside ($C_{10}H_{20}O_6$ is acicular. *c* 4.41 Å. X = *c*. $N_X = 1.465$, N_Y = ?, $N_Z \geqslant 1.535$, $N_Z - N_X \geqslant 0.070$. Ref: 60.

2,3,4,6-Tetramethyl-α-*D*-glucopyranose is orthorhombic disphenoidal with[2] *a*:*b*:*c* = 0.812 : 1 : 0.259. Space group $P2_12_12_1$; *a* 14.85, *b* 18.29, *c* 4.74 Å. U.C. 4. Crystals show {100}, {110}, and {001}. D 1.22, X = *c*; Y = *b*. (-)2V = ?. $N_X = 1.475$, N_Y = ?, $N_Z \geqslant 1.54$, $N_Z - N_X \geqslant 0.065$. Ref: 60.

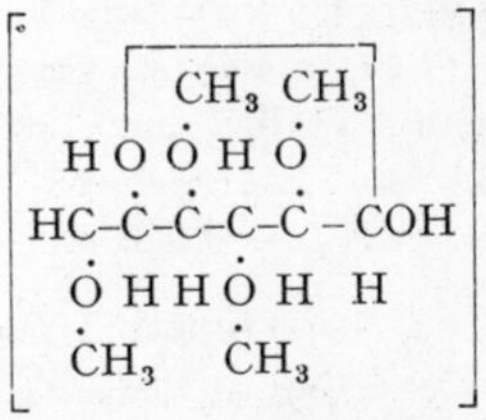

β-2,3,4,6-Tetra-acetyl-*D*-glucopyranose ($C_{14}H_{20}O_{10}$) seems to have two crystal phases which are isomorphous. M.P. 120°. Crystals of both have parallel extinction with $N_X = 1.483$, N_Y = ?, $N_Z = 1.495$, $N_Z - N_X = 0.012$, Biaxial positive with large optic angle, ∴ $N_Y = 1.49$ *ca.* [α] = - 2.2° to - 82.7°. Ref: 139.

α-1,2,3,4,6-Penta-acetyl-*D*-glucopyranose [$C_{16}H_{22}O_{11}$] or α-*D*-glucose penta-acetate is monoclinic with M.P. 112 - 113°. $N_X = 1.460$, $N_Y = 1.500$, $N_Z = 1.515$; $N_Z - N_X = 0.055$. ∴ (-)2V = 60° *ca.* [α] = - 101.6° (chloroform). Ref: 291.

---

[1] *a b c* changed to *b a c* to make *b* > *a* > *c*.

[2] *a b c* changed to *b a c* to make *b* > *a* > *c*.

β-1,2,3,4,6-Penta-acetyl-*D*-glucopyranose or *β*-*D*-glucose penta-acetate [$C_{16}H_{22}O_{11}$] is probably orthorhombic with[1] $a:b:c = 0.601:1:0.233$. *a* 14.9, *b* 24.3, *c* 5.65 Å. U.C. 4. M.P. 131 - 134°. $N_X = 1.47$, $N_Y = 1.48$ *ca.*, $N_Z = 1.50$, $N_Z - N_X = 0.03$ Na. $[\alpha] = -3.8°$ (chloroform). Ref: 291, 540.

Hexa-acetyl-*al*-*D*-glucose oxime or *aldehydo*-*d*-glucose oxime hexa-acetate [$C_6H_7O_6N(CH_3CO)_6$] is orthorhombic in prisms elongated along *c* with parallel extinction and positive elongation. M.P. 119.5°. The optic plane is probably 010. (–)2V = small. $N_X = 1.460$, $N_Y = 1.497$, $N_Z = 1.504$, $N_Z - N_X = 0.044$. Another form which melts at 79° changes to the first one by mere heating. $[\alpha] = -45.9°$. Ref: 381.

α-Methyl *D*-glucopyranoside or *α*-methyl *d*-glucoside [$C_6H_{11}O_6(CH_3)$] is orthorhombic disphenoidal with $a : b : c = 0.767 : 1 : 0.360$. Space group $P2_12_12_1$; *a* 11.21, *b* 14.57, *c* 5.29 Å. U.C. 4. Crystals prismatic with {110}, {120}, {010}, {101}, etc. Piezoelectric. D 1.48. M.P. 166°. Y = *b*; Z = *c*. (+) 2 V = = 86°32′ Li, 85°18′ Na, 85°9′ Tl. $N_Y = 1.5420$ Li, 1.5431 Na, 1.5446 Tl. $[\alpha] = -158.9°$. Ref: 58, 117.

β-Methyl *D*-glucopyranoside or *β*-methyl *d*-glucoside [$C_6H_{11}O_6(CH_3)$] is tetragonal with $c/a = 4.596$. Space group $P4_12$; *a* 7.32, *c* 33.6 Å. U.C. 8. Crystals {001} tablets with {111}, {100}. Perfect 001 cleavage. D 1.49. M.P. 104°. Uniaxial negative with $N_O = 1.5274$ Li, 1.5287 Na, 1.5336 Tl; $N_E = 1.5113$ Li, 1.5126 Na, 1.5200 Tl; $N_O - N_E = 0.0161$ Na. {001} plates may show twinning in four parts, giving slightly biaxial interference figures. $[\alpha] = +34.2°$. Ref: 58, 117.

2, 3, 4-Trimethyl-*β*-methyl-*D*-glucopyranoside is orthorhombic disphenoidal with[2] $a : b : c = 0.917 : 1 : 0.254$. Space group $P2_12_12$; *a* 16.08, *b* 17.54, *c* 4.45 Å. Crystals acicular along *c* with {010}, {110}, and {001}. D 1.25. M.P. 92°. X = *c*. $N_X = 1.465$, $N_Y = ?$, $N_Z \geqslant 1.525$, $N_Z - N_X \geqslant 0.060$ *ca.* Ref: 60.

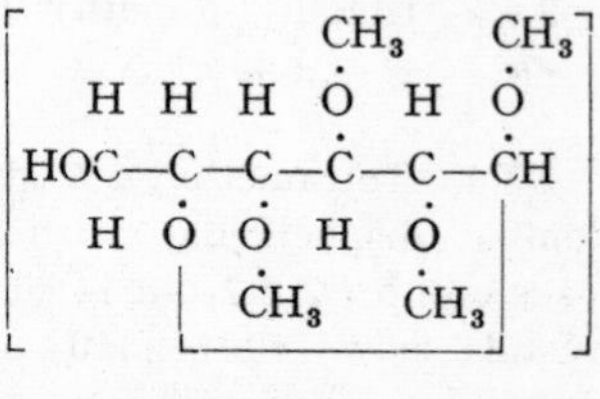
CH3 CH3
H H H O H O
HOC—C—C—C—C—CH
H O O H O
CH3 CH3

2, 3, 6-Trimethyl-*β*-methyl-*D*-glucopyranoside ($C_{10}H_{20}O_6$) is acicular. *c* 4.41 Å. X = *c*. $N_X = 1.47$, $N_Y = ?$, $N_Z = 1.555$, $N_Z - N_X = 0.085$. Ref: 60.

α-Ethyl *D*-glucopyranoside or *α*-ethyl *d*-glucoside [$C_6H_{11}O_6(C_2H_5)$] is orthorhombic sphenoidal with $a : b : c = 0.851 : 1 : 0.594$. Crystals show {110}, {1$\bar{1}$1}, {111}, {001}, etc. M.P. 114°. Perfect 001 and imperfect 110 cleavages. X = *a*; Y = *b*. (—) 2 V = 51°34′ Li, 51°14′ Na, 51°0′ Tl. $N_Y = 1.4808$ Li, 1.4841 Na, 1.4864 Tl; $N_Z - N_X$ = weak. $[\alpha] = -152.0°$. Ref: 117.

Glucoseanil sulfanilamide ($C_{18}H_{24}O_7N_3S$) is monoclinic. M.P. 211°. Elongation negative. (+) 2 V < 22° calc., r > v. $N_X = 1.569$, $N_Y = 1.574$, $N_Z > 1.676$ (crystals dissolve in index liquids with N > 1.676), $N_Z - N_X > 0.107$. Ref: 617a.

[1] *a b c* changed to *b a c* to make *b* > *a* > *c*.

[2] *a b c* changed to *b a c* to make *b* > *a* > *c*.

Saligenin glucoside or salicin $(CH_2OHC_6H_4OC_6H_{11}H_5)$ forms needles which melt at 201°. $N_X = 1.505$, $N_Y = 1.590$, $N_Z = 1.603$, $N_Z - N_X = 0.098$, ∴ (—) $2V = 45°$ calc.   Ref: 524.

l-Gulono-1,4-lactone-2,3-enediol or hexuronic acid or l-ascorbic acid or cevitamic acid or vitamin C {CH_2OHCHOHCHC(OH):C(OH)CO} is monoclinic

$$\overset{\cdot}{O}\text{————————}$$

sphenoidal with $a:b:c = 2.802:1:1.010$, $\beta = 102.5°$. Space group $P2_1$. a 16.95, b 6.32, c 6.38 Å. U.C. 4. Crystals may be {100} plates. Good 010 cleavage. D 1.65 (1.74). M.P. 188 – 192°. Oxidizes in air. Soluble in water or alcohol; insoluble in chloroform or ether. $[\alpha]_D^{25} = 20.5 - 21.5°$. Colorless or yellowish and weakly pleochroic.   X = b, Z ∧ c = 41° in acute β. (+)2V = 88°, r > v. In red 2V passes 90° with change of sign. $N_X = 1.474$, $N_Y = 1.595$, $N_Z = 1.746$, $N_Z - N_X = 0.272$, (McCrone). Again for $\lambda = 5.780$: $N_X = 1.465$, $N_Y = 1.600$, $N_Z = 1.747$, $N_Z - N_X = 0.282$ (Hendricks).   Also reported as $(-)2V = 3°$, $N_X = 1.466$, $N_Y = 1.680$, $N_Z = 1.705$, $N_Z - N_X = 0.239$.

Ref: 55a, 57, 135, 343b, 518, 552a, 560a, 611a.

$$\overset{\text{————}O\text{————}}{}$$

Calcium ascorbate dihydrate {(COCOHCOHCHCHOHCH_2OH)_2Ca·2H_2O} is triclinic, probably pinacoidal. Crystals somewhat elongated with inclined extinction and ± elongation. X inclined some to the shortest dimension of the crystals. (–)2V near 90°, $N_X = 1.53$, $N_Y = 1.61$ ca., $N_Z = 1.680$, $N_Z - N_X = 0.15$. These crystals formed on the sides and bottom of the vessel containing the saturated solution; on the upper surface other crystals formed which are perhaps another phase (or an oxalate?); they were prisms (with nearly rectangular cross section) 5 – 10 times as long as their width. Uniaxial (or nearly so) positive (from the indices). $N_O = 1.530$ +, $N_E = 1.535$ +, $N_E - N_O = 0.007$ ca. Ref: 607, 608.

Hydroquinone-β-D-glucopyranoside or arbutin melts at 195°; it has parallel extinction and positive elongation with $N_1 = 1.55$, $N_2 = 1.58$, $N_2 - N_1 = 0.03$.
Ref: 34, 35.

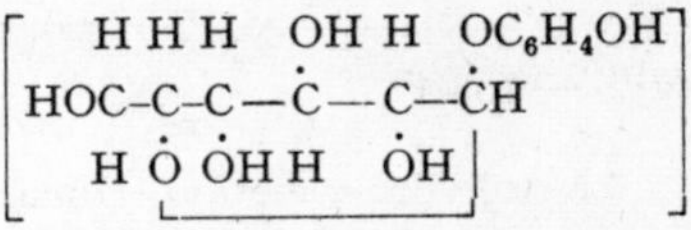

$$\begin{bmatrix} \text{H H H} & \text{OH H} & OC_6H_4OH \\ \text{HOC–C–C—}\overset{\cdot}{\text{C}}\text{—C—}\overset{\cdot}{\text{C}}\text{H} \\ \text{H }\overset{\cdot}{\text{O}}\text{ OH H} & \overset{\cdot}{\text{OH}} \end{bmatrix}$$

1-[2,4-Dihydroxy-6-(β-D-glucopyranosidoxy)phenyl]-3-(4-hydroxyphenyl)-1-propanone dihydrate or phlorizoside dihydrate or phlorizin dihydrate $(C_{21}H_{24}O_{10}\cdot 2H_2O)$ is probably orthorhombic, with $a:b:c = ?:1:0.245$. Crystals {100} plates elongated along c, with {010}, {001}, {110}. Poor 001 cleavage. D 1.431. M.P. 105°. Y = b; Z = a. (+)2V = large. $N_X = 1.604$, $N_Y = 1.615$, $N_Z = 1.628$, $N_Z - N_X = 0.024$, all ± .003. On heating in vaseline the crystals lose water at 105° and change to $C_{21}H_{24}O_{10}$ of nearly the same shape, with D 1.452, M.P. 150°, and N = 1.62 (mean). The hydrous crystals absorb various organic coloring agents (0.5 to 0.01 percent), and become much larger, and pleochroic and fluorescent with ultraviolet.   Ref: 102.

β-$D(+)$-Mannose [CH_2OH(CHOH)_4CHO] is orthorhombic disphenoidal with $a:b:c = 0.414:1:0.312$. Space group $P2_12_12_1$; a 7.62, b 18.18, c 5.67 Å. U.C. 4. Crystals in plates and rods show {110}, {011}, {010}. D 1.501. M.P.

132°. Y = *a*; Z = *c*. Elongation ±. (+)2V = 55° *ca.* calc. N_X = 1.529, N_Y = 1.536, N_Z = 1.563 ± .002, $N_Z - N_X$ = 0.034 Na. [α] = + 16.3° (initial) to - 14.5° (equilibrium). Ref: 117, 170, 546a.

Mannoseanil sulfanilamide ($C_{18}H_{24}O_7N_3S$) is monoclinic. M.P. 202°. Elongation positive. (-)2V = 77° calc., r > v. N_X = 1.581, N_Y = 1.615, N_Z = 1.636, $N_Z - N_X$ = 0.055. Ref: 617a.

D- or *L*-Mannose phenylhydrazone [$C_6H_5NHN{:}CH(CHOH)_4CH_2OH$] is triclinic in rhombic {001} tablets with angles of 74° and 106°, the small angle sometimes truncated by a small face. An optic axis is nearly normal to 001; the optic plane nearly bisects the acute angle on 001. (+)2V = large. N_X = 1.600 *ca.*, N_Y = 1.650, N_Z = 1.82 *ca.*, $N_Z - N_X$ = 0.22 *ca.* Ref: 251.

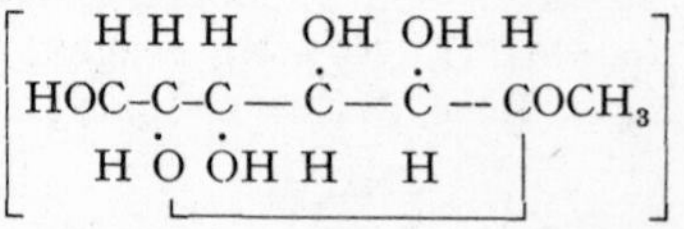

α-Methyl *D*-mannopyranoside or α-methyl *d*-mannoside is orthorhombic disphenoidal with *a*:*b*:*c* = 0.938:1:0.928. Space group $P2_12_12_1$; *a* 9.38, *b* 9.99, *c* 9.23 Å. U.C. 4. Crystals sphenoidal with {111}, {1̄1̄1}, {110}, {011}, etc. D 1.48. M.P. 194°. Y = *b*; Z = *a*. (+)2V = 46°40′ Li, 46°58′ Na, 47°24′ Tl. N_X = 1.5273 Li, 1.5280 Na, 1.5314 Tl; N_Y = 1.5280 Li, 1.5294 Na, 1.5326 Tl; N_Z = 1.5322 Li, 1.5368 Na, 1.5390 Tl; $N_Z - N_X$ = 0.0088 Na. [α] = - 78.6°. Ref: 56, 117.

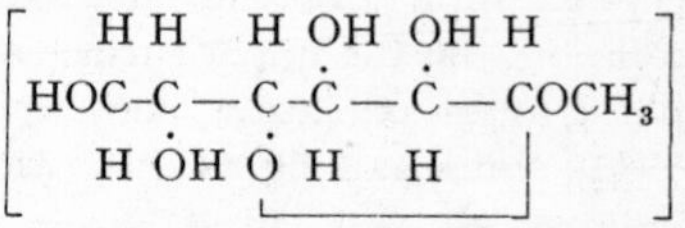

α-Methyl *D*-mannofuranoside is probably orthorhombic disphenoidal with[1] *a*:*b*:*c* = 0.739:1:0.292. Space group $P2_12_12_1$; *a* 11.73, *b* 15.87, *c* 4.64 Å. U.C. 4. Crystals acicular along *c* and flattened on 010. D 1.48. M.P. 118 - 119°. X = *c*; Y = *b*. (-)2V = moderate. N_X = 1.518, N_Y = 1.54 *ca.*, N_Z = 1.549, $N_Z - N_X$ = 0.031. [α] = - 108.4°. Ref: 56.

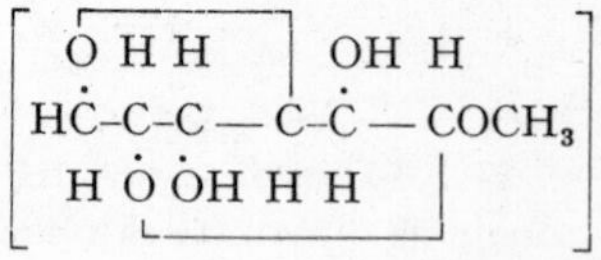

3,6-Anhydro-α-methyl-*D*-mannopyranoside is orthorhombic disphenoidal with *a*:*b*:*c* = 0.936:1:1.057. Crystals of varied habit may be {010} or {012} tablets with {110}, {212}, {210}, {011}, etc. M.P. 133°. Y = *a*; Z = *b*. (+)2V = 60°, r > v. N_X = 1.521, N_Y = 1.522, N_Z = 1.526, $N_Z - N_X$ = 0.005. [α] = 97.7° in water. Ref: 263.

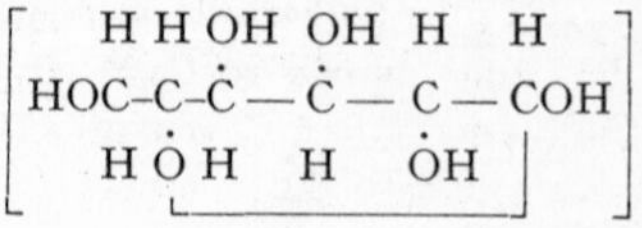

α-*D*-Galactopyranose is orthorhombic with[2] *a*:*b*:*c* = 0.613:1:0.608. Crystals prismatic. D 1.58. X = *b*; Y = *c*. (-)2V = large. N_X = 1.530, N_Y = 1.56 *ca.*, N_Z = 1.569, $N_Z - N_X$ = 0.039 Na. Ref: 59.

---

[1] *a b c* changed to *b a c* to make *b* > *a* > *c*.

[2] *a b c* changed to *b a c* to make *b* > *a* > *c*.

α-Methyl D-galactopyranoside mo-nohydrate or α-methyl d-galactoside monohydrate is orthorhombic disphen-oidal with[1] $a:b:c = 0.349:1:0.287$.

$$\begin{bmatrix} \text{H} & \text{H} & \text{OH} & \text{OH} & \text{H} & \text{H} \\ \text{HOC-C-}\overset{\cdot}{\text{C}} & — & \overset{\cdot}{\text{C}} & — \text{C} & — \text{COCH}_3 \cdot \text{H}_2\text{O} \\ \text{H} & \overset{\cdot}{\text{O}} & \text{H} & \text{H} & \overset{\cdot}{\text{O}}\text{H} & \end{bmatrix}$$

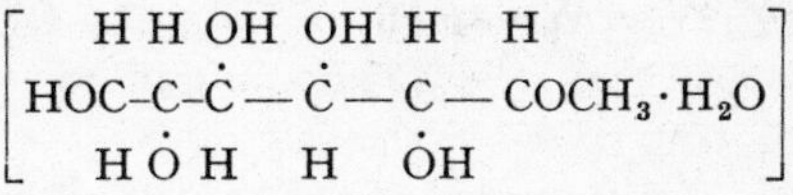

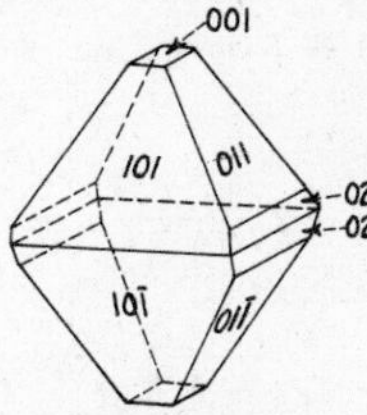

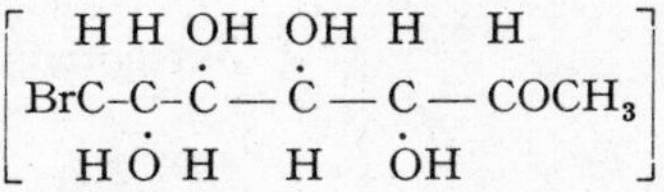

Space group $P2_12_12_1$; a 7.45, b 21.33, c 6.21 Å. U.C. 4. Crystals equant with {101}, {011}, etc. Fig. 127. No distinct cleavage. M.P. 111°. $Y = b$; $Z = c$. $(+)2V = 52°59'$ Li, $53°5'$ Na, $53°41'$ Tl. $N_X = 1.5202$ Li, 1.5215 Na, 1.5244 Tl; $N_Y = 1.5217$ Li, 1.5230 Na, 1.5260 Tl; $N_Z = 1.5273$ Li, 1.5286 Na, 1.5316 Tl; $N_Z - N_X = 0.0071$ Na. $[\alpha] = -178.8°$.
Ref: 59, 117.

Fig. 127.
α-Methylgalactoside monohydrate.

α-Methyl D-galactopy-ranoside-6-bromide is or-thorhombic disphenoidal with $a:b:c = 0.771:1:$

$$\begin{bmatrix} \text{H} & \text{H} & \text{OH} & \text{OH} & \text{H} & \text{H} \\ \text{BrC-C-}\overset{\cdot}{\text{C}} & — & \overset{\cdot}{\text{C}} & — \text{C} & — \text{COCH}_3 \\ \text{H} & \overset{\cdot}{\text{O}} & \text{H} & \text{H} & \overset{\cdot}{\text{O}}\text{H} & \end{bmatrix}$$

1.051. Space group $P2_12_12_1$; a 7.81, b 10.58, c 11.23 Å. U.C. 4. Crystals elongated along a with {001}, {010}, {111}, etc. Perfect 010 cleavage. D 1.86. M.P. 157 – 163°. $X = a$; $Y = c$. $(-)2V = $ very large. $N_X = 1.581$ Na, $N_Y = 1.584$, $N_Z = 1.586$, $N_Z - N_X = 0.005$. $[\alpha] = -157°$.

Ref: 263.

α-Ethyl D-galactopyranoside is ortho-rhombic disphenoidal with $a:b:c = 0.507:$ 1:0.733. Crystals {010} plates with {011}, etc. Good 010 cleavage. M.P. 140°. $X = a$;

$$\begin{bmatrix} \text{H} & \text{H} & \text{OH} & \text{OH} & \text{H} \\ \text{HOC-C-}\overset{\cdot}{\text{C}} & — & \overset{\cdot}{\text{C}} — \text{C} & - \text{COC}_2\text{H}_5 \\ \text{H} & \overset{\cdot}{\text{O}} & \text{H} & \text{H} & \overset{\cdot}{\text{O}}\text{H} \end{bmatrix}$$

$Y = b$. $(-)2V = 69°30'$ red, $69°46'$ Na, $70°20'$ green. $N_Y = 1.52$. Ref: 117.

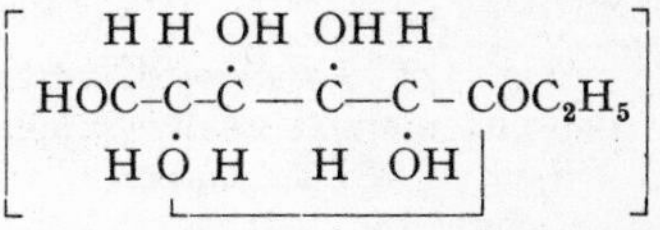

2,3,4,6-Tetramethyl-β-methyl-D-galacto-pyranoside is acicular in flattened needles with $c = 4.74$ Å. $X = c$. $N_X = 1.47$, $N_Z - N_X = $ strong. Ref: 60.

$$\begin{bmatrix} & \text{CH}_3 & \text{CH}_3 & & \text{CH}_3 \\ \text{H} & \text{H} & \overset{\cdot}{\text{O}} & \overset{\cdot}{\text{O}} & \text{H} & \overset{\cdot}{\text{O}} \\ \text{CH}_3\text{OC-C-}\overset{\cdot}{\text{C}} & — & \overset{\cdot}{\text{C}} — \text{C} & - \overset{\cdot}{\text{C}}\text{H} \\ \text{H} & \overset{\cdot}{\text{O}} & \text{H} & \text{H} & \overset{\cdot}{\text{O}} \text{-} \text{CH}_3 \end{bmatrix}$$

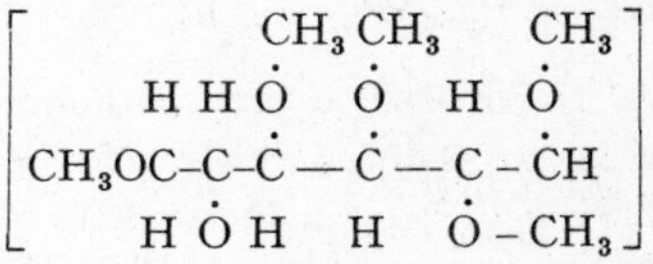

d-Galactose diethyl mercaptal penta-acetate $[(C_2H_5S)_2C_6H_7O_5(CH_3CO)_5]$ is trimorphous. The first phase (I) melts at 77° and has $[\alpha] = -9.8°$ in chloroform. It forms six-sided plates with $(-)2V = 65°$ calc. $N_X = 1.480$, $N_Y = 1.518$, $N_Z = 1.532$, $N_Z - N_X = 0.052$. The second phase (II) melts at 81°; it forms small elongated prisms with $(-)2V = 60°$ calc. $N_X = 1.496$, $N_Y = 1.535$, $N_Z = 1.549$, $N_Z - N_X = 0.053$. $[\alpha] = -7.3°$. The third phase (III) melts at 91°; it forms (nearly?) rectangular plates with $(-)2V = $ "small" (70° calc.). $N_X = 1.482$, $N_Y = 1.505$, $N_Z = 1.517$, $N_Z - N_X = 0.035$. $[\alpha] = -7.4°$.
Ref: 344a.

β-D(-)-Fructose or levulose $[CH_2OH(CHOH)_3COCH_2OH]$ is orthorhombic disphenoidal with $a:b:c = 0.801:1:0.907$. Space group $P2_12_12_1$; a 8.06, b 10.06, c 9.12 Å. U.C. 4. Crystals rod-like with {110}, {011}, etc. Twinning on 110. M.P. 102 – 104°. The optic plane is 001 for red and 010 for blue. $X = c$.

---

[1] $a\,b\,c$ changed to $b\,a\,c$ to make $b > a > c$.

(+)2V = very small. N_X = 1.558, N_Y = 1.558 *ca.* calc., N_Z = 1.561, $N_Z - N_X$ = 0.003. [α] = + 133.5° (initial) to + 92.0° (equilibrium).
Ref: 117, 170, 292, 487.

Fructose dihydrate or levulose dihydrate ($C_6H_{12}O_6 \cdot 2H_2O$) is orthorhombic disphenoidal. Crystals short prisms with a prism angle of 68°. Fig. 128. M.P. 21.3°. X = *c* (elongation). Z = *a*. (+)2V = 79° (again 81.5°), N_X = 1.5061, N_Y = 1.5221, N_Z = 1.5444, $N_Z - N_X$ = 0.0383. N_Y' seen on crystals lying on a prism face = 1.5303.
Ref: 628b, 628c.

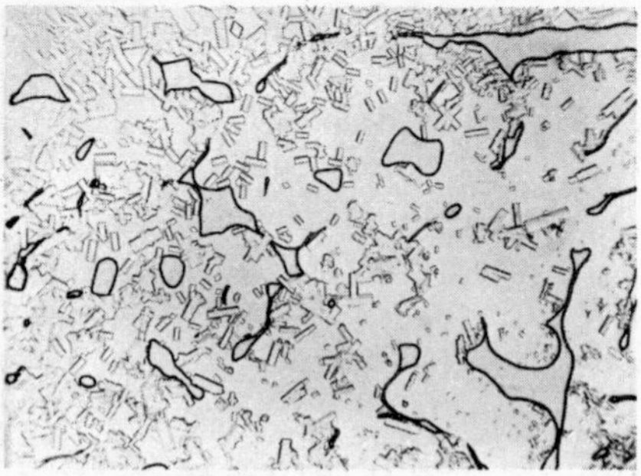

Fig. 128. Levulose dihydrate. Photomicrograph kindly supplied by F. T. Jones.

1,3,4-Trimethyl-*D*-fructose [$CH_2OCH_3CO(CHOCH_3)_2CHOHCH_2OH$] is orthorhombic disphenoidal with[1] *a*:*b*:*c* = 0.465:1:0.386. Space group $P2_12_12_1$; *a* 8.60, *b* 18.49, *c* 7.14 Å. U.C. 4. Crystals {210} prisms with {201}, {101}. Imperfect 010 cleavage D 1.29. X = *b*; Y = *a*. (-)2E = 28° *ca.*, 2V=18°. N_X = 1.49, N_Y = 1.52 *ca.*, N_Z = 1.525, $N_Z - N_X$ = 0.035.
Ref: 60.

1,3,4,5-Tetramethyl-*β*-*D*-fructopyranose [$C_{10}H_{20}O_5$) is orthorhombic with[2] *a*:*b*:*c*=0.623:1:0.606 in nearly square {100} plates bounded by {011}. Good 100 cleavage. The optic plane is 100. 2V = 90° approx. N_X = 1.51, N_Y = 1.52, N_Z = 1.53, $N_Z - N_X$ = 0.02.
Ref: 60, 629.

D-Sorbose is orthorhombic disphenoidal with *a*:*b*:*c* = 0.361:1:0.348. Space group $P2_12_12_1$; *a* 6.51, *b* 18.01, *c* 6.26 Å. U.C. 4. Crystals equant or prismatic with {110}, {101}, {100}, {010}, etc. D 1.63. X = *b*; Y = *a*. (-)2V = 70° calc.

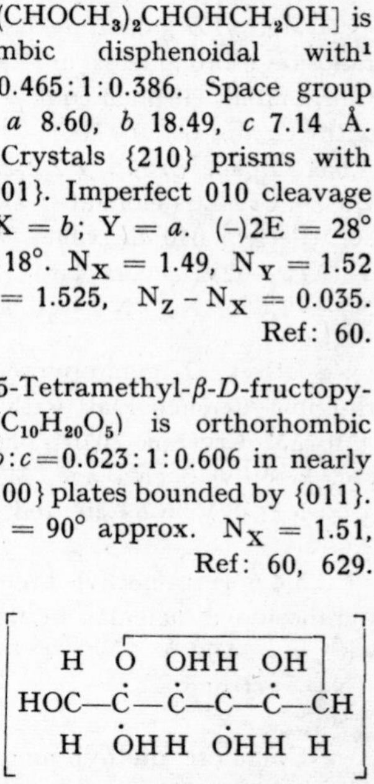

N_X = 1.553 Na, N_Y = 1.566, N_Z = 1.572, all ± .002, $N_Z - N_X$ = 0.019. [α] = - 42.9°.
Ref: 59.

Altrosazone or allosazone [$CH_2OH(CHOH)_3C(:NNHC_6H_5)CH:NNHC_6H_5$] forms needles with positive elongation and Z = *c*. M.P. 175°. 2V = ?, N_X = 1.740, N_Y = ?, N_Z = 1.805, $N_Z - N_X$ = 0.065. Characteristic blue and orange-yellow interference colors.
Ref: 386.

D- or *L*-Mannosazone or fructosazone or glucosazone [$CH_2OH(CHOH)_3C(:NNHC_6H_5)CH:NNHC_6H_5$] forms needles in radial groups with ± elongation and 0° to large extinction angle. Abnormal interference colors (green, blue, purple). M.P. 208°. 2V = ?, N_X = 1.800, N_Y = ?, N_Z = 1.835, $N_Z - N_X$ =

---

[1] *a b c* changed to *b a c* to make *b* > *a* > *c*.

[2] *a b c* changed to *c a b* to make *b* > *a* > *c*.

0.035. A second phase (II) forms needles elongated on b and flattened on 100. The optic plane is 010. $(+)2V$ = medium. $N_X = 1.755$, $N_Y = 1.780$, $N_Z = 1.850$, $N_Z - N_X = 0.095$. Ref: 251, 386.

Mannose methylphenylosazone or fructose methylphenylosazone or methyl-phenyl-d-fructosazone $[C_6H_5N(CH_3)N:CHC(:NN[CH_3]C_6H_5)(CHOH)_3CH_2OH]$ is orthorhombic in {100} plates elongated along c. $Y = b$; $Z = a$. Negative elongation. $(+)2V$ = small. $N_X = 1.589$, $N_Y = 1.603$, $N_Z = 1.82$ +, $N_Z - N_X = 0.231$ +. Pleochroic with X = yellow, Y = dark yellow, Z = brown. Ref: 251.

Gulosazone or idosazone or sorbosazone $[CH_2OH(CHOH)_3C(:NNHC_6H_5)$ $CH:NNHC_6H_5]$ forms single needles with positive elongation and $Z = c$. M.P. 168°. $2V$ = ?, $N_X = 1.670$, N_Y = ?, $N_Z = 1.820$, $N_Z - N_X = 0.150$. Blue, green, and yellow interference colors. Ref: 386.

Galactosazone or talosazone or tagatosazone $[CH_2OH(CHOH)_3C(:NNHC_6H_5)$ $CH:NNHC_6H_5]$ forms needles in radial groups with $\pm$ elongation and 0° to large extinction angle. Strong dispersion of the bisectrices; yellow and green interference colors. M.P. 208°. $2V$ = ?. $N_X = 1.825$, N_Y = ?, $N_Z = 1.850$, $N_Z - N_X = 0.025$. Also in blades flattened on 100. $X \wedge c = 30°$; $Y = b$. $(+)2V$ = small. $N_X = 1.790$, $N_Y = 1.800$, $N_Z = 1.845$, $N_Z - N_X = 0.055$. Ref: 251, 386.

2,3-Enedimethoxy-D-gluconoheptono-1,3-lactone or dimethyl D-glucoascorbic acid is monoclinic sphenoidal with $a:b:c = 1.254:1:$ 1.139, $\beta = 115°59'$. Space group $P2_1$; a 9.66, b 7.70, c 8.77 Å. U.C. 2. Crystals show {100}, {10$\bar{1}$}, and {011}. D 1.45. M.P. 94°. $[\alpha]$ = + 22° in water (c. 4.0). X = b. $N_X = 1.46$, N_Y = ?, $N_Z = 1.60$, $N_Z - N_X = 0.14$.

$$\begin{array}{l} \text{H} \quad \text{H} \quad \text{H} \quad \text{O} \\ \text{HOC–C—C—C-C}=\text{C—CO} \\ \text{H} \quad \text{OHOHHO} \quad \text{O} \\ \qquad\qquad \text{CH}_3\text{CH}_3 \end{array}$$

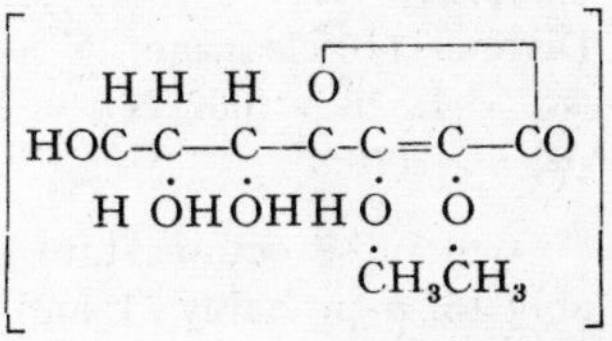

Ref: 57.

2,3-Enediol-D-galactoheptano-1,4-lactone monohydrate or D-galactoascorbic acid monohydrate is triclinic pedial with $a:b:c$ = 0.6966:1:0.5551, $\alpha = 91°48'$, $\beta = 102°23'$, $\gamma = 79°6'$. Space group $P1$; a 5.96, b 8.56, c 4.75 Å. Crystals asymmetric with {100},

$$\begin{array}{l} \text{H} \quad \text{H} \quad \text{OH} \text{O} \\ \text{HOC–C—C—C-C}=\text{C—CO·H}_2\text{O} \\ \text{H} \quad \text{OHH} \quad \text{H} \quad \text{OH} \text{OH} \end{array}$$

{$\bar{1}$00}, {010}, {0$\bar{1}$0}, {001}, {00$\bar{1}$}, {110}, and {0$\bar{1}$1}. D 1.60. X makes an angle of 30° $\pm$ 5° with a normal to 001 and 74° $\pm$ 5° with a normal to 0$\bar{1}$0. $2V = 90°$ $ca.$ calc. $N_X = 1.46$, $N_Y = 1.57$, $N_Z = 1.68$, $N_Z - N_X = 0.22$. Ref: 57.

D-1-Imino-2,3-enediolgalactoheptano-1,4-lactone, or D-imino-galactoascorbic acid is orthorhombic with $a:b:c = 1.000:1:5.758$. a and b 6.7, c 38.5 Å. U.C. 8. Crystals pseudotetragonal, often twinned on 110 with {104}, {014}, {001}. D 1.58. $Z = c$. (+)

$$\begin{array}{l} \text{H} \quad \text{H} \quad \text{OH} \text{O} \\ \text{HOC–C—C—C-C}=\text{C—C:NH} \\ \text{H} \text{OH} \text{H} \quad \text{H} \quad \text{OH} \quad \text{OH} \end{array}$$

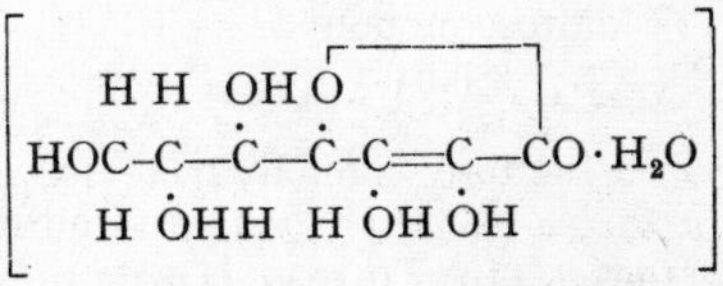

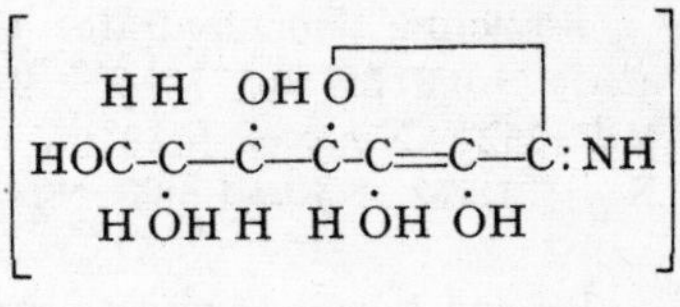

$2E = 47°$, $r > v$ strong. $2V = 28°$ calc. N_X and $N_Y = 1.623 \pm .002$ ($N_Y - N_X = 0.001$), $N_Z = 1.64$ D, $N_Z - N_X = 0.017$.   Ref: 57.

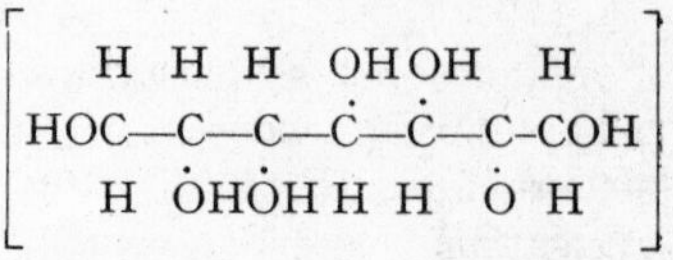

$D(+)$-Mannoheptulose or $D(+)$-mannoketoheptose is monoclinic sphenoidal with $a:b:c = 1.458:1:0.921$, $\beta = 116°36'$. Crystals thick tabular or equant with {001}, {100}, {110}, {1$\bar{1}$0}, {$\bar{1}$01}, etc. No observed cleavage. M.P. 182°. $Y = b$; $Z \wedge c = 26°36'$. $(+)2V = 89°$. $N_X = 1.547$,

$$\begin{bmatrix} \text{H H H OHOH H} \\ \text{HOC—C—C—C—C—C-COH} \\ \text{H OHOH H H O H} \end{bmatrix}$$

$N_Y = 1.570$, $N_Z = 1.595$, $N_Z - N_X = 0.048$. No appreciable dispersion of bisectrices or optic axes. This sugar exists in the free state in avocados. $[\alpha] = -29.4°$.   Ref: 388.

Naringin dihydrate or naringenin-5-rhamnoglucoside dihydrate ($C_{27}H_{32}O_{14} \cdot 2H_2O$) is apparently orthorhombic in needles with parallel extinction and negative elongation. M.P. 171°. $(-)2V = 60°$ (calc.), $N_X = 1.480$, $N_Y = 1.625$, $N_Z = 1.668$, $N_Z - N_X = 0.188$. Color yellow. Taste bitter. Formed on grapefruit.   Ref: 520.

Trehalose dihydrate or mykose dihydrate $\left[CH_2OHCH(CHOH)_3CH \cdot O \cdot \right.$ $\left. CH(CHOH)_3CHCH_2OH \cdot 2H_2O \right]$ is orthorhombic disphenoidal with $a:b:c = 0.681:1:0.417$. Crystals short prismatic with {120}, {110}, {101}, {011}, etc. Distinct 110 cleavage. $Y = b$; $Z = c$. $(+)2V = 48°2'$ Li, $50°16'$ Na, $51°26'$ Tl. $N_X = 1.528 \pm .002$, $N_Y = 1.529$ calc., $N_Z = 1.533 \pm .002$, $N_Z - N_X = 0.005$ Na. $[\alpha] = -178.8°$.   Ref: 117, 170, 192a.

Cellobiose octa-acetate $C_{28}H_{38}O_{19}$ is probably orthorhombic with[1] a probably 15, b probably 21, and c 5.7 Å. U.C. 2. Crystals tiny rods with Y parallel to elongation. D 1.275. $(+)2V = $ large, $N_X = 1.470$, $N_Y = 1.480$, $N_Z = 1.505$, $N_Z - N_X = 0.035$ Na.   Ref: 372, 540.

Maltose monohydrate [$C_{12}H_{22}O_{11} \cdot H_2O$] is granular with $N_1 = 1.54$, $N_2 = 1.55$, $N_2 - N_1 = 0.01$.   Ref: 34, 35.

α-Lactose monohydrate [$C_{12}H_{22}O_{11} \cdot H_2O$] is monoclinic sphenoidal with $a:b:c = 0.368:1:0.214$, $\beta = 99°47'$. Crystals of tomahawk shape show {0$\bar{1}$1}, {100}, {110}, {010}, {1$\bar{1}$0}, {0$\bar{1}$0}. Perfect 001(?) and distinct 100 and 010 cleavages. D 1.525. M.P. 201.6°. $X \wedge c = -10°$ to $-11°$; $Z = b$. $(-)2V = 21.5°$, $r < v$. $N_X = 1.517$, $N_Y = 1.553$, $N_Z = 1.555$, $N_Z - N_X = 0.038$.   Also $N_X = 1.517$, $N_Y = 1.542$, $N_Z = 1.550$, $N_Z - N_X = 0.033$.   Ref: 117, 170, 343c, 359.

β-Lactose monohydrate ($C_{12}H_{22}O_{11} \cdot H_2O$) is monoclinic sphenoidal with $a:b:c = 0.817:1:0.377$, $\beta = 91°45'$. Crystals show {001}, {110}, {2$\bar{1}$0}, etc. M.P. 252°. $X \wedge c = +30°$; $Y = b$. $(-)2E = 120°$; $2V = 67°$ calc. $N_X = 1.542$, $N_Y = 1.572$, $N_Z = 1.585$, $N_Z - N_X = 0.043$.   Ref: 359.

---

[1] a and b interchanged to make $b > a$.

Melibiose dihydrate $\left[CH_2OH\overset{\lceil\text{——O——}\rceil}{CH(CHOH)_3CH}\cdot O\cdot CH_2\overset{\lceil\text{——O——}\rceil}{CH(CHOH)_3CHOH}\cdot 2H_2O \right]$ (galactose) (glucose)
is probably orthorhombic in rods often quadrilateral. Parallel extinction and positive elongation. (+)2V = large. $N_X = 1.526$, $N_Y = 1.541$, $N_Z = 1.560$, $N_Z - N_X = 0.034$, all ± .002. Ref: 170.

Sucrose or saccharose $[C_6H_{11}O_5 \cdot C_6H_{11}O_6]$ is monoclinic sphenoidal with $a:b:c = 1.260:1:0.878$, $\beta = 103°30'$. Crystals thick {100} tablets with {110}, {001}, {10$\bar{1}$}, {1$\bar{1}$0}, etc. Fig. 129. Distinct 100 cleavage. D 1.488. M.P. 160° (190°, Bryant). $X \wedge c = -67°$; Y = *b*. (-)2V = 47°56′ Li, 48°0′ Na, 48°8′ Tl. $N_X = 1.5379$ Li, 1.5397 Na, 1.5442 Tl; $N_Y =$ 1.5638 Li, 1.5667 Na, 1.5685 Tl; $N_Z = 1.5693$ Li, 1.5716 Na, 1.5734 Tl; $N_Z - N_X = 0.0319$ Na. Also $N_X = 1.5383$ Na, $N_Y = 1.5654$, $N_Z = 1.5709$, $N_Z - N_X = 0.0326$. A plate 1 cm. thick rotates the plane of polarization + 22° for light along the optic axis normal to 100 and - 64° for light along the other optic axis. Ref: 117, 293, 556a.

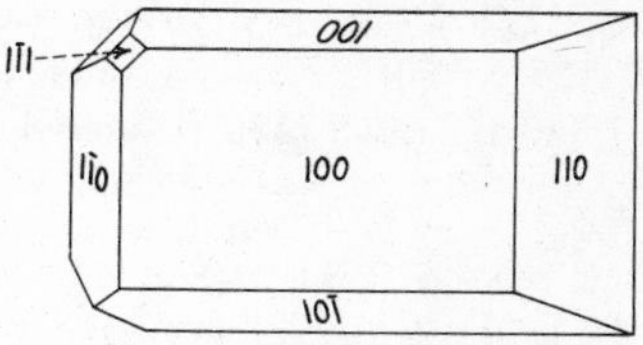

Fig. 129. Saccharose.

Sucrose hemipentahydrate $[C_{12}H_{22}O_{11} \cdot 2.5H_2O]$ is monoclinic sphenoidal in lath-like or acicular crystals long || *b*. $\beta = 122°$. M.P. 45.7°. X = *b*; $Z \wedge c = 18°$; $Y \wedge a = 14°$. (-)2V = 51°, r > v weak. $N_X = 1.5170$, $N_Y = 1.5255$, $N_Z = 1.5275$, $N_Z - N_X = 0.0105$. Ref: 628a.

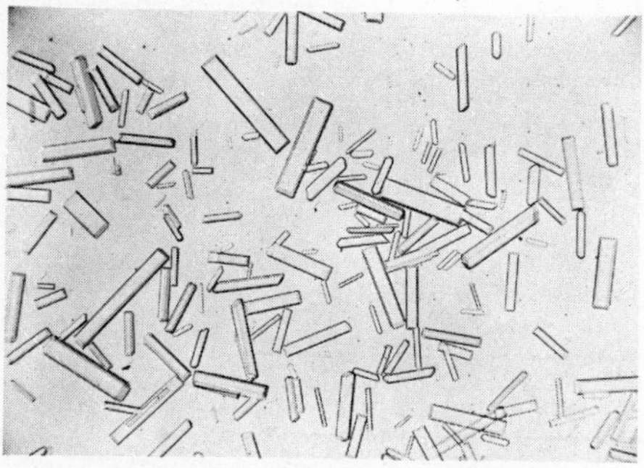
Fig. 130. Sucrose hemiheptahydrate. Photomicrograph kindly supplied by F. T. Jones.

Sucrose hemiheptahydrate $[C_{12}H_{22}O_{11} \cdot 3.5H_2O]$ is orthorhombic. Crystals spherulitic aggregates of needles or elongated prisms. Fig. 130. M.P. 27.8°. X || elongation. (-)2V= 52°, $N_X = 1.5135$, $N_Y = 1.5190$, $N_Z = 1.5205$, $N_Z - N_X = 0.007$. Ref: 628a, 628b.

Sucrose octa-acetate or octa-acetylsaccharose $[C_{12}H_{14}O_3(O_2CCH_3)_8]$ has two phases. One (I) is orthorhombic with[1] $a:b:c = 0.823:1:0.379$. Crystals show {001}, {100} and {010}, and are elongated along *a*. X = *c*; Y = *b*. (-)2V = 80° calc. $N_X = 1.470$, $N_Y = 1.488$, $N_Z = 1.500$, $N_Z - N_X = 0.030$. Another (II) is monoclinic with β nearly equal to 90°; the optic plane is near 100 and X = *b*. Fresh crystals show: (+)2V = 76°44′, $N_X \leqslant 1.455$, $N_Y \leqslant 1.462$, $N_Z = 1.473$ calc. $N_Z - N_X \leqslant 0.018$ calc. Crystals change slowly and after two years they show: (+)2V = 80°54′, $N_X < 1.455$, $N_Y < 1.455$. Ref: 74, 346a.

[1] *a* and *b* interchanged to make $b > a$.

Maltose phenylosazone, or maltosazone $[C_{12}H_{20}O_9(:NNHC_6H_5)_2]$ is orthorhombic in {100} blades elongated along *c*. M.P. 206°. X = *b*; Y = *a*. (-)2V = 55° *ca.* $N_X = 1.655$, $N_Y = 1.715$, $N_Z = 1.730$, $N_Z - N_X = 0.075$.
Ref: 251.

Raffinose pentahydrate or melitriose pentahydrate $[C_{18}H_{32}O_{16}\cdot 5H_2O]$ is orthorhombic disphenoidal with *a*:*b*:*c* = 0.974:1:0.506. Crystals prismatic with {110}, {101}, {010}, {011}, etc. No distinct cleavage. The optic plane is 001; X ∥ elongation. (+)2V = 87° *ca.* red, 80° *ca.* blue. $N_X = 1.522$, $N_Y = 1.529$ calc., $N_Z = 1.537$, $N_Z - N_X = 0.015$.
Ref: 117, 170.

Melezitose dihydrate $[C_{18}H_{30}O_{15}\cdot 2H_2O]$ is orthorhombic with[1] *a*:*b*:*c* = 0.822:1:0.408. Crystals show {010}, {011}, {100}, etc. X = *b*; Y = *a*. (-)2V = 50°. $N_X = 1.538$ (650), 1.540 D, 1.550 (450); $N_Y = 1.545$ (650), 1.548 D, 1.558 (450); $N_Z = 1.547$ (650), 1.550 D, 1.561 (450); $N_Z - N_X = 0.010$ D.
Ref: 354.

Starch $(C_6H_{10}O_5)$ is tetragonal with *c*/*a* = 0.850; *a* 5.94, *c* 5.05 Å. U.C. 1. D 1.50. Uniaxial negative with N = 1.53 and $N_O - N_E$ = strong. But starch probably has at least three phases.
Ref: 152, 511b, 588, 595.

Cellulose $(C_6H_{10}O_5)_n$ is monoclinic sphenoidal with *a*:*b*:*c* = 0.811:1:0.767, β = 96°. Space group $P2_1$; *a* 8.35, *b* 10.3, *c* 7.9 Å. U.C. 4. Fibrous parallel to *b*, with D 1.60 ± .01. Parallel extinction and positive elongation. In spite of its monoclinic structure cellulose (like many other fibers) has one refractive index along the fiber axis and another which is the same (or, in some cases very nearly the same) in all directions normal to the fiber axis. It is therefore reasonable to designate the first N_E and the second N_O. Cellulose is sensibly uniaxial and positive with, for ramie (at 3° C.) $N_O = 1.5308$ C, 1.5325 D, 1.5384 F, $N_E = 1.5982$ C, 1.6007 D, 1.6078 F, $N_E - N_O = 0.0674$ C, 0.0682 D, 0.0694 F; and at 20.6° C., $N_O = 1.5297$ C, 1.5322 D, 1.5396 F, $N_E = 1.5965$ C, 1.5993 D, 1.6075 F, $N_E - N_O = 0.0668$ C, 0.0671 D, 0.0679 F and $N_F - N_C = 0.0099$ for N_O and 0.0110 for N_E.

The indices vary with the tenor of water; for example:

Vol. % H_2O = 0.0	8.2	24.4
$N_O = 1.5312$	1.5299	1.5281
$N_E = 1.5956$	1.5931	1.5900
$N_E - N_O = 0.0643$	0.0632	0.0619

But these results are decidedly at variance with those obtained by Kanamaru who reported that ordinary cellulose with $N_O = 1.528$ and $N_E = 1.596$ changed under hydrating conditions so that $N_O = 1.537$ and $N_E = 1.603$. He reported that oxidizing conditions changed the refractive indices of cellulose the same amount.

---

[1] *a* and *b* interchanged to make *b* > *a*.

Cotton is almost pure natural cellulose; it has $N_O = 1.533$, $N_E = 1.580$, $N_E - N_O = 0.047$. Cotton mercerized under tension has $N_O = 1.522$, $N_E = 1.586$, $D_E - N_O = 0.064$. Cotton mercerized without tension has $N_O = 1.524$, $N_E = 1.554$, $N_E - N_O = 0.030$.

"Kipawa" and "forshaga" are artificially purified cellulose; they have $N_O = 1.533$, $N_E = 1.564$, $N_E - N_O = 0.031$.

Ref: 282, 463, 511, 554, 555, 572, 584.

Agave, straw, hemp, bamboo, jute, ramie, and flax are all composed largely of cellulose, but like all other natural cellulose fibers have other ingredients. Data follow:

Agave americana	Agave sisalana	Agave cantala	Agave fourcroydes (Henequen)	Straw
$N_O = 1.522$	1.521	1.522	1.519	1.542 – 1.524
$N_E = 1.530$	1.543	1.547	1.546	1.566 – 1.575
$N_E - N_O = 0.008$	0.022	0.025	0.027	0.024 – 0.051

Manila hemp	Bamboo	Jute	Flax	Flax	Hemp
$N_O = 1.529 - 1.525$	1.541 – 1.540	1.532 – 1.528	1.528	1.532	1.527 – 1.525
$N_E = 1.564 - 1.574$	1.566 – 1.580	1.568 – 1.586	1.595	1.594	1.578 – 1.596
$N_E - N_O = 0.035 - 0.049$	0.025 – 0.040	0.036 – 0.058	0.067	0.062	0.051 – 0.071

Ramie	Ramie	Ramie	Ramie	Ramie	Ramie	Ramie
$N_O = 1.532$	1.534	1.528	1.5307	1.533	1.525	1.525 – 1.528
$N_E = 1.599$	1.595	1.596	1.6015	1.595	1.596	1.571 – 1.596
$N_E - N_O = 0.067$	0.061	0.068	0.0708	0.062	0.071	0.046 – 0.068

Mercerized flax	Mercerized ramie			Mercerized ramie without tension
$N_O = 1.517$	1.525	1.524	1.532	1.529
$N_E = 1.571$	1.574	1.584	1.587	1.579
$N_E - N_O = 0.054$	0.049	0.060	0.055	0.050

Ref: 411, 460, 461, 462, 482, 488, 510, 572.

Cisalfa (protein and cellulose) forms fibers with $N_O = 1.533$, $N_E = 1.546$, $N_E - N_O = 0.013$. Ref: 587.

Zealon (from maize) forms fibers with $N_O = 1.532$, $N_E = 1.539$, $N_E - N_O = 0.007$. Ref: 587.

Aralac (from milk casein) forms fibers with $N_O = 1.537$, $N_E = 1.537 +$, $N_E - N_O = 0.000 +$. Ref: 587.

Soya bean fibers have $N_O = 1.545$, $N_E = 1.545 +$. $N_E - N_O = 0.000 +$.
Ref: 587.

Vinyon $(C_4H_6O_2 \cdot 9C_2H_3Cl)_n$ forms fibers with D 1.35, $N_O = 1.536$, $N_E = 1.536$, $N_E - N_O = 0.000 -$ but very weak birefringence can be detected with the sensitive tint plate. Optic sign + (in one case). Ref: 587.

Polyacrylonitrile fibers (C_3H_3N ?) are uniaxial negative with $N_O = 1.520$, $N_E = 1.517$, $N_E - N_O = 0.003$. Ref: 438.

Nylon $(C_{12}H_{22}O_2)_n$ forms fibers with parallel extinction and positive elongation. D 1.14, $N_O = 1.520$, $N_E = 1.580$, $N_E - N_O = 0.060$. Elliptical cross section. Strong photo-elasticity. Ref: 461.

Wool (contains C,N,H,S, etc.) varies in structure; when stretched it is orthorhombic with[1] *a* 10.3, *b* 2.7, *c* 9.8 Å, elongated along *b*; when unstretched it is also orthorhombic with[1] *a* 6.64, *b* 9.3, *c* 9.8 Å, and elongated along *b*. Both are apparently uniaxial positive with N_O (normal to elongation) $= 1.545$, $N_E = 1.555$, $N_E - N_O = 0.010$. Also reported to have $N_E - N_O$ varying from 0.009 to 0.012.
Ref: 409, 482, 591.

Silk ($C_{18}H_{25}N_5O_7$ approx. ?) is orthorhombic with *a* 9.27, *b* 10.4, *c* 7.00 Å. U.C. 4. D 1.33 - 1.46. Apparently uniaxial positive with N_O (normal to elongation) $= 1.538$, $N_E = 1.595$, $N_E - N_O = 0.057$. Again $N_O = 1.529$, $N_E = 1.584$, $N_E - N_O = 0.055$. Also (another phase ?) monoclinic with *c* 6.95 Å, *a* and *b* uncertain. Certain varieties and derivatives of silk have properties as follows:

Gelatine silk	Spinning silk (Nephila Madagascar)	Viscose	silk	"Copper Nitrate Silk"	Silk
$N_O = 1.539$	1.542	1.521	1.523	1.527	1.518
$N_E = 1.540$	1.581	1.547	1.548	1.548	1.548
$N_E - N_O = 0.001$	0.039	0.026	0.025	0.021	0.030

Degummed silk varies in index so that $N_E - N_O$ varies from 0.048 to 0.057.
Ref: 422, 461, 482, 535, 591.

Acetate silk is of two types. One kind is soluble in acetone. It has N_O (normal to elongation) $= 1.470$, $N_E = 1.476$, $N_E - N_O = 0.006$. Another kind is soluble in chloroform. It is apparently uniaxial negative with N_O (normal to elongation) $= 1.479$, $N_E = 1.474$, $N_O - N_E = 0.005$.

Acetate rayon (soluble in chloroform) varies in composition from nearly $(C_{10}H_{13}O_7)_n$ to nearly $(C_{12}H_{15}O_9)_n$. It forms fibers with parallel extinction and negative elongation. D 1.32. $N_O = 1.479$, $N_E = 1.474$, $N_O - N_E = 0.005$. This is the completely acetylated rayon used for a short time many years ago. Acetate rayon (insoluble in chloroform) is only partly acetylated. It forms

[1] *a* and *b* interchanged to make $b > a$.

fibers with parallel extinction and positive elongation. D 1.33. $N_O = 1.473$. $N_E = 1.478$, $N_E - N_O = 0.005$. Ref: 482, 591.

Viscose rayon with L.A.[1] and 0% stretch has: $N_O = 1.5336$, $N_E = 1.5560$, $N_E - N_O = 0.0224$. With L.A.[1] and 70% stretch it has: $N_O = 1.5320$, $N_E = 1.5673$, $N_E - N_O = 0.0353$. With H.A.[1] and 10% stretch it has: $N_O = 1.5335$, $N_E = 1.5600$, $N_E - N_O = 0.0265$. With H.A. and 80% stretch it has: $N_O = 1.5310$, $N_E = 1.5680$, $N_E - N_O = 0.0370$. With H.A. and 120% stretch it has: $N_O = 1.5280$, $N_E = 1.5730$, $N_E - N_O = 0.0450$. Viscose (no-skin) has $N_O = 1.523$, $N_E = 1.549$, $N_E - N_O = 0.026$; viscose (thick-skin) has $N_O = 1.516$, $N_E = 1.541$, $N_E - N_O = 0.025$; viscose (no-skin) with 50% Godet stretch $N_O = 1.526$, $N_E = 1.554$, $N_E - N_O = 0.028$; viscose (no-skin) with 0% Godet stretch has $N_O = 1.526$, $N_E = 1.548$, $N_E - N_O = 0.022$. Sedura[2] has: $N_O = 1.531$, $N_E = 1.576$, $N_E - N_O = 0.045$. Bemberg[3] has: $N_O = 1.534$, $N_E = 1.571$, $N_E - N_O = 0.037$.

Viscose impregnated with urea formaldehyde resin has $N_O = 1.530$ *ca.*, $N_E = 1.545$ *ca.*, $N_E - N_O = 0.015$ *ca.*

Cellulose hydrate or mercerized cotton ($3C_6H_{10}O_5 \cdot 2H_2O$?) is monoclinic sphenoidal with $a:b:c = 0.790:1:0.887$, $\beta = 118°$. Space group $P2_1$; a 8.14, b 10.30, c 9.14 Å. U.C. 4. D 1.55 – 1.60. Fibers are elongated along b and show parallel extinction. Another hydrate is probably $3C_6H_{10}O_5 \cdot H_2O$.
Ref: 408, 488, 594.

Nitrocellulose ($C_6H_8(NO_2)_2O_5$, etc.) is orthorhombic with a 9.77, b 10.10, c 8.56 Å. U.C. 4. D 1.65. Fibers have parallel extinction and indices varying with the tenor of N as follows:

%N = 5.6	11.6	12.6	13.7
$N_O = 1.528$	1.5108	1.519	1.511
$N_E = 1.567$	1.5108	1.508	1.509
$N_E - N_O = 0.039$	0.0000	-0.001	-0.002

Ref: 494, 511a.

Pectin (formula ?) is uniaxial negative with $N_O = 1.5037$, $N_E = 1.5029$, $N_O - N_E = 0.0008$. (Form double refraction present.) Ref: 623.

Pectic acid (formula ?) is uniaxial negative with $N_O = 1.5328$, $N_E = 1.5265$, $N_O - N_E = 0.0063$. (Form double refraction present.) Ref: 623.

---

[1] L.A ± low alkali content: H.A. = High alkali content.

[2] Sedura = Lilienfeld process yarn.

[3] Bemberg = Cuprammonium rayon.

3. Steroids or Derivatives of Perhydrocyclopentanophenanthrene

5-Cholesten-3-ol or Cholesterol and its Derivatives

Cholesterol [$C_{27}H_{46}O$] is monoclinic with $a:b:c = 1.36:1:3.806$, $\beta = 117°$. *a* 14.0, *b* 10.3, *c* 3.92. D 1.067. M.P. 147.5 – 148.5°. $N_X = 1.520$ D, $N_Y = 1.532$, $N_Z = 1.566$, $N_Z - N_X = 0.046$. ∴ (+)2V = 60° *ca.* Ref: 136, 418.

Cholesteryl ether [$(C_{27}H_{46})_2O$] is biaxial with (+)2V = 60° calc. $N_X = 1.520$, $N_Y = 1.532$, $N_Z = 1.562$, $N_Z - N_X = 0.042$. Ref: 136.

Cholesteryl formate [$CHO_2(C_{27}H_{45})$] is monoclinic sphenoidal with $a:b:c = 3.279:1:1.317$, $\beta = 109°44'$. Crystals acicular with {100}, {001}, {101}, etc. M.P. 96°. No distinct cleavage. The optic plane is 010; $Z \wedge c = 21.5°$. (+)2V = ?. $N_Y = 1.5243$, $N_Z = 1.5655$. Ref: 117.

Calciferol or vitamin D_2 ($C_{28}H_{43}OH$) forms rectangular laths. D 1.047. M.P. 115°. (+)2V = 43°, $N_X = 1.515$, $N_Y = 1.535$, $N_Z = 1.572$, $N_Z - N_X = 0.057$. Ref: 436b.

Cholesteryl acetate ($CH_3CO_2 \cdot C_{27}H_{45}$) forms liquid crystals which are uniaxial negative with (at 95°) $N_O = 1.499$, $N_E = 1.482$, $N_O - N_E = 0.017$. Ref: 464.

Cholesteryl propionate ($C_2H_5CO_2C_{27}H_{45}$) forms liquid crystals in two phases. Phase I (between 60° and 80° F) is uniaxial positive with (at 60°) $N_O = 1.482$, $N_E = 1.527$, $N_E - N_O = 0.045$. Phase II (between 80° and 105°) is uniaxial negative with (at 95°) $N_O = 1.495$, $N_E = 1.480$, $N_O - N_E = 0.015$. Ref: 464.

Cholesteryl capronate ($C_5H_{11}CO_2 \cdot C_{27}H_{45}$) forms liquid crystals in two phases. Phase I is uniaxial positive with (at 80°). $N_O = 1.481$, $N_E = 1.524$, $N_E - N_O = 0.043$. Phase II is uniaxial negative with (at 85°) $N_O = 1.489$, $N_E = 1.479$, $N_O - N_E = 0.010$. Ref: 464.

Cholesteryl propyl carbonate ($C_3H_7CO_3 \cdot C_{27}H_{45}$) forms liquid crystals (between 54° and 100°) which are uniaxial negative with (at 63°) $N_O = 1.5041$, $N_E = 1.4802$, $N_O - N_E = 0.0239$. Ref: 218.

Cholesteryl amyl carbonate ($C_5H_{11}CO_3 \cdot C_{27}H_{45}$) forms liquid crystals (between 52° and 68°) which are uniaxial negative with (at 59°) $N_O = 1.499$, and (at 56.9°) $N_E = 1.4814$, $N_O - N_E = 0.018$. Ref: 218.

Cholesteryl phenyl carbonate [$C_6H_5CO_3 \cdot C_{27}H_{45}$] forms liquid crystals (between 73° and 102°) which are uniaxial negative with $N_O = 1.5255$, $N_E = 1.4998$, $N_O - N_E = 0.0257$. Ref: 218.

Cholesteryl benzoate [$C_6H_5CO_2(C_{27}H_{45})$] is tetragonal with $c/a = 3.627$. Crystals {001} plates or tablets with {114}, {113}, {112}, {111}, etc. Fig. 131. Perfect 001 cleavage. M.P. 146°. Uniaxial negative with $N_O = 1.579$, $N_E = 1.540$, $N_O - N_E = 0.039$ Na. Between 130° and 150° it forms liquid crystals which are uniaxial negative with (at 130°) $N_O = 1.508$, $N_E = 1.491$, $N_O - N_E = 0.017$. Ref: 118, 464.

Cholesteryl salicylate [$C_6H_4(OH)CO_2(C_{27}H_{45})$] is triclinic pedial with $a:b:c$ = 0.774:1:0.504, α = 92°55′, β = 101°58′, γ = 95°14′. Space group $P1$: a 9.68, b 12.52, c 6.31 Å. U.C. 1. Crystals show {100}, {010}, {$1\bar{1}\bar{0}$}, {$0\bar{1}0$}, {001}, etc. M.P. 178.5°. Extinction in $0\bar{1}0$ at 36° to c in obtuse angle β. Distinct dispersion of the bisectrix. An optic axis visible through $0\bar{1}0$ on the edge of the field. (+)2V = 60° *ca.*, N_X = 1.522 D, N_Y = 1.56, N_Z = 1.661, $N_Z - N_X$ = 0.139. Ref: 118, 136.

5,6-Dibromocholestane, or cholestene dibromide or hydrocholesterilene dibromide ($C_{27}H_{46}Br_2$) is orthorhombic with $a:b:c$=0.546:1:0.534. Crystals prismatic or thick {010} tablets with {110}, {120}, {010}, {011}. M.P. 141 - 142°. Distinct 001 and 010 cleavages. Y = a; Z = c. (+)2V = 30°, r < v. N_Y = 1.54 *ca.* $N_Z - N_Y$=0.007, $N_Y - N_X$=0.055, $N_Z - N_X$=0.062; ∴ N_X = 1.49 *ca.* N_Z = 1.55 *ca.* Ref: 117.

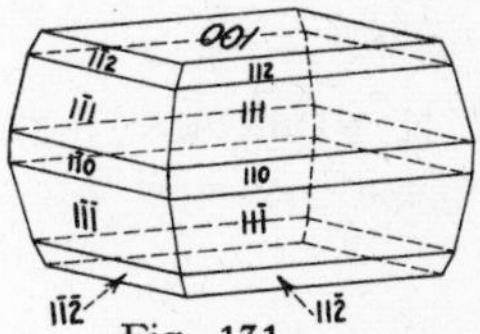

Fig. 131.
Cholesteryl benzoate.

Sterol glucoside tetra-acetate ($C_{43}H_{68}O_{10}$) is probably orthorhombic in thin laths with M.P. 165 - 166°. It is obtained from soybean oil and is derived from stigmasterol and sitosterol. (-)2V = ?. N_X = 1.512, N_Y = 1.522, N_Z = ?. An optic axis normal to some laths; an obtuse bisectrix normal to others; the latter have positive elongation and parallel extinction. [α] = + 24.5°. Ref: 333a.

Sapogenin from agave ($C_{15}H_{24}O_2$) is monoclinic with $a:b:c$ = 1.515:1:2.006, β = 94°15′. Crystals {001} tablets with {100}, {110}, {101}, {111}. M.P. 183.5°. Extinction parallel to b (elongation). An optic axis oblique to 001. N_X = 1.535, N_Y = 1.550, N_Z = 1.570, $N_Z - N_X$ = 0.035. (+)2V = large, with distinct dispersion. Ref: 368.

Equiline ($C_{18}H_{20}O_2$) is orthorhombic disphenoidal with $a:b:c$ = 0.720:1:2.88. Crystals {001} plates with {$\bar{1}\bar{1}\bar{1}$}, {010}, {110}, {100}. Distinct 100 cleavage. M.P. 240°. X = b; Y = a. (-)2V = 40° *ca.* N_X = 1.534 ± .003, N_Y = 1.677 ± .005, N_Z = 1.705 ± .005, $N_Z - N_X$ = 0.171. Fluoresces in clear violet. Ref: 109.

Equilenin ($C_{18}H_{18}O_2$) is orthorhombic in six-sided {001} plates much elongated along b with {110} and {011}. Poor 110 cleavage. 110 ∧ $1\bar{1}0$ = 90 - 91°. M.P. 259°. X = b; Y = a. (-)2V = rather large. N_X = 1.51 *ca.*, N_Y = 1.718 ± .003, N_Z = ?, $N_Z - N_X$ is notably greater than 0.2, and probably about 0.3. Ref: 106.

Estrone, or theelin or folliculin ($C_{18}H_{22}O_2$) has three phases. Estrone I is monoclinic sphenoidal with $a:b:c$ = 0.344:1:0.413, β = 111°30′. Space group $P2_1$; a 7.60, b 22.1, c 9.22 Å. U.C. 4. Crystals {010} tablets with {110}, {011}, etc. Twinning on 100. Perfect 001 cleavage. D 1.24. M.P. 256°. X ∧ c = - 12°; Z = b. (-)2V = 60°, r > v weak. Also (-)2V = 50 - 55°. N_X = 1.520, N_Y = 1.642, N_Z = 1.692, $N_Z - N_X$ = 0.172. Estrone II is orthorhombic disphenoidal with $a:b:c$ = 0.742:1:0.460. Space group $P2_12_12_1$; a 12.1, b 16.3, *c* 7.5 Å. U.C. 4. Crystals show {011}, {120}, {110}. (Orientation of Neuhaus.) Perfect 01̄1 and distinct 010 cleavages. D 1.22. M.P. 259°. X = *b*; Y = *c*. (-)2V = 75°, r > v weak. N_X = 1.511 D, N_Y = 1.621, N_Z = 1.697, $N_Z - N_X$ = 0.186. Also: N_X = 1.512, N_Y = 1.619, N_Z = 1.692, $N_Z - N_X$ = 0.180. (-)2V = 73°. Estrone III is orthorhombic disphenoidal with[1] *a*:*b*:*c* = 0.465: 1:0.386. Space group $P2_12_12_1$; *a* 9.9, *b* 18.2, *c* 7.7 Å. U.C. 4. Metastable crystals six-sided {010} plates. D 1.236. M.P. 254°. X = *c*; Y = *b*. (-)2V = 73° *ca.* N_X = 1.594, N_Y = 1.628, N_Z = 1.647, $N_Z - N_X$ = 0.053.

Ref: 29, 109, 210, 211, 257, 296.

3,17-Dihydroxy-1,3,5-estratriene or estradiol benzoate ($C_{25}H_{28}O_3$) is white or slightly yellowish to brownish. It has N_1 = 1.586, N_2 = 1.632, $N_2 - N_1$ = 0.046.

Ref: 518.

Estriol or estrone hydrate [$C_{18}H_{22}O_2 \cdot H_2O$] is monoclinic sphenoidal with *a*:*b*:*c* = 0.329:1:0.402, β = 109.5°. Space group $P2_1$; *a* 7.50, *b* 22.8, *c* 9.16 Å. U.C. 4. D 1.27 (Röntg.). X ∧ ⊥001 = 17°; Z = *b*. (-)2V = 65° *ca.* N_X = 1.533, N_Y = 1.642, N_Z = 1.686, $N_Z - N_X$ = 0.153. Ref: 29, 257.

Ergosterol ($C_{27}H_{42}O$) is monoclinic in laths or plates with β = 98°. D 1.047. M.P. 155°. X ∧ *c* = 7°. Y = *b*. (+)2V = 89°. N_X = 1.502, N_Y = 1.555, N_Z = 1.612, $N_Z - N_X$ = 0.110. Ref: 436b.

Ergosterol monohydrate ($C_{27}H_{42}O \cdot H_2O$) is monoclinic in laths or plates with β = 101°. D 1.047. X ∧ *a* = 2°. Y = *b*. (+)2V = 88°. N_X = 1.505, N_Y = 1.550, N_Z = 1.610, $N_Z - N_X$ = 0.105. Ref: 436b.

3, 20-Allopregnanedione ($C_{21}H_{32}O_2$) is biaxial with M.P. 202° and N_X = 1.528, N_Y = 1.576, N_Z = 1.638, $N_Z - N_X$ = 0.110. (+)2V = 85° *ca.* Ref: 29, 258.

4-Pregnene-3,20-dione or progesterone ($C_{21}H_{30}O_2$) has two phases. The α-phase (I), called luteosteron C, is orthorhombic disphenoidal with *a*:*b*:*c* = 0.750:1:0.905. Space group $P2_12_12$; *a* 10.27, *b* 13.88, *c* 12.31 Å. U.C. 4. Crystals show {011}, {110}, {010}. Poor 011 cleavage. D 1.163. M.P. 128 - 129°. X = *c*; Y = *b*. (+)2V = 40° D, r > v. N_X = 1.542 D, N_Y = 1.554, N_Z = 1.663, $N_Z - N_X$ = 0.121. The β-phase (II), called luteosteron D, is orthorhombic with *a*:*b*:*c* = 0.563:1:0.275. Crystals acicular with parallel extinction and negative elongation. Cleavage on 001 and 110. D 1.167. M.P. 121 - 122°. Y = *b*; Z = *a*. (+)2V = 68° ± 3°, r > v distinct. N_X = 1.529 D, N_Y = 1.575, N_Z = 1.676, $N_Z - N_X$ = 0.149.

Ref: 29, 258.

Allopregnan-20-on-3-ol, or 3 luteosterone [$C_{21}H_{30}O_2$] is orthorhombic in short {001} plates elongated along *b*. M.P. 195°. X = *a*; Y = *b*. (+)2V = 40° D. N_X = 1.559, N_Y = 1.566, N_Z = 1.622, $N_Z - N_X$ = 0.063. Ref: 297a.

---

[1] *a b c* changed to *a c b* to make *b* > *a* > *c*.

4. Alkaloids

Alkaloids of the Aromatic Amine Type

Carpaine ($C_{14}H_{25}O_2N$) has parallel extinction and negative elongation. $N_1 = 1.51$, $N_2 = 1.52$, $N_2 - N_1 = 0.01$. Ref: 35.

Alkaloids with a Pyrrole Nucleus

3-(1-Methyl-2-pyrrolidyl)pyridine, or Nicotine, and its Salts

3-Pyridine-carboxylic acid or nicotinic acid or niacin ($C_5H_4 \cdot NCOOH$) is monoclinic with $a:b:c = 0.614:1:0.618$, $\beta = 113°23'$. Space group $P2_1/c$. a 7.175, b 11.682, c 7.220 Å. U.C. 4. Crystals {010} plates with {100} and {001}, or small rods. All crystals show twinning about c or on 100. D 1.472. $X \wedge c = 13.5°$ in obtuse β. $Z = b$. (-)2V = 46°, $N_X = 1.424$, $N_Y = 1.717$, $N_Z > 1.75$ and ≈ 1.79, $N_Z - N_X > 0.326$ (≈ 0.37). Again: $N_X = 1.420$, $N_Y = 1.717$, $N_Z = 1.79$, $N_Z - N_X = 0.37$. Colorless. Ref: 436b, 517, 622a.

3-Pyridinecarboxamide or nicotinamide or niacinamide [$C_5H_4N \cdot CO \cdot CH_2$] is polymorphous, crystallizing from the melt in any one of four phases. Phase I (low temperature) is monoclinic with $a:b:c = 0.603:1:0.254$, $\beta = 99°8'$. a 9.435, b 15.65, c 3.974 Å. It forms needles along c which melt at 129 - 132°. D 1.40. $X \wedge c = +23.5°$; $Y = b$. (-)2V = 32°, $N_X = 1.466$, $N_Y = 1.74$, $N_Z > 1.75$ and ≈ 1.77, $N_Z - N_X \approx 0.3$. Again: $N_X = 1.485$, $N_Y = 1.734$, $N_Z > 1.734$, $N_Z - N_X > 0.249$. Phase II is acicular in spherulites with negative elongation and $N_Z - N_X = 0.05$. Phase III forms plates with $\pm$ elongation, and $N_Z - N_X =$ 0.02 - 0.03. Phase IV is acicular in spherulites with - elongation and $N_Z - N_X =$ 0.02 - 0.03. Colorless. Ref: 517, 553, 617b, 622a.

Nicotinamide with nitric acid ($C_6H_6ON_2$ with HNO_3) gives rods or fragments which are monoclinic. Elongation positive, Extinction inclined. $X = b$. (+)2V = 40 - 60°. $N_X = 1.410$, $N_Y > 1.46$ and < 1.49, calc., $N_Z > 1.730$ and < 1.741, $N_Z - N_X > 0.32$ and < 0.341. Ref: 617b.

3-Pyridenecarboxamide with 1,2-ethanediol or nicotinamide with ethylene glycol [$4(C_5H_4NCONH_2OH) \cdot 2(CH_2OHCH_2OH$] is monoclinic with $a:b:c =$ $0.459:1:0.486$, $\beta = 116°$. Space group $P2_1/c$. a 7.16, b 5.6, c 7.58 Å. U.C. 4(?). Crystals prisms $\parallel c$, twinned. D 1.346. $X \wedge c = 18°$ probably in obtuse β. $Z = b$. (-)2V = 23°. $N_X = 1.449$, $N_Y = 1.685$, $N_Z = 1.694$, $N_Z - N_X = 0.245$. Colorless. Perhaps McCrone's data for nicotinamide ($X \wedge c = 25°$, (-)2V = 29°, $r < v$; $N_X = 1.445$, $N_Y = 1.683$, $N_Z = 1.711$, $N_Z - N_X = 0.266$) were measured on this substance. Ref: 553, 622a.

Nicotine tartrate [$CH:CHCH:NCH:CH \cdot CHN(CH_3)CH_2CH_2CH_2 \cdot C_4H_6O_6$] has parallel extinction and positive elongation. $N_1 = 1.56$, $N_2 = 1.57$, $N_2 - N_1 = 0.01$. Ref: 35.

Nicotine salicylate [$CH:CHCH:NCH:CH \cdot CHN(CH_3)CH_2CH_2CH_2 \cdot C_6H_4(OH)CO_2H$] has parallel extinction and positive elongation. $N_1 = 1.545$, $N_2 = 1.635$, $N_2 - N_1 = 0.09$. Ref: 35.

Pyridine Alkaloids

Hemlock Alkaloids

d-2-Propylpiperidine acid tartrate dihydrate or *d*-coni-ine bitartrate dihydrate [$CH_2(CH_2)_3NHCH(C_3H_7) \cdot C_4H_6O_6 \cdot 2H_2O$] is orthorhombic disphenoidal with $a:b:c = 0.777:1:0.586$. Crystals short prisms with {110}, {100}, {0$\bar{1}$1}, {0$\bar{1}$0}, etc. Fig. 132. Perfect 100 cleavage. Y = *a*; Z = *c*. (+)2E = 43°10′ Li, 43°33′ Na, 44°1′ Tl. Bolland gives for "coni-ine tartrate" (no mention of water): parallel extinction and positive elongation with $N_1 = 1.50$, $N_2 = 1.53$, $N_2 - N_1 = 0.03$. (This is probably the dihydrate, and the common form and cleavage render it probable that N_1 is N_X and N_2 is N_Z; then (+)2V = 29° *ca.* and $N_Y = 1.502$ *ca.* - A.N.W.) Ref: 23, 34, 35, 218.

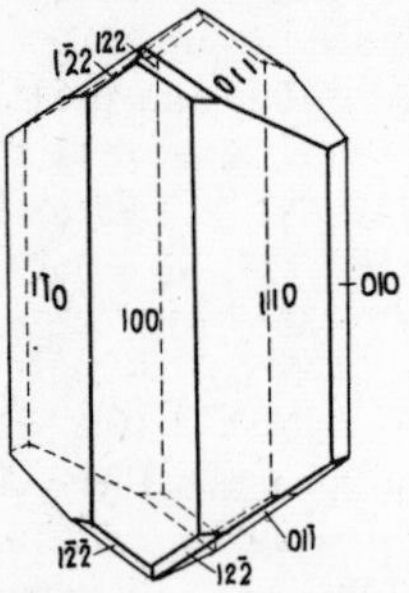

Fig. 132. Coni-ine bitartrate dihydrate.

2-(1-Hydroxypropyl)piperidine or conhydrine [$CH_3CH_2CHOHCH(CH_2)_4NH$] has parallel extinction and positive elongation. M.P. 133 - 134°. $N_1 = 1.54$, $N_2 = 1.55$, $N_2 - N_1 = 0.01$. Ref: 33a, 34, 35.

5-Hydroxy-2-propyl piperidine or pseudoconhydrine [$CH_3CH_2CH_2CHNCH_2CHOHCH_2CH_2$] has two indices of refraction which are very close to 1.55. Ref: 34, 35.

Lobelia Alkaloids

Lobeline hydrochloride ($C_{22}H_{27}NO_2 \cdot HCl$) has $N_1 = 1.520$, $N_Y = 1.645$, $N_3 = 1.67$, $N_3 - N_1 = 0.150$. Ref: 343c.

Areca Alkaloids

3-Carbomethoxy-1,2,5,6-tetrahydro-1-methylpyridine, or Arecoline, and its Salts

Arecoline hydrochloride [$CH_2CH:C(CO_2CH_3)CH_2N(CH_3)CH_2 \cdot HCl$] has parallel extinction and negative elongation with $N_1 = 1.45$, $N_2 = 1.545$, $N_2 - N_1 = 0.095$. Ref: 34, 35.

Arecoline hydrobromide [$CH_2CH:C(CO_2CH_3)CH_2N(CH_3)CH_2 \cdot HBr$] has parallel extinction and negative elongation with $N_1 = 1.57$, $N_2 = 1.62$, $N_2 - N_1 = 0.05$. Again: Z || elongation, $N_X = 1.555$, $N_Y = 1.590$, $N_Z = 1.655$, $N_Z - N_X = 0.100$. ∴ (+)2V = 73° *ca.* Ref: 35.

Alkaloids of Pepper

1-[5-(3,4-Methylenedioxyphenyl)-2,4-pentadienoyl]piperidine or piperine [$C_5H_{10}NCOCH:CHCH:CHC_6H_3 \cdot O \cdot CH_2 \cdot O$] is monoclinic with $a:b:c$ = 0.966:1:0.587, β = 109°27′. Crystals prisms with {110}, {010}, {001}. Fig. 133. No distinct cleavage. M.P. 129°. Extinction at 9° to c in 110. $N_1 = 1.55$, $N_2 = 1.70$, $N_2 - N_1 = 0.15$. Ref: 23, 119.

Anabasine Derivatives

2-(3-Pyridyl)piperidine picrate or anabasine picrate or nicotimine picrate [$C_5H_4N \cdot C_5H_9NH \cdot C_6H_2(NO_2)_3OH$] forms yellow plate-like rods often six-sided. Extinction usually parallel, but may be inclined. $N_X = 1.585$, $N_Y > 1.74$, N_Z = ?, $N_Z - N_X > 0.15$. Ref: 191.

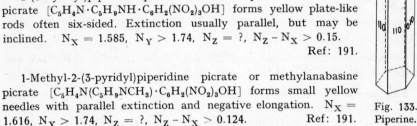

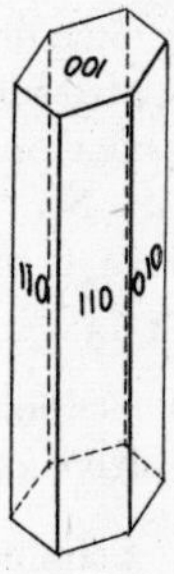

Fig. 133. Piperine.

1-Methyl-2-(3-pyridyl)piperidine picrate or methylanabasine picrate [$C_5H_4N(C_5H_9NCH_3) \cdot C_6H_2(NO_2)_3OH$] forms small yellow needles with parallel extinction and negative elongation. $N_X = 1.616$, $N_Y > 1.74$, N_Z = ?, $N_Z - N_X > 0.124$. Ref: 191.

Alkaloids with Condensed Pyrrolidine and Piperidine Rings

8-Methyl-8-azabicyclo[3,2,1]octan-3-ol tropate or Tropic acid tropine ester or *dl*-Hyoscyamine or Atropine or Daturine and its Salts

Atropine [$HOCH_2CH(C_6H_5)CO_2CHCH_2CHCH_2CH_2CHCH_2$] (bridged by $N(CH_3)$) is orthorhombic with $a:b:c$ = 0.630:1:?. Crystals long prisms with {110}, {010}. No distinct cleavage. M.P. 116°. The optic plane is 001, and optic axes are nearly normal to the prism faces. (−)2V = large. $N_1 = 1.58$, $N_2 = 1.60$, $N_2 - N_1 = 0.02$. Also: $N_1 = 1.555$, $N_2 = 1.595$, $N_2 - N_1 = 0.040$. Again: $N_X = 1.550$, $N_Z = 1.595$, $N_Z - N_X = 0.045$. (Probably $N_X = 1.555$, $N_Y = 1.58$, $N_Z = 1.60$ – A.N.W.) Ref: 35, 168, 196, 518.

Atropine arsenate ($C_{17}H_{23}O_3N \cdot H_3AsO_4$) has parallel extinction and positive elongation. $N_1 = 1.555$, $N_2 = 1.600$, $N_2 - N_1 = 0.045$. Ref: 35.

Atropine valerate ($C_{17}H_{23}O_3N \cdot C_5H_{10}O_2$) has parallel extinction and positive elongation. $N_1 = 1.515$, $N_2 = 1.53$, $N_2 - N_1 = 0.015$. Ref: 35.

Atropine salicylate ($C_{17}H_{23}O_3N \cdot C_6H_4(OH)CO_2H$) has parallel extinction and negative elongation. $N_1 = 1.56$, $N_2 = 1.62$, $N_2 - N_1 = 0.06$. Ref: 35.

Atropine methobromide ($C_{17}H_{23}O_3N \cdot CH_3Br$) has an extinction angle of 41°. $N_1 = 1.53$, $N_2 = 1.625$, $N_2 - N_1 = 0.095$. Ref: 35.

Atropine sulfate [$(C_{17}H_{23}O_3N)_2 \cdot H_2SO_4$] is granular with $N_1 = 1.555$, $N_2 = 1.60$, $N_2 - N_1 = 0.045$ (with H_2O ?). Ref: 35.

Atropine nitrate ($C_{17}H_{23}O_3N \cdot HNO_3$) is granular with $N_1 = 1.57$, $N_2 = 1.59$, $N_2 - N_1 = 0.02$.   Ref: 35.

Atropine hydrochloride [$C_{17}H_{23}O_3N \cdot HCl$] is granular with $N_1 = 1.58$, $N_2 = 1.61$, $N_2 - N_1 = 0.03$.   Ref: 35.

Atropine hydrobromide ($C_{17}H_{23}O_3N \cdot HBr$) has parallel extinction and positive elongation. $N_1 = 1.60$, $N_2 = 1.62$, $N_2 - N_1 = 0.02$.   Ref: 35.

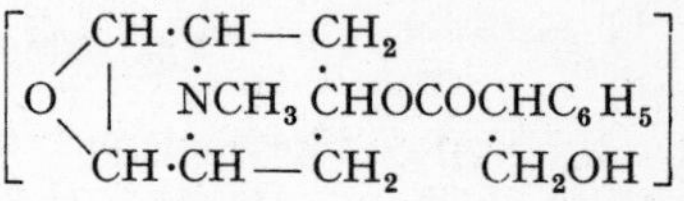

Scopolamine or hyoscine or "duboisine" or atroscine has parallel extinction and positive elongation with $N_1 = 1.555$, $N_2 = 1.57$, $N_2 - N_1 = 0.015$. d-Scopolamine monohydrate is monoclinic with $a:b:c = 2.145:1:1.48$, $\beta = 100°40'$. Good $02\bar{1}$ cleavage.   Ref: 35, 119.

$$\left[\begin{array}{c} CH \cdot CH - CH_2 \\ O \quad | \qquad NCH_3 \ \dot{C}HOCOCHC_6H_5 \\ CH \cdot CH - CH_2 \qquad CH_2OH \end{array} \right]$$

Scopolamine hydrochloride ($C_{17}H_{21}O_4N \cdot HCl$) has parallel extinction and positive elongation. $N_1 = 1.56$, $N_2 = .1.61$, $N_2 - N_1 = 0.05$.   Ref: 35.

Scopolamine hydrobromide trihydrate [$C_{17}H_{21}O_4N \cdot HBr \cdot 3H_2O$] is orthorhombic disphenoidal with $a:b:c = 0.601:1:0.411$. Crystals show {010}, {110}, {100}, {021}, etc. Perfect 010 and distinct 021 cleavages. $X = c$; $Y = b$. $(-)2E = 100°23'$ Li, $101°12'$ Na, $102°14'$ Tl. "Hyoscine hydrobromide" (with no mention of water) has parallel extinction and positive elongation with $N_1 = 1.555$, $N_2 = 1.605$, $N_2 - N_1 = 0.050$. Also $N_1 = 1.568$, $N_2 = 1.586$. It is probable that these indices were measured on the trihydrate, since anhydrous scopolamine hydrobromide is monoclinic with $a:b:c = 0.847:1:1.288$, $\beta = 123°26.5'$. It has distinct $10\bar{1}$ cleavage. The optic plane is 010; $Z \wedge c = +7°$. $(+)2V = ?$. Also though Groth considers atroscine a synonym of scopolamine, Bolland gives for "atroscine hydrobromide" $N_1 = 1.60$, $N_2 = 1.61$, $N_2 - N_1 = 0.01$.   Ref: 35, 119, 343c.

Scopolamine hydroiodide hemihydrate [$C_{17}H_{21}O_4N \cdot HI \cdot 0.5H_2O$] is monoclinic sphenoidal with $a:b:c = 0.938:1:1.357$, $\beta = 94°40'$. Crystals elongated along b with {100}, {001}, {110}, {1$\bar{1}\bar{1}$}. Perfect 100 and imperfect 010 cleavage. The optic plane is 010; extinction on 010 at $-56°$ to c. An optic axis visible through 001 and another through 100 on the edge of the field. For "hyoscine hydroiodide", with no mention of water, Bolland gives: parallel extinction and $N_X = 1.60$, $N_Y = 1.61$, $N_Z = 1.64$, $N_Z - N_X = 0.04$. $\therefore$ $(+)2V = 60°$ calc. (These data probably belong to the hemihydrate – A.N.W.)   Re : 35, 119.

8-Methyl-8-azabicyclo[3.2.1]octan-3-ol mandelate, or Homatropine, and its Salts

Homatropine [$CHOH(C_6H_5)CO_2CHCH_2CHCH_2CH_2CHCH_2$] has parallel extinction and negative elongation. $N_1 = 1.56$, $N_2 = 1.62$, $N_2 - N_1 = 0.06$.
(with $N(CH_3)$ bracket over the middle portion)
                                                                                                                                          Ref: 34, 35.

Homatropine hydrochloride ($C_{16}H_{21}O_3N \cdot HCl$) has parallel extinction and negative elongation. $N_1 = 1.60$, $N_2 = 1.61$, $N_2 - N_1 = 0.01$.   Ref: 35.

Homatropine hydrobromide ($C_{16}H_{21}O_3N \cdot HBr$) is orthorhombic with $a:b:c = 0.414:1:0.472$. Crystals {010} tablets limited by {110}. Imperfect 001 cleavage. M.P. 212°. $X = b$; $Y = c$ (-)$2E = 69 - 70°$. $N_1 = 1.615$, $N_2 = 1.645$, $N_2 - N_1 = 0.030$. Again: $N_X = 1.603$, $N_i = 1.610$, $N_Z = 1.645$, $N_Z - N_X = 0.042$. Ref: 35, 518.

Homatropine sulfate ($C_{16}H_{21}O_3N \cdot H_2SO_4$) has parallel extinction and positive elongation. $N_1 = 1.57$, $N_2 = 1.60$, $N_2 - N_1 = 0.03$. Ref: 35.

8-Methyl-8-azabicyclo[3.2.1]octan-3-ol chloroplatinate or tropine chloroplatinate [($CH_2CH_2CHN(CH_3)CHCH_2CHOHCH_2 \cdot HCl)_2 \cdot PtCl_4$] is monoclinic with $a:b:c = 0.553:1:0.979$, $\beta = 92°28'$. Crystals varied in habit with {110}, {010}, {001}, {101}, {134}, etc. Imperfect 010 cleavage. M.P. 198°. $X \wedge c = -81.5°$ Na, $r < v$; $Z = b$. (-)$2V = 52°12'$ Na, $r < v$. $N_X = 1.6366$ Na, $N_Y = 1.6500$, $N_Z = 1.6595$, $N_Z - N_X = 0.0229$ Na. Ref: 119.

8-Methyl-8-azabicyclo[3.2.1]octan-3-ol atropate [[$CH_2:C(C_6H_5)CO_2CHCH_2CHCH_2CH_2CHCH_2 \cdot HCl$] —$N(CH_3)$—] hydrochloride or apoatropine hydrochloride or atropamine hydrochloride has parallel extinction and negative elongation. $N_1 = 1.58$, $N_2 = 1.65$, $N_2 - N_1 = 0.07$. Ref: 34, 35.

Apoatropine sulfate (+5H_2O?) [[$CH_2:C(C_6H_5)CO_2CHCH_2CHCH_2CHCH_2CH_2CHCH_2$]$H_2SO_4$] (—$NCH_3$— bridge) has parallel extinction and positive elongation. $N_1 = 1.555$, $N_2 = 1.63$, $N_2 - N_1 = 0.075$. Ref: 35.

Homatropine salicylate [$C_{16}H_{21}O_3N \cdot C_6H_4(OH)CO_2H$] is biaxial with parallel extinction. (+)$2V = 45°$ calc. $N_X = 1.56$, $N_Y = 1.57$, $N_Z = 1.625$, $N_Z - N_X = 0.065$. Ref: 35.

l-8-Methyl-8-azabicyclo[3,2,1]octan-3-ol tropate, or *l*-Hyoscyamine and its Salts

Hyoscyamine [$HOCH_2CH(C_6H_5)CO_2CHCH_2CHCH_2CH_2CHCH_2$] (—$N(CH_3)$— bridge) is tetragonal with $c/a = 2.708$. Crystals equant with {001}, {111}. Fig. 134. Also in very thin needles with negative elongation. No observed cleavage. M.P. 109°. Uniaxial negative with $N_O = 1.58$, $N_E = 1.60$, $N_E - N_O = 0.02$. Ref: 35, 196.

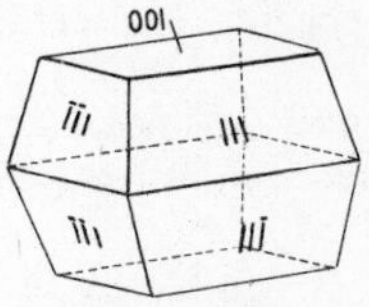

Fig. 134. Hyoscyamine.

Hyoscyamine hydrochloride ($C_{17}H_{23}O_3N \cdot HCl$) is granular with $N_1 = 1.575$, $N_2 = 1.61$, $N_2 - N_1 = 0.035$. Ref: 35

Hyoscyamine hydrobromide ($C_{17}H_{23}O_3N \cdot HBr$) has parallel extinction and positive elongation. $N_1 = 1.61$, $N_2 = 1.63$, $N_2 - N_1 = 0.02$. Ref: 35.

Hyoscyamine hydroiodide ($C_{17}H_{23}O_3N \cdot HI$) is granular with $N_1 = 1.61$, $N_2 = 1.615$, $N_2 - N_1 = 0.005$. Ref: 35.

Hyoscyamine sulfate ($C_{17}H_{23}O_3N \cdot H_2SO_4$) has parallel extinction and negative elongation. $N_1 = 1.55$, $N_2 = 1.57$, $N_2 - N_1 = 0.02$. Ref: 35

Hyoscyamine salicylate ($C_{17}H_{23}O_3N \cdot C_6H_4(OH)CO_2H$) is granular with $N_1 = 1.54$, $N_2 = 1.63$, $N_2 - N_1 = 0.09$. Ref: 35.

Cocaine Group

Methyl *l*-3-hydroxy-8-methyl-8-azabicyclo[3.2.1]octane-1-carboxylate benzoate, or *l*-Cocaine, and its Salts

Cocaine [$CH_2CH_2CHN(CH_3)CHCH(CO_2CH_3)CH(O_2CC_6H_5)CH_2$] is monoclinic with $a:b:c = 0.848:1:1.032$, $\beta = 106°10'$. Crystals {001} tablets with {100}, {011}, etc. Fig. 135. Perfect 001 and $10\bar{1}$ cleavages. M.P. 98°. Optic angle very large. $N_X = 1.49$, $N_Y = ?$, $N_Z = 1.58$, $N_Z - N_X = 0.09$. Also: $N_1 = 1.50$ (parallel to elongation), $N_2 = 1.62$ *ca.*, $N_2 - N_1 = 0.12$. Soluble in index liquids. Ref: 119, 196, 386.

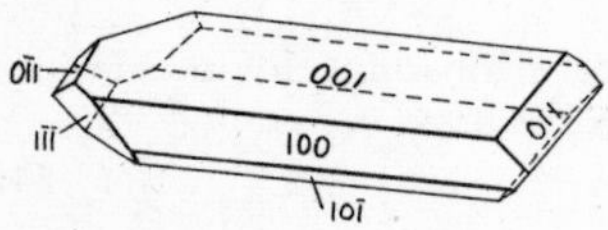

Fig. 135. *l*-Cocaine.

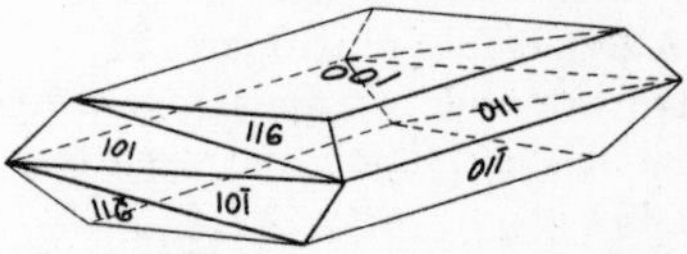

Fig. 136. *l*-Cocaine hydrochloride.

Cocaine hydrochloride ($C_{17}H_{21}O_4N \cdot HCl$) is orthorhombic disphenoidal with $a:b:c = 0.329:1:0.976$. Crystals {001} plates with {011}, {101}. Fig. 136. Perfect 001 cleavage. M.P. 187°. X = *c*; Y = *b*. (–)2V = 60° calc. $N_X = 1.522$, $N_Y = 1.594$, $N_Z = 1.616$, $N_Z - N_X = 0.094$. Again: $N_X = 1.570$, $N_Y = 1.596$, $N_Z = 1.618$, $N_Z - N_X = 0.048$. Ref: 119, 152, 343c, 518.

Cocaine hydrochloride with gold chloride ($C_{17}H_{21}O_4N \cdot HCl$ with $AuCl_3$) forms long rods with many shorter ones nearly at right angles. $N_1 = 1.570$, $N_2 = 1.734$, $N_2 - N_1 = 0.164$. Ref: 523h.

Cocaine tartrate [$(C_{17}H_{21}O_4N)_2 \cdot C_4H_6O_6$] has parallel extinction and negative elongation. $N_1 = 1.52$, $N_2 = 1.56$, $N_2 - N_1 = 0.04$. Ref: 34, 35.

8-Methyl-8-azabicyclo[3.2.1]octan-3-ol benzoate hydrochloride or tropacocaine hydrochloride [$C_6H_5CO_2CHCH_2CHCH_2CH_2CHCH_2 \cdot HCl$, with $N(CH_3)$ bridge] forms rhombic and prismatic crystals and needles, easily soluble in water. M.P. 271° with decomposition. $N_1 = 1.531$, $N_2 = 1.659$, $N_2 - N_1 = 0.128$. Colorless. Ref: 239.

9-Methyl-9-azabicyclo[3:3.1] nonan-3-one, or Pseudopelletierine, or *N*-Methylgranatonine Salts

Pseudopelletierine hydrochloride [$CH_2CH_2CH_2CHN(CH_3)CHCH_2COCH_2 \cdot HCl$] has parallel extinction and positive elongation with $N_1 = 1.56$, $N_2 = 1.62$, $N_2 = N_1 = 0.06$. Ref: 35.

Pseudopelletierine sulfate [(CH$_2$CH$_2$CH$_2$CHN(CH$_3$)CHCH$_2$COCH$_2$)$_2$·H$_2$SO$_4$] (4H$_2$O ?) has extinction at 20° with positive elongation and $N_1 = 1.545$, $N_2 = 1.55$, $N_2 - N_1 = 0.005$. Ref: 35.

Alkaloids of the Broom and Lupin Group

Lupinine hydrochloride ($C_{10}H_{19}ON \cdot HCl$) is orthorhombic disphenoidal with $a:b:c = 0.872:1:0.526$. Crystals equant or {100} tablets with {110}, {101}, {1$\bar{1}$1}, etc. Fig. 137. Distinct 010 and imperfect 100 cleavages. M.P. 112 - 113°. $Y = c$; $Z = a$. (+)2V = 60°17′ Li, 59°18′ Na, 57°42′ Tl. $N_Y = 1.5658$ Li, 1.5700 Na, 1.5756 Tl. Ref: 119.

Lupinine thiocyanate monohydrate ($C_{15}H_{24}ON_2 \cdot HCNS \cdot H_2O$) is monoclinic sphenoidal with $a:b:c = 0.484:1:0.569$, $\beta = 123°24'$. Crystals varied in habit with {0$\bar{1}$0}, {010}, {110}, {011}, {001}, etc. May be twinned on 010. $X = b$: Z nearly normal to 100. (+)2V = 68° *ca.* Na, $N_Y = 1.641$ Na. Ref: 119.

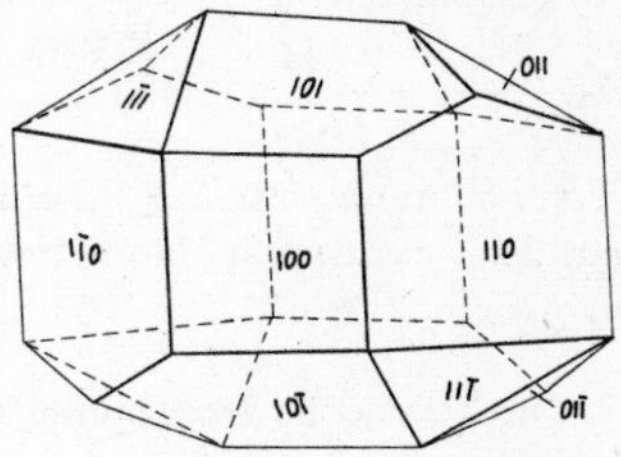

Fig. 137.
Lupinine hydrochloride.

Sparteine hydrochloride ($C_{15}H_{26}N_2 \cdot HCl$) is granular with no distinct prism edges. $N_1 = 1.56$, $N_2 = 1.575$, $N_2 - N_1 = 0.015$. Ref: 34.

Sparteine hydriodide ($C_{15}H_{26}N_2 \cdot HI$) is orthorhombic disphenoidal with $a:b:c = 0.575:1:0.559$. Crystals {010} tablets or brachydomatic with {011}, {010}, {110}, etc. Distinct 010 and imperfect 011 cleavages. $Y = b$; $Z = a$, Parallel extinction and positive elongation. (+)2V = very small. $N \perp a = 1.645$. $N_Z = 1.665$, $N_Z - N_X = 0.02$ *ca.* Ref: 35, 119.

Sparteine sulfate [$(C_{15}H_{26}N_2)_2 \cdot H_2SO_4$] is probably biaxial with parallel extinction and positive elongation. $N_1 = 1.52$, $N_2 = 1.535$, $N_2 - N_1 = 0.015$. Ref: 35.

Oxysparteine ($C_{15}H_{24}ON_2$) is granular with $N_1 = 1.615$, $N_2 = 1.67$, $N_2 - N_1 = 0.055$. Ref: 35.

Quinoline Alkaloids

Cinchona Alkaloids

d-2-[Hydroxy(4-quinolyl)methyl]-5-vinyl-1-azabicyclo[2.2.2]octane, or Cinchonine and its Salts

α-Cinchonine ($C_{19}H_{22}ON_2$) is monoclinic sphenoidal with $a:b:c = 1.483:1:?$, $\beta = 107°53'$. Crystals thick {001} tablets with {110}, {100}, etc. Perfect 001 and distinct 100 cleavages. M.P. 264°. $X \wedge c = -57°$; $Z = b$. Elongation is parallel to *b* and positive with parallel extinction. (-)2V = 21° calc.; 2E = 30°48′ Li, 35°52′ Na, 40°58′ Tl. $N_X = 1.570$, $N_Y = 1.685$, $N_Z = 1.690$, $N_Z - N_X = 0.120$ D. Ref: 119, 196, 239, 294, 365, 386.

Cinchonine salt of 2-(*o*-carboxyphenyl)-3-pyridine carboxylic acid or cinchonine 2-phenylpyridine-2',3-dicarboxylate [$C_{13}H_9O_4N \cdot 2(C_{19}H_{22}ON_2)$] is probably orthorhombic with parallel extinction and negative elongation. $N_1 = 1.557$ (along *c*). $N_2 = 1.665$ (normal to elongation, which is assumed to be along *c*), $N_2 - N_1 = 0.108$. Ref: 268.

Cinchonine disulfate ($C_{19}H_{22}N_2O \cdot 2H_2SO_4$) forms colorless rods with positive elongation and parallel extinction. Blue fluorescence. Biaxial with $N_X = 1.56$, $N_Y = ?$, $N_Z = 1.62$, $N_Z - N_X = 0.06$. Ref: 294.

Cinchonine dihydrochloride ($C_{19}H_{22}N_2O \cdot 2HCl$) is orthorhombic disphenoidal with $a:b:c = 0.824:1:1.833$. Crystals prisms with {110}, {012}, {001}. Positive elongation and parallel extinction with $N_X = 1.55$, $N_Y = 1.62$, $N_Z = 1.67$, $N_Z - N_X = 0.12$; ∴ (-)2V = 80° calc. Also $N_1 = 1.60$, $N_2 = 1.655$, $N_2 - N_1 = 0.055$. Ref: 35, 119, 294.

Cinchonine nitrate (hemihydrate?) [$C_{19}H_{22}N_2O \cdot HNO_3 \cdot (0.5H_2O\,?)$] has parallel extinction and negative elongation with $N_1 = 1.555$, $N_2 = 1.64$, $N_2 - N_1 = 0.085$. Ref: 34, 35.

Cinchonine hydrobromide(monohydrate?) ($C_{19}H_{22}ON_2 \cdot HBr \cdot H_2O$), is orthorhombic disphenoidal with $a:b:c = 0.243:1:0.314$. Crystals show {110}, {011}, etc. Perfect 010 cleavage. Y = *b*; Z = *c*. (+)2E = 150°. $N_X = ?$, $N_Y = 1.649$, $N_Z = 1.691$. ∴ (+)2V = 72° *ca.*, $N_X = 1.627$ *ca.* "Cinchonine hydrobromide" (with H_2O?) is biaxial positive with parallel extinction and positive elongation; it has: $N_X = 1.61$, $N_Y = ?$, $N_Z = 1.69$, $N_Z - N_X = 0.08$. Ref: 119, 277, 294.

Cinchonine methanetrisulfonate octahydrate [$HC(SO_3H)_3 \cdot 3C_{19}H_{22}ON_2 \cdot 8H_2O$] is orthorhombic and pseudotetragonal with $a:b:c = 1:1:1.307$. Crystals show {011}, {001}, {101}, {1$\bar{1}$1}, etc., often elongated along *a*. X = *b*; Y = *a*. (-)2V = 50° calc. $N_X = 1.510$, $N_Y = 1.527$, $N_Z = 1.531$ D, $N_Z - N_X = 0.021$. Ref: 15.

Cinchonine hydrochloride dihydrate ($C_{19}H_{22}N_2OHCl \cdot 2H_2O$) is monoclinic with $a:b:c = 4.082:1:2.116$, $\beta = 106°2'$. Crystals {001} plates with {100}, {011}, etc. Perfect 100 cleavage. $X \wedge c = -35°$; Z = *b*. (-)2E = 102°, r < v. Also said to form rods with positive elongation and extinction at 24° to length. $N_X = 1.545$, $N_Y = 1.617$, $N_Z = 1.661$, $N_Z - N_X = 0.116$; ∴ (-)2V = 57.5° calc. Ref: 119, 277.

Cinchonine hydroiodide monohydrate ($C_{19}H_{22}N_2O \cdot HI \cdot H_2O$) is monoclinic with $a:b:c = 0.810:1:?$, $\beta = 95°9'$. Crystals acicular with positive elongation and extinction at 19° to elongation. (-)2V = 80° calc., r > v. $N_X = 1.596$, $N_Y = 1.649$, $N_Z = 1.684$, $N_Z - N_X = 0.088$. Ref: 119, 277.

Cinchonine chlorate monohydrate ($C_{19}H_{22}N_2O \cdot HClO_3 \cdot H_2O$) is monoclinic in needles and rods with positive elongation. (-)2E = 101°, r < v. $N_X = 1.573$, $N_Y = 1.641$, $N_Z = 1.664$, $N_Z - N_X = 0.091$. (-)2V = 56° calc. Ref: 277.

Cinchonine bromate dihydrate ($C_{19}H_{22}N_2O \cdot HBrO_3 \cdot 2H_2O$) is monoclinic in fine needles with positive elongation. (-)2E = 53°, r < v. $N_Y = 1.636$, $N_Z = 1.670$, ∴ $N_X = 1.27$ *ca.* calc., $N_Z - N_X = 0.40$ *ca.* calc., and (-)2V = 31°40′ calc. Ref: 277.

Cinchonine iodate monohydrate ($C_{19}H_{22}N_2O \cdot HIO_3 \cdot H_2O$) is monoclinic in fine needles with positive elongation. (-)2V = large. $N_X = 1.600$, $N_Y = 1.660$, $N_Z > 1.700$, $N_Z - N_X > 0.100$. [∴ N_Z must be less than 1.72 and 2V must be 80 - 90° - A.N.W.] Ref: 277.

Cinchonine perchlorate monohydrate ($C_{19}H_{22}N_2O \cdot HClO_4 \cdot H_2O$) is monoclinic (or triclinic ?) in needles and rods with positive elongation and extinction at 12° to elongation. Perfect 010 cleavage. (-)2E = large, r < v. $N_X = 1.518$, $N_Y = 1.572$, $N_Z = 1.620$, $N_Z - N_X = 0.102$. ∴ (-)2V = 87° calc. Ref: 119, 277.

Cinchonine nitrate monohydrate ($C_{19}H_{22}N_2O \cdot HNO_3 \cdot H_2O$) is monoclinic in plates with positive elongation and extinction at 45° to elongation. (+)2E = 59°, r < v. $N_X = 1.550$, $N_Y = 1.568$, $N_Z = 1.655$, $N_Z - N_X = 0.105$. From 2E and N_Y, 2V = 36°40′. Ref: 277.

Cinchonine sulfate dihydrate ($C_{19}H_{22}N_2O \cdot H_2SO_4 \cdot 2H_2O$) is monoclinic in plates with positive elongation and extinction at 38° to elongation. (-)2V = 70° calc., r < v. $N_X = 1.587$, $N_Y = 1.641$, $N_Z = 1.667$, $N_Z - N_X = 0.080$. This is probably the compound described by Schabus as monoclinic with $a:b:c$ = 2.417:1:?, β = 96°43′; crystals short prismatic with perfect 100 and 001 cleavages. Ref: 119, 277.

Cinchonine thiosulfate dihydrate ($C_{19}H_{22}N_2O \cdot H_2S_2O_3 \cdot 2H_2O$) is monoclinic with ± elongation and extinction at 35° thereto. (-)2E = 82°, r < v. $N_X = 1.578$, $N_Y = 1.673$, calc., $N_Z = 1.690$, $N_Z - N_X = 0.112$. ∴ (-)2V = 46° *ca.* Ref: 277.

Cinchonine thiocyanate ($C_{19}H_{22}N_2O \cdot HCNS$) is monoclinic sphenoidal with $a:b:c$ = 2.034:1:1.221, β = 97°24′. Crystals show {001}, {$20\bar{1}$}, {$10\bar{1}$}, {100}, {$11\bar{1}$}, {110}. Perfect 100 cleavage. Plates and rods have negative elongation. (-)2E = large, r > v. $N_X = 1.554$, $N_Y = 1.651$, $N_Z = 1.700$, $N_Z - N_X = 0.146$. ∴ 2V = 71° calc. Again: $N_X = 1.545$, $N_Y = 1.650$, $N_Z = 1.705$, $N_Z - N_X$ = 0.160. Ref: 119, 277, 525.

Cinchonine benzoate ($C_{19}H_{22}N_2O \cdot C_6H_5CO_2H$) is monoclinic in needles and rods with ± elongation and positive optic sign. $N_X = 1.547$, $N_Y = 1.596$, $N_Z = 1.684$, $N_Z - N_X = 0.137$. ∴ (+)2V = 73° calc. Ref: 277.

Cinchonine *o*-chlorobenzoate ($C_{19}H_{22}N_2O \cdot ClC_6H_4CO_2H$) is monoclinic in needles and rods with negative elongation. (+)2E = large. $N_X = 1.519$, N_Y = ?, $N_Z = 1.625$, $N_Z - N_X = 0.106$. ∴ N_Y is about 1.54 to 1.56. Ref: 277.

Cinchonine sulfate tetrahydrate ($C_{19}H_{22}N_2O \cdot H_2SO_4 \cdot 4H_2O$) is said to be orthorhombic with $a:b:c$ = 0.689:1:0.599. Crystals prisms with {110}, {101}, {011}, {111}, having 110 cleavage. Microscopically seem to be orthorhombic tablets, all plates showing interference figures. Elongation is negative. $N_1 = 1.59$, $N_2 = 1.67$, $N_2 - N_1 = 0.08$. Colorless rods with parallel extinction and positive elongation. (-)2V = 65°, calc. $N_X = 1.59$, $N_Y = 1.64$, $N_Z = 1.66$, $N_Z - N_X = 0.07$. Ref: 119, 196, 294.

Cinchonine ethobromide monohydrate ($C_{19}H_{22}N_2O \cdot C_2H_5Br \cdot H_2O$) is orthorhombic with $a:b:c = 0.375:1:0.259$. Crystals prismatic with {110}, {320}, {011}, {010}. Perfect 010 cleavage. $Y = b$; $Z = c$. (+)2V = 87°50′, r > v. $N_X = 1.6407$, $N_Y = 1.6539$, $N_Z = 1.6701$, $N_Z - N_X = 0.0294$ Na. Ref: 119.

Cinchonine *l*-2-hydroxy-2-phenylethanoate or cinchonine *l*-phenylglycolate or cinchonine *l*-mandelate ($C_{19}H_{22}N_2O \cdot C_6H_5CHOHCO_2H$) is orthorhombic disphenoidal with $a:b:c = 0.712:1:1.825$. Crystals show {1$\bar{1}$1}, {001}, {1$\bar{2}$4}, etc. Perfect 001 cleavage. $Y = b$; $Z = c$. (+)2H (in cedar oil) = 91°22′ Na, 90°56′ Tl. $N_Z = 1.6614$ Na, 1.6688 Tl. Ref: 119.

2-(4-Quinolylcarbonyl)-5-vinyl-1-azabicyclo[2.2.2]octane or cinchoninone ($C_{19}H_{20}N_2O$) is orthorhombic disphenoidal with $a:b:c = 0.458:1:0.445$. Crystals {001} tablets with {111}, {331}, etc. Perfect 001 and imperfect 110 cleavages. D 1.23. M.P. 126 - 127°. $X = b$; $Y = c$. (-)2V = 65°20′ Na. $N_X = 1.5287$, $N_Y = 1.6704$, $N_Z = 1.7161$, $N_Z - N_X = 0.1874$ Na. Ref: 119.

d-5-Ethyl-2-[hydroxy(4-quinolyl)methyl]-1-azabicyclo[2.2.2]octane dihydrobromide or hydrocinchonine dihydrobromide ($C_{19}H_{24}N_2O \cdot 2HBr$) is orthorhombic disphenoidal with $a:b:c = 0.979:1:0.849$. Crystals equant with {010}, {101}, {011}, {110}, etc. Distinct 010, 101, 100, and 001 cleavages. $Y = a$; $Z = c$. (+)2V = 62°. $N_X = 1.601$, $N_Y = 1.632$, $N_Z = 1.733$, $N_Z - N_X = 0.132$. Ref: 301.

l-2-[Hydroxy(4-quinolyl)methyl]-5-vinyl-1-azabicyclo[2.2.2]octane or Cinchonidine and its Salts

Cinchonidine ($C_{19}H_{22}N_2O$) is orthorhombic disphenoidal with $a:b:c = 0.649:1:0.941$. Crystals brachydomatic or {001} tablets with {001}, {110}, {021}, {010}, etc. Elongation parallel to *a*. Perfect 001 and distinct 010 cleavages. M.P. 210°. $Y = b$; $Z = a$. (+)2V = 59° calc., r > v weak. $N_X = 1.610$, $N_Y = 1.625$, $N_Z = 1.675$, $N_Z - N_X = 0.065$. Also $N_1 = 1.62$, $N_2 = 1.68$, $N_2 - N_1 = 0.06$. Again: $N_X = 1.61$, $N_Y = 1.62$, $N_Z = 1.68$, $N_Z - N_X = 0.07$. $[\alpha] = +109.2°$ ($c = 1$ percent in ethanol). Ref: 119, 196, 294, 365.

Cinchonidine tetrasulfate ($C_{19}H_{22}N_2O \cdot 4H_2SO_4$) forms colorless rods with positive elongation and parallel extinction. Bright fluorescence. (+)2V = 35° calc. $N_X = 1.55$, $N_Y = 1.56$, $N_Z = 1.65$, $N_Z - N_X = 0:10$ Ref: 294.

Cinchonidine hydrobromide [$C_{19}H_{22}N_2O \cdot HBr \cdot (2/3H_2O$?)] is orthorhombic disphenoidal with $a:b:c = 0.863:1:0.366$. Crystals {010} tablets with perfect 010 cleavage. $Y = a$; $Z = c$. Positive elongation. (+)2E = 140°; 2V = 69° calc. $N_X = 1.63$, $N_Y = 1.66$, $N_Z = 1.72$ calc., $N_Z - N_X = 0.09$. Ref: 119; 294.

Cinchonidine dihydrochloride ($C_{19}H_{22}N_2O \cdot 2HCl$) forms colorless rods with positive elongation and parallel extinction. Biaxial with $N_X = 1.59$, $N_Y = ?$, $N_Z = 1.70$, $N_Z - N_X = 0.11$. Ref: 294.

Cinchonidine salt of 2-(*o*-carboxyphenyl)-3-pyridinecarboxylic acid or cinchonidine 2-phenylpyridine-2′,3-dicarboxylate [$C_{13}H_9O_4N \cdot 2(C_{19}H_{22}N_2O)$] is orthorhombic disphenoidal with $a:b:c = 0.654:1:0.796$. Crystals show {001}, {020}, {110}, {021} of hexagonal aspect. $X = c$; $Y = b$. (-)2V = 30°, $r < v$. $N_X = 1.613$, $N_Y = 1.648$, $N_Z = 1.651$ (all ± .003), $N_Z - N_X = 0.038$. Ref: 268.

Cinchonidine acetate ($C_{19}H_{22}N_2O \cdot CH_3CO_2H$) forms colorless rods with positive elongation and parallel extinction. (+)2V = 80° calc. $N_X = 1.59$, $N_Y = 1.61$, $N_Z = 1.64$, $N_Z - N_X = 0.05$. Ref: 294.

Cinchonidine benzene solvate ($C_{19}H_{22}N_2O + C_6H_6$) is orthorhombic in rods with cleavage parallel thereto; parallel extinction and positive elongation. (+)2V = large. $N_X = 1.595$, $N_Y = 1.620$, $N_Z = 1.655$, $N_Z - N_X = 0.060$. $[\alpha] = +87.0°$. Ref: 365.

Cinchonidine sulfate trihydrate [$(C_{19}H_{22}ON_2)_2 \cdot H_2SO_4 \cdot 3H_2O$] is monoclinic. Crystals acicular with parallel extinction. $N_X = 1.562$, $N_Y = 1.604$, $N_Z = 1.660$, $N_Z - N_X = 0.098$ ∴ (+)2V = 85° calc. Colorless. Ref. 524.

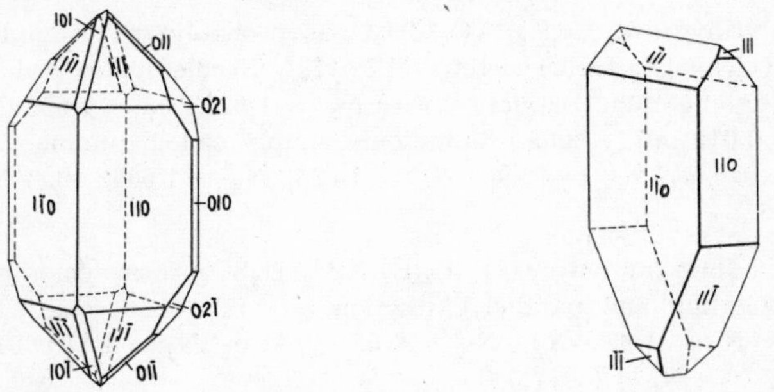

Fig. 138, 139. Cinchonidine ethiodide methiodide dihydrate.

Cinchonidine sulfate pentahydrate ($C_{19}H_{22}N_2O \cdot H_2SO_4 \cdot 5H_2O$) is monoclinic sphenoidal with $a:b:c = 0.513:1:0.167$, $\beta = 97°19'$. Crystals orthodomatic with {100}, {101}, {10$\bar{1}$}, {010}, {110}. Perfect 100 and 010 cleavages. $X = b$; $Z \wedge c = -59°$. (+)2V = 64° calc., weak dispersion. Described as needles with parallel extinction and positive elongation with $N_1 = 1.58$, $N_2 = 1.62$, $N_2 - N_1 = 0.04$. Ref: 119, 196.

Cinchonidine thiocyanate ($C_{19}H_{22}ON_2 \cdot HCNS$) forms rods with Z parallel to elongation and $N_X = 1.600$, $N_Y = 1.645$, $N_Z = 1.700$, $N_Z - N_X = 0.100$; ∴ (+)2V = 85° calc. Ref: 525.

Cinchonidine ethiodide methiodide dihydrate ($C_{19}H_{22}N_2O \cdot CH_3I \cdot C_2H_5I \cdot 2H_2O$) is orthorhombic disphenoidal with $a:b:c = 0.699:1:0.966$. Crystals prismatic with {110}, {011}, {101}, etc. Figs. 138, 139. Distinct 001 cleavage. Loses

$2H_2O$ at 150° and fuses with decomposition at 242 – 245°. The optic plane is 010; the acute bisectrix is *a*. 2V = 73°36′ Na, r > v. $N_Y = 1.6613$ Na. Color reddish yellow. Ref: 119.

Cinchonidine sulfanilamide sulfate ($C_{25}H_{29}O_6N_4S \cdot H_2SO_4$) is monoclinic. M.P. 183°. Elongation positive. (+)2V = ?, $N_X = 1.507$, $N_Y = 1.594$, $N_Z > 1.671$ (also < 1.681, since the optic sign is +. – A.N.W.), $N_Z - N_X > 0.164$. Crystals dissolve in index liquids with N > 1.671. Ref: 617a.

Cinchonidine tartrate [$(C_{19}H_{22}N_2O)_2 \cdot C_4H_6O_6 \cdot (2H_2O$?)] has parallel extinction and positive elongation. $N_1 = 1.56$, $N_2 = 1.58$, $N_2 - N_1 = 0.02$. Ref: 35.

l-5-Ethyl-2-[hydroxy(4-quinolyl)methyl]-1-azabicyclo[2.2.2]octane dihydrobromide dihydrate or hydrocinchonidine dihydrobromide dihydrate ($C_{19}H_{24}N_2O \cdot 2HBr \cdot 2H_2O$) is monoclinic sphenoidal with *a*:*b*:*c* = 1.102:1:1.169, β = 79°23′. Crystals {001} tablets, equant, or prismatic with {001}, {101}, {011}, {110}, {111}, etc. Distinct 100 and 110 cleavages. Slowly volatile. X ∧ *a* = small; Z = *b*. (–)2V = 63°, r < v. $N_X = 1.56$, $N_Y = 1.67$, $N_Z = 1.718$, $N_Z - N_X = 0.158$. Ref: 300.

l-2-[Hydroxy(6-methoxy-4-quinolyl)methyl]-5-vinyl-1-azabicyclo[2.2.2]octane or Quinine and its Salts

Quinine trihydrate ($C_{20}H_{24}N_2O_2 \cdot 3H_2O$) is probably orthorhombic in small needles with cleavage parallel thereto. M.P. 172°. Needles have parallel extinction and negative elongation. Biaxial (?) with $N_X = 1.620$, $N_Y = 1.625$, $N_Z = 1.630$, $N_Z - N_X = 0.010$, all ± .005. Commonly simply called quinine. Dehydrates easily – then (?): $N_X = 1.596$, $N_Y = 1.624$, $N_Z = 1.689$, $N_Z - N_X = 0.093$. (+)2V = 65°. Ref: 239, 365.

Quinine sulfate (anhydrous ?) ($C_{20}H_{24}N_2O_2 \cdot H_2SO_4$) forms colorless rods with positive elongation and parallel extinction. (+)2V = 50° calc. $N_X = 1.62$, $N_Y = 1.63$, $N_Z = 1.67$, $N_Z - N_X = 0.05$. Also $N_1 = 1.610$, $N_2 = 1.635$, $N_3 = 1.687$, $N_3 - N_1 = 0.077$. Ref: 294, 334c.

Quinine sulfate heptahydrate ($C_{20}H_{24}N_2O_2 \cdot H_2SO_4 \cdot 7H_2O$) is orthorhombic disphenoidal with *a*:*b*:*c* = 0.984:1:0.310. Changes to the dihydrate in dry air. M.P. 205°. Crystals show {010}, {110}, {100}, {101}, etc. Perfect 100 and distinct 001 cleavages. The optic plane is 100 for red and yellow, 010 for green and blue. X = *c*. Z ∧ *c* also reported. (–)2V = 11.5°. $N_1 = 1.60$, $N_2 = 1.69$, $N_2 - N_1 = 0.09$. Also: $N_X = 1.595$, $N_Y = 1.635$, $N_Z = 1.690$, $N_Z - N_X = 0.095$. ∴ (+)2V = 80° *ca.* Ref: 23, 119, 294, 518.

Quinine ethyl carbonate ($C_{20}H_{24}N_2O_2 \cdot CO_3 \cdot C_2H_5$) is acicular with $N_1 = 1.57$, $N_2 = 1.59$, $N_3 = 1.68$, $N_3 - N_1 = 0.11$. M.P. 95°. Ref: 239, 343c.

Quinine benzene solvate ($C_{20}H_{24}N_2O_2 \cdot C_6H_6$) is found in two phases. The stable phase (I) is orthorhombic in rods and needles with cleavage parallel thereto; they have parallel extinction and positive elongation. (+)2V = large. $N_X = 1.608$, $N_Y = 1.611$, $N_Z = 1.615$, $N_Z - N_X = 0.007$. The metastable phase (II) is also orthorhombic in shreds with cleavage. The extinction is parallel and elongation positive. (-)2V = 61° calc., r < v. N_X = 1.525, N_Y = 1.630, N_Z = 1.655, $N_Z - N_X$ = 0.130. Ref: 365.

Quinine (iso-?)valerate ($C_{20}H_{24}N_2O_2 \cdot C_5H_{12}O_2$) is biaxial with N_1 = 1.502, N_2 = 1.682, $N_2 - N_1$ = 0.174. Ref: 239.

Quinine succinate ($C_{20}H_{24}N_2O_2 \cdot C_4H_6O_4$) forms colorless rods with positive elongation and parallel extinction. Biaxial with N_X = ?, N_Y = 1.59, N_Z = 1.68. Bolland gives N_1 = 1.63, N_2 = 1.675, $N_2 - N_1$ = 0.045. (Perhaps N_X = 1.59?, and N_Y = 1.63; then (+)2V = large – A.N.W.) Ref: 34, 294.

Quinine tartrate [$(C_{20}H_{24}N_2O_2)_2 \cdot C_4H_6O_6$] has parallel extinction and positive elongation. N_1 = 1.61, N_2 = 1.67, $N_2 - N_1$ = 0.06. Ref: 35.

Quinine *dl*-lactate ($C_{20}H_{24}N_2O_2 \cdot C_3H_6O_3$) is uniaxial positive with N_O = 1.608, N_E = 1.655, $N_E - N_O$ = 0.047. M.P. 165°. Ref: 391.

Quinine *d*-(or *l*-?) lactate ($C_{20}H_{24}N_2O_2 \cdot C_3H_6O_3$) is uniaxial positive with N_O = 1.588, N_E = 1.660, $N_E - N_O$ = 0.072. Ref: 391.

Quinine salicylate [$C_{20}H_{24}N_2O_2 \cdot C_6H_5CO_2H(OH)$] forms colorless rods with positive elongation and parallel extinction. (+)2V = 50° calc. N_X = 1.62, N_Y = 1.63, N_Z = 1.67, $N_Z - N_X$ = 0.05. Bolland gives N_1 = 1.62, N_2 = 1.705, $N_2 - N_1$ = 0.085. Again: N_X = 1.602, N_Y = 1.620, N_Z = 1.682, $N_Z - N_X$ = 0.080. ∴ (+)2V = moderate. Ref: 34, 294, 524.

Quinine carbonic acid ester or 0,0′-carbonyl diquinine or diquinine carbonic acid ester [$(C_{20}H_{23}N_2O)_2CO_3$] is granular and insoluble in water. M.P. 189°. (+)2V = large. N_X = 1.57, N_Y = 1.62, N_Z = 1.684, $N_Z - N_X$ = 0.114. Ref: 239.

Quinine hydrochloride ($C_{20}H_{24}N_2O_2 \cdot HCl$) forms colorless rods with positive elongation and parallel extinction. (+)2V = 70°, calc. N_X = 1.59, N_Y = 1.61, N_Z = 1.67, $N_Z - N_X$ = 0.08. Again: N_X = 1.588, N_Y = 1.615, N_Z = 1.656, $N_Z - N_X$ = 0.068. Ref: 294, 518.

Quinine hydrobromide ($C_{20}H_{24}N_2O_2 \cdot HBr$) forms colorless rods with positive elongation and parallel extinction. (+)2V = 65°, calc. N_X = 1.61, N_Y = 1.63, N_Z = 1.68, $N_Z - N_X$ = 0.07. Ref: 294.

Quinine salt of 2-(*o*-carboxyphenyl)-3-pyridinecarboxylic acid or quinine 2-phenylpyridine-2′,3-dicarboxylate [$C_{13}H_9O_4N \cdot 2(C_{20}H_{24}N_2O_2)$] is orthorhombic disphenoidal with $a:b:c$ = 0.628:1:0.777. Crystals show {001}, {110}, {022}, {021} of hexagonal aspect. The optic plane is 100; X = *c*. Data follow:

	(-)2V	N_X	N_Y	N_Z	$N_Z - N_X$	
Li	13°27′	1.580	1.660	1.661	0.081	all ± .001
Na	16°42′	1.583	1.665	1.667	0.084	all ± .001
Tl	21°17′	1.594	1.679	1.683	0.089	all ± .002

Ref: 268.

Quinine carbamate dihydrochloride ($C_{20}H_{24}N_2O_2 \cdot NH_2CO_2H \cdot 2HCl$) forms colorless rods with inclined extinction and positive elongation. (+)2V = 80° calc. $N_X = 1.58$, $N_Y = 1.64$, $N_Z = 1.72$, $N_Z - N_X = 0.14$. Ref: 294.

Quinine dihydrobromide ($C_{20}H_{24}N_2O_2 \cdot 2HBr$) forms yellow rods with positive elongation and parallel extinction. Yellow fluorescence. (-)2V = 69° calc. $N_X = 1.58$, $N_Y = 1.61$, $N_Z = 1.69$, $N_Z - N_X = 0.11$. Ref: 294.

Quinine 1,2-benzene dicarboxylate or quinine phthalate [$C_{20}H_{24}N_2O_2 \cdot C_6H_4(CO_2H)_2$] forms colorless rods with positive elongation and parallel extinction. (+)2V = 40° calc. $N_X = 1.61$, $N_Y = 1.62$, $N_Z = 1.69$, $N_Z - N_X = 0.08$. It is also described as orthorhombic with (+)2V = 60°, $N_X = 1.620$, $N_Y = 1.625$, $N_Z = 1.69$, $N_Z - N_X = 0.07$. (Indices and 2V are inconsistent - A.N.W.) Ref: 294, 396.

Quinine benzoate ($C_{20}H_{24}N_2O_2 \cdot C_6H_5CO_2H$) forms colorless rods with positive elongation and parallel extinction. (-)2V = 70° calc. $N_X = 1.60$, $N_Y = 1.66$, $N_Z = 1.69$, $N_Z - N_X = 0.09$. Ref: 294.

Quinine 1,2,2-trimethyl-1,3-cyclopentanedicarboxylate or quinine camphorate [$C_{20}H_{24}N_2O_2 \cdot C_8H_{14}(CO_2H)_2$] forms yellow rods with positive elongation and parallel extinction. (-)2V = 60° calc. $N_X = 1.58$, $N_Y = 1.61$, $N_Z = 1.62$, $N_Z - N_X = 0.04$. Ref: 294.

Quinine chromate ($C_{20}H_{24}N_2O_2 \cdot H_2CrO_4$) forms yellow rods with positive elongation and parallel extinction. Biaxial with N_X = ?, $N_Y = 1.65$, $N_Z = 1.69$. Ref: 294.

Quinine chlorate ($C_{20}H_{24}N_2O_2 \cdot HClO_3$) forms colorless rods with positive elongation and parallel extinction. (+)2V = 65° calc. $N_X = 1.62$, $N_Y = 1.64$, $N_Z = 1.69$, $N_Z - N_X = 0.07$. Ref: 294.

Quinine 2-hydroxy-1,2,3-propane-tricarboxylate or quinine citrate ($C_{20}H_{24}N_2O_2 \cdot C_6H_8O_7$) forms colorless rods with positive elongation and parallel extinction. Biaxial with $N_X = 1.58$, $N_Y = 1.65$, N_Z = ? Ref: 294.

Quinine salt of *l*-abietic acid ($C_{20}H_{24}N_2O_2 \cdot C_{20}H_{30}O_2$) is probably orthorhombic in fine needles with parallel extinction and positive elongation. M.P. 185 - 187°. $N_X = 1.570$, N_Y = ?, $N_Z = 1.615$, $N_Z - N_X = 0.045$. $[\alpha] = +140.3°$. Ref: 190.

Quinine phosphate ($C_{20}H_{24}N_2O_2 \cdot H_3PO_4$) forms colorless rods with positive elongation and parallel extinction. Biaxial with $N_X = 1.58$, N_Y = ?, $N_Z = 1.64$, $N_Z - N_X = 0.06$. Again: $N_X = 1.575$, $N_Y = 1.595$, $N_Z = 1.655$, $N_Z - N_X = 0.080$. ∴ (+)2V = moderate. Ref: 294, 524.

Quinine arsenate ($C_{20}H_{24}N_2O_2 \cdot H_3AsO_4$) forms pink rods with positive elongation and parallel extinction. (+)2V = 40° calc. $N_X = 1.61$, $N_Y = 1.62$, $N_Z = 1.69$, $N_Z - N_X = 0.08$. Ref: 294.

Quinine 4-methoxybenzoate or quinine anisate [$C_{20}H_{24}N_2O_2 \cdot (CH_3O)C_6H_4CO_2H$] forms yellow diamond-shaped crystals insoluble in water. Biaxial with $N_X = 1.58$, $N_Y = 1.62$, $N_Z = ?$ Ref: 294.

Quinine acetate ($C_{20}H_{24}N_2O_2 \cdot CH_3CO_2H$) forms needles soluble in water, Positive elongation and parallel extinction. Biaxial with $N_X = ?$, $N_Y = 1.62$. $N_Z = 1.68$. Colorless. Ref: 294.

Quinine ethanedioate or quinine oxalate [$C_{20}H_{24}N_2O_2 \cdot (CO_2H)_2$] forms colorless rods with positive elongation and parallel extinction. (+)2V = 35° calc. $N_X = 1.60$, $N_Y = 1.61$, $N_Z = 1.69$, $N_Z - N_X = 0.09$. Ref: 294.

Quinine nitrate ($C_{20}H_{24}N_2O_2 \cdot HNO_3$) forms orange rods with negative elongation and parallel extinction. (-)2V = 75° calc. $N_X = 1.56$, $N_Y = 1.61$, $N_Z = 1.64$, $N_Z - N_X = 0.08$. (Is this the monohydrate? If so, it is monoclinic with $a:b:c = 0.749:1:1.078$, $\beta = 105°29'$; elongation along c.) Ref: 119, 294.

Quinine thiosulfate ($C_{20}H_{24}N_2O_2 \cdot H_2S_2O_3$) forms colorless rods with positive elongation and parallel extinction. Biaxial with $N_X = ?$, $N_Y = 1.64$, $N_Z = 1.70$. Ref: 294.

Quinine hypophosphite ($C_{20}H_{24}N_2O_2 \cdot H_4P_2O_6$) forms colorless rods with positive elongation and parallel extinction. (+)2V = 80° calc. $N_X = 1.60$[1], $N_Y = 1.62$, $N_Z = 1.65$, $N_Z - N_X = 0.05$. Ref: 294.

Quinine hydrofluosilicate ($C_{20}H_{24}N_2O_2 \cdot H_2SiF_6$) forms colorless rods with positive elongation and parallel extinction. (+)2V = 70° calc. $N_X = 1.56$, $N_Y = 1.58$, $N_Z = 1.62$, $N_Z - N_X = 0.06$. Ref: 294.

Quinine formate ($C_{20}H_{24}N_2O_2 \cdot HCO_2H$) forms colorless rods with positive elongation and parallel extinction. Biaxial with $N_X = ?$, $N_Y = 1.62$, $N_Z = 1.69$. Ref: 294.

Quinine disulfate heptahydrate ($C_{20}H_{24}N_2O_2 \cdot 2H_2SO_4 \cdot 7H_2O$) forms colorless rods with positive elongation and parallel extinction; blue fluorescence. Biaxial with $N_X = 1.58$, $N_Y = ?$, $N_Z = 1.67$, $N_Z - N_X = 0.09$. Again: $N_1 = 1.555$, $N_2 = 1.620$, $N_2 - N_1 = 0.065$. Ref: 294, 518.

Quinine picrate [$C_{20}H_{24}N_2O_2 \cdot (NO_2)_3C_6H_2OH$] forms yellow rods with negative elongation and parallel extinction. (+)2V = 60° calc. $N_X = 1.61$, $N_Y = 1.64$, $N_Z = 1.72$, $N_Z - N_X = 0.11$. Ref: 294.

Quinine thiocyanate (monohydrate?) [$C_{20}H_{24}N_2O_2 \cdot 2HCNS \cdot (H_2O\ ?)$] is monoclinic sphenoidal with $a:b:c = 0.688:1:1.020$, $\beta = 101°47'$; it forms tablets or colorless rods with positive elongation and parallel extinction. Biaxial with $N_X = ?$, $N_Y = 1.61$, $N_Z = 1.69$. The monohydrate forms rods with Z parallel to elongation. $N_X = 1.604$, $N_Y = 1.614$, $N_Z = 1.687$, $N_Z - N_X = 0.083$; ∴ (+)2V = 40° *ca.* Ref: 119, 294, 525.

[1] Value of N_X as corrected in personal communication from Mary L. Willard, January 26, 1938.

Quinine trisulfate dihydroiodide tetraiodide hexahydrate ($4C_{20}H_{24}O_2N_2 \cdot 3H_2SO_4 \cdot 2HI \cdot I_4 \cdot 6H_2O$) is orthorhombic[1] with $a:b:c = 0.577:1:0.455$. Crystals {010} plates with {011}, {031}, {110}, {120}, and {121}. D 1.645 for brown crystals, but green crystals show D 1.70! Y = b; Z = a. (+)2V = 10° (est.) with r > green. $N_X = 1.608$ Na, $N_Y = 1.625$, N_Z = ?. If 2V = 10°, N_Z must be about 2.97 and $N_Z - N_X$ about 1.36! Because of very strong absorption, N_Z cannot be measured in Na light. This substance has been called "herapathite", and is very useful in making "polaroid" in large sheets. Ref: 345.

Quinine sulfanilamide sulfate ($C_{26}H_{31}O_4N_4S \cdot H_2SO_4$) is monoclinic. M.P. 209°. Elongation positive. (-)2V = 83° calc., r > v. $N_X = 1.596$, $N_Y = 1.657$, $N_Z = 1.668$, $N_Z - N_X = 0.072$. Ref: 617a.

Quinine sulfanilamide sesquisulfate ($C_{26}H_{31}O_4N_4S \cdot 1.5H_2SO_4$) is monoclinic. M.P. 186°. Elongation positive. (+)2V < 72° calc., $N_X = 1.574$, $N_Y = 1.618$, $N_Z > 1.703$, $N_Z - N_X > 0.129$. Ref: 617a.

l-5-Ethyl-2-[hydroxy(6-methoxy-4-quinolyl)methyl]-1-azabicyclo[2.2.2)-octane hydrochloride or hydroquinine hydrochloride [$C_{20}H_{26}N_2O_2 \cdot HCl \cdot (2H_2O\,?)$] is granular and easily soluble in water. $N_1 = 1.592$, $N_2 = 1.71$ *ca.*, $N_2 - N_1 = 0.118$. Ref: 239.

d-2-[Hydroxy(6-methoxy-4-quinolyl)methyl]-5-vinyl-1-azabicyclo[2.2.2]-octane, or Quinidine, and its Salts

Quinidine ($C_{20}H_{24}N_2O_2$) is monoclinic sphenoidal according to Schabus with $a:b:c = 2.156:1:2.075$, $\beta = 102°40'$. It is orthorhombic according to Wherry, in needles with cleavage parallel thereto; they have parallel extinction and positive elongation. (-)2V = 55° calc. $N_X = 1.580$, $N_Y = 1.665$, $N_Z = 1.690$, $N_Z - N_X = 0.110$. According to Mayrhofer, $N_1 = 1.544$, $N_2 = 1.711$, $N_2 - N_1 = 0.167$. Also (-)2V = 70°, $N_1 = 1.54$, $N_2 = 1.70$, $N_2 - N_1 = 0.16$. Ref: 119, 196, 239, 365.

Quinidine benzene solvate ($3C_{20}H_{24}N_2O_2 \cdot C_6H_6$) is orthorhombic disphenoidal with $a:b:c = 0.692:1:1.005$. Crystals {001} tablets with {110}, {111}, etc. Perfect 001 cleavage. Shreds and rods have parallel extinction and positive elongation. The optic plane is 010; Z = c. (+)2V = 50° calc., r < v. $N_X = 1.575$, $N_Y = 1.595$, $N_Z = 1.685$, $N_Z - N_X = 0.110$. Ref: 119, 365.

Quinidine sulfate dihydrate [$(C_{20}H_{24}N_2O_2)_2 \cdot H_2SO_4 \cdot 2H_2O$] forms colorless rods with positive elongation and parallel extinction. (+)2V = 60° calc. $N_X = 1.59$, $N_Y = 1.61$, $N_Z = 1.65$, $N_Z - N_X = 0.06$. Behrens gives $N_1 = 1.58$, $N_2 = 1.62$. Again: $N_X = 1.565$, $N_Y = 1.607$, $N_Z = 1.670$, $N_Z - N_X = 0.105$. Ref: 23, 294, 518.

Quinidine thiocyanate ($C_{20}H_{24}O_2N_2 \cdot HCNS$) forms rods with X parallel to elongation and $N_X = 1.549$, $N_Y = 1.643$, $N_Z > 1.734$, $N_Z - N_X > 0.185$; ∴ probably (+)2V = large. Ref: 525.

[1] $a\ b\ c$ changed to $b\ c\ a$ to make $b > a > c$.

Quinidine ethyl alcohol solvate ($C_{20}H_{24}N_2O_2 \cdot C_2H_5OH$) is orthorhombic disphenoidal with $a:b:c = 0.800:1:0.589$. Crystals prismatic with {110}, and {101}. Cleavage parallel to elongation of rods, which have parallel extinction and positive elongation. (+)2V = 48° calc., r < v. $N_X = 1.550$, $N_Y = 1.570$, $N_Z = 1.690$, $N_Z - N_X = 0.140$. Ref: 119, 365.

Quinidine hydrobromide ($C_{20}H_{24}N_2O_2 \cdot HBr$) forms colorless rods with positive elongation and parallel extinction. (+)2V = 55° calc. $N_X = 1.58$, $N_Y = 1.60$, $N_Z = 1.68$, $N_Z - N_X = 0.10$. Ref: 294.

Quinidine salt of 2-(*o*-carboxyphenyl)-3-pyridinecarboxylic acid or quinidine 2-phenylpyridine-2′,3-dicarboxylate [$C_{13}H_9O_4N \cdot 2(C_{20}H_{24}N_2O_2)$] is monoclinic sphenoidal with $a:b:c = 0.485:1:0.451$, $\beta = 103°6'$. Crystals show {100}, {010}, {0$\bar{1}$0}, {001}, {110}, {0$\bar{1}$1}. Perfect 010 cleavage. $X = b$; $Z \wedge c = -38.5°$. (-)2V = 55° ± 5°, r < v. $N_X = 1.526$, $N_Y = 1.641$, $N_Z = 1.672$, $N_Z - N_X = 0.146$. Ref: 268.

Cupreine ($C_{19}H_{22}N_2O_2$) is monoclinic and pseudo-orthorhombic by twinning. Negative elongation and extinction angle less than 35°. (-?)2V = large. $N_1 = 1.62$, $N_2 = 1.64$, $N_2 - N_1 = 0.02$. Ref: 196.

Cinchonamine ($C_{19}H_{24}N_2O$) is pseudotrigonal with a rhombohedral angle of 84°42′. Crystals hexagonal prisms {1120}, with {1011}, etc. M.P. 185°. Positive elongation. (+)2V = small. $N_X = 1.61$, $N_Y = 1.61+$, $N_Z = 1.67$, $N_Z - N_X = 0.06$ Na. Ref: 119, 196.

Quinamine ($C_{19}H_{24}N_2O_2$) is probably orthorhombic in needles with parallel extinction and positive elongation. (-)2V = 30°. $N_1 = 1.58$, $N_2 = 1.62$, $N_2 - N_1 = 0.04$. Ref: 196.

Conquinamine ($C_{19}H_{24}N_2O_2$) has negative elongation with $N_1 = 1.58$, $N_2 = 1.60$, $N_2 - N_1 = 0.02$. Ref: 23, 196.

Isoquinoline Alkaloids

Anhalonium Group

1,2,3,4-Tetrahydro-8-hydroxy-6,7-dimethoxy-1,2-dimethylisoquinoline or pellotine ($C_{13}H_{19}O_3N$) is granular with $N_1 = 1.66$, $N_2 = 1.67$, $N_2 - N_1 = 0.01$. Ref: 35.

1,2,3,4-Tetrahydro-6-methoxy-7,8-methylenedioxy-1-methylisoquinoline hydrochloride, or anhalonine hydrochloride ($C_{12}H_{15}O_3N \cdot HCl$) has parallel extinction and negative elongation with $N_1 = 1.60$, $N_2 = 1.615$, $N_2 - N_1 = 0.015$. Ref: 35.

Papaverine Group

1-(3,4-Dimethoxybenzyl)-6,7-dimethoxyisoquinoline or papaverine ($C_{20}H_{21}O_4N$) is orthorhombic with $a:b:c = 0.319:1:0.427$. Crystals, which may be formed by sublimation at 135 – 140° at 11 mm. pressure and at 1 – 2 mm. distance, are prisms with {110}, {010}, {011}. D 1.337. M.P. 147°. $X = c$; $Y = b$. 2V =

large. $N_X = 1.625$, $N_Y = ?$, $N_Z = 1.690$, $N_Z - N_X = 0.065$. Also $N_1 = 1.62$, $N_2 = 1.68$, $N_2 - N_1 = 0.06$. Parallel extinction. Also (+)2V = 87°, $N_X = 1.634$, $N_Y = 1.68$, $N_Z > 1.74$, $N_Z - N_X > 0.106$. Ref: 35, 119, 196, 208, 386.

1-(3,4-Dimethoxybenzyl)-6,7-dimethoxyisoquinoline hydrochloride or papaverine hydrochloride ($C_{20}H_{21}O_4N \cdot HCl$) is monoclinic with $a:b:c = 0.829:1:0.583$, $\beta = 92°21'$. Crystals prisms with {110}, {100}, and {011}. M.P. 220°. $N_X = 1.555$, $N_Y = 1.734$, $N_Z > 1.734$, $N_Z - N_X > 0.179$. Also[1] (+)2V = 87°, $N_X = 1.634$, $N_Y = 1.68$, $N_Z > 1.734$, $N_Z - N_X > 0.106$. Ref: 524.

Narcotine ($C_{22}H_{23}O_7N$) is orthorhombic disphenoidal with $a:b:c = 0.95:1:0.489$. Crystals formed by sublimation at 150 - 160° under 11 mm. pressure and at 2 mm. distance are {001} tablets or elongated along *c* with {010}, {100}, {110}, {011}, {111}. Perfect 010 and imperfect 001 and 100 cleavages. D 1.37 - 1.395. M.P. 176°. X = *c*; Y = *a*. (-)2E = 50° *ca.* r < v strong. Also (-)2V = 22°, $N_X = 1.525$, $N_Y = 1.687$ *ca.*, $N_Z = 1.697$ *ca.*, $N_Z - N_X = 0.172$.

(-)2V	N_1	N_2	$N_Z - N_X$ or $N_2 - N_1$	Authority
20°	1.50	1.69	0.19	Kley
	1.54	1.69	0.15	Bolland
	1.525	1.69	0.165	Kerbosch

Ref: 35, 119, 193, 196, 208.

Narceine and its Salts

Narceine (trihydrate) ($C_{23}H_{27}NO_8 \cdot 3H_2O$) assumes minute hairlike forms with negative elongation. $N_1 = 1.57$, $N_2 = 1.61$, $N_2 - N_1 = 0.04$. Ref: 23, 196.

Narceine hydrochloride ($C_{23}H_{27}NO_8 \cdot HCl$) is biaxial with parallel extinction and negative elongation. 2V = very large. $N_X = 1.55$, $N_Y = 1.57$, $N_Z = 1.59$, $N_Z - N_X = 0.04$. Ref: 34, 35.

Narceine sulfate hexahydrate [$(C_{23}H_{27}NO_8)_2 \cdot H_2SO_4 \cdot 6H_2O$] has parallel extinction and negative elongation. $N_1 = 1.545$, $N_2 = 1.64$, $N_2 - N_1 = 0.095$. Ref: 35.

Narceine meconate ($C_{23}H_{27}NO_8 \cdot C_{10}H_{11}O_5$) is probably monoclinic with extinction at 23°. $N_1 = 1.53$, $N_2 = 1.69$, $N_2 - N_1 = 0.16$. Ref: 35.

Hydrastine ($C_{21}H_{21}NO_6$) is orthorhombic disphenoidal with $a:b:c = 0.846:1:0.376$. Crystals equant with {110}, {230}, {130}, {203}, {101}, etc. No distinct cleavage. M.P. 132°. Z ∥ elongation. (+)2V = ?, $N_X = 1.550$, $N_1 = 1.734$, $N_Z > 1.734$, $N_Z - N_X > 0.184$. Again: $N_1 = 1.56$, $N_2 = 1.74$(?). Colorless. Ref: 119, 196, 523a, 523h.

Hydrastine bitartrate [$C_{21}H_{21}O_6N \cdot (C_4H_6O_6)_2$] has parallel extinction and positive elongation. $N_1 = 1.54$, $N_2 = 1.58$, $N_2 - N_1 = 0.04$. Ref: 35.

[1] Data given by Kofler for "papaverine", but perhaps measured on the hydrochloride.

Hydrohydrastinine hydrochloride ($C_{11}H_{13}NO_2 \cdot HCl$) has parallel extinction and negative elongation. $N_1 = 1.535$, $N_2 = 1.63$, $N_2 - N_1 = 0.095$. Ref: 35.

Berberine Group

Berberine hexahydrate ($C_{20}H_{19}NO_5 \cdot 6H_2O$) is probably orthorhombic with X parallel with elongation of needles. (–?)2V = ?. $N_1 > 1.50$, $N_2 = 1.74$, $N_2 - N_1 < 0.24$. Again: $N_X = 1.490$, $N_i = 1.565$, $N_Y = 1.701$, $N_Z > 1.74$, $N_Z - N_X > 0.25$. Strongly pleochroic from clear yellow to dark brown. Ref: 196, 523a.

Berberine hydrochloride hemipentahydrate ($C_{20}H_{19}NO_5 \cdot HCl \cdot 2.5H_2O$) has parallel extinction and negative elongation. $N_1 = 1.50$, $N_2 = 1.95$, $N_2 - N_1 = 0.45$. Ref: 35.

Berberine sulfate ($C_{20}H_{19}NO_5 \cdot H_2SO_4$) has parallel extinction and negative elongation. $N_1 = 1.50$, $N_2 = 1.59$, $N_2 - N_1 = 0.09$. Ref: 35.

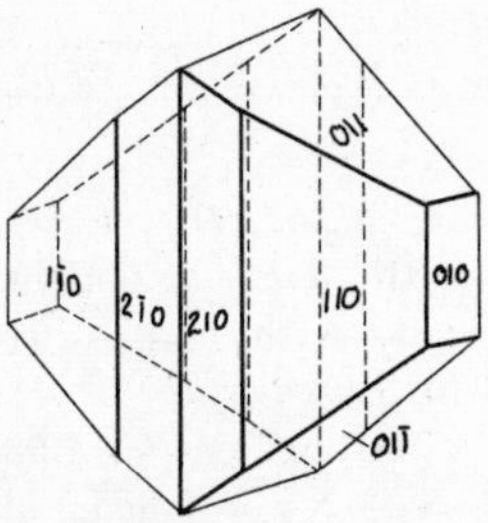

Fig. 140. Bulbocapnine.

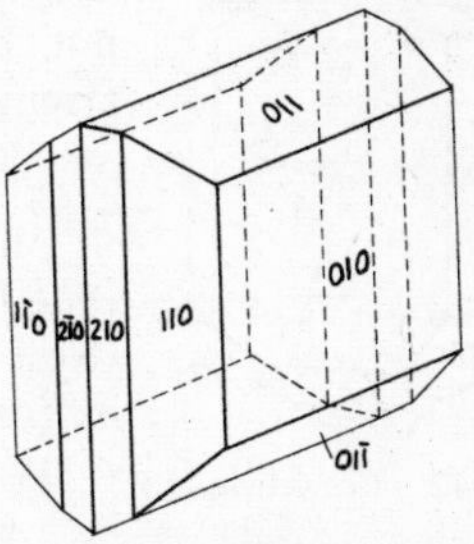

Fig. 141. Benzoylbulbocapnine.

Bulbocapnine ($C_{19}H_{19}NO_4$) is orthorhombic disphenoidal with $a:b:c = 0.725:1:0.718$. Crystals short prisms with {110}, {210}, {011}, {010}. Fig. 140. Perfect 010 and imperfect 001 cleavages. M.P. 199 – 200°. X = *b*; Y = *a*. (–)2V = ?. $N_X = 1.6411$ Li, 1.6519 Na, 1.6752 Tl; N_Y = ?; $N_Z = 1.7555$ Li, 1.7684 Na, 1.7828 Tl; $N_Z - N_X = 0.1165$ Na. Ref: 119.

Bulbocapnine hydrochloride ($C_{19}H_{19}O_4N \cdot HCl$) has parallel extinction and positive elongation. $N_1 = 1.32$, $N_2 = 1.68$, $N_2 - N_1 = 0.36$. Ref: 35.

d- or *l*-Bulbocapnine methyl ether [$C_{19}H_{18}O_4N(CH_3)$] is tetragonal trapezohedral with $c/a = 1.055$. Crystals show {111} and {001}. Imperfect 110 cleavage. M.P. 130 – 131°. Uniaxial negative with $N_O = 1.6714$ Li, 1.6802 Na, 1.6890 Tl; $N_E = 1.6086$ Li, 1.6217 Na, 1.6255 Tl; $N_O - N_E = 0.0585$ Na. Ref: 119.

d-Benzoylbulbocapnine ($C_{19}H_{18}O_4N \cdot COC_6H_5$) is orthorhombic disphenoidal with $a:b:c = 0.894:1:0.631$. Crystals {010} tablets with {011}, {110}, etc. Fig. 141. Cleavage on (100 or 010?). M.P. 202 – 203°. X = *b*; Y = *c*. (–)2V = 76°54′ Li, 78°34′ Na, 80°6′ Tl; $N_X = 1.2762$ Li, 1.2798 Na, 1.2873 Tl; $N_Y = 1.2809$ Li, 1.2855 Na, 1.2875 Tl; $N_Z = 1.2831$ Li, 1.2894 Na, 1.2920 Tl; $N_Z - N_X = 0.0096$ Na. (These indices are so very low that new measurements are desirable – A.N.W.) Ref: 119.

Corydine ($C_{20}H_{23}O_4N$) is tetragonal trapezohedral with $c/a = 0.399$. Crystals short prisms with {110}, {111}, {100}, {201}. Fig. 142. Perfect 100 and distinct 001 cleavages. M.P. 149°. Uniaxial with very weak birefringence and N = 1.6290 Li, 1.6348 Na, 1.6410 Tl. Rotation of polarization plane for 1 mm. = 10°28′ Li, 13°9′ Na, 14°19′ Tl. Ref: 119.

Morphine and Cryptopine Alkaloids: Colchicine

Morphine ($C_{17}H_{19}NO_3$) is orthorhombic in both its phases. The metastable phase (I) melts at 197°. Crystals short columnar with many faces, or large thin plates, often bent. Parallel extinction and ± elongation. Z normal to plates. If plates are {100}, then there is good cleavage parallel to 010 and distinct cleavage parallel to 001. (-)2V = 32° *ca.* $N_X = 1.573$, $N_Y = 1.625$, $N_Z = 1.630$, $N_Z - N_X = 0.057$. The stable phase (II) melts above 240° with decomposition, but may sublime before melting. Crystals show {100}, {110}, {011}, {101}; probably not holohedral. $Y = a$; $Z = c$. (+)2V = 56°, r > v strong. $N_X = 1.653$, $N_Y = 1.657$, $N_Z = 1.671$, $N_Z - N_X = 0.018$. Ref: 207.

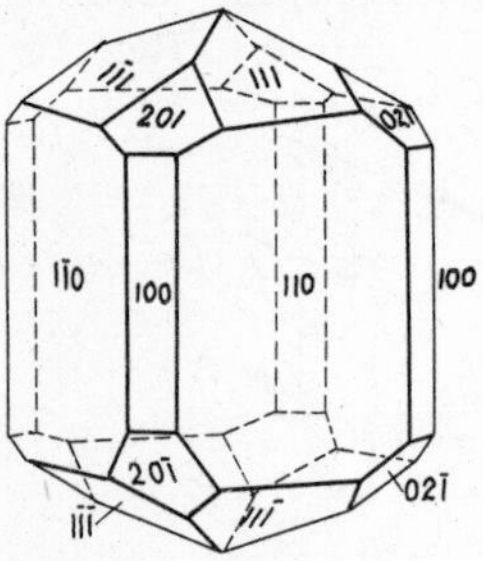

Fig. 142. Corydine.

Morphine monohydrate ($C_{17}H_{19}NO_3 \cdot H_2O$) is orthorhombic disphenoidal with $a{:}b{:}c = 0.4999{:}1{:}0.9285$. Crystals elongated vertically with {110}, {010}, {011}, or {012}. Cleavage on 010. Loses water at 130°. $Y = c$. (-)2V = 66° calc., r > v strong. $N_X = 1.580$ D, $N_Y = 1.625$, $N_Z = 1.645$, $N_Z - N_X = 0.065$, all ± .005. Kofler gives: (-)2V = 74°, $N_X = 1.582$, $N_Y = 1.623$, $N_Z = 1.644$, $N_Z - N_X = 0.062$. Ref: 119, 206, 207, 366.

Morphine with KI, CdI_2 and H_2O forms needles with X parallel with elongation. $N_X = 1.654$, $N_Y = 1.695$, $N_Z > 1.694$ and < 1.734, $N_Z - N_X > 0.040$ and < 0.080. Ref: 523h.

Morphine hydrochloride monohydrate ($C_{17}H_{19}NO_3 \cdot HCl \cdot H_2O$) has parallel extinction and negative elongation. $N_1 = 1.545$, $N_2 = 1.59$, $N_2 - N_1 = 0.045$. Also $N_1 = 1.545$, $N_2 = 1.59$, $N_3 = 1.63$, $N_3 - N_1 = 0.085$. Again: $N_X = 1.540$, $N_Y = 1.590$, $N_Z = 1.635$, $N_Z - N_X = 0.095$. Ref: 34, 35, 343c, 524.

Morphine hydrobromide (monohydrate?) ($C_{17}H_{19}O_3N \cdot HBr \cdot H_2O$?) is orthorhombic with negative elongation. $N_1 = 1.57$, $N_2 = 1.63$, $N_2 - N_1 = 0.06$. Ref: 35.

Morphine sulfate heptahydrate [$(C_{17}H_{19}O_3N)_2 \cdot H_2SO_4 \cdot 7H_2O$] is orthorhombic disphenoidal with $a{:}b{:}c = 0.966{:}1{:}0.281$. Crystals brachydomatic with {011}, {110}, {010}. $X = a$; $Y = b$. Therefore parallel extinction and negative elongation. (-)2E = 69°37′ red, 67°55′ blue. $N_1 = 1.545$, $N_2 = 1.64$, $N_2 - N_1 = 0.095$. Again: $N_X = 1.545$, $N_Y = 1.620$, $N_Z = 1.632$, $N_Z - N_X = 0.087$. Ref: 35, 119, 518.

Morphine tartrate dihydrate ($C_{17}H_{19}O_3N \cdot C_4H_6O_6 \cdot 2H_2O$) has parallel extinction and negative elongation. $N_1 = 1.54$, $N_2 = 1.64$, $N_2 - N_1 = 0.10$. Ref: 35.

Codeine or methylmorphine ($C_{17}H_{18}O_2N \cdot OCH_3$) is orthorhombic disphenoidal with $a:b:c = 0.931:1:0.509$. Crystals equant with {100}, {101}, {010}, {120}, {110}, {101}, etc. Fig. 143. No distinct cleavage. D 1.315. M.P. 155°. $Y = c$; $Z = b$. (+)2V = 77°44′ Li, 75°8′ Na, 72°52′ Tl. $N_X = 1.62$, $N_Y = 1.63$, $N_Z = 1.65$, $N_Z - N_X = 0.03$. Also $N_X = 1.616$ *ca.*, $N_Y = 1.622$ *ca.*, $N_Z = 1.645$ *ca.*, $N_Z - N_X = 0.029$ *ca.* Also $N_1 = 1.56$, $N_2 = 1.66$, $N_2 - N_1 = 0.10$.
Ref: 119, 196, 208, 366.

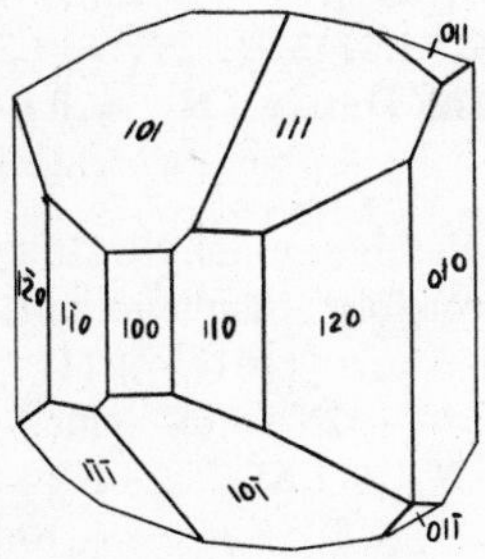

Fig. 143. Codeine.

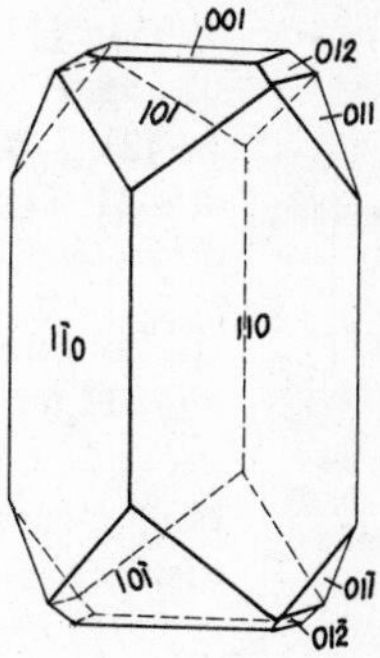

Fig. 144. Codeine monohydrate.

Codeine monohydrate ($C_{18}H_{21}O_3N \cdot H_2O$) is orthorhombic sphenoidal with $a:b:c = 0.960:1:0.835$. Crystals columnar or equant with {110}, {101}, {011}, {001}, etc. Fig. 144. Distinct 001 cleavage. D 1.31 - 1.32. Loses water at 60° or fuses at 64 - 67°. $X = c$; $Y = b$. (-)2V = 53° D, $r < v$. $N_X = 1.5402$ C, 1.5428 D; 1.5507 F, $N_Y = 1.6285$ C, 1.6355 D, 1.6514 F; $N_Z = 1.6730$ C, 1.6838 D, $N_Z - N_X = 0.141$ D (Heydrich). Wherry's data confirm Heydrich's. Kofler gives (-)2V = 80°. Ref: 119, 143, 208, 366.

Codeine hydrochloride monohydrate [$C_{18}H_{21}NO_3 \cdot HCl \cdot H_2O$] has parallel extinction and negative elongation. $N_1 = 1.55$, $N_2 = 1.62$, $N_2 - N_1 = 0.07$.
Ref: 35, 523h.

Codeine hydrobromide monohydrate [$C_{18}H_{21}NO_3 \cdot HBr \cdot H_2O$] has parallel extinction and negative elongation. $N_1 = 1.55$, $N_2 = 1.65$, $N_2 - N_1 = 0.10$. Ref: 35.

Codeine sulfate pentahydrate [$(C_{18}H_{21}NO_3)_2 \cdot H_2SO_4 \cdot 5H_2O$] is orthorhombic disphenoidal with $a:b:c = 0.257:1:0.440$. Crystals prisms with {110}, {010}, {011}. Cleavage on 010. Parallel extinction and negative elongation. $N_1 = 1.545$, $N_2 = 1.62$, $N_2 - N_1 = 0.075$. Also $N_1 = 1.560$, $N_2 = 1.660$, $N_2 - N_1 = 0.100$. Again: $N_X = 1.561$, $N_Y = 1.642$, $N_Z = 1.661$, $N_Z - N_X = 0.100$. ∴ (-)2V = 50° *ca.* Ref: 35, 119, 168, 518, 523h.

Codeine phosphate (dihydrate?) [$C_{18}H_{21}NO_3 \cdot H_3PO_4 \cdot (2H_2O\,?)$] melts at 235°; it has parallel extinction and negative elongation. $N_1 = 1.63$, $N_2 = 1.65$, $N_2 - N_1 = 0.02$. Also $N_1 = 1.545$, $N_2 = 1.634$. Ref: 35, 343c.

Codeine salicylate ($C_{18}H_{21}NO_3 \cdot HOC_6H_4CO_2H$) has parallel extinction and negative elongation. $N_1 = 1.62$, $N_2 = 1.645$, $N_2 - N_1 = 0.025$. Ref: 35.

Isocodeine ($C_{18}H_{21}NO_3$) is orthorhombic disphenoidal with $a:b:c = 0.632:1:0.560$. Crystals prismatic or {010} tablets with {110}, {120}, {011}, etc. Fig. 145. Perfect 010 cleavage. D 1.36. M.P. 171 - 172°. $X = c$; $Y = b$. (-)2V = 88° *ca.* calc. $N_X = 1.6026$ C, 1.6070 D, 1.6149 F, $N_Y = 1.6364$ C, 1.6422 D, 1.6557 F; $N_Z = 1.6697$ C, 1.6754 D; $N_Z - N_X = 0.0684$ D. Ref: 119.

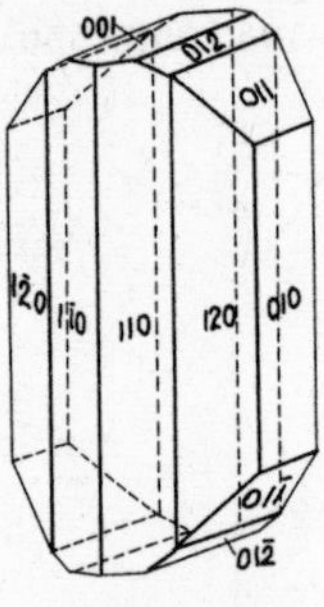

Fig. 145.
Isocodeine.

Pseudocodeine ($C_{18}H_{21}NO_3$) is monoclinic sphenoidal with $a:b:c = 2.194: 1:1.104$, $\beta = 108°14$. Crystals show {100}, {001}, {110}, etc. Fig. 146. Perfect 100 and distinct 001 cleavage. D 1.29. M.P. 181°. $X \wedge c = +22°$; $Z = b$. (+)2V = 77° calc. $N_X = 1.5705$ C, 1.5743 D; $N_Y = 1.5974$ C, 1.6021 D; $N_Z = 1.6426$ C, 1.6472 D; $N_Z - N_X = 0.0729$ D. Ref: 119.

Codethyline or morphine ethyl ether monohydrate ($C_{19}H_{23}NO_3 \cdot H_2O$) is orthorhombic, probably disphenoidal[1], with $a:b:c = 0.687:1:0.543$. Crystals show {101}, {011}, {110}, etc., cleavage on 100. M.P. 83°. (+)2V = 68° calc., r > v distinct. $N_X = 1.55$, $N_Y = 1.58$, $N_Z = 1.65$, $N_Z - N_X = 0.10$. Ref: 366.

Ethylmorphine hydrochloride trihydrate or dionine trihydrate ($C_2H_5 \cdot C_{17}H_{18}NO_3 \cdot HCl \cdot 3H_2O$) melts at about 123°. N = 1.557. Ref: 343c.

Heroine or diacetylmorphine [$C_{17}H_{17}(CH_3CO_2)_2NO$] is orthorhombic disphenoidal with $a:b:c = 0.895:1:0.497$. Crystals {010} tablets with {110}, {111}, {201}, etc. D 1.32. M.P. 172°. $Y = b$. (-)2V = 61.5° calc. $N_X = 1.56$, $N_Y = 1.60$, $N_Z = 1.61$, $N_Z - N_X = 0.05$ D. Ref: 366.

Diacetylmorphine hydrochloride monohydrate [$C_{21}H_{23}NO_5 \cdot HCl \cdot H_2O$] melts at 231° C. $N_1 = 1.576$, $N_2 = 1.591$, $N_2 - N_1 = 0.015$. Ref: 343c.

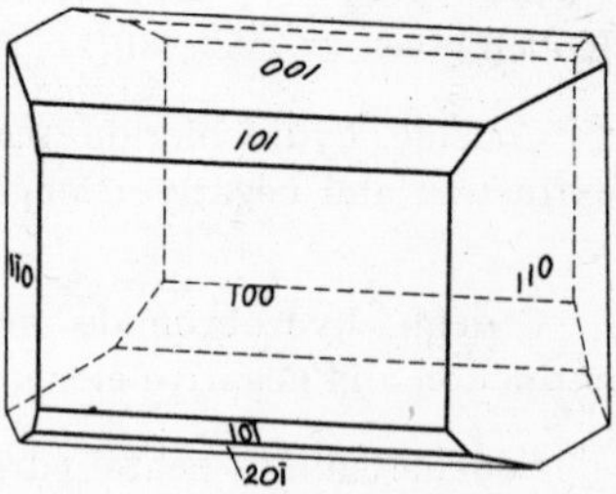

Fig. 146. Pseudocodeine.

Thebaine [$C_{17}H_{15}NO(OCH_3)_2$] is orthorhombic in rectangular plates with parallel extinction and negative elongation. It may be crystallized by sublimation at 170 - 180° under atmospheric pressure and at 1 mm. distance. It has two rectangular cleavages (010 and 001?). (+?)2V = large. $N_1 = 1.63$, $N_2 = 1.69$, $N_2 - N_1 = 0.06$. Also (+)2V = 50°, r < v. $N_X = 1.62$ *ca.*, $N_Y = 1.63$ *ca.*, $N_Z = 1.68$ *ca.*, $N_Z - N_X = 0.06$ *ca.* Ref: 193, 208.

Thebaine tartrate [$(C_{19}H_{21}NO_3)_2 \cdot C_4H_6O_6$] is probably biaxial with parallel extinction and negative elongation. $N_1 = 1.59$, $N_2 = 1.62$, $N_2 - N_1 = 0.03$. Ref: 35.

[1] a and b interchanged to make $b > a > c$.

Apomorphine hydrochloride (+ 0.75H_2O ?) ($C_{17}H_{17}NO_2 \cdot HCl$) has parallel extinction and positive elongation. $N_1 = 1.66$, $N_2 = 1.69$, $N_2 - N_1 = 0.03$. Also $N_1 = 1.636$, $N_2 = 1.662$, $N_Z = 1.694$. Ref: 35, 343c.

Apomorphine sulfate ($C_{17}H_{17}NO_2 \cdot H_2SO_4$) is probably orthorhombic in prisms with parallel extinction and positive elongation. $N_1 = 1.66$, $N_2 = 1.70$, $N_2 - N_1 = 0.04$. Ref: 196.

Colchicine ($C_{22}H_{25}NO_6$) has $N_1 = 1.63$, $N_2 = 1.65$, $N_2 - N_1 = 0.02$. Ref: 34, 35.

Carboline Alkaloids

Quebrachine or yohimbine $(C_{21}H_{26}N_2O_3)_2$ is probably biaxial with parallel extinction and negative elongation. M.P. 228°. $N_1 = 1.545$, $N_2 = 1.67$, $N_2 - N_1 = 0.125$. It is orthorhombic with (+)2V = 42°. $N_X = 1.548$, $N_Y = 1.563$, $N_Z = 1.688$, $N_Z - N_X = 0.140$. Ref: 35, 295.

Yohimbine hydrochloride ($C_{21}H_{26}N_2O_3 \cdot HCl$) forms thin plates and crystals showing prisms and acute pyramids. M.P. 285 - 290°. It is orthorhombic with parallel extinction and negative elongation. (+)2V = moderate. $N_X = 1.580 - 1.585$, $N_Y = 1.590 - 1.600$, $N_Z = 1.630 - 1.635$, $N_Z - N_X = 0.045 - 0.055$. Ref: 239, 295.

Yohimbine chloroacetate ($C_{21}H_{26}N_2O_3 \cdot ClCH_2CO_2H$) is triclinic in rod-shaped crystals with inclined extinction; $Y \wedge b = 34°$. (+)2V = 35° calc. $N_X = 1.530$, $N_Y = 1.542$, $N_Z = 1.654$, $N_Z - N_X = 0.124$. Colorless. Ref: 295.

Yohimbine picrate [$C_{21}H_{26}N_2O_3 \cdot (NO_2)_3C_6H_2OH$] forms rod-shaped crystals with parallel extinction and negative elongation. 2V = large. $N_1 = 1.55 - 1.56$, $N_2 = 1.68 - 1.70$, $N_2 - N_1 = 0.12 - 0.15$. Ref: 295.

Vasicine tartrate or peganine tartrate ($C_{11}H_{12}N_2O \cdot C_4H_6O_6$) has parallel extinction and negative elongation. $N_1 = 1.475$, $N_2 = 1.67$, $N_2 - N_1 = 0.195$. Ref: 34, 35.

Alkaloids of Ergot, Pilocarpine, and Eserine

Ergotoxine with ergosinine [$(C_{35}H_{41}N_5O_6) \cdot n(C_{30}H_{37}N_5O_5)$] is monoclinic in plates elongated along *b*. M.P. 170 - 171°. The optic plane is 010; elongation negative. (+)2V = 60°, $r < v$. $N_Y = 1.545$. Ref: 204.

Ergotoxine benzene solvate or hydroergotinine (?) benzene solvate ($C_{35}H_{41}N_5O_6 \cdot nC_6H_6$) is orthorhombic in {010} plates with {110}, {001}, and {101}. Unstable even at room temperature because of loss of benzene. Unchanged by rapid heating to about 100°; melts at about 165 - 180°. $Y = b$; $Z = c$. (+)2V = moderate. $N_X = 1.56$ *ca.*, $N_Y = 1.57$ *ca.*, $N_Z = 1.60$ *ca.*, $N_Z - N_X = 0.04$ *ca.* but the indices change rather rapidly with increase in the optic angle as decomposition occurs. Ref: 202.

Ergotinine ($C_{35}H_{39}N_5O_5$) is orthorhombic in plates of varied habit with {100}, {110}, {011}, {010}, {001}. Crystallizes easily from various solvents, including alcohol, ether, acetone, benzene, and chloroform. Perfect 001 and 100 cleavages. Becomes colored yellow to brown above 150° and isotropic at 210 - 215°. X = *c*; Y = *a*. (+)2V = 30°. N_X = 1.575, N_Y = 1.580, N_Z = 1.655, $N_Z - N_X$ = 0.080. [α] = - 36.5° (in chloroform). When crystallized from benzene, ergotinine seems to have two crystal phases. One is granular with radial structure, which inverts at 90 - 100° to the stable phase already described. Moreover, large spindle-shaped crystals may form which alter easily and may be a solvate of ergotinine and benzene. Ref: 202.

Ergocristine with ergosinine [($C_{35}H_{39}N_5O_5$)·*n*($C_{30}H_{37}N_5O_5$)] is monoclinic in plates elongated along *b*. M.P. 171 - 172°. Y = *b*. (+)2V = 80°, r < v. N_Y = 1.565. Ref: 204.

Ergocristine ($C_{35}H_{39}N_5O_5$) is monoclinic in plates elongated along *b*. Y = *b*. (+)2V = 50°. N_X = 1.585, N_Y = ?, N_Z > 1.659, $N_Z - N_X$ > 0.066. [α] = + 186° (in chloroform). Ref: 204.

Ergosinine methyl alcohol solvate or ergoclavinine [($C_{30}H_{37}N_5O_5$)·*n*(CH_3OH)] is orthorhombic in {100} and {010} plates with pyramid faces. M.P. 190 - 192°. Soluble in high index immersion liquids. X = *b*; Y = *c*. (-)2V = 80°, r > v. N_X = 1.54, N_Y = 1.603, N_Z = 1.64 calc., $N_Z - N_X$ = 0.10 calc. Ref: 203.

Ergosinine ($C_{30}H_{37}N_5O_5$) is orthorhombic in {100} tablets with {010} and domes or pyramids. M.P. 210 - 215° (228°). Readily soluble in chloroform and acetone; less easily in benzene and ethyl alcohol. X = *a*; Y = *c*. (+)2V = 36°, r < v. N_X = 1.570, N_Y = 1.578, N_Z = 1.656, $N_Z - N_X$ = 0.086. [α] = -420° (in chloroform). Ref: 203.

Ergosinine with ergosine [($C_{30}H_{37}N_5O_5$)·*n*($C_{30}H_{37}N_5O_5$)] is monoclinic sphenoidal in plates elongated along *b* M.P. 169 - 170°. Y = *b*; elongation negative. (+)2V = 60°, r < v. N_X = ?, N_Y = 1.546, N_Z = 1.56 - 1.57. Ref: 204.

Ergosine ($C_{30}H_{37}N_5O_5$) is orthorhombic in {100} tablets with {110} and {001}. M.P. 208 - 212° dec. Readily soluble in chloroform; less soluble in methyl alcohol, acetone, ethyl acetate, and benzene. Crystallizes slowly from ethyl acetate, acetone, methyl, and ethyl alcohol. Y = *b*; Z = *c*. (-)2V = 18° (red), r < v very strong. N_X = 1.520, N_Y = 1.601, N_Z = 1.603, $N_Z - N_X$ = 0.083, measured with the use of a Lifa filter 200c. Shows abnormal brown interference colors in 100 plates. [α] = + 161° (in chloroform). Ref: 203.

Ergotamine water solvate ($C_{30}H_{35}N_5O_5 \cdot nH_2O$) is monoclinic sphenoidal. Crystals elongated along *c* and plainly hemimorphic with {100}, {011}, {010}, and {001}. Crystals separate into polygonal plates at 60° and melt at 174 - 176°. Soluble in pyridine. Distinct 001 cleavage. X ∧ *c* = 50° *ca.*; Z = *b*. (-)2V = 75°. N_X = 1.565 calc., N_Y = 1.626 calc., N_Z = 1.660 calc., (N_X' = 1.600 along *c*), $N_Z - N_X$ = 0.095 calc. Ref: 201.

Ergotamine with ergotinine $[(C_{33}H_{35}N_5O_5)\cdot n(C_{35}H_{39}N_5O_5)]$ is monoclinic in plates elongated along *b*. M.P. 164 - 165°. Y = *b*; elongation negative. (+)2V = small, r < v. $N_Y = 1.686$. Ref: 204.

Ergotamine with ergosinine $[(C_{33}H_{35}N_5O_5)\cdot n(C_{30}H_{37}N_5O_5)]$ is monoclinic in plates elongated along *b*. M.P. 176 - 177°. Y = *b*; elongation negative. (+)2V = 80°. $N_Y = 1.570$. Ref: 204.

Ergotamine tartrate $(C_{33}H_{35}N_5O_5\cdot H_2C_4H_4O_6)$ is orthorhombic; it has $N_1 = 1.518$, $N_2 = 1.625$, $N_2 - N_1 = 0.107$. Colorless; darkens at 177° and decomposes at 184°C. Ref: 518.

Ergotamine acetone dihydrate $[(C_{33}H_{35}N_5O_5)\cdot 2(CH_3)_2CO\cdot 2H_2O]$ is monoclinic sphenoidal. Crystals lie on {100}, or rarely on {001} and then show {100} and {110}. β is nearly 90°. Loses birefringence at 60°, becomes yellow at 140°, and melts at 172 - 174°. Y = *b*; Z ∧ *c* = 15°. (+ ?)2V = near 90° with distinct dispersion. $N_X' < 1.540$ ($N_X = 1.533$ calc.), $N_Y = 1.580$, $N_Z' > 1.621$ ($N_Z = 1.627$ calc.), $N_Z' - N_X' > 0.081$ ($N_Z - N_X = 0.093$ calc.). Ref: 201, 306.

Ergotamine pyridine solvate $(C_{33}H_{35}N_5O_5\cdot nC_5H_5N)$ is monoclinic sphenoidal in crystals with {100}, {110}, {001}. M.P. 172 - 176°. Good 010 cleavage. Y = *b*; Z ∧ *c* = moderate. (+)2V = 80°. $N_X < 1.579$ calc., $N_Y = 1.604$, $N_{Z'} = 1.640$ (measured on 100), $N_Z' - N_X > 0.061$. Ref: 201.

Ergotamine benzene solvate $[(C_{33}H_{35}N_5O_5\cdot n(C_6H_6)]$ is orthorhombic in crystals with {100}, {110}, {101}, and {001}. Becomes cloudy at 130 - 135° and melts at 168 - 172° to brown liquid. X = *a*; Y = *c*. (-)2V = 56°, r < v. $N_X = 1.545$, $N_Y = 1.616$, $N_Z = 1.635$, $N_Z - N_X = 0.90$. Ref: 201.

Ergotamine methyl alcohol solvate $(C_{33}H_{35}N_5O_5\cdot nCH_3OH)$ is monoclinic sphenoidal. Crystals show {100}, {001}, {010}, etc. β = 140° *ca.* M.P. 208 - 210° dec. Y = *b*; Z ∧ *c* = - 5°. (+)2V = 60°. $N_X < 1.595$, $N_Y = 1.610$, $N_Z = 1.660$, $N_Z - N_X > 0.066$. Ref: 201.

Ergotamine ethyl alcohol solvate $(C_{33}H_{35}N_5O_5\cdot nC_2H_5OH)$ is monoclinic sphenoidal, very much like the methyl alcohol solvate. Crystals show {100}, {001}, {010}, {011}. β = 140° *ca.* M.P. 208 - 210°. Y = *b*; Z ∧ *c* = - 5° *ca.* (+)2V = 70° *ca.* $N_X = 1.604$ calc., $N_Y = 1.620$, $N_Z = 1.653$ calc., $N_Z - N_X =$ 0.049 calc. ($N_{Z'} = 1.652$, $N_X' = ?$, measured on 100). Ref: 201.

Ergotamine dichloroethylene solvate $(C_{33}H_{35}N_5O_5\cdot nClCH:CHCl)$ is orthorhombic in crystals showing {001}, {100}, {110}, etc. Good 010, 100, and 001 cleavages. M.P. 182 - 186°. Y = *b*; Z = *c*. (-)2V = 50° *ca.* All indices > 1.60, $N_Z - N_X$ weak. Ref: 201.

Ergotamine ethyl ether solvate $(C_{33}H_{35}N_5O_5\cdot n(C_2H_5)_2O)$ is monoclinic (or triclinic) in prisms with M.P. 183 - 185°. The elongation is ± with Y ∧ *c* = 15°. $N_Y = 1.602$ *ca.* Ref: 201.

Ergotaminine $(C_{33}H_{35}N_5O_5)$ is monoclinic sphenoidal in lamellar or columnar crystals with {100}, {110}, {010}, etc. M.P. above 220°. Y = *b*. (+)2V = 60° *ca.* $N_X < 1.590$, $N_Y = 1.655$, $N_Z > 1.855$ calc., $N_Z - N_X > 0.265$. Ref: 201.

Ergometrine or ergonovine ($C_{19}H_{23}O_2N_3$) crystallizes from solvents in six-sided or rhomboidal plates, often in aggregates, which darken at about 190° and fuse at about 204°. They are orthorhombic (or nearly so). Z is normal to six-sided plates which have four interior angles of 123° and two of 132°. The optic plane and X (nearly ?) bisect the larger angles. (+)2V = ?. $N_X = 1.622$, $N_Y = 1.655$, $N_Z = ?$ $[\alpha] = +44°$ (in chloroform). Ref: 204a.

Ergometrine ethyl acetate solvate or ergonovine ethyl acetate solvate ($C_{19}H_{23}O_2N_3 \cdot nCH_3CO_2C_2H_5$) forms orthorhombic crystals at room temperature which usually lie on 010. Perfect 010 and distinct transverse 001 cleavages. Inverts at 100° or fuses at about 160°. After inversion, fuses at 200°. X = *c*; Y = *b*. (+)2V = moderate. $N_X = 1.536$, $N_Y = ?$, $N_Z > 1.659$, $N_Z - N_X > 0.123$. At moderate temperature pseudo-orthorhombic rhomboidal plates form which fuse at 130 – 132° or invert to a fibrous aggregate fusing at 200°. The optic plane is parallel to the short diagonal of the rhomb, which is divided into four sectors under crossed nicols, whose extinction directions differ only about 3°. (–)2V = large. $N_1 = 1.642$, $N_2 > 1.659$, $N_2 - N_1 > 0.017$. These two types seem to be addition products in different ratios, not different phases of the same composition. From boiling acetic acid still different crystals are formed, which are almost certainly pure ergometrine, since crystals of the same kind can also be obtained from various other solvents. Ref: 204a.

Ergocristine acetone solvate ($C_{35}H_{39}O_5N_5 \cdot nCH_3COCH_3$) forms orthorhombic prisms with {100}, {110}, {001}. Alters at 145° and fuses at 160 – 165°. Y = *a*; Z = *c*. (+)2V = rather large. $N_X = 1.552$, $N_Y = 1.587$, $N_Z > 1.659$, $N_Z - N_X > 0.107$. Ref: 204a.

Pseudoergotinine ($C_{35}H_{39}O_5N_5$?) forms orthorhombic crystals with {100}, {110}, {001}, etc., with distinct 001 cleavage. Alters at about 200° to 214°. The optic plane is 100 in red light and 001 in blue light because of strong dispersion, which also causes abnormal interference colors. Z = *b*. (+)2V = small (in 100) to 0 – 10° (in 001). $N_X = 1.573$ *ca.*, N_Y nearly $= N_Z = 1.645$ *ca.*, $N_Z - N_X = 0.072$ *ca.* Ref: 204a.

Ergocristine benzene solvate ($C_{35}H_{39}O_5N_5 \cdot nC_6H_6$) forms orthorhombic crystals with {100}, {010}, {110}, etc. Loses benzene at 30° and fuses at 160 – 165°. Soluble in high index liquids. Y = *c*; Z = *a*. (–)2V = 74°, r > v. $N_X = 1.58$ *ca.*, $N_Y = 1.60$ *ca.*, $N_Z = 1.64$ calc., $N_Z - N_X = 0.06$ *ca.* calc. Ref: 204a.

Ergometrine ethyl alcohol solvate or ergonovine ethyl alcohol solvate ($C_{19}H_{23}O_2N_3 \cdot nC_2H_5OH$) forms monoclinic crystals having $\beta = 132°$, often elongated along *b*. Distinct 100 cleavage. Alters at about 135 – 140° and fuses at 156 – 158°. X = *b*; $Z \wedge c = +15°$ *ca.* (+)2V = moderate. $N_X = 1.538$. Ergometrine and propyl alcohol give very similar crystals. Ref: 204a.

Ergometrine acetone solvate or ergonovine acetone solvate ($C_{19}H_{23}O_2N_3 \cdot nCH_3COCH_3$) gives monoclinic crystals similar to those of ergometrine and ethyl alcohol; they alter at about 130° and fuse at about 160°. Commonly elongated along *b*. X = *b*. (+)2V = 45°, r > v. $N_X = 1.544$, $N_Y = 1.56$, $N_Z > 1.70$ (indices and optic angle give 1.664), $N_Z - N_X$ probably about 0.16. Ref: 204a.

Ergometrine benzene solvate or ergonovine benzene solvate ($C_{19}H_{23}O_2N_3 \cdot nC_6H_6$) forms monoclinic crystals very much like those of ergometrine and ethyl alcohol; they alter at 50° and fuse at 156 - 158°. X = *b*; $Z \wedge c = +15°$ *ca.* (+)2V = rather large. $N_X = 1.553$, $N_Y = 1.610$, $N_Z > 1.70$, $N_Z - N_X > 0.147$. Ref: 204a.

Ergometrinine ethyl acetate solvate ($C_{19}H_{23}O_2N_3 \cdot nCH_3CO_2C_2H_5$) gives apparently orthorhombic crystals which are rhomboidal when lying on 010 and six-sided when on 001 or 110. X = *b*; Y = *c*. (-)2V = 55°. $N_X = 1.572$, $N_Y > 1.659$, N_Z = ?, $N_Z - N_X$ = ? (If $N_Y = 1.672$, N_Z would be 1.69 *ca.*) Ref: 204a.

Ergotoxine acetone solvate ($C_{35}H_{39}O_5N_5 \cdot nCH_3COCH_3$) forms orthorhombic crystals. Y = *a*; Z = *c*. N_X = ?, $N_Y = 1.580$, $1.659 > N_Z > 1.63$. (Soluble in high index liquids.) Ref: 204a.

Ergocristinine ($C_{35}H_{39}O_5N_5$) forms orthorhombic needles with {100}, {110}, etc. Alters at 210° and fuses at 215°. X = *c*; Y = *a*. (+)2V = 50°, r > v distinct. $N_X = 1.585$, $N_Y = 1.602$, $N_Z = 1.68$ calc., $N_Z - N_X = 0.095$. [α] = — 365° (in chloroform). Ref: 204a.

Ergocristinine alcohol solvate ($C_{35}H_{39}O_5N_5 \cdot nC_2H_5OH$) forms needles and plates with parallel extinction. Y=*a*. 2V=15°, r > v. $N_Z \leqslant 1.659$. Ref: 204a.

Pilocarpine hydrochloride ($C_{11}H_{16}N_2O_2 \cdot HCl$) has parallel extinction and positive elongation. $N_1 = 1.535$, $N_2 = 1.61$, $N_2 - N_1 = 0.075$. Again: $N_X = 1.515$, $N_Y = 1.570$, $N_Z = 1.594$, $N_Z - N_X = 0.081$: ∴ (-)2V = 66° calc. Ref: 34, 35, 524.

Pilocarpine hydrobromide ($C_{11}H_{16}N_2O_2 \cdot HBr$) is biaxial with parallel extinction and negative elongation. (+)2V = large. $N_X = 1.535$, $N_Y = 1.55$, $N_Z = 1.63$, $N_Z - N_X = 0.095$. Ref: 34, 35.

Pilocarpine sulfate [$(C_{11}H_{16}N_2O_2)_2 \cdot H_2SO_4$)] has parallel extinction and negative elongation. $N_1 = 1.55$, $N_2 = 1.615$, $N_2 - N_1 = 0.065$. Ref: 34, 35.

Pilocarpine nitrate ($C_{11}H_{16}N_2O_2 \cdot HNO_3$) has parallel extinction and positive elongation. $N_1 = 1.55$, $N_2 = 1.60$, $N_2 - N_1 = 0.05$. Again: $N_X = 1.475$, $N_Y = 1.588$, $N_Z = 1.608$, $N_Z - N_X = 0.123$: ∴ (-)2V = 45° *ca.* Ref: 34, 518.

Pilocarpine borate ($C_{11}H_{16}N_2O_2 \cdot HBO_3$) has parallel extinction and negative elongation. $N_1 = 1.51$, $N_2 = 1.52$, $N_2 - N_1 = 0.01$. Ref: 34, 35.

Pilocarpine (iso-?)valerate ($C_{11}H_{16}N_2O_2 \cdot C_4H_9CO_2H$) has parallel extinction and positive elongation. $N_1 = 1.51$, $N_2 = 1.55$, $N_2 - N_1 = 0.04$. Ref: 34, 35.

Pilocarpine salicylate ($C_{11}H_{16}N_2O_2 \cdot HOC_6H_4CO_2H$) has parallel extinction and positive elongation. $N_1 = 1.54$, $N_2 = 1.61$, $N_2 - N_1 = 0.07$. Ref: 34, 35.

Pilocarpidine nitrate ($C_{10}H_{14}N_2O_2 \cdot HNO_3$) has parallel extinction and positive elongation with $N_1 = 1.55$, $N_2 = 1.605$, $N_2 - N_1 = 0.055$. Ref: 34, 35.

Aconitine ($C_{34}H_{45}NO_{11}$) is orthorhombic sphenoidal[1] with $a:b:c = 0.917:1:0.714$. Crystals show {100}, {010}, {111}, {120}, etc. Cleavage on 010. M.P. 198°, Negative elongation. Y = *a*, Z = *b*. (+)2V = 36° Na. 2E = 47°0′ Li, 56°10′ Na. 65°5′ Tl. $N_1 = 1.56$, $N_2 = 1.57$, $N_2 - N_1 = 0.01$. Ref: 23, 119, 196.

Aconitine hydrochloride hemipentahydrate ($C_{34}H_{45}NO_{11} \cdot HCl \cdot 2.5\ H_2O$) is orthorhombic disphenoidal with $a:b:c = 0.875:1:1.304$. Crystals {001} plates with {111}, {100}, {102}. Parallel extinction and positive elongation. $N_1 = 1.56$, $N_2 = 1.58$, $N_2 - N_1 = 0.02$. Ref: 34, 35, 119.

Aconitine hydrobromide hemipentahydrate ($C_{34}H_{45}NO_{11} \cdot HBr \cdot 2.5H_2O$) is orthorhombic disphenoidal with $a:b:c = 0.865:1:1.310$. Crystals {001} plates with {111}, {100}, etc. (+)2V = small. $N_X = 1.545$, $N_Y = 1.55$, $N_Z = 1.61$, $N_Z - N_X = 0.065$ D. Ref: 34, 35, 119.

Aconitine nitrate ($C_{34}H_{45}NO_{11} \cdot HNO_3$) is granular with $N_1 = 1.54$, $N_2 = 1.61$, $N_2 - N_1 = 0.07$. Ref: 34, 35.

Aconitine sulfate [$(C_{34}H_{45}NO_{11})_2 \cdot H_2SO_4$] has parallel extinction and negative elongation. $N_1 = 1.54$, $N_2 = 1.55$, $N_2 - N_1 = 0.01$. Ref: 34, 35.

Aconitine phosphate [$(C_{34}H_{45}NO_{11})_2 \cdot H_3PO_4$] has parallel extinction and positive elongation. $N_1 = 1.555$, $N_2 = 1.60$, $N_2 - N_1 = 0.045$. Ref: 34, 35.

Aconitine arsenate [$(C_{34}H_{45}NO_{11})_2 \cdot H_3AsO_4$] has parallel extinction and positive elongation. $N_1 = 1.600$, $N_2 = 1.605$, $N_2 - N_1 = 0.005$. Ref: 34, 35.

Aconitine salicylate ($C_{34}H_{45}NO_{11} \cdot HOC_6H_4CO_2H$) is granular with $N_1 = 1.53$, $N_2 = 1.56$, $N_2 - N_1 = 0.03$. Ref: 34, 35.

Physostigmine or eserine ($C_{15}H_{21}N_3O_2$) is orthorhombic disphenoidal with $a:b:c = 0.977:1:0.498$. Crystals show {110}, {101}, {1$\bar{1}$1}, {100}, {011}. M.P. 106°. X = *c*; Y = *b*. (−)2V = 79°3′ Li, 77°42′ Na, 76°16′ Tl. N_Y = 1.5976 Li, 1.6023 Na, 1.6073 Tl. Kley gives (+)2V = 20°; also $N_1 = 1.54$, $N_2 = 1.66$, with positive elongation. (Probably $N_X = 1.54$, $N_Z = 1.66$, $N_Z - N_X = 0.12$. ∴ $N_Y = 1.55$ – A.N.W.) Ref: 119, 147, 196.

Physostigmine (or eserine) hydrochloride ($C_{15}H_{21}N_3O_2 \cdot HCl$) is granular with $N_1 = 1.55$, $N_2 = 1.56$, $N_2 - N_1 = 0.01$. Ref: 34, 35.

Physostigmine (or eserine) hydrobromide ($C_{15}H_{21}N_3O_2 \cdot HBr$) has parallel extinction and positive elongation with $N_1 = 1.625$, $N_2 = 1.64$, $N_2 - N_1 = 0.015$. Ref: 34, 35.

Physostigmine (or eserine) salicylate ($C_{15}H_{21}N_3O_2 \cdot HOC_6H_4CO_2H$) has parallel extinction and negative elongation. $N_1 = 1.56$, $N_2 = 1.66$, $N_2 - N_1 = 0.10$. Also $N_1 = 1.559$, $N_2 = 1.649$. Ref: 34, 35, 343c.

---

[1] *a* and *b* interchanged to make $b > a > c$.

Emetine hydrochloride ($C_{29}H_{40}N_2O_4 \cdot HCl$) has parallel extinction and positive elongation. $N_1 = 1.565$, $N_2 = 1.57$, $N_2 - N_1 = 0.005$. Ref: 34, 35.

Cytisine ($C_{11}H_{14}N_2O$) is orthorhombic with $a:b:c = 0.677:1:0.557$. Crystals short prisms with {110}, {100}, {101}, etc. Fig. 147. No good cleavage. M.P. 153°. The optic plane is 100; $Z = c$. $(+)2V = 61°36'$ $r < v$ very strong. $N_1 = 1.64$, $N_2 = 1.73$, $N_2 - N_1 = 0.09$. Ref: 119, 196.

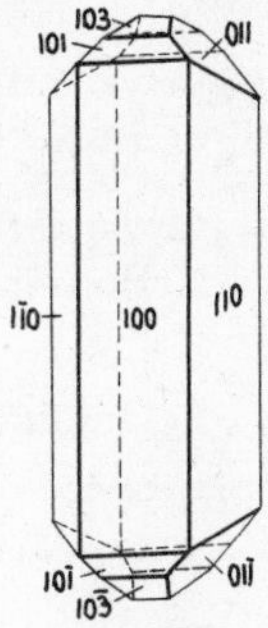

Fig. 147. Cytisine.

Cytisine hydrochloride trihydrate ($C_{11}H_{14}N_2O \cdot 4HCl \cdot 3H_2O$) is biaxial with parallel extinction and $(-)2V$ = very large. $N_X = 1.60$, $N_Y = 1.65$, $N_Z = 1.69$, $N_Z - N_X = 0.09$. Ref: 34.

Alkaloids of unknown constitution

Pseudoyohimbine ($C_{21}H_{26}N_2O_3$) is orthorhombic[1] with $a:b:c = 0.617:1:0.592$. Crystals {010} tablets with {111}, {011}, etc. Perfect 010 and another (111 ?) distinct cleavage. $X = c$; $Y = a$. $(-)2V = 80°30'$ calc. $N_X = 1.571$ D, $N_Y = 1.642$, $N_Z = 1.655$, $N_Z - N_X = 0.084$. Ref: 153.

Sabadinine ($C_{27}H_{43}NO_8$) melts at 160°. It has parallel extinction and positive elongation. $N_1 = 1.53$, $N_2 = 1.55$, $N_2 - N_1 = 0.02$. Ref: 34, 35.

Sabadinine hydrochloride ($C_{27}H_{43}NO_8 \cdot HCl$) is granular with no distinct prism edges. $N_1 = 1.57$, $N_2 = 1.595$, $N_2 - N_1 = 0.025$. Ref: 34, 35.

Sabadinine bisulfate ($C_{27}H_{43}NO_8 \cdot 2H_2SO_4$) is biaxial with parallel extinction. $N_X = 1.555$, $N_Y = 1.56$, $N_Z = 1.575$, $N_Z - N_X = 0.020$; $\therefore$ $(+)2V$ = large. Ref: 34, 35.

Sabadine ($C_{29}H_{51}NO_8$) is granular with two indices between 1.52 and 1.53; $N_Z - N_X$ = weak, probably. Ref: 34, 35.

Sabadine hydrochloride ($C_{29}H_{51}NO_8 \cdot HCl$) is granular with no distinct prism edges. $N_1 = 1.54$, $N_2 = 1.56$, $N_2 - N_1 = 0.02$. Ref: 34, 35.

Sabadine nitrate ($C_{29}H_{51}NO_8 \cdot HNO_3$) is probably monoclinic with an extinction angle of 29°. $N_1 = 1.545$, $N_2 = 1.56$, $N_2 - N_1 = 0.015$. Ref: 34, 35.

Sabadine sulfate ($C_{29}H_{51}NO_8H_2SO_4$) has one index, $N = 1.54$. Ref: 34, 35.

Conessine ($C_{24}H_{40}N_2$) is granular with $N_1 = 1.56$, $N_2 = 1.615$, $N_2 - N_1 = 0.055$. Ref: 34, 35.

Gelseminine hydrochloride ($C_{42}H_{47}O_{14}N \cdot HCl$) is biaxial with parallel extinction. $(+)2V$ = large. $N_X = 1.62$, $N_Y = 1.63$, $N_Z = 1.645$, $N_Z - N_X = 0.025$. Ref: 34, 35.

Gelseminine hydrobromide ($C_{42}H_{47}O_{14}N \cdot HBr$) has parallel extinction and negative elongation. $N_1 = 1.65$, $N_2 = 1.675$, $N_2 - N_1 = 0.025$. Ref: 34, 35.

---

[1] *a b c* changed to *a c b* to make $b > a > c$.

Anagyrine hydrobromide ($C_{15}H_{22}ON_2 \cdot HBr$) is granular with $N_1 = 1.66$, $N_2 = 1.67$, $N_2 - N_1 = 0.01$. Ref: 34, 35.

Ditaine tetrahydrate or echitamine tetrahydrate ($C_{22}H_{28}O_4N_2 \cdot 4H_2O$) has parallel extinction and positive elongation. $N_1 = 1.615$, $N_2 = 1.65$, $N_2 - N_1 = 0.035$. Ref: 34, 35.

Oxyacanthine ($C_{19}H_{21}NO_3$) has parallel extinction and positive elongation. $N_1 = 1.62$, $N_2 = 1.69$, $N_2 - N_1 = 0.07$. Ref: 34, 35.

Oxyacanthine sulfate hexahydrate [$(C_{19}H_{21}NO_3)_2 \cdot H_2SO_4 \cdot 6H_2O$] has parallel extinction and positive elongation. $N_1 = 1.57$, $N_2 = 1.63$, $N_2 - N_1 = 0.06$. Ref: 35.

Solanidine ($C_{27}H_{43}NO_9$?) has parallel extinction with $N_1 = 1.49$, $N_2 = 1.53$, $N_2 - N_1 = 0.04$. Ref: 33a.

Solanine ($C_{52}H_{91}NO_{18}$?) is granular with $N_1 = 1.52$, $N_2 = 1.53$, $N_2 - N_1 = 0.01$. Ref. 35.

Cevadine or veratrine ($C_{37}H_{53}O_{11}N$) is described as amorphous with M.P. 150 – 155°, and also as turning deep green and then brown on heating, but it is also said to have $N_1 = 1.52$, $N_2 = 1.55$, $N_2 - N_1 = 0.03$. Ref: 23, 239.

Strychnos Alkaloids

Strychnine ($C_{21}H_{22}N_2O_2$) is orthorhombic disphenoidal with $a:b:c = 0.983:1:0.931$. Space group $P2_12_12_1$; a 11.92, b 12.13, c 11.39 Å. U.C. 4. Crystals equant or prisms with {110}, {101}, {011}, {111}, etc. Fig. 148. Imperfect 110 cleavage. D 1.36. M.P. 265°. Y = a; Z = c. Parallel extinction and positive elongation. (+ ?)2V = very large. $N_X = 1.61$, $N_Y = 1.68$, $N_Z = 1.74$, $N_Z - N_X = 0.13$. Kofler gives $N_X = 1.612$, $N_Y = 1.653$, $N_Z < 1.74$, $N_Z - N_X < 0.128$. Mayrhofer gives $N_X = 1.620$, $N_Y = 1.631$, $N_Z = 1.73$, $N_Z - N_X = 0.110$. Ref: 119, 206, 239, 386, 545.

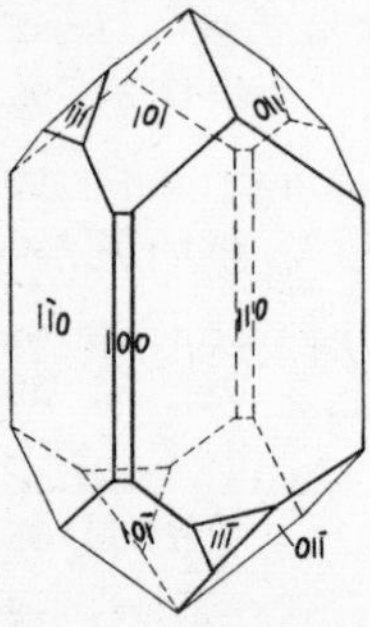

Fig. 148. Strychnine.

Strychnine hydrobromide monohydrate ($C_{21}H_{22}N_2O_2 \cdot HBr \cdot H_2O$) is monoclinic in needles with negative elongation. (+)2V = small, with weak dispersion. $N_X = 1.646$, $N_Y = 1.650$, $N_Z = 1.73$ *ca.*, $N_Z - N_X = 0.084$; ∴ (+)2V = 20° calc. Ref: 276a.

Strychnine hydroiodide monohydrate ($C_{21}H_{22}N_2O_2 \cdot HI \cdot H_2O$) is monoclinic in stout needles with negative elongation. (+)2V = small, r > v. $N_X = 1.661$ (1.657), $N_Y = 1.665$, $N_Z = 1.73$, $N_Z - N_X = 0.069$. ∴ (+)2V = 30° calc. Also $N_1 = 1.66$, $N_2 = 1.69$, $N_2 - N_1 = 0.03$. Ref: 35, 276a.

Strychnine hydrochloride dihydrate ($C_{21}H_{22}N_2O_2 \cdot HCl \cdot 2H_2O$) is orthorhombic in fine needles with negative elongation. (+)2V = large, r > v weak. $N_X = 1.609$, $N_Y = 1.627$, $N_Z = 1.662$, $N_Z - N_X = 0.053$. ∴ (+)2V = 72° calc. Ref: 276a.

Strychnine chlorate monohydrate ($C_{21}H_{22}N_2O_2 \cdot HClO_3 \cdot H_2O$) is monoclinic in fine needles with negative elongation and X = *b*. (+)2V = moderate, with horizontal dispersion. $N_X = 1.605$, $N_Y = 1.611$, $N_Z = 1.663$, $N_Z - N_X = 0.058$. ∴ (+)2V = 37°, calc. Ref: 276a.

Strychnine perchlorate monohydrate ($C_{21}H_{22}N_2O_2 \cdot HClO_4 \cdot H_2O$) is monoclinic in stout needles with ± elongation and an extinction angle of 22°. (+)2V = moderate, with inclined dispersion. $N_X = 1.589$, $N_Y = 1.598$. $N_Z = 1.654$, $N_Z - N_X = 0.065$. ∴ (+)2V = 45°, calc. Ref: 276a,

Strychnine nitrate ($C_{21}H_{22}N_2O_2 \cdot HNO_3$) is monoclinic in fine needles with negative elongation. (+)2V = large, r > v. $N_X = 1.610$, $N_Y = 1.624$, $N_Z = 1.675$, $N_Z - N_X = 0.065$. ∴ (+)2V = 54°, calc. Also $N_1 = 1.62$, $N_2 = 1.67$, $N_2 - N_1 = 0.05$. Ref: 35, 276a, 343c.

Strychnine sulfate pentahydrate ($C_{21}H_{22}N_2O_2 \cdot H_2SO_4 \cdot 5H_2O$) is monoclinic sphenoidal with $a:b:c = 4.739:1:1.036$, $\beta = 107°33'$. Crystals usually elongated along *b* with {100}, {001}, {510}, {110}, etc. Perfect 100 and imperfect 001 cleavages. May be twinned on 100. Needles have negative elongation. X = *b*; $Z \wedge c = -32°43'$, with strong dispersion. (+)2E = 16°30′ Na, r < v, weak. $N_X = 1.592$, $N_Y = 1.597$, $N_Z = 1.661$, $N_Z - N_X = 0.069$. Also $N_Z = 1.594$ red. From 2E and N_Y, 2V = 10°. Ref: 69, 119, 276a.

Strychnine sulfate hexahydrate ($C_{21}H_{22}N_2O_2 \cdot H_2SO_4 \cdot 6H_2O$) is tetragonal trapezohedral with $c/a = 3.18$. D 1.398. Crystals {001} plates with {111}, etc. Uniaxial negative or (-)2E up to 30°. $N_X = 1.595$, $N_Y = 1.613$, $N_Z = 1.615$, $N_Z - N_X = 0.020$. Crystals 1 mm. thick rotate the polarization plane 9 - 10° to the left. Ref: 276a.

Strychnine selenate pentahydrate ($C_{21}H_{22}N_2O_2 \cdot H_2SeO_4 \cdot 5H_2O$) is monoclinic sphenoidal with $a:b:c = 4.74:1:1.04$, $\beta = 108°$ *ca.* Crystals usually elongated along *b* with {100}, {110}, {1$\bar{1}$0}, {111}, etc. Perfect 100 cleavage. Needles have negative elongation. X = *b*; $Z \wedge c = -31°$. (+)2V = small, r < v. 2E = 10°, $N_X = 1.598$, $N_Y = 1.600$, $N_Z = 1.661$, $N_Z - N_X = 0.063$. Also (+)2E = 14°, r < v, strong. From 2E = 10° and $N_Y = 1.600$, 2V = 6°15′. Ref: 119, 276a.

Strychnine phosphate dihydrate ($C_{21}H_{22}N_2O_2 \cdot H_3PO_4 \cdot 2H_2O$) is monoclinic in needles with ± elongation and Y = *b*. (+)2V = moderate, with inclined dispersion. $N_X = 1.589$, $N_Y = 1.597$, $N_Z = 1.655$, $N_Z - N_X = 0.066$; ∴ (+)2V = 38° calc. Ref: 276a.

Strychnine thiocyanate monohydrate ($C_{21}H_{22}N_2O_2 \cdot HCNS \cdot H_2O$) is monoclinic in stout needles with ± elongation and Y = *b*. (+)2V = small with inclined dispersion. $N_X = 1.651$, $N_Y = 1.654$, $N_Z = 1.695$, $N_Z - N_X = 0.044$; ∴ (+)2V = 35° calc. Ref: 276a.

Strychnine oxalate heminonahydrate [$C_{21}H_{22}N_2O_2 \cdot (CO_2H)_2 \cdot 4.5H_2O$] is monoclinic in needles with ± elongation. (+)2V = small, r > v. $N_X = 1.592$, $N_Y = 1.598$, $N_Z = 1.662$ *ca.*, $N_Z - N_X = 0.070$ *ca.* ∴ (+)2V = 35° calc. Ref: 276a

Strychnine bioxalate sesquihydrate [$C_{21}H_{22}N_2O_2 \cdot (CO_2H)_2 \cdot 1.5H_2O$] is monoclinic in stout needles with $\pm$ (but usually negative) elongation. Extinction at 69.5° to elongation. (+)2V = large, r > v. $N_X = 1.592$, $N_Y = 1.603$, $N_Z = 1.665$, $N_Z - N_X = 0.073$. ∴ (+)2V = 45° calc. Ref: 276a.

Strychnine malonate hexahydrate [$(C_{21}H_{22}N_2O_2)_2 \cdot CH_2(CO_2H)_2 \cdot 6H_2O$] is tetragonal. Uniaxial negative with $N_O = 1.610$, N_E = ?. Ref: 276a.

Strychnine bisuccinate monohydrate ($C_{21}H_{22}N_2O_2 \cdot HO_2CCH_2CH_2CO_2H \cdot H_2O$) is orthorhombic (?) in needles with negative elongation. (–)2V = large. $N_X = 1.588$, $N_Y = 1.646$ *ca.*, $N_Z = 1.662$, $N_Z - N_X = 0.074$. ∴ (–)2V = 55° calc., r > v. Ref: 276a.

Strychnine glutarate [$C_{21}H_{22}N_2O_2 \cdot HO_2C(CH_2)_3CO_2H$] has negative elongation of needles and negative optic sign. $N_X = 1.575$, N_Y = ?, $N_Z = 1.655$, $N_Z - N_X = 0.080$. Ref: 276a.

Strychnine maleate monohydrate ($C_{21}H_{22}N_2O_2 \cdot HO_2CCH{:}CHCO_2H \cdot H_2O$) is orthorhombic in rods with negative elongation. (–?)2V = large. $N_X = 1.544$, $N_X = 1.598$, $N_Z = 1.667$, $N_Z - N_X = 0.123$. ∴ (+)2V = 85° calc. Ref 276a.

Strychnine bitartrate trihydrate [$C_{21}H_{22}N_2O_2 \cdot HO_2C(CHOH)_2CO_2H \cdot 3H_2O$] is monoclinic in stout needles. (+)2V = large, r > v, marked. $N_X = 1.596$, $N_Y = 1.603$, $N_Z = 1.632$, $N_Z - N_X = 0.036$. ∴ (+)2V = 52° calc. Ref: 276a.

Strychnine salicylate ($C_{21}H_{22}N_2O_2 \cdot HOC_6H_4CO_2H$) has parallel extinction and positive elongation with $N_1 = 1.69$, $N_2 = 1.72$, $N_2 - N_1 = 0.03$. Ref: 35.

Strychnine 1,2-benzenedicarboxylate monohydrate or strychnine phthalate monohydrate [$C_{21}H_{22}N_2O_2 \cdot C_6H_4(CO_2H)_2 \cdot H_2O$] is orthorhombic in prismatic crystals with parallel extinction. (+)2V = 60°. $N_X = 1.565$, $N_Y = 1.596$ calc., $N_Z = 1.69$, $N_Z - N_X = 0.125$. Ref: 396.

Brucine ($C_{23}H_{26}N_2O_4$) is probably monoclinic in long thin needles with negative elongation and extinction less then 20°. (–?)2V = ?, $N_1 = 1.48$, $N_2 = 1.66$, $N_2 - N_1 = 0.18$. Ref: 196.

Brucine salt of sucrose disulfuric acid [$C_{12}H_{22}O_{11} \cdot (SO_3H)_2 \cdot 2C_{23}H_{26}N_2O_4$] has inclined extinction. $N_1 = 1.556$, $N_2 = 1.655$, $N_2 - N_1 = 0.099$. Ref: 288.

Brucine sulfate ($C_{23}H_{26}N_2O_4 \cdot H_2SO_4$) forms rods with parallel extinction and positive elongation. $N_1 = 1.535$, $N_2 = 1.686$, $N_2 - N_1 = 0.151$. Again: $N_X = 1.512$, $N_Y = 1.595$, $N_Z = 1.688$, $N_Z - N_X = 0.176$. ∴ (+)2V near 90°. Ref: 168, 524.

Brucine sulfate with platinic chloride [$(C_{23}H_{26}O_4N_2)_2 \cdot H_2SO_4$ with $PtCl_4$] forms rods and needles with Z || elongation. $N_X = 1.592$, N_Y = ?, $N_Z = 1.734$, $N_Z - N_X = 0.142$. Ref: 523f.

Brucine sulfate with potassium iodide [$(C_{23}H_{26}O_4N_2)_2 \cdot H_2SO_4$ with KI] forms rectangular plates and squares with Z || elongation and $N_X = 1.550$. Ref: 523f.

Brucine 1,2-benzenedicarboxylate, or brucine phthalate [$C_{23}H_{26}N_2O_4 \cdot C_6H_4(CO_2H)_2$] is orthorhombic in colorless needles with parallel extinction. 2V = large. $N_X = 1.535$, N_Y = ?, $N_Z = 1.69$, $N_Z - N_X = 0.155$. Ref: 396.

V. MISCELLANEOUS COMPOUNDS

Nitrogeneous substances

Aureomycin hydrochloride $(C_{22}H_{27-29}O_8N_2Cl \cdot HCl)$ is orthorhombic with $a:b:c = 0.833:1:0.728$. a 12.89, b 15.48, c 11.27 Å. U.C. 4. Crystals are {010} plates with {101} and {011}. D 1.54. $X = b$; $Y = c$. $(-)2V = 59°$, $r < v$. $N_X = 1.635$, $N_Y = 1.706$, $N_Z = 1.730$, $N_Z - N_X = 0.095$. Ref: 535c.

Bios $(C_6H_{11}NO_3)$ is isometric and isotropic with $N = 1.525$. Ref: 467.

N[4-{[(-2-Amino-4-hydroxyl-6-pteridyl)methyl]amino}benzoyl] glutamic acid

or pteroyl glutamic acid or folic acid {NC(NH$_2$)NC(CH)CCNCCCH$_2$NHC$_6$H$_4$ $\underset{N}{\llcorner \quad \lrcorner}$ CONHCH(CO$_2$H)CH$_2$CO$_2$H} forms lenticular crystals with $N_1 = 1.559$, $N_2 = 1.744$, $N_2 - N_1 = 0.185$. Ref: 529.

Gliotoxin $(C_{13}H_{14}O_4N_2S_2)$ is monoclinic; the angle $\beta = 79°$. Crystals are {100} tablets, long parallel with b. Decompose at 221°. $Y \wedge c = 23°$, $Z = b$. $(+)2V = 53°$, $2E = 90°$, $N_X = 1.644$, $N_Y = 1.658$, $N_Z = 1.7075$, $N_Z - N_X = 0.0335$. $\alpha_D^{25} = -255°$ in chloroform. Ref: 505a.

Methylisatoid $(C_{17}H_{10}N_2O_4)$ is monoclinic prismatic with $a:b:c = 0.513:1:0.429$, $\beta = 100.5°$. Space group $P2_1/m$; a 9.42, b 18.36, c 7.87 Å. U.C. 4. Crystals columnar with {011}, {001}, {010}, {100}. D 1.49 (obs.), 1.51 (X-rays). $X = b$; $Z \wedge c = 10° \pm$. $(+)2V = 80°$ calc. $N_X = 1.57 \pm 0.01$, $N_Y = 1.68 \pm 0.02$, $N_Z = 1.83 \pm 0.02$, $N_Z - N_X = 0.26$. Color yellow. Ref: 61.

Klement compound $(C_{23}H_{16}ON_2)$ is monoclinic prismatic with $a:b:c = 0.501:1:0.313$, $\beta = 101°22'$. a 11.045, b 22.05, c 6.90 Å. Crystals columnar. D 1.344. M.P. 249°. $N_1 < 1.74$, $N_2 > 1.78$, $N_2 - N_1 > 0.04$. Color yellow. Ref: 494a.

Moser compound {4$(C_{22}H_{14}ON_2)$ + 2(CH$_3$·CO·OC$_2$H$_5$)} is triclinic pinacoidal with $a:b:c = 0.492:1:0.353$, $\alpha = 99°55'$, $\beta = 104°30'$, $\gamma = 74°59'$. a 10.92, b 22.18, c 7.84 Å. Crystals short columnar. D 1.362. $N_1 < 1.67$, $N_2 > 1.74$. $N_2 - N_1 > 0.07$. Color yellow. Ref: 494a.

Sodium penicillin G $(C_{16}H_{17}N_2SO_4Na)$ is probably orthorhombic disphenoidal. Crystals platy or acicular with $Z \parallel$ length. $(-)2V = 45°$ calc. $N_X = 1.550$, $N_Y = 1.609$, $N_Z = 1.620$, $N_Z - N_X = 0.070$. Colorless. Plates commonly give an optic axis interference figure. Ref: 451.

Dihydrostreptomycin trihydrochloride $(C_{21}H_{41}O_{12}N_7 \cdot 3HCl)$ is probably orthorhombic in fine needles. Z parallel to length. $(-)2V = 80°$. $N_X = 1.522$, $N_Y = 1.548$, $N_Z = 1.566$, $N_Z - N_X = 0.044$. Colorless. Ref: 620c.

Dihydrostreptomycin trisulfate $(C_{21}H_{41}O_{12}N_7)_2 \cdot 3H_2SO_4$ is probably monoclinic in trapezoidal plates which melt at about 250°, with decomposition. Extinction parallel on some plates, but the extinction angle is 18°. $(+)2V = 89°$ calc. $N_X = 1.552$, $N_Y = 1.558$, $N_Z = 1.566$, $N_Z - N_X = 0.014$. Colorless. Ref: 620c.

Terramycin dihydrate $\{C_{22}H_{25}O_9N_2 \cdot 2H_2O\}$ is probably orthorhombic. Crystals are thick six-sided plates with Y parallel with the elongation. M.P. 185°. $(+)2V = 28°$, $N_X = 1.634$, $N_Y = 1.646$, $N_Z > 1.700$, $N_Z - N_X > 0.066$. $[\alpha]_D^{25} = 196°$. Ref: 458a.

Vitamin B_{12} (formula ?) is orthorhombic with[1] $a:b:c = 0.876:1:0.659$. It forms needles which darken at about 210° and melt at about 300°. D 1.34. $X = b$; $Y = a$. $(-)2V$ = moderate, $N_X = 1.616$, $N_Y = 1.652$, $N_Z = 1.664$, $N_Z - N_X = 0.048$. Again: $(-)2V = 25°$ *ca.*, $N_X = 1.591$, $N_Y = 1.652$, $N_Z = 1.656$, $N_Z - N_X = 0.065$. Color red. Ref: 568a, 574.

Vitamin B_{12a} (formula ?) containing 4.58% Co and 2.43% P, has $(-)2V$ = moderate, $N_X = 1.580$, $N_Y = 1.640$, $N_Z = 1.654$, $N_Z - N_X = 0.074$. Ref: 509a.

Nitrogen-free substances

Agathendicarbonic acid $(C_{20}H_{30}O_4)$ is orthorhombic with $a:b:c = 0.960:1:1.019$. Crystals elongates along c, showing {110}, {010}, and {011}. $Y = b$, $Z = c$. $(-)2V = 26°46'$ red, $30°24'$ D, $33°42'$ green. $N = 1.559$, $N_Z - N_X$ = strong. Ref: 469.

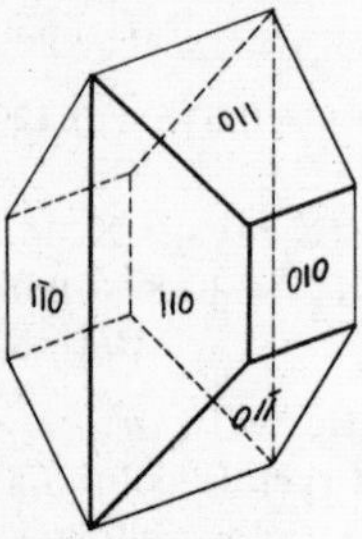

Fig. 149.
Atranoric acid.

β-Amyrin anisate $(C_{38}H_{56}O_3)$ is probably monoclinic with $\beta = 96°$ *ca.* Crystals {001} plates bounded by {110}. Cleavage on 001. $X = b$; $Z \wedge c = +5°$ $(+)2V = 46°12'$, no visible dispersion. $N_X = 1.533$ *ca.*, $N_Y = 1.552$, $N_Z = 1.67$ calc., $N_Z - N_X = 0.14$. Ref: 231.

γ-Hydroxysantonin or artemisin $(C_{15}H_{18}O_4)$ is orthorhombic with $a:b:c = 0.687:1:0.504$. Crystals prisms along a. M.P. 202°. $Z = a$. $2V = 40°$; $N_Y = 1.5715$, $N_Z = 1.6078$. Again: $N_1 = 1.57$, $N_2 = 1.615$, $N_2 - N_1 = 0.045$. Ref: 34, 35, 557a.

Atranoric acid $(C_{20}H_{18}O_9)$ is orthorhombic with $a:b:c = 0.771:1:2.579$. Crystals equant with {110}, {011}, {010}. Fig. 149. Cleavage reported on 110 and 100. M.P. 195 - 197°. $Y = c$; $Z = a$. $(+)2V$ = ?. $N_X = 1.5960$, N_Y = ?, $N_Z = 1.7788$, $N_Z - N_X = 0.1828$. Ref: 119, 164.

Deguelin $(C_{23}H_{22}O_6)$ is probably monoclinic with $\beta = 113.5°$. M.P. 171°. Negative elongation and extinction inclined at 14°. $(+)2V = 40°$ calc., $N_X = 1.571$ Na, $N_Y = 1.593$, $N_Z = 1.745$, $N_Z - N_X = 0.174$. Again: $N_X = 1.570$, $N_Y = 1.590$, $N_Z > 1.739$, $N_Z - N_X > 0.169$. Colorless. Ref: 32, 171.

Dehydrodeguelin $(C_{23}H_{20}O_6)$ is probably orthorhombic with parallel extinction and negative elongation. M.P. 171°. $(+)2V = 85°$ calc. $N_X = 1.638$, $N_Y = 1.689$, $N_Z = 1.749$, $N_Z - N_X = 0.113$. Colorless or pale yellow. Again: $N_X = 1.635$, $N_Y = 1.687$, $N_Z > 1.74$, $N_Z - N_X > 0.105$. Ref: 32, 171.

[1] a and b interchanged to make $b > a$.

Dihydrodeguelic acid ($C_{23}H_{26}O_8$) is probably monoclinic. M.P. 80° and again at 144°. $N_X = 1.490$, $N_Y = ?$, $N_Z > 1.740$, $N_Z - N_X > 0.250$. Intermediate indices include 1.605 and 1,740. Ref: 173a.

Dihydrodehydrodeguelin or dehydro-β-dihydrorotenone ($C_{23}H_{22}O_6$) is probably monoclinic. M.P. 267°. 2V = very small. $N_X = 1.498$, $N_Y = ?$, $N_Z > 1.74$, $N_Z - N_X > 0.24$. Color yellow. Ref: 173a.

Oxydehydrodeguelin ($C_{23}H_{20}O_8$) is probably orthorhombic. M.P. 303. Parallel extinction and negative elongation. (+)2V < 75° calc. $N_X = 1.490$, $N_Y = 1.595$, $N_Z > 1.740$, $N_Z - N_X > 0.250$. Color yellow. Ref: 173a.

Squash-seed α-globulin is tetragonal and nearly isometric; crystals pyramidal with N = 1.546 to 1.548. $N_Z - N_X < 0.001$. Ref: 186, 187.

Helenalin ($C_{15}H_{18}O_4$) forms rods with parallel extinction and positive elongation. (+)2V = 70° *ca.*, calc. $N_X = 1.550$, $N_Y = 1.568$, $N_Z = 1.603$ (all ± .003), $N_Z - N_X = 0.053$. $[\alpha] = + 101.9$. Ref: 180.

Tetrahydrohelenalin ($C_{15}H_{22}O_4$) forms long needles which melt at 176°. They have parallel extinction and negative elongation. (+)2V = 55° *ca.*, calc. $N_X = 1.545$, $N_Y = 1.550$, $N_Z=1.570$ (all ± .003), $N_Z - N_X=0.025$. Ref: 180.

Methoxyacetylhelanalin ($C_{18}H_{22}O_6$) forms six-sided rods which melt at 135°. They have parallel extinction and positive elongation. (–)2V = 45° *ca.*, calc. $N_X = 1.525$, $N_Y = 1.580$, $N_Z=1.590$ (all ± .003), $N_Z - N_X=0.065$. Ref: 180.

Insulin with Zn ($nC_8H_{14}O_4N_3S_2$?, with Zn)[1] forms rhombohedral crystals often having a basal plane. Also acicular. Space group R3. *a* 74.8, *c* 30.9 Å. D 1.31. M.P. 230°, after turning brown at about 220°. Uniaxial positive with $N_O = 1.550$, $N_E = 1.562$, $N_E - N_O = 0.012$. Again: N_O slightly above 1.544, $N_E = 1.556$, $N_E - N_O$ nearly = 0.012. Once more: N_O a little less than 1.531, N_E a little more than 1.537, $N_E - N_O = 0.007$ (Meas.). Also reported as uniaxial negative with $N_O = 1.535$ Li, $N_E - N_O = 0.005$. Crystals studied in the mother liquor have D 1.27, *a* 83.0, *c* 34.0 Å. Ref: 437, 442, 443.

Kosin ($C_{23}H_{30}O_7$?) melts at 142°; it has parallel extinction and negative elongation. $N_1 = 1.49$, $N_2 = 1.715$, $N_2 - N_1 = 0.225$. Ref: 34, 35.

Lepranthin ($C_{25}H_{40}O_{10}$) is monoclinic sphenoidal with $a:b:c = 2.402:1:0.927$, $\beta = 93°2'$. Crystals show {100}, {101}, {010}, etc. M.P. 183°. Y = *b*; and an optic axis appears on the edge of the field through 100. $N_Y = 1.503$ Na. Ref: 47a, 119, 382a.

Lonchocarpic acid ($C_{26}H_{26}O_6$) forms short prisms with M.P. 201°. $N_X = 1.510$, $N_Y = 1.718$, N_Z is "considerably greater than" 1.77, $N_Z - N_X > 0.260$. Ref: 110, 382b, 382c, 382d, 382e.

---

[1] Said to contain 288 (or 292) units of which 72 are leucine, 72 are glutamic acid, 36 are cysteine, 24 are tyrosine, 18 are histidine, 12 are serine, 8 are threonine, 6 are hydro-oxyamino acids, 6 are arginine, and 6 are lysine. See Jensen: Insulin, 1938.

Limonin ($C_{26}H_{30}O_8$) is orthorhombic with $a:b:c = 0.819:1:0.500$. Space group $P2_12_12_1$; a 14.53, b 17.75, c 8.88 Å. U.C. 4. Crystals are six-sided plates with angles of 81° ($110 \wedge 0\bar{1}\bar{0}$) and 127° ($011 \wedge 0\bar{1}\bar{1}$). M.P. 298°. D 1.36. X = a, Y = c, Z = b. (+)2E = 87°, 2V = 53°, r > v weak. $N_X = 1.557$, $N_Y = 1.562$, $N_Z = 1.582$, $N_Z - N_X = 0.025$. $[\alpha]_D^{30,5} = -129°$ in acetone Ref: 289b, 506a.

Limonin monomethylene chloride solvate ($C_{26}H_{30}O_8 \cdot CH_2Cl$?) is orthorhombic. Crystals are plates with an angle of 101°. X || elongation and bisects angle of 101°. Crystals often give $N_Z = 1.546$. (+)2E = 108°, 2V = 63°, r > v weak. $N_X = 1.540$, $N_Y = 1.543$, $N_Z = 1.551$, $N_Z - N_X = 0.011$. Ref: 506a.

Limonin hemimethylene chloride solvate ($C_{26}H_{30}O_8 \cdot 0.5CH_2Cl$) is orthorhombic in acicular crystals. Z parallel to elongation. $N_Z = 1.542$, $N_Z - N_X$ = very weak. Ref: 506a.

Limonin monoacetic acid solvate ($C_{26}H_{30}O_8 \cdot CH_3CO_2H$?) is orthorhombic with $a:b:c = 0.757:1:0.736$. Space group $P2_12_12_1$; a 12.75, b 16.85, c 12.40 Å. U.C. 4. Crystals acicular. D 1.32. X = b; Y = a; Z = c. (+)2E = 83°, 2V = 51°, r > v moderate. $N_X = 1.543$, $N_Y = 1.545$, $N_Z = 1.553$, $N_Z - N_X = 0.010$. Ref: 506a.

Lupeol ($C_{30}H_{50}O$) is probably orthorhombic. Crystals long prisms or laths with X || elongation, and Y normal to one face. M.P. 214 - 215°. $N_X = 1.551$, N_Y = ?, $N_Z = 1.565$, $N_Z - N_X = 0.014$. Ref: 602a.

Lupeol acetate ($C_{30}H_{49} \cdot CO_2CH_3$) is monoclinic (?), some faces showing strong dispersion and poor extinction; others have parallel extinction. M.P. 216°. (-)2V = large. $N_X = 1.540$, $N_Y = 1.567$, N_Z = ? (probably about 1.58 - 1.59 - A.N.W.), $N_Z - N_X < 0.094$. Ref: 602a.

Lupeol benzoate ($C_{30}H_{49} \cdot CO_2C_6H_5$) is probably orthorhombic. Crystals like rods with X || elongation. (+)2V = small, $N_X = 1.565$, $N_Y = 1.567$, $N_Z = 1.634$, $N_Z - N_X = 0.069$. Ref: 602a.

Lysozyme chloride (formula ?) is tetragonal. Crystals dipyramidal. Uniaxial positive with indices rising as crystals lose water. With maximum water: $N_O = 1.492$, $N_E = 1.495$, $N_E - N_O = 0.003$. When air-dried: $N_O = 1.554$, $N_E = 1.558$, $N_E - N_O = 0.004$. Colorless. Ref: 506.

Mibulactone ($C_{15}H_{22}O_4$) is orthorhombic. Crystals {010} plates with {100} and {101}. M.P. 268°. (+)2V = 76°, $N_X = 1.509$, $N_Y = 1.573$, $N_Z = 1.579$, $N_Z - N_X = 0.070$. (Indices and 2V are inconsistent; if 2V is +, N_Y should be about 1.537; if 2V is –, N_Y should be about 1.553 - A.N.W.). Ref: 557b.

Dehydronetoric acid ($C_{12}H_{12}O_5$) is apparently orthorhombic in short rods and needles with parallel extinction and negative elongation. M.P. 212° dec. (+)2V = large, $N_X = 1.533$, $N_Y = 1.678$, $N_Z > 1.74$ (not much greater), $N_Z - N_X > 0.20$. Brownish yellow color. Ref: 174.

Hydroxynetoric acid ($C_{12}H_{14}O_6$) is biaxial in irregular grains and rhombs with M.P. 189°. $N_X = 1.513$, $N_Y = ?$, $N_Z = 1.660$, $N_Z - N_X = 0.147$.
Ref: 174.

Picrotoxin ($C_{30}H_{34}O_{13}$) is orthorhombic with $a:b:c = 0.748:1:1.350$. Crystals {001} plates with {110}, {111}. Imperfect 001 cleavage. M.P. 203 - 204°. $N_X = 1.520$, $N_Y = ?$, $N_Z = 1.565$, $N_Z - N_X = 0.045$. $[\alpha] = +30°$ in water.
Ref: 119, 178, 227.

Picrotoxinin ($C_{15}H_{16}O_6 \cdot H_2O$) melts at 209.5°. It forms colorless rods with parallel extinction and negative elongation. $Y = c$; $Z = a$. $N_X = 1.5259$, $N_Y = 1.6030$, $N_Z = ?$ But Keenan gives (+) 2V = 60° calc. $N_X = 1.550$, $N_Y = 1.555$ *ca.*, $N_Z = 1.570$, $N_Z - N_X = 0.020$. Ref: 178, 219.

Picrotin ($C_{15}H_{18}O_7$) is orthorhombic with $a:b:c = 0.977:1:0.702$. Crystals {110} prisms or {010} plates with {101}, {012}, etc. M.P. 252°. $X = a$; $Y = c$. (-)2V = ?. Parallel extinction and positive elongation with $N_X = 1.535$, $N_Y = ?$, $N_Z = 1.565$, $N_Z - N_X = 0.030$. (If Keenan's plates were {010}, he may have measured N_Y instead of N_Z.) $[\alpha] = +70°$ in alcohol. (Picrotin may form a hydrate also.)
Ref: 119, 178, 219.

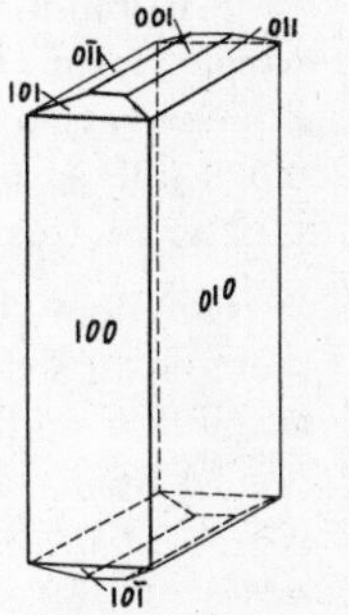

Fig. 150.
Pinastric acid.

Pinastric acid ($C_{20}H_{16}O_6$) is orthorhombic with[1] $a:b:c = 0.969:1:0.356$. Crystals {100} tablets with {010}, {001}, etc. Fig. 150. Perfect 001 cleavage. M.P. 203 - 205°. Easily soluble in chloroform or benzene. $Y = b$; $Z = c$. Described as optically positive with $N_X = 1.5185$ Na, $N_Y = 1.9418$, $N_Z = 2.0497$, $N_Z - N_X = 0.5312$ Na. (These indices require that the sign must be negative with 2V = 53°, but they lead to such extreme birefringence as to be open to question. A.N.W.) Color dark red-brown, strongly pleochroic (red-brown and yellow).
Ref: 119.

Pinoresinol ($C_{20}H_{22}O_6$) is orthorhombic with[2] $a:b:c = 0.880:1:0.762$. Crystals show {100}, {110}, {011}, {102}, etc. No cleavage. H = 1 –. M.P. 112°. D 1.385. Color pale yellow. $Y = a$; $Z = c$. (+)2V = 69°54′, $r < v$ very weak. $N_X = 1.508$ D, $N_Y = 1.532$, $N_Z = 1.552$, $N_Z - N_X = 0.044$.
Ref: 241.

Quassin ($C_{32}H_{40}O_{10}$) is biaxial with (+)2V = large, $N_X = 1.57$, $N_Y = 1.59$, $N_Z = 1.62$, $N_Z - N_X = 0.05$.
Ref: 34, 35.

Anhydroquassin ($C_{22}H_{28}O_5$) melts at 196°. It is probably biaxial with $N_X = 1.575$, $N_Y = ?$, $N_Z = 1.615$, $N_Z - N_X = 0.040$.
Ref: 181.

Dehydroquassin ($C_{22}H_{28}O_6$) melts at 264°. It has parallel extinction and ± elongation with (+)2V = 60° calc. $N_X = 1.560$, $N_Y = 1.575$, $N_Z = 1.615$, $N_Z - N_X = 0.055$. Colorless six-sided rods.
Ref: 181.

---

[1] a and b interchanged to make $b > a$.

[2] a and b interchanged to make $b > a$.

Ethoxyneoquassin ($C_{24}H_{34}O_6$) melts at 180°. It has Z || elongation. (+ ?)2V = 30° *ca.* calc. $N_X = 1.523$, $N_Y = 1.535$ *ca.*, $N_Z = 1.583$, $N_Z - N_X = 0.060$. Colorless. Ref: 181.

α-Robinin ($C_{33}H_{40}O_{19}$) is probably orthorhombic in rods with square ends which melt at 195 - 197°. They have X || elongation. (-)2V = 80° calc. $N_X = 1.490 \pm .003$, $N_Y = 1.612$, $N_Z = 1.702 \pm .005$, $N_Z - N_X = 0.212 \pm .004$. (This may be hydrated, as it is formed from aqueous solution.) Ref: 364.

β-Robinin ($C_{33}H_{40}O_{19}$) is probably orthorhombic in rods with square ends which form from alcoholic solution and melt at 249 - 250°. They have Z || elongation. Biaxial with $N_X = 1.600$, N_Y = ?, $N_Z = 1.620$, $N_Z - N_X = 0.020$ (all ± .003). Abnormal interference colors in blue and purple are characteristic of this substance. Ref: 364.

Rotenone ($C_{23}H_{18}O_6$) has two crystal phases. The low temperature phase (II) melts at 163°; it is probably orthorhombic in six-sided plates with symmetrical extinction and the optic plane parallel to the plate. 2V = large. $N_X = 1.616$, $N_Y = 1.635$, $N_Z = 1.662$ (all ± .003), $N_Z - N_X = 0.046$. Keenan gives $N_X = 1.610 \pm .003$, N_Y = ?, $N_Z = 1.662$. The high temperature phase (I) melts at 180°; it is also probably orthorhombic in nearly equant crystals or thick plates with symmetrical extinction. Many crystals are flattened and the optic plane is parallel to this face. (-)2V = 65°. $N_X = 1.600$, $N_Y = 1.650$, $N_Z = 1.685$ (all ± .003), $N_Z - N_X = 0.085$. The inversion temperature is perhaps 125°. Both phases have D 1.33. Ref: 112, 182.

Dihydrorotenone ($C_{23}H_{24}O_6$) has two phases. One (I) forms rectangular and six-sided prisms which melt at 164°. They have X || elongation. 2V = biaxial. $N_X = 1.550$, N_Y = ?, $N_Z = 1.682$, $N_Z - N_X = 0.132 \pm .003$. Another phase (II) forms short prisms and wedges which melt at 216°. An optic axis of a biaxial crystal is easily obtained. $N_X = 1.600$, $N_Y = 1.625$, $N_Z = 1.680$, all ± .003, $N_Z - N_X = 0.080$: ∴ (+)2V = 70° calc. Ref: 217.

Rotenone carbon tetrachloride solvate or carbon tetrachloride solvate of rotenone ($C_{23}H_{22}O_6 \cdot CCl_4$) is orthorhombic. Crystals are long prisms somewhat flattened. D 1.40. Dec. 87°. X || elongation. (-)2V = 65° calc. $N_X = 1.563$, $N_Y = 1.612$, $N_Z = 1.631$, $N_Z - N_X = 0.068$. Colorless. Ref: 112.

α-Santonin ($C_{15}H_{18}O_3$) is orthorhombic disphenoidal with *a*:*b*:*c* = 0.613:1:0.410. Crystals {010} tablets elongated along *a* with {012}, {120}, {011}, etc. Perfect 010 cleavage (also 100 ?). D 1.87. M.P. 170°. Y = *a*; Z = *b*. (-)2V = 25° D calc. $N_X = 1.589$, $N_Y = 1.592$, $N_Z = 1.639$, $N_Z - N_X = 0.050$. At 3°, 2E = 35°25′ C, 41°17′ D, 54°8′ F. At 15°, 2E = 36°6′ C, 41°34′ D, 54°32′ F. At 70°, 2E = 38°18′ C, 43°33′ D, 55°20′ F. Again: $N_1 = 1.59$, $N_2 = 1.60$, $N_3 = 1.63$.
Ref: 119, 192, 239, 343c, 524.

β-Santonin ($C_{15}H_{18}O_3$) is monoclinic with *a*:*b*:*c* = 0.835:1:0.778, β = 108°15′. *a* 14.00, *b* 16.65, *c* 13.2 Å. U.C. 8. Crystals prismatic. M.P. 218°. (-)2V = 70°. $N_X = 1.490$, $N_Y = 1.640$, $N_Z = 1.663$, $N_Z - N_X = 0.173$. (From the indices 2V = 40°.) Ref: 557c.

Hyposantonin ($C_{15}H_{18}O_2$) is orthorhombic with $a:b:c = 0.730:1:0.378$. Basal plates. M.P. 152 - 153°. (+)2V = 65°, $N_X = 1.4818$, $N_Y = 1.64$, $N_Z = 1.693$, $N_Z - N_X = 0.2112$. Ref: 557c.

Isohyposantonin ($C_{15}H_{18}O_2$) is orthorhombic with $a:b:c = 0.551:1:0.499$. Crystals long prisms with 010 cleavage. M.P. 167 - 168°. $Y = b$, $Z = a$. (+)2V = 47°, $N_X = 1.5839$, $N_Y = 1.659$, $N_Z = 1.665$, $N_Z - N_X = 0.0811$. (From the indices: 2V = 30°.) Ref: 557c.

Dihydrosantinic acid (active) ($C_{15}H_{20}O_2$) is monoclinic with $a:b:c = 0.652:1:0.504$, $\beta = 95°$. a 10.32, b 15.60, c 7.82 Å. U.C. 4. Crystals prismatic. (-)2V = 68°, $N_X = 1.492$, $N_Y = 1.657$, $N_Z = 1.710$, $N_Z - N_X = 0.218$. Ref: 557d.

Dihydrosantinic acid (inactive) ($C_{15}H_{20}O_2$) is monoclinic with $a:b:c = 0.566:1:0.696$, $\beta = 95°$. a 8.35, b 14.75, c 10.26 Å. U.C. 4 (-)2V = 77°, $N_X = 1.477$, $N_Y = 1.710$, $N_Z = 1.743$, $N_Z - N_X = 0.266$. Ref: 557d.

α-Desmotroposantonin ($C_{15}H_{19}O_3$) is orthorhombic with[1] $a:b:c = 0.647:1:0.289$. Crystals acicular along c. $X = b$; $Y = c$. (+)2V = 84°. $N_X = 1.553$, $N_Y = 1.5985$, $N_Z = 1.689$, $N_Z - N_X = 0.136$. (From the indices: 2V = 70°.) Ref: 557c.

β Desmotroposantonin ($C_{15}H_{19}O_3$) is orthorhombic with $a:b:c=0.876:1:0.939$. Crystals (010) plates along c. $X = c$; $Y = b$. (+)2V = 58°, $N_X = 1.587$, $N_Y = 1.6055$ calc., $N_Z = 1.6364$, $N_Z - N_X = 0.0494$. Ref: 557c.

α-Tetrahydrosantonin or dihydromonoginin ($C_{15}H_{22}O_3$) is orthorhombic with $a:b:c = 0.598:1:0.704$. Crystals {010} plates. M.P. 155°. $X = a$; $Z = c$. $N_X = 1.4810$, $N_Y = ?$, $N_Z = 1.5694$, $N_Z - N_X = 0.884$. Ref: 557b.

Shellolic acid dimethyl ester [$C_{13}H_{16}(OH)_2(CO_2CH_3)_2$] is monoclinic with $a:b:c = 1.042:1:1.054$, $\beta = 99°4'$. Crystals show {100}, {001}, {010}, {111}. Good 010 cleavage. D 1.32. M.P. 149°. $Y = b$; $Z \wedge c = +40°$. (+)2V = 55°12′, $r > v$ strong. $N_Y = 1.586 \pm .006$. Ref: 129.

Stearopten {($C_{17}H_{35})_2CO$?} forms spherulitic masses which (at 36°) are uniaxial positive with $N_O = 1.5076$, $N_E = 1.5172$, $N_E - N_O = 0.0096$. Ref: 611.

Sumatrol ($C_{23}H_{22}O_7$) is probably triclinic in needles or blades with negative elongation and extinction at about 35°. M.P. 189°. (-)2V = 40° calc. $N_X = 1.529$, $N_Y = 1.716$, $N_Z = 1.745$, $N_Z - N_X = 0.216$. Colorless. Ref: 32.

Temisin ($C_{15}H_{22}O_3$) is monoclinic (?) with $a:b:c = 0.627:1:0.663$. Measured on minute planes extinction is 0 - 3°. M.P. 228°. $Z = c$. (-)2V = 80°, $N_X = 1.4912$, $N_Y = 1.5401$, $N_Z = 1.5727$ calc., $N_Z - N_X = 0.0815$ calc. Ref: 557b.

Isotemisin ($C_{15}H_{22}O_3$) is orthorhombic with $a:b:c = 0.607:1:0.541$. Crystals are {010} plates with {101}, {001}, etc. M.P. 70 - 73°. $Z = c$. (+)2V = 64°. $N_X = 1.4920$, $N_Y = 1.502$ calc., $N_Z = 1.5280$, $N_Z - N_X = 0.036$. Ref: 557b.

---

[1] a and b interchanged to make $b > a$.

Tetrahydrotemisin ($C_{15}H_{26}O_3$) in crystals has M.P. 231° and $N_X = 1.498$, $N_Y = ?$, $N_Z = 1.552$, $N_Z - N_X = 0.054$. Ref: 557b.

Tetrahydroisotemisin monohydrate ($C_{15}H_{26}O_3 \cdot H_2O$) in crystals has M.P. 112°. $N_X = 1.480$, $N_Y = ?$, $N_Z = 1.514$, $N_Z - N_X = 0.0341$. Ref: 557b.

α-Tetrahydrotemisol ($C_{15}H_{30}O_3$) is orthorhombic with $a:b:c = 0.872:1:0.533$. Crystals {010} plates. M.P. 148° ± 4°. (+)2V = 81°. $N_X = 1.5190$, $N_Y = 1.523$ calc., $N_Z = 1.5271$, $N_Z - N_X = 0.0081$. Ref: 557b.

Tephrosin ($C_{23}H_{22}O_7$) is probably monoclinic with $\beta = 106°$. M.P. 193°. The optic plane and Z seem to be normal to 010; $X \wedge c = 9°$; negative elongation. (-)2V = large. $N_X = 1.593$, $N_Y = 1.68$ *ca.*, $N_Z = 1.763$, $N_Z - N_X = 0.170$ Na. Again, $N_X = 1.590$, $N_Z > 1.74$. Ref: 32, 172.

Tephrosindicarboxylic acid ($C_{23}H_{22}O_{11}$) is probably monoclinic with inclined extinction and positive elongation. M.P. 221° dec. $N_X = 1.530$, $N_Y = ?$, $N_Z = 1.640$, $N_Z - N_X = 0.110$. Ref: 172.

Isotephrosin ($C_{23}H_{22}O_7$) melts at 252°. Rhombic plates, biaxial with $N_X = 1.547$, $N_Y = ?$, $N_Z = 1.582$, $N_Z - N_X = 0.035$. Ref: 176.

Isotephrosindicarboxylic acid ($C_{23}H_{22}O_{11}$) melts at 187°. Apparently biaxial with $N_X = 1.485$, $N_Y = ?$, $N_Z = 1.660$, $N_Z - N_X = 0.175$. Colorless. Ref: 176.

Monoacetate of dehydrotoxicarol ($C_{25}H_{22}O_8$) melts at 231 - 232°. It has inclined extinction and negative elongation. $N_X = 1.563$, $N_Y = ?$, $N_Z > 1.740$, $N_Z - N_X > 0.177$. Ref: 173.

Apotoxicarol methyl ether ($C_{19}H_{18}O_7$) is apparently monoclinic in needles with inclined extinction and negative elongation. $N_X = 1.600$, $N_Y = ?$, $N_Z > 1.740$, $N_Z - N_X > 0.14$. Colorless. Ref: 174.

Dehydroapotoxicarol ($C_{18}H_{14}O_7$) is apparently orthorhombic in rods with M.P. 298°. X || elongation. (-?)2V = ?, $N_X = 1.543$, $N_Y = 1.685$, $N_Z > 1.74$ (but not much greater), $N_Z - N_X > 0.20$. Ref: 174.

Dehydrotoxicarol ($C_{23}H_{20}O_7$) melts at 234°. X || elongation. (-?)2V > 50°, calc., $N_X = 1.460$, $N_Y = 1.685$, (both ± .003), $N_Z > 1.740$, $N_Z - N_X > 0.280$. Yellow, acicular. Ref: 173.

Dihydrotoxicarol ($C_{23}H_{24}O_7$) melts at 206°. An optic axis normal to plates, often. (-)2V = 75°, calc., $N_X = 1.575$, $N_Y = 1.627$, $N_Z = 1.658$, (all ± .003), $N_Z - N_X = 0.083$. Colorless six-sided plates. Ref: 173.

Dihydrodesoxytoxicarol ($C_{23}H_{26}O_6$) melts at 188°. X || elongation with (-)2V = 87°, calc., $N_X = 1.567$, $N_Y = 1.625$, $N_Z = 1.680$ (all ± .003), $N_Z - N_X = 0.113$. Colorless rods. Ref: 173.

Dehydrodihydrotoxicarol ($C_{23}H_{22}O_7$) is apparently monoclinic. M.P. 260°. Extinction usually inclined. (-?)2V > 60° *ca.* calc., $N_X = 1.500$, $N_Y = 1.680$ (both ± .003), $N_Z > 1.740$, $N_Z - N_X > 0.240$. Yellow rods. Ref: 173.

Monoacetate of dihydrodesoxytoxicarol ($C_{25}H_{28}O_7$) melts at 156°. It has inclined extinction and negative elongation. (+)2V < 85°, calc., $N_X = 1.547$, $N_Y = 1.633$, (both ± .003), $N_Z > 1.740$, $N_Z - N_X > 0.193$. Colorless. Ref: 173.

Diacetate of dihydrotoxicarol ($C_{27}H_{28}O_9$) melts at 238°. It has X || elongation with $N_X = 1.48$, $N_Y = ?$, $N_Z \geqslant 1.74$, $N_Z - N_X \geqslant 0.26$. Colorless. Ref: 173.

Monoacetate of dihydrotoxicarol ($C_{25}H_{26}O_6$) melts at 207°. It has X || elongation. $N_X = 1.583$, $N_Y = ?$, $N_Z = 1.655$ (both ± .003), $N_Z - N_X = 0.072$. An intermediate index, 1.615, is often found. Colorless prisms. Ref: 173.

Diacetate of toxicarol ($C_{27}H_{26}O_9$) melts at 233°. It is biaxial with $N_X = 1.500$, $N_Y = ?$, $N_Z > 1.74$, $N_Z - N_X > 0.24$. Colorless plates. Ref: 173.

Dihydrotoxicarolic acid ($C_{23}H_{26}O_9$) forms six-sided plates often elongated with M.P. 129°. X || elongation. $N_X = 1.515$, $N_Y = ?$, $N_Z = 1.600$, $N_Z - N_X = 0.085$. (But described as birefringence "extremely strong". Is 1.600 actually N_Y? - A.N.W.) Ref: 174.

Dihydrotoxicarolic acid methyl ether ($C_{24}H_{28}O_9$) forms thin plates and rhombs with M.P. 174°. Extinction parallel. Biaxial. $N_X = 1.535$, $N_Y = ?$, $N_Z = 1.740$, $N_Z - N_X = 0.205$. Ref: 174.

7-Hydroxytoxicarol ($C_{23}H_{22}O_8$) forms yellow prisms with M.P. 227°. Crystals often rhombs. (+)2V = large. $N_X = 1.580$, $N_Y = 1.650$, N_Z slightly more than 1.737, $N_Z - N_X = 0.160$ *ca.* Ref: 177.

Monoacetate of dihydro-7-hydroxytoxicarol ($C_{25}H_{26}O_9$) forms prisms and rhombs (with M.P. 196°) which give an inclined optic axis. $N_X = 1.550$, $N_Y = ?$, $N_Z = 1.685$, $N_Z - N_X = 0.135$. Ref: 177.

7-Hydroxydihydrotoxicarol ($C_{23}H_{24}O_8$) forms prisms and rhombs with M.P. 223°. (+)2V = very large. $N_X = 1.575$, $N_Y = 1.630$, $N_Z = 1.695$, $N_Z - N_X = 0.120$. Ref: 177.

Monoacetate of 7-hydroxytoxicarol ($C_{25}H_{24}O_9$) forms thick rhomboidal plates with M.P. 184° and parallel extinction. $N_X = 1.555$, $N_Y = ?$, $1.737 > N_Z > 1.700$, $0.18 > N_Z - N_X > 0.145$. Ref: 177.

Triacetate of apotoxicarol ($C_{24}H_{22}O_{10}$) is biaxial in square micaceous plates. $N_X = 1.547$, $N_Y' = 1.645$, $N_Z > 1.74$, $N_Z - N_X > 0.20$. Ref: 174.

Ursolic acid ($C_{30}H_{48}O_3$) is probably orthorhombic in bladed crystals with parallel extinction and ± elongation. Cleavage across the blades. M.P. 285°. (+)2E = 130° ± 10°, 2V = 70°, calc., $N_X = 1.55$, $N_Y = 1.56$, $N_Z = 1.58$ (all ± .01), $N_Z - N_X = 0.03$. Ref: 364.

Methyl monoacetylursolate or monoacetate of methyl ursolate ($CH_3CO_2C_{29}H_{46}CO_2CH_3$) is probably orthorhombic in platy rods which melt at 246 - 247°. X || elongation. (+)2E = 85° ± 5°, 2V = 50°, calc., r > v. $N_X = 1.530$, $N_Y = 1.537$, $N_Z = 1.565$ (all ± .003), $N_Z - N_X = 0.035$. Ref: 364.

d-(or *l*-) Usnic acid ($C_{18}H_{16}O_7$) is orthorhombic with $a:b:c = 0.937:1:0.397$. Space group probably $P2_12_12_1$. U.C. 8. Crystals {010 tablets with {110}, {011}, {111}, etc. Fig. 151. Distinct 001 cleavage. D 1.46. M.P. 203°. $Y = a$; $Z = b$. (−)2V = 72°, r < v strong. $N_X = 1.611$, $N_Y = 1.710$, $N_Z = 1.772$, $N_Z - N_X = 0.161$ Na. Color greenish yellow, weakly pleochroic, clear green and clear yellow.
Ref: 119, 164, 308, 506b.

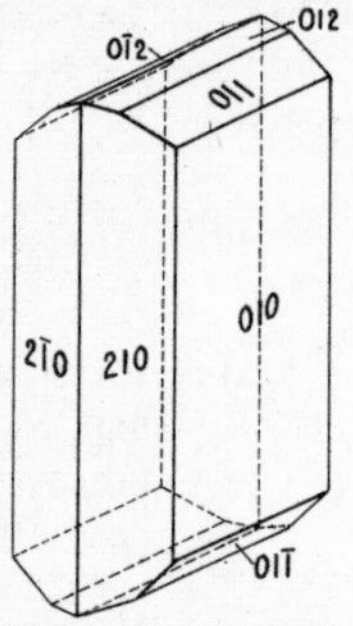

Fig. 151. Usnic acid.

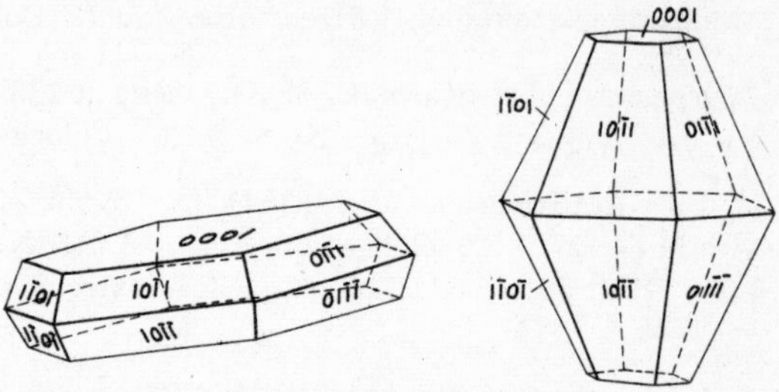

Fig. 152, 153. Zeorin.

Zeorin ($C_{52}H_{88}O_4$) is hexagonal with $c/a = 1.733$. Crystals pyramidal or basal tablets with {$10\bar{1}1$}. Figs. 152, 153. No cleavage observed. M.P. 249 − 251°. Uniaxial positive with $N_O = 1.5404$, $N_E = 1.5462$, $N_E - N_O = 0.0058$.
Ref: 119, 164.

Addendum

Dimethylglyoxime $\left[\begin{matrix} \text{HON NOH} \\ H_3C \cdot \ddot{C} \cdot \ddot{C} \cdot CH_3 \end{matrix}\right]$ is triclinic with $a:b:c = 0.950:1:0.703$, $\alpha = 125°$, $\beta = 91°$, $\gamma = 79°$. *a* 6.07, *b* 6.39, *c* 4.48 Å. U.C. 1. Crystals often {100} tablets with common twinning on 001 and good 001 and 100 cleavages. D 1.35. M.P. 260 − 266°. Optic plane roughly parallel with 100; Z nearly parallel with *b*; $Z \wedge b = 1°$ on 100. (+)2V = 80°, r > v. $N_X = 1.40$, $N_Y = 1.54$, $N_Z = 1.85$, $N_Z - N_X = 0.45$.
Ref: 553 a.

REFERENCES.

1. Agafonoff: Bull. soc. franç. minéral., 53 : 25 (1930).
2. Agafonoff: Bull. soc. franç. minéral., 54 : 54 (1931).
3. Amadori: Atti accad. Lincei Classe sci. fis., mat. nat., (6) 1 : 244 (1925).
4. Ambler (and Wherry): Ind. Eng. Chem. Ind. Ed., 12 : 1081, 1085 (1920).
5. Artini: Atti accad. Lincei Rend. adun. sol., 26 : 392, 420 (1917).
6. Artini: Z. Kryst., 25 : 172 (1894).
7. Ashton, Houston, and Saylor: J. Res. Nat. Bur. Stand., 11 : 233 (1933).
8. Backer: Rec. trav. chim. 54 : 905 (1935).
9. Backer and Bente: Rec. trav. chim., 54 : 523 (1935).
10. Backer and Mulder: Rec. trav. chim., 55 : 357 (1936).
11. Backer and Stienstra: Rec. trav. chim., 54 : 607 (1935).
12. Backer and Stienstra: Rec. trav. chim., 54 : 833 (1935).
13. Backer and Stienstra: Rec. trav. chim., 54 : 905 (1935).
14. Backer, Strating, and Zuithof: Rec. trav. chim., 55 : 761 (1931).
15. Backer, Terpstra, and Dykstra: Rec. trav. chim., 50 : 1073 (1931).
16. Backer, Terpstra, and Dykstra: Rec. trav. chim., 51 : 289 (1932).
17. Backer, Terpstra, and Dykstra: Rec. trav. chim., 51 : 1166 (1932).
18. Baier: Z. Krist. 65 : 719 (1927).

18a. Balas and Bryok: Coll. Czechoslav. Chem. Comm., 1 : 306 (1929).

19. Bannister and Hey: Discovery Rep., 13 : 60 (1936).
20. Bartalini: Z. Kryst. 25 : 406 (1896).
21. Beger: Centr. Mineral. Geol., 1920, 129.
22. Beger: Z. Krist., 57 : 303 (1922).
23. Behrens-Kley: Org. Mikroch. Anal. Leipzig, 1922.
24. Beintema, Terpstra, and de Vrieze: Pharm. Weekblad, 72 : 1287 (1936).
25. Beintema, Terpstra, and Van Weerden: Rec. trav. chim., 54 : 627 (1935).
26. Beintema, Terpstra, and Van Weerden: Rec. trav. chim., 54 : 745, 962 (1935).
27. Bennett: J. Chem. Soc. London, 127 : 1277 (1925).
28. Bent, Larsen, and Berman: J. Am. Chem. Soc., 58 : 1522 (1936).

28a. Bernal: Z. Krist. 78 : 363 (1931).

29. Bernal and Crowfoot: Z. Krist., 93 : 464 (1936).
30. Bhagavantam: Proc. Roy. Soc., A 126 : 143 (1930).
31. Blodgett and Langmuir: Phys. Rev., 51 : 964 (1937).
32. Boam, Cahn, and Stuart: J. Soc. Chem. Ind., 56 : 91 (1937).
33. Bodewig: Z. Kryst., 3 : 381 (1877).

33a. Bolland: Sitzb. Akad. Wiss. Wien, 117, Abt. IIb : 671 (1908).

34. Bolland: Sitzb. Akad. Wiss. Wien, 119, Abt. IIb : 275 (1910). Almost the same data can be found in 35.
35. Bolland: Monatsh., 31 : 390 (1910).

35a. Bowen, in Ksanda and Tunell: Am. J. Sci., 35a : 173 (1938).

36. Brun: Arch. Sci. phys. nat., (4) 7 : 284 (1899); Z. Kryst., 34 : 630 (1901).
37. Bryant: Am. Miner., 20 : 281 (1935).
38. Bryant: J. Am. Chem. Soc., 54 : 3758 (1932).
39. Bryant: J. Am. Chem. Soc., 55 : 3201 (1933); 58: 2335 (1936). 60 : 2815 (1938).
39a. Bryant: J. Am. Chem. Soc., 63 : 511 (1941).
40. Bryant: Personal comm., March 16, 1938.
41. Bryant and Mitchell: J. Am. Chem. Soc., 60 : 2748 (1938).
42. Bücking: Z. Kryst. I : 304 (1877).
43. Buckley: Mineral. Mag., 20 : 159 (1924).
44. Buckley: Mineral. Mag., 21 . 55 (1926).
45. Buhs: Z. Krist., 63 : 601 (1926).
46. Burgess and Lowry: J. Chem. Soc. London, 125 : 2088 (1924).
47. Burgess and Lowry: J. Chem. Soc. London, 127 : 271 (1925).
47a. Busz: in Zopf: Ann. Chem., 336 : 48 (1904). also Z. Kryst. 44 : 528 (1908).
48. Bygden: J. parkt. Chem., 96 : 86 (1917).
49. Bygden· J. parkt. Chem., 100 : 1 (1920).
50. Campbell and Willard: Z. Kryst., 100 : 111 (1938).
51. Chatelain: Bull. soc. franç. minéral., 60 : 280 (1937).
52. Chatelain: Compt. rend., 200 : 412 (1935).
53. Chatelain: Compt. rend., 203 : 266 (1936).
54. Chatelain: Compt. rend., 203 : 1169 (1936).
55. Ciamician and Boeris: Gazz. chim. ital., 24 : 303 (1894).
55a. Cox: Nature, 130 : 205 (1932).
56. Cox and Goodwin: J. Chem. Soc. London, 1932 : 1824.
57. Cox and Goodwin: J. Chem. Soc. London, 1936 : 769.
58. Cox and Goodwin: Z. Krist., 85 : 462 (1933).
59. Cox, Goodwin and Wagstaff: J. Chem. Soc. London, 1935 : 978.
60. Cox, Goodwin and Wagstaff: J. Chem. Soc. London, 1935 : 1495.
61. Cox, Goodwin and Wagstaff: Proc. Roy. Soc., A 157 : 399 (1936).
62. Cox, Sharrot, Wardlaw and Webster: J. Chem. Soc. London, 1936 : 129.
63. Cox, Wardlaw and Webster: J. Chem. Soc. London, 1936 : 775.
64. Cox and Webster: J. Chem. Soc. London, 1935 : 731.
65. Crosby, Kirk (and Pabst): Mikrochem., 18 : 137 (1935).
65a. Crowfoot: J. Chem. Soc. London, 1938 : 1241.
66. Cunningham, MacIntyre, and Kirk: Mikrochem. 21 : 245 (1936).
67. Davis, Ashdown, and Couch: J. Am. Chem. Soc. 47 : 1063 (1925).
68. Dennis, Staneslow, and Forgeng: J. Am. Chem. Soc. 55 : 4392 (1933).
69. Des Cloiseaux: Ann. Mines, 14 : 389 (1858).
70. Des Cloiseaux: Manuel de Minéral. (Paris) 2 : 38 (1874).
71. Des Cloiseaux: Nouv. Rech., 3 (Mem. Sav. Étrang. Acad. Paris, 18 : 621 (1867).
72. Drugman: Z. Krist. 53 : 240 (1913).
73. Duffaur: Z. Krist. 63 : 359 (1926).
73a. Dunn, Inouye, and Kirk: Mikrochem. 27 : 154 (1939).
74. Duparc and Galopin: Helv. Chim. Acta, 13 : 702 (1930).
75. Dupré la Tour: Compt. rend., 193 : 180 (1931).
76. Ekeley and Portratz: J. Am. Chem. Soc. 58 : 907 (1936).
76a. Emery: J. Am. Pharm. Assn., 16 : 932 (1927).

77. Emmons: Pers. comm. April 27, 1937.
78. Eppler: Z. Kryst. 30 : 118 (1899).
79. Eykman: Ber. 24 : 1278 (1894); Z. Kryst., 23 : 599 (1894).
80. Faber: Centr. Mineral. Geol., 1933, A, 191.
81. Faber: Z. Krist., 70 : 497 (1929).
82. Faber: Z. Krist. 75 : 147 (1930).
83. Faber: Z. Krist. 86 : 161 (1933).
84. Fels: Z. Kryst. 37 : 485 (1903).
84a. Ferla: Period. Mineral., 10 : 25 (1931).
85. Fischer: Ann., 270 : 64 (1892).
86. Fischer and Kofler: Arch. Pharm., 270 : 207 (1932).
87. Fischer and Kofler: Arch. Pharm., 270 : 433 (1932).
88. Fischer and Kofler: Mikrochem. 19 : 38 (1935).
89. Fisher: Am. J. Sci., 10 : 201 (1925).
90. Ford, in Johnson and Coghill: J. Am. Chem. Soc. 47 : 2843 (1925).
91. Frey: Z. Krist. 63 : 347 (1926).
91a. Frey-Wyssling and Wuhrmann: Helv. Chim. Acta, 22 : 981 (1939).
92. Gatewood: J. Am. Chem. Soc. 45 : 146 (1923).
93. Gatewood: J. Am. Chem. Soc. 45 : 3056 (1923).
94. Gatewood: J. Am. Chem. Soc. 47 : 407 (1925).
95. Gatewood: J. Am. Chem. Soc. 47 : 2175 (1925).
96. Gatewood: J. Am. Chem. Soc. 47 : 2181 (1925).
97. Gaubert: Bull. soc. franç. minéral., 33 : 335 (1910).
98. Gaubert: Bull. soc. franç. minéral., 41 : 198 (1918).
99. Gaubert: Bull. soc. franç. minéral., 55 : 235 (1932).
100. Gaubert: Compt. rend., 149 : 1005 (1909).
101. Gaubert: Compt. rend., 195 : 1088 (1932).
102. Gaubert: Compt. rend., 196 : 554 (1933).
103. Gaubert: Compt. rend., 200 : 1120 (1935).
104. Gaubert: Compt. rend., 202 : 1192 (1936).
105. Gaudefroy: Bull soc. franç. minéral., 52 : 55 (1929).
106. Gaudefroy, in Girard, Sandulesco, Fridenson and Rutgers: Compt, rend., 195 : 981 (1932).
107. Gibson, Markley and Merwin: J. Am. Chem. Soc. 55 : 2399 (1933).
108. Gill, in Orndorff and Nichols: J. Am. Chem. Soc., 45 : 1536 (1923).
109. Girard, Sandulesco, Fridenson, Gaudefroy and Rutgers: Compt. rend., 194 : 1020 (1932).
110. Gooden, in Jones: J. Am. Chem. Soc. 56 : 1247 (1934).
111. Gooden and Smith: J. Am. Chem. Soc., 57 : 2616 (1935).
112. Gooden and Smith: J. Am. Chem. Soc., 59 : 787 (1937).
113. Gottfried and Steinmetz: N. J. Mineral. Geol. Bl. Bd. 57, A: 249 (1928).
114. Greenwood: Am. Mineral., 16 : 473 (1931).
115. Greenwood: Mineral. Mag., 20 : 123 (1923).
116. Greenwood: Mineral. Mag., 20 : 393 (1923).
117. Groth: Chem. Kryst., Vol. 3, Leipzig, 1910.
118. Groth: Chem. Kryst., Vol. 4, Leipzig, 1917.
119. Groth: Chem. Kryst., Vol. 5, Leipzig, 1919.

120. Groth: Z. Kryst. 5 : 476 (1881).
120a. Grove and Keenan: J. Am. Chem. Soc., 63 : 97 (1941).
121. Grütter: Z. Krist., 62 : 314 (1925).
121a. Grütter: Z. Krist., 102 : 48 (1939).
121b. Grutterink: Z. anal. Chem., 51 : 175 (1912).
122. Guaisnet-Pilaud: Compt. rend., 197 : 419 (1933).
123. Haas: Mikrochem., Emich Festschrift, 1930, 83.
124. Haller, Adams, and Wherry: J. Am. Chem. Soc., 42 : 1840 (1920).
125. Hann and Keenan: J. Phys. Chem., 31 : 1082 (1920).
125a. Hann, Maclay, and Hudson: J. Am. Chem. Soc., 61 : 2432 (1939).
126. Hartley, Drugman, Vlieland, and Bourdillon: J. Chem. Soc. London, 103 : 1747 (1913).
127. Hartline: Unpubl. B.S. thesis, Mass. Inst. Tech., 1931.
128. Hartshorne and Stuart: Crystals and the Polarising Microscope, Arnold and Co., London (1934).
129. Hartwig: Z. Kryst., 60 : 310 (1924).
130. Hayman, Wagner, and Holden: J. Am. Pharm. Assn., 14 : 388 (1925).
131. Heide: Z. Krist., 64 : 177 (1926).
132. Heilbron and Wilson: J. Chem. Soc. London, 101 : 1489 (1912).
133. Hémon: Bull. soc. franç. minéral., 54 : 47 (1931).
134. Hendricks: J. Am. Chem. Soc., 57 : 552 (1935).
135. Hendricks: Nature, 133 : 178 (1934).
136. Hendricks: Z. Krist., 89 : 427 (1934).
136a. Hendricks: Z. Krist. 91 : 48 (1935).
137. Hendricks and Deming: Z. Krist., 91 : 290 (1935).
138. Hendricks and Jefferson: J. Optical Soc. Am., 23 : 299 (1933).
139. Hendricks, Wulf, and Liddel: J. Am. Chem. Soc., 58 : 1997 (1936).
140. Henriques, in Groth: Z. Kryst., 5 : 476 (1881).
141. Herbette: Bull. soc. franç. minéral., 29 : 97 (1906).
142. Hey: Z. Kryst., 48 : 243 (1910).
143. Heydrich: Z. Kryst., 48 : 243 (1910).
144. Hirsjarvi: Bull. com. géol. Finlande, 119 . 119 (1937).
145. Hlawatsch, in Kohn and Grun: Monatsh., 46 : 75 (1925): Sitzb. Akad. Wiss. Wien, 134, Abt. IIb: 75 (1925).
146. Hlawatsch, in Kohn and Mendelewitsch: Sitzb. Akad. Wiss. Wien, 130, Abt. IIb: 235 (1921).
147. Hoefinghoff: Z. Kryst., 20 : 305 (1892).
148. Hultquist and Poe: Ind. Eng. Chem., Anal. Ed., 7 : 398 (1935).
149. Hutchinson, in McCleland and Whitworth: J. Chem. Soc. London, 1927 : 2753.
150. Iball: Proc. Roy. Soc., A 146 : 140 (1934).
151. Inslay and Glaze: J. Res. Nat. Bur. Stand., 12 : 471 (1934).
152. Intern. Crit. Tables, Vol I, McGraw Hill Book Co., N. Y., 1926.
153. Ito: Z. Krist., 65 : 303 (1927).
154. Jablonski: Arch. Mineral. soc. sci. Varsovie, 9 : 128 (1933).
155. Jaeger: Proc. Acad. Sci. (Konink. Akad. Wetensch.), Amsterdam, 20:263 (1918).
156. Jaeger: Proc. Acad. Sci. (Konink. Akad. Wetensch.) Amsterdam, 38:243 (1935).
156a. Jaeger: Proc. Acad. Sci. (Konink. Akad. Wetensch.), Amsterdam, 40:116 (1940).

157. Jaeger: Rec. trav. chim., 33 : 343 (1914).
157a. Jaeger: Z. Kryst., 44 : 561 (1908).
158. Jaeger: and Beintema: Proc. Acad. Sci. (Konink. Akad. Wetensch.), Amsterdam, 38 : 243 (1935).
159. James and Soper: J. Chem. Soc. London, 1936 : 133.
160. James, King, and Horroks: Proc. Roy. Soc., A 153 : 225 (1936).
161. Jeffery, in Mann and Pope: Proc. Roy. Soc., A 107 : 88 (1925).
162. Kahrs: Z. Kryst., 40 : 482 (1905).
163. Kaplanova: Rosp. Ces. Akad., 2 cl., 24 (1915), No. 23; abstracted in Z. Krist., 63 : 574 (1926). and N. J. Mineral. Geol. 1917, I : 123.
164. Kappen: Z. Kryst., 37 : 151 (1903).
165. Karandéeff: Z. Kryst., 43 : 76 (1907).
166. Karandejew: Festschrift Vernadsky, 92 (1914).
167. Kasparova: Rosp. Ces. Akad., 2 cl. 26, No. 29 (1917).
168. Keenan: J. Am. Pharm. Ass., 16 : 837 (1927).
169. Keenan: J. Biol. Chem., 62 : 163 (1924).
170. Keenan: J. Wash. Acad. Sci., 16 : 433 (1926).
171. Keenan, in Clark: J. Am. Chem. Soc., 53 : 313 (1931).
172. Keenan, in Clark: J. Am. Chem. Soc., 53 : 729 (1931).
173. Keenan, in Clark: J. Am. Chem. Soc., 53 : 2264 (1931).
173a. Keenan, in Clark: J. Am. Chem. Soc., 53 : 2369 (1931).
174. Keenan, in Clark: J. Am. Chem. Soc., 54 : 2537 (1932).
175. Keenan, in Clark: J. Am. Chem. Soc., 54 : 3000 (1932).
176. Keenan, in Clark: J. Am. Chem. Soc., 54 : 4454 (1932).
177. Keenan, in Clark: J. Am. Chem. Soc., 56 : 987 (1934).
178. Keenan, in Clark: J. Am. Chem. Soc., 57 : 1111 (1935).
179. Keenan, in Clark: J. Am. Chem. Soc., 58 : 1009 (1936).
180. Keenan, in Clark: J. Am. Chem. Soc., 58 : 1982 (1936).
181. Keenan, in Clark: J. Am. Chem. Soc., 59 : 2511 (1937).
182. Keenan, in Clark: Science, 70 : 478 (1929).
183. Keenan, in Czonka and Nicolet: J. Biol. Chem., 99 : 213 (1932).
184. Keenan, in LaForge: J. Am. Chem. Soc., 53 : 3896 (1931).
185. Keenan, in LaForge: J. Am. Chem. Soc., 53 : 4450 (1931).
186. Keenan, in Jones and Gersdorff: J. Biol. Chem., 56 : 79 (1923).
187. Keenan, in Jones and Gersdorff: J. Biol. Chem., 75 : 213 (1927).
188. Keenan, in Montgomery, Hann, and Hudson: J. Am. Chem. Soc., 59: 1124 (1937).
189. Keenan, in Nelson: J. Am. Chem. Soc., 52 : 2928 (1930).
189a. Keenan, in Palkin and Harris: J. Am. Chem. Soc., 55 : 3677 (1933).
190. Keenan, in Palkin and Harris: J. Am. Chem. Soc., 56 : 1935 (1934).
191. Keenan, in Smith: J. Am. Chem. Soc., 54 : 397 (1932).
192. Keenan and Weisberg: J. Phys. Chem. 33 : 792 (1929).
192a. Keenan: Pers. Communic., May 25th, 1939.
193. Kerbosch: Arch. Pharm., 284 : 536 (1910).
194. Klasens, Perdok, and Terpstra: Z. Krist., 96 : 227 (1937).
194a. Klasens and Backer: Rec. trav. chim., 58 : 941 (1939).
195. Klasens and Terpstra: Rec. trav. chim., 56 : 673 (1937).
196. Kley: Z. Anal. Chem. 43 : 160 (1904).

197. Knaggs: J. Chem. Soc. London, 121 : 2069 (1922).
198. Knaggs: J. Chem. Soc. London, 123 : 71 (1923).
199. Knaggs: Proc. Roy. Soc., A, 150 : 576 (1935).
200. Knaggs, in Bansor, Gibson, and Pope: J. Chem. Soc. London, 117 : 1454 (1920).
201. Kofler: Arch. Pharm., 274 : 398 (1936).
202. Kofler: Arch. Pharm., 275 : 455 (1937).
203. Kofler: Arch. Pharm., 276 : 40 (1938).
204. Kofler: Arch. Pharm., 276 : 61 (1938).
204a. Kofler: Arch. Pharm., 276 : 525 (1938).
205. Kofler: Mikrochem., 15 : 319 (1934).
206. Kofler: Mikroskopische Methoden in der Mikrochemie. Emil Haim and Co., Leipzig, 1936.
207. Kofler and Kofler: Arch. Pharm., 271 : 387 (1933).
208. Kofler and Kofler: Arch. Pharm. 272 : 537 (1934).
209. Kofler and Fischer: Arch. Pharm., 273 : 483 (1935).
210. Kofler and Hauschild: Mikrochemie, 15 : 55 (1934).
211. Kofler and Hauschild: Z. Physiol. Chem., 224 : 150 (1934).
211a. Kofler and Mayrhofer: Mikrochemie, 10 : 460 (1934).
212. Kohn and Grün: Monatsh., 46 : 75 (1925); Sitzb. Akad. Wiss. Wien, 134, Abt. IIb : 75 (1924).
213. Kozik: Bull. intern. acad. polonaise, Series B, Sci., 1927 : 229.
214. Kozik: Bull. intern. acad. polonaise, Series B, Sci., 1931 : 247.
214a. Kurtz, Fry, and Willard: Unpubl. thesis at Penna. State Coll. Kindly sent to writer.
215. LaForge: J. Biol. Chem., 41 : 251 (1920).
216. LaForge and Hudson: J. Biol. Chem., 30.: 68 (1917).
217. LaForge and Keenan: J. Am. Chem. Soc., 53 : 4450 (1931).
218. Landolt-Bornstein: Physikalische-chemische Tabell., 3 Erg., 2: (1935).
219. Lang: Sitz. Akad. Wiss. Wien, 117, Abt. IIb : 287 (1908). Z. Krist. 49 : 638 (1911).
220. Laskiewicz: Arch. Chem. Farm., 2 : 219 (1935).
221. Laskiewicz: Arch. mineral. soc. sci. Varsovie, 6 : 119 (1930).
221a. Laskiewicz: Arch. mineral. soc. sci. Varsovie, 9 : 20 (1933).
222. Laskiewicz: N. J. Mineral. Geol., 1935: I, 552.
223. Lebedev: Festschrift Vernandsky, 1914.
224. Linck: Z. Kryst., 12 : 442 (1887).
224a. Liweh: Z. Kryst., 10 : 268 (1885).
225. Lonchambon: Bull. soc. franç. minéral., 48 : 367 (1925).
225a. Longchambon: Compt. rend., 178 : 951 (1924).
226. Lonsdale: Proc. Roy. Soc. A 123 : 494 (1929).
227. Loschmidt, in Barth and Kretschy: Sitzb. Akad. Wiss. Wien, 81, Abt. II:23 (1880).
228. Lowry, Steele, and Burgess: J. Chem. Soc. London, 121 : 633 (1922).
229. Lu, Hughes, and Giguere: J. Am. Chem. Soc., 63 : 1507 (1941).
230. Machatschki: Z. Krist., 59 : 209 (1924).
231. Machatschki: Z. Krist., 64 : 311 (1926).
231a. Malmquist: Bull. Geol. Inst. Univ. Upsala, 24 : 243 (1933).
232. Manasse: Atti accad. Lincei Rend. adur. sol. (5a), 19 : 138 (1910).
233. Mann and Pope: Proc. Roy. Soc., A 109 : 444 (1925).

234. Maquenne: Compt. rend., 107 . 583 (1888).
235. Martin: N. J. Mineral. Geol., Bl. Bd., 7 : 1 (1891).
236. Mason: Pers. commun., Oct. 30, 1936.
236a. Mason, in Bruce and Todd: J. Am. Chem. Soc., 61 : 157 (1939).
237. Mason, in Smith, Wilcoxon, and Browne: J. Am. Chem. Soc., 45 : 2604 (1923).
238. Matignon and Dode: Bull. soc. franç. minéral., 56 : 351 (1933).
239. Mayrhofer: Mikrochemie der Arzneimittel and Gifte, Bd. 2. Berlin, 1928.
240. Mayrhofer: Pharm. Monatsh. 7 : 61, 81, 109, 129 (1926).
241. Meixner: Z. Krist., 89 : 496 (1934).
242. Mercer and Robertson: J. Chem. Soc. London, 1936 : 291.
243. Merwin: J. Wash. Acad. Sci., 9 . 429 (1918).
244. Meyer and Rampoldt: Z. anorg. allgem. Chemie, 214 : 1 (1935).
245. Minder and Stocker: Z. Krist., 94 : 137 (1936).
245a. Minguzzi: Per. Mineral., 9 : 347 (1938).
246. Mochizuki: J. Chem. Soc. Japan, 54 : 894 (1933).
247. Monke, in Geisenheimer and Anschutz: Ann. chim., 306 : 38 (1899).
248. Moore and Gatewood: J. Am. Chem. Soc., 45 : 135 (1923).
249. Moroschkina: Bull. Imp. Acad. St. Petersburg, 1913 : 225.
250. Morozewicz: Bull. intern. acad. sci. Cracovie, 1908 : 1067.
251. Morris: J. Am. Chem. Soc., 54 : 2843 (1932).
252. Moses: Sch. Mines Quart., New York, 16 : 226 (1895).
253. Mottern and Keenan: J. Am. Chem. Soc., 53 : 2347 (1931).
254. Mügge: Centr. Mineral. Geol., 1915 : 481.
255. Mügge: N. J. Mineral. Geol., 1899, II : 12.
256. Mylius: Acta acad. Aboensi Math. Phys., 7, No. 3 (1933).
257. Neuhaus: Z. Krist., 89 : 505 (1934).
258. Neuhaus: Z. Krist. 90 : 415 (1935).
259. Nichols and Howes: Carnegie Inst. Wash. Pub., 298 : 207 (1919).
260. Niini: Z. Krist., 79 : 532 (1931).
261. Nováček: Z. Krist., 72 : 419 (1930).
262. Nováček: Z. Krist., 76 : 569 (1931).
263. Nováček: Z. Krist., 88 : 82 (1934).
264. Oftedahl: Z. Krist., 64 : 351 (1926).
265. Orndorff and Pratt: Am. Chem. J., 47 : 95 (1912).
266. Pabst: Am. J. Sci., 26 : 72 (1933).
267. Page: Ind. Eng. Chem., Ind. Ed., 28 : 856 (1936); as corrected by West: J. Am. Chem. Soc., 59 : 742 (1937).
268. Peacock: Univ. Toronto Studies Geol., Ser. 41 : 49 (1938).
269. Peterson: Ind. Eng. Chem., Ind. Ed., 20 : 388 (1928).
270. Philippe: Ann. chim. phys., 26 : 289 (1912).
271. Phillips and Keenan: J. Am. Chem. Soc., 53 : 1924 (1931).
272. Pichetto: Atti accad. Lincei, Classe sci. fis., mat., nat., (50)31 (2) : 143 (1922).
273. Pickett: Proc. Roy. Soc., A 142 : 334 (1933); Nature, 131 : 513 (1933).
274. Pierce: J. Biol. Chem., 23 : 334 (1915).
275. Pinck and Blair: J. Am. Chem. Soc., 49 : 509 (1927).
276. Piotrowski: Arch. Minéral. soc. sci. Varsovie, 13 : 63 (1937); N.J. Mineral. Geol., 1938, I : 483.

276a. Poe and Sellers: J. Am. Chem. Soc., 54 : 349 (1932); Ind. Eng. Chem. IV, 69 (1932).
277. Poe and Swisher: J. Am. Chem. Soc., 57 : 748 (1935).
278. Porter: Z. Krist., 66 : 217 (1928).
279. Porter: Z. Krist., 68 : 531 (1928).
280. Reuter: N. J. Mineral. geol., 1899, I : 155.
280a. Rochow, Stafford, Davis and Gilbert: Ind. Eng. Chem., 32 : 1187 (1940).
281. Rosch: Z. Krist., 65 : 681 (1927).
282. Rose: Centr. Mineral. Geol., 1917 : 85.
283. Rose: N. J. Mineral. Geol., 1918, I : 1.
284. Rost: Bull. Int. Acad. Sci. Bohème, 1937.
285. Rupe and Diehl: Helv. Chim. Acta, 5 : 906 (1922).
286. Rupe, Steiger, and Fiedler: Ber., 47 : 73 (1914).
287. Ruzicka, Huyser, and Geidel: Rec. trav. chim., 47 : 363 (1928).
288. Sada: Bull. Chem. Soc. Japan, 9 : 1 (1934).
289. Sanero and Fornaseri: Period. Mineral. (Rome), 9 : 213 (1938).
289a. Sarrero: Period. Mineral. 8 : 265 (1937); abstr. in N. J. Mineral. Geol. 1939, II : 284.
289b. Schechter and Haller: J. Am. Chem. Soc., 62 : 1307 (1940).
290. Schrauf: Sitzb. Akad. Wiss. Wien, 42 : 128 (1860).
291. Schurink, in Landolt-Bornstein: Physikalische-chemische Tabellen, 3 Erg., II : 1595 (1935).
292. Schuster: Tschermak's mineral. petrog. Mitt., 9 : 216 (1887).
293. Schwietring: Z. Krist., 76 : 87 (1931).
294. Shaner and Willard: J. Am. Chem. Soc., 58 : 1977 (1936).
295. Shaner and Willard: Mikrochem., 19 : 222 (1936).
296. Slawson: J. Biol. Chem., 77 : 373 (1930).
297. Slawson, in Blicke and Smith: J. Am. Chem. Soc., 51 : 1874 (1929).
297a. Slotta, Ruschig and Fels: Ber., 67 : 1270 (1934).
298. Smith, Mason, and Carroll: J. Am. Chem. Soc., 53 : 4103 (1933).
299. Smith, Miale, and Mason: J. Am. Chem. Soc., 55 : 3759 (1933).
300. Spaenhauer: Z. Krist., 77 : 159 (1931).
301. Spaenhauer: Z. Krist., 83 : 113 (1932).
302. Spaenhauer: Z. Krist., 88 : 176 (1934).
302a. Spaenhauer: Z. Krist., 88 : 330 (1934).
303. Stefl: Z. Krist., 54 : 343 (1914).
304. Steinmetz: Z. Krist., 53 : 463 (1914).
305. Steinmetz: Z. Krist., 67 : 434 (1928).
306. Stoll: Schweiz. Apoth. Z., 60 : 374 (1922).
307. Stortenbeker: Rec. trav. chim., 32 : 226 (1913).
308. Strüver: Z. Kryst., 6 : 538 (1882).
309. Stumpf: Ann. Physik, (4) 37 : 351 (1912).
310. Sundararajan: Z. Krist., 93 : 238 (1936).
311. Sutton: Phil. Mag., 15 : 1001 (1933).
312. Takahashi, Yaginuma, and Hayakawa: Proc. Imp. Acad. Japan, 7 : 57 (1931); J. Soc. Chem. Ind. Japan, 34 : 215B, 216B (1931).
313. Takayama: J. Chem. Soc. Japan, 52 : 245 (1931).
314. Terpstra: Physica, 8 : 95 (1928).

315. Terpstra: Z. Krist., 64 : 150 (1926).
316. Terpstra: Z. Krist., 67 : 484 (1928).
317. Terpstra, in Backer: Rec. trav. chim., 49 : 559 (1930).
318. Terpstra, in Backer: Rec. trav. chim., 49 : 729 (1930).
319. Terpstra, in Backer: Rec. trav. chim., 49 : 1107 (1930).
320. Terpstra, in Backer: Rec. trav. chim., 50 : 1073 (1931).
321. Terpstra, in Backer: Rec. trav. chim., 54 : 745 (1935).
322. Terpstra, in Backer: Rec. trav. chim., 54 : 832 (1935).
323. Terpstra, in Backer: Rec. trav. chim., 55 : 591 (1936).
324. Terpstra, in Backer: Rec. trav. chim., 55 : 602 (1936).
325. Terpstra, in Backer and Bottema: Rec. trav. chim., 54 : 627 (1932).
326. Terpstra, in Backer and Dijken: Rec. trav. chim., 54 : 627 (1935).
327. Terpstra, in Backer and Dijken: Rec. trav. chim., 55 : 22 (1936).
328. Terpstra, in Backer and Klasens: Rev. trav. chim., 49 : 1045 (1930).
329. Terpstra, in Backer and Strating: Rec. trav. chim., 53 : 525 (1934).
330. Terpstra, in Backer and van der Boan: Rec. trav. chim., 56 : 1175 (1937).
331. Terpstra, in Jaeger and Byjkerk: Proc. Acad. Sci. (Konink. Akad. Wetensch.), Amsterdam, 40 : 246 (1937).
332. Theilacker: Z. Krist., 90 : 51, 77 (1935).
333. Thibaud and Dupré la Tour: Compt. rend., 191 : 200 (1930).
333a. Thornton, Kraybill, and Mitchell: J. Am Chem. Soc., 62 : 2006 (1940).
334. Topsøe and Christiansen: Ann. chim. phys., (5) 1 : 64 (1874).
335. Tutton: Proc. Roy. Soc., A 108 : 548 (1925).
336. Ulrich, in Ruzicka and Balas: Ann., 460 : 202 (1928).
337. Van der Veen: Z. Krist, 55 : 627 (1920).
338. Venable: J. Am. Chem. Soc., 40 : 1099 (1918).
339. Viehoever: J. Ass. Off. Agric. Chem., 6 : 489 (1923).
340. Walcott, in Collins: J. Am. Med. Assoc., 90 : 25 (1928).
341. Walcott, in Gordon: J. Am. Pharm. Assoc., 17 : 1195 (1928).
342. Walcott, in Hurd and Spence: J. Am. Chem. Soc., 49 : 266 (1927).
342a. Waldman and Brandenberger: Z. Krist., 82 : 77 (1932).
343. Walter: J. Am. Chem. Soc., 62 : 3273 (1914).
343a. Ward: New and Nonofficial Remedies, 1938 : 480. Amer. Med. Assoc.
343b. Watanabe: J. Pharm. Soc. Japan, 58 : 145 (1938).
343c. Watanabe: J. Pharm. Soc. Japan, 59 : 30 (1939).
343d. Watanabe: J. Pharm. Soc. Japan, 60 : 163 (1940).
344. Watanabe and Watanabe: Proc. Imp. Acad. (Tokyo), 2 : 379 (1935). Mineral. Abstr., 6 : 516 (1937).
344a. Welsh and Keenan: J. Am. Chem. Soc., 64 : 183 (1942).
345. West: Am. Mineral., 22 : 731 (1937).
346. West: J. Am. Chem. Soc., 59 : 742 (1937).
346a. West: J. Am. Chem. Soc., 63 : 630 (1941).
347. West: Personal commun. Nov. 2, 1936.
348. West: Z. Krist., 88 : 195 (1934).
349. West: Z. Krist., 96 : 459 (1937).
350. Wherry: Int. Crit. Tables, 1 : 261 (1926).
351. Wherry: J. Am. Chem. Soc., 40 : 1852 (1918).

352. Wherry: J. Am. Chem. Soc., 41 : 1115 (1919).
353. Wherry: J. Am. Chem. Soc., 42 : 1840 (1920).
354. Wherry: J. Am. Chem. Soc., 42 : 125 (1920).
355. Wherry: J. Biol. Chem., 42 : 377 (1920).
356. Wherry: J. Wash. Acad. Sci., 8 : 277 (1918).
357. Wherry: J. Wash. Acad. Sci., 12 : 196 (1922).
358. Wherry: J. Wash. Acad. Sci., 16 : 433 (1926).
359. Wherry: J. Wash. Acad. Sci., 18 : 302 (1928).
360. Wherry and Adams: J. Wash. Acad. Sci., 9 : 396 (1919).
361. Wherry, in Hann: J. Am. Chem. Soc., 45 : 82 (1923).
362. Wherry and Hann: J. Wash. Acad. Sci., 12 : 286 (1922).
363. Wherry and Keenan, in Ambler: Ind. Eng. Chem., 12 : 1081 (1920).
364. Wherry and Keenan, in Sando: J. Biol. Chem., 90 : 477, 675 (1931).
365. Wherry and Yanovsky: J. Am. Chem. Soc., 40 : 1063, 1955 (1918).
366. Wherry and Yanovsky: J. Wash. Acad. Sci., 9 : 505 (1919).
366a. Wherry, in Eagles and Johnson: J. Am. Chem. Soc., 49 : 575 (1927).
367. Wherry, in Hudson and Chernoff: J. Am. Chem. Soc., 40 : 1005 (1918).
368. Wherry, Johns, Chernoff, and Viehofer: J. Biol. Chem., 52 : 335 (1922).
369. Wherry, in Nelson: J. Am. Chem. Soc., 41 : 1115 (1919).
370. Wherry, in Nelson: J. Am. Chem. Soc., 41 : 2121 (1919).
371. Wherry, in Nelson and Dawson: J. Am. Chem. Soc., 45 : 2179 (1923).
372. Wherry, in Wise and Russell: Ind. Eng. Chem., 15 : 815 (1923).
373. Whitmore and Gebhart: Ind. Eng. Chem., Anal. Ed., 10 : 654 (1938).
374. Widmer: Z. Krist., 60 : 181 (1924).
375. Widmer: Z. Krist., 72 : 442 (1930).
376. Wilcox: Personal Commun. Dec. 6, 1937.
377. Willard: Personal Commun., Jan. 26, 1938.
377a. Willard: Personal Commun., Dec. 21, 1938.
377b. Willard and Jones: J. Am. Chem. Soc., 62 : 2876 (1940).
377c. Willard and Maresh: J. Am. Chem. Soc., 62 : 1253 (1940).
378. Wilson and Keenan: J. Assoc. Off. Agric. Chem., 13 : 389 (1920).
379. Winchell: Am. Mineral., 22 : 1088 (1937).
379a. Winchell: Optical Mineralogy, 3d Ed., Part 2. John Wiley and Sons, New York, 1933.
380. Winterstein: Z. Krist., 64 : 351 (1926).
381. Wolfram and Thompson: J. Am. Chem. Soc., 53 : 622 (1931).
382. Wood and Ayliffe: Phil. Mag., (7) 21 : 321 (1936).
383. Wooster: Crystal Physics, Cambridge, 1938.
384. Wooster, in Jones: J. Chem. Soc. London, 1933 : 951.
385. Woyno: Arch. mineral. soc. sci. Varsovie, 2 : 1 (1926).
386. Wright: J. Am. Chem. Soc., 38 : 1647 (1916).
387. Wright: J. Am. Chem. Soc., 52 : 1276 (1930).
388. Wright: J. Biol. Chem., 28 : 523 (1917).
389. Wright and Allen: Am. Mineral., 11 : 67 (1926).
390. Wright and Allen: Am. Mineral., 15 : 169 (1930).
391. Wright, in Phelps and Palmer: J. Am. Chem. Soc., 39 : 136 (1917).
392. Wright, in Phelps and Palmer: J. Am. Chem. Soc., 39 : 1515 (1917).

393. Wulff and Schaller: Z. Krist., 87 : 43 (1934).
394. Wyrouboff: Bull soc. franç. minéral., 23 : 65 (1900).
395. Yaginuma, Arai, and Hagakawa: Proc. Imp. Acad. (Tokyo), 8 : 91 (1932).
396. Yorks and Willard: Mikrochem., 19 : 227 (1935).
396a. Yosiki: J. Soc. Chem. Ind. Japan, 43. Sup. 83 (1940).
397. Young, in Hartline: Unpubl. B.S. thesis, Mass. Inst. Tech., 1931.
398. Young: in unpubl. report received from N.W. Buerger, Feb. 1937.
398a. Young and Spiers: Z. Krist., 78 : 101 (1931).
399. Zadoc-Kahn: Compt. rend., 187 : 1138 (1928).
400. Zartner: Z. Krist., 59 : 555 (1924).
401. Zartner: Z. Krist., 62 : 144 (1924).
402. Zenzen: Arkiv Kemi, Mineral. Geol., 8 Heft, 6 (1923); Abstract in N. J. Mineral. Geol. 1930, I : 171.
403. Zeynek: Z. physiol. Chem., 114 : 275 (1921).

REFERENCES ADDED FOR THE SECOND EDITION.

404. Albrecht and Corey: J. Am. Chem. Soc., 61 : 1087 (1939).
405. Ambler, Turer and Keenan: J. Am. Chem. Soc., 67 : 1 (1945).
405a. Amer. Cyanamid Co.: New Products Bull., Vol. I (1949).
406. Andress: Z. Krist., 78 : 477 (1931).
407. Andress: Z. Phys. Chem., B2 : 380 (1929).
408. Andress: Z. Phys. Chem., B4 : 190 (1929).
409. Astbury: J. Text. Soc., B4 : 1900 (1929).
410. Astbury: Proc. Roy. Soc., 107 : 506 (1923).
411. Atsuki and Okajima: J. Soc. Chem. Ind. Japan, 40 : 360 B (1937).
411a. Auerswald, Günthard and Epprecht: Helv. Chim. Acta, 34 : 222 (1951).
412. Backer and Bijhen: Rec. trav. chim. Pays-Bas, 55 : 22 (1936).
413. Banerjee and Ahmad: Indian J. Phys., 12 : 249 (1938).
414. Banerjee and Sinha: Indian J. Phys., 11 : 21 (1937).
415. Banerjee and Sinha: Indian J. Phys., 11 : 409 (1938).
416. Bernal: Trans. Faraday Soc., 29 : 1032 (1933).
417. Bernal and Crowfoot: J. Chem. Soc. London, 93 (1935).
418. Bernal and Crowfoot: J. Soc. Chem. Ind., 54 : 701 (1935).
418a. Biles, Witt and Poe: Mikrochem., 38 : 591 (1951).
418aa. Bokiĭ and Lyashenko: Trudy Inst. Krist. 1947, No. 3, 21 – 28. From Chem. Abst. 44 : 7702 (1950).
418b. Bond *et al.*: Anal. Chem. 20 : 491 (1948).
419. Bragg: J. Chem. Soc. London, 121 : 2756 (1931).
420. Brandstätter: Z. Phys. Chem., 192 : 76 (1943).
421. Bredig and Möller: Z. Krist., 71 : 331 (1929).
422. Brill: Ann. Chim., 331 : 204 (1923).
423. Brill *et al.*: Ann. Phys. 34 : 393 (1939).
424. Bryant: J. Am. Chem. Soc., 60 : 1394 (1938).
425. Bryant: J. Am. Chem. Soc., 65 : 96 (1943).
426. Bunn: Trans. Faraday Soc., 35 : 482 (1939).
427. Buerger: Am. Mineral., 30 : 551 (1945).

428. Burgers: Phil. Mag., 1 : 289 (1926).
429. Burgers: Proc. Roy. Soc. London, 116 : 553 (1927).
429a. Cannon and George: Nature, 151 : 53 (1943).
430. Carson, Waisbrot, and Jones: J. Am. Chem. Soc., 65 : 1777 (1943).
431. Caspari: J. Chem. Soc. London, 3235 (1925).
432. Caspari: J. Chem. Soc. London, 129 : 2944 and 131 : 1093 (1927).
433. Caspari: Phil. Mag., 4 : 1276 (1927).
433a. Castle: J. Am. Pharm. Assn., 33 : 47 (1949).
433b. Castle: Mikrochem., 38 : 92 (1951).
434. Castle and Witt: J. Am. Chem. Soc., 68 : 64 (1946).
434a. Castle, Witt, and Poe: J. Am. Chem. Soc., 71 : 228 (1949).
435. Clark, Kaye and Parks: Ind. Eng. Chem. Anal. Ed. 18 : 310 (1946).
435a. Clarke and Krc: Anal. Chem., 24 : 1378, 1516 (1952).
436. Clark and Smith: Ind. Eng. Chem., 23 : 697 (1931).
436a. Cock *et al.*: Anal. Chem., 20 : 593 (1948).
436b. Cook and McCrone: unpubl. vol. on Vitamins, Armour Res. Found.
437. Council on Pharm. and Chem.; J. Am. Med. Assn., 121 : 592 (1943).
438. Coven: Unpubl. data of the Am. Cyanamid Co.
439. Cox: J. Chem. Soc. London, 2313 (1931).
440. Cox *et al.*: J. Chem. Soc. London, 129 (1936).
441. Cox *et al.*: Proc. Roy. Soc., 157 : 399 (1936).
442. Crowfoot: Proc. Roy. Soc., 164 : 580 (1938).
443. Crowfoot and Riley: Nature, 144 : 1011 (1939).
443a. Daasch: Anal. Chem., 19 : 779 (1947).
443b. Datta: Indian J. Phys. 21 : 303 (1947).
444. Davies and Hartshorne: J. Chem. Soc. London, 1830 (1934).
445. Dewey and Plein: Ind. Eng. Chem., Anal. Ed. 17 : 515 (1946).
446. Dhar: Indian J. Physics, 7 : 43 (1932).
446a. Doll and Grison: Compt. rend., 226 : 679 (1948).
447. Dorn and Lohmann: Ann. Phys. 29 : 533 (1909).
448. Dresser *et al.*: J. Am. Chem. Soc., 53 : 4235 (1931).
449. Dufet: Bull. soc. franç. minéral., 25 : 127 (1902); Z. Krist. 29 : 311 (1902).
450. Dupré la Tour: Ann. phys. 18 : 199 (1932).
451. Eisenberg and Keenan: J. Am. Pharm. Assn., 36 : 294 (1947).
451a. Eisenberg and Keenan: J. Assn. Off. Agric. Chem., 27 : 177 (1944).
452. Eisenberg and Keenan: J. Assn. Off. Agric. Chem., 27 : 458 (1944).
452a. Eisenberg and Wilson: J. Assn. Off. Agric. Chem., 30 : 563 (1947).
453. Elliott: Z. Krist. 98 : 180 (1937).
454. Evans: Z. Krist. 92 : 154 (1935).
455. Fankuchen: Phys. Rev. 45 : 563 (1934).
456. Fankuchen: *et al.*: Science, 103 : 25 (1946).
456a. Fenimore: Acta Cryst., 1 : 295 (1948).
456b. Feneglio: Atti accad. Sci. Torino, 84 : 208 (1949 – 50).
457. Ferrari and Curti: Z. Krist., 84 : 8 (1932).
458. Ferguson, Rosevear, and Nordsieck: J. Am. Chem. Soc., 69 : 141 (1947).
458a. Finlay *et al.*: Science, 111 : 85 (1950); modified by J. A. Means: pers. commun., March 29, 1950.

459. Fisher: Proc. Geol. Soc. Am., 444 (1933).
460. Frey-Wyssling: Kolloidchem., 23 : 40 (1927).
461. Frey-Wyssling: Nature, 145 : 821 (1940).
462. Frey-Wyssling: Pringsheim Jahrb. 31 : 211 (1926).
463. Frey-Wyssling: and Wuhrmann: Helv. Chim. Acta, 22 : 981 (1939).
464. Gaubert: Compt. rend., 153 : 573 (1911).
465. Gaubert: Compt. rend., 177 : 1123 (1923).
466. Gerstäcker *et al.*: Z. Krist., 66 : 355 (1927).
467. Gibb: Opt. Meth. Chem. Anal., 307 and 309 (1942).
468. Gilbert: Unpubl. data of the Am. Cyanamid Co.
468a. Gilpin *et al.*: Anal. Chem. 20 : 779, 879, 1124 (1948).
468b. Gilpin and McCrone: Anal. Chem., 22 : 368 (1950).
469. Goedhart, in Rusicka and Hosking: Ann. Chim., 349 : 147 (1929).
470. Gooden: J. Am. Chem. Soc., 67 : 1616 (1945).
471. Goodwin and Hardy: Proc. Roy. Soc., 164 : 369 (1938).
472. Gossner and Neff: Z. Krist., 85 : 370 (1933).
473. Gossner and Neff: Z. Krist., 86 : 32 (1933).
473a. Gottardi: Chem. Abst., 44 : 9209 (1950).
474. Gottfried and Steinmetz: N.J. Min. Bl. Bd. 57 : 249 (1928).
474a. Grabar and McCrone: Anal. Chem., 22 : 620 and 1338 (1950).
475. Greenwood: Min. Mag, 21 : 1 (1926).
475a. Grove and Keenan: J. Am. Chem. Soc., 63 : 97 (1941).
476. Guaisnet-Pilaud: Compt. rend. 197 : 419 (1933).
477. Guha: Phil. Mag., 26 : 213 (1938).
477a. Haley and Keenan: J. Am. Pharm. Assn., 39 : 85 (1949).
477b. Haley and Keenan: J. Am. Pharm. Assn., 38 : 381 and 384 (1949).
477c. Haley and Keenan: J. Am. Pharm. Assn., 39 : 212 (1950).
477d. Haley and Keenan: J. Am. Pharm. Assn., 39 : 526 (1950).
478. Halla and Zimmerman: Z. Krist., 82 : 497 (1932).
479. Hallimond in Robinson and Jones: J. Chem. Soc. London, 101 : 62 (1912).
480. Hassel and Luzanski: Zeit. Phys. Chem., B 3 : 282 (1929).
481. Hassel and Mark: Zeit. Phys. Chem., 111 : 357 (1924).
482. Heerman and Herzog: Mikro. Mech. Tech. Textile, 89 (1937).
483. Hendricks: J. Am. Chem. Soc., 50 : 2455 (1928).
484. Hendricks: J. Phys. Chem., 37 : 1109 (1933).
485. Hendricks: Z. Krist., 84 : 85 (1933).
485a. Hendricks: Z. Krist., 91 : 48 (1935).
485b. Hendricks and Jefferson: J. Chem. Phys., 4 : 102 (1936).
486. Hengstenberg: Z. Krist., 67 : 583 (1928).
487. Hengstenberg and Mark: Z. Krist., 72 : 301 (1929).
488. Hermans: Phys. Cellulose Fibers, 1946.
489. Herrmann: Z. Krist., 67 : 189 (1928).
490. Hertel: Z. Phys. Chem., B 11 : 279 (1930–31).
491. Hertel: Z. Phys. Chem. Festb., 272 (1931).
491a. Hertel: Z. Phys. Chem., B 29 : 117 (1935).
492. Hertel and Römer: Z. Phys. Chem., B 21 : 292 (1933).
493. Hertel and Schneider: Z. Phys. Chem., B12 : 139 (1931).

494. Herzog: Helv. Chim. Acta, 9 : 631 and 798 (1926).
494a. Hotz: Schw. Min. Pet. Mit., 31 : 188 (1951).
495. Hubbard: Am. Mineral., 30 : 645 (1945).
495a. Hubach and Jones: Anal. Chem., 22 : 595 (1950).
496. Hughes: J. Am. Chem. Soc., 62 : 1258 (1940).
497. Hughes: J. Am. Chem. Soc., 63 : 1737 (1941).
498. Huggins and Noble: Am. Mineral. 16 : 519 (1931).
499. Hultgreen: J. Chem. Phys. 4 : 84 (1936).
499a. Hultquist, Poe, and Witt: Ind. Eng. Chem. Anal. Ed., 14 : 219 (1942).
499b. Hultquist, Poe, and Witt: J. Am. Chem. Soc., 67 : 688 (1945).
500. Iball: Z. Krist., 94 : 7 (1936).
501. Iball: Z. Krist., 94 : 397 (1936).
502. Ivanov and Savinova: Compt. rend. Acad. Sci. USSR, 48 : 31 (1945).
503. Jaffe: Phys. Rev., 51 : 43 (1939).
504. Jaffray: Compt. rend. 213 : 132 (1941).
505. Jefferson: J. Chem. Phys., 4 : 102 (1936).
505a. Joel and Canepa: Acta Cryst., 4 : 283 (1951).
505b. Johnson, Bruce and Dutcher: J. Am. Chem. Soc., 65 : 2005 (1943).
506. Jones: J. Am. Chem. Soc., 68 : 854 (1946).
506a. Jones and Palmer: J. Am. Chem. Soc., 71 : 1935 (1949).
506b. Jones and Palmer: J. Am. Chem. Soc., 72 : 1820 (1950).
507. Jones and White: J. Am. Chem. Soc., 68 : 1339 (1946).
508. Jong: Physica, 10 : 101 (1930).
509. Kabraji: Indian J. Phys., 6 : 81 (1931).
509a. Kaezka, Wolf and Folkers: J. Am. Chem. Soc., 71 : 1514 (1949).
510. Kanamaru: Helv. Chim. Acta, 17 : 1047 (1934).
511. Kanamaru: Helv. Chim. Acta, 17 : 1066 (1934).
512. Kanamaru: Helv. Chim. Acta, 17 : 1429 (1934).
513. Katz *et al.*: Z. Phys. Chem., 171 : 181 (1934).
514. Keenan: J. Biol. Chem., 83 : 137 (1929).
515. Keenan: J. Assn. Off. Agric. Chem., 25 : 830 (1942).
516. Keenan: J. Am. Pharm. Assn., 32 : 248 (1943).
517. Keenan: J. Assn. Off. Agric. Chem., 26 : 514 (1943).
518. Keenan: J. Assn. Off. Agric. Chem., 27 : 153 (1944).
519. Keenan: J. Am. Pharm. Assn., 33 : 183 (1944).
520. Keenan: Science, 104 : 211 (1946).
521. Keenan: J. Am. Pharm. Assn., 35 : 338 (1946).
522. Keenan: J. Assn. Off. Agric. Chem., 29 : 327 (1946).
523. Keenan: J. Am. Pharm. Assn., 36 : 281 (1947).
523a. Keenan: J. Am. Pharm. Assn., 37 : 41 (1948).
523b. Keenan: J. Am. Pharm. Assn., 37 : 202 (1948).
523c. Keenan: J. Am. Pharm. Assn., 37 : 479 (1948).
523d. Keenan: J. Am. Pharm. Assn., 37 : 519 (1948).
523e. Keenan: Science, 110 : 304 and 404 (1949): J. Am. Pharm. Assn. 38 : 313 (1949).
523f. Keenan: Chem. Anal., 39 : 33 and 52 (1950).
523g. Keenan: J. Am. Pharm. Assn., 39 : 215 (1950).
523h. Keenan: Chem. Anal., 40 : 3 (1951).

524. Keenan and Eisenberg: J. Am. Pharm. Assn., 35 : 94 (1946).
524a. Keenan and Haley: J. Am. Pharm. Assn., 39 : 333 (1950).
525. Keenan and Warren: J. Am. Pharm. Assn., 29 : 300 (1945).
526. Keenan and Welsh: J. Am. Pharm. Assn., 33 : 128 (1944).
527. Keenan, in McCalip and Seibert: Ind. Eng. Chem., 33 : 637 (1941).
527a. Keihn and King: Acta Cryst., 4 : 473 (1951).
527b. Keller and Ungnade: Acta Cryst., 2 : 193 (1949).
528. Ketelaar: Physica 4 : 619 (1937).
528a. Kirkpatrick: personal communication, April 24, 1950.
529. Kirkpatrick: Unpublished data of the Am. Cyanamid Co.
530. Kirkpatrick: Unpublished Ph. D. thesis, Penna. State Coll., 1943.
530a. Kleber, Stackelberg and Wallraf: N. Jahrb. Min. 1950, 241.
531. Klug: Z. Krist., 90 : 495 (1933).
532. Knaggs: J. Chem. Physics, 3 : 241 (1935).
533. Kofler and Brandstätter: Zeit. Phys. Chem., 192 : 229 (1943).
534. Kofler and Dernbach: Arch. Pharm., 270 : 153 (1932).
535. Kratky: Zeit. Phys. Chem. B, 5 : 297 (1929); B, 11 : 363 (1930).
535a. Krc and McCrone: Anal. Chem., 22 : 720, 845, 1576 (1950).
535b. Krc: Anal. Chem., 23 : 932 (1951).
535c. Krc: Anal. Chem., 24 : 1070 (1952).
536. Kreider and Menotti: J. Am. Chem. Soc., 69 1227 (1942).
537. Kurnakov and Andreevskii: Anorg. Chem., 189 : 137 (1930).
537a. Kutina: Chem. Abstr., 44 : 1209 (1950).
538. Lambot: Bull. Soc. Roy. Sci. Liège, No. 11, Nov. 1946.
539. Lambot: Bull. Soc. Roy. Sci. Liège, No. 12, Dec. 1946.
539a. Larsen, Witt, and Poe: Mikrochem., 34 (1948).
539b. Larsen, Poe, and Witt: Mikrochem., 35 (1949).
540. Leuck and Mark: J. Am. Chem. Soc., 56 : 1959 (1934).
541. Llewellyn, Cox, and Goodwin: J. Chem. Soc. London, 1937 : 883.
541a. Llewellyn and Whitmore: J. Chem. Soc., 1948 : 1316.
542. Lonsdale: Mineral. Mag., 27 : 120 (1945).
542a. Magnano: Atti accad. Sci. Torino, 85 : 83 (1950 – 51).
543. Maresh and Perry: Unpubl. data of the Amer. Cyanamid Co.
544. Mark: Z. Krist., 69 : 105 (1928).
545. Marwick: Nature, 24 : 438 (1930).
546. Marwick: Proc. Roy. Soc., 131 : 172 (1927).
546a. Marwick: Proc. Roy. Soc., 135 : 621 (1931).
547. Mason, in Smith *et al.*: J. Am. Chem. Soc., 45 : 2604 (1923).
548. Mauguin: Bull. soc. chim. Belg., 36 : 172 (1927).
549. McCabe and Quirke: Am. Inst. Min. Eng. Tech. Publ., 791 (1937).
550. McCombie, Scarborough, and Waters: J. Chem. Soc. London, 1928, p. 353.
551. McCrea: Nature, 117 : 162 (1931).
551a. McCrone: personal communication to A. N. Winchell, Jan. 18, 1951 and Feb. 27, 1951.
552. McCrone: Personal communication to T. G. Rochow, June 2, 1947.
552a. McCrone *et al.*: Anal. Chem., 20 : 274, 385, 593, 683, 986, 1249 (1948).
553. McCrone and Cook: Frontier, 10, No. 2, 12, and 23 (1947).

553a. McCrone *et al.*: Anal. Chem. 21: 191, 306, 421, 531, 645, 757, 882, 1293, 1428 (1949).
553b. McCrone *et al.*: Anal. Chem., 22 : 500, 954, 1067, 1225 (1950).
553c. McCrone *et al.*: Anal. Chem., 23 : 205, 543, 1042, 1188, 1339, 1523, 1718, 1884 (1951).
553d. McCrone *et al.*: Anal. Chem., 24 : 225, 421, 592 (1952).
554. Meyer and Frey-Wyssling: Helv. Chim. Acta, 18 : 1428 (1935).
555. Meyer and Milsch: Helv. Chim. Acta, 20 : 232 (1937).
556. Merwin: Proc. Am. Soc. Test. Mat. 17, (2), 494 (1917).
556a. Mitchell: Anal. Chem., 21 : 448 (1949).
557. Mitchell and Bryant: J. Am. Chem. Soc., 65 : 128 (1943).
557a. Mitsuhashi: Cryst. Stud. Org. Pharm., 1 : 201 (1948).
557b. Mitsuhashi: J. Pharm. Soc. Japan, 70 : 711 (1950).
557c. Mitsuhashi: J. Pharm. Soc. Japan, 71 : 1115 (1951).
557d. Mitsuhashi: J. Pharm. Soc. Japan, 72 : 830 (1952).
557e. Murray and Walter: J. Am. Chem. Soc., 67 : 1422 (1945).
558. Neuhaus: Z. Krist., 101 : 177 (1939).
559. Neuhaus: Z. Krist., 104 : 401 (1942).
560. Neuhaus: Z. Krist., 105 : 161 (1943).
560a. Niggli: Schw. Min. Pet. Mit., 22 (1942).
560b. Nitta and Osaki: X-Rays, 5 : 37 (1948).
560c. Nitta and Saito: X-Rays, 5 : 89 (1949).
561. Nitta and Watanabe: Sci. Pap. Inst. Phys. Chem. Res., 26 : 164 (1934).
562. Nitta and Watanabe: Sci. Pap. Inst. Phys. Chem. Res., 31 : 125 (1937).
563. Orelkin and Lonsdale: Proc. Roy. Soc., A, 144 : 630 (1934).
563a. Paden and MacLean: Chem. Abst., 42 : 3426 (1948).
564. Page: Ind. Eng. Chem. Ind. Ed., 28 : 856 (1936), as corrected by West: J. Am. Chem. Soc., 59 : 742 (1937).
565. Pal and Guha: Z. Krist., 92 : 392 (1935).
565a. Palin and Powell: J. Chem. Soc., 1948, p. 815.
566. Patterson and White: Z. Krist., 78 : 86 (1931).
566a. Pellet and Chatelain: Bull. soc. franc. mineral., 73 : 154 (1950).
566aa. Plein: J. Am. Pharm. Assn., 38 : 535 (1949).
567. Plein and Dewey: Ind. Eng. Chem., Anal. Ed., 15 : 534 (1943).
567a. Plein and Dewey: Ind. Eng. Chem., Anal. Ed., 18 : 515 (1946).
567b. Pebeguin: Bull. soc. franç. minéral., 82 : 189 (1949).
567c. Poe, Witt, and Snodgrass: Mikrochem., 35 (1949).
568. Pope and Whitworth: Proc. Roy. Soc., A, 134 : 357 (1932).
568a. Porter and Spiller: Barker Index of Crystals, I, 2 (1951).
569. Prasad, de Sousa, and Shanker: J. Univ. Bombay, 5, 2 : 109 (1936).
570. Prasad and Mapara: Indian J. Phys., 6 : 41 (1936).
571. Prasad and Shanker: J. Indian Chem. Soc., 13 : 123 (1936).
572. Preston: Trans. Faraday Soc., 29 : 65 (1933).
572a. Prien and Frondel: J. Urol., 46 : 748 (1941).
573. Prien and Frondel: J. Urol., 46 : 756 (1941).
573a. Reis and Schneider: Z. Krist., 68 : 543 (1928).
574. Rickes *et al.*: Science, 107 : 396 (1948).
575. Rieck: Rec. Trav. Chim. Pays-Bas, 63 : 171 (1944).
576. Riskin: J. Appl. Chem. Russ., 14 : 1036 (1941).

577. Riskin and Zimatskaya: J. Appl. Chem. Russ., 13 : 1596 (1940). Accuracy for N_Z is $\pm$ .02 and for N_X is $\pm$ .001 to $\pm$ .002.
578. Robertson: Proc. Roy. Soc., 140 : 79 (1933).
579. Robertson: Proc. Roy. Soc., 141 : 594 (1933).
580. Robertson: Proc. Roy. Soc., 146 : 473 (1934).
581. Robertson and Ubbelohde: Proc. Roy. Soc., A, 157 : 122 (1938).
582. Robertson and Woodward: J. Chem. Soc. London, 1936, p. 1817.
583. Robertson and Woodward: Proc. Roy. Soc., 162 : 568 (1937).
584. Rochow: Unpubl. data of the American Cyanamid Co.
585. Rochow, Stafford, Davis, and Gilbert: Ind. Eng. Chem., 32 : 1187 (1940).
585a. Rose: Anal. Chem., 24 : 1680 (1952).
586. Rost: Mineral. Abstr., 9 : 186 (1946).
587. Royer and Maresh: J. Soc. Dyers Col., 63 : 287 (1947).
588. Rundle and French: J. Am. Chem. Soc., 65 : 558 (1943).
588a. Rupe and Gassman: Helv. Chim. Acta, 17 : 283 (1934).
588b. Sanero: Atti accad. Sci. Torino, 85 : 67 (1950–51).
588c. Saunder: Proc. Roy. Soc. A, 190 : 508 (1947).
588d. Schiavinato: Per. Mineral., 16 : 138 (1947).
589. Schoon: Z. Phys. Chem., B, 39 : 385 (1938).
589a. Schweizer: J. Org. Chem., 15 : 471 (1950).
590. Sen: Sci. Cult., 5 : 717 (1940); Indian J. Phys., 19 : 243.
591. Sherman: The New Fibers, 1946, p. 31.
592. Sidhu: J. Appl. Phys., 10 : 83 (1939).
593. Snaauw and Wiebenga: Rec. trav. chim. Pays-Bas, 61 : 253 (1942).
594. Sobu, Kiessig and Hess: Z. Phys. Chem. B 43: 309 (1939).
595. Sponsler: J. Gen. Physiol. 5 : 757 (1923).
596. Sponsler and Dore: J. Am. Chem. Soc., 53 : 1639 (1931).
597. Stafford: Ind. Eng. Chem. Anal. Ed., 14 : 698 (1942).
598. Stafford: Unpubl. data of the Am. Cyanamid Co.
598a. Stafford and Williams: Protect. Decor. Coatings, 5 (1946).
599. Staritzky and Singer: Acta Cryst., 5 : 536 (1952).
599a. Steward: Nature, 165 : 406 (1950).
599b. Steward: Acta Cryst., 4 : 184 (1951); 5 : 390 (1952).
600. Stora: Compt. rend., 220 : 248 (1945).
601. Stumpf: Ann. Phys. 37 : 351 (1912).
602. Swamy: Curr. Sci. (India), 10 : 197 (1941).
602a. Swift and Walter: J. Am. Chem. Soc., 64 : 2539 (1942).
603. Ten Broeck and Van der Meulen: J. Am. Chem. Soc., 53 : 3596 (1931).
604. Theilacker: Z. Krist., 76 : 203 (1931).
605. Thibault and Dupré la Tour: J. Chim. Phys., 29 : 153 (1932).
605a. Toussaint: Bull. Soc. Roy. Sci. Liége, 12, 533 (1943).
605b. Toussaint: Bull. Soc. Roy. Sci. Liége, 17 : 10, 18, 157 (1948).
606. Toussaint: Bull. Soc. Chim. Belg., 54 : 319 (1945).
607. Valentine: pers. commun., May 31, 1947.
608. Valentine, in Ruskin and Merrill: Science, 105 : 504 (1947).
609. Van Tassel: Bull. Mus. Roy. Nat. Hist. Belg., 21, No. 26 (1945).
610. Verweel and MacGilvary: Z. Krist., 102 : 60 (1939).

610a. Vloten, Kruissink, Strijk and Bigvoet: Acta Cryst., 3 : 139 (1950).
611. Vorlander and Salke: Z. phys. Chem., 129 : 435 (1927).
611a. Waldmann: Schw. Min. Pet. Mit., 27 (1947).
612. Waldmann and Brandenberger: Z. Krist. 82 : 77 (1932).
612a. Walter: J. Am. Chem. Soc., 66 : 419 (1947).
613. Warren: Phys. Rev., 43 : 500 (1933).
614. Welsh and Keenan: J. Am. Pharm. Assn., 30 : 123 (1941).
615. Wendekamm: Z. Krist., 85 : 35 (1933).
616. Wetzel: Z. Krist., 104 : 305 (1942).
617. White: Z. Krist., 78 : 91 (1931).
617a. White *et al.*: Anal. Chem., 22 : 950 (1950).
617b. Wickstrøm: J. Pharm. Pharmacol., 2 : 444 (1950).
617c. Wickstrøm: J. Pharm. Pharmacol., 3 : 431 (1951).
618. Wiebenga and Moerman: Z. Krist., 99 : 217 (1938).
618a. Wilkerson: J. Am. Chem. Soc., 64 : 2230 (1942).
619. Williams: Unpubl, data of the Am. Cyanamid Co.
620. Williams and Keenan: J. Assn. Off. Agric. Chem., 27 : 446 (1944).
620a. Williams and Van Meter: Anal. Chem., 24 : 762, 911, 1220 (1952).
620b. Wittnauer and Senti: J. Am. Chem. Soc., 72 : 2803 (1950).
620c. Wolf *et al.*: Science, 109 : 515 (1949) and 110 : 310 (1949).
621. Wood: Proc. Univ. Durham, 7 : 168 (1928); Strukturber., 2 : 820 (1932).
622. Wood, Ayliffe, and Cullinane: Phil; Mag., 19 : 405 (1935).
622a. Wright and King: Acta Cryst., 3 : 31 (1950).
623. Wuhrmann and Pilnik: Experimentia, 1 : 330 (1945).
624. Wurstlin: Z. Krist., 88 : 185 (1934).
625. Wyckoff and Corey: Z. Krist., 81 : 386 (1931).
626. Yakshin and Lyashenko: Chem. Abst., 41 : 4987 (1947).
627. Yardley: J. Chem. Soc. London, 127 : 2207 (1925).
628. Yardley: Proc. Roy. Soc., 105 : 451 (1924).
628a. Young and Jones: J. Phys. Chem., 53 : 1334 (1949).
628b. Young and Jones: pers. commun., April 14, 1949.
628c. Young, Jones and Lewis: J. Phys. Chem., 56 : 738 (1952).
629. Young and Spiers: Z. Krist., 78 : 101 (1931).
630. Zachariasen: Phys. Rev., 53 : 917 (1931).
631. Zvyagintsev and Matatashvili: Chem. Abst., 41 : 2956 (1947).

DETERMINATIVE TABLES BASED ON REFRINGENCE

Table I includes substances for which one or two indices of refraction have been measured in random position (usually N_1 and N_2) but occasionally only one index N, N_O, N_E, N_X, N_Y, N_Z, or a third random index, N_3; it also includes substances for which indices have been measured in correct position, but not enough data obtained to permit inclusion on either diagram for example, N_X and N_Z may be reported, but not N_Y nor 2V. Table I is arranged in the order of increasing value of the highest measured index of refraction, but substances for which only one index of refraction has been measured are included, except when that index is known to be N_X.

Table II is similar, but is arranged in order of the increasing value of the lowest measured index of refraction and substances for which only one index has been measured are not included except when that index is known to be N_X.

Uniaxial substances are included in a similar way. If both N_O and N_E have been measured the substances can be found on the diagram and are not included in the tables. Of only one of these has been measured the substance is included in Table I if the measured index is the higher one (or if the optic sign is unknown) and it is included in Table II if the measured index is the lower one.

Of course isometric crystals are not included in either table since they are shown in the diagrams.

Approximate measurements of refractive indices can be made with very small crystals or fragments by the use of a series of immersion liquids of known refractive indices for mounts to be observed microscopically. More accurate measurements require the use of large crystals and a refractometer, or the double variation method, which involves the use of the universal stage (with a petrographic microscope) as described[1] especially by Emmons.

---

[1]R. C. Emmons: Geol. Soc. Amer. Memoir 8 (1943).

TABLE I. BASED ON THE HIGHER MEASURED REFRACTIVE INDEX.

N_2(orN_3),N	N_1	Sign	2V	Name	Composition	Opt. Orient., etc.,	Page
1.416 = N_Y		?	?	Acetoxime	C_3H_7ON	D 0.97. MP 60°	12
1.465	1.452	?	0°	Potassium oleate	$C_{18}H_{33}O_2K$	Tetrag.	25
1.469 = N_Y		?	59°	Bromophenylparaconic acid	$C_{11}H_9O_4Br$	Tetrag.	189
1.47	1.46	?	?	1-Methylbutyl carbamate	$C_5H_{13}O_2N$	MP 76°	38
1.471 = N_Y		?	?	Sodium glycerophosphate · 4 H_2O	$C_3H_7O_6PNa_2 \cdot 4\,H_2O$	Y = *b*. D 1.634	8
1.477 = N_Z	1.472 = N_X	+	?	Barium butanone sulfonate	$C_8H_{14}O_2SO_3Ba$	Y = *b*, Z = *c*.	61
1.478 = N_Y		?	51°	4-Cyano-3-ethyl-2, 4-dihydroxy-2-methylpentanoic-1,4-lactone	$C_9H_{13}O_3N$	Y = *c*. MP 109°	190
1.480 = N_Z	1.475 = N_Y	?	?	Sodium zinc uranyl acetate · 6 H_2O	$(CH_3 \cdot CO_2)_9NaZn(UO_2)_3 \cdot 6\,H_2O$	X ∧ *c* = 20° *ca*. Z = *b*.	18
1.481 = N_Y		?	44°	3,5-Diphenyl-1,2-diazole	$C_{15}H_{12}N_2$	$Bx_a \wedge c = 44°$	205
1.485	1.46	?	?	Ammonium valerate	$C_4H_9CO_2NH_4(2\,H_2O\,?)$	Extinction angle = 33°	21
1.488		?	68°	3-Methyl-1, 5-diphenyl-1, 2-diazole	$C_{16}H_{14}N_2$	Y = *b*. MP 63°	205
1.49	1.40	?	?	Sodium succinate · 6 H_2O	$(CH_2CO_2)_2Na_2 \cdot 6\,H_2O$	Z ‖ elongation	33
1.495 *ca.*		?	?	*trans*-Bromopyrocamphoric acid	$C_9H_{13}O_4Br$	Extinc. ∧ *a* = 17.5° 001 cleav. MP 207°	122
1.495	1.463	?	?	α-Hydroxyisobutyric acid	$C_4H_8O_3$	N_2 ‖ elong.	46
1.50 = N_3	1.45	+	?	Magnesium lactate (· 3 H_2O ?)	$(C_3H_5O_3)_2Mg(\cdot 3\,H_2O\,?)$	Parallel extinc. N_2 = 1.46	45
1.50	1.40	−	Lg.	Lithium acetate · 2 H_2O	$CH_3CO_2Li \cdot 2\,H_2O$	X = *a*, Y = *b*. 110 cleav.	16
1.503 = N_Z	1.495 = N_X	?	?	Lithium zinc uranyl acetate · 6 H_2O	$(CH_3CO_2)_9LiZn(UO_2)_3 \cdot 6\,H_2O$	Z = *b*.	18
1.506		?	88°	Barium methyluvinate · 4 H_2O	$C_{14}H_{14}O_6Ba \cdot 4\,H_2O$	Y = *a*.	187
1.507 = N_Y		?	?	Diethylaniline azyline	$C_{20}H_{28}N_4$	MP 170°	178

N_2 (or N_3), N	N_1	Sign	2V	Name	Composition	Opt. Orient., etc.	Page
$1.51 = N_Z$	$1.465 = N_X$	?	?	2, 3, 6-Trimethyl-α-D-glucopyranose	$C_9H_{18}O_6$	X = *c*.	261
$1.510 = N_3$	1.470	–	Mod.	Sodium citrate · 2 H_2O	$C_6H_5O_3Na_3 \cdot 2\,H_2O$	110 and $10\bar{1}$ cleav. $N_2 = 1.500$	58
$1.514 = N_Z$	$1.480 = N_X$	?	?	Tetrahydrotemisin · H_2O	$C_{15}H_{26}O_3 \cdot H_2O$	MP 112°	316
1.515	1.495	?	?	Zinc valerate	$(C_4H_9CO_2)_2Zn$	X ‖ elongation	22
1.515	1.485	?	?	Calcium lactate · 3 H_2O	$(C_3H_5O_3)_2Ca \cdot 3\,H_2O$	MP 100°	45
$1.517 = N_Y$		?	90° *ca.*	*cis*-1, 4-Cyclohexanediol	$C_6H_{12}O_2$	Y ∧ elong. = 10°	96
1.52	1.51	?	?	Pilocarpine borate	$C_{11}H_{17}O_5N_2B$	X ‖ elong.	303
1.52	1.51	?	?	Carpaine	$C_{14}H_{25}O_2N$	X ‖ elong.	277
1.521	1.49	?	?	Uranyl acetate · 2H_2O	$(CH_3CO_2)UO_2 \cdot 2H_2O$	1.49 = N along *c*.	16
$1.522 = N_Y$	$1.512 = N_X$	–	?	Sterol glucoside tetraacetate	$C_{43}H_{68}O_{10}$	Z ‖ elong.	275
1.523	1.477	?	?	Pentobarbital sodium	$C_{11}H_{17}O_3N_2Na$	Colorless	229
1.523	1.515	?	?	Orthoform hydrate	$C_8H_9O_3N \cdot nH_2O$	MP 55° *ca.*	165
$1.525 = N_Z$	$1.465 = N_X$	?	?	2,3,4-Trimethyl-β-methyl-*D*-glucopyranoside	$C_{10}H_{20}O_6$	X = *c*. MP 92°	262
$1.525 = N_Y$	$1.51 = N_X$	?	?	Agaric acid · 1.5H_2O	$C_{22}H_{40}O_7 \cdot 1.5H_2O$	MP 142°	58
1.525 *ca.*	1.51	?	?	Sodium uroxanate · 8H_2O	$C_5H_6O_6N_4Na_2 \cdot 8H_2O$	Y ⊥ plates, Z ‖ elong.	58
1.525 *ca.*	1.525 *ca.*	?	?	Sabadine	$C_{29}H_{51}O_8N$	Granular	305
$1.526 = N_Y$		?	67°	Racemic acid · H_2O	$C_4H_6O_6 \cdot H_2O$	Opt. Pl. nearly ‖ 110 Perf. 010 cleav.	55
< 1.527	1.52 *ca.*	?	?	Aspartic acid picrolonate	$C_{14}H_{13}O_9N_5$	Z ‖ elong.	210
1.527	1.523	?	32°	Lauroylcholine bromide	$C_{14}H_{31}O_2NBr$	Triclinic	65
$1.527 = N_O$		?	0°	Propyl-*n*-(*p*-phenylbenzalamino)-α-ethylcinnamate II	$C_{26}H_{27}O_2N$	Measured at 110°	164
$1.530 = N_Z$	$1.386 = N_X$	?	83° (2H)	4,5-Dihydro-5-keto-3-furancarboxylic acid	$C_5H_4O_4$	X = *b*; Y = *a*. 001 cleav.	188
1.530	1.525	?	27°	Palmitoylcholine bromide	$C_{18}H_{39}ONBr$	Extinc. at 15°	65
1.53	1.515	?	?	Atropine valerate	$C_{17}H_{23}O_3N \cdot C_5H_{10}O_2$	Z ‖ elong.	279

TABLE I. BASED ON THE HIGHER MEASURED REFRACTIVE INDEX

N_2(orN_3),N	N_1	Sign	2V	Name	Composition	Opt. Orient., etc.	Page
1.53	1.48	?	?	Lithium citrate (H_2O ?)	$C_6H_5O_7Li_3 \cdot (H_2O\ ?)$	Z ‖ elong.	58
1.53	1.49	?	?	Solanidine	$C_{27}H_{43}ON$?	Parallel extinc.	306
1.530	1.420	?	?	Dipotassium fumarate	$(CH \cdot CO_2K)_2$	Needles	35
1.53	1.52	?	?	Solanine	$C_{52}H_{91}O_{18}N$	Granular	306
1.53	1.49	–	?	Ferrous lactate($3H_2O$?)	$(C_3H_5O_3)_2Fe \cdot (3H_2O\ ?)$	Parallel extinc.	145
$1.531 = N_Y$		?	61°	4,4-Bisantipyrine	$C_{22}H_{22}O_2N_4$	$Bx_a \wedge c = 37°$	249
$1.533 = N_3$	1.47	+	70°(2H)	*d*-Camphoric acid	$C_{10}H_{16}O_4$	$X = b$; $Z \wedge c = -64°$. Perf. cleav. $N_2 = 1.48$	122
1.533	$1.508 = N_Y$	+	Lg.	α-Palmitic acid	$C_{15}H_{31}CO_2H$	$Y = b$. MP 63°	23
1.534		?	?	Sodium ammonium methanedisulfonate	$CH_2(SO_3)_2NaNH_4$	$N_1 \parallel c$	60
1.535	1.52	?	?	Sparteine sulfate	$C_{30}H_{54}O_4N_4S$	Z ‖ elong.	283
$1.535 = N_Z$	$1.465 = N_X$	?	?	2,4,6-Trimethyl-β-methyl-*D*-glucopyranoside	$C_{10}H_{20}O_6$	$X = c$	261
1.535	$1.510 = N_X$	+	Mod.	β-Stearic acid	$C_{17}H_{35}CO_2H$	N_1 in 001	24
1.536	1.493	?	?	Proponal	$C_{10}H_{16}O_3N_2$	MP 146°	228
1.538	1.522	?	?	Copper aspartate	$C_4H_5O_4NCu \cdot (5H_2O\ ?)$	Z ‖ elong.	69
$1.538 = N_Y$		?	74°	3,4,4-Trimethyl-1-phenyl-5-pyrazolone	$C_{12}H_{14}ON_2$	Extinc. $\wedge c = 65°$	212
1.54	1.475	–	?	2,3,4,6-Tetramethyl-α-*D*-glucopyranose	$C_{10}H_{20}O_6$	$X = c$. D 1.22	261
1.54		?	?	Potassium nickel dithio-oxalate	$(COS)_4NiK$	Parallel extinc. Red to black.	32
1.54	1.51	?	?	Sorbitol	$C_6H_{14}O_6$	Z ‖ elongation	10
1.542	1.530	?	?	Cupric 2-aminopentanoate	$C_5H_{10}O_2NCu$	X ‖ elong.	68
$1.542 = N_Z$		?	?	Limonin hemimethylene chloride solvate	$C_{26}H_{30}O_8 \cdot 0.5CH_2Cl$	Z ‖ elong.	312
1.545		?	?	Ethyl *p*-methoxycinnamate	$C_{12}H_{14}O_3$	$Y = b$; extinc. $\wedge c = -49°$	130

TABLE I. BASED ON THE HIGHER MEASURED REFRACTIVE INDEX

N_2(orN_3),N	N_1	Sign	2V	Name	Composition	Opt. Orient., etc.	Page
$1.545 = N_Y$	$1.528 = N_X$	?	?	Tetrakis(hydroxymethyl)cyclopentanone	$C_9H_{16}O_5$	Orthorhombic	110
1.545	1.54	?	?	Adonitol	$C_5H_{12}O_5$	X ‖ elong. MP 102°	9
1.545 *ca.*	1.53 *ca.*	?	?	Sodium uroxanate·nH_2O	$C_5H_6O_4N_4Na \cdot nH_2O$	After heating to 110°	58
1.545	1.45	?	?	Arecoline·HCl	$C_8H_{13}O_2N \cdot HCl$	X ‖ elong.	278
1.545	1.49	?	?	Sodium tartrate ($2H_2O$?)	$C_4H_4O_6Na_2(2H_2O\ ?)$	Z ‖ elong.	50
1.545	1.535	?	?	Dulcitol	$C_6H_{14}O_6$	$X = b$; $Z \wedge c = -77°$. MP 188°	10
1.547		?	0°	Squash-seed α-globulin	?	Pyramidal	311
1.547	1.534	?	?	Cupric 2-amino-3-methylpentanoate	$C_{12}H_{24}O_2N_2Cu$	Sym. extinc. —elong.	69
$1.548 = N_Z$	$1.513 = N_X$	?	?	Diamylamine abietate	$C_{30}H_{43}O_2N$	Z ‖ elong.	120
$1.548 = N_Z$	$1.510 = N_X$	?	?	Magnesium palmitate	$(C_{15}H_{31}CO_2)_2Mg$	X ‖ elong. MP 105°	23
$1.548 = N_Z$	$1.503 = N_X$	?	?	Calcium palmitate	$(C_{15}H_{31}CO_2)_2Ca$	X ‖ elong.	23
$1.548 = N_Y$		?	30°	4-Ethylantipyrine	$C_{13}H_{16}ON_2$	$Bx_a \wedge c = 40°$	208
$1.549 = N_O$		?	0°	Ethyl-*p*-(*p*-ethoxybenzalamino)-α-ethylcinnamate II	$C_{22}H_{25}O_3N$	MP 58°	164
$1.549 = N_Z$	$1.504 = N_X$	?	?	Trional	$C_8H_{18}O_4S_2$	MP 76°	11
$1.550 = N_Z$	$1.501 = N_X$	?	?	Calcium stearate	$(C_{17}H_{35} \cdot CO_2)_2Ca$	X ‖ elongation	24
1.55	1.43	?	?	Parabanic acid	CONHCOCONH	X ‖ elongation	215
1.55		?	?	Methoxyacetol	$C_8H_{16}O_4$	MP 127°	191
1.55	1.545	?	?	Pseudopelletierine sulfate	$C_{18}H_{32}O_5NS$	$Z \wedge$ elong. = 20°	283
1.55	1.54	?	?	Chloral urethan	$C_5H_8O_3NCl_3$	Z ‖ elong. MP 103°	38
1.55	1.54	?	?	Conhydrine	$C_8H_{17}ON$	Z ‖ elong.	278
1.55	1.54	?	?	Copper formate·$2H_2O$	$(HCO_2)_2Cu \cdot 2H_2O$	X ‖ elong. 100 cleav.	14
1.55		?	?	Pseudoconhydrine	$C_8H_{17}ON$		78
1.550		?	80°	5-Hydantoinacetamide	$C_5H_7O_3N_3$	$Y = b$.	237
1.55	1.51	?	?	Pilocarpine (iso ?)valerate	$C_{15}H_{26}O_4N_2$	Z ‖ elong.	303
1.55	1.501	?	?	Tetronal	$C_9H_{20}O_2S$	MP 85°	11

Table I. Based on the Higher Measured Refractive Index

N_2(orN_3),N	N_1	Sign	2V	Name	Composition	Opt. Orient., etc.	Page
1.55	1.54	?	?	Aconitine sulfate	$C_{68}H_{92}O_{26}N_2S$	X $\parallel$ elong.	304
1.55	1.545	?	?	Copper acetate·(H_2O ?)	$(CH_3CO_2)_2Cu\cdot(H_2O\ ?)$	X $\wedge$ elong. = 20°. 001 and 110 cleav.	16
1.55	1.53	?	?	Sabadinine	$C_{27}H_{43}O_8N$	Z $\parallel$ elong.	305
1.55	1.52	?	?	Cevadine	$C_{37}H_{53}O_{11}N$	MP 150° *ca.*	306
1.551 = N_Y	1.515	?	?	Potassium tartrate (H_2O ?)	$C_4H_4O_6K_2(H_2O\ ?)$		49
1.552	1.541	?	?	Cupric 2-aminohexanoate	$C_8H_{24}O_4N_2Cu$	Sym. extinc.; – elong.	69
1.552 = N_Z	1.498 = N_X	?	?	Tetrahydrotemisin	$C_{15}H_{26}O_3$	MP 231°	316
1.554 = N_Y		?	60°	Dextropimaric acid·HCl	$C_{20}H_{31}O_2Cl$	X nearly ⊥ 100; Y = *b*	120
1.554 = N_Y		?	71°	Terpinene nitrolethylamine	$C_{12}H_{22}ON_2$	$Bx_a \wedge c = 26°$. MP 131°. 100 cleav.	160
1.555 = N_Z	1.475	?	?	2,3,4-Trimethyl-α-methyl-*D*-arabinopyranoside	$C_8H_{16}O_5$	X = *c*	258
1.555	1.534	?	?	Cupric 2-amino-3-methylbutanoate	$C_{10}H_{18}O_4N_2Cu$	X $\parallel$ elong.	68
1.555 = N_Z	1.48 = N_X	?	?	2,3,4-Trimethyl-α-*D*-xylopyranose	$C_8H_{15}O_5$	X = *b*	259
1.555	1.508	?	?	Lauron	$C_{23}H_{46}O$	Indices at 41°	13
1.555 = N_Z	1.47 = N_X	?	?	2,3,6-Trimethyl-β-methyl-*D*-glucopyranoside	$C_{10}H_{20}O_6$	X = *c*.	262
1.555 = N_Z		?	Biax	Isocaffuric acid	$C_6H_9O_4N_3$	Z $\wedge$ elong. = 35°	237
1.557	1.466	?	?	Dipotassium alcohol phthalate	$C_{10}H_{10}O_5K_2$	Laths	122
1.557		?	?	Dionine·$3H_2O$	$C_{19}H_{24}O_3NCl\cdot 3H_2O$	MP 123°	298
1.557 = N_Z	1.537 = N_X	?	?	α-*L*-Fucose	$C_6H_{12}O_5$	D 1.49	260
1.558	1.498	?	Biax	Methyl palmitate	$C_{17}H_{34}O_2$	MP 30°	24
1.559		–	30°	Agathendicarbonic acid	$C_{20}H_{30}O_4$	X = *a*; Y = *b*.	310
1.559	1.502	?	Biax.	Methyl stearate	$C_{19}H_{38}O_2$	Liquid crystals	25
1.560	1.551	?	72°	Stearoylcholine bromide	$C_{11}H_{25}ONBr$	Z at 27° on 001. Opt. Pl. at 6° on 100	65
1.56	1.55	?	?	Physostigmine·HCl	$C_{15}H_{22}O_2N_3Cl$	Granular	304

TABLE 1. BASED ON THE HIGHER MEASURED REFRACTIVE INDEX

N_2(orN_3),N	N_1	Sign	2V	Name	Composition	Opt. Orient., etc.	Page
1.56	1.51	?	?	Malic acid	$C_4H_6O_5$	Z ‖ elongation	45
1.56	1.53	?	?	Aconitine salicylate	$C_{41}H_{51}O_{14}N$	Granular	304
1.56	1.52	?	?	Cocaine tartrate	$C_{38}H_{48}O_{14}N_2$	X ‖ elong.	282
1.56	1.55	?	?	Quinic acid	$C_7H_{12}O_6$	X ‖ elong. Y = *b*. MP 162°	132
1.56	1.54	?	?	Hydroxyvaline picrolonate	$C_{15}H_{19}O_8N_5$	Z ‖ elong.	210
1.56 = N_Z	1.55 = N_X	?	Lg.	Verdigris	$CuO(CH_3CO_2)_2Cu$	Pleoch. X = blue, Z green	18
1.56	1.54	?	?	Sabadine · HCl	$C_{29}H_{52}O_8NCl$	Granular	305
1.56	1.55	−	74.5°	1,2,3,5-Cyclohexanetetrol-5-carbonate	$C_7H_{12}O_6$	Y = *b*; Z ∧ *c* = −6°	101
1.56	1.545	?	?	Sabadine nitrate	$C_{29}H_{52}O_{11}N_2$	Extinc. ∧ = 29°	305
1.56 = N_Y		+	?	Allobetulin	$C_{30}H_{48}(OH_2)$	Z′ in 001 at 4° to 010 and 35° to 1$\bar{1}$0.	100
1.565 = N_Z	1.535 = N_X	−	?	Picrotin	$C_{15}H_{18}O_7$	Z ‖ elong.	313
1.565 = N_Z	1.495 = N_X	?	?	1-Valine	$C_5H_{11}O_2$	Z ‖ elong.	68
1.565 = N_Z	1.520 = N_X	?	?	Picrotoxin	$C_{30}H_{34}O_{13}$	MP 203 – 204°	313
1.565	1.553	−	74°(2H)	*D*-Glucosamine · HCl	$C_5H_{12}O_5N \cdot HCl$	X ∧ *c* = 40°; Y = *b*. 10$\bar{1}$ cleav.	66
1.565 = N_Z	1.551 = N_X	?	?	Lupeol	$C_{30}H_{50}O$	X ‖ elong.	312
1.566 = N_Z	1.524 = N_Y	+	?	Cholesteryl formate	$C_{28}H_{46}O_2$	Y = *b*. MP 96°	274
1.567	1.530	?	?	Serine picrolonate I	$C_{13}H_{15}O_8N_5$	Z ∧ elong. = 40°	211
1.569 = N_Z	1.481 = N_X	?	?	α-Tetrahydrosantonin	$C_{15}H_{22}O_9$	X = *a*; Z = *c*. MP 155°	315
1.57	1.565	?	?	Emetine · HCl	$C_{29}H_{41}O_4N_2Cl$	Z ‖ elong.	305
1.570	1.534	?	?	Cupric 1-2-aminopentanoate	$C_6H_{13}O_2NCu$	Z ∧ elong. = 29°	68
1.57	1.56	+	36°	Aconitine	$C_{34}H_{45}O_{11}N$	Y = *b*, Z = *a*.	304
1.57	1.56	?	?	Nicotine tartrate	$C_{14}H_{21}O_6N_2$	Z ‖ elong.	277
1.57	1.55	?	?	Hyoscyamine sulfate	$C_{17}H_{25}O_7NS$	X ‖ elong.	282
1.57 = N_Z	1.56 = N_X	?	?	N-Vanillylcaprylamide	$C_{16}H_{25}O_3N$	X ‖ elong. MP 42°	159
1.57	1.555	?	?	Scopolamine	$C_{17}H_{21}O_3N$	Z ‖ elong.	280
1.57 = N_3	1,53	?	?	Cerous lactate($3H_2O$?)	$(C_3H_5O_3)_2Ce \cdot (3H_2O\ ?)$	Opt. + ? $N_2 = 1.54$	45

N_2(orN_3),N	N_1	Sign	2V	Name	Composition	Opt. Orient., etc.	Page
$1.574=N_Y$		?	55°	Terpinene nitrolmethylamine	$C_{11}H_{20}ON_2$	$Bx_a \wedge c=31°$. MP 141°	160
$1.574=N_Y$	$1.487=N_X$	?	?	Sodium *p*-toluenesulfon-chloramide·$3H_2O$	$C_7H_7O_2NClSNa \cdot 3H_2O$	Colorless prisms	134
1.575	1.56	?	?	Sparteine·HCl	$C_{15}H_{27}N_2Cl$	Granular	283
1.575	1.48	?	?	*p*-Methoxybenzoic acid	$C_6H_4O \cdot CH_3 \cdot CO_2H$	Y=*b*; extinc. $\wedge c=18°$. MP 184°	128
1.58	1.56	?	?	Aconitine·HCl·$2.5H_2O$	$C_{34}H_{46}O_{11}NCl \cdot 2.5H_2O$	Z ‖ elong.	304
1.58	1.49	?	Lg.	Cocaine	$C_{17}H_{21}O_4N$	MP 98°	282
1.58	1.575	?	?	Alanine picrolonate	$C_{14}H_{15}O_7N_5$	X ‖ elong.	209
1.58	1.54	?	?	Lithium acid tartrate·$1.5H_2O$	$C_4H_4O_6HLi \cdot 1.5H_2O$	Z ‖ elong.	48
1.58	1.55	?	?	Arbutin	$C_{12}H_{16}O_7$	Z ‖ elong.	263
1.58	1.56	?	?	Cinchonidine tartrate	$C_{42}H_{50}O_8N_4(2H_2O\ ?)$	Z ‖ elong.	288
1.58	1.49	?	?	2-Methylbutanedioic acid	$C_5H_8O_4$	Z ‖ elongation	34
1.58	1.54	?	?	Hydrastine bitartrate	$C_{29}H_{33}O_{18}N$	Z ‖ elong.	294
$1.58=N_Y$	$1.571=N_X$	?	?	Strontium phthalate	$C_6H_4(CO_2)_2Sr(H_2O\ ?)$	Parallel extinc.	123
>1.580	<1.549	?	?	Dibromotyrosine picrolonate	$C_{19}H_{17}O_8N_5Br_2$	X ∧ elong.=44°	210
$1.582=N_Z$	$1.547=N_X$	?	Biax.	Isotephrosin	$C_{23}H_{22}O_7$	Rhombic	316
1.583	1.545	?	Lg.	5-Hydroxy-3-phenyl-5-hydantoincarboxymethylamide	$C_{11}H_{11}O_4N_3$	X ‖ elong.	238
1.584	$1.516=N_X$	−	90° *ca.*	Dial	$C_{10}H_{12}O_3N_2$	Sym. extinc.	232
$1.585=N_Y$	$1.549=N_X$	+	?	Ethylmethylphenylbetaine·H_2O	$C_{11}H_{17}O_3N$	X ‖ elong.	144
$1.585=N_Y$	1.549	+	Sm.	Ethylmethylphenylbetaine·$2H_2O$	$C_{11}H_{19}O_4N$	Y=*b*. Two cleav.	144
$1.59=N_Z$	$1.57=N_X$	?	?	*N*-Vanillylpelargonamide	$C_{17}H_{27}O_3N$	X ‖ elong. MP 50°	159
1.59	1.57	?	?	Atropine nitrate	$C_{17}H_{24}O_6N_2$	Granular	280
1.59	1.46	?	Lg.	Allocaffuric acid	$C_7H_{11}O_4N_3$	Sym. extinc.	237
1.59	1.50	?	?	Berberine sulfate	$C_{20}H_{21}O_9NS$	X ‖ elong.	295
1.59	1.505	?	?	Dixanthyl biguanide	$C_{28}H_{23}O_2N_5$	Tablets	188
$1.590=N_Y$	$1.508=N_X$	−	?	Phenylamine nitrate	$C_6H_8O_3N_2$	X=*c*; Y=*a*.	139

Table I. Based on the Higher Measured Refractive Index

N_2(orN_3),N	N_1	Sign	2V	Name	Composition	Opt. Orient., etc.	Page
1.59 $=N_Z$	1.52 $=N_X$	?	?	Tanacetone semicarbazone	$C_{11}H_{19}ON_3$	MP 170°	103
1.590$=N_Z$	1.538$=N_X$	?	?	Partheniol	$C_{15}H_{26}O$	X ‖ elong.	85
1.59 $=N_Z$	1.528$=N_X$	?	?	l-Menthone semicarbazone	$C_{11}H_{21}ON_3$	MP 184°	103
1.59 $=N_3$	1.54	?	?	l-Acetamido-4-ethoxybenzene	$C_{10}H_{13}O_2N$	$N_2=1.58$	155
1.59	1.52	?	?	Ammonium acid succinate	$C_4H_9O_4N$	Extinc. at 37°	33
1.591	1.576	?	?	Diacetylmorphine·HCl·H_2O	$C_{21}H_{24}O_5NCl \cdot H_2O$	MP 231°	298
1.592		?	55°	Pentamethyleneaminotetrazole	$C_6H_{11}N_5$	Y$=b$. MP 91°	252
⟨1.595$=N_Y$	⟨1.555$=N_X$	+	Sm.	Methylphenylpropylbetaine·$2H_2O$	$C_{12}H_{21}O_4N$	Z ⊥ plates	144
1.595$=N_Y$	1.555$=N_X$	+	?	Methylphenylpropylbetaine·H_2O	$C_{12}H_{19}O_3N$	Y ‖ elong. Z ⊥ plates	144
1.595	1.57	?	?	Sabadinine·HCl	$C_{27}H_{44}O_8NCl$	Granular	305
1.595	1.555	−	Lg.	Atropine	$C_{17}H_{23}O_3N$	Y$=c$; MP 116°	279
1.595 *ca.*		?	?	Isopral	$C_3H_5OCl_3$	Z′ ‖ length. MP 51°	7
1.596	1.529	?	?	Tyrosine picrolonate	$C_{19}H_{19}O_8N_5$	Z ∧ elong.$=37°$	212
1.596$=N_Y$	1.485$=N_X$	-	?	Aniline *cis*-β-sulfoacrylate·H_2O	$C_9H_{13}O_6NS$	X$=a$; Y$=c$.	139
1.596	1.574	?	?	Glutamic acid picrolonate	$C_{15}H_{17}O_9N_5$	X ‖ elong.	210
1.598$=N_Y$		?	Biax.	*N,N′*-Dimethyl-α-(phenylureido)-malonamide	$C_{12}H_{16}O_3N_4$	Y ‖ elong. MP 225°	143
1.599	1.536	?	?	Cupric 2-amino-3-hydroxypropionate	$C_3H_6O_3NCu$	Sym. extinc.	71
1.600$=N_Z$	1.553$=N_X$	?	?	Butylamine abietate	$C_{24}H_{41}O_2N$	MP 165°	120
1.60 $=N_Z$	1.46 $=N_X$	?	?	Dimethyl-*D*-glucoascorbic acid	$C_9H_{14}O_7$	X$=b$. MP 94°	267
1.60	1.555	?	?	Atropine arsenate	$C_{17}H_{23}O_3N \cdot H_3AsO_4$	Z ‖ elong.	279
1.600$=N_Z$	1.515$=N_X$	?	?	Dihydrotoxicarolic acid	$C_{23}H_{26}O_9$	X ‖ elong.	317
1.60	1.555	?	?	Aconitine phosphate	$C_{68}H_{93}O_{26}NP$	Z ‖ elong.	304
1.60	1.58	?	?	Conquinamine	$C_{19}H_{24}O_2N_2$	X ‖ elong.	293
1.6$=N_Z$	1.487$=N_X$	?	5°	Potassium phthalate	$C_6H_4(CO_2K)_2(H_2O\ ?)$	Very soluble	122
1.600	1.548	?	?	Cystine picrolonate	$C_{16}H_{20}O_9N_6S$	Z ‖ elong.	210
1.60	1.555	?	?	Atropine sulfate	$(C_{17}H_{23}O_3N)_2 \cdot H_2SO_4$	Granular	279
1.6 est.	⟩1.35	+	Lg.	Azidodithiocarbonic acid	$HSCSN_3$	X ∧ $c=30°$	44

Table I. Based on the Higher Measured Refractive Index

N_2(orN_3),N	N_1	Sign	2V	Name	Composition	Opt. Orient., etc.	Page
1.60	1.57	?	?	Homatropine sulfate	$C_{16}H_{23}O_7NS$	Z ‖ elong.	281
1.601	1.532	?	?	Uroxanic acid	$C_5H_6O_5N_3$	Irregular solids	59
1.602=N_Y		?	53°	5-Methyl-2-phenyl-1-propyl-3-pyrazolone	$C_{13}H_{16}ON_2$	Extinc. ∧ c=20°, MP 93°	212
1.602=N_Y		?	70°	4,4′-Dicyanodibenzylamine	$C_{16}H_{13}N_3$	Opt. plane nearly ‖ 001. $Bx_a \wedge a$=36°. MP 106°	164
1.602=N_Y		?	?	Ergotamine ethyl ether solvate	$C_{33}H_{35}O_5N_5 \cdot n(C_2H_5)_2O$	Y ∧ c=15°	301
1.603=N_Y	1.486=N_X	–	Lg.	Propyl 3,5-dinitrobenzoate	$C_{10}H_{10}O_6N_2$	Y ‖ elong. (*b*) MP 74°	115
1.603	1.504	–	?	Alypine	$C_{16}H_{26}O_2N_2 \cdot 2HCl$	MP 173°	112
1.603	1.548	?	90° *ca.*	9,10-Dihydro-9,9,10,10-tetraiso-butylanthracene	$C_{30}H_{44}$	Poor 001 cleav. Triclinic	81
1.603=N_Z	1.577=N_X	?	?	Vonedrine·HCl	$C_{10}H_{15}N \cdot HCl$	X ‖ elong.	151
1.605	1.60	?	?	Aconitine arsenate	$C_{68}H_{93}O_{26}N_2As$	Z ‖ elong.	304
1.605	1.55	?	?	Pilocarpidine nitrate	$C_{10}H_{15}O_5N_3$	Z ‖ elong.	304
1.605	1.530	?	?	Proline picrolonate	$C_{15}H_{17}O_7N_5$	X ‖ elong.	211
1.605	1.505	?	?	2-Hydroxypropanedioic acid	$CHOH \cdot CO_2H$	Granular	45
1.605	1.545	?	?	9-Allyl-1,3-dimethylpseudouric acid	$C_{10}H_{14}O_4N_4$	MP 190°	241
1.605	1.40	?	?	Guanidine nitrate	$CNH(NH_2)_2 \cdot HNO_3$	Z ‖ elong. MP 214°	43
1.605	1.555	?	?	Scopolamine·HBr·3H_2O	$C_{17}H_{22}O_4NBr \cdot 3H_2O$	X=c; Y=b.	280
1.608	1.520	?	?	Isoserine picrolonate II	$C_{13}H_{15}O_8N_5$	Z ‖ elong.	211
⟨1.610	⟩1.445	?	Biax.	*N′*-Phenyl-*N*-carbethoxyurea	$C_{10}H_{12}O_3N_2$	Z ‖ elong.	142
1.61	1.55	?	?	Neurodine	$C_{12}H_{10}O_4N$	X ‖ elong.	156
1.61	1.58	?	?	Atropine·HCl	$C_{17}H_{24}O_3NCl$	Granular	280
1.610	1.520	?	?	Isoleucine picrolonate	$C_{16}H_{21}O_7N_5$	Z ‖ elong.	211
1.61	1.56	?	?	Scopolamine·HCl	$C_{17}H_{22}O_4NCl$	Z ‖ elong.	280
1.61	1.54	?	?	Pilocarpine salicylate	$C_{18}H_{22}O_5N_2$	Z ‖ elong.	303
1.610	1.550	?	Biax.	Diethyl(phenylureido)malonate	$C_{14}H_{18}O_5N_2$	X ‖ elong. MP 113°	142
1.61	1.60	?	?	Homatropine·HCl	$C_{16}H_{22}O_3NCl$	X ‖ elong.	280

TABLE I. BASED ON THE HIGHER MEASURED REFRACTIVE INDEX

N_2(orN_3),N	N_1	Sign	2V	Name	Composition	Opt. Orient., etc.	Page
1.61 = N_Z	1.520 = N_X	?	Biax.	Histidine	$C_6H_9O_2N_3$	X ‖ elong.	242
1.61	1.575	?	?	Hyoscyamine·HCl	$C_{17}H_{24}O_3NCl$	Granular	281
1.61	1.56	?	?	Eucatropine·HCl	$C_{17}H_{26}O_3NCl$	MP 184°	197
1.61	1.57	?	?	Narceine·$3H_2O$	$C_{23}H_{27}O_8N\cdot 3H_2O$	– elong.	294
1.61	1.523	+	70°	Sodium 4-hydroxybenzene-sulfonate·$2H_2O$	$C_6H_4OH\cdot SO_3Na\cdot 2H_2O$	Y = b; Z ∧ c = 9°. N_2 = 1.58	137
1.61	1.595	?	?	Caffeine·H_2SO_4	$C_8H_{10}O_2N_4\cdot H_2SO_4$		249
1.610	1.513	?	?	Dipotassium maleate	$(HC)_2\cdot(CO_2K)_2$	Laths	36
1.61	1.54	?	?	Aconitine nitrate	$C_{34}H_{46}O_{14}N_2$	Granular	304
1.611	1.582	?	?	Barium monochloroacetate	$(CH_2ClCO_2)_2Ba$	X ‖ elongation	19
1.612	1.599	?	?	Copper β-phenylalanine salt	$C_{18}H_{20}O_4N_2Cu$	X ‖ elong.	164
1.612	1.564	?	?	Cupric 2-amino-4-methylpentanoate	$C_{12}H_{24}O_4N_2Cu$	Blue color	69
1.613 = N_Z	1.547 = N_X	?	?	Methyl phenaceturate	$C_{11}H_{13}O_3N$	Y = b; Z = a.	117
1.613	1.570	?	?	Barium gluconate·H_2O	$C_{12}H_{22}O_8Ba\cdot H_2O$	Granular. Biaxial	57
1.614 = N_Y	1.387 = N_X	?	?	Fumaric acid	$(HO_2C\cdot CH)_2$	Z ⊥ plates.	35
1.615 = N_Z	1.578 = N_X	?	?	Anhydroquassin	$C_{22}H_{28}O_5$	MP 196°	313
1.615	1.56	?	?	Conessine	$C_{24}H_{40}N_2$	Granular	305
1.615	1.55	?	?	Pilocarpine sulfate	$C_{22}H_{34}O_8N_4S$	X ‖ elong.	303
1.615 = N_Z	1.570 = N_X	?	?	Quinine abietate	$C_{40}H_{54}O_4N_2$	Z ‖ elong.	290
1.615	1.61	?	?	Hyoscyamine·HI	$C_{17}H_{24}O_3NI$	Granular	281
1.615	1.60	?	?	Anhalonine·HCl	$C_{12}H_{16}O_3N\cdot Cl$	X ‖ elong.	293
1.616	1.557	?	?	Histidine picrolonate	$C_{16}H_{17}O_7N_7$	Z ‖ elong.	210
1.616	1.531	?	?	Glycine picrolonate	$C_{12}H_{13}O_7N_5$	Z ‖ elong.	210
1.617	1.591	?	?	2-Naphthol-3,6-disulfonic acid benzoate	$C_{17}H_{12}O_8S_2$	Z ‖ elong.	138
1.617	1.527	?	?	Leucine picrolonate	$C_{16}H_{21}O_7N_5$	Z ‖ elong.	211
1.618	1.432	?	?	Ethyl cyanoguanidine carboxylate	$C_5H_8O_2N_4$	Twinning common	42
1.619 = N_Z	1.513 = N_X	?	?	Ethylhydrocupreine·HCl	$C_{21}H_{28}O_2N_2\cdot HCl$	MP 253°	207

TABLE I. BASED ON THE HIGHER MEASURED REFRACTIVE INDEX

N_2(orN_3),N	N_1	Sign	2V	Name	Composition	Opt. Orient., etc.	Page
1.620 = N_Z	1.600 = N_X	?	Biax.	β-Robinin	$C_{33}H_{40}O_{19}$	Z ‖ elong.	314
1.62	1.61	?	90° *ca.*	Santonic acid	$C_{15}H_{20}O_4$	$Bx_a = c$; Y = *a*. 010 cleav.	133
1.62	1.59	?	?	Thebaine tartrate	$C_{23}H_{27}O_9N$	X ‖ elong.	298
1.62	1.56	?	?	Atropine salicylate	$C_{24}H_{29}O_6N$	X ‖ elong.	279
1.62	1.51	?	?	5-Hydroxy-3-methyl-1-phenyl-5-hydantoin carboxymethylamide·H_2O	$C_{12}H_{13}O_4N_4 \cdot H_2O$	Z ‖ elong.	238
1.62	1.56	?	?	Pseudopelletierine·HCl	$C_9H_{16}ONCl$	Z ‖ elong.	282
1.62	1.55	?	?	Codeine·HCl·H_2O	$C_{18}H_{22}O_3NCl \cdot (2H_2O\ ?)$	X ‖ elong.	297
1.62	1.58	−	30°	Quinamine	$C_{19}H_{24}O_2N_2$	Z ‖ elong.	293
1.62	1.555	?	?	Quinine·$2H_2SO_4 \cdot 7H_2O$	$C_{20}H_{28}O_{10}N_2S_2 \cdot 7H_2O$	Z ‖ elong.	291
1.62 = N_Y	1.58 = N_X	?	Biax.	Quinine anisate	$C_{28}H_{32}O_5N_2$	Yellow	291
1.62	1.58	+	64°	Cinchonidine·$H_2SO_4 \cdot 5H_2O$	$C_{19}H_{24}O_5N_2S \cdot 5H_2O$	X = *b*, Z ∧ *c* = 59°	287
1.62	1.56	?	Biax.	Cinchonine·$2H_2SO_4$	$C_{19}H_{26}O_9N_2S_2$	Z ‖ elong.	284
1.620	1.571	?	Lg.	3-Phenyl-5-isohydantoin carboxymethylamide	$C_{11}H_{11}O_5N_3$	X ‖ elong. MP 249 – 250°	237
1.62 = N_Y		?	65°	7-Isopropyl-hydrocarbostyril	$C_{12}H_{15}ON$	Y = *b*. MP 134°	197
1.62		+	60° *ca.*	*d*-Glutamic acid·HI	$C_5H_9O_4N \cdot HI$	Y = *c*; Z = *b*; $N_Z - N_X$ = very strong.	71
1.62	1.571	?	Lg.	Dimethylphenyluric acid	$C_{13}H_{12}O_3N_4$	X ‖ elongation	251
1.62		+	Mod.	*dl*-Glutamic acid·HI	$C_5H_9O_4N \cdot HI$	Opt. ax. ⊥ 010; opt. pl. ∧ *c* = 15°	71
1.62	1.494	?	?	Methionine picrolonate	$C_{15}H_{19}O_7N_5S$	Z ‖ elong.	211
1.62	1.54	?	?	Succinimide	$C_4H_5O_2N$	MP 125°	198
1.620	1.545	?	Biax.	6-Benzamido-2-naphthalenesulfonic acid II	$C_{17}H_{13}O_4NS$	Z ‖ elong.	170
1.62	1.56	?	?	Homatropine	$C_{16}H_{21}O_2N$	X ‖ elong.	280

N_2(orN_3),N	N_1	Sign	2V	Name	Composition	Opt. Orient., etc.	Page
1.62	1.58	–	30°	Quinamine	$C_{19}H_{24}O_2N_2$	Z ‖ elong.	293
1.620	›1.545	?	Biax.	Ethyl oxamate	$C_4H_7O_3N$	X ‖ elongation	32
1.62	1.60	?	?	Atropine·HBr	$C_{17}H_{24}O_3NBr$	Z ‖ elong.	280
›1.620	1.468	?	?	Potassium acid uroxanate	$C_5H_7O_6N_4K$	Z ‖ elong.	59
1.625	1.518	?	?	Ergotamine tartrate	$C_{37}H_{41}O_{11}N_5$	Orth.	301
1.625	1.530	?	?	*N*-Methyl-*N*-phenylcarbamylglycine	$C_{10}H_{12}O_3N_2$	X ‖ elong.	142
1.625	1.53	?	?	Atropine methobromide	$C_{18}H_{26}O_3NBr$	Extinc. ∧ = 41°	279
1.626 = N_Z	1.457 = N_X	?	?	Sodium calcium aconitate·$2H_2O$	$C_6H_3O_6CaNa\cdot 2H_2O$	N_i = 1.572	37
1.627	1.602	+	45°	Phenylurea	$C_7H_8ON_2$	X = *b*; Z ∧ *c* = 78°. 100 cleav. MP 147°	141
1.627 = N_Y		?	79°	2,6,2′,5′-Tetrahydroxybenzohydrol ethyl ether	$C_{15}H_{11}O_{10}$	Bx_a = *b*; Y = *a*.	102
1.628 = N_Z		–	30°	*l*-Dichlorotyrosine	$C_9H_9O_3NCl_2$	Y = *b*.	165
1.63	1.57	?	?	Morphine·HBr(H_2O ?)	$C_{17}H_{20}O_3NBr\cdot(H_2O\ ?)$	– elong.	296
1.630	1.572	?	?	Cupric 2-amino-4-methylmercapto-butanoate	$C_5H_{10}O_2NSCu$	X ‖ elong.	72
1.63	1.555	?	?	Apoatropine sulfate	$(C_{17}H_{21}O_2N)_2\cdot H_2SO_4$	Z ‖ elong.	281
1.63	1.61	?	?	Hyoscyamine·HBr	$C_{17}H_{24}O_3NBr$	Z ‖ elong.	281
1.63	1.41	?	?	Chloroacetic acid	$CH_2Cl\cdot CO_2H$	Z ‖ elong ?	19
1.63	1.54	?	?	Hyoscyamine salicylate	$C_{24}H_{29}O_6N$	Granular	282
1.630	1.527	?	?	Cupric 2-aminopropionate·H_2O	$C_4H_9O_2NCu\cdot H_2O$	X ‖ elong.	67
1.63	1.535	?	?	Hydrohydrastinine·HCl	$C_{11}H_{14}O_2NCl$	X ‖ elong.	295
1.63 = N_Z	1.580 = N_Y	?	?	Ergotoxine acetone solvate	$C_{35}H_{39}O_5N_5\cdot nC_3H_6O$	Y = *a*; Z = *c*.	303
1.63	1.57	?	?	Oxyacanthine·$H_2SO_4\cdot 6H_2O$	$C_{40}H_{44}O_{10}N_2S\cdot 6H_2O$	Z ‖ elong.	306
1.632 = N_Z		–	69°(2E)	*dl*-Bromotyrosine	$C_9H_{10}O_3NBr$	X = *a*; Y = *b*.	165
1.632	1.586	?	?	Estradiol benzoate	$C_{25}H_{28}O_3$	White to brown	276

Table I. Based on the Higher Measured Refractive Index

N_2(orN_3),N	N_1	Sign	2V	Name	Composition	Opt. Orient., etc.	Page
1.633	1.576	?	?	5-Benzamido-1-naphthalene sulfonic acid	$C_{17}H_{13}O_4NS$	X ‖ elong.	170
1.634	1.545	?	?	Codeine phosphate·($2H_2O$?)	$C_{18}H_{24}O_7NP$(·$2H_2O$?)	X ‖ elong.	297
1.635		?	0°	Corydine	$C_{20}H_{23}O_4N$	MP 149°	296
1.635	1.545	?	?	Nicotine salicylate	$C_{17}H_{21}O_3N_2$	Z ‖ elong.	278
1.635=N_Z	1.600=N_X	?	Biax.	Diphenylhydantoin	$(C_6H_5)_2$NHCONHCOCH$_2$	X ‖ elong.	213
1.635=N_Z	1.625=N_X	+	?	Tryptophan	$C_{11}H_{12}O_2N_2$	Biaxial	203
1.636	1.513	?	?	*N*-Methyl-*N′*-phenylurea	$C_8H_{10}ON_2$	Parallel extinc.	143
1.637=N_Y		?	?	Triethylsulfonium chloroplatinate	$[(C_2H_5)_3SCl]_2PtCl_4$	Monoclinic	7
1.637=N_Y		?	43°	3-Methyl-1-phenyl-5-pyrazolone	$C_{10}H_{10}ON_2$	MP 127°	207
1.639=N_Z	1.520=N_X	?	?	Tricalcium aconitate·$3H_2O$	$(C_6H_3O_6)_2Ca_3 \cdot 3H_2O$	Parallel extinc.	37
1.64	1.555	?	?	Cinchonine nitrate	$C_{19}H_{23}O_4N_3$	X ‖ elong.	284
1.64=N_Z	1.53=N_X	?	?	Tephrosindicarboxylic acid	$C_{23}H_{22}O_{11}$	Z ∧ elong.= ?	316
1.64	1.62	– ?	Lg.	Cupreine	$C_{19}H_{22}O_2N_2$	X ∧ elong. < 35°	293
1.640=N_Z	1.585=N_X	?	?	Lithium benzoate	$C_6H_5CO_2Li$	Thin flakes	111
1.64	1.545	?	?	Narceine·$H_2SO_4 \cdot 6H_2O$	$C_{46}H_{56}O_{20}N_2S \cdot 6H_2O$	X ‖ elong.	294
1.64 *ca.*	⟨1.63	?	?	Nirvanol	$C_{11}H_{12}O_2N_2$	MP 200°	213
1.64	1.54	?	?	Morphine tartrate·$2H_2O$	$C_{23}H_{25}O_9N \cdot 2H_2O$	X ‖ elong.	297
1.64	1.54	?	?	Guanidine hydrochloride	$CNH(NH_2)_2 \cdot HCl$	Orth.	40
1.64	1.625	?	?	Physostigmine·HBr	$C_{15}H_{22}O_2N_3Br$	Z ‖ elong.	304
1.64	1.53	?	?	Uranyl acetate(·$2H_2O$?)	$(CH_3CO_2)_2UO_2$	Z ‖ elong. Yellow pleoch.	16
1.642=N_Z	1.475=N_X	?	Biax.	Aconitic acid	$C_6H_6O_6$	MP 195°	36
1.645	1.62	?	?	Codeine salicylate	$C_{25}H_{27}O_6N$	X ‖ elong.	298
1.645	1.615	–	70°(2E)	Homatropine·HBr	$C_{16}H_{22}O_3NBr$	X=*b*; Y=*c*.	281
1.645	1.520	?	?	Lysine picrolonate	$C_{16}H_{22}O_7N_6$	Z ‖ elong.	211
1.645=N_Z	1.445=N_X	?	?	Methyl-*p*-tolyl ketone semicarbazone	$C_{11}H_{16}ON_3$	MP 210°	104
1.645	1.62	?	?	Antimony acid tartrate·$4H_2O$	$C_{12}H_{15}O_{18}Sb \cdot 4H_2O$?	Prismatic	48

TABLE I. BASED ON THE HIGHER MEASURED REFRACTIVE INDEX

N_2(orN_3),N	N_1	Sign	2V	Name	Composition	Opt. Orient., etc.	Page
1.646=N_Z	1.58=N_X	?	?	Ethoxytris(4-methylphenyl) methane	$C_{24}H_{26}O$		96
1.646	1.628	?	?	5-Benzamido-2-naphthalenesulfonic acid	$C_{17}H_{13}O_4NS$	Z ‖ elong.	170
1.646	1.628	?	?	2-Naphthol-6-sulfonic acid benzoate	$C_{17}H_{12}O_5S$	Z ‖ elong.	138
1.647	1.525	?	Lg.	1,3-Dimethyl-9-phenylpseudouric acid	$C_{13}H_{14}O_4N_4$	Extinc. at 25 – 37°	241
1.648	1.430	–	40° *ca.*	Sodium fumarate (H_2O ?)	$(CHCO_2Na)_2 \cdot (H_2O$?)	X ∧ *c*=10° *ca.* N_2=1.62	35
1.648	1.514	?	?	Guanidine anthranilate	$C_8H_{12}O_2N_4$	N_1 ‖ width	162
1.649=N_Y		?	77°	4,4-Methylenediantipyrine·H_2O	$C_{23}H_{24}O_2N_4 \cdot H_2O$	Bx_a ∧ *c*=56°	249
⟩1.649=N_Z	1.532=N_X	?	?	Phenylbiuret	$C_8H_9O_2N_3$	Extinc. at 33°. MP 190°	142
1.65	1.58	?	?	Apoatropine·HCl	$C_{17}H_{22}O_2NCl$	X ‖ elong.	281
1.65	1.55	?	?	Codeine·HBr·H_2O	$C_{18}H_{22}O_3NBr \cdot H_2O$	X ‖ elong.	297
1.65	1.63	?	?	Colchicine	$C_{22}H_{25}O_6N$		299
1.65	1.615	?	?	Ditaine ·4H_2O	$C_{22}H_{28}O_4N_2 \cdot 4H_2O$	Z ‖ elong.	306
1.65=N_Z	1.52=N_X	?	Biax.	2-Methoxy-4-propylphenyl 3,5-dinitrobenzoate	$C_{17}H_{16}O_7N_2$	MP 116°	117
1.65=N_Z	1.58	?	?	Genistin	$C_{21}H_{20}O_{10}$	Z ‖ elong. MP 256°	187
1.65	1.61	?	Biax.	Carbolic acid	C_6H_5OH	Y=*b*. MP. 43°	85
1.65=N_Y	1.58=N_X	?	Biax.	Quinine citrate	$C_{26}H_{32}O_9N_2$	Z ‖ elong.	290
1.65=N_Z	1.52=N_X	+	70°	Acetolsalicylate	$C_{10}H_{10}O_4$	Y=*b*; Z ∧ elong.=43°	128
1.651	1.60	?	?	Leucine flavianate	$C_{16}H_{20}O_{10}N_3S$	Z ‖ elong.	137
1.652	1.589	?	?	Cupric 2-aminoacetate·H_2O	$C_4H_8O_4N_2Cu \cdot H_2O$	X ‖ elong. Color blue	67
1.653	1.537			4-Benzamido-1-naphthalenesulfonic acid	$C_{17}H_{13}O_4NS$	Sym. extinc. N_1 bisects 104°	170
1.654	1.460	?	?	1-Benzoxy-4-naphthalenesulfonic acid	$C_{17}H_{12}O_5S$	Extinc. at 31°	138
1.654=N_Z	1.585=N_X	+	?	*m*-Chlorobenzyl phanodorn	$C_{26}H_{26}N_2O_3Cl_2$	MP 102°	233
1.655	1.556	?	?	Brucine salt of sucrose disulfuric acid	$C_{58}H_{76}O_{22}N_4S_2$	Incl. extinc.	308
1.655=N_Z	1.575=N_X	–	?	Strychnine glutarate	$C_{26}H_{30}O_6N_2$	– elong.	308
1.655=N_Z	1.583=N_X	?	?	Monoacetate of dihydrotoxicarol	$C_{25}H_{26}O_8$	X ‖ elong.	317

TABLE I. BASED ON THE HIGHER MEASURED REFRACTIVE INDEX

N_2(orN_3),N	N_1	Sign	2V	Name	Composition	Opt. Orient., etc.	Page
1.655=N_Y	1.622=N_X	+	?	Ergometrine	$C_{19}H_{23}O_2N_3$	MP 204°	302
1.656=N_Y		?	83°	*N*-Ethoxybenzamidine	$C_9H_{12}ON_2$	Bx_a = *a*; Y = *c*. MP 67°	113
1.656=N_Y		?	61°	Pulvinic acid ethyl alcoholate	$C_{19}H_{18}O_6$	Y = *a*. Yellow	189
1.657=N_Z	1.459=N_X	?	?	Monopotassium aconitate	$C_6H_5O_6K$	Thin plates	36
1.657	1.598	?	?	Orthoform	$C_8H_9O_3N$	MP 120°	164
1.658=N_Z	1.595=N_X	?	Lg.	*N,N'*-Dibenzylurea	$C_{15}H_{16}ON_2$	Z ǁ elong.	151
1.658	1.493	?	?	Hydroxyproline picrolonate	$C_{15}H_{17}O_{10}N_5$	Z ǁ elong.	210
1.658	1.651	?	?	*m*-Nitrobenzoic acid I	$C_6H_4NO_2CO_2H$	Y = *b*; extinc. $\wedge c = 50°$	114
1.658=N_Y		?	86°	4-Methylantipyrine	$C_{12}H_{14}ON_2$	Extinc. $\wedge c = 47°$	208
1.659	1.531	?	?	Tropacocaine·HCl	$C_{15}H_{20}O_2NCl$	MP 271°	282
>1.659	1.642	–	Lg.	Ergometrine ethyl acetate solvate	$C_{19}H_{23}O_2N_3 \cdot nC_4H_8O_2$	MP 130 – 132°	302
1.659=N_Z		?	15°	Ergocristinine alcohol solvate	$C_{35}H_{39}O_5N_5 \cdot nC_2H_6O$	Y = *a*.	303
1.659=N_Z	1.536=N_X	+	Mod.	Ergometrine ethyl acetate solvate	$C_{19}H_{23}O_2N_3 \cdot nC_4H_8O_2$	X = *c*; Y = *b*.	302
1.659=N_Z	1.585=N_X	+	50°	Ergocristine	$C_{35}H_{39}O_5N_5$	Y = *b* ǁ elong.	300
<1.66=N_Z	1.536	?	Lg.	Methyl phenyl ketone methyl phenylhydrazone	$C_{15}H_{16}N_2$	Bx_a nearly ⊥ 100; Y = *b*. MP 124°	172
<1.66	1.579	?	67°	Allantoin	$C_4H_6O_3N_4$	X ǁ elong.	241
1.66	1.605	?	Lg.	Diphenylamine	$C_{10}H_{11}N$	X ǁ elong. ?	140
1.66	1.565	?	?	Caffeine·HCl	$C_8H_{10}O_2N_4 \cdot HCl$	X ǁ elong.	249
1.66	1.51	?	?	Opianic acid	$C_{10}H_{10}O_5$	X ǁ elong.	133
1.66	1.56	?	?	Physostigmine salicylate	$C_{22}H_{27}O_5N_3$	X ǁ elong.	304
1.66	1.58	–	48°(2E)	*p*-Aminophenol	C_6H_7ON	X = *a*; Y = *c*. 100 cleav. MP 184°	155
1.660=N_Z	1.485=N_X	?	?	Isotephrosindicarboxylic acid	$C_{22}H_{22}O_{11}$	MP 187°	316
1.660	1.529	?	?	Isoserine picrolonate III	$C_{13}H_{15}O_8N_5$	Z ǁ elong.	211
1.66=N_Z	1.50=N_X	+	Lg.	Ferrous 2-naphthalenesulfonate·6H_2O	$(C_{10}H_7SO_3)_2Fe \cdot 6H_2O$	Y ⊥ plates.	134
1.66	1.48	-?	?	Brucine	$C_{23}H_{26}O_4N_2$	X $\wedge$ elong. < 20°	308

TABLE I. BASED ON THE HIGHER MEASURED REFRACTIVE INDEX

N_2(orN_3),N	N_1	Sign	2V	Name	Composition	Opt. Orient., etc.	Page
1.660=N_Z	1.447=N_X	?	?	Magnesium acid aconitate·$4H_2O$	$C_6H_3O_6MgH \cdot 4H_2O$	Small prisms	37
1.660=N_Z	1.513=N_X	?	Biax.	Hydroxynetoric acid	$C_{12}H_{14}O_6$	MP 189°	313
1.660=N_Z	1.560=N_X	?	?	Citral semicarbazone	$C_{11}H_{19}ON_3$	MP 132°	42
>1.66	1.56	+	?	Coumarin	$C_8H_6O_2$	Y=*c*; Z=*a*. MP 67°	182
>1.66	1.50	?	92°(2H)	Phenyl salicylate	$C_{13}H_{10}O_3$	Y=*a*. MP 42°	127
1.661		?	74°	Cinchonidine·$CH_3I \cdot C_2H_5I \cdot 2H_2O$	$C_{22}H_{30}ON_2 \cdot 2H_2O$	Y=*b*.	287
1.661 ?	1.55	?	Biax.	Citrophen	$C_{14}H_{19}O_8N$	MP 186°	155
1.661		+	91°(2H)	Cinchonine-l-mandelate	$C_{27}H_{30}O_4N_2$	Y=*b*; Z=*c*.	286
1.662	1.606	?	?	Biguanide sodium ferricyanide	$C_8H_{10}N_{11}NaFe$		42
1.663=N_Z	1.578=N_X	?	?	Sulfaguanidine with HNO_3	$C_7H_{10}O_2N_4S$ with HNO_3	Z nearly ‖ elong.	168
1.665	1.39	-	49°(2E)	Meconic acid·$3H_2O$	$C_7H_4O_7 \cdot 3H_2O$	X=*c*; Y=*b*. 001 cleav.	190
1.665	1.515	?	?	3-Methyl-1-phenylhydantoin	$C_{10}H_{10}O_2N_2$	Z ‖ elong.	212
1.665	1.645	+	Sm.	Sparteine·HI	$C_{15}H_{27}N_2I$	Y=*b*; Z=*a*.	283
1.665	1.557	?	?	Cinchonine-2-phenylpyridine-2,3-dicarboxylate	$C_{51}H_{53}O_6N_5$	X ‖ elong.	284
1.666	1.616	?	?	Isoleucine flavianate	$C_{16}H_{20}O_{10}N_2S$	X ‖ elong.	137
1.666	1.626	?	90° *ca.*	Sodium tobiasate	$C_{10}H_8O_3NSNa$	Sym. and inclined extinc.	169
1.667=N_Y	1.662=N_X	?	?	*dl*-Methionine nitroindandionate	$C_{14}H_{16}O_6N_2S$	Z ‖ elong. MP 193°	107
1.668=N_3	1.63	?	?	Phenolphthalein	$C_{19}H_{14}O_4$	N_2=1.65. MP 250–253°	186
1.67	1.66	?	?	Pellotine	$C_{13}H_{19}O_3N$	Granular	293
1.67	1.520	?	?	Lobeline·HCl	$C_{22}H_{27}ON_2 \cdot HCl$	N_Y=1.645	278
1.67	1.615	?	?	Oxysparteine	$C_{15}H_{24}ON_2$	Granular	283
1.67	1.66	?	?	Anagyrine·HBr	$C_{15}H_{23}ON_2Br$	Granular	306
1.67	1.475	?	?	Vasicine tartrate	$C_{15}H_{18}O_7N_2$	X ‖ elong.	299
1.67=N_Z	1.58=N_X	?	Biax.	Quinine·$2H_2SO_4 \cdot 7H_2O$	$C_{20}H_{28}O_{10}N_2S_2 \cdot 7H_2O$	Z ‖ elong.	291
1.67	1.61	?	?	Quinine tartrate	$C_{44}H_{54}O_{10}N_4$	Z ‖ elong.	289
1.674=N_Y		?	?	2-Aminodiphenyl	$C_{12}H_{11}N$	MP 49°	153

N_2(orN_3),N	N_1	Sign	2V	Name	Composition	Opt. Orient., etc.	Page
1.674	1.557	?	?	Diethyleneglycoldinitrobenzoate	$C_{18}H_{14}O_{13}N_4$	N_2 || elong.	117
1.674	1.557	?	?	Methylphenyluric acid	$C_{12}H_{10}O_3N_4$	Z || elong.	251
1.675	1.65	?	?	Gelseminine·HBr	$C_{42}H_{48}O_{14}NBr$	X || elong.	305
1.675=N_3	1.412	+	35° *ca.*	Cyanamide	$H_2N \cdot CN$	$Z \wedge c=80°$, MP 44°. $N_2=1.556$	40
1.678=N_Z	1.656=N_Y	+	Lg.	Copper pyridine disaccharin·$2H_2O$	$C_{24}H_{18}O_6N_4S_2Cu \cdot 2H_2O$	$Y=b$; $Z=c$. D 1.509	253
1.68	1.57	+	45°(2E)	2,2,4,4,6-Pentachloro-6-methyl-1,3,5-cyclohexanetrione	$C_7H_3O_3Cl_5$	Z || elong.	106
1.68=N_3	1.57	?	?	Quinine ethyl carbonate	$C_{23}H_{29}O_5N_2$	$N_2=1.59$. MP 95°	288
1.680	1.490	?	?	Sodium benzoate·H_2O	$C_7H_5O_2N \cdot H_2O$	Loses H_2O at 120°	111
1.680=N_Z	1.590=N_X	?	Lg.	Thenfanil·HCl	$C_{15}H_{19}N_3 \cdot HCl$	MP 151°	199
1.68=N_Z	1.59=N_Y	?	?	Quinine succinate	$C_{24}H_{30}O_6N_2$	Z || elong.	289
1.68	1.47	?	?	Pyridine nitrate	$C_5H_5N \cdot HNO_3$	X || elong.	193
1.680	1.590	?	Biax.	Ethyl phenyloxalurate I	$C_{11}H_{12}O_4N_2$	X || elong.	141
1.68=N_Z	1.62=N_Y	?	Biax.	Quinine acetate	$C_{22}H_{28}O_4N_2$	Z || elong.	291
1.680	1.621	?	?	Phenylisoguanylurea·HCl	$C_8H_{10}ON_4Cl$	N_2|| width	143
1.68	1.32	?	?	Bulbocapnine·HCl	$C_{19}H_{20}O_4NCl$	Z || elong.	295
1.681	1.572	?	?	Salophen	$C_{15}H_{13}O_4N$	MP 187°	156
1.681	1.547	?	?	2-Naphthol-6,8-disulfonic acid benzoate	$C_{17}H_{12}O_8S_2$	X || elong.	138
1.682=N_Z	1.550=N_X	?	Biax.	Dihydrorotenone I	$C_{23}H_{24}O_6$	X || elong.	314
1.682	1.508	?	Biax.	Quinine (iso?)valerate	$C_{25}H_{36}O_4N_2$		289
1.683	1.635	?	?	Methionine flavianate	$C_{15}H_{18}O_{10}N_3S_2$	X || elong.	138
1.684	1.155	?	Lg.	Dimethylphenyluric acid	$C_{13}H_{12}O_3N_4$	MP > 300°	251
1.684	1.662	?	?	8-Benzamido-1-naphthol-5-sulfonic acid benzoate	$C_{24}H_{17}O_6NS$	X || elong.	171
1.685	1.606	?	?	8-Benzamido-2-naphthalenesulfonic acid	$C_{17}H_{13}O_4NS$	X || elong.	170

TABLE I. BASED ON THE HIGHER MEASURED REFRACTIVE INDEX

N_2(orN_3),N	N_1	Sign	2V	Name	Composition	Opt. Orient., etc.	Page
1.685=N_Z	1.550=N_X	?	Biax.	Monoacetate of dihydro-7-hydroxy-toxicarol	$C_{25}H_{26}O_9$	MP 196°	317
1.685	1.460	+	Lg.	Dimelamine phthalate	$C_{14}H_{17}O_4N_{12}$	X′ ∧ elong.=30°	245
1.685=N_Y	1.56=N_X	?	?	Benzaldehyde semicarbazone	$C_8H_9ON_3$	MP 217°	103
1.686=N_Y		+	Sm.	Ergotamine with ergotinine	$C_{33}H_{35}O_5N_5$+ +$n(C_{35}H_{39}O_5N_5)$	Y=*b*. MP 164 - 165°	301
1.69	1.528	?	?	1,3-Dimethylxanthine·H_2O	$C_7H_8O_2N_4 \cdot H_2O$	X ∧ *c*=43°	247
1.69	1.64	?	?	Embelic acid	$C_{18}H_{28}O_4$	X ‖ elong.	110
1.69	1.591	?	?	Allylpseudouric acid·H_2O	$C_8H_{10}O_4N_4 \cdot H_2O$	X ‖ elong.	241
1.69	1.54	?	?	Thermodine	$C_{13}H_{17}O_4N$	MP 86°	156
1.69 =N_Z	1.65 =N_Y	?	Biax.	Quinine chromate	$C_{20}H_{26}O_6N_2Cr$	Z ‖ elong.	290
1.690=N_Z	1.468=N_X	?	?	Zinc acid aconitate·$4H_2O$	$C_6H_3O_6ZnH \cdot 4H_2O$	Decomposes at 110°	37
1.69 =N_Z	1.62 =N_Y	?	Biax.	Quinine formate	$C_{21}H_{26}O_4N_2$	Z ‖ elong.	291
1.69 =N_Z	1.45 =N_X	?	?	3,5-Acetoxylide	$C_{10}H_{13}ON$	X ∧ elong.=12°	151
1.69	1.53	?	?	Narceine meconate	$C_{33}H_{38}O_{13}N$	Extinc. ∧ =23°	294
1.69 =N_Z	1.45 =N_X	?	?	3,5-Xylidine	$C_8H_{11}N$	X ∧ *c*=12°; Y=*b*.	151
1.69 *ca.*	1.555 *ca.*	?	Lg.	Yohimbine picrate	$C_{27}H_{29}O_{10}N_5$	X ‖ elong.	299
1.69 =N_Z	1.59 =N_Y	?	?	Cupric acetylacetonate	$(C_5H_7O_2)_2Cu$	X=*b*. D 1.57. Blue	12
1.69	1.62	?	?	Oxyacanthine	$C_{19}H_{21}O_3N$	Z ‖ elong.	306
1.69	1.66	–	Lg.	Bromal hydrate·H_2O	$CBr_3 \cdot CH(OH)_2 \cdot H_2O$	Z=*b*. MP 51°	12
1.69	1.535	?	Lg.	Brucine phthalate	$C_{31}H_{32}O_8N_2$	Parallel extinc.	308
1.691	1.510	?	?	7-Benzamido-3-naphthalene disulfonic acid	$C_{17}H_{13}O_7NS_2$	X ‖ elong.	170
1.691	1.502	+	60°	*m*-Nitrophenol	$C_6H_4NO_2OH$	Extinc. ∧ *c*=1.5° in 110. MP 96°	86
1.692=N_Y	1.675=N_X	–?	?	*N*-*β*-Hydroxyethyl-*N*-phenylthiourea	$C_9H_{12}ON_2S$	Parallel extinc.	151
1.692		–	45°(2E)	*dl*-Dichlorotyrosine	$C_9H_9O_3NCl_2$	Y=*a*.	165

TABLE I. BASED ON THE HIGHER MEASURED REFRACTIVE INDEX

N_2(orN_3),N	N_1	Sign	2V	Name	Composition	Opt. Orient., etc.	Page
1.693=N_Z	1.485=N_X	?	?	Strontium salicylate·$2H_2O$	$(C_6H_4OHCO_2)_2Sr\cdot 2H_2O$	White powder	127
1.693	1.462	?	?	*dl*-Tryptophane diliturate·$3H_2O$	$C_{15}H_{15}O_7N_5\cdot 3H_2O$	Elong. –. Decomp. 191°	226
1.694	1.592	?	?	8-Benzamido-1-naphthol-3,6-disulfonic acid benzoate	$C_{24}H_{17}O_9NS_2$	X′ ∧ elong. =17°	171
1.694	1.662	?	?	Apomorphine·HCl·(0.75H_2O ?)	$C_{17}H_{18}O_2NCl\cdot(.75H_2O$?)	Z ‖ elong.	299
1.695	1.555	?	?	Dimethylphenylpseudouric acid	$C_{13}H_{14}O_4N_4$	MP 220°	241
1.695	1.540	?	?	Guaiacol carbonate	$(C_7H_7O)_2CO_3$	MP 88°	98
1.696=N_Z	1.563=N_X	?	?	1,3-*bis*(*p*-Nitrobenzyl)-5-ethyl-5-isopropylbarbituric acid	$C_{23}H_{24}O_7N_4$	X ∧ elong. =35°. MP 157°	229
1.696	1.563	?	?	*p*-Nitrobenzyl ipral	$C_{26}H_{30}O_7N_4$	X ∧ elong. =35°. MP 157°	229
1.696	1.629	?	?	6-Benzamido-1-naphthol-3-sulfonic acid benzoate	$C_{24}H_{17}O_6NS$	Z ‖ elong.	170
1.696	1.548	?	?	*p*-Nitrobenzyl pentobarbital	$C_{25}H_{28}O_7N_4$	Z ‖ elong. MP 151°	230
1.697	1.552	?	?	2-Naphthol-3,6-disulfonic acid benzoate	$C_{17}H_{12}O_8S_2$	Z ‖ elong.	138
1.697	1.535	?	?	Guanylurea anthranilate	$C_9H_{13}O_3N_5$	N_1‖ width	163
⟩1.698	⟩1.618	?	?	Dichlorotyrosine picrolonate	$C_{19}H_{17}O_8N_5Cl$	Z ‖ elong.	210
1.700	1.595	?	?	Phenyloxaluric acid methylamide	$C_{10}H_{11}O_3N_3$	X ‖ elong.	141
1.70=N_Z	1.64=N_Y	?	Biax.	Quinine thiosulfate	$C_{20}H_{26}O_5N_2S_2$	Z ‖ elong.	291
1.70	1.55	?	?	Caffeine·HBr	$C_8H_{10}O_2N_4\cdot HBr$	Z ‖ elong.	249
1.70	1.43	?	?	Cyanuric acid	$C_3H_3O_3N_3$	Z ‖ elong.	244
1.70	1.55	?	?	Piperine	$C_{17}H_{19}O_3N$	MP 129°	279
1.700=N_Y	1.62=N_X	– ?	Lg.	*N*-Isoamyl-*N′*-phenylthiourea	$C_{12}H_{18}N_2S$	Sym. extinc. MP 102°	143
1.70	1.59	?	Biax.	Cinchonine·2HCl	$C_{19}H_{24}ON_2Cl_2$	Z ‖ elong.	284
1.70	1.66	?	?	Apomorphine sulfate	$C_{17}H_{19}O_6NS$	Z ‖ elong.	299

Table I. Based on the Higher Measured Refractive Index

N_2(orN_3),N	N_1	Sign	2V	Name	Composition	Opt. Orient., etc.	Page
1.70=N_3	1,489	?	?	Gallic acid·H_2O	$C_7N_6O_5 \cdot H_2O$	X ‖ elong. Y=*b*. N_2=1.68	131
>1.70	1.514	?	?	2,4-Dichlorophenol	$C_6H_3Cl_2OH$	N_2 ‖ length. MP 45°	86
>1.70 =N_Z	1.555=N_X	?	?	Monoacetate of 7-hydroxytoxicarol	$C_{25}H_{24}O_9$	Parallel extinc.	317
>1.70 =N_Y	1.57 *ca.*	?	Lg.	Trinitroresorcinol I	$C_6H_3O_8N_3$	X ∧ *c*=7°; Y=*b*. MP 177°	99
1.701=N_Y	1.435=N_X	?	?	Ammonium dicyanoguanidine	$C_3H_2N_5 \cdot NH_4$	X ‖ elong.	42
1.701	1.468	?	?	1-Tyrosine diliturate·$3H_2O$	$C_{13}H_{14}O_8N_4 \cdot 3H_2O$	Decomp. 172°	225
1.702		?	81°	Benzoyl disulfide	$C_{14}H_{10}O_2S_2$	Y=*b*; Z ∧ *c*=18°	117
1.703	1.632	?	?	2-Benzamido-1-naphthalene sulfonic acid	$C_{17}H_{13}O_4NS$	X ‖ elong.	169
1.705	1.525	?	Biax.	1,3,9-Trimethyluric acid	$C_8H_{10}O_3N_4$	Z ‖ elong.	250
1.705=N_Z	1.548=N_X	?	?	Barium monobromoacetate	$(CH_2BrCO_2)_2Ba$	Z ‖ elongation.	20
1.705 *ca.*	1.670=N_X	–	84°(2H)	*m*-Bromonitrobenzene	$C_6H_4BrNO_2$	X=*c*; Y=*a*. MP 56°	75
1.706=N_Y	1.470=N_X	–	?	Isobutylamine diliturate	$C_8H_{14}O_5N_4$	X ∧ elong. =41°	216
1.709	1.534	?	?	Acetopyrine	$C_{20}H_{20}O_5N_2$	MP 63 – 65°	208
1.710=N_Z	1.525=N_X	?	?	Nitroguanidine II	$NH_2C(NH)_2 \cdot NO_2$	Long plates	43
1.71	1.612	?	?	6-Benzamido-2-naphthalenesulfonic acid I	$C_{17}H_{13}O_4NS$	X ‖ elong.	170
1.71 *ca.*	1.592	?	?	Hydroquinine·HCl·($2H_2O$?)	$C_{20}H_{26}O_2N_2$ HCl ($2H_2O$?)	Granular	292
1.71	1.515=N_X	–	?	*o*-Bromonitrobenzene	$C_6H_4BrNO_2$	X ∧ *c*=14.5°; Z=*b*.	75
1.71	1.55	?	?	Phenylamine sulfate	$(C_6H_5NH_2)_2 \cdot H_2SO_4$	Extinc. at 32°	139
1.71	1.70	+	Sm.	*p*-Nitrobenzaldehyde	$C_6H_4NO_2CHO$	Opt. plane for red ⊥ opt. pl. for blue	104
1.71	1.512=N_X	?	?	*p*-Chloronitrobenzene	$C_6H_4ClNO_2$	X ∧ *c*=20°; Y=*b*.	74
>1.71	1.624	?	?	7-Benzamido-1-naphthol-3-sulfonic acid benzoate	$C_{24}H_{17}O_6NS$	X ‖ elong.	171
1.714	1.636	?	?	7-Methyl-9-phenylpseudouric acid	$C_{12}H_{12}O_4N_4$	Z ‖ elong.	241

N_2(orN_3),N	N_1	Sign	2V	Name	Composition	Opt. Orient., etc.	Page
1.715	1.600	?	Lg.	2-Ketopropanedioic acid monomethylamide phenylhydrazone	$C_{10}H_{11}O_3N_3$	Sym. extinc.	172
1.716	1.580	?	?	Arginine picrolonate	$C_{16}H_{22}O_7N_8(H_2O\,?)$	Z ‖ elong.	209
1.717 = N_Z	1.525 = N_X	?	?	9-Phenyluric acid·$2H_2O$	$C_{11}H_8O_3N_4 \cdot 2H_2O$	Z ‖ elong.	250
1.718 = N_Y	1.51 = N_X	–	Lg.	Equilenin	$C_{18}H_{18}O_2$	X = *b*; Y = *a*.	275
1.72	1.49	?	?	Pyrogallol	$C_6H_3(OH)_3$	Z ‖ elong. 001 cleav.	100
1.72	1.545	?	?	Diphenylamine·HCl	$C_{12}H_{12}NCl$	Z ‖ elong.	140
1.72 = N_Y		?	29°	*N*-(*o*-Chlorophenyl)-*N′*-phenylthiourea	$C_{13}H_{11}N_2SCl$	Parallel extinc. MP 158°	145
1.72	1.69	?	?	Strychnine salicylate	$C_{28}H_{28}O_5N_2$	Z ‖ elong.	308
1.720	1.495	?	?	Di-iodotyrosine flavianate	$C_{19}H_{15}O_{11}N_3SI_2$	X ‖ elong. Yellow	166
1.72	1.477 = N_X	– ?	?	*o*-Nitrobenzyl alcohol	$C_7H_7O_3N$	X ‖ elong. Brown	93
1.72	1.515 = N_X	– ?	?	*p*-Nitrobenzyl alcohol	$C_7H_7O_3N$	X′ ∧ elong. = 24°. MP 93°. Str. dispersion	93
1.72	1.59	?	?	Ammonium salicylate·$0.5H_2O$	$C_7H_9O_3 \cdot 0.5H_2O$	Z ‖ elong.	127
1.72	1.55	?	?	Monoguanyl melamine·HCl·H_2O	$C_4H_9N_8Cl \cdot H_2O$	N_2 ‖ elong.	245
1.72	1.545	?	?	*p*-Aminophenol·HCl	C_6H_8ONCl	Z ‖ elong.	155
1.72	1.706	?	?	Oxanilide	$C_{14}H_{12}O_2N_2$	N_2 ‖ length; N_1 ‖ width. MP 245°	141
1.72	1.533	?	?	Salipyrine	$C_{18}H_{18}O_4N$	MP 91°	208
›1.72	1.49	?	Biax.	2-Methylphenyl 3,5-dinitrobenzoate	$C_{14}H_{10}O_6N_2$	MP 138°	116
1.721 = N_E		?	?	2-Methyl-butyl-3-[4-(4-cyanobenzal-amino)-phenyl] propenoate	$C_{22}H_{22}O_2N_2$	Also forms liquid crystals.	166
1.723	1.626	?	?	Biguanide anthranilate	$C_9H_{14}O_2N_6$	N_2 ‖ width	162
1.725	1.58	?	?	Heliotropin semicarbazone	$C_9H_9O_3N_3$	MP 234°	191
1.725	‹1.445	?	?	3-Methyl-1-phenylbiuret	$C_9H_{11}O_2N_3$	X ‖ elong. MP 183°	142
1.729	1.507	–	?	4,4′-Dichloro-3,3′ditolyl	$C_{14}H_{12}Cl_2$	Z ∧ plates = 70°	88

Table I. Based on the Higher Measured Refractive Index

N_2(orN_3),N	N_1	Sign	2V	Name	Composition	Opt. Orient., etc.	Page
$1.73=N_Z$	$1.64=N_X$	?	?	2-Naphthylamine-2-naphthalene-sulfonate	$C_{20}H_{17}O_3NS$	MP 278°	152
1.730	1.665	?	?	Allyldimethyluric acid	$C_{10}H_{12}O_3N_4$	X ‖ elong.	251
$1.7=N_Y$	$1.583=N_X$	?	Biax.	Apiole	$C_{12}H_{14}O_4$	MP 29.5°	191
1.73	1.64	+	62°	Cytisine	$C_{11}H_{14}ON_2$	$Y=a$; $Z=c$.	305
$1.73=N_Z$	$1.53=N_X$	?	?	Uric acid(H_2O ?)	$C_5H_4O_3N_4(H_2O$?)		249
$1.73=N_Z$	$1.54=N_X$	+	Lg.	Mercuric phthalate	$C_6H_4(CO_2)_2Hg(H_2O$?)	Parallel extinc.	122
1.73 *ca.*	1.48	?	Lg.	*p*-Bromonitrobenzene	$C_6H_4BrNO_2$	X ∧ elong. = 14° 010 cleav. MP 127°	75
1.73	1.454	−	25° *ca.*	Melamine sulfate	$C_3H_8O_4N_6S$		245
$>1.73=N_Z$	$1.559=N_X$	?	?	Phenylbiuret	$C_8H_9O_2N_3$	Extinc at 33°. MP 197°	142
$1.732=N_Z$	$1.500=N_X$	−	?	Pyramidone	$C_{13}H_{17}ON_3$	MP 108°	240
>1.732	1.550	?	?	2-Methoxy-6-chloroacridone	$C_{14}H_{10}O_2NCl$	X ‖ elong.	198
1.733	1.555	?	?	Adrenalin	$C_9H_{13}O_3N$	Colorless to brown	160
$1.733=N_Z$	$1.55=N_X$	?	?	*N*-Cinnamyl-*l*-ephedrine·HCl	$C_{12}H_{18}ONCl$	MP 182°	157
$1.733=N_Z$	$1.57=N_X$	?	?	*N*-Cinnamyl-*dl*-ephedrine	$C_{12}H_{17}ON$	X ‖ elong. MP 67°	157
$1.733=N_Z$	$1.582=N_X$	?	?	*N*-Cinnamyl-*l*-ephedrine	$C_{12}H_{17}ON$	X ‖ elong. MP 86°	157
>1.733	1.500	?	?	Atabrine (·$2H_2O$?)	$C_{23}H_{30}O_3NCl(2H_2O$?)	Yellow color	203
$>1.733=N_3$	1.522	?	?	Atabrine·2HCl·$2H_2O$	$C_{23}H_{36}O_5NCl_3$	$N_2=1.733$. Color yellow	203
$>1.733=N_Z$	$1.582=N_X$	?	?	Sulfathiazole with picrolonic acid	?	X inclined to elong.	255
$>1.733=N_3$	1.447	?	?	1,3-Dimethylxanthine·H_2O	$C_7H_8O_2N_4\cdot H_2O$	X ∧ $c=43°$. $N_2=1.695$	248
$>1.733=N_3$	1.448	?	?	Tetracaine·HCl	$C_{15}H_{25}O_2N_2Cl$	$N_2=1.733$. MP 150°	163
$1.734=N_Z$	$1.592=N_X$	?	?	Brucine sulfate with $PtCl_4$	$(C_{23}H_{26}O_4N_2)_2\cdot H_2SO_4$ with $PtCl_4$	Z ‖ elong.	308
$1.734=N_Z$	$1.59=N_X$	?	?	Sulfanilamide·$H_2O+AgNO_3$	$C_6H_8O_2N_2S\cdot nH_2O\cdot nAgNO_3$	X ‖ elong.	167
1.734	1.570	?	?	Cocaine·HCl with $AuCl_3$	$C_{17}H_{21}O_4N\cdot HCl$ with $AuCl_3$	Rods.	282

TABLE I. BASED ON THE HIGHER MEASURED REFRACTIVE INDEX

N_2(orN_3),N	N_1	Sign	2V	Name	Composition	Opt. Orient., etc.	Page
1.734 = N_Z	1.580 = N_X	?	?	*d*-Desoxyephedrine with $AuCl_3$	$C_{10}H_{15}N$ with $AuCl_3$	X ‖ elong.	151
1.734 = N_Y		?	?	3-Amino-1,5-diphenyl-1,2,4-triazole	$C_{14}H_{12}N_4$	Extinc. ∧ *c* = 56°	250
1.734 = N_Z	1.603 = N_X	?	?	Vonedrine with $AuCl_3$	$C_{10}H_{15}N$ with $AuCl_3$	Inclined extinction	151
$>$1.734 = N_Y	1.734 = N_X	?	?	Copper picrolonate	$(C_{10}H_7O_5N_4)_2Cu$	Z ‖ elong.	209
$>$1.744 = N_Z		?	?	*dl*-Desoxyephedrine·HCl	$C_{10}H_{15}N \cdot HCl$	X ‖ elong.	151
$>$1.734	1.650	?	?	Zinc picrolonate	$(C_{10}H_7O_5N_4)_2Zn$	Z ‖ elong.	209
$>$1.734	1.448	?	?	Strontium picrolonate	$(C_{10}H_7O_5N_4)_2Sr(H_2O\ ?)$	X ∧ elong. $>$ 0° and $<$ 45°	209
$>$1.734	1.644	?	?	Ammonium picrolonate	$C_{10}H_7O_5N_4NH_4$	Z ‖ elong. N_i = 1.734	209
$>$1.734	1.505	+?	Sm.?	Potassium picrolonate	$C_{10}H_7O_5N_4K$	N_i = 1.519 (= N_Y ?)	209
$>$1.734	1.616	?	?	Sodium picrolonate	$C_{10}H_7O_5N_4Na$	X ‖ elong.	209
$>$1.734	1.428	?	Biax.	Nicotinic acid	$C_6H_5O_2N$	Extinc. ‖	277
$>$1.734 = N_Y	1.555 = N_X	?	?	Papaverine·HCl	$C_{20}H_{21}O_4N \cdot HCl$	MP 220°	294
1.735 *ca.*	1.492	?	?	Cinchophen with HNO_3	$C_{16}H_{11}O_2N$ with HNO_3	Z ≈ elong.	201
1.735 *ca.*		?	74°	2-Methoxyphenazine	$C_{13}H_{12}O_2N$	Extinc. ∧ *c* = 61°	207
1.735	1.546	?	?	Lysine flavianate	$C_{16}H_{21}O_{10}N_4S$	X ‖ elong. Yellow	137
1.735	1.546	?	?	Histidine flavianate	$C_{16}H_{16}O_{10}N_5S$	Extinc. at 18°. Yellow	242
1.736 = N_Z	1.445 = N_X	−	15°	3-Ethoxy-4-hydroxybenzaldehyde semicarbazone	$C_{10}H_{13}O_3N_3$	N_i = 1.69, common. MP 175°	109
1.736	1.616 = N_Y	+ ?	?	Aminomethylphenyltriazole·$PtCl_4$	$(C_9H_{10}N_4 \cdot HCl)_2 \cdot PtCl_4$	MP 245°	244
1.737 = N_Z	1.690 = N_X	?	?	Pyrrolazote hydrochloride	$C_{16}H_{16}N_2S \cdot HCl$	MP 198°	256
$<$1.74	$>$1.658	?	?	Norleucine picrolonate	$C_{16}H_{21}O_7N_5$	X ‖ elong.	211
1.74 ?	1.583	−	57°(2H)	*N,N'*-Diphenylurea	$C_{13}H_{12}ON_2$	X = *c*; Y = *a*. MP 235°	141
1.74 = N_Z	1.568 = N_Y	?	?	Phenobarbital-*p*-chlorobenzyl	$C_{26}H_{22}O_3N_2Cl_2$	Z ∧ elong. = 8°	235
1.74	1.61	?	?	*trans*-Cinnamic acid	$C_9H_8O_2$	X = *b*, Z ∧ *c* = 58°	119
1.74	1.42	?	?	Theobromine salicylate	$C_{14}H_{13}O_5N_5$	X ‖ elong.	248
1.74 = N_Z	1.50 = N_X	?	Biax.	4-Methylphenyl 3,5-dinitrobenzoate	$C_{14}H_{10}O_6N_2$	MP 187°	116
1.74 = N_Z	1.51 = N_X	−	?	Opianic acid	$C_{10}H_{10}O_5$	X ‖ elong.	133

TABLE I. BASED ON THE HIGHER MEASURED REFRACTIVE INDEX

N_2(orN_3),N	N_1	Sign	2V	Name	Composition	Opt. Orient., etc.	Page
1.74	1.515	?	?	Asaron	$C_{11}H_{16}O_4$	$Bx_a \wedge c = 18°$; $Y = b$.	101
1.74	1.56	+	?	Hydrastine	$C_{21}H_{21}O_6N$	Z ‖ elong.	294
1.74 = N_Z	1.535 = N_X	?	Biax.	Dihydrotoxicarolic acid methyl ether	$C_{24}H_{28}O_9$	Parallel extinc.	317
1.74		?	Lg.	Diphenyliodonium chloride	$(C_6H_5)_2ICl$	$Y = b$. $N_Z - N_X = .02$	79
1.74	1.495	+	?	*m*-Nitrobenzaldehyde	$C_7H_5O_3N$	Opt. plane ‖ elong. MP 58°	104
1.74 = N_Z	1.48 = N_X	?	?	Diacetate of dihydrotoxicarol	$C_{27}H_{28}O_9$	X ‖ elong.	317
>1.74	1.70 *ca.*	?	Lg.	Benzaldehyde 4-nitrophenylhydrazone	$C_{13}H_{11}O_2N_3$	$Z = b$. MP 262°	173
>1.74	1.684	?	?	Norvaline picrolonate II	$C_{15}H_{19}O_7N_5$	X ‖ elong.	211
>1.74	<1.67	?	?	Moser compound	$C_{22}H_{14}ON_2 + C_4H_8O_2$	Yellow columnar	309
>1.74	>1.66	?	Sm.	α-Naphthol	$C_{10}H_7OH$	$Bx_a = b$; $Bx_0 \wedge c = 15°$	94
>1.74	1.549	?	?	Dibromotyrosine picrolonate	$C_{19}H_{17}O_8N_5Br_2$	Z ‖ elong.	210
>1.74	1.70 *ca.*	?	?	Isoserine picrolonate I	$C_{13}H_{15}O_8N_5$	Z ‖ elong.	211
$>1.74 = N_Z$	1.500 = N_X	?	Biax.	Diacetate of toxicarol	$C_{27}H_{26}O_9$	MP 233°	317
$>1.74 = N_Z$	1.600 = N_X	?	?	Apotoxicarol methyl ether	$C_{19}H_{18}O_7$	X ∧ elong. = ?	316
$>1.74 = N_Z$	1.563 = N_X	?	?	Monoacetate of dehydrotoxicarol	$C_{25}H_{22}O_8$	X ∧ elong. = ?	316
$>1.74 = N_Z$	1.498 = N_X	?	Sm.	Dihydrodehydrodeguelin	$C_{23}H_{22}O_6$	MP 267°	311
>1.74	1.549	?	?	Valine picrolonate	$C_{15}H_{19}O_7N_5$	X ‖ elong.	212
$>1.74 = N_Z$	1.455 = N_X	?	?	Nicouic acid	$C_{12}H_{12}O_8$	Incl. extinc. MP 196°	132
>1.74	1.563	?	?	Phenobarbital-*p*-bromobenzyl	$C_{26}H_{22}O_3N_2Br_2$	Z ∧ elong. = 9°	234
>1.74	1.74	?	?	Cysteine picrolonate	$C_{13}H_{15}O_7N_5S$	X ‖ elong.	210
$>1.74 = N_Z$	1.52	+ ?	?	Ethyl-*p*-aminobenzoate	$C_9H_{11}O_2N$	Z ‖ elong. MP 90°	163
$>1.74 = N_Y$	1.616 = N_X	?	?	Methylanabasine picrate	$C_{17}H_{19}O_7N_5$	X ‖ elong.	279
>1.74	1.55	?	?	Vanillin	$C_8H_8O_3$	Opt. plane ⊥ 010. MP 81°	108
>1.74	1.50	− ?	?	Berberine · $6H_2O$	$C_{20}H_{19}O_5N \cdot 6H_2O$	X ‖ elong.	295
>1.74	1.53 = N_X	?	Biax.	2-Methoxyphenyl 3,5-dinitrobenzoate	$C_{14}H_{10}O_7N_2$	MP 141°	117
$>1.74 = N_Y$	1.585 = N_X	?	?	Anabasine picrate	$C_{16}H_{17}O_7N_5$		279

TABLE I. BASED ON THE HIGHER MEASURED REFRACTIVE INDEX

N_2(orN_3),N	N_1	Sign	2V	Name	Composition	Opt. Orient., etc.	Page
>1.74	1.523	?	?	Barium-*p*-(*p*-aminobenzoyl) benzenesulfonate	$C_{26}H_{20}O_8N_2S_2Ba$	Y=*b*; $Z \wedge c=6°$. 100 cleav.	171
>1.74=N_Z	1.490=N_X	?	?	Dihydrodeguelic acid	$C_{23}H_{26}O_8$	MP 80° and 144°	311
>1.74	1.587	?	?	(*p*-Methoxyphenyl) phenetyl-guanidine·HCl	$C_{23}H_{25}O_3N_3\cdot HCl$	MP 176°	101
>1.74		?	?	Aspartic acid picrolonate	$C_{14}H_{13}O_9N_5$	X ‖ elong.	210
>1.74	1.511	?	?	*o*-Nitrobenzaldehyde	$C_7H_5O_3N$	X ‖ elong. MP 114°	103
>1.74	>1.74	?	?	Phenylalanine picrolonate II	$C_{19}H_{19}O_7N_5$	Incl. extinc. MP 238°	211
>1.743	1.468=N_X	–	Mod.	Potassium nitranilate I	$C_6O_8N_2K_2$	Y=*b*; $Z \wedge c=42°$. X=yellow, Y and Z=golden	109
1.744	1.568	?	Sm.	Dibromobenzene	$C_6H_4Br_2$	Y=*b*, $Bx_a \wedge c=40°$	74
1.744	1.559	?	?	Folic acid	$C_{18}H_{16}O_6N_7$	Lenticular	309
1.745	1.614	?	?	Dixanthyl urea	$C_{27}H_{20}O_2N_2$	X′‖ elong.	188
1.75	1.72	?	?	Theobromine·HCl (H_2O ?)	$C_7H_8O_2N_4\cdot HCl(H_2O\ ?)$	Z ‖ elong.	248
1.75	1.705	?	?	Dixanthyl thiourea	$C_{27}H_{20}O_2N_2S$	X′‖elong.	188
1.75 *ca.*	1.458	?	?	Dichlorotyrosine flavianate	$C_{19}H_{15}O_{11}N_3SCl_2$	X ‖ elong. Yellow	165
1.75	1.66	?	?	Chalcone semicarbazone	$C_{16}H_{15}ON_3$	X ‖ elong.	104
1.75	1.60	?	?	Carbazole	$C_{12}H_8N$	MP 245°	196
1.75=N_Z	1.58=N_X	?	?	*p*-Sulfobenzene-azo-α-naphthol	$C_{16}H_{12}O_4N_2S$	Z ‖ elong.	176
1.75=N_Z	1.55=N_X	–	?	Salicylic acid	$C_7H_6O_3$	Y=*b*; $Z \wedge c=42.5°$. MP 156°	126
1.755=N_Y		?	?	Ammonium fulminurate	$C_3H_6O_3N_4$	Monoclinic	33
1.755	1.675	?	?	Ethyl phenyloxalurate II	$C_{11}H_{12}O_4N_2$	Extinc. at 18° *ca.*	141
1.755	1.661	–	25°	Triphenylarsine	$C_{18}H_{15}As$	Optic plane $\wedge$ 010=67°	180
>1.755	1.540	?	?	Dimethylphenyluric acid	$C_{13}H_{12}O_3N_4$	MP > 280°	251
1.758=N_Y	1.543	–	?	Tobias acid·H_2O	$C_{10}H_{11}O_4NS$	Y=*a*. Sym. extinc.	169

Table I. Based on the Higher Measured Refractive Index

N_2(orN_3),N	N_1	Sign	2V	Name	Composition	Opt. Orient., etc.	Page
1.76	1.55	?	?	Silver picolinate	$(C_5H_4NCO_2)_2Ag$	Thin needles	200
>1.76	1.50	?	?	α-Cupric picolinate·$2H_2O$	$(C_5H_4NCO_2)_2Cu \cdot 2H_2O$	Blue	200
>1.76	1.54	?	?	Cupric picolinate	$(C_5H_4NCO_2)_2Cu$	Blue	200
1.761=N_Z	1.745=N_Y	–	Sm.	Sulfapyridine	$C_{11}H_{11}O_2N_3S$	Anom. dispersion	202
1.764=N_Y	1.720=N_X	?	?	Germanium tetrakis(p-tolylmercaptide)	$(C_7H_7S)_4Ge$	Y=*b*, Z=*c*.	93
1.768=N_Z	1.652=N_X	–	?	Bulbocapnine	$C_{19}H_{19}O_4N$	X=*b*, Y=*a*.	295
>1.768	1.583	?	?	1,3-Dimethyl-9-phenylpseudouric acid·H_2O	$C_{13}H_{14}O_4N_4 \cdot H_2O$	X ‖ elong.	241
1.775=N_Y	1.728=N_X	–	?	Germanium tetrakis (phenylmercaptide)	$(C_6H_5S)_4Ge$	X=*c*, Y=*b*.	93
1.776=N_Z	1.483=N_X	+	?	Aminophenyltriazole·HCl·H_2O	$C_8H_8N_4 \cdot HCl \cdot H_2O$	X=*b*; Z ∧ *c*=44°	243
1.778	1.493	?	?	Tyrosine flavianate	$C_{19}H_{17}O_{10}N_3S$	X ‖ elong. Yellow	165
1.780	1.620	?	?	Dipyridinodichloroplatinum	$(C_5H_5N)_2PtCl_2$	Yellow	194
1.78=N_Z	1.53=N_X	?	?	Copper phthalate	$C_8H_4O_4Cu(H_2O\,?)$	Extinc. at 22°. Blue	122
1.78	1.53	?	?	Benzothiazole guanidine nitrate	$C_8H_{10}N_4S \cdot HNO_3$	Z′ ‖ elong.	254
1.78	1.56	?	?	β-Cupric picolinate·$2H_2O$	$(C_5H_4NCO_2)_2Cu \cdot 2H_2O$	Blue	200
>1.78=N_Z	1.57=N_X	?	?	Copper benzoylacetonate	$C_{20}H_{18}O_4Cu$	X ∧ ⊥ 001=21°	105
>1.78	<1.74	?	?	Klement compound	$C_{23}H_{16}ON_2$	Yellow, columnar	309
>1.78=N_Y	<1.47=N_X	– ?	?	*o*-Nitrophenol	$C_6H_5O_3N$	Bx_a ∧ *c*=5°. Pleochroic in green MP 45°	86
1.78	1.484	+	65° *ca.*	*p*-Nitrophenol	$C_6H_5O_3N$	X ∧ elong. =21°. MP 113°	86
1.783		–	17° *ca.*	3,3-*bis*(Iodomethyl)oxetone	$C_5H_8OI_2$	X nearly ‖ *b*.	181
>1.785=N_Y	1.454=N_X	–	?	Ethylenediamine diliturate	$C_6H_{11}O_5N_5$	X ∧ elong. =44°	217
1.785=N_Z	1.608=N_X	?	?	Pyridineethylenedichloroplatinum	$C_5H_5NC_2H_4PtCl_2$	‖ extinc. Yellow	194
>1.785=N_Y	1.452=N_X	–	?	Propylenediamine diliturate	$C_7H_{13}O_5N_5$	Y ∧ elong. =28°	217
1.79=N_Y		–	Lg.	Tri-*o*-phenylenediarsine	$C_{18}H_{12}As_2$	Z=*b*.	180

Table I. Based on the Higher Measured Refractive Index

N_2(orN_3), N	N_1	Sign	2V	Name	Composition	Opt. Orient., etc.	Page
1.79 *ca.*	$1.652 = N_X$	?	48°	3,4,5-Tribromo-2,6-dimethoxyphenol	$C_8H_7O_3Br_3$	Y = *b* elong. D 2.29	100
$1.795 = N_Z$	$1.600 = N_X$	?	?	1-Naphthylamine 1,5-naphthalene disulfonate	$C_{30}H_{26}O_6N_2S_2$	Y ⊥ plates.	152
$1.795 = N_Z$	$1.552 = N_X$	?	?	1-Naphthylamine 1-naphthalene-sulfonate	$C_{20}H_{17}O_3N$	Parallel extinc. MP 232°	152
$1.80 = N_Z$	$1.485 = N_X$	?	?	Sodium salt of *m*-sulfobenzene-azodiphenylamine	$C_{18}H_{12}O_3N_3SNa$	X ‖ elong.	178
1.8 *ca.*	1.53	–	?	*p*-α-β-Trimethylcinnamic acid	$C_{12}H_{14}O_2$	X = *b*; Y = *a*.	121
$>1.80 = N_Z$	$1.44 = N_X$	?	?	5-Methyl cytosine picrate	$C_{11}H_{10}O_8N_6$	X ‖ elong.	214
>1.80	1.45	?	?	2-Ketopropanedioic acid phenyl-hydrazone	$C_9H_8O_4N_2$	X ‖ elong. MP 165°	172
>1.80	1.50	?	?	Cytosine picrate	$C_{10}H_8O_8N_6$	X ∧ *c* = 48°. Yellow	214
$>1.80 = N_Y$	$1.55 = N_X$	–	Lg.	Alizarin	$C_{14}H_8O_4$	X = *c*; Y = *b*. Yellow to red	110
$1.827 = N_Y$		?	?	Thallous picrate	$C_6H_2O_7N_3Tl$	Y = *b*. Color red	87
$1.829 = N_Z$	$1.70 = N_X$	?	Biax.	Triphenylstibine	$C_{18}H_{15}Sb$	X ∧ *a* = 5°. MP 48°	181
$1.830 = N_Z$	$1.670 = N_X$	?	?	Gulosazone	$C_{18}H_{17}O_4N_4$	Z = *c*.	267
$1.830 = N_Z$	$1.573 = N_X$	?	?	Uric acid	$C_5H_4O_3N_4$	X = *a*; Y = *c*.	249
$1.835 = N_Z$	$1.800 = N_X$	?	?	Mannosazone I	$C_{18}H_{20}O_4N_4$	Extinc. ∧ = 0° to large	266
<1.84	>1.80	?	?	Diguanylmelamine·H_2O	$C_5H_{10}N_{10}\cdot H_2O$	N_1 ‖ elong. $N_3 = 1.461$	246
1.85 *ca.*	1.80 *ca.*	?	?	Arginine flavianate	$C_{16}H_{21}O_{10}N_6S$	Z ‖ elong.	137
$1.85 = N_Z$	$1.825 = N_X$	?	?	Galactosazone I	$C_{18}H_{22}O_4N_4$	Y ∧ elong. = large	267
$1.856 = N_Z$	$1.518 = N_X$	–	?	Vulpinic acid	$C_{18}H_{14}O_5$	X near *c*. Y = *b*. MP 148°	189
$1.87 = N_Z$	$1.514 = N_X$	?	?	Disodium 1-phenylazo-2-naphthol-6,8-disulfonate	$C_{16}H_{10}O_7N_2SNa$	X ‖ elong. Orange	178
$1.87 = N_Z$	$1.465 = N_X$	?	?	3-Methyl-4-phenylazo-1-(4-sul-fophenylazo)-5-pyrazolone	$C_{16}H_{15}ON_4S$	X ‖ elong.	242
1.884	1.618	?	Biax.	4-Nitro-methyldiphenyl sulfide	$C_{13}H_{11}NO_2S$	$N_2 \approx N_Z$; $N_1 \approx N_X$	93

Table I. Based on the Higher Measured Refractive Index

N_2(orN_3),N	N_1	Sign	2V	Name	Composition	Opt. Orient., etc.	Page
1.89 ?	1.44 $=N_X$	–	Sm.	2,4-Dioximino-5-cyclohexene-1,3-dione·H_2O	$C_6H_4O_4N \cdot H_2O$	X=*c*. Y=*a*. 001 cleav.	108
1.90 $=N_Z$	1.46 $=N_X$	–	?	α-(4-Chloro-2-nitrophenylazo)-acetoacetanilide	$C_{15}H_{12}O_4N_4Cl_2$	X ‖ elong. 110 cleav.	175
1.9 *ca.*	1.495	?	?	Benzoselenazoleguanidine picrate	$C_{14}H_{13}O_7N_7Se$	Extinc. ∧ =0° to 18°	254
1.915$=N_Z$	1.704$=N_X$	–	?	Salicylaminoanthraquinone	$C_{21}H_{13}O_4N$	Z ‖ elong. MP 273°	161
1.95	1.62	?	?	4-Isopropylphenylamine	$C_9H_{13}N$	X ‖ elong. MP 63°	152
1.95	1.50	?	?	Berberine·HCl·2.5H_2O	$C_{20}H_{20}O_5NCl \cdot 2.5H_2O$	X ‖ elong.	295
1.95	1.75	?	?	α-Nitroso-β-naphthol	$C_{10}H_6(NO)OH$	Extinc. at 44°. MP 110°	95
>1.95	1.52	?	?	Curcumin	$C_{21}H_{20}O_6$	X ‖ elong.	111
>1.95	1.56	?	?	*o*-Coumaric acid	$C_9H_8O_3$	X ‖ elong.	130
>1.95	1.515	?	?	Phloretin	$C_{15}H_{15}O_5$	Extinc. at 41°	110
>1.95	1.68	?	?	Chrysoidine	$C_{12}H_{12}N_4$	Z ‖ elong.	179
>1.95	1.46	?	?	Sorbic acid	$C_6H_8O_2$	X ‖ elongation	26
>1.95	1.555	?	?	Quinoline-hydroquinone	$(C_9H_7N)_2 \cdot nC_6H_6O_2$	X ‖ elongation	195
1.96 $=N_Z$	1.564$=N_X$	?	?	Lithol fast yellow GG	$C_{13}H_{10}O_4N_4Cl_2$?	X ‖ elong.	140
2.00 $=N_Z$	1.73 $=N_X$	?	?	1-(Phenylazo)-2-naphthol-6,8-disulfonate	$C_{16}H_{12}O_7N_2S_2$	X ‖ length	177
>2.0 $=N_Y$	>1.70 $=N_X$	+	80°(2E)	Lead nitroaminoguanidine	$C_2O_4N_{10}Pb$	Yellow tablets	43
2.065$=N_Z$	1.46 $=N_X$	–	?	4-(2,5-Dichlorophenylazo)-3-methyl-1-phenyl-5-pyrazolone	$C_{15}H_9ON_4Cl_2$	N_i=1.526(=N_Y ?)	243
2.07 $=N_Z$	1.465$=N_X$	?	Biax.	Fast yellow 4R	$C_{15}H_{10}ON_4Cl$	X ∧ *c*=43°. N_Y=1.49 ?	242
2.07 $=N_Z$	1.465$=N_X$	–	Lg.	Hansa yellow 3R	?	X ∧ *c*=5°	175
2.13 $=N_Z$	1.45 $=N_X$	–	?	α-(4-Methyl-2-nitrophenylazo)aceto-acetanilide	$C_{17}H_{15}O_4N_4$	X ∧ *c*=18°	175
2.135$=N_Z$	1.915$=N_X$	?	?	1-Benzamido-4-hydroxyanthraquinone	$C_{21}H_{13}O_4N$	Z ‖ elong.	162
2.14 $=N_Z$	1.90 $=N_X$	–	?	1-(1-Sulfo-2-naphthylazo)-2-naphthol	$C_{20}H_{14}O_4N_2S$	X ∧ elong. =18°	177

Table I. Based on the Higher Measured Refractive Index

N_2(orN_3),N	N_1	Sign	2V	Name	Composition	Opt. Orient., etc.	Page
2.14 $=N_Z$	1.522 $=N_X$	?	?	2,7-(1-Anthraquinonylamino)-anthraquinone	$C_{42}H_{22}O_6N_2$	X ∧ elong. =80°. Yellow to red	161
›2.14 $=N_Z$	1.783 $=N_X$	?	?	Lake Red C	$C_{17}H_{13}O_4N_2SCl$?	Incl. extinc. Yellow to red.	177
2.20 $=N_Z$	1.455 $=N_X$	?	Biax.	Hansa yellow GSA	?	X ∧ c=45°	175
2.20 $=N_Z$	1.46 $=N_X$	−	Lg.	Hansa yellow GR	?	X ∧ c=43°	175
2.23 $=N_Z$	1.465 $=N_X$	?	?	Hansa yellow 3R (impure)	?	X ∧ c=43°	175
2.23 $=N_Z$	2.06 $=N_X$	?	?	Sodium salt of 6-sulfo-4-chloro-3-toluene-azo-β-hydroxynaphthoic acid	$C_{18}H_{12}O_6N_2SClNa$	X ‖ . elong.	177
2.23 $=N_Z$	2.06 $=N_X$	?	?	Lithol ruby GK	$C_{17}H_{12}O_6N_2SCl$	Z ‖ elong.	176
2.26 $=N_Z$	1.56 $=N_X$	?	?	Lake Bordeaux BK	$C_{20}H_{14}O_4N_2S$	Z ‖ elong. Orange to red.	177
2.26 $=N_Z$	1.47 $=N_X$	?	?	α-Naphthaleneazo-β-naphthol	$C_{20}H_{13}ON$	X ∧ elong. =5°. MP 220°	176
2.29 $=N_Z$	1.495 $=N_X$	+	?	1-(1-Naphthylazo)-2-naphthol-6,8-disulfonate	$C_{20}H_{14}O_7N_2S_2$	Y ⊥ plates. Z ∧ length=19°	178
2.32 $=N_Z$	1.745 $=N_X$	?	?	Hansa ruby G	$C_{17}H_{10}O_{10}N_4S$	Z ‖ elong. Yellow to red.	177
2.33 $=N_Z$	1.49 $=N_X$	?	?	1-(2,4-Dinitrophenylazo)-2-naphthol	$C_{16}H_{10}O_5N_4$	X ‖ elong.	176
2.35 $=N_Z$	2.06 $=N_X$	?	?	Lake Bordeaux BN	$C_{21}H_{15}O_6N_2S$	Z ‖ elong.	177
2.37 $=N_Z$	1.505 $=N_X$	?	?	Fast red R	$C_{16}H_{10}O_3N_3Cl$	X ‖ elong.	176
2.45 $=N_Z$	1.52 $=N_X$	−	?	Methylnitrophenylazonaphthol	$C_{17}H_{13}O_3N_3$	X ∧ c=10°	176
2.5 $=N_Z$	1.455 $=N_X$	?	?	Nitrophenylazonaphthol	$C_{16}H_{11}O_3N_3$	X ∧ c=10°	176
2.52 $=N_Z$	1.52 $=N_X$	−	?	Nitrotolueneazonaphthol	$C_{17}H_{13}O_3N_3$	X ‖ elong.	176
2.53 $=N_Z$	2.0 $=N_X$	?	?	α-Naphthaleneazo-β-naphthol	$C_{20}H_{13}ON$	Z ‖ elong.	176
2.55 $=N_Z$	2.0 $=N_X$	?	?	Permanent ruby PhB-ASH	?	Z ‖ elong.	178
2.67 $=N_Z$	2.06 $=N_X$	+	?	1-(4-Nitro-2-sulfophenylazo-2-naphthol	$C_{16}H_{11}O_6N_3S$	Z ∧ elong. =18° ?	177

TABLE II. BASED ON THE LOWER MEASURED REFRACTIVE INDEX

N_1	N_2	Sign	2V	Name	Composition	Opt. Orient., etc.	Page
1.155 +	1.684	?	Lg.	Dimethylphenyluric acid	$C_{13}H_{12}O_3N_4$	MP ⟩ 300°	251
1.32	1.68	?	?	Bulbocapnine·HCl	$C_{19}H_{20}O_4NCl$	Z ‖ elong.	295
⟩1.35	1.60 est.	+	Lg.	Azidodithiocarbonic acid	$HSCSN_3$	X ∧ *c*=30°	44
1.386=N_X	1.530=N_Z	?	83°	4,5-Dihydro-5-keto-3-furancarboxylic acid	$C_5H_4O_4$	X=*b*; Y=*a*; 001 cleav.	188
1.387=N_X	1.614=N_Y	?	?	Fumaric acid	$(HO_2C\cdot CH)_2$	Z ⊥ plates	35
1.39	1.665	–	49°(2E)	Meconic acid·$3H_2O$	$C_7H_4O_7\cdot 3H_2O$	X=*c*; Y=*b*; 001 cleav.	190
1.40	1.49	?	?	Sodium succinate·$6H_2O$	$(CH_2CO_2)_2Na_2\cdot 6H_2O$	Z ‖ elongation	33
1.40	1.50	–	Lg.	Lithium acetate·$2H_2O$	$CH_3CO_2Li\cdot 2H_2O$	X=*a*, Y=*b*; 110 cleav.	16
1.40	1.605	?	?	Guanidine nitrate	$CNH(NH_2)_2\cdot HNO_3$	Z ‖ elong. MP 214°	43
1.41	1.63	?	?	Chloroacetic acid	$CH_2Cl\cdot CO_2H$	Z ‖ elong. ?	19
1.412	1.556	+	35° *ca.*	Cyanamide	$H_2N\cdot CN$	Z ∧ *c*=80°. MP 44° N_3=1.675	40
1.420	1.530	?	?	Dipotassium fumarate	$(CH\cdot CO_2K)_2$	Needles	35
1.42	1.74	?	?	Theobromine salicylate	$C_{14}H_{13}O_5N_5$	X ‖ elong.	248
1.428	⟩1.734	?	Biax.	Nicotinic acid	$C_6H_5O_2N$	Extinc. ‖ elong.	277
1.43	1.55	?	?	Parabanic acid	CONHCOCONH	X ‖ elong.	215
1.430	1.620	–	40° *ca.*	Sodium fumarate (H_2O ?)	$(CHCO_2Na)_2\cdot(H_2O\ ?)$	X ∧ *c*=10° *ca.* N_3=1.648	35
1.43	1.70	?	?	Cyanuric acid	$C_3H_3O_3N_3(\cdot 2H_2O\ ?)$	Z ‖ elong.	244
1.432	1.618	?	?	Ethyl cyanoguanidine carboxylate	$C_5H_8O_2N_4$	Twinning common	42
1.435=N_X	1.701=N_Y	?	?	Ammonium dicyanoguanidine	$C_3H_2N_5\cdot NH_4$	X ‖ elong.	42
1.44 =N_X	1.80⟨N_Z	?	?	5-Methyl cytosine picrate	$C_{11}H_{10}O_8N_6$	X ‖ elong.	214
1.44 =N_X	1.89 ?	–	Sm.	2,4-Dioximino-5-cyclohexene-1,3-dione·H_2O	$C_6H_2O_2(NOH)_2\ H_2O$	X=*c*, Y=*a*. 001 cleav.	108
⟨1.445	1.725	?	?	3-Methyl-1-phenylbiuret	$C_9H_{11}O_2N_3$	X ‖ elong. MP 183°	142
1.445 +	1.610 –	?	Biax.	*N′*-Phenyl-*N*-carbethoxyurea	$C_{10}H_{12}O_3N_2$	Z ‖ elong.	142
1.445=N_X	1.645=N_Z	?	?	Methyl *p*-tolyl ketone semi-carbazone	$C_{11}H_{16}ON_3$	MP 210°	104

TABLE II. BASED ON THE LOWER MEASURED REFRACTIVE INDEX

N_1	N_2	Sign	2V	Name	Composition	Opt. Orient., etc.	Page
$1.445=N_X$	$1.736=N_Z$	–	15°	3-Ethoxy-4-hydroxybenzaldehyde semicarbazone	$C_{10}H_{13}O_3N_3$	$N_i=1.69$ common. MP 175°	109
$1.447=N_X$	$1.660=N_Z$	?	?	Magnesium acid aconitate·$4H_2O$	$C_6H_3O_6MgH\cdot 4H_2O$	Small prisms	37
1.447	1.695	?	?	1,3-Dimethylxanthine·H_2O	$C_7H_8O_2N_4\cdot H_2O$	$X \wedge c=43°$. $N_3 > 1.733$	248
1.448	1.733	?	?	Tetracaine·HCl	$C_{15}H_{25}O_2N_2Cl$	$N_3 > 1.733$. MP 150°	163
1.448	>1.734	?	?	Strontium picrolonate	$(C_{10}H_7O_5N_4)_2Sr(H_2O\ ?)$	$X \wedge$ elong. $> 0°$ and $< 45°$	209
1.45	1.46	+ ?	?	Magnesium lactate(·$3H_2O$?)	$(C_3H_5O_3)_2Mg(\cdot 3H_2O\ ?)$	Parallel extinc. $N_3=1.50$	45
1.45	1.545	?	?	Arecoline·HCl	$C_8H_{13}O_2N\cdot HCl$	X ‖ elong.	278
$1.45\ =N_X$	$1.69\ =N_Z$	?	?	3,5-Xylidine	$C_8H_{11}N$	$X \wedge c=12°$; $Y=b$.	151
$1.45\ =N_X$	$1.69\ =N_Z$	?	?	3,5-Acetoxylide	$C_{10}H_{13}ON$	$X \wedge$ elong. $=12°$	151
1.45	>1.80	?	?	2-Ketopropanedioic acid phenyl-hydrazone	$C_9H_8O_4N_2$	X ‖ elong. MP 165°	172
$1.45\ =N_X$	$2.13\ =N_Z$	–	?	α-(4-Methyl-2-nitrophenylazo) acetoacetanilide	$C_{17}H_{15}O_4N_4$	$X \wedge c=18°$	175
1.452	1.465	?	0°	Potassium oleate	$C_{18}H_{33}O_2K$	Tetrag.	25
$1.452=N_X$	$>1.785=N_Y$	–	?	Propylenediamine diliturate	$C_7H_{13}O_5N_5$	$Y \wedge$ elong. $=28°$	217
1.454	1.73	–	25° *ca.*	Melamine sulfate	$C_3H_8O_4N_6S$		245
$1.454=N_X$	$>1.785=N_Y$	–	?	Ethylenediamine diliturate	$C_6H_{11}O_5N_5$	$X \wedge$ elong. $=44°$	217
$1.455=N_X$	$>1.74\ =N_Z$	?	?	Nicouic acid	$C_{12}H_{12}O_8$	MP 196°	132
$1.455=N_X$	$2.20\ =N_Z$	?	Biax.	Hansa yellow GSA	?	$X \wedge c=45°$	175
$1.455=N_X$	$2.5\ \ =N_Z$	?	?	Nitrophenylazonaphthol	$C_{16}H_{11}O_3N_3$	$X \wedge c=10°$	176
$1.457=N_X$	$1.626=N_Z$	?	?	Sodium calcium aconitate·$2H_2O$	$C_6H_3O_6CaNa\cdot 2H_2O$	$N_i=1.572$	37
1.458	1.75 *ca.*	?	?	Dichlorotyrosine flavianate	$C_{19}H_{15}O_{11}N_3SCl$	X ‖ elong. Yellow	165
$1.459=N_X$	$1.657=N_Z$	?	?	Monopotassium aconitate	$C_6H_5O_6K$	Thin plates	36
1.46	1.47	?	?	2-Methylbutyl carbamate	$NH_2CO_2CH(CH_3)(C_3H_7)$	MP 76°	38
1.46	1.485	?	?	Ammonium valerate	$C_4H_9CO_2NH_4(2H_2O\ ?)$	Extinction angle$=33°$	21
1.46	1.59	?	Lg.	Allocaffuric acid	$C_7H_{11}O_4N_3$	Sym. extinc.	237
$1.46\ =N_X$	$1.60\ =N_Z$	?	?	Dimethyl-*D*-glucoascorbic acid	$C_9H_{14}O_7$	$X=b$. MP 94°	267

Table II. Based on the Lower Measured Refractive Index

N_1	N_2	Sign	2V	Name	Composition	Opt. Orient., etc.	Page
1.460	1.654	?	?	1-Benzoxy-4-naphthalenesulfonic acid	$C_{17}H_{12}O_5S$	Extinc. at 31°	138
1.460	1.685	+	Lg.	Dimelamine phthalate	$C_{14}H_{17}O_4N_{12}$	$X' \wedge$ elong. $=30°$	245
1.46 $=N_X$	1.90 $=N_Z$	−	?	α-(4-Chloro-2-nitrophenylazo)-acetoacetanilide	$C_{15}H_{12}O_4N_4Cl_2$	X ‖ elong. 110 cleav.	175
1.46	›1.95	?	?	Sorbic acid	$CH_3\cdot(CH)_4\cdot CO_2H$	X ‖ elong.	26
1.46 $=N_X$	2.065 $=N_Z$	−	?	4-(2,5-Dichlorophenylazo)-3-methyl-1-phenyl-5-pyrazolone	$C_{15}H_9ON_4Cl_2$	$N_i=1.526(=N_Y\ ?)$	243
1.46 $=N_X$	2.20 $=N_Z$	−	Lg.	Hansa Yellow GR	?	$X \wedge c=43°$	75
1.461	›1.80	?	?	Diguanylmelamine·H_2O	$C_5H_{10}N_{10}\cdot H_2O$	N_1 ‖ elong. N_3 ‹ 1.84	246
1.462	1.693	?	?	*dl*-Tryptophane diliturate·$3H_2O$	$C_{15}H_{15}O_7N_5\cdot 3H_2O$	− elong. Decomp. 191°	226
1.463	1.495	?	?	α-Hydroxyisobutyric acid	$C_4H_8O_3$	N_i ‖ elong.	46
1.465 $=N_X$		+	?	2,3,4-Trimethyl-xylonolactone	$C_8H_{14}O_5$	$X=c$.	185
1.465 $=N_X$	1.525 $=N_Z$	?	?	2,3,4-Trimethyl-β-methyl-*D*-glucopyranoside	$C_{10}H_{20}O_6$	$X=c$. MP 92°	262
1.465 $=N_X$	1.535 $=N_Z$	?	?	2,4,6-Trimethyl-β-methyl-*D*-glucopyranoside	$C_{10}H_{20}O_6$	$X=c$.	261
1.465 $=N_X$	1.87 $=N_Z$	?	?	3-Methyl-4-phenylazo-1-(4-sulfophenylazo)-5-pyrazolone	$C_{16}H_{15}ON_4S$	X ‖ elong.	242
1.465 $=N_X$	2.07 $=N_Z$	−	Lg.	Hansa Yellow 3R	?	$X \wedge c=5°$	175
1.465 $=N_X$	2.07 $=N_Z$	?	Biax.	Fast Yellow 4R	$C_{15}H_{10}ON_4Cl$	$X \wedge c=43°$. $N_Y=1.49$?	242
1.465 $=N_X$	2.23 $=N_Z$	?	?	Hansa Yellow 3R (impure)	?	$X \wedge c=43°$	175
1.466	1.557	?	?	Dipotassium alcohol phthalate	$C_{10}H_{10}O_5K_2$	Laths	122
1.468	›1.620	?	?	Potassium acid uroxanate	$(NH_2\cdot CO\cdot NH)_2CCO_2H\cdot CO_2K$	Z ‖ elong.	59
1.468 $=N_X$	1.690 $=N_Z$	?	?	Zinc acid aconitate·$4H_2O$	$C_6H_3O_6ZnH\cdot 4H_2O$	Decomp. 110°	37
1.468	1.701	?	?	*l*-Tyrosine diliturate·$3H_2O$	$C_{13}H_{14}O_8N_4\cdot 3H_2O$	Decomp. 172°	225
1.468 $=N_X$	›1.743	−	Mod.	Potassium nitranilate I	$C_6(NO_2)_2(OK)_2O_2$	$Y=b$, $Z \wedge c=42°$. Pleoch.	109
‹1.47 $=N_X$		?	?	2,3,5-Trimethyl-lyxono-lactone	$C_8H_{14}O_5$	$X \wedge c=20°$	185

TABLE II. BASED ON THE LOWER MEASURED REFRACTIVE INDEX

N_1	N_2	Sign	2V	Name	Composition	Opt. Orient., etc.	Page
⟨1.47 $=N_X$	⟩1.78 $=N_Y$	– ?	?	*o*-Nitrophenol	$C_6H_4NO_2OH$	$Bx_a \wedge c=5°$. MP 45°	86
1.47 $=N_X$		?	?	2,3,4,6-Tetramethyl-*β*-methyl-*D*-galactopyranoside	$C_{11}H_{22}O_6$	X = *c*.	265
1.47	1.48	+	70°(2H)	*d*-Camphoric acid	$C_5H_5\cdot(CH_3)_3\cdot(CO_2H)_2$	X = *b*; $Z \wedge c = -64°$. MP 187°. $N_3 = 1.533$	122
1.47 $=N_X$	1.555 $=N_Z$	?	?	2,3,6-Trimethyl-*β*-methyl-*D*-glucopyranoside	$C_{10}H_{20}O_6$	X = *c*.	262
1.47	1.68	?	?	Pyridine nitrate	$C_5H_5N\cdot HNO_3$	X ‖ elong.	193
1.470 $=N_X$	1.706 $=N_Y$	–	?	Isobutylamine diliturate	$C_8H_{14}O_5N_4$	$X \wedge$ elong. = 41°	216
1.47 $=N_X$	2.26 $=N_Z$	?	?	*α*-Naphthaleneazo-*β*-naphthol	$C_{20}H_{13}ON$	$X \wedge$ elong. = 5°. MP 220°	176
1.471 $=N_X$		–	46°(2E)	2,4,2′, 4′-Tetramethylpyrocoll	$C_{14}H_{14}O_2N_2$	X = *c*; Y = *a*.	214
1.472 $=N_X$	1.477 $=N_Z$	+	?	Barium butanone sulfonate	$C_8H_{14}O_2SO_3Ba$	Y = *b*, Z = *c*.	61
1.475 $=N_X$	1.480 $=N_Z$	?	?	Sodium zinc uranyl acetate·$6H_2O$	$(CH_3\cdot CO_2)_9NaZn(UO_2)_3\cdot 6H_2O$	$X \wedge c = 20°$ *ca*. Z = *b*.	18
1.475	1.54	–	?	2,3,4,6-Tetramethyl-*α*-*D*-glucopyranose	$C_{10}H_{20}O_6$	X = *c*. D 1.22	261
1.475	1.555 $\leqslant N_Z$	?	?	2,3,4-Trimethyl-*α*-methyl-*D*-arabinopyranoside	$C_8H_{16}O_3$	X = *c*.	258
1.475 $=N_X$	1.642 $=N_Z$	?	Biax.	Aconitic acid	$C_6H_6O_6$	MP 195°	36
1.475	1.67	?	?	Vasicine tartrate	$C_{15}H_{18}O_7N_2$	X ‖ elong.	299
1.477	1.523	?	?	Pentobarbital sodium	$C_{11}H_{17}O_3N_2Na$	Colorless	229
1.477 $=N_X$	1.72	– ?	?	*o*-Nitrobenzyl alcohol	$C_7H_7O_3N$	X ‖ elong. Brown	93
1.48 $=N_X$		?	?	2,3,4-Trimethyl-*α*-*L*-lyxopyranose	$C_8H_{16}O_5$	X = *a* or *c*.	259
1.480 $=N_X$	1.514 $=N_Z$	?	?	Tetrahydrotemisin·H_2O	$C_{15}H_{26}O_3\cdot H_2O$	MP 112°	316
1.48	1.53	?	?	Lithium citrate (H_2O ?)	$C_6H_5O_7Li_3\cdot(H_2O$?)	Z ‖ elong.	58
1.48 $=N_X$	1.555 $=N_Z$	?	?	2,3,4-Trimethyl-*α*-*D*-xylopyranose	$C_8H_{15}O_5$	X = *b*.	259
1.48	1.575	?	?	*p*-Methoxybenzoic acid	$C_6H_4O\cdot CH_3\cdot CO_2H$	Y = *b*; extinc. $\wedge c = 18°$.	128
1.48	1.66	?	?	Brucine	$C_{23}H_{26}O_4N_2$	$X \wedge$ elong. ⟨ 20°	308

TABLE II. BASED ON THE LOWER MEASURED REFRACTIVE INDEX

N_1	N_2	Sign	2V	Name	Composition	Opt. Orient., etc.	Page
1.48	1.73 *ca.*	+ ?	Lg.	*p*-Bromonitrobenzene	$C_6H_4BrNO_2$	X ∧ elong. = 14°. 010 cleav. MP 127°	75
1.48 $=N_X$	1.74 $\leq N_Z$	?	?	Diacetate of dihydrotoxicarol	$C_{27}H_{28}O_9$	X ‖ elong.	317
1.481 $=N_X$	1.569 $=N_Z$	?	?	α-Tetrahydrosantonin	$C_{15}H_{22}O_3$	X = *a*; Z = *c*. MP 155°	315
1.483 $=N_X$	〉1.776 $=N_Z$	+	?	Aminophenyltriazole·HCl·H_2O	$C_8H_9 \cdot N_4Cl \cdot H_2O$	X = *b*; Z ∧ *c* = 44°	243
1.484	〉1.78	+	65° *ca.*	*p*-Nitrophenol	$C_6H_4NO_2OH$	X ∧ elong. = 21°. MP 113°	86
1.485	1.515	?	?	Calcium lactate·$3H_2O$	$(C_3H_5O_3)_2Ca \cdot 3H_2O$	MP 100°	45
1.485 $=N_X$	1.596 $=N_Y$	−	?	Aniline *cis*-β-sulfoacrylate·H_2O	$C_9H_{13}O_6NS$	X = *a*; Y = *c*.	139
1.485 $=N_X$	1.660 $=N_Z$	?	?	Isotephrosinedicarboxylic acid	$C_{22}H_{22}O_{11}$	MP 187°	316
1.485 $=N_X$	1.693 $=N_Z$	?	?	Strontium salicylate·$2H_2O$	$(C_6H_4OHCO_2)_2Sr \cdot 2H_2O$	White powder	127
1.485 $=N_X$	1.80 $=N_Z$	?	?	Sodium salt of *m*-sulfobenzene-azodiphenylamine	$C_{18}H_{12}O_3N_3SNa$	X ‖ elong.	178
1.486 $=N_X$	1.603 $=N_Y$	−	Lg.	Propyl-3,5-dinitrobenzoate	$(NO_2)_2C_6H_3 \cdot CO_2CH_2 \cdot CH_2 \cdot CH_3$	Y ‖ elong. (*b*). MP 74°	115
1.487 $=N_X$	1.574 $=N_Y$	?	?	Sodium *p*-toluenesulfonchloramide·$3H_2O$	$C_7H_7O_2NClSNa \cdot 3H_2O$	Colorless prisms	134
1.487 $=N_X$	1.6 $=N_Z$	?	5°	Potassium phthalate	$C_6H_4(CO_2K)_2(H_2O\,?)$	Very soluble	122
1.489	1.68	?	?	Gallic acid·H_2O	$C_7H_6O_5 \cdot H_2O$	X ‖ elong. Y = *b*. $N_3 = 1.70$	131
1.49	1.521	?	?	Uranyl acetate·$2H_2O$	$(CH_3CO_2)UO_2 \cdot 2H_2O$	1.49 for X along *c*.	16
1.49	1.53	?	?	Solanidine	$C_{27}H_{43}ON$?	Parallel extinc.	306
1.49	1.545	?	?	Sodium tartrate($2H_2O$?)	$C_4H_4O_6Na_2(2H_2O\,?)$	Z ‖ elong.	50
1.49	1.53	−	?	Ferrous lactate($3H_2O$?)	$(C_3H_5O_3)_2Fe \cdot (3H_2O\,?)$	Opt. −. Parallel extinc.	145
1.49	1.58	?	?	2-Methylbutanedioic acid	$HO_2C \cdot CHCH_3CH_2 \cdot CO_2H$	Z ‖ elong.	34
1.49	1.58	?	Lg.	Cocaine	$C_{17}H_{21}O_4N$	MP 98°	282
1.490	1.680	?	?	Sodium benzoate·H_2O	$C_6H_5 \cdot CO_2N \cdot H_2O$	Loses H_2O at 120°	111
1.49	〉1.72	?	Biax.	2-Methylphenyl 3,5-dinitrobenzoate	$CH_3 \cdot C_6H_4 \cdot O_2C \cdot C_6H_3(NO_2)_2$	MP 138°	116

Table II. Based on the Lower Measured Refractive Index

N_1	N_2	Sign	2V	Name	Composition	Opt. Orient., etc.	Page
1.49	1.72	?	?	Pyrogallol	$C_6H_3(OH)_3$	Z ‖ elong. 001 cleav.	100
1.490 = N_X	1.74 < N_Z	?	?	Dihydrodeguelic acid	$C_{23}H_{26}O_8$	MP 80° and 144°	311
1.49 = N_X	2.33 = N_Z	?	?	1-(2,4-Dinitrophenylazo)-2-naphthol	$C_{16}H_{10}O_5N_4$	X ‖ elong.	176
1.492	1.735 *ca.*	?	?	Cincophen with HNO_3	$C_6H_{11}O_2N$ with HNO_3	Z ≈ elong.	201
1.493	1.778	?	?	Tyrosine flavianate	$C_{19}H_{17}O_{10}N_3S$	X ‖ elong. Yellow	165
1.493	1.658	?	?	Hydroxyproline picrolonate	$C_{15}H_{17}O_{10}N_5$	Z ‖ elong.	210
1.494	1.62	?	?	Methionine picrolonate	$C_{15}H_{19}O_7N_5S$	Z ‖ elong.	211
1.495 = N_X	1.503 = N_Z	?	?	Lithium zinc uranyl acetate · $6H_2O$	$(CH_3 \cdot CO_2)_9LiZn(UO_2)_3 \cdot 6H_2O$	Z = *b*.	18
1.495	1.515	?	?	Zinc valerate	$(C_4H_9CO_2)_2Zn$	X ‖ elong.	22
1.495 = N_X	1.565 = N_Z	?	?	*l*-Valine	$(CH_3)_2 \cdot CH \cdot CH(NH_2) \cdot CO_2H$	Z ‖ elong.	68
1.495	1.720	?	?	Di-iodotyrosine flavianate	$C_{19}H_{15}O_{11}N_3SI_2$	X ‖ elong. Yellow	166
1.495	1.74	+	?	*m*-Nitrobenzaldehyde	$C_6H_4NO_2CHO$	Opt. plane ‖ elong. MP 58°	104
1.495	1.9 *ca.*	?	?	Benzoselenazoguanidine picrate	$C_{14}H_{13}O_7N_7Se$	Extinc. angle = 0°–18°	254
1.495 = N_X	2.29 = N_Z	+	?	1-(1-Naphthylazo)-2-naphthol-6,8-disulfonate	$C_{20}H_{14}O_7N_2S_2$	Y ⊥ plates. Z ∧ length = 19°	178
1.498 = N_X	1.552 = N_Z	?	?	Tetrahydrotemisin	$C_{15}H_{26}O_3$	MP 231°	316
1.498	1.558	?	Biax.	Methyl palmitate	$C_{17}H_{34}O_2$	MP 30°	24
1.498 = N_X	1.74 < N_Z	?	Sm.	Dihydrodehydrodeguelin	$C_{23}H_{22}O_6$	MP 267°	311
1.50 = N_X		?	?	Potassium nitranilate II	$C_6O_8N_2K_2$	B = very strong. Color yellow	109
1.50	1.59	?	?	Berberine sulfate	$C_{20}H_{21}O_9NS$	X ‖ elong.	295
1.50	> 1.66	?	92°(2H)	Phenyl salicylate	$C_6H_4OH \cdot CO \cdot O \cdot C_6H_5$	Y = *a*. MP 42°	127
1.50 = N_X	1.66 = N_Z	+	Lg.	Ferrous 2-naphthalenesulfonate · $6H_2O$	$(C_{10}H_7SO_3)_2Fe \cdot 6H_2O$	Y ⊥ plates	134
1.500	> 1.733	?	?	Atabrine · $2H_2O$?	$C_{23}H_{30}O_3NCl(2H_2O\,?)$	Yellow color	203
1.500 = N_X	1.732 = N_Z	–	?	Pyramidone	$C_{13}H_{17}ON_3$	MP 108°	240

N_1	N_2	Sign	2V	Name	Composition	Opt. Orient., etc.	Page
1.50 $=N_X$	1.74 $=N_Z$	?	Biax.	4-Methylphenyl 3,5-dinitrobenzoate	$CH_3\cdot C_6H_4\cdot O_2C\cdot C_6H_3(NO_2)_2$	MP 187°	116
1.500 $=N_X$	$>$1.74 $=N_Z$	?	Biax.	Diacetate of toxicarol	$C_{27}H_{26}O_9$	MP 233°	317
1.50	$>$1.74	– ?	?	Berberine·$6H_2O$	$C_{20}H_{19}O_5N\cdot 6H_2O$	X ‖ elong.	295
1.50	$>$1.76	?	?	Cupric picolinate·$2H_2O$	$(C_5H_4NCO_2)_2Cu\cdot 2H_2O$	Blue	200
1.50	1.80 $<N_Z$	?	?	Cytosine picrate	$C_{10}H_8O_8N_6$	$X \wedge c=48°$. Yellow	214
1.50	1.95	?	?	Berberine·HCl·$2.5H_2O$	$C_{20}H_{20}O_5NCl\cdot 2.5H_2O$	X ‖ elong.	295
1.501	1.55	?	?	Tetronal	$(C_2H_5)_2:C:(SO_2\cdot C_2H_5)_2$	MP 85°	11
1.501 $=N_X$	1.550 $=N_Z$	?	?	Calcium stearate	$(C_{17}H_{35}\cdot CO_2)_2Ca$	X ‖ elong.	24
1.502	1.559	?	Biax.	Methyl stearate	$C_{19}H_{38}O_2$	Liquid crystals	25
1.502	1.691	+	60°	*m*-Nitrophenol	$C_6H_4NO_2OH$	Extinc. $\wedge c=1.5°$ in 110. MP 96°	86
1.503 $=N_X$	1.548 $=N_Z$	?	?	Calcium palmitate	$(C_{15}H_{31}CO_2)_2Ca$	X ‖ elong.	23
1.504 $=N_X$	1.549 $=N_Z$	?	?	Trional	$CH_3\cdot C\cdot(SO_2C_2H_5)_2\cdot C_2H_5$	MP 76°	11
1.504	1.603	–	?	Alypine	$C_{16}H_{26}O_2N_2\cdot 2HCl$	MP 173°	112
1.505	1.59	?	?	Dixanthyl biguanide	$C_{28}H_{23}O_2N_5$	Tablets	188
1.505	1.605	?	?	2-Hydroxypropanedioic acid	$CHOH\cdot CO_2H$	Granular	45
1.505	$>$1.734	+ ?	Sm.?	Potassium picrolonate	$C_{10}H_7O_5N_4K$	$N_i=1.519(=N_Y\,?)$	209
1.505 $=N_X$	2.37 $=N_Z$	?	?	Fast red R	$C_{16}H_{10}O_3N_3Cl$	X ‖ elong.	176
1.507	1.729	–	?	4,4′-Dichloro-3,3′-ditolyl	$ClCH_3\cdot C_6H_3ClCH_3$	$Z \wedge$ plates $=70°$	88
1.508 $=N_Y$	1.533	+	Lg.	α-Palmitic acid	$C_{15}H_{31}CO_2H$	$Y=b$. MP 63°	23
1.508	1.555	?	?	Lauron	$CH_3(CH_2)_{10}CO(CH_2)_{10}CH_3$	Indices at 41°	13
1.508 $=N_X$	1.590 $=N_Y$	–	?	Phenylamine nitrate	$C_6H_8O_3N_2$	$X=c$; $Y=a$.	139
1.508	1.682	?	Biax.	Quinine (iso ?) valerate	$C_{25}H_{36}O_4N_2$		289
1.51	1.525 *ca.*	?	?	Sodium uroxanate·$8H_2O$	$(NH_2CONH_2)_2C(CO_2Na)_2\, 8H_2O$	Y ⊥ plates; Z ‖ elong.	58
1.51 $=N_X$	1.525 $=N_Y$	?	?	Agaric acid·$1.5H_2O$	$C_{19}H_{36}OH(CO_2H)_3\cdot 1.5H_2O$	MP 142°	58

TABLE II. BASED ON THE LOWER MEASURED REFRACTIVE INDEX

N_1	N_2	Sign	2V	Name	Composition	Opt. Orient., etc.	Page
1.510 = N_X	1.535	+	Mod.	β-Stearic acid	$C_{17}H_{35}CO_2H$	N_i in 001	24
1.51	1.54	?	?	Sorbitol	$C_6H_{14}O_6$	Z ǁ elong.	10
1.510 = N_X	1.548 = N_Z	?	?	Magnesium palmitate	$(C_{15}H_{31}CO_2)_2Mg$	X ǁ elong. MP 105°	23
1.51	1.55	?	?	Pilocarpine (iso ?) valerate	$C_{15}H_{26}O_4N_2$	Z ǁ elong.	303
1.51	1.56	?	?	Malic acid	$CO_2H \cdot CHOH \cdot CH_2 \cdot CO_2H$	Z ǁ elong.	45
1.51	1.62	?	?	5-Hydroxy-3-methyl-1-phenyl-5-hydantoin carboxy-methylamide·H_2O	$C_{12}H_{13}O_4N_4 \cdot H_2O$	Z ǁ elong.	238
1.51	1.66	?	?	Opianic acid	$C_{10}H_{10}O_5$	X ǁ elong.	133
1.510	1.691	?	?	7-Benzamido-1,3-naphthalene disulfonic acid	$C_{17}H_{13}O_7NS_2$	X ǁ elong.	170
1.51 = N_X	1.718 = N_Z	−	Lg.	Equilenin	$C_{18}H_{18}O_2$	X = *b*; Y = *a*.	275
1.51 = N_X	1.74 = N_Z	−	?	Opianic acid	$C_{10}H_{10}O_5$	X ǁ elong.	133
1.511	>1.74	?	?	*o*-Nitrobenzaldehyde	$C_6H_4NO_2CHO$	X ǁ elong. MP 114°	103
1.512 = N_X	1.522 = N_Y	−	?	Sterol glucoside tetraacetate	$C_{43}H_{68}O_{10}$	Z ǁ elong.	275
1.512 = N_X	1.71	?	?	*p*-Chloronitrobenzene	$C_6H_4ClNO_2$	X ∧ *c* = 20°; Y = *b*.	74
1.513 = N_X	1.548 = N_Z	?	?	Diamylamine abietate	$C_{30}H_{43}O_2N$	Z ǁ elong.	120
1.513	1.610	?	?	Dipotassium maleate	$(HC)_2 \cdot (CO_2K)_2$	Laths	36
1.513 = N_X	1.619 = N_Z	?	?	Ethylhydrocupreine·HCl	$C_{21}H_{28}O_2N_2 \cdot HCl$	MP 253°	207
1.513	1.636	?	?	*N*-Methyl-*N′*-phenylurea	$C_8H_{10}ON_2$	Parallel extinc.	143
1.513 = N_X	1.660 = N_Z	?	Biax.	Hydroxynetoric acid	$C_{12}H_{14}O_6$	MP 189°	313
1.514	1.648	?	?	Guanidine anthranilate	$C_8H_{12}O_2N_4$	N_i ǁ width	162
1.514	>1.70	?	?	2,4-Dichlorophenol	$C_6H_3Cl_2OH$	N_2 ǁ length. MP 45°	86
1.514 = N_X	1.87 = N_Z	?	?	Disodium 1-phenylazo-2-naphthol-6,8-disulfonate	$C_{16}H_{10}O_7N_2SNa$	X ǁ elong. Orange	178
1.515	1.523	?	?	Orthoform hydrate	$C_8H_9O_3N \cdot nH_2O$	MP 55° *ca.*	165
1.515	1.53	?	?	Atropine valerate	$C_{17}H_{23}O_3N \cdot C_5H_{10}O_2$	Z ǁ elong.	279

Table II. Based on the Lower Measured Refractive Index

N_1	N_2	Sign	2V	Name	Composition	Opt. Orient., etc.	Page
1.515	$1.551 = N_Y$	?	?	Potassium tartrate(H_2O ?)	$C_4H_4O_6K_2(H_2O\ ?)$		49
$1.515 = N_X$	$1.600 = N_Z$	?	?	Dihydrotoxicarolic acid	$C_{23}H_{26}O_9$	X ‖ elong.	317
1.515	1.665	?	?	3-Methyl-1-phenylhydantoin	$C_{10}H_{10}O_2N_2$	Z ‖ elong.	212
$1.515 = N_X$	1.71	–	?	*o*-Bromonitrobenzene	$C_6H_4BrNO_2$	$X \wedge c = 14.5°$; $Z = b$.	75
1.515	1.72	– ?	?	*p*-Nitrobenzylalcohol	$C_6H_4NO_2CH_2OH$	$X' \wedge$ elong. $= 24°$, MP 93°. Str. dispersion	93
1.515	1.74	?	?	Asaron	$C_6H_2CH{:}CHCH_3(OCH_3)_3$	$Bx_a \wedge c = 18°$; $Y = b$.	101
1.515	>1.95	?	?	Phloretin	$C_{15}H_{15}O_5$	Extinc. at 41°	110
$1.516 = N_X$	1.584	–	90° *ca.*	Dial	$C_{10}H_{12}O_3N_2$	Sym. extinc.	232
$1.517 < N_E$		–	0°	*cis*-1,4-Cyclohexanediol II	$C_6H_{12}O_2$	X ‖ elong.	96
$1.517 = N_Y$		?	90° *ca.*	*cis*-1,4-Cyclohexanediol III	$C_6H_{12}O_2$	$Y \wedge$ elong. $= 10°$	96
1.518	1.625	?	?	Ergotamine tartrate	$C_{37}H_{41}O_{11}N_5$	Decomposes at 184°	301
$1.518 = N_X$	$1.856 = N_Z$	–	?	Vulpinic acid	$C_{18}H_{14}O_5$	X near *c*; $Y = b$. MP 148°	189
$1.52 = N_X$		–	Sm.	*dl*-Amphetamine sulfate	$C_9H_{15}O_4NS$	X ‖ elong.	148
1.52 *ca.*	<1.527	?	?	Aspartic acid picrolonate	$C_{14}H_{31}O_2NBr$	Triclinic	210
1.52	1.53	?	?	Solanine	$C_{52}H_{91}O_{18}N$?	Granular	306
1.52	1.535	?	?	Sparteine sulfate	$C_{30}H_{54}O_4N_4S$	Z ‖ elong.	283
1.52	1.55	?	?	Cevadine	$C_{37}H_{53}O_{11}N$	MP 150° *ca.*	306
1.52	1.56	?	?	Cocaine tartrate	$C_{38}H_{48}O_{14}N_2$	X ‖ elong.	282
$1.520 = N_X$	$1.565 = N_Z$	?	?	Picrotoxin	$C_{30}H_{34}O_{13}$	MP 203 – 204°	313
$1.52 = N_X$	$1.59 = N_Z$	?	?	Tanacetone semicarbazone	$C_{10}H_{16}{:}N \cdot NH \cdot CONH_2$	MP 170°	103
1.52	1.59	?	?	Ammonium acid succinate	$(CH_2CO_2)_2HNH_4$	Extinc. at 37°	38
1.520	1.608	?	?	Isoserine picrolonate II	$C_{13}H_{15}O_8N_5$	Z ‖ elong.	211
1.520	1.610	?	?	Isoleucine picrolonate	$C_{16}H_{21}O_7N_5$	Z ‖ elong.	211
$1.52 = N_X$	$1.61 = N_Z$	?	Biax.	Histidine	$C_6H_9O_2N_3$	X ‖ elong.	242
$1.520 = N_X$	$1.639 = N_Z$	?	?	Tricalcium aconitate·$3H_2O$	$(C_6H_3O_6)_2Ca_3 \cdot 3H_2O$	Parallel extinc.	37
1.520	1.645	?	?	Lysine picrolonate	$C_{16}H_{22}O_7N_6$	Z ‖ elong.	211
1.520	$1.645 = N_Y$	?	?	Lobeline·HCl	$C_{22}H_{28}ON_2Cl$	$N_3 = 1.67$	278

Table II. Based on the Lower Measured Refractive Index

N_1	N_2	Sign	2V	Name	Composition	Opt. Orient., etc.	Page
1.52 $=N_X$	1.65 $=N_Z$	+	70°	Acetolsalicylate	$HOC_6H_4CO_2CH_2COCH_3$	Y = *b*; Z ∧ elong. = 43°	128
1.52 $=N_X$	1.65 $=N_Z$	?	Biax.	2-Methoxy-4-propylphenyl 3,5-dinitrobenzoate	$C_{17}H_{16}O_7N_2$	MP 116°	117
1.52	⟩1.74 $=N_Z$	+ ?	?	Ethyl-*p*-aminobenzoate	$C_9H_{11}O_2N$	Z ‖ elong. MP 90°	163
1.52	⟩1.95	?	?	Curcumin	$(CH_3\cdot O\cdot HO\cdot C_6H_3\cdot \cdot CH{:}CH\cdot CO)_2CH_2$	X ‖ elong.	111
1.52 $=N_X$	2.45 $=N_Z$	?	?	Methylnitrophenylazonaphthol	$C_{17}H_{13}O_3N_3$	X ∧ *c* = 10°	176
1.52 $=N_X$	2.52 $=N_Z$	−	?	Nitrotolueneazonaphthol	$C_{17}H_{13}O_3N_3$	X ‖ elong.	176
1.52 $=N_X$		?	?	Phthaloxime	$C_8H_5O_3N$	X ‖ elong.	183
1.522	1.538	?	?	Copper aspartate	$O_2C\cdot CHNH_2\cdot CH_2CO_2Cu\cdot(5H_2O\ ?)$	Z ‖ elong.	69
1.522	1.733	?	?	Atabrine·2HCl·$2H_2O$	$C_{23}H_{32}O_3NCl_3\cdot 2H_2O$	N_3 ⟩ 1.733. Color yellow	203
1.522 $=N_X$	2.14 $=N_Z$	?	?	2,7-(1-Anthroquinonylamino)-anthraquinone	$C_{42}H_{22}O_6N_2$	X ∧ elong. = 80° Yellow to red.	161
1.523	1.58	+	70°	Sodium 4-hydroxybenzenesulfonate·$2H_2O$	$C_6H_4OH\cdot SO_3Na\cdot 2H_2O$	Y = *b*; Z ∧ *c* = + 9°. N_3 = 1.61	137
1.523	1.527	?	32°	Lauroylcholine bromide	$CH_3(CH_2)_{10}CH_3\cdot NOHCH_3CH_3OBr$	Triclinic	65
1.523	⟩1.74	?	?	Barium-p-(*p*-aminobenzoyl)-benzenesulfonate	$C_{26}H_{20}O_8N_2S_2Ba$	Y = *b*; Z ∧ *c* = 6°. 100 cleav.	171
1.524 $=N_Y$	1.566 $=N_Z$	+	?	Cholesteryl formate	$C_{28}H_{46}O_2$	Y = *b*; MP 96°	274
1.525 *ca.*	1.525 *ca.*	?	?	Sabadine	$C_{29}H_{51}O_8N$	Granular	305
1.525	1.530	?	27°	Palmitoylcholine bromide	$CH_3(CH_2)_{14}CH_3\cdot NOHCH_2CH_2Br$	Extinc. at 15°	65
1.525	1.647	?	Lg.	1,3-Dimethyl-9-phenylpseudouric acid	$C_{13}H_{14}O_4N_4$	Extinc. at 25° – 37°	241
1.525	1.705	?	Biax.	1,3,9-Trimethyluric acid	$C_8H_{10}O_3N_4$	Z ‖ elong.	250
1.525 $=N_X$	1.710 $=N_Z$	?	?	Nitroguanidine II	$NH_2C(NH)_2\cdot NO_2$	Long plates	43
1.525 $=N_X$	1.717 $=N_Z$	?	?	9-Phenyluric acid·$2H_2O$	$C_{11}H_8O_3N_4\cdot 2H_2O$	Z ‖ elong.	250

N_1	N_2	Sign	2V	Name	Composition	Opt. Orient., etc.	Page
1.527	1.617	?	?	Leucine picrolonate	$C_{16}H_{21}O_7N_5$	Z ‖ elong.	211
1.527	1.630	?	?	Cupric 2-aminopropionate·H_2O	$(CH_3)_2(O_2C \cdot CHNH_2)Cu \cdot H_2O$	X ‖ elong.	67
$1.528 = N_X$	$1.545 = N_Z$	?	?	Tetrakis(hydroxymethyl)cyclopentanone	$C_9H_{16}O_5$	Orthorhombic	110
1.528	1.69	?	?	1.3-Dimethylxanthine·H_2O	$C_7H_8O_2N_4 \cdot H_2O$	$X \wedge c = 43°$	247
$1.528 = N_X$	$1.59 = N_Z$	?	?	*l*-Menthone semicarbazone	$CH_3(CH_3)_2CHC_6H_8{:}N \cdot NH \cdot CONH_2$	MP 184°	103
1.529	1.596	?	?	Tyrosine picrolonate	$C_{19}H_{19}O_8N_5$	Z ∧ elong. = 37°	212
1.529	1.660	?	?	Isoserine picrolonate III	$C_{13}H_{15}O_8N_5$	Z ‖ elong.	211
1.53	1.54	?	?	Cerous lactate ($3H_2O$?)	$(C_3H_5O_3)_2Ce \cdot (3H_2O\ ?)$	Opt. + ? $N_3 = 1.57$	45
1.530	1.542	?	?	Cupric 2-aminopentanoate	$\{CH_3(CH_2)_2CHNH_2CO_2\}Cu$	X ‖ elong.	68
1.53	1.545	?	?	Sodium uroxanate·nH_2O	$(NH_2CONH)_2C \cdot (CO_2Na)_2 \cdot nH_2O$	After heating to 110°	58
1.53	1.55	?	?	Sabadinine	$C_{27}H_{43}O_8N$	Z ‖ elong.	305
1.53	1.56	?	?	Aconitine salicylate	$C_{41}H_{51}O_{14}N$	Granular	304
1.530	1.567	?	?	Serine picrolonate	$C_{13}H_{15}O_8N_5$	Z ∧ elong. = 40°	211
1.530	1.625	?	?	*N*-Methyl-*N*-phenylcarbamylglycine	$C_{10}H_{12}O_3N_2$	X ‖ elong.	142
1.53	1.625	?	?	Atropine methobromide	$C_{18}H_{26}O_3NBr$	Extinc. ∧ = 41°	279
1.53	1.64	?	?	Uranyl acetate (·$2H_2O$?)	$(CH_3CO_2)_2UO_2$	Z‖elong. Yellow; pleoch.	16
$1.53 = N_X$	$1.64 = N_Z$	?	?	Tephrosindicarboxylic acid	$C_{23}H_{22}O_{11}$	Z ∧ elong. = ?	316
1.53	1.69	?	?	Narceine meconate	$C_{33}H_{38}O_{13}N$	Extinc. ∧ = 23°	294
1.53 *ca.*	1.69 *ca.*	?	Lg.	Yohimbine picrate	$C_{27}H_{29}O_{10}N_5$	X ‖ elong.	294
$1.52 = N_X$	$1.73 = N_Z$	?	?	Uric acid (H_2O ?)	$C_5H_4O_3N_4(H_2O\ ?)$		249
$1.53 = N_X$	›1.74	?	Biax.	2-Methoxyphenyl 3,5-dinitrobenzoate	$CH_3O \cdot C_6H_4 \cdot O_2C \cdot C_6H_3(NO_2)_2$	MP 141°	117

N_1	N_2	Sign	2V	Name	Composition	Opt. Orient., etc.	Page
1.53	1.8 *ca.*	–	?	*p*-α-β-Trimethylcinnamic acid	$CH_3 \cdot C_6H_4 \cdot C(CH_3) \cdot C(CH_3)CO_2 \cdot H$	X = *b*; Y = *a*.	121
1.53	1.78	?	?	Benzothiazole guanidine nitrate	$C_8H_{11}O_3N_5S$	Z′ ‖ elong.	254
$1.53 = N_X$	$1.78 = N_Z$	?	?	Copper phthalate	$C_6H_4(CO_2)_2Cu(H_2O\ ?)$	Extinc. at 22°. Blue	122
1.531	1.616	?	?	Glycine picrolonate	$C_{12}H_{13}O_7N_5$	Z ‖ elong.	210
1.531	1.659	?	?	Tropacocaine·HCl	$C_{15}H_{20}O_2NCl$	MP 271°	282
1.532	1.601	?	?	Uroxanic acid	$NH_2(CO \cdot NH)_2C(CO_2H)_2$	Irregular solids	59
$1.532 = N_X$	$>1.649 = N_Z$	?	?	Phenylbiuret	$C_8H_9O_2N_3$	Extinc. at 33°. MP 190°	142
1.533	1.72 ?	?	?	Salipyrine	$C_{18}H_{18}O_4N$	MP 91°	208
1.534	1.547	?	?	Cupric 2-amino-3-methylpentanoate	$\{O_2C \cdot CHNH_2CH(OH_3) \cdot CH_2 \cdot CH_3\}_2Cu$	Sym. extinc. – elong.	69
1.534	1.555	?	?	Cupric 2-amino-3-methylbutanoate	$\{O_2C \cdot CHNH_2 \cdot CH(OH_3)_2\}_2Cu$	X ‖ elong.	68
1.534	1.570	?	?	Cupric *l*-2-aminopentanoate	$O_2C \cdot CHNH_2 \cdot (CH_2)_2 \cdot (CH_3)_2Cu$	Z ∧ elong. = 29°	68
1.534	1.709	?	?	Acetopyrine	$C_{20}H_{20}O_5N_2$	MP 63 – 65°	208
1.535	1.545	?	?	Dulcitol	$CH_2OH \cdot (CHOH)_4 \cdot CH_2OH$	X = *b*; Z ∧ *c* = – 77°, MP 188°	10
$1.535 = N_X$	$1.565 = N_Z$	–	?	Picrotin	$C_{15}H_{18}O_7$	Z ‖ elong.	313
1.535	1.63	?	?	Hydrohydrastinine·HCl	$C_{11}H_{14}O_2NCl$	X ‖ elong.	295
1.535	1.69	?	?	Brucine phthalate	$C_{31}H_{32}O_8N_2$	Parallel extinc.	308
1.535	1.697	?	?	Guanylurea anthranilate	$C_9H_{13}O_3N_5$	N_1 ‖ width	163
$1.535 = N_X$	$1.74 = N_Z$	?	Biax.	Dihydrotoxicarolic acid methyl ether	$C_{24}H_{28}O_9$	Parallel extinc.	317
1.536	1.599	?	?	Cupric 2-amino-3-hydroxypropionate	$(O_2C \cdot CHNH_2 \cdot CH_2OH)Cu$	Sym. extinc.	71
$1.536 = N_X$	$>1.659 = N_Z$	+	Mod.	Ergometrine ethyl acetate solvate	$C_{19}H_{20}O_2N_3 \cdot nC_4H_8O_2$	X = *c*; Y = *b*.	302
1.536	$<1.66 = N_Z$	?	Lg.	Methyl phenyl ketone methylphenylhydrazone	$C_{15}H_{16}N_2$	Bx_a nearly ⊥ 100; Y = *b*. MP 124°	172

Table II. Based on the Lower Measured Refractive Index

N_1	N_2	Sign	2V	Name	Composition	Opt. Orient., etc.	Page
$1.537 = N_X$	$1.557 = N_Z$	?	?	α-*L*-Fucose	$C_6H_{12}O_5$	D 1.49	260
1.537	1.653	?	?	4-Benzamido-1-naphthalenesulfonic acid	$C_{17}H_{13}O_4NS$	Sym. extinc. N_1 bisects 104°	170
$1.538 = N_X$		+	Mod.	Ergometrine ethyl alcohol solvate	$C_{19}H_{20}O_2N_3 \cdot nC_2H_6O$	$X = b$; $Z \wedge c = 15°$	302
$1.538 = N_X$	$1.590 = N_Z$	?	?	Partheniol	$C_{15}H_{26}O$	X ‖ elong.	85
$1.54 = N_X$		−	?	Purpurin	$C_{13}H_8O_5$	$X = c$. Orange to red.	110
1.54	1.545	?	?	Adonitol	$CH_2OH \cdot (CHOH)_3 \cdot CH_2OH$	X ‖ elong. MP 102°	9
1.54	1.55	?	?	Choral urethan	$CCl_3CH(OH)NHCO_2C_2H_5$	Z ‖ elong. MP 103°	38
1.54	1.55	?	?	Copper formate·$2H_2O$	$(HCO_2)_2Cu \cdot 2H_2O$	X ‖ elong. 100 cleav.	14
1.54	1.55	?	?	Conhydrine	$C_8H_{17}ON$	Z ‖ elong.	278
1.54	1.55	?	?	Aconitine sulfate	$C_{68}H_{92}O_{26}N_2S$	X ‖ elong.	304
1.54	1.56	?	?	Hydroxyvaline picrolonate	$C_{15}H_{19}O_8N_5$	Z ‖ elong.	210
1.54	1.56	?	?	Sabadine·HCl	$C_{29}H_{52}O_8NCl$	Granular	305
1.54	1.58	?	?	Hydrastine bitartrate	$C_{29}H_{33}O_{18}N$	Z ‖ elong.	294
1.54	1.58	?	?	Lithium acid tartrate·$1.5H_2O$	$C_4H_4O_6HLi \cdot 1.5H_2O$	Z ‖ elong.	48
1.54	1.61	?	?	Aconitine nitrate	$C_{34}H_{46}O_{14}N_2$	Granular	304
1.54	1.61	?	?	Pilocarpine salicylate	$C_{18}H_{22}O_5N_2$	Z ‖ elong.	303
1.54	1.62	?	?	Succinimide	$C_4H_5O_2N$	MP 125°	198
1.54	1.63	?	?	Hyoscyamine salicylate	$C_{24}H_{29}O_6N$	Granular	282
1.54	1.64	?	?	Guanidine hydrochloride	$CNH(NH_2)_2 \cdot HCl$	Orth.	40
1.54	1.64	?	?	Morphine tartrate·$2H_2O$	$C_{23}H_{25}O_9N \cdot 2H_2O$	X ‖ elong.	297
1.54	1.69	?	?	Thermodine	$C_{13}H_{17}O_4N$	MP 86°	156
1.540	1.695	?	?	Guaiacol carbonate	$(C_7H_7O)_2CO_3$	MP 88°	98
$1.54 = N_X$	$1.73 = N_Z$	+	Lg.	Mercuric phthalate	$C_6H_4(CO_2)_2Hg(H_2O\,?)$	Parallel extinc.	122
1.540	> 1.755	?	?	Dimethylphenyluric acid	$C_{13}H_{12}O_3N_4$	MP > 280°	251
1.54	> 1.76	?	?	Cupric picolinate	$(C_5H_4NCO_2)_2Cu$	Blue	200

TABLE II BASED ON THE LOWER MEASURED REFRACTIVE INDEX

N_1	N_2	Sign	2V	Name	Composition	Opt. Orient., etc.	Page
1.541	1.552	?	?	Cupric 2-aminohexanoate	$\{O_2C \cdot CHNH_2 \cdot (CH_2)_3CH_3\}_2Cu$	Sym. extinc.; – elong.	69
1.543	$1.758 = N_Y$	–	?	Tobias acid · H_2O	$C_{10}H_{11}O_4NS$	Y = *a*. Sym. extinc.	169
1.545	1.55	?	?	Copper acetate · (H_2O ?)	$(CH_3CO_2)_2Cu \cdot (H_2O\ ?)$	X ∧ elong. = 20°. 001 and 110 cleav.	16
1.545	1.55	?	?	Pseudopelletierine sulfate	$C_{18}H_{32}O_5NS$	Z ∧ elong. = 20°	283
1.545	1.56	?	?	Sabadine nitrate	$C_{29}H_{52}O_{11}N_2$	Extinc. angle = 29°	305
1.545	1.583	?	Lg.	5-Hydroxy-3-phenyl-5-hydantoin-carboxymethylamide	$C_{11}H_{11}O_4N_3$	X ‖ elong.	238
1.545	1.605	?	?	9-Allyl-1,3-dimethylpseudouric acid	$C_{10}H_{14}O_4N_4$	MP 190°	241
1.545	1.620	?	Biax.	6-Benzamide-2-naphthalenesulfonic acid II	$C_{17}H_{13}O_4NS$	Z ‖ elong.	170
1.545	1.634	?	?	Codeine phosphate($2H_2O$?)	$C_{18}H_{24}O_7NP \cdot (2H_2O\ ?)$	X ‖ elong.	297
1.545	1.635	?	?	Nicotine salicylate	$C_{17}H_{21}O_3N_2$	Z ‖ elong.	278
1.545	1.64	?	?	Narceine · $H_2SO_4 \cdot 6H_2O$	$C_{46}H_{56}O_{20}N_2S \cdot 6H_2O$	X ‖ elong.	294
1.545	1.72	?	?	Diphenylamine · HCl	$C_{12}H_{12}NCl$	Z ‖ elong.	140
1.545	1.72	?	?	*p*-Aminophenol · HCl	C_6H_8ONCl	Z ‖ elong.	155
⟨1.545	1.620	?	Biax.	Ethyl oxamate	$NH_2 \cdot CO \cdot CO_2(C_2H_5)$	X ‖ elong.	32
1.546	1.735	?	?	Histidine flavianate	$C_{16}H_{16}O_{10}N_5S$	Extinc. at 18°. Yellow	242
1.546	1.735	?	?	Lysine flavianate	$C_{16}H_{21}O_{10}N_4S$	X ‖ elong. Yellow	137
$1.547 = N_X$	$1.582 = N_Z$	?	Biax.	Isotephrosin	$C_{23}H_{22}O_7$	Rhombic	316
$1.547 = N_X$	$1.613 = N_Z$	?	?	Methyl phenaceturate	$C_6H_5 \cdot CH_2 \cdot CO \cdot NH(CH_2 \cdot CO_2 \cdot CH_3)$	Y = *b*; Z = *a*.	117
$1.547 = N_X$	$1.681 = N_Z$	?	?	2-Naphthol-6,8-disulfonic acid benzoate	$C_{17}H_{12}O_8S_2$	X ‖ elong.	138
1.548	1.600	?	?	Cystine picrolonate	$C_{16}H_{20}O_9N_6S$	Z ‖ elong.	210
1.548	1.603	+ ?	90° *ca.*	9,10-Dihydro-9,9,10,10-tetraiso-butylanthracene	$C_{30}H_{44}$	Poor 001 cleav. Triclinic	81

Table II. Based on the Lower Measured Refractive Index

N_1	N_2	Sign	2V	Name	Composition	Opt. Orient., etc.	Page
1.548	1.696	?	?	*p*-Nitrobenzyl pentobarbital	$C_{25}H_{28}O_7N_4$	Z ‖ elong. MP 151°	230
$1.548 = N_X$	$1.705 = N_Z$	?	?	Barium monobromoacetate	$(CH_2BrCO_2)_2Ba$	Z ‖ elong.	20
$<1.549 = N_X$		+ ?	80°	*β*-Naphthalene-acetic acid II	$C_{11}H_9O_3$	Optic axis seen	121
<1.549	>1.580	?	?	Dibromotyrosine picrolonate	$C_{19}H_{17}O_8N_5Br_2$	X ∧ elong. = 44°	210
$1.549 = N_X$	$1.585 = N_Y$	+	?	Ethylmethylphenylbetaine·H_2O	$C_{11}H_{15}O_2N \cdot H_2O$	X ‖ elong.	144
1.549	$<1.585 = N_Y$	+	Sm.	Ethylmethylphenylbetaine·$2H_2O$	$C_{11}H_{15}O_2N \cdot 2H_2O$	Y = *b*. Two cleav.	144
1.549	$<1.74 = N_Z$	?	?	Valine picrolonate	$C_{15}H_{19}O_7N_5$	X ‖ elong.	212
>1.549	>1.74	?	?	Dibromotyrosine picrolonate	$C_{19}H_{17}O_8N_5Br_2$	Z ‖ elong.	210
1.55	1.56	?	?	Physostigmine·HCl	$C_{15}H_{22}O_2N_3Cl$	Granular	304
1.55	1.56	?	?	Quinic acid	$C_7H_{12}O_6$	X ‖ elong. Y = *b*. MP 162°	132
$1.55 = N_X$	$1.56 = N_Z$	?	I.g.	Verdigris	$CuO \cdot (CH_3CO_2)_2Cu$?	Pleoch. X = blue, Z = green	18
1.55	1.56	-	74.5°	1,2,3,5-Cyclohexanetetrol-5-carbonate	$C_7H_{12}O_6$	Y = *b*; Z ∧ *c* = −6°	101
1.55	1.57	?	?	Hyoscyamine sulfate	$C_{17}H_{25}O_7NS$	X ‖ elong.	282
1.55	1.58	?	?	Arbutin	$C_{12}H_{16}O_7$	Z ‖ elong.	263
1.55	1.605	?	?	Pilocarpidine nitrate	$C_{10}H_{15}O_5N_3$	Z ‖ elong.	304
1.550	1.610	?	Biax.	Diethyl(phenylureido)malonate	$C_{14}H_{18}O_5N_2$	X ‖ elong. MP 113°	142
1.55	1.61	?	?	Neurodine	$C_{12}H_{10}O_4N$	X ‖ elong.	156
1.55	1.615	?	?	Pilocarpine sulfate	$C_{22}H_{34}O_8N_4S$	X ‖ elong.	303
1.55	1.62	?	?	Codeine·HCl·H_2O.	$C_{18}H_{22}O_3NCl \cdot H_2O$	X ‖ elong.	297
1.55	1.65	?	?	Codeine·HBr·H_2O	$C_{18}H_{22}O_3NBr \cdot H_2O$	X ‖ elong.	297
1.55	1.661 ?	?	Biax.	Citrophen	$C_{14}H_{19}O_8N$	MP 186°	155
$1.550 = N_X$	$1.682 = N_Z$	?	Biax.	Dihydrorotenone I	$C_{23}H_{24}O_6$	X ‖ elong.	314
$1.550 = N_X$	$1.685 = N_Z$	?	Biax.	Monoacetate of dihydro-7-hydroxy-toxicarol	$C_{25}H_{26}O_9$	MP 196°	317
$1.550 = N_X$		?	?	Brucine sulfate with KI	$(C_{23}H_{26}O_4N_2)_2 \cdot H_2SO_4$ with KI	Z ‖ elong.	308

Table II. Based on the Lower Measured Refractive Index

N_1	N_2	Sign	2V	Name	Composition	Opt. Orient., etc.	Page
1.55	1.70	?	?	Caffeine·HBr	$C_8H_{11}O_2N_4Br$	Z ‖ elong.	249
1.55	1.70	?	?	Piperine	$C_{17}H_{19}O_3N$	MP 129°	279
1.55	1.71	?	?	Phenylamine sulfate	$(C_6H_5NH_2)_2 \cdot H_2SO_4$	Extinc. at 32°	139
1.55	1.72	?	?	Monoguanyl melamine·HCl·H_2O	$C_4H_9N_8Cl \cdot H_2O$	N_2 ‖ elong.	245
1.550	>1.732	?	?	2-Methoxy-6-chloroacridone	$C_{14}H_{10}O_2NCl$	X ‖ elong.	198
$1.55 = N_X$	$1.733 = N_Z$	?	?	*N*-Cinnamyl-1-ephedrine·HCl	$C_{11}H_{15}OCl$	MP 182°	157
1.55	>1.74	?	?	Vanillin	$C_6H_3(OH)OCH_3 \cdot CHO$	Opt. plane ⊥ 010. MP 81°	108
$1.55 = N_X$	$1.75 = N_Z$	−	?	Salicylic acid	$C_6H_4(OH) \cdot CO_2H$	$Y = b$; $Z \wedge c = 42.5°$. MP 156°	126
1.55	1.76	?	?	Silver picolinate	$(C_5H_4NCO_2)_2Ag$	Thin needles	200
$1.55 = N_X$	$>1.80 = N_Y$	−	Lg.	Alizarin	$C_{14}H_8O_4$	$X = c$; $Y = b$. Yellow to red	110
1.551	1.560	?	72°	Stearoylcholine bromide	$C_{11}H_{25}ONBr$	Z at 27° on 001	65
$1.551 = N_X$	$1.565 = N_Z$	?	?	Lupeol	$C_{30}H_{50}O$	X ‖ elong.	312
1.552	1.697	?	?	2-Naphthol-3,6-disulfonic acid benzoate	$C_{17}H_{12}O_8S_2$	Z ‖ elong.	138
$1.552 = N_X$	$1.795 = N_Z$	?	?	1-Naphthylamine 1-naphthalene-sulfonate	$C_{20}H_{17}O_3N$	Parallel extinc. MP 232°	152
$1.553 = N_X$	$1.600 = N_Z$	?	?	Butylamine abietate	$C_{24}H_{41}O_2N$	MP 165°	120
$<1.555 = N_X$	$<1.595 = N_Y$	+	Sm.	Methylphenylpropylbetaine·$2H_2O$	$C_{12}H_{17}O_2N \cdot 2H_2O$	Z ⊥ plates	144
$1.555 = N_X$		+	55°	*β*-Naphthalene-acetic acid I	$C_{11}H_9O_3$	Z ⊥ plates	121
1.555	1.565	−	74°(2H)	*D*-Glucosamine·HCl	$C_6H_{14}O_4NCl$	$X \wedge c = 40°$; $Y = b$. $10\bar{1}$ cleav.	66
1.555	1.57	?	?	Scopolamine	$C_{17}H_{21}O_3N$	Z ‖ elong.	280
$1.555 = N_X$	$1.595 = N_Y$	+	?	Methylphenylpropylbetaine·H_2O	$C_{12}H_{17}O_2N \cdot H_2O$	Y ‖ elong. Z ⊥ plates. MP 172°	144
1.555	1.60	?	?	Atropine sulfate	$C_{34}H_{48}O_{10}N_2S$	Granular	279
1.555	1.595	−	Lg.	Atropine	$C_{17}H_{23}O_3N$	$Y = c$. MP 116°	279

Table II. Based on the Lower Measured Refractive Index

N_1	N_2	Sign	2V	Name	Composition	Opt. Orient., etc.	Page
1.555	1.60	?	?	Aconitine phosphate	$C_{68}H_{93}O_{26}NP$	Z ‖ elong.	304
1.555	1.60	?	?	Atropine arsenate	$C_{17}H_{23}O_3N \cdot H_3AsO_4$	X ‖ elong.	279
1.555	1.605	?	?	Scopolamine · HBr · $3H_2O$	$C_{17}H_{22}O_4NBr \cdot 3H_2O$	X = *c*; Y = *b*.	280
1.555	1.62	?	?	Quinine · $2H_2SO_4 \cdot 7H_2O$	$C_{20}H_{28}O_{10}N_2S_2 \cdot 7H_2O$	Z ‖ elong.	291
1.555	1.63	?	?	Apoatropine sulfate	$C_{34}H_{44}O_8N_2S$	Z ‖ elong.	281
1.555	1.64	?	?	Cinchonine nitrate	$C_{19}H_{23}O_4N_3$	X ‖ elong.	284
1.555	1.695	?	?	Dimethylphenylpseudouric acid	$C_{13}H_{14}O_4N_4$	MP 220°	241
$1.555 = N_X$	$1.70 = N_Z$	?	?	Monoacetate of 7-hydroxytoxicarol	$C_{25}H_{24}O_5$	Parallel extinc.	317
1.555	1.733	?	?	Adrenalin	$C_9H_{13}O_3N$	Colorless to brown	160
$1.555 = N_X$	$>1.734 = N_Y$	?	?	Papaverine · HCl	$C_{20}H_{21}O_4N \cdot HCl$	MP 220°	294
1.555	>1.95	?	?	Quinoline-hydroquinone	$(C_9H_7N)_2 \cdot nC_6H_6O_2$	X ‖ elong.	195
1.556	1.655	?	?	Brucine salt of sucrose disulfuric acid	$C_{58}H_{76}O_{22}N_4S_2$	Incl. extinc.	308
1.557	1.616	?	?	Histidine picrolonate	$C_{16}H_{17}O_7N_7$	Z ‖ elong.	210
1.557	1.665	?	?	Cinchonine-2-phenylpyridine-2,3-dicarboxylate	$C_{51}H_{53}O_6N_5$	X ‖ elong.	284
1.557	1.674	?	?	Methylphenyluric acid	$C_{12}H_{10}O_3N_4$	Z ‖ elong.	251
1.557	1.674	?	?	Diethylglycol dinitrobenzoate	$C_{18}H_{14}O_{13}N_4$	N_2 ‖ elong.	117
$1.559 = N_X$	$>1.73 = N_Z$	?	?	Phenylbiuret	$C_8H_9O_2N_3$	Extinc. at 33°. MP 197°	142
1.559	1.744	?	?	Folic acid	$C_{18}H_{16}O_6N_7$	Lenticular	309
1.56	1.57	+	36°	Aconitine	$C_{34}H_{45}O_{11}N$	Y = *b*; Z = *a*.	304
1.56	1.57	?	?	Nicotine tartrate	$C_{14}H_{21}O_6N_2$	Z ‖ elong.	277
$1.56 = N_X$	$1.57 = N_Z$	?	?	*N*-Vanillylcaprylamide	$C_{16}H_{25}O_3N$	X ‖ elong. MP 42°	159
1.56	1.575	?	?	Sparteine · HCl	$C_{15}H_{27}N_2Cl$	Granular	283
1.56	1.58	?	?	Aconitine · HCl · $2.5H_2O$	$C_{34}H_{46}O_{11}NCl \cdot 2.5H_2O$	Z ‖ elong.	304
1.56	1.58	?	?	Cinchonidine tartrate	$C_{42}H_{50}O_8N_4(2H_2O\,?)$	Z ‖ elong.	288
1.56	1.61	?	?	Eucatropine · HCl	$C_{17}H_{26}O_3NCl$	MP 184°	197
1.56	1.61	?	?	Scopolamine · HCl	$C_{17}H_{22}O_4NCl$	Z ‖ elong.	280
1.56	1.615	?	?	Conessine	$C_{24}H_{40}N_2$	Granular	305

Table II. Based on the Lower Measured Refractive Index

N_1	N_2	Sign	2V	Name	Composition	Opt. Orient., etc.	Page
1.56	1.62	?	?	Atropine salicylate	$C_{24}H_{29}O_6N$	X ‖ elong.	279
1.56	1.62	?	Biax.	Cinchonine · $2H_2SO_4$	$C_{19}H_{26}O_9N_2S_2$	Z ‖ elong.	284
1.56	1.62	?	?	Homatropine	$C_{16}H_{21}O_2N$	X ‖ elong.	280
1.56	1.62	?	?	Pseudopelletierine · HCl	$C_9H_{16}ONCl$	Z ‖ elong.	282
1.56	1.66	?	?	Physostigmine salicylate	$C_{22}H_{27}O_5N_3$	X ‖ elong.	304
1.56	>1.66	+	?	Coumarin	$C_8H_6O_2$	$Y=c$; $Z=a$. MP 67°	182
$1.560=N_X$	$1.660=N_Z$	?	?	Citral semicarbazone	$C_{11}H_{19}ON_3$	MP 132°	42
$1.56=N_X$	$1.685=N_Y$	?	?	Benzaldehyde semicarbazone	$C_6H_5 \cdot CH{:}N \cdot NHCONH_2$	MP 217°	103
1.56	1.74	+	?	Hydrastine	$C_{21}H_{21}O_6N$	Z ‖ elong.	294
1.56	1.78	?	?	β-Cupric picolinate · $2H_2O$	$(C_5H_4NCO_2)_2Cu \cdot 2H_2O$	Blue	200
1.56	>1.95	?	?	*o*-Coumaric acid	$C_9H_8O_3$	X ‖ elong.	130
$1.56=N_X$	$2.26=N_Z$	?	?	Lake Bordeaux BK	$C_{20}H_{14}O_4N_2S$	Z ‖ elong. Orange to red	177
$1.561=N_E$		–	0°	Barium *cis*-diaminodinitro-oxalate-cobaltiate · $3H_2O$	$C_2H_{12}O_{11}N_4BaCo \cdot 3H_2O$	D 2.14	31
1.563	1.696	?	?	*p*-Nitrobenzyl ipral	$C_{23}H_{24}O_7N_2$	X ∧ elong. = 35° MP 157°	229
1.563	>1.74	?	?	Phenobarbital-*p*-bromobenzyl	$C_{26}H_{22}O_3N_2Br_2$	Z ∧ elong. = 9°	234
$1.563=N_X$	$>1.74=N_Z$	?	?	Monoacetate of dehydrotoxicarol	$C_{25}H_{22}O_8$	X ∧ elong. = ?	316
1.564	1.612	?	?	Cupric 2-amino-4-methylpentanoate	$\{O_2C \cdot CHNH_2 \cdot CH_2 \cdot CH(CH_3)_2\}_2Cu$	Blue color	69
$1.564=N_X$	$1.96=N_Z$	?	?	Lithol fast yellow GG	$C_{13}H_{10}O_4N_4Cl_2$?	X ‖ elong.	140
1.565	1.57	?	?	Emetine · HCl	$C_{29}H_{41}O_4N_2Cl$	Z ‖ elong.	305
1.565	1.66	?	?	Caffeine · HCl	$C_8H_{11}O_2N_4Cl$	X ‖ elong.	249
$1.568=N_Y$	$1.74=N_Z$	?	?	Phenobarbital-*p*-chlorobenzyl	$C_{26}H_{22}O_3N_2Cl_2$	Z ∧ elong. = 8°	235
1.568	1.744	?	Sm.	Dibromobenzene	$C_6H_4Br_2$	$Y=b$; $Bx_a \wedge c=40°$	74
$1.57=N_X'$	?	?	?	Copper dimethylglyoxime dichloride	$C_4H_8O_2N_2CuCl_2$	D 1.98	12
1.57	1.59	?	?	Quinine ethyl carbonate	$C_{23}H_{29}O_5N_2$	$N_3=1.68$. MP 95°	288
$1.57=N_X$	$1.59=N_Z$	?	?	*N*-Vanillylpelargonamide	$C_{17}H_{27}O_3N$	X ‖ elong. MP 50°	159

TABLE II. BASED ON THE LOWER MEASURED REFRACTIVE INDEX

N_1	N_2	Sign	2V	Name	Composition	Opt. Orient., etc.	Page
1.57	1.595	?	?	Sabadinine·HCl	$C_{27}H_{44}O_8NCl$	Granular	305
1.57	1.60	?	?	Homatropine sulfate	$C_{16}H_{23}O_7NS$	Z ∥ elong.	281
1.57	1.61	?	?	Narceine·$3H_2O$	$C_{23}H_{27}O_8N \cdot 3H_2O$	X ∥ elong.	294
1.570	1.613	?	Biax.	Barium gluconate·H_2O	$\{CH_2OH \cdot (CHOH)_4CO_2\}Ba \cdot H_2O$	Granular.	57
1.570 = N_X	1.615 = N_Z	?	?	Quinine abietate	$C_{40}H_{54}O_4N_2$	Z ∥ elong.	290
1.57	1.63	?	?	Oxyacanthine·$H_2SO_4 \cdot 6H_2O$	$C_{40}H_{44}O_{10}N_2S \cdot 6H_2O$	Z ∥ elong.	306
1.57	1.63	?	?	Morphine·HBr(H_2O ?)	$C_{17}H_{20}O_3NBr(H_2O\,?)$	– elong.	296
1.57	1.68	+	45°(2E)	2,2,4,4,6-Pentachloro-6-methyl-1,3.5-cyclohexanetrione	$C_7H_3O_3Cl_5$	Z ∥ elong.	106
1.57 *ca.*	›1.70 = N_Y	?	Lg.	Trinitroresorcinol I	$C_6H_3O_8N_3$	X ∧ *c* = 7°; Y = *b*. MP 177°	99
1.57 = N_X	1.733 = N_Z	?	?	*N*-Cinnamyl-*dl*-ephedrine	$C_{12}H_{17}ON$	X ∥ elong. MP 67°	157
1.570	1.734	?	?	Cocaine·HCl with $AuCl_2$	$C_{17}H_{21}O_4N$ with $AuCl_3$	Rods	282
1.57 = N_X	›1.78 = N_Z	?	?	Copper benzoylacetonate	$C_{20}H_{18}O_4Cu$	X ∧ ⊥ 001 = 21°	105
1.571 = N_X	1.58 = N_Y	?	?	Strontium phthalate	$C_6H_4(CO_2)_2Sr(H_2O\,?)$	Parallel extinc.	123
1.571	1.620	?	Lg.	3-Phenyl-5-isohydantoincarboxy-methylamide	$C_{11}H_{11}O_5N_3$	X ∥ elong. MP 249–250°	237
1.571	1.62	?	Lg.	Dimethylphenyluric acid	$C_{13}H_{12}O_3N_4$	X ∥ elong.	251
1.572	1.630	?	?	Cupric 2-amino-4-methylmercapto-butanoate	$\{O_2C \cdot CHNH_2 \cdot (CH_2)_2 \cdot S \cdot CH_3\}Cu$	X ∥ elong.	72
1.572	1.681	?	?	Salophen	$C_{15}H_{13}O_4N$	MP 187°	156
1.573 = N_X	1.830 = N_Z	?	?	Uric acid	$C_5H_4O_3N_4$	X = *a*; Y = *c*.	249
1.574	1.596	?	?	Glutamic acid picrolonate	$C_{15}H_{17}O_9N_5$	X ∥ elong.	210
1.575	1.58	?	?	Alanine picrolonate	$C_{14}H_{15}O_7N_5$	X ∥ elong.	209
1.575	1.61	?	?	Hyoscyamine·HCl	$C_{17}H_{24}O_3NCl$	Granular	281
1.575 = N_X	1.655 = N_Z	–	?	Strychnine glutarate	$C_{26}H_{30}O_6N_2$	– elong.	308
1.576	1.591	?	?	Diacetylmorphine·HCl·H_2O	$C_{21}H_{24}O_5NCl \cdot H_2O$	MP 231°	298

TABLE II. BASED ON THE LOWER MEASURED REFRACTIVE INDEX

N_1	N_2	Sign	2V	Name	Composition	Opt. Orient., etc.	Page
1.576	1.633	?	?	5-Benzamido-1-naphthalene sulfonic acid	$C_{17}H_{13}O_4NS$	X ‖ elong.	170
$1.577=N_X$	$1.603=N_Z$	?	?	Vonedrine·HCl	$C_{10}H_{15}N \cdot HCl$	X ‖ elong.	151
$1.578=N_X$	$1.615=N_Z$	?	?	Anhydroquassin	$C_{22}H_{28}O_5$	MP 196°	313
$1.578=N_X$	$1.663=N_Z$			Sulfaguanidine with HNO_3	$CNHNH_2SO_2$? with HNO_3	Z nearly ‖ elong.	168
$1.579=N_X$		–	72°(2H)	Methyl ether of *p*-toluhydroxamic acid	$C_6H_4(CH_3) \cdot C(OH):(NOCH_3)$	$X=b$; $Z \wedge c=32°$. 100 cleav.	118
1.579	<1.66	?	67±	Allantoin	$C_4H_6O_3N_4$	X ‖ elong.	241
1.58	1.60	?	?	Conquinamine	$C_{19}N_{24}O_2N_2$	X ‖ elong.	293
1.58	1.61	?	?	Atropine·HCl	$C_{17}H_{24}O_3NCl$	Granular	280
1.58	1.62	–	30°	Quinamine	$C_{19}H_{24}O_2N_2$	Z ‖ elong.	293
1.58	1.62	+	64°	Cinchonidine·$H_2SO_4 \cdot 5H_2O$	$C_{19}H_{24}O_5N_2S \cdot 5H_2O$	$X=b$; $Z \wedge c=59°$	287
$1.58=N_X$	$1.62=N_Y$	?	Biax.	Quinine anisate	$C_{28}H_{32}O_5N_2$	Yellow	291
$1.580=N_X$	$1.63=N_Z$	?	?	Ergotoxine acetone solvate	$C_{35}H_{39}O_5N_5 \cdot nC_3H_6O$	$Y=a$; $Z=c$.	303
$1.58=N_X$	$1.646=N_Z$	?	?	Ethoxytris(4-methylphenyl) methane	$C_{24}H_{26}O$		96
1.58	$1.65=N_Z$	?	?	Genistin	$C_{21}H_{20}O_{10}$	Z ‖ elong. MP 256°	187
$1.58=N_X$	$1.65=N_Z$	?	Biax.	Quinine citrate	$C_{26}H_{32}O_9N_2$	Z ‖ elong.	290
1.58	1.66	–	48°(2E)	*p*-Aminophenol	C_6H_7ON	$X=a$; $Y=c$. 100 cleav. MP 184°	155
$1.58=N_X$	$1.67=N_Z$	?	Biax.	Quinine·$2H_2SO_4 \cdot 7H_2O$	$C_{20}H_{28}O_{10}N_2S_2 \cdot 7H_2O$	Z ‖ elong.	291
1.58	1.65	?	?	Apoatropine·HCl	$C_{17}H_{22}O_2NCl$	X ‖ elong.	281
1.580	1.716	?	?	Arginine picrolinate	$C_{16}H_{22}O_7N_2(H_2O\,?)$	Z ‖ elong.	209
1.58	1.725	?	?	Heliotropin semicarbazone	$C_9H_9O_3N_3$	MP 234°	191
$1.58=N_X$	$1.75=N_Z$	?	?	*p*-Sulfobenzene-azo-α-naphthol	$C_{16}H_{12}O_4N_2S$	Z ‖ elong.	176
1.582	1.611	?	?	Barium monochloroacetate	$(CH_2ClCO_2)_2Ba$	X ‖ elong.	19
$1.582=N_X$	$>1.733=N_Z$	?	?	Sulfathiazole with picrolonic acid	$C_9H_9O_2N_3S_2$+p. acid	X inclined to elong.	255
$1.582=N_X$	$1.733=N_Z$	?	?	*N*-Cinnamyl-*l*-ephedrine	$C_{12}H_{17}ON$	X ‖ elong. MP 86°	157

Table II. Based on the Lower Measured Refractive Index

N_1	N_2	Sign	2V	Name	Composition	Opt. Orient., etc.	Page
$1.583 = N_X$	$1.655 = N_Z$	?	?	Monoacetate of dihydrotoxicarol	$C_{25}H_{26}O_8$	X ‖ elong.	317
$1.583 = N_X$	$1.73 = N_Y$	?	Biax.	Apiole	$C_{12}H_{14}O_4$	MP 29.5°	191
1.583	1.74 ?	–	57°(2H)	*N,N'*-Diphenylurea	$C_{13}H_{12}ON_2$	X = *c*; Y = *a*. MP 235°	141
$1.585 = N_X$	$1.640 = N_Z$	?	?	Lithium benzoate	$C_6H_5CO_2Li$	Thin flakes	111
$1.585 = N_X$	$1.654 = N_Z$	+	?	*m*-Chlorobenzyl phanodorn	$C_{26}H_{26}N_2O_3Cl_2$	MP 102°	233
$1.585 = N_X$	$1.659 = N_Z$	+	50°	Ergocristine	$C_{35}H_{39}O_5N_5$	Y = *b* ‖ elong.	300
$1.585 = N_X$	$<1.74 = N_Z$	?	?	Anabasine picrate	$C_{16}H_{17}O_7N_5$		279
1.586	1.632	?	?	Estradiol benzoate	$C_{25}H_{28}O_3$	White to brown	276
1.587	>1.74	?	?	(*p*-Methoxyphenyl)phenetyl-guanidine·HCl	$C_{23}H_{25}O_3N_3 \cdot HCl$	MP 176°	101
1.589	1.652	?	?	Cupric 2-aminoacetate·H_2O	$(O_2C \cdot CH_2NH_2)_2Cu \cdot H_2O$	X ‖ elong. Color blue	67
$1.59 = N_X$		+	?	Betulin diacetate	$C_{30}H_{48}(O_2C \cdot CH_3)_2$	Y = *a*, Z = *b*.	100
$1.59 = N_X$		–	?	Zinc phthalate	$C_6H_4(CO_2)_2Zn(H_2O\,?)$	Prisms	123
1.59	1.62	?	?	Thebaine tartrate	$C_{23}H_{27}O_9N$	X ‖ elong.	298
$1.590 = N_X$	$1.680 = N_Z$	?	Lg.	Thenfanil·HCl	$C_{15}H_{19}N_3 \cdot HCl$	MP 151°	199
1.590	1.680	?	Biax.	Ethyl phenyloxalurate I	$C_{11}H_{12}O_4N_2$	X ‖ elong.	141
$1.59 = N_Y$	$1.68 = N_Z$	?	?	Quinine succinate	$C_{24}H_{30}O_6N_2$	Z ‖ elong.	289
$1.59 = N_X$	$1.69 = N_Z$	?	?	Cupric acetylacetonate	$(C_5H_7O_2)_2Cu$	X = *b*. D 1.57. Blue	12
1.59	1.70	?	Biax.	Cinchonine·2HCl	$C_{19}H_{24}ON_2Cl_2$	Z ‖ elong.	284
1.59	1.72	?	?	Ammonium salicylate·$0.5H_2O$	$NH_4CO_2 \cdot C_6H_4OH \cdot 0.5H_2O$	Z ‖ elong.	127
$1.59 = N_X$	$1.734 = N_Z$	?	?	Sulfanilamide·$H_2O + AgNO_3$	$C_6H_8O_2N_2S \cdot H_2O \cdot nAgNO_3$	X ‖ elong	167
1.591	1.617	?	?	2-Naphthol-3,6-disulfonic acid benzoate	$C_{17}H_{12}O_8S_2$	Z ‖ elong.	138
1.591	1.69	?	?	Allylpseudouric acid·H_2O	$C_8H_{10}O_4N_4 \cdot H_2O$	X ‖ elong.	241
1.592	1.694	?	?	8-Benzamido-1-naphthol-3,6-disulfonic acid benzoate	$C_{24}H_{17}O_9NS_2$	X′ ∧ elong. = 17°	171

N_1	N_2	Sign	2V	Name	Composition	Opt. Orient., etc.	Page
1.592	1.71 *ca.*	?	?	Hydroquinine·HCl (2H_2O ?)	$C_{20}H_{27}O_2N_2Cl\cdot(2H_2O\ ?)$	Granular	292
1.592=N_X	1.734=N_Z	?	?	Brucine sulfate with $PtCl_4$	$(C_{23}H_{26}O_4N_2)_2\cdot H_2SO_4$ with $PtCl_4$	Z ‖ elong.	308
1.595	1.61	?	?	Caffeine·H_2SO_4	$C_8H_{10}O_2N_4\cdot H_2SO_4$	Granular	249
1.595	1.700	?	?	Phenyloxaluric acid methylamide	$C_{10}H_{11}O_3N_3$	X ‖ elong.	141
1.595=N_X′	1.658=N_Z	?	Lg.	*N,N′*-Dibenzylurea	$C_{15}H_{16}ON_2$	Z ‖ elong.	151
1.598	1.657	?	?	Orthoform	$C_8H_9O_3N$	MP 120° ?	164
1.599	1.612	?	?	Copper *β*-phenylalanine salt	$C_{18}H_{20}O_4N_2Cu$	X ‖ elong.	164
1.60	1.605	?	?	Aconitine arsenate	$C_{68}H_{93}O_{26}N_2As$	Z ‖ elong.	304
1.60	1.615	?	?	Anhalonine·HCl	$C_{12}H_{16}O_3NCl$	X ‖ elong.	293
1.60	1.62	?	?	Atropine·HBr	$C_{17}H_{24}O_3Br$	Z ‖ elong.	280
1.600=N_X	1.620=N_Z	?	Biax.	*β*-Robinin	$C_{33}H_{40}O_{19}$	Z ‖ elong.	314
1.600=N_X	1.635=N_Z	?	Biax.	Diphenylhydantoin	$(C_6H_5)_2\overline{NHCONHCOCH_2}$	X ‖ elong.	213
1.60	1.65	?	?	Leucine flavianate	$C_{16}H_{20}O_{10}N_3S$	Z ‖ elong.	137
1.60	1.61	?	?	Homatropine·HCl	$C_{16}H_{22}O_3NCl$	X ‖ elong.	280
1.600	1.715	?	Lg.	2-Ketopropanedioic acid monomethylamide phenylhydrazone	$C_{10}H_{11}O_3N_3$	Sym. extinc.	172
1.600=N_X	›1.74=N_Z	?	?	Apotoxicarol methyl ether	$C_{19}H_{18}O_7$	X ∧ elong. = ?	316
1.600=N_X	1.795=N_Z	?	?	1-Naphthylamine 1,5-naphthalene-disulfonate	$C_{30}H_{26}O_6N_2S_2$	Y ⊥ plates	152
1.602	1.627	+	45°	Phenylurea	$C_7H_8ON_2$	X=*b*; Z ∧ *c*=78°. MP 147°	141
1.603=N_X	1.734=N_Z	?	?	Vonedrine with chloro-auric acid	($C_{10}H_{15}N$ with $AuCl_3$	Incl. extinc. Yellow	151
1.605	1.66	?	Lg.	Diphenylamine	$C_{10}H_{11}N$	X ‖ elong. ?	140
1.606	1.662	?	?	Biguanide sodium ferricyanide	$C_8H_{10}N_{11}NaFe$		42
1.606	1.685	?	?	8-Benzamido-2-naphthalenesulfonic acid	$C_{17}H_{13}O_4NS$	X ‖ elong. ?	170

Table II. Based on the Lower Measured Refractive Index

N_1	N_2	Sign	2V	Name	Composition	Opt. Orient., etc.	Page
$1.608 = N_X$	$1.785 = N_Z$	?	?	Pyridinethylene dichloroplatinum	$C_5H_5NC_2H_4PtCl_2$	‖ extinc. Yellow	194
1.61	1.615	?	?	Hyoscyamine·HI	$C_{17}H_{24}O_3NI$	Granular	281
1.61	1.62	?	90° *ca.*	Santonic acid	$C_{15}H_{20}O_4$	$Bx_a = c$; $Y = a$. 010 cleav.	133
1.61	1.63	?	?	Hyoscyamine·HBr	$C_{17}H_{24}O_3NBr$	Z ‖ elong.	281
1.61	1.65	?	Biax.	Carbolic acid	C_6H_5OH	$Y = b$. MP 43°	85
1.61	1.67	?	?	Quinine tartrate	$C_{44}H_{54}O_{10}N_4$	Z ‖ elong.	289
1.61	1.74	?	?	*trans.*-Cinnamic acid	$C_6H_5 \cdot CH:CH \cdot CO_2H$	$X = b$; $Z \wedge c = 58°$	119
1.612	1.71	?	?	6-Benzamido-2-naphthalene sulfonic acid I	$C_{17}H_{13}O_4NS$	X ‖ elong.	170
1.614	1.745	?	?	Dixanthyl urea	$C_{27}H_{20}O_2N_2$	X′ ‖ elong.	188
$1.615 = N_X$		–	?	Metrazole	$C_6H_{10}N_4$	$Z = b$.	246
1.615	1.645	–	70°(2E)	Homatropine·HBr	$C_{16}H_{22}O_3NBr$	$X = b$; $Y = c$.	281
1.615	1.65	?	?	Ditaine·$4H_2O$	$C_{22}H_{28}O_4N_2 \cdot 4H_2O$	Z ‖ elong.	306
1.615	1.67	?	?	Oxysparteine	$C_{15}H_{24}ON_2$	Granular	283
1.616	1.666	?	?	Isoleucine flavianate	$C_{16}H_{20}O_{10}N_2S$	X ‖ elong.	137
1.616	〉1.734	?	?	Sodium picrolonate	$C_{10}H_7O_5N_4Na$	X ‖ elong.	209
$1.616 = N_Y$	1.736	+ ?	?	Aminomethylphenyltriazole·$PtCl_4$	$C_{18}H_{22}N_4Cl_6Pt$	MP 245°	244
$1.616 = N_X$	1.74 〈N_Y	?	?	Methylanabasine picrate	$C_{17}H_{19}O_7N_5$	X ‖ elong.	279
1.618	1.884	?	Biax.	4-Nitro-methyldiphenyl sulfide	$C_{13}H_{11}NO_2S$	$N_1 \approx N_Z$; $N_2 \approx N_X$	93
〉1.618	〉1.698	?	?	Dichlorotyrosine picrolonate	$C_{19}H_{17}O_8N_5Cl$	Z ‖ elong.	210
$1.62 = N_O$	?	+	0°	1,3-Indandione	$C_6H_4(CO)_2CH_2$	Tetrag. D 1.18	106
1.62	1.64	?	?	Cupreine	$C_{19}H_{22}O_2N_2$	X ∧ elong. 〈 35°	293
1.62	1.645	?	?	Codeine salicylate	$C_{25}H_{27}O_6N$	X ‖ elong.	298
1.62	1.645	?	?	Antimony acid tartrate·$4H_2O$?	$C_{12}H_{15}O_{18}Sb \cdot 4H_2O$?	Prismatic	48
$1.62 = N_Y$	$1.68 = N_Z$	?	Biax.	Quinine acetate	$C_{22}H_{28}O_4N_2$	Z ‖ elong.	291
1.62	1.69	?	?	Oxyacanthine	$C_{19}H_{21}O_3N$	Z ‖ elong.	306
$1.62 = N_Y$	$1.69 = N_Z$	?	Biax.	Quinine formate	$C_{21}H_{26}O_4N_2$	Z ‖ elong.	291
$1.62 = N_X$	$1.700 = N_Y$	– ?	Lg.	*N*-Isoamyl-*N′*-phenylthiourea	$C_{12}H_{18}N_2S$	Sym. extinc. MP 102°	143

Table II. Based on the Lower Measured Refractive Index

N_1	N_2	Sign	2V	Name	Composition	Opt. Orient., etc.	Page
1.62	1.95	?	?	4-Isopropylphenylamine	$C_9H_{13}N$	X $\parallel$ elong. MP 63°	152
1.620	1.780	?	?	Dipyridinodichloroplatinum	$(C_5H_5N)_2PtCl_2$	Yellow	194
1.621	1.680	?	?	Phenylisoguanylurea · HCl	$C_8H_{10}ON_4Cl$	$N_1 \parallel$ width	143
1.622 = N_X	1.655 = N_Y	+	?	Ergometrine	$C_{19}H_{23}O_2N_3$	MP 204°	302
1.624	›1.71	?	?	7-Benzamido-1-naphthol-3-sulfonic acid benzoate	$C_{24}H_{17}O_6NS$	X $\parallel$ elong.	171
1.625 = N_X	1.635 = N_Z	+	?	Tryptophan	$C_{11}H_{12}O_2N_2$	Biaxial	203
1.625	1.64	?	?	Physostigmine · HBr	$CNH(NH_2)_2 \cdot HCl$	Orthorhombic	304
1.626	1.666	?	90° *ca.*	Sodium tobiasate	$C_{10}H_8O_3NSNa$	Sym. and inclined extinc.	169
1.626	1.723	?	?	Biguanide anthranilate	$C_9H_{14}O_2N_6$	$N_1 \parallel$ width	162
1.628	1.646	?	?	2-Naphthol-6-sulfonic acid benzoate	$C_{17}H_{12}O_5S$	Z $\parallel$ elong.	138
1.628	1.646	?	?	5-Benzamido-2-naphthalene-sulfonic acid	$C_{17}H_{13}O_4NS$	Z $\parallel$ elong.	170
1.629	1.696	?	?	6-Benzamido-1-naphthol-3-sulfonic acid benzoate	$C_{24}H_{17}O_6NS$	Z $\parallel$ elong.	170
‹1.63	1.64 *ca.*	?	?	Nirvanol	$C_{11}H_{12}O_2N_2$	MP 200°	213
1.63 = N_E		–	0°	2-Amino-1,2-diphenylethanol · HCl	$C_{14}H_{16}ONCl$	Cruciform twins	158
1.63	1.65	?	?	Phenolphthalein	$C_{19}H_{14}O_4$	N_3 = 1.668. MP 250–253°	186
1.63	1.65	?	?	Colchicine	$C_{22}H_{25}O_6N$		299
1.632	1.703	?	?	2-Benzamido-1-naphthalene sulfonic acid	$C_{17}H_{13}O_4NS$	X $\parallel$ elong.	169
1.635	1.683	?	?	Methionine flavianate	$C_{15}H_{18}O_{10}N_3S_2$	X $\parallel$ elong.	138
1.636	1.714	?	?	7-Methyl-9-phenylpseudouric acid	$C_{12}H_{12}O_4N_4$	Z $\parallel$ elong.	241
1.64	1.69	?	?	Embelic acid	$C_{18}H_{28}O_4$	X $\parallel$ elong.	110
1.64 = N_Y	1.70 = N_Z	?	Biax.	Quinine thiosulfate	$C_{20}H_{26}O_5N_2S_2$	Z $\parallel$ elong.	291
1.64 = N_X	1.73 = N_Z	?	?	2-Naphthylamine-2-naphthalene-sulfonate	$C_{20}H_{17}O_3NS$	MP 278°	152

Table II. Based on the Lower Measured Refractive Index

N_1	N_2	Sign	2V	Name	Composition	Opt. Orient., etc.	Page
1.64	1.73	+	62°	Cytisine	$C_{11}H_{14}ON_2$	$Y=a$; $Z=c$.	305
1.642	>1.659	–	Lg.	Ergometrine ethyl acetate solvate	$C_{19}H_{23}O_2N_3 \cdot nC_4H_8O_2$	MP 130° – 132°	302
1.644	>1.734	?	?	Ammonium picrolonate	$C_{10}H_7O_5N_4NH_4$	Z ‖ elong. $N_i=1.734$.	209
1.645	1.665	+	Sm.	Sparteine·HI	$C_{15}H_{27}N_2I$	$Y=b$; $Z=a$.	283
$1.65=N_Y$	$1.69=N_Z$	?	Biax.	Quinine chromate	$C_{20}H_{26}O_6N_2Cr$	Z ‖ elong.	290
1.65	1.675	?	?	Gelseminine·HBr	$C_{42}H_{48}O_{14}NBr$	X ‖ elong.	305
1.650	>1.734	?	?	Zinc picrolonate	$(C_{10}H_7O_5N_4)_2Zn$	Z ‖ elong.	209
1.651	1.658	?	?	*m*-Nitrobenzoic acid I	$C_6H_4NO_2CO_2H$	$Y=b$; extinc. $\wedge c=50°$	114
$1.652=N_X$	$1.768=N_Z$	–	?	Bulbocapnine	$C_{19}H_{19}O_4N$	$X=b$; $Y=a$.	295
$1.652=N_X$	1.79 *ca.*	?	48°	3,4,5-Tribromo-2,6-dimethoxyphenol	$C_6Br_3(OCH_3)_2OH$	$Y=b=$elong. D 2.29	100
1.656	1.678	+	Lg.	Copper pyridine disaccharin·$2H_2O$	$C_{24}H_{18}O_6N_4S_2Cu \cdot 2H_2O$	$Y=b$; $Z=c$. D 1.509	253
>1.658	<1.74	?	?	Norleucine picrolonate	$C_{16}H_{21}O_7N_5$	X ‖ elong.	211
1.66	1.67	?	?	Pellotine	$C_{13}H_{19}O_3N$	Granular	293
1.66	1.67	?	?	Anagyrine·HBr	$C_{15}H_{23}ON_2Br$	Granular	306
1.66	1.69	–	Lg.	Bromal hydrate·H_2O	$CBr_3 \cdot CH(OH)_2 \cdot H_2O$	$Z=b$. MP 51°	12
1.66	1.70	?	?	Apomorphine sulfate	$C_{17}H_{19}O_6NS$	Z ‖ elong.	299
1.66	1.75	?	?	Chalcone semicarbazone	$C_6H_5 \cdot CH:CHC(C_6H_5):NNH \cdot CONH_2$	X ‖ elong.	104
1.66 +	>1.74	?	Sm.	α-Naphthol	$C_{10}H_7OH$	$Bx_a=b$; $Bx_o \wedge c=15°$	94
1.6603		+	0°	Furfurylhydrophenanthraquinone	$C_{19}H_{12}O_4$?	Pleochroic in yellow	188
1.661	1.755	–	25°	Triphenylarsine	$C_{18}H_{15}As$	Optic plane $\wedge$ 010=67°	180
$1.662=N_X$	$1.667=N_Y$	+ ?	?	*dl*-Methionine nitroindandionate	$C_{14}H_{16}O_6N_2S$	Z ‖ elong. MP 193°	107
1.662	1.684	?	?	8-Benzamido-1-naphthol-5-sulfonic acid benzoate	$C_{24}H_{17}O_6NS$	X ‖ elong.	171
1.662	1.694	?	?	Apomorphine·HCl·($0.75H_2O$?)	$C_{17}H_{18}O_2NCl \cdot (0.75H_2O$?)	Z ‖ elong.	299
1.665	1.730	?	?	Allyldimethyluric acid	$C_{10}H_{12}O_3N_4$	X ‖ elong.	251
<1.67	>1.74	?	?	Moser compound	$C_{22}H_{14}ON_2$ with $C_4H_8O_2$	Yellow, columnar	309
$1.670=N_X$	1.705 *ca.*	–	84°(2H)	*m*-Bromonitrobenzene	$C_6H_4BrNO_2$	$X=c$; $Y=a$. MP 56°	75

TABLE II. BASED ON THE LOWER MEASURED REFRACTIVE INDEX

N_1	N_2	Sign	2V	Name	Composition	Opt. Orient., etc.	Page
1.670 = N_X	1.830 = N_Z	?	?	Gulosazone	$C_{18}H_{17}O_4N_4$	Z = *c*	267
1.675 = N_X	1.693 = N_Y	– ?	?	*N*-*β*-Hydroxyethyl-*N*-phenylthiourea	$C_9H_{12}ON_2S$	Parallel extinc.	151
1.675	1.755	?	?	Ethyl phenyloxalurate II	$C_{11}H_{12}O_4N_2$	Extinc. at 18° *ca.*	141
1.68	>1.95	?	?	Chrysoidine	$C_{12}H_{12}N_4$	Z ‖ elong.	179
1.684	>1.74	?	?	Norvaline picrolonate II	$C_{15}H_{19}O_7N_5$	X ‖ elong.	211
1.69	1.72	?	?	Strychnine salicylate	$C_{28}H_{28}O_5N_2$	Z ‖ elong.	308
1.690 = N_X	1.737 = N_Z	?	?	Pyrrolazote·HCl	$C_{16}H_{16}N_2S \cdot HCl$	MP 198°	256
1.692 = N_X		?	Biax.	Vanillin semicarbazone	$C_9H_{11}O_3N_3$	MP 230°	109
1.70	1.71	+	Sm.	*p*-Nitrobenzaldehyde	$C_6H_4NO_2CHO$	Opt. plane for red ⊥ opt. plane for blue	104
1.70 *ca.*	>1.74	?	?	Isoserine picrolonate I	$C_{13}H_{15}O_8N_5$	Z ‖ elong.	211
1.70 *ca.*	>1.74	?	Lg.	Benzaldehyde 4-nitrophenylhydrazone	$C_{13}H_{11}O_2N_3$	Z = *b*. MP 262°	173
1.70 = N_X	1.829 = N_Z	?	Biax.	Triphenylstibine	$C_{18}H_{15}Sb$	X ∧ *a* = 5°. MP 48°	181
1.70 = N_X	>2.0 = N_Y	+	80°(2E)	Lead nitroaminoguanidine	$C_2O_4N_{10}Pb$	Yellow tablets	43
1.704 = N_X	1.915 = N_Z	–	?	Salicylaminoanthraquinone	$C_{21}H_{13}O_4N$	Z ‖ elong. MP 273°	161
1.705	1.75	?	?	Dixanthyl thiourea	$C_{27}H_{20}O_2N_2S$	X′ ‖ elong.	188
1.706	1.72	?	?	Oxanilide	$C_{14}H_{12}O_2N_2$	N_1 ‖ length; N_2 ‖ width. MP 245°	141
1.72	1.75	?	?	Theobromine·HCl·(H_2O ?)	$C_7H_9O_2N_4Cl \cdot (H_2O\ ?)$	Z ‖ elong.	248
1.720 = N_X	1.764 = N_Y	?	?	Germanium tetrakis(*p*-tolylmercaptide)	$(C_7H_7S)_4Ge$	Y = *b*; Z = *c*.	93
1.728 = N_X	1.775 = N_Y	–	?	Germanium tetrakis(phenylmercaptide)	$(C_6H_5S)_4Ge$	X = *c*; Y = *b*.	93
1.73 = N_X	2.00 = N_Z	?	?	1-(Phenylazo)-2-naphthol-6,8-disulfonate	$C_{16}H_{12}O_7N_2S_2$	X ‖ length.	177
1.734 = N_X	>1.734	?	?	Copper picrolonate	$(C_{10}H_7O_5N_4)_2Cu$	Z ‖ elong.	209
<1.74	>1.78	?	?	Klement compound	$C_{23}H_{16}ON_2$	Yellow, columnar	309
1.74	>1.74	?	?	Cysteine picrolonate	$C_{13}H_{15}O_7N_5S$	X ‖ elong.	210

Table II. Based on the Lower Measured Refractive Index

N_1	N_2	Sign	2V	Name	Composition	Opt. Orient., etc.	Page
⟩1.74	⟩1.74	?	?	Phenylalanine picrolonate II	$C_{19}H_{19}O_7N_5$	Inc. extinc. MP 238°	211
1.745 = N_Y	1.761 = N_Z	–	Sm.	Sulfapyridine	$C_{11}H_{11}O_2N_3S$	Anom. dispersion	202
1.745 = N_X	2.32 = N_Z	?	?	Hansa ruby G	$C_{17}H_{10}O_{10}N_4S$	Z ‖ elong. Yellow to red.	177
1.75	1.95	?	?	α-Nitroso-β-naphthol	$C_{10}H_6(NO)OH$	Extinc. at 44°. MP 110°	95
1.783 = N_X	⟩2.14 = N_Z	?	?	Lake red C ?	$C_{17}H_{13}O_4N_2SCl$?	Incl. extinc. Yellow to red.	177
1.783		–	17° *ca.*	3,3-*bis*(Iodomethyl)oxetone	C_5H_8OI	X nearly ‖ *b*.	181
1.800 = N_X	1.835 = N_Z	?	?	Mannosazone I	$C_{18}H_{20}O_4N_4$	Extinc. ∧ = 0° to large	266
1.80 *ca.*	1.85 *ca.*	?	?	Arginine flavianate	$C_{16}H_{21}O_{10}N_6S$	Z ‖ elong.	137
1.825 = N_X	1.85 = N_Z	?	?	Galactosazone I	$C_{18}H_{22}O_4N_4$	Y ∧ elong. = large	267
1.90 = N_X	2.14 = N_Z	–	?	1-(Sulfo-2-naphthylazo)-2-naphthol	$C_{20}H_{14}O_4N_2S$	X ∧ elong. = 18°	177
1.915 = N_X	2.135 = N_Z	?	?	1-Benzamido-4-hydroxyanthraquinone	$C_{21}H_{13}O_4N$	Z ‖ elong.	162
1.92 = N_X	2.32 = N_Z	?	?	Hansa ruby G	$C_{17}H_{10}O_{10}N_4S$	Light to dark red.	177
2.0 = N_X	2.53 = N_Z	?	?	α-Naphthaleneazo-β-naphthol	$C_{20}H_{13}ON$	Z ‖ elong.	176
2.0 = N_X	2.55 = N_Z	?	?	Permanent ruby PhB–ASH	?	Z ‖ elong.	178
2.06 = N_X	2.23 = N_Z	?	?	Lithol red GG	$C_{18}H_{12}O_6N_2SClNa$	X ‖ elong.	177
2.06 = N_X	2.23 = N_Z	?	?	Lithol ruby GK	$C_{17}H_{12}O_6N_2SCl$	Z ‖ elong.	176
2.06 = N_X	2.35 = N_Z	?	?	Lake Bordeaux BN	$C_{21}H_{15}O_6N_2S$	Z ‖ elong.	177
2.06 = N_X	2.67 = N_Z	+	?	1-(4-Nitro-2-sulfophenylazo)-2-naphthol	$C_{16}H_{11}O_6N_3S$	Z ∧ elong. = 18° ?	177

Index

D

E

F

I

O

P

Q

R

S

Z

EXPLANATION AND KEY
TO THE
DIAGRAMS FOR DETERMINATION OF COMPOUNDS

Explanation of the Diagrams for the Determination of Compounds

For many years chemists have recognized that the melting point of any pure substance (under fixed vapor pressure) is definite and is therefore an important aid in identifying it. Similarly, the optical properties can be used to determine the nature of any crystallized substance; instead of a single characteristic value the optical properties nearly always furnish three or more. — Therefore the measurement of these properties goes far toward the determination of the substance.

Of course no substance can be identified by measuring its physical properties unless those properties have been measured previously on samples of known substances. In the following discussion it will be assumed that no substances are included whose properties have not been measured.

The most important optical properties are the indices of refraction. Only a few crystallized organic substances are isometric, and have only a single index of refraction. Indeed, they are so rare that the measurement of this single index usually suffices to identify them, as may be seen by the fact that all of those thus far measured are found along the central horizontal line of Plate I and along a single topmost line of Plate II. For example, an isometric organic substance having only one refractive index, which is 1.578, must be number 134, according to the Plates, and the key shows that this is arginine picrolonate.

Indices of refraction may be measured in several ways. If large crystals are available, a refractometer may be used to measure indices by the method of minimum deviation with a prism, or that of total reflection from a plane surface. Polarized light should be used so as to get both values from a given prism or plane surface. Often a second prism, or surface in a different crystal direction, is needed to obtain a third index. However, large crystals are only rarely available. In their absence minute crystals, or even microscopic fragments of crystals, can be used to measure indices of refraction by means of a set of immersion liquids and simple comparisons under the microscope for approximate results (± .003), or liquids with the universal stage and the double variation method[1] for greater accuracy.

Nearly all crystallized organic compounds have two or three indices of refraction. In measuring indices microscopically, tiny crystals (or fragments) are used. In general, every crystal (in any position) has two indices of refraction, both of which should be measured. They can be found by merely examining the crystal in its two positions of extinction between crossed nicols. If all the crystals of a given substance have one index which is the same, the crystal is uniaxial and the substance has only two indices of refraction: one is the constant index (N_O), and the other (N_E), is given by the crystal whose other index differs most

[1] Detailed directions for such work can be found, for example, in the author's Optical Mineralogy, Part I, Chapter XX.

from N_O. If N_E is greater than N_O, the optic sign is positive and N_O should be sought in the upper half of the diagram. If N_E is less than N_O, the optic sign is negative and N_O should be sought in the lower half of the diagrams. The difference between N_E and N_O is the measure of the birefringence. For example, if the constant index is 1.615 and the other index is 1.830, the sign is positive, the birefringence is 0.215, and plate I shows that the substance is number 191, which the key shows to be benzoselenazole guanidine sulfate.

If a given substance has three indices of refraction, that fact can be proved by finding that the various crystals (or grains) do not have one index which is common to all. All three indices can be found even without a universal stage by measuring both indices of enough grains; it is then true that the highest index of any grain is N_Z, the lowest is N_X, and the intermediate index (N_Y) can be derived on the basis of the fact that every grain must have one index which is equal to (or greater than) N_Y, and another which is equal to (or less than) N_Y. Let us assume that several grains have been measured with the following results:

Grain	Indices of refraction	
	Larger	Smaller
1	1.602	1.560
2	1.616	1.535
3	1.595	1.570
4	1.611	1.589
5	1.602	1.593
6	1.599	1.522

Then the highest index (N_Z) must be equal to (or greater than) 1.616, the lowest (N_X) must be equal to (or lower than) 1.522, and the intermediate index (N_Y) must be at least as great as 1.593 and at least as low as 1.595. Further the optic sign must be negative, because N_Y is nearer to N_Z than to N_X. Also the birefringence is the difference between N_Z and N_X, namely .094. Using $1.594 \pm .001$ for N_Y, a negative sign and a birefringence of .094, we find that the substance must be number 434 on Plate I, and the key shows that this is cocaine hydrochloride.

There are other ways to find the three indices of refraction of a biaxial substance. It can be done conveniently by properly orienting a crystal (or grain) in two different positions by means of the universal stage and using the double refraction method to measure both indices in both positions. It is true that the index of the liquid cannot always be changed enough to make it equal all of the indices of the crystal. In that case it is sufficient to measure two of the indices, and then measure the optic angle and determine the optic sign. Then the little inset chart at the bottom of Plate I will suffice to give the third index. For example, if an unknown crystal is oriented with the acute bisectrix in the axis of the microscope and if the index of refraction for light vibrating normal to the optic plane is 1.685 and for light vibrating in the optic plane is 1.690, the first value must be N_Y, the second must be N_Z, and the sign must be negative.

If the optic angle is then measured and found to be 21°, the inset chart shows that the partial birefringence $(N_Z - N_Y)$ of .005 is about .04 of the total birefringence; therefore $N_Z - N_X = .12$ and N_X must be 1.57. Using the optic sign, the birefringence, and the value of N_Y, we discover that the substance is number 407 and the key reveals that this is α-cinchonine.

There is still another way to find the three indices of refraction of a biaxial crystal. Select a grain or crystal or fragment so oriented that it is dark, or nearly so, in all positions of rotation of the stage; it will have only one index of refraction, which is N_Y. Then select another grain or fragment that shows the highest interference color (for the given thickness); it will have two indices of refraction, N_Z and N_X. The optic sign is easily determined from a centered interference figure and also from the fact[1] that $N_Z - N_Y > N_Y - N_X$ in positive crystals, and $N_Z - N_Y < N_Y - N_X$ in negative crystals. It is not always possible to measure both N_Z and N_X from a single plate or grain in one liquid, because the two indices may differ more than the difference that can be produced in the index of the liquid. In that case the crystal may be transferred from one liquid to another. Or, if a crystal plate of uniform thickness is involved, a measurement of that thickness will permit a determination of the birefringence (without measuring either index), if the interference color is not too high. For this purpose a color chart showing relation between birefringence and thickness is needed.

Any of the substances entered on Plate I can be identified by these methods. A few substances are so similar in optical properties as to make determination uncertain, and some other physical or chemical property must be used to discriminate between the possibilities. More than seventeen hundred substances are included on Plate I — all whose indices of refraction have been accurately measured. Different crystal phases of the same compound are included as different substances, so the diagram can be used to distinguish between the different crystal phases of the same compound, as well as to distinguish between different compounds.

All the indices of refraction of any substance may be obtained from the data on Plate I and the optic angle given in the key. Any substance having an optic angle of 0° has only two indices of refraction; one (N_O) is used in placing the substance on the diagram, and the other may be obtained by adding to N_O the value of the positive birefringence or subtracting from N_O the value of the negative birefringence. For example, iodoform (848) has an N_O index of 1.800; its N_E index is obtained by subtracting its birefringence (.05) from 1.80. Any substance having two optic axes has three indices of refraction; the intermediate index, N_Y, is used on the diagram. If the optic sign is positive, N_Z may be obtained by adding to N_Y that major fraction of the birefringence which corresponds to the value of the optic angle (2V), shown in the inset diagram, and N_X may be obtained by subtracting from N_Y the minor fraction of the birefringence. If the optic sign is negative, N_Z may be obtained by adding the

[1] In the rare case in which the optic angle is very near 90° this relation does not hold true. For precision it is necessary to use squares; in fact, for negative crystals $1/N_X^2 - 1/N_Y^2 > 1/N_Y - N_Z$, and for positive crystals $1/N_X^2 - 1/N_Y^2 < 1/N_Y^2 - 1/N_Z^2$.

minor fraction of the birefringence to N_Y, and N_X may be derived by subtracting the major fraction. For example, *o*-chlorobenzoic acid (358) has an optic angle of 60°, a refractive index, N_Y, of 1.686, a birefringence, $N_Z - N_X$, of 0.320, and a negative sign; therefore $N_Z = N_Y + 1/4\ (0.320) = 1.686 + 0.08 = 1.766$; and $N_X = N_Y - 3/4\ (0.320) = 1.686 - 0.24 = 1.446$. These are the reported values. if they were not, it would prove the existence of some inaccuracy in the data;

Since more than eighty percent of the organic substances whose optic properties have been measured are biaxial and have three indices of refraction it is nearly always necessary to find two crystals (or fragments) in two different and suitable crystallographic orientations in order to be able to measure the three refractive indices and therefore be able to use Plate I. Therefore Plate II has been added; it is based upon one index of refraction (N, N_O, or N_Y), the optic angle, and the optic sign, which can all be determined from a single crystal (or fragment) having an orientation which is easily recognized since it produces the lowest interference color. For example, *o*-chlorobenzoic acid (358) is located on Plate II by means of its negative optic sign, optic angle of 60°, and intermediate refractive index, N_Y, of 1.686. All of these properties can be determined from any crystal showing the lowest interference color, since such a crystal is normal to an optic axis and therefore gives N_Y in any position of rotation, and permits the determination of the optic sign by means of an accessory mica or gypsum plate, and gives an approximate value of the optic angle from the curvature of the isogyre at the 45° position. About one sixth of the organic substances whose optical properties have been measured are uniaxial; such substances would be too crowded in some places on the diagram if they were put on only two lines (one for uniaxial positive and one for uniaxial negative). They are distributed over two areas (for positive and negative) on the basis of their birefringence. Fortunately this can be estimated from the number of colored circles seen in the interference figure of the crystal being studied.

The abundance of numbers on Plate II at $2V_X$ and N = about 1.52 to 1.54 is due in part to the large number of measured samples of natural cellulose, such as cotton, wool, silk, straw, hemp, bamboo, jute, and flax, and related artificial products such as zealon, vinyon, nylon, and rayon.

All organic compounds whose optical properties have been adequately described are to be found on both Plates. In a few cases the refractive index, N_Y, and the birefringence, $N_Z - N_X$, have been measured with no measure of the optic angle; such substances are included on Plate I, but cannot be placed on Plate II. In a few other cases the refractive index N_Y and the optic angle have been measured with no measure of the birefringence; such substances are included on Plate II, but cannot be placed on Plate I. Finally, about six hundred organic substances have been measured optically in such an incomplete way that they cannot be placed on either Plate. They are nevertheless described in the text and entered in tables 1 and 2.

In round numbers there are fourteen hundred substances on both Plates, fifteen hundred on Plate II, eighteen hundred on Plate I, and nineteen hundred on one or both Plates.

The key to Plates I and II appears on pages 445–487. The diagrams may be found inside the back cover.

Key to Diagrams 1 and 2

No.	Sign	$N_Z - N_X$	N, N_O, N_Y	2V	Substance	Page
1	−	.108	1.578	75°	*l*-Abietic acid	119
2	−	.085	1.590	38°	*l*-Abietic acid	119
3	+	.214	1.468	70°	Acenaphthene	80
4	+	.216	1.463	70°	Acenaphthylene	81
5	−	.02	1.48	0°	Acetaldehyde ammonia	243
6	−	.480	1.969	38°	Acetaldehyde 2,4-dinitrophenol hydrazone I	173
7	−	.666	2.078	4°	Acetaldehyde 2,4-dinitrophenol hydrazone II	173
8	−	.08	1.54	0°	Acetamide(stable)	18
9	−	.042	1.497	0°	Acetamide(stable ?)	18
10	−	.215	1.485	85°	Acetamide(metastable)	18
11	+	⟩.215	1.574	63°	1-Acetamido-4-ethoxybenzene I	155
12	−	⟩.227	1.627	70°	1-Acetamido-4-ethoxybenzene II	155
13	+	.220	1.620	88°	Acetanilide	140
14	+	.006	1.470	0°	Acetate silk	272
15	−	.005	1.479	0°	Acetate silk	272
16	+	.195	1.678	71°	Acet-*p*-bromanilide (metastable)	145
17	+	.448	1.663	86°	Acet-*p*-bromanidide (stable)	145
17 a	+	.141	1.603	74°	Acetoacetanilide	141
18	+	.144	1.587	58°	*o*-Acetotoluide	149
19	+	.312	1.625	88°	*p*-Acetotoluide	150
20	−		1.492	71°	Acetoxycarboxymethylbutanedioic anhydride	190
21	−	.176	1.520	36°	*N*-Acetyl-*dl*-alanine	67
22	−	.143	1.658	83°	Acetylmetanilamidopyrimidine	239
23	+	.089	1.603	83°	Acetyloxydiphenyldesoxycaffeine	250
23 a	+	.165	1.609	48°	Acetylphenplhydrazine	171
24	−	.179	1.650	70°	Acetylsulfamethyldiazine	240
25	−	.194	1.697	0°	Acetylsulfanilamide	168
26	−		1.658	70°*ca.*	Acetylsulfanilamidochloropyrimidine	240
27	−?	⟩.110	1.70	Lg.	Acetylsulfanilamidopyridine	202
28	−	.106	1.623	Lg.	Acetylsulfanilyldimethylpyrimidine	240
29	−	.2(est.)	1.695	?	Acetylsulfanilylguanidine·H_2O	169
30	−	.125	1.763	Sm.	Acetylsulfathiazole	255
31	−	⟩.248	1.685	Mod.?	*d*-1-Acetyl-2-thio-5-methylhydantoin	213
32	+	.065	1.55	Sm.	Aconitine·HBr·2.5H_2O	304
32 a	+	⟩.116	1.636?	45°	Acridyldimethylaminoethane·HCl	196
32 b	+	.224	1.669	Mod.	Adenine·HCl·0.5H_2O	247
32 c	−	.377	1.688	64°	Adenine sulfate·2H_2O	247
33	+	.105	1.505	74°	Adipic acid	34

No.	Sign	$N_Z - N_X$	N, N_O, N_Y	2V	Substance	Page
34	−	.253	1.611	89°	Adrenaline·HCl(H_2O) (metastable)	161
35	−	.245	1.647	74°	Adrenaline·HCl(H_2O) (stable)	161
36	−		1.559?	27°	Agathendicarbonic acid	310
37	+	.008	1.522	0°	Agave americana	271
38	+	.022	1.521	0°	Agave sisalana (Sisal)	271
39	+	.060	1.540	80°	α-Alanine	67
39 a	−	.081	1.591	48°	β-Alanine	67
40	+	.204	1.605	Lg.	Alanine diliturate·H_2O	218
41	−	>.392	1.738	Lg.	Alanine nitroindandionate	106
42	+	.110	1.576	85°	Allopregnanedione	276
43	−		1.657	72.5°	Allyliminotriethyldihydrothia-phosphirane	72
44	−	.114	1.566	70°	Allylisopropylbarbituric acid	230
45	−	.079	1.558	70°	Allylisopropylbarbituric acid	230
46	−	.138	1.684	77°	Allylthiourea	44
47	−	.05	1.775	0°	9-Allyluric acid	251
47 a	+	.094	1.578	67°	Alphenal	235
48	−	.028	1.539	0°	Aluminum mellitate·$18H_2O$	126
49	+	.126	1.630	0°	Amarine·HBr	206
50	+	.124	1.623	0°	Amarine·HCl	206
51	+	.345	1.81	85°	*p*-Aminoazobenzene	178
51 a	−	.27	1.74	39°	*o*-Aminobenzoic acid I	162
51 b	−	.20	1.73	46°	*o*-Aminobenzoic acid II	162
51 c	−	.22	1.78	73°	*o*-Aminobenzoic acid III	162
52	−	.210	1.650	25°	2-Aminobutane diliturate	216
53	−	.171	1.648	40°	2-Aminocymene diliturate	225
54	−	.289	1.659	67°	*p*-Aminodiethylaniline diliturate	223
55	−	.136	1.675	40°	Amino-dimethylaminotriazine	245
56	−	>.323	1.668	>75°	*p*-Aminodimethylaniline diliturate	223
57	+	>.115	1.670	<83°	2-Amino-1,3-dimethylbenzene diliturate	222
58	+	.180	1.657	87°	2-Amino-1,4-dimethylbenzene diliturate	222
59	−	>.263	1.671	>82°	4-Amino-1,3-dimethylbenzene diliturate	222
60	−	.180	1.642	85°	5-Amino-1,3-dimethylbenzene diliturate	222
61	−	>.324	1.774	>25°	*o*-Aminodiphenyl diliturate	222
62	+	>.182	1.653	<62°	*p*-Aminodiphenyl diliturate	223
63	−	.243	1.651	85°	2-Amino-5-hydroxyltoluene diliturate	224
64	−	.150	1.683	0°	2-Amino-4,6-methylamine-1,3,5-triazine	245
65	−	.331	1.850	54°	2-Aminomethylcyclopentylamine picrate	154
66	+	>.113	1.722	<84°	2-Amino-4-nitrophenol diliturate	224
67	−	.178	1.635	30°	2-Amino-*n*-octane diliturate	217
68	−	.178	1.69	55°	*p*-Aminophenaceturic acid	163
69	+	.158	1.632	39°	*o*-Aminophenol	154
70	−	>.305	1.750	>37°	*m*-Aminophenol diliturate I	224
71	−	>.284	1.689	>72°	*m*-Aminophenol diliturate II	224
72	+	>.167	1.673	<70°	*o*-Aminophenol diliturate	223
73	−	>.277	1.715	>60°	*p*-Aminophenol diliturate	224
73 a	−?	.185	1.754	>42°	Aminopyridinopyridinodichloroplatinum	201
74	−	.358	1.873	23°	3-Aminoquinoline	203
75	−	.254	1.670	18°	Aminotetrazole	252

No.	Sign	N_Z-N_X	N, N_O, N_Y	2V	Substance	Page
75 a	−	⩾.185	1.740	55°	Amminopyridinonitrochloroplatinum	193
76	−	.145	1.550	40°	Ammonium acid dioxalate·$2H_2O$	27
77	−	.163	1.658	33°	Ammonium acid phthalate	123
78	−	.072	1.561	80°	Ammonium acid tartrate	47
79	−	.128	1.653	32°	Ammonium-*o*-amino-benzoate·HCl	162
80	−		1.503	48°	Ammonium bimalate	46
81	+	.095	1.520	62°	Ammonium carbamate	37
82	−		1.496	54°	Ammonium carboxybenzene sulfonate	138
83	+	.191	1.709	81°	Ammonium catechol molybdate·$0.5H_2O$	97
84	−	).358	1.772	)20°	Ammonium diliturate	215
85	−	).220	1.73	88°	Ammonium dinitrocresol·H_2O	93
85 a	−	.195	1.724	63°	Ammonium ethylenetrichloroplatinate	5
86	−	.067	1.555	40°	Ammonium gluconate	57
87	−		1.550	80°	Ammonium methanedisulfonate	59
88	−	.185	1.729	49°	Ammonium-1.5-naphthalene disulfonate	134
89	−	.157	1.548	62°	Ammonium oxalate·H_2O	28
90	−	.400	1.872	29°	Ammonium picrate	87
91	+		1.564	61°	Ammonium racemate	55
92	−	.182	1.587	68°	Ammonium shikimate	131
93	−	.04?	1.581	59°	Ammonium *d*-tartrate	49
94	+	.013	1.481	0°	Ammonium uranyl acetate	16
95	+	.083	1.614	55°	*n*-Amylamine diliturate	217
96	+	).145	1.582	Lg.	Amylcaine·HCl I	163
97	−	.009	1.582	0°	Amylcaine·HCl II	163
98	+	.129	1.680	0°	Amylcyanbenzalaminocinnamate	164
99	+		1.587	88°	Amylene nitrolaniline	140
100	+		1.573	76°	Amylene nitrolaniline·HCl	140
101	−		1.509	62°	Amylene nitrosate	13
102	−		1.596	66°	Amylnitrophthalimide	125
103	+	.140	1.630	20°	*N*-Amyl-*N′*-phenylthiourea	143
104	+	.083	1.581	72°	*d*-α-Amyrilene	78
105	+	.029	1.570	29°	*d*-β-Amyrilene	79
106	+	.140	1.552	46°	β-Amyrin anisate	310
107	−	.481	1.748	68°	Amyrolin	10
108	−	.093	1.533	65°	Amytal	229
108 a	+	.096	1.640	61°	Aneurin·H_2O I	256
108 b	+	.085	1.639	87°	Aneurin·H_2O II	256
109	+	.005	1.522	60°	Anhydro-α-methylmannopyranoside	264
110	−	.338	1.738	)44°	Aniline diliturate I	219
111	−	.237	1.659	82°	Aniline diliturate II	219
112	−	.070	1.532	35°	Aniline hexafluorogermanate	139
113	+	.04	1.57	60°	Aniline·HCl	139
114	−	.132	1.677	18°	Anilinoacetic acid·HCl	143
114 a	+	.301	1.539	0°	Anisaldazine	108
115	+	).083	1.692	87°	Anisaldehyde semicarbazone	108
116	+		1.620	71°	Anisbenztolhydroxylamine	130
117	+		1.627	65°	Anistolbenzhydroxylamine	130
118	+		1.561	50°	Anistolhydrozamic acid	129
118 a	−	.15	1.67	84°	Antabase	63

No.	Sign	$N_Z - N_X$	N, N_O, N_Y	2 V	Substance	Page
118 b	+	.147	1.635	70°	Antergan·HCl	149
118 c	−	.112	1.585	65°	Anthallan·HCl	191
118 d	see	No 124			Anthistine·HCl	20
119	−	.403	1.786	72°	Anthracene	81
120	+	.3	1.75	Sm.	Anthraquinone I	107
121	−	.310	1.698	75°	Anthraquinone II	107
122	−	.163	1.694	54°	Antipyrine	208
123	+	.132	1.576	Sm.	Antipyrine	208
124	+	›.05	1.650	Mod.	Anthistine·HCl	205
125	+	.040	1.765	40°	Arabinosazone	259
126	−	.022	1.573	48°	β-*L*(+)-or D(-)-Arabinose	258
127	−	.020	1.567	Lg.	α-*D*(-) or *L*(+)-Arabinose	258
128	+	.108	1.674	85°	*D* or *L*-Arabinose diphenylhydrazone	258
129	+	040	1.472	Lg.	*aldehydo-D*-Arabinose hexa-acetate	258
130	+	very weak	1.537	0°	Aralac	271
131	+	.100	1.590	Lg.	Arecoline·HBr	278
132	+	.062	1.562	Mod.	Arginine	68
133	+	.051	1.549	Lg.	Arginine·$2H_2O$	68
134		.000	1.578		Arginine picrolonate	209
135	−	.094	1.559	81°	α-Arsonobutyric acid	73
136	+	.071	1.580	86°	Asparagine·H_2O	69
137	+	.115	1.560	80°	Aspartic acid	69
138	−	.223	1.636	35°	Aspartic acid dilituräte·$3H_2O$	218
139	+	›.239	1.683	Lg.	Aspartic acid nitroindandionate	106
140	−	.151	1.642	15°	Aspirin	127
141	+	.20	1.543	Lg.	Atophan I	201
142	−	.085	1.590	Lg.	Atophan II	201
143	−	.045	1.58	Lg.	Atropine	279
143 a	−	.095	1.706	59°	Aureomycin·HCl	309
144	−	.056	1.761	0°	Aurodibenzylsulfonium chloride	94
144 a	+	.63	1.634	50°	Axerophthol	94
144 b	+	.166	1.495	63°	Azelaic acid	35
145	+	.144	1.720	36°	*trans*-Azobenzene	175
146	−	.379	1.715	68°	Azobenzene-*o*-phenetole	175
147	+	.647	1.573	14°	*p,p'*-Azoxydianisole	179
148	+	.576	1.584	49°	*p,p'*-Azoxydiphenetole	179
149	+	.040	1.540	0°	Bamboo	271
150	+	.025	1.541	0°	Bamboo	271
151	−	.136	1.679	40°	Barbital-*m*-bromobenzyl	227
152	−	.107	1.640	55°	Barbital-*o*-bromobenzyl	227
153	+	.142	1.577	30°	Barbital-*p*-bromobenzyl	227
154	−	.050	1.642	45°	Barbital-*p*-bromophenacyl	228
155	−	.152	1.640	70°	Barbital-*m*-chlorobenzyl	227
156	−	.148	1.649	60°	Barbital-*o*-chlorobenzyl	227
157	+	.119	1.563	45°	Barbital-*p*-chlorobenzyl	228
158	+	›.21	1.642	‹25°	Barbital-*p*-iodobenzyl	228
159	+	.228	1.626	80°	Barbital-*m*-nitrobenzyl	227

No.	Sign	$N_Z - N_X$	N, N_O, N_Y	2V	Substance	Page
160	+	.196	1.606	90°	Barbital-*p*-nitrobenzyl	227
161	−	.047	1.626	40°	Barbitalphenacyl	227
161 a	−	.318	1.696	31°	Barbituric acid	215
161 b	−	.256	1.642	14°	Barbituric acid·$2H_2O$	215
161 c	−	.025	1.517	70°	Barium acetate·H_2O	16
162	+?	.02	1.56	Lg.	Barium acetate·$3H_2O$	17
163	−	.021	1.553	75°	Barium 2-butanone-4-sulfonate	61
164		.0	1.444		Barium dicalcium propionate	20
165	+	.063	1.597	78°	Barium formate	14
166	−	.171	1.559	56°	Barium-3-methyl-1,2-diazole-5-carboxylate·$1.5H_2O$	236
167	+	.058	1.533	56°	Barium monofluoroacetate	19
168	−?	.049	1.498	Lg.	Barium monofluoroacetate·H_2O	19
169	−	.217	1.75	Lg.	Barium mono-iodoacetate	20
170	−	.115	1.714	30°	Barium-1,5-naphthalene disulfonate·H_2O	135
171	−		1.624	62°	Barium phenoldisulfonate·$4H_2O$	137
172	−		1.518	82°	Barium propionate·H_2O	20
173	+	.060	1.491	0°	Barium stearate	24
173 a	+	.053	1.580	0°	Barium succinate	33
174	−	.028	1.625	50°	Benadryl	95
175	+	.142	1.736	63°	Benzalaminophenol	155
176	+	.289	1.666	87°	Benzamide	113
177	+	.267	1.638	79°	α-Benzanis-*p*-tolhydroxylamine I	129
178	+		1.638	56°	α-Benzanis-*p*-tolhydroxylamine II	129
178 a	+	.117	1.604	45°	Benzazoline·HCl	204
179	−	.228	1.645	55°	Benzedrine diliturate	221
179 a	−	.026	1.602	30°	α-Benzene hexachloride	73
179 b		.000	1.630		β-Benzene hexachloride	73
179 c	+	.5	1.64	60°	γ-Benzene hexachloride	73
180	+	.014	1.633	55°	γ-Benzene hexachloride	73
180 a	+	.035	1.612	75°	ε-Benzene hexachloride	73
181	+	.049	1.600	0°	Benzenesulfonanilide	144
182	+	>.214	1.684	<87°	Benzidine diliturate	225
183	+	.021	1.658	0°	Benzil	107
184	+	.007	1.612	87°	Benzimidazole	205
184 a	−	.156	1.662	82°	Benzimidazole	205
185	+	.116	1.612	64°	Benzoic acid	111
186	+		1.695	75° *ca.*	Benzoin	108
187	+	.191	1.471	30°	*o*-Benzoic acid sodium sulfimide	253
188	+	.26	1.780	30°	Benzoselenazoleguanidine	254
189	−	.42	1.785	Lg.	Benzoselenazoleguanidine·HCl	254
190	−	.41	1.480	60°	Benzoselenazoleguanidine·HNO_3	254
191	+	.215	1.615	0°	Benzoselenazoleguanidine·H_2SO_4	254
192	+	>.100	1.740	52°	Benzothiazoleguanidine I	253
193	−	.275	1.745	Sm.	Benzothiazoleguanidine II	253
194	+	>.22	1.60	30°	Benzothiazoleguanidine III	253
195	−	>.23	1.765	Lg.	Benzothiazoleguanidine·HCl	254
196	−	.139	1.585	20°?	4-Benzoxy-2,2,6-trimethylpiperidine·HCl	196
197	+		1.627	72°	Benzoylanishydroxamic acid ethyl ether	130

No.	Sign	$N_Z - N_X$	N, N_O, N_Y	2V	Substance	Page
198	−	.010	1.286	78°	*d*-Benzoylbulbocapnine	295
199	−	.05	1.66	0°	3-Benzoylcamphor beryllate	107
200	+	.111	1.569	56°	4-(Benzoylmethylamino)butanoic acid	113
201	+	.292	1.546	4°	Benzoyl peroxide	113
202	−	.094	1.668	22°	*N*-Benzoyl-*m*-toluidine	149
203	+	.070	1.654	87°	*N*-Benzoyl-*o*-toluidine	149
204	+	.182	1.646	74°	*N*-Benzoyl-*p*-toluidine	150
205	+	.087	1.592	50°	Benzyl alurate	230
206	−	>.338	1.766	>25°	Benzylamine dilituràte	222
207	−		1.601	74°	Benzyl benzilate	131
207 a	+	.195	1.651	82°	Benzyl *p*-hydroxybenzoate	128
208	−	>.286	1.618	80°	Benzylideneacetone semicarbazone	104
209	+	.288	1.643	36°	α-Benzylidene-4-methyl acetophenone	105
209 a	+	>.36	1.676	?	Benzylidene sulfanilamide	167
210	−	.110	1.670	Sm.	*S*-Benzylisothiourea 1,5-naphthalene disulfonate	136
211	+	.105	1.580	Sm.	*S*-Benzylisothiourea 1,6-naphthalene disulfonate	136
212	+	.100	1.585	Sm.	*S*-Benzylisothiourea 2,6-naphthalene disulfonate	136
213	+	.075	1.587	58°	*S*-Benzylisothiourea 2,7-naphthalene disulfonate	136
214	−	.069	1.672	Sm.	*S*-Benzylisothiourea 1-naphthalene sulfonate	134
215	+	.105	1.590	40°	*S*-Benzylisothiourea 2-naphthalene sulfonate	134
216	−	.118	1.612	64°	β-Benzylmalimide	199
217	+		1.640	72°	Benzylnitrophthalimide	126
217 a	−	.054	1.686	86°	Benzylphenoxydimethylethanolamine dihydrogen citrate	95
218	−	.058	1.683	Sm.	Benzylthiopseudourea·HCl	94
219	−	.040	1.657	88°	Benzyltriphenylmethylether	96
220	−	>.250	1.701	?	Berberine·$6H_2O$	295
221	+		1.487	84°	Beryllium oxalate·$3H_2O$	29
222	+	.079	1.535	62°	Betaine·HCl	67
222 a	−?	.204	1.660	70°	Betaine·HCl with $AuCl_3$	67
223	+	.020	1.551	12°	Bicyclodecane peroxide	85
224	−	>.08	1.613	0°	Biguanidine disodium ferrocyanide	42
225		.000	1.525		Bios	309
226	+	.38	1.654	69°	Biphenyl	79
227	−	.177	1.657	78°	Bisdimethylfulvene	76
228	−		1.649	89.9°	Bismethoxyphenolpropane	100
229	+	.144	1.647	60°	Bismuth *m*-nitrobenzene sulfonate·$7H_2O$	133
230	−	.221	1.616	16°	Biuret	39
231	+	1.16±.24	1.649	66°	Bixin methyl ester	257
232	+	.012	1.542	76°	*d*-Bornylmethylene ether	84
233	−		1.68	85°	Bromoacetanilide III	145
234	+	>.207	1.679	$<88°$	3-Bromo-4-aminotoluene dilituràte	221

No.	Sign	N_Z-N_X	N, N_O, N_Y	2V	Substance	Page
235	−	.210	1.708	55°	*m*-Bromoaniline diliturate	220
236	+	.208	1.647	70°	*o*-Bromoaniline diliturate	220
237	+	>.329	1.749	<90°	*p*-Bromoaniline diliturate I	221
238	+	>.188	1.688	<88°	*p*-Bromoaniline diliturate II	221
239	−	.088	1.581	0°	4-Bromoantipyrine	208
240	−	.127	1.655	38°	*m*-Bromobenzyl alurate	230
241	−	.064	1.631	61°	*o*-Bromobenzyl alurate	230
242	+	.113	1.581	50°	*p*-Bromobenzyl alurate	231
243	+	.103	1.573	42°	*p*-Bromobenzyl amytal	230
244	−	.004	1.646	0°	*p*-Bromobenzyl cyanide	118
245	+	>.131	1.589	<45°	Bromobenzyldiallylbarbiturate	232
246	+	.138	1.582	40°	Bromobenzyl ipral	228
247	−	.186	1.644	70°	Bromobenzyl neonal	229
248	+	.114	1.611	20°	Bromobenzyl nostal	232
249	−	.175	1.638	75°	*p*-Bromobenzyl pentobarbital	230
250	−	.079	1.654	62°	*m*-Bromobenzyl phanodorn	233
251	+	.063	1.608	69°	*o*-Bromobenzyl phanodorn	233
252	+	.109	1.618	82°	*p*-Bromobenzyl phanodorn	233
253	+	.158	1.574	47°	Bromobenzyl sandoptal	231
254	−	.038	1.579	69°	*d*-α-Bromocamphor	103
255	+	.03	1.56	Lg.	β-Bromocamphor-α-sulphonyl chloride	138
256	−	.089	1.575	86°	Bromodiethylacetylurea I	39
257	+	.076	1.532	28°	Bromodiethylacetylurea II	39
258	+	.170	1.670	52°	1-Bromo-2,4-dinitrobenzene	75
259	−	.245	1.744	42°	Bromodinitromesitylene	76
260	+	.067	1.533	64°	Bromoethylbutanamide	23
261	+	.300	1.650	Lg.	5-Bromomethyl-4,5-dihydro-2-hydroxythiazole	253
262	−	.060	1.57	68°	α-Bromoisovalerylurea I	39
263	−	.080	1.583	50°	α-Bromoisovalerylurea II	39
264	−	.056	1.55	Lg.	α-Bromoisovalerylurea II	39
265	+		1.526	70°	Bromomethyltriphenylpyrrolone	198
266	+?	.31	1.700	90°	4-Bromophthalic anhydride	184
266 a	+	.117	1.654	70°	Bromothen	204
267	+	.042	1.584	0°	Bromoshikimilactone	131
267 a	−	>.402	1.761	Lg.	5-Bromouracil	214
268	+	.176	1.595	90°	Brucine sulfate	308
269	−	.059	1.680	0°	*d*- or *l*-Bulbocapnine methyl ether	295
270	−		1.666	43°	Butanedinitrile disilver nitrate	34
271	−		1.654	44°	Butanedinitrile tetrasilver nitrate	34
272	+		1.496	64°	Butanedioic anhydride	183
273	−	.307	1.704	60°	*n*-Butylamine diliturate	216
274	−	.355	1.753	40°	Butylamine picrate	90
275	+	.153	1.577	56°	Butylbenzamide	118
276	−	.23	1.596	86°	*p*-*sec*.-Butylbenzamide	118
277	−	.047	1.481	7°	*n*-Butyl carbamate	37
278	−	.177	1.621	59°	Butyl-3,5-dinitrobenzoate	115
279	−	.138	1.578	70°	*sec*-Butyl-3,5-dinitrobenzoate	115
280	+	.006	1.622	0°	*tert*-Butyl ester of tetrathiogermanic acid	8

No.	Sign	N_Z-N_X	N, N_O, N_Y	2V	Substance	Page
281	+	.008	1.604	0°	*tert*-Butyl ester of tetrathiosilicic acid	7
282	+	.003	1.640	0°	*tert*-Butyl ester of tetrathiostannic acid	8
282 a	−	.308	1.645	61°	*n*-Butyl *p*-hydroxybenzoate	128
283	+	.122	1.567	0°	Butylmelamine	245
284	+		1.623	34°	Butylnitrophthalimide	125
285	+	.054	1.463	0°	Butyl palmitate	24
286	+	.185	1.603	37°	*N*-Butyl-*N'*-phenylthiourea	143
287	+	.049	1.467	0°	Butyl stearate	25
288	+	.130	1.570	45°	Butyn	163
289	+	.065	1.482	63°	Butyramide	22
290	+	.305	1.615	88°	Butyr-*p*-bromoanilide	146
291	+	.036	1.552	0°	(*bis*)-α-Butyrolactone-α,α-spiran	192
292	+	.140	1.588	41°	Butyrylsulfanilamide	168
293	−	.023	1.633	Sm.	Cadmium bromide cadmium xylonate·$2H_2O$	46
294	+	.097	1.607	25°	Cadmium formate	14
295	+	.051	1.506	40°	Cadmium formate·$2H_2O$	15
296	−	.072	1.533	32°	Cadmium monochloroacetate·$6H_2O$	19
297	−	.126	1.552	30°	Caesium acid dioxalate·$2H_2O$	27
298	−	.140	1.653	38°	Caesium acid phthalate	123
299	−	.061	1.556	81°	Caesium acid tartrate	48
299 a	−	.113	1.801	0°	Caesium cuprous barium thiocyanate	43
299 b	−	.154	1.853	0°	Caesium cuprous strontium thiocyanate	43
300	+	.021	1.552	45°	Caesium methanetrisulfonate·H_2O	60
301	+	.119	1.540	80°	Caesium oxalate · H_2O	28
301 a	−	.097	1.776	0°	Caesium silver barium thiocyanate	43
302	−	.254	1.70	0°	Caffeine	248
303	−	.268	1.661	Sm.	Caffeine·H_2O	248
303 a	+	.057	1.535	43°	Calciferol	274
304	+?	.02	1.56	Lg.	Calcium acetate	16
305	+	.052	1.507	62°	Calcium acid *d*-malate·$6H_2O$	46
306	+	.060	1.535	70°	Calcium aconitate	36
307	−	.011	1.549	0°	Calcium aluminum basic acetate·$8H_2O$	18
308	−	.300	1.712	39°	Calcium ammelide·$2H_2O$	244
309	−	$>$.30	1.626	80°	Calcium ammeline·$5H_2O$	244
310	−	.15	1.61 *ca.*	90° *ca.*	Calcium ascorbate·$2H_2O$	263
311	+	.007	1.530	0°	Calcium ascorbate·$2H_2O$?	263
312	−	.147	1.648	87°	Calcium chloro-oxalate·$2H_2O$	29
313	−	.068	1.545	71°	Calcium chloro-oxalate·$7H_2O$	30
314	+	.065	1.530	60°	Calcium citrate·$4H_2O$	58
315	−	.046	1.486	0°	Calcium copper acetate·$6H_2O$	18
316	−	.150	1.567	55°	Calcium crotonate	25
317	−	.055	1.502	58°	Calcium dichloroacetate·$10H_2O$	19
318	+	.047	1.515	80°	Calcium dichloroacetate·$10H_2O$	19
319	+	.415	1.480	55°	Calcium dicyanimide·$2H_2O$	40
319 a	−	.381	1.642	70°	Calcium dicyanoguanidine·$4H_2O$	42
320	−	.050	1.462	68°	Calcium ethyl sulfate·$2H_2O$	5
321	+	.068	1.514	26°	Calcium formate	13

No.	Sign	$N_Z - N_X$	N, N_O, N_Y	2V	Substance	Page
322	−	.198	1.602	22°	Calcium fumarate·$2H_2O$	35
323	+		1.452	35°	Calcium glycerate·$2H_2O$	45
324	+	.049	1.522	Sm.	Calcium magnesium stearate	24
325	+	.030	1.555	70°	Calcium *l*-malate·$3H_2O$	46
326	−	.145	1.580	77°	Calcium maleate·H_2O	36
327	−	.085	1.525	73°	Calcium mesotartrate·$3H_2O$	57
328	−	.260	1.643	32°	Calcium nitrotetronate·nH_2O	183
329	+	.02	1.523	0°	Calcium oxalate·$2H_2O$	29
330	+	.160	1.555	51°	Calcium oxalate·H_2O	28
331	+	.031	1.552	0°	Calcium oxalate·$3H_2O$	29
332	+	.038	1.505	Lg.	Calcium pantothenate	67
333	−	.150	1.540	87°	Calcium succinate·$3H_2O$	33
334	−	.092	1.583	70°	Calcium sulfate-urea	39
335	+?	.025	1.535	80°	Calcium *d*-tartrate·$4H_2O$	51
336	−	.03	1.50	Sm.	Calcium *d*-tartrate·$6H_2O$	56
337	−	.001	1.545	0°	Camphor (Matico)	103
338	+	.069	1.54	89°	Cantharidin	189
339	+	.088	1.534	86°	ε-Caprolactam	197
340	+	.060	1.540	30°	Capsaicin	159
341	−	.523	1.90	35°	Carbamylguanidine picrate	87
342	+	.46 *ca.*	1.633	Lg.	Carbethoxydicyandiamide	42
343	−	.068	1.612	Mod.	Carbon tetrachloride solvate of rotenone	314
344	−	.220	1.645	66°	*d*-Carvone semicarbazone	103
345	+	.035	1.480	Lg.	Cellobiose octa-acetate	268
346	+	.064	1.531	0°	Cellulose with no H_2O	270
347	+	.062	1.528+	0°	Cellulose with 24% H_2O	273
348	−	.008	1.482	0°	Cerium ethyl sulfate·$18H_2O$	6
349	+	.048	1.481	0°	Cetyl alcohol	8
350	+	.274	1.594	88°	Cevitamic acid	263
351	−	.239	1.680	3°	Cevitamic acid	263
352	+	.003	1.545	0°	Champaca oil	85
353	−	.063	1.600	21°	Chloral hydrate	12
354	−	>.231	1.777	>17°	*m*-Chloroaniline dilituraté	219
355	+	.257	1.657	88°	*o*-Chloroaniline dilituraté	219
356	+	>.210	1.670	<85°	*p*-Chloroaniline dilituraté	219
357	−	.232	1.680	55°	Chloroantipyrine	208
358	−	.320	1.686	60°	*o*-Chlorobenzoic acid	113
359	−	.280	1.676	45°	*p*-Chlorobenzoic acid	113
360	+	.118	1.587	81°	*m*-Chlorobenzyl alurate	231
361	−	.156	1.649	74°	*o*-Chlorobenzyl alurate	231
362	+	.150	1.560	51°	*p*-Chlorobenzyl alurate	231
363	+	.155	1.574	58°	*p*-Chlorobenzyl amytal	229
364	+	>.140	1.592	40°	Chlorobenzyldiallylbarbiturate	232
364 a	+	>.38	1.703 *ca.*	?	*o*-Chlorobenzylidene sulfanilamide	167
364 b	+	>.334	1.703 *ca.*	?	*p*-Chlorobenzylidene sulfanilamide	167
365	+	.123	1.568	42°	Chlorobenzyl ipral	228
366	−	.183	1.640	70°	Chlorobenzyl neonal	229
367	+	.111	1.605	25°	Chlorobenzyl nostal	232
368	−	.157	1.631	70°	*p*-Chlorobenzylpentobarbital	230

No.	Sign	N_Z-N_X	N, N_O, N_Y	2V	Substance	Page
369	−	.087	1.623	70°	*o*-Chlorobenzyl phanodorn	233
370	+	.113	1.600	68°	*p*-Chlorobenzyl phanodorn	233
371	+	.145	1.567	45°	Chlorobenzyl sandoptal	231
372	−	weak	2.06	0°	Chloromethylsulfophenylazonaphthol	177
373	−	.078	1.74	49°	*m*-Chloronitrobenzene	74
374	−	.23	1.70	Sm.	*o*-Chloronitrobenzene	74
375	−	.275	1.700	57°	4-Chlorophthallic anhydride	184
376	+	>.181	1.625	80°	Chlorothen·HCl	203
376 a	+?	<.181	1.668	75°	Chlorotrimeton maleate	203
377	−	.055	1.67	55°	Chlorotriphenylmethane	82
377 a	−	>.426	1.754	Lg.	5-Chlorouracil	213
378	+	.046	1.532	60°	Cholesterol	274
379	−	.017	1.499	0°	Cholesteryl acetate	274
380	−	.018	1.499	0°	Cholesterylamyl carbonate	274
381	−	.039	1.579	0°	Cholesteryl benzoate	274
382	−	.017	1.508	0°	Cholesteryl benzoate	274
383	+	.043	1.481	0°	Cholesteryl capronate I	274
384	−	.010	1.489	0°	Cholesteryl capronate II	274
385	+	.042	1.532	60°	Cholesteryl ether	274
386	−	.026	1.526	0°	Cholesterylphenyl carbonate	274
387	+	.045	1.482	0°	Cholesteryl propionate I	274
388	−	.015	1.495	0°	Cholesteryl propionate II	274
389	−	.024	1.504	0°	Cholesterylpropyl carbonate	274
390	−	.139	1.56	60°	Cholesteryl salicylate	275
391	−	.125	1.700	0°	Chromium chloride dipyridine·HBr	195
392	−	.190	1.720	40°	Chromium chloride dipyridine·HCl	195
393	−	.047	1.647	0°	Chromium chloride diquinoline·HBr	195
394	−	.200	1.710	40°	Chromium chloride diquinoline·HCl	195
395	−	.195	1.700	Lg.	Chromium chloride tetraquinoline·HCl	195
396		.000	1.61		Chromium tripyrocatechol arsenate · $12H_2O$	98
397	+	.163	1.782	0°	Chrysazine	110
398	−	.483	1.787	88°	Chrysene	82
399	+	.06	>1.61	Sm.	Cinchonamine	293
400	+	.065	1.625	59°	Cinchonidine	286
401	+	.05	1.61	80°	Cinchonidine acetate	287
402	+	.060	1.620	Lg.	Cinchonidine benzene solvate	287
403	+	.09	1.66	69°	Cinchonidine·HBr	286
404	−	.038	1.648	30°	Cinchonidine 2-phenylpyridine-2′,3-dicarboxylate	287
404 a	+	>.164	1.594	?	Cinchonidine sulfanilamide sulfate	288
405	+	.098	1.604	85°	Cinchonidine sulfate·$3H_2O$	287
406	+	.10	1.56	35°	Cinchonidine·$4H_2SO_4$	286
406 a	+	.100	1.645	85°	Cinchonidine thiocyanate	287
407	−	.120	1.685	21°	α-Cinchonine	283
408	+	.137	1.596	73°	Cinchonine benzoate	285
409	−	.40	1.636	31°	Cinchonine bromate·$2H_2O$	285
410	−	.091	1.641	56°	Cinchonine chlorate·H_2O	284
411	+	.106	1.55	Lg.	Cinchonine-*o*-chlorobenzoate	285

No.	Sign	$N_Z - N_X$	N, N_O, N_Y	2V	Substance	Page
412	−	.12	1.62	80°	Cinchonine·2HCl	284
413	+	.029	1.654	88°	Cinchonine ethobromide·H_2O	286
414	+	.08	1.649	Lg.	Cinchonine·HBr·H_2O	284
415	−	.116	1.617	58°	Cinchonine·HCl·$2H_2O$	284
416	−	.088	1.649	80°	Cinchonine·HI·H_2O	284
417	−	>.100	1.660	Lg.	Cinchonine iodate·H_2O	285
418	−	.021	1.527	50°	Cinchonine methanetrisulfonate·H_2O	284
419	+	.105	1.568	36°	Cinchonine nitrate·H_2O	285
420	−	.102	1.572	87°	Cinchinine perchlorate·H_2O	285
421	−	.080	1.641	70°	Cinchonine sulfate·$2H_2O$	285
422	−	.07	1.64	65°	Cinchonine sulfate·$4H_2O$	285
423	−	.146	1.651	71°	Cinchonine thiocyanate	285
424	−	.112	1.673	46°	Cinchonine thiosulfate·$2H_2O$	285
425	−	.187	1.670	65°	Cinchoninone	286
426	−	.022	1.520	25°	*l*-Cineolic acid·H_2O	188
426 a	+	.35	1.703+	?	Cinnamylidene sulfanilamide	168
427	+	.013	1.533	0°	Cisalfa	271
428	+	.016	1.498	66°	Citric acid·H_2O	57
429	−		1.542	31°	Cobalt acetate·$4H_2O$	17
430	−	.057	1.545	22°	Cobalt monochloroacetate·$6H_2O$	19
431	−	.133	1.628	60°	Cobalt 1,5-naphthalene disulfonate·$6H_2O$	135
432	−	.129	1.595	72°	Cobalt phthalate	122
433		.0	1.595		Cobalt tripyrocatechol arsenate·$8H_2O$	98
434	−	.094	1.594	60°	Cocaine·HCl	282
435	+	.03	1.63	75°	Codeine	297
436	−	.141	1.636	53°	Codeine·H_2O	297
437	−	.100	1.642	50°	Codeine·H_2SO_4·$5H_2O$	297
438	+	.10	1.58	68°	Codethyline·H_2O	298
439	+	.03	1.502	29°	*d*-Coni-ine ditartrate·$2H_2O$	278
440	−	.392	1.764	40°	Copper dimethylglyoxime	12
441	+	>.36	1.73	90° *ca.*	Copper disalicylaldoxime	108
442	−	.144	1.542	35°	Copper formate·$4H_2O$	15
443	−	.119	1.625	63°	Copper 1,5-naphthalenedisulfonate·$6H_2O$	135
444	−	.255	1.700	45°	Copper saccharin·$6H_2O$	253
445	+	.021	1.527	0°	Copper nitrate silk	272
446	+	.047	1.533	0°	Cotton	271
447	+	.030	1.524	0°	Cotton(mercerized)	271
448	+	.064	1.522	0°	Cotton(tension mercerized)	271
449	+	.090	1.570	55°	Cresol 3,5-dinitrobenzoate	117
450	−	.265	1.700	45°	*m*-Cresol 3,5-dinitrobenzoate	116
451	+	.061	1.587	44°	*β*-Cuminuraminocrotonic acid ethyl ester	236
452	+	.513	1.734	88°	Curtisite	83
453	−	.131	1.680	0°	*p*-Cyanobenzylideneaminocinnamate of active amyl alcohol	166
454	−	.294	1.737	20°	2-Cyano-1,3-dimethylbenzene	119
455	+	.326	1.549	38°	Cyanoguanidine	41
456	−	.325	1.615	38°	Cyanoguanidine nitrate	41
457	−	>.360	1.705	29°	Cyanuric acid·$2H_2O$	244
458	−	.305	1.740	15°	Cyanuric chloride	243

No.	Sign	N_Z-N_X	N, N_O, N_Y	2V	Substance	Page
459	−	.484	1.862	0°	Cyanuric triazide	246
460		.0	〉1.517		*cis*-1,4-Cyclohexanediol I	96
460 a	−	?	〉1.517	0°	*cis*-1,4-Cyclohexanediol II	96
461	−	.214	1.648	57°	Cyclohexylamine diliturate	217
462	+	.038	1.549	70° *ca.*	*cis*-4-Cyclohexylcyclohexanol	85
463	−?	.026	1.535	90° *ca.*	*trans*-4-Cyclohexylcyclohexanol	85
464	−	.187	1.625	80°	*p*-Cyclohexylphenyl 3,5-dinitrobenzoate	116
464 a	−	.024	1.597	53°	Cyclonite	154
464 b	−	.106	1.575	85°	Cyclopal	233
464 c	+	.141	1.594	20°	Cyclotetramethylene tetranitramine I	154
464 d	+	.17 *ca.*	1.564	20° *ca.*	Cyclotetramethylene tetranitramine II	154
464 e	+	.129	1.585	75°	Cyclotetramethylene tetranitramine III	154
464 f	−	.041	1.607	0°	Cyclotetramethylene tetranitramine IV	154
465	−	.288	1.682	52°	Cysteine diliturate	219
466	−	〉.357	1.748	Lg.	Cysteine nitroindandionate·H_2O	106
467	−	.060	1.700	0°	*l*-Cystine	72
468	−	.107	1.724	37°	Cystine di-diliturate·$3H_2O$	219
469	+	.034	1.584	2°	*l*-Cystine·HCl	72
470	−	.09	1.65	Lg.	Cytisine·HCl·$3H_2O$	305
471	−	.337	1.747	36°	Cytosine hydrate	239
472	+	.020	1.550	12°	Decahydronaphthalene peroxide	85
472 a	−	.427	1.871	56°	Decarboxyl-monomethyl Ciba yellow	212
473	−	.179	1.655	45°	Decarboxyrissic acid	132
474	+?		1.581	89° *ca.*	Decylnitrophthalimide	126
475	+	.174	1.593	40°	Deguelin	310
476	−	〉.20	1.685	?	Dehydroapotoxicarol	316
477	+	.113	1.689	85°	Dehydrodeguelin	310
478	+	.161	1.580	75°	Dehydrodiacetyllevulinic acid	188
479	−	〉.240	1.680	60°	Dehydrodihydrotoxicarol	316
480	+	〉.20	1.678	Lg.	Dehydronetoric acid	312
481	+	.055	1.575	60°	Dehydroquassin	313
482	−	〉.28	1.685	50°	Dehydrotoxicarol	316
482 a	+	.166	1.544	61°	Delvinal	233
483	+?	.073	1.581	90°?	Demerol·HCl	200
484	+	.048	1.625	80°	Demerol·HCl·KI ?	200
485	+	.065	1.582	90°?	Demerol·HCl·sodium nitroprusside ?	200
485 a	+	.115	1.565	70°	Derric acid	132
485 b	+	.136	1.599	84°	α-Desmotroposantonin	315
486	+	.049	1.606	58°	β-Desmotroposantonin	315
486 a	+	.085	1.537	Mod.	*d*-Desoxyephedrine·HCl	151
486 b	−	.233	1.653	55°	Dexedrine diliturate	221
486 c	+	.103	1.545	Sm.	Dexedrine sulfate	148
487	−	.168	1.617	81°	Diacetoxystilbene	100
488	−	.050	1.647	88°	*N,N'*-Diacetylhydrazobenzene	172
489	+	.035	1.507	40°	α-Diacetonedulcitol	192
489 a	−	.001	1.515	0°	Diacetyl-α-2,4-diaminopentane	65
490	−	.092	1.567	85°	Dial	232
491	+		1.697	86°	Diallylphenylbenzimidazolium iodide	206

No.	Sign	N_Z-N_X	N, N_O, N_Y	2V	Substance	Page
492	+	.03	1.56	Lg.	Diaminoacetoxime·2HCl	66
493	−	>.330	1.761	>30°	2,4-Diaminobutane dilitarate	217
494	−	.070	1.688	0°	2,4-Diamino-6-dimethylamine-1,3,5-triazine	245
495	−		1.633	81°	Diaminoethane·2HCl	64
496	−		1.635	51°	Diaminoethane dithiocyanate	64
497	−	>.277	1.701	>66°	2,4-Diaminophenol dilitarate I	224
498	−	>.287	1.695	>69°	2,4-Diaminophenol dilitarate II	224
499	−	>.315	1.751	>37°	2,4-Diaminotoluene dilitarate	223
500	−	>.272	1.749	>42°	2,5-Diaminotoluene dilitarate	223
501		.000	2.419		Diamond	1
502	−	.129	1.675	85°	Diatrin·HCl	191
503	−	.123	1.555	77°	1,2-Diazole-3,5-dicarboxylic acid·H_2O	236
504	−?	>.175	1.734	?	2,3,5,6-Dibenzo-1,4-thiazine	252
505	+	.307	1.682	28°	*β*-Dibenzoylmethane enol	110
506	−	.101	1.698	0°	Dibenzoylpropane dioxime	107
507	+	.227	1.629	89°	Dibenzyl	80
507 a	−	.126	1.628	42°	Dibenzyl succinate	93
508	+	>.195	1.653	<70°	2,6-Dibromo-4-aminophenol dilitarate	224
509	−		1.512	56°	Dibromocamphor	103
510	+	.062	1.54	30°	Dibromocholestane	275
510 a	+	.184	1.662	50°	Dibromodiphenylsulfone	92
510 b	−	.027	1.612	0°	Dibromomethylcyclohexyl-4-acetic acid	111
511	+	.043	1.662	76°	Dibromotrihydroshikimic acid	131
512	−	.082	1.698	48°	*s*-Dibromotetrachloroethane	3
513	+	.057	1.573	35°	Dibromotrimethylacetic acid	22
514	−	.263	1.743	52°	Dibutylamine picrate	90
515	−	.353	1.711	62°	Di-*sec*-butylamine picrate	90
516	+	.050	1.479	0°	Dicetyl I	5
517	+	.050	1.515	0°	Dicetyl II	5
518	+	>.213	1.660	<80°	2,4-Dichloroaniline dilitarate	220
519	+	>.253	1.700	<90°	2,5-Dichloroaniline dilitarate	220
519 a	−	.399	1.724	83°	4-4′-Dichlorobenzophenone	105
520	−	.039	1.554	0°	1,4-Dichloro-2,3-butanediol	8
521	+	>.11	1.65	31°	*β,β′*-Dichlorodiethyl selenide dichloride	7
521 a	+	.182	1.653	66°	4-4′-Dichlorodiphenylsulfone	92
522	+		1.594	62°	Dichlorodinitrosocyclohexane	73
522 a	+	.144	1.554	77°	5-5-Dichloro-6-hydroxydihydrouracil	236
523	−	.220	1.645	52°	Dichlorophenoxyacetic acid	86
524	−	.605	1.526?	?	Dichlorophenylazomethylphenyl-pyrazolone	243
525	+	.100	1.623	87°	Dichlorotyramine	156
526	+	.23	1.590	>80°	Dicyanodiamide benzylsulfonate	134
527	+		1.608	75° *ca.*	Dicyanodiamide·2HCl	41
528	−	.072	1.551	54°	Dicyanodiamide ethylsulfonate	42
529	−	.043	1.645	41°	Dicyanodiamide·HCl	41
530	−	.310	1.692	17°	Dicyanodiamide maleate	42
531	+		1.541	29°	Dicyanodiamide oxalate	41
532	+	.17	1.72	76°	Dicyanodiamide picrate	88

No.	Sign	N_Z-N_X	N, N_O, N_Y	2V	Substance	Page
533	−		1.567	48°	Dicyanodiamide sulfate	41
534	−	.051	1.582	68°	Dicyanodiamide-*p*-toluene sulfonate	134
535	+	.064	1.537	75°	Di(2-cyanoethyl)amine·HCl	67
536	−	.315	1.787	38°	Diethanolamine picrate	91
537	+	.267	1.640	72°	Diethylamine picrate	88
538	+	.038	1.552	80°	Di(ethylamine sulfate)di-indium sulfate· $7H_2O$	63
539	−	.342	1.793	20°	Diethylaminoethanol picrate	91
540	+	⟩.150	1.556	37°	2-Diethylaminoethyl-*p*-aminobenzoate· HCl	163
541	+	⟩.164	1.580	37°	2-Diethylaminoethyl-*p*-aminobenzoate· HCl	163
542	+	.045	1.496	64°	Diethyl α,β-diacetyl succinate I	58
543	+	.049	1.479	50°	Diethyl α,β-diacetyl succinate II	58
544	−	.290	1.731	10°	Diethylenetriamine diliturate	217
545	−	.391	1.858	16°	Diethylenetriamine picrate	90
546	+	.02	1.535	Sm.	Diethyl hydrazone of phenyl isocyanate	143
547	+	.017	1.687	0°	Diethylmethylsulfonium chloroplatinate	7
548	+		1.572	70°	Diethyltoluidine·HBr	150
549	+		1.636	63°	Diethyltoluidine·$2H_2PtCl_6$	150
550	+	.040	1.554	84°	Diethyl ureindihydroxysuccinate	238
551	+	.090	1.648	65°	2,2′-Difluorobiphenyl	79
552	−	.309	1.698	71°	4,4′-Difluoro-3,3′-ditolyl	80
553	+	.251	1.594	64°	4,4′-Difluoro-2-nitrodiphenyl	79
553 a	−	.082	1.716	50°	Difluoropyridinodichloroplatinum	194
554	−	.113	1.625	87°	Dihydrodesoxytoxicarol	316
555	+	.080	1.625	70°	Dihydrorotenone	314
556	+	.101	1.550	67°	Dihydrosandaraco-pimaric acid	121
556 a	−	.218	1.657	68°	Dihydrosantinic acid (active)	315
556 b	−	.266	1.710	77°	Dihydrosantinic acid (inactive)	315
557	−	.044	1.548	80°	Dihydrostreptomycin·3HCl	309
558	+	.014	1.558	89°	Dihydrostreptomycin trisulfate	309
559	−	.083	1.627	75°	Dihydrotoxicarol	316
560	−	.131	1.575	21°	Dihydroxyacetone	13
561	+	.129	1.614	35°	1,2-Dihydroxybenzene	97
562	−	.040	1.549	65°	*cis*-3,4-Dihydroxy-3,4-dimethyl- thiacyclopentane 1-dioxide·$0.5H_2O$	182
563	+	.114	1.654	86°	α,β-Dihydroxy-α,β-diphenylethylene dibenzoate	111
564	+	.005	1.516	0°	β,β′-Dihydroxypivalic acid	45
565	+	.094	1.787	63°	1,5-Di-iodo-2,4-dinitrobenzene	75
566	+	⟩.102	1.786	Lg.	Di-iodotyrosine nitroindandionate	166
567	−	.319	1.770	44°	Di-isobutylamine picrate	90
568	−	.357	1.759	45°	Di-isopropylamine picrate	89
569	−	⟩.397	1.684	⟩60°	Dilituric acid	215
569 a	−?	⟩.373	1.678	Lg.	Dilituric acid·$3H_2O$	215
570	−	.255	1.725	⟨60°	Dimelamine phthalate	245
571	−	.195	1.670	35°	3,4-Dimethoxybenzylamime·HCl	158
571 a	+	⟩.048	1.674	⟨80°	2,4-Dimethoxybenzylidene sulfanilamide	168

No.	Sign	N_Z-N_X	N, N_O, N_Y	2V	Substance	Page
571 b	+	>.182	1.605	<85°	3,4-Dimethoxybenzylidene sulfanilamide	168
572	+	.207	1.689	56°	Dimethylamine picrate	88
573	+	.063	1.536	85°	6-Dimethylaminocarvone·$HClO_4$	161
574	−	.123	1.615	53°	Dimethylamino-*tert*.-butyl benzoate·HCl	112
575	−	.077	1.595	7°	(2-Dimethylaminoethyl(dimethyl-carbinyl benzoate·HCl	112
576	−	.023	1.528	72°	1-Dimethylamino-6-hydroxydihydro-carvone·$HClO_4$	161
577	+	.037	1.543	58°	3-Dimethylaminopropyldimethyl-carbinyl benzoate·HCl	112
578	−	.047	1.614	0°	Dimethylammonium hexachlorostannate	61
579	+?	.172	1.53	90° *ca.*	Dimethylaniline hexafluorogermanate	139
580	+	.108	1.591	81°	2,6-Dimethylbenzamide	118
581	−	.095	1.577	40°	3,4-Dimethyl-3-butylene sulfone	181
582	−	.16	1.59	80°	Dimethyl-butylbenzoic anhydride	119
583	+	.45	1.54	80°	Dimethylglyoxime	318
584	+	.125	1.565	Lg.	1,3-Dimethyl-5-hydantoincarboxy-methylamide	237
585	+	.107	1.510	38°	Dimethylmalonamide	34
586	+	.069	1.197	0°	Dimethylmalonic acid	34
586 a	+	.151	1.590	45°	2,3′-Dimethyl-2-nitrobiphenyl	81
587	+	.141	1.468	74°	Dimethyloxalate	32
588	−		1.657	47°	Dimethyloxindole	197
589	+?	>.173	1.645	Lg.	2,4-Dimethylphenyl-3,5-dinitrobenzoate	116
590	−	.253	1.665	90° *ca.*	2,5-Dimethylphenyl-3,5-dinitrobenzoate	116
591	+?	>.228	1.670	Lg.	2,6-Dimethylphenyl-3,5-dinitrobenzoate	116
592	−?	>.232	1.670	Lg.	3,4-Dimethylphenyl-3,5-dinitrobenzoate	116
593	−?	>.255	1.650	Lg.	3,5-Dimethylphenyl-3,5-dinitrobenzoate	116
594	+		1.512	63°	Dimethyl racemate diacetate	56
594 a	−	.023	1.808	0°	Dimethyl thallium bromide	73
595	+		1.717	58°	Dimethyltritan	82
596	+	.039	1.501	72°	Dimethyl ureindihydroxysuccinate	238
596 a	+	>.16	1.706	<65°	Di(monochloropyridene)dichloroplatinum	194
597	−	.407	1.766	50°	*m*-Dinitrobenzene	74
598	+	.109	1.647	65°	*p*-Dinitrobenzene	74
598 a	+	.79	1.64	37°	4,4′-Dinitrodiphenyl with 4-bromodi-phenyl	79
598 b	+	.37	1.63	29°	4,4′-Dinitrodiphenyl with dihydroxy-diphenyl	95
598 c	+	.44	1.64	45°	4,4′-Dinitrodiphenyl with 4-hydroxy-diphenyl	95
598 d	+	.51	1.65	34°	4,4′-Dinitrodiphenyl with 4-iododiphenyl	79
598 e	−	.07	1.553	0°	Dinitroethane	4
598 f	−	.226	1.763	80°	1,8-Dinitronaphthalene II	78
599	+	.52	1.715	31°	2,4-Dinitrophenylhydrazine·HCl	173
600	−	.539	1.869	40°	2,4-Dinitrophenylhydrazone of butyraldehyde	174
601	−	.576	1.906	38°	2,4-Dinitrophenylhydrazone of iso-butyraldehyde	174

No.	Sign	N_Z-N_X	N, N_O, N_Y	2V	Substance	Page
602	−	.313	1.662	70°	2,4-Dinitrotoluene	78
603	−	.255	1.669	60°	2,6-Dinitrotoluene	78
604	−		1.476	12°	Dinitrotoluidine	151
605	+	.163	⟩1.78	⟩0°	1,8-Dioxyanthraquinone	110
605 a	+	.075	1.610	78°	Diparalene·HCl	204
606	+	.040	1.629	52°	*N,N'*-Diphenylacetamide	141
607	+	.420	1.687	68°	*p*-Diphenylbenzene	82
608	+	⟩.164	1.650	Lg.	1,5-Diphenylbiuret	142
608 a	−	.13	1.677	83°	1,5-Diphenyl carbohydrazide	172
609	+	.076	1.664	78°	Diphenyldesoxycaffeine	247
610	−	.101	1.659	77°	Diphenyl(2,4-dihydroxyphenyl) acetic acid	131
611	−	.074	1.658	82°	Diphenyl ether	85
612	+	.325	1.512	Sm.	Diphenylmaleic anhydride	184
612 a	−		1.800	34°	Diphenylmelamine	246
613	+	.097	1.632	64°	Diphenyl sulfone	92
614	+	.17 *ca.*	1.716	65°	*N,N'*-Diphenylthiourea	145
615	+	.237	1.624	50°	*N,N'*-Diphenylurea	141
615 a	+	.058	1.651	38°	*unsym.*-Diphenylurea	142
616	−	.203	1.751	30°	Dipropylamine picrate	89
617	+	.177	1.618	87°	Dipyridinebetaine·HBr·H_2O	195
618	+	.174	1.608	84°	Dipyridinebetaine·HCl·H_2O	195
618 a	−?	⟩.202	1.770	⟩20°	Dipyridinodichloroplatinum	194
619	−	.16	1.77	40° *ca.*	α,α'-Dipyridyl	196
620	+	.114	1.62	Lg.	Diquinine carbonic acid ester	289
620 a	−	.009	1.568	24°	Di-(tetraethyl ammonium) plutonium hexachloride	63
620 b	−	.027	1.568	0°	Di(tetraethyl ammonium) plutonyl tetrachloride	63
620 c	−	.008	1.555	35°	Di(tetraethyl ammonium) uranium hexachloride	63
620 d	−	.028	1.558	33°	Di-(tetraethyl ammonium) uranyl tetrachloride	63
620 e		.000	1.509		Di-(tetramethyl ammonium) hexachlorostannate	62
620 f		.000	1.526		Di-(tetramethyl ammonium) plutonium hexachloride	62
620 g	+	.015	1.526	0°	Di-(tetramethyl ammonium) plutonyl tetrachloride	62
620 h		.000	1.511		Di-(tetramethyl ammonium) uranium hexachloride	62
621	+	.010	1.516	0°	Di-(tetramethyl ammonium) uranyl tetrachloride	62
621 a	−	.296	1.880	52°	Dithiobiuret	44
622	+	.14	1.687	79°	Di-*o*-tolylguanidine	149
623	+	.157	1.631	61°	Di-*o*-tolylguanidine·$ZnCl_2$	149
623 a	+	.335	1.83	80°	Di-*p*-tolylselenium dibromide	92
624	+	.085	1.685	43°	*N,N'*-Di-*p*-tolylthiourea	145
625	+	.070	1.663	66°	*N,N'*-Di-*o*-tolylthiourea	149

No.	Sign	$N_Z - N_X$	N, N_O, N_Y	2V	Substance	Page
626	+	.025	1.589	46°	Dulcine	155
627	−	.013	1.495	0°	Dysprosium ethyl sulfate·$18H_2O$	7
628	+	.075	1.512	0°	Elaidic acid	25
629	−	.111	1.619	70°	Ephedrine diliturate	225
630	−	.06	1.608	70°	*dl*-Ephedrine·HCl	157
631	−	.108	1.603	70°	*l*-Ephedrine·HCl	157
632	+	.064	1.288	66°	Ephedrinephenylthiocarbamide	156
633	+	⟩.05	1.565	Lg.	*l*-Ephedrine sulfate	157
634	−	.171	1.677	40°	Equiline	275
635	−	.011	1.497	0°	Erbium ethyl sulfate·$18H_2O$	7
636	+	⟩.107	1.587	Lg.	Ergocristine acetone solvate	302
637	−	.06	1.60	74°	Ergocristine benzene solvate	302
638	+		1.565	80°	Ergocristine + ergosinine	300
639	+	.095	1.602	50°	Ergocristinine	303
640	+	⟩.147	1.610	Lg.	Ergometrine benzene solvate	303
641	−	.083	1.601	18°	Ergosine	300
642	+	.086	1.578	36°	Ergosinine	300
643	−	.10	1.603	80°	Ergosinine methyl alcohol solvate	300
643 a	+	.110	1.555	89°	Ergosterol	276
643 b	+	.105	1.550	88°	Ergosterol·H_2O	276
644	+	⟩.081	1.580	90° *ca.*	Ergotamine acetone·$2H_2O$	301
645	−	.090	1.616	56°	Ergotamine benzene solvate	301
646	+		1.570	80°	Ergotamine + ergosinine	301
647	+	.049	1.620	70°	Ergotamine ethyl alcohol solvate	301
648	+	⟩.066	1.610	60°	Ergotamine methyl alcohol solvate	301
649	+	⟩.061	1.604	80°	Ergotamine pyridine solvate	301
650	−	.095	1.626	75°	Ergotamine water solvate	300
651	−	.118	1.61	55°	Ergothioneine	242
652	−		1.562	48°	Ergothioneine·HCl·$2H_2O$	242
653	+	.080	1.580	30°	Ergotinine	300
654	+	.04 *ca.*	1.57 *ca.*	Mod.	Ergotoxine benzene solvate	299
655	+		1.545	60°	Ergotoxine + ergosinine	299
656	+	.037	1.500	0°	Eruca acid	26
657	−	.023	1.544	0°	*dl*-Erythritol	8
658	−	.172	1.642	59°	Estrone I	275
659	−	.186	1.621	75°	Estrone II	275
660	−	.053	1.628	73°	Estrone III	275
661	−	.153	1.642	65°	Estrone hydrate	276
662	−	.319	1.744	37°	Ethanolamine diliturate	218
662 a	−	.066	1.549	20°	Ethanolamine hydrogen *d*-tartrate	65
663	−	.211	1.618	75°	2-Ethoxy-4-hydroxypyrimidine	213
664	−	.254	1.652	51°	4-Ethoxy-2-hydroxypyrimidine	214
665	+		1.630	75°	Ethoxymethylphenyldiazole methiodide	207
666	+?	.060	1.535	30°	Ethoxyneoquassin	314
667		.00	1.72		Ethyl alcohol cobalt bromide	5
668	−	⟩.326	1.734	⟩45°	Ethylamine diliturate	216
669	−	.420	1.513	0°	Ethylazoxymethyl-cinnamate I	180
670	+?		1.553	0°	Ethylazoxymethyl-cinnamate II	180

No.	Sign	$N_Z - N_X$	N, N_O, N_Y	2V	Substance	Page
671	+	.146	1.592	71°	*o*-Ethylbenzamide	118
672	−	.221	1.638	72°	*p*-Ethylbenzamide	118
673	−	.092	1.562	32°	Ethyl *d*-or *l*-bornylxanthate	85
673 a	+	.086	1.622	65°	Ethylchloroethoxyphenylhydrindone	108
674	+	.16	1.660	40° *ca.*	3-Ethylchloranthrene	83
675	−	.124	1.42	72°	Ethyl 3,5-dichloro-2-hydroxybenzoate	128
676	+	.13	1.576	45°	Ethyl 3,5-dinitrobenzoate	115
677	−	.026	1.610	62°	Ethyl diphenylacetate	121
677 a	+	>.02	1.770	0°	Ethyleneamminodibromoplatinum	5
677 b	+	>.063	1.732	0°	Ethyleneamminodichloroplatinum	5
678	−	>.331	1.785	?	Ethylenediamine diliturate	217
679	−	.449	1.916	5°	Ethylenediamine picrate	90
679 a	−	.084	1.589	21°	Ethylenediamine *d*-tartrate	64
680	−	.010	1.552	26°	Ethylenediamine *d*-tartrate·H_2O	64
680 a	−	.127	1.734	60°	Ethylenediamminoamminodinitrochloroplatinum nitrate	64
680 b	−	.080	1.740	40°	Ethylenediammino(methylammino)-nitrochloronitroplatinum chloride	64
680 c	−	.050	1.690	78°	Ethylenediamminonitrochloromethylamminochloroplatinum chloride sesquihydrate	64
680 d	−	.303	1.686	44°	Ethylene dinitramine	65
681	−?	>.30	>1.95	?	Ethylene iodide	4
681 a	+	.157	1.563	47°	Ethyleneurea II	207
681 b	+	>.039	1.521	0°	Ethyleneurea·$0.5H_2O$	207
682	−	.394	1.726	68°	Ethyl ester phenylhydrazone of pyruvic acid	172
683	+	.389	1.529	0°	Ethylethoxybenzalaminoethylcinnamate I	164
684	+?		1.549	0°	Ethylethoxybenzalaminoethylcinnamate II	164
685	+	.370	1.516	0°	Ethylethoxybenzalaminomethylcinnamate I	164
686	+	.270	1.535	0°	Ethylethoxybenzalaminomethyl cinnamate II	164
687	−		1.52	70°	Ethylgalactopyranoside	265
688	−		1.484	51°	α-Ethylglucoside	262
688 a	−	.345	1.648	64°	Ethyl *p*-hydroxybenzoate	128
689	−		1.652	88° *ca.*	Ethylnitrophthalimide	125
690	+	.055	1.463	0°	Ethyl palmitate	24
691	−?	.072?	1.628	40°	Ethyl phenaceturate	117
692	+	.070	1.680	82°	*N*-Ethyl-*N'*-phenylthiourea	143
693	+	.142	1.568	48°	Ethyl-*d*-pimarate	120
694	−	.291	1.690	15°	Ethylprotocatechualdehyde semicarbazone	109
695	+	.017	1.533	64°	Ethyl santonate	133
696	+	.055	1.466	0°	Ethyl stearate	25
697	−	.024	1.500	80°	Ethyl tetra-acetylquinate	132

No.	Sign	N_Z-N_X	N, N_O, N_Y	2V	Substance	Page
698	−	.098	1.578	65°	Ethyl 2,3,3-trimethyl-2-phenyl-cyclopentanecarboxylate	121
699	−	.055	1.712	Sm.	1-Ethyl-3,3,5-triphenyl-2(3)-pyrrolone	198
700	−	.010	1.494	0°	Europium ethyl sulfate·$18H_2O$	6
701	−	.088	1.609	71°	Evipal	234
702	+?	.605	1.49?	?	Fast yellow 4R	242
703	+	.062	1.532	0°	Flax	271
704	+	.065	1.566	45°	Fenchyl acid phthalate	123
705	+	.160	1.56 *ca.*	Lg.	Ferrous 2-naphthalenesulfonate·$6H_2O$	134
706	+	.198	1.561	Lg.	Ferrous oxalate·$2H_2O$	29
707	+	.341	1.663	67°	Fluorene	81
707 a	+	.085	1.600	50°	Fluorobenzyl D.P.E·HCl	199
708	−	.32	1.72 *ca.*	⟨30°	3-Fluoro-4-nitrotoluene	76
709	−	.34	1.74	3°–5°	4-Fluorophthalic anhydride	184
710	−		1.901	57°	Formaldehyde dinitrophenylhydrazene	173
711	+	.018	1.507	37°	*N*-Formyl-*l*-leucine	69
712	+	.078	1.507	68°	*N*-Formyl-*d*-norleucine	68
713	+	.003	1.558	Sm.	Fructose	265
713 a	+	.038	1.522	79°	Fructose·$2H_2O$	266
714	+	⟩.231	1.603	Sm.	Fructose methylphenylosazone	267
714 a	+	⟩.307	1.651	?	Furfurylidene sulfanilamide	182
715	+	.024	1.493	83°	Gadolinium acetate·$4H_2O$	17
716	+	.009	1.475	70°	Gadolinium butyrate·$2H_2O$	22
717	−	.008	1.490	0°	Gadolinium ethyl sulfate·$18H_2O$	7
718	−	.029	1.738	0°	Gadolinium formate	14
719	−	.003	1.495	45°	Gadolinium propionate·$3H_2O$	20
720	+?	.22	1.57	90° *ca.*	*d*-Galactoascorbic acid·H_2O	267
721	+	.055	1.800	Sm.	Galactosazone	267
722	−	.052	1.518	65°	*d*-Galactose diethylmercaptal penta-acetate I	265
723	−	.053	1.535	60°	*d*-Galactose diethylmercaptal penta-acetate II	265
724	−	.035	1.505	Sm.	*d*-Galactose diethylmercaptal penta-acetate III	265
725	−	.039	1.56 *ca.*	Lg.	α-*D*-Galactopyranose	264
726	+	.001	1.539	0°	Gelatin silk	272
727	+	.025	1.63	Lg.	Gelseminine·HCl	305
728	−?	⟩.203	1.645 *ca.*	Lg.	Genistein	187
729	+	⟩.225	1.556	55°	Genistein triacetate	187
730	−	.057	1.556	75°	*l*-Genistin hexa-acetate	187
731	+	.034	1.658	53°	Gliotoxin	309
732	+	.010	1.550	Lg.	α-Glucoheptitol	10
733	−	.010	1.550	50°	*β*-Glucoheptitol	10
734	+	.060	1.544	Lg.	*D* or *L*-Glucono-1,4-lactone	186
734 a	+	⟩.107	1.574	⟨22°	Glucoseanil sulfanilamide	262
735	−	.037	1.556	60°	Glucose	260
736	+	.042	1.528	68°	Glucose·H_2O	261

No.	Sign	N_Z-N_X	N, N_O, N_Y	2V	Substance	Page
737	−	.055	1.500	60°	α-*D*-Glucose penta–acetate	262
738	+?	.03	1.48 *ca.*	?	β-*D*-Glucose penta–acetate	262
738 a	−	.04	1.578	60°	Glucurone	187
739	−	.130	1.605	40°	Glutamic acid	70
740	−	.121	1.621	62°	Glutamic acid diliturate·$2.5H_2O$	218
741	+	.029	1.582	80°	Glutamic acid·HBr	71
742	+	.037	1.561	71°	Glutamic acid·HCl	70
743	−	›.421	1.689	Lg.	Glutamic acid nitroindandionate	107
743 a	+	.134	1.502	80°	Glutaric acid	34
744	−	.155	1.615	62°	α-Glycine	66
745	−	.162	1.608	62°	β-Glycine	66
746	−	.333	1.677	Lg.	Glycine diliturate·H_2O	218
747	+	›.254	1.717	Lg.	Glycine nitroindandionate	106
748	−	.084	1.511	38°	Glycolic acid	44
749	+	.074	1.551	0°	Glyoxaline-4(or 5)-sulfonic acid	238
750	+	.097	1.569	0°	Guaiacol	98
751	−	.160	1.530	0°	Guanidine ammelide	244
752	−	.010	1.496	0°	Guanidine carbonate	40
753	−	.196	1.745	0°	Guanidine·HI	40
754	+	.090	1.547	79°	Guanidine lactate	40
755	−	.130	1.575	33°	Guanidine nitrate	40
756	−	.76	1.998	44°	Guanidine picrate	88
757		.0	1.462		Guanidine sulfate	40
757 a	+	.249	1.622	49°	Guanine·HCl·$2H_2O$	248
757 b	−	.349	1.713	47°	Guanine sulfate·$2H_2O$	248
758	+	.306	1.535	81°	Guanylazide nitrate	43
758 a	−	.308	1.660	36°	Guanylurea nitrate	41
758 b	−	.193	1.553	64°	Guanylurea phosphate	41
758 c	−	.183	1.585	45°	Guanylurea sulfate·$2H_2O$	41
759	+	.010	1.560	75°	α-Guloheptitol	10
760	+	.021	1.570	60°	β-Guloheptitol	10
761	+	.575	1.92	Lg.	Hansa ruby G	177
762	−	.74	1.9 *ca.*	Lg.	Hansa yellow GR	175
763	−	.605	1.8 *ca.*	Lg.	Hansa yellow 3R	175
764	−	.73	2.10	70°	Harrison red	95
765	+	.022	1.480	0°	Hatchettite	5
766	+	.070	1.523	30°	Hatchettite	5
767	+	.053	1.568	70°	Helenalin	311
767 a	+	›.6	1.605	63°	Helianthin	178
768	+	›.8	1.605	35°	Helianthin	178
769	+	.05	1.64	Sm.	Hematoxylin·$3H_2O$	182
770	−	.243	1.636	47°	Hemimellitic acid	126
771	+	.071	1.525	0°	Hemp	271
772	+	.051	1.527	0°	Hemp	271
773	+	.068	1.616	73°	*n*-Heptylamine diliturate	217
774	−?		1.591	88° *ca.*	Heptylnitrophthalimide	125
775	−	.05	1.60	61°	Heroine	298
776	+	.039	1.543	70°	Hexa(acetoxymethyl)benzene	102

No.	Sign	$N_Z - N_X$	N, N_O, N_Y	2V	Substance	Page
777	−	.044	1.497	Sm.	Hexa-acetyl-glucose oxime	262
778	−	.123	1.847	37°	Hexabromoethane	3
779	−	.120	1.799	0°	Hexa(bromomethyl)benzene	296
780	−	.078	1.598	38°	Hexachloroethane	3
781	+	.012	1.643	89°	Hexachloro-keto-tetrahydronaphthalene	104
782	−	.126	1.726	0°	Hexa(chloromethyl)benzene	77
783	+	.059	1.574	70°	Hexa(dimethylamino)benzene	154
784	+	.123	1.529	71°	Hexaethylbenzene	77
785	−	.239	1.679	50°	Hexamethylbenzene	77
786	−	.399	1.842	21°	Hexamethylenediamine picrate	65
787		.00	1.589		Hexamethylenetetramine	11
788	−	.327	1.822	71°	Hexamethylenetetramine picrate	91
789	−	⟩.170	1.604	70°	Hexamethylenetetramine salicylate I	127
790		.00	1.480		Hexamethylethane	4
791	−	.262	1.692	0°	Hexamethylmelamine	245
792	−	.125	1.826	0°	Hexa(methylmercaptomethyl) benzene	102
792 a	−	.07	1.80	62°	Hexanitrodiphenylamine	140
793	−		1.590	84°	Hexylnitrophthalimide	125
193 a	−	.559	1.972	65°	Highest yellow U	215
794	+	.225	1.592	66°	Hippuric acid	113
795	−	⟩.107	1.654	88°	Histadyl	203
796	−	.316	1.723	40°	Histidine di-diliturate·$3H_2O$	242
797	−	⟨.244	1.758	Lg.	Histidine dinitroindandionate	242
798	+	.061	1.714	73°	Histamine monopicrate	239
799	−?	⟨.217	1.600	?	Holocaine	156
800	+	.065	1.57	45°	Homatropine salicylate	281
801	+		1.656	88°	Homobetaine·$PtCl_4$	67
802	−	.085	1.558	37°	Hydracrylamide	46
803	−	.325	1.748	37°	Hydrazine diliturate	216
804	−	.158	1.67	63°	Hydrocinchonidine·2HBr·$2H_2O$	288
805	+	.132	1.632	62°	Hydrocinchonine·2HBr	286
806	+	.045	1.520	55°	Hydrogenated capsaicin	159
807	−	.006	1.633	0°	Hydroquinone	99
807 a	+	.06	1.606	0°	Hydroquinone acetonitrile complex	99
807 b	+	.02	1.613	0°	Hydroquinone formic acid complex	99
807 c	−	.006	1.630	0°	Hydroquinone methyl alcohol complex	99
807 d	+	.026	1.629	0°	Hydroquinone sulfur dioxide complex	99
808	+		1.559	55°	Hydrosantonide	185
809	−	.05	1.69	60°	*d*-Hydroxybenzoyl camphor enol	108
810	+	⟩.369	1.689	Lg.	N^4-(2-Hydroxybenzylidene)sulfacetimide	169
811	+	⟩.283	1.686	Lg.	N^4-(2-Hydroxybenzylidene) sulfadiazine	239
812	+	⟩.299	1.668	Lg.	N^4-(2-Hydroxybenzylidene) sulfaguanidine	169
813	+	⟩.307	1.679	Lg.	N^4-(2-Hydroxybenzylidene) sulfamerazine	240
813 a	−	.40	1.680	?	*o*-Hydroxybenzylidene sulfanilamide	167
813 b	−	.308	1.666	?	*p*-Hydroxybenzylidene sulfanilamide	167
814	+	⟩.251	1.750	Lg.	N^4-(2-Hydroxybenzylidene) sulfapyridine	202
815	+	⟩.259	1.735	Lg.	N^4-(2-Hydroxybenzylidene) sulfathiazole	256

No.	Sign	N_Z-N_X	N, N_O, N_Y	2V	Substance	Page
816	+	.120	1.630	Lg.	7-Hydroxydihydrotoxicarol	317
817	−	.018	1.526	39°	1-Hydroxy-6-dimethylaminodihydro-carvone perchlorate	161
818	+	.305	1.688	66°	2-Hydroxyethylamine picrate	87
819	−	.304	1.837	38°	Hydroxyethylethylenediamine picrate	91
820	−	.276	1.748	25°	Hydroxylamine diliturate	216
821	+	).353	1.682	Lg.	N^4-(2-Hydroxy-3-methoxybenzylidene) sulfacetamide	169
822	+	).297	1.695	Lg.	N^4-(2-Hydroxy-3-methoxybenzylidene) sulfadiazine	239
823	+	).283	1.614	Sm.	N^4-(2-Hydroxy-3-methoxybenzylidene) sulfaguanidine	169
824	+	).312	1.669	Lg.	N^4-(2-Hydroxy-3-methoxybenzylidene) sulfamerazine	240
825	−	).318	1.750	Lg.	N^4-(2-Hydroxy-3-methoxybenzylidene) sulfapyridine	203
826	+	).228	1.734	Lg.	N^4-(2-Hydroxy-3-methoxybenzylidene) sulfathiazole	256
827	−	.060	1.689	50°	*p*-Hydroxymethylbenzoate	128
828	−	.079	1.590	0°	Hydroxymethylglyoxime	59
829	−	.023	1.546	82°	4-Hydroxy-1,2,2,6,6-pentamethyl-4-piperidine carboxylic acid	201
830	−	.113	1.602	77°	Hydroxyproline diliturate·$2.5H_2O$	226
831	+	.341	1.621	85°	Hydroxyproline nitroindandionate	200
832	−	.02	1.58	0°	Hyoscyamine	281
832 a	+	.211	1.64	65°	Hyposantonin	315
832 b	−	).394	1.748	Mod.	Hypoxanthine·HCl·H_2O	247
832 c	−	.412	1.720	43°	Hypoxanthine nitrate·$1.5H_2O$	247
833	+	.017	1.624	28°	*D*-Iminogalactoascorbic acid	267
833 a	+	.379	1.836	60°	Indigo yellow 3G Ciba	215
834		.00	1.559		Indium bromide (tetramethylammonium bromide)	62
835	+	.005	1.609	0°	Indium bromide tetraethylammonium bromide	64
836	−	(.015	1.550	Lg.	Indium chloride (tetramethylammonium chloride)	62
837	−	.018	1.583	0°	Indium chloride (tetraethylammonium chloride)	63
838	+	.024	1.560	80°	Indium chloride tetrakis(dimethyl-ammonium chloride)	62
839	+	.013	1.582	0°	Indium chloride tetrakis(methyl-ammonium chloride)	61
840	+	.003	1.546	0°	Indium chloride tris(trimethylammonium chloride)	62
841	−	).096	1.552	Mod.	Indium sulfate benzylamine sulfate·$6H_2O$	151
841 a	−	.013	1.562	Mod.	*l*-Inositol	102
842	−	.042	1.526	Mod.	*l*-Inositol·$2H_2O$	102
843	+	.005	1.473	0°	Insoluble acetate rayon	272

No.	Sign	N_Z-N_X	N, N_O, N_Y	2V	Substance	Page
844	+	.007	1.531	0°	Insulin (with Zn)	311
845	+	.012	1.550	0°	Insulin (with Zn)	311
846	+	>.285	1.751	90°	*p*-Iodoaniline diliturate	221
847	−	.169	1.646	0°	4-Iodoantipyrine	208
848	−	.344	2.11 *ca.*	0°	Iodoform	3
849	−	.050	1.800	0°	Iodoform	3
850	−	.31 *ca.*	1.77	65° *ca.*	4-Iodophthalic anhydride	184
851	−	.024	1.697	0°	*N*-Iodosuccinimide	198
851 a	+	.188	1.727	Mod.	5-Iodouracil	214
852	−	.147	1.573	73°	Ipral	228
852 a	+	.061	1.734	82°	Iridium dichlorodimethylglyoximic acid	12
853	−	.44	1.80	50°	Isatin	198
854	−	.216	1.644	45°	Isoamylamine diliturate	217
855	−	.378	1.821	26°	Isobutylamine picrate	90
856	−	.260	1.605	79°	*p*-Isobutylbenzamide	119
857	+	.23	1.588	73°	Isobutyr-*p*-bromoanilide	146
858	+	.051	1.466	0°	Isobutyl stearate	25
859	+	.109	1.605	75°	Isobutyrylsulfanilamide	168
860	+	.029	1.527	60°	Isocitric acid	57
861	−	.068	1.642	88°	Isocodeine	298
862	+	.348	1.642	80°	Isocytosine	213
862 a	−	.43	1.700	76°	Isocytosine	213
862 b	−	.434	1.688	Lg.	Isocytosine	213
862 c	+	.129	1.552	65°	Isodrine sulfate	157
862 d	+	<.036	1.78	?	α-Isodypnopinacoline	86
862 e	+	.081	1.659	47°	Isohyposantonin	315
863	−	.168	1.592	35°	Isoleucine diliturate · $3H_2O$	218
864	−	.321	1.652	75°	Isoleucine nitroindandionate	106
865	−	.335	1.701	60°	Isopropylamine diliturate	216
866	−	.380	1.806	24°	Isopropylamine picrate	89
867	+	.05	1.69	40° *ca.*	3-Isopropylcholanthrene	83
868	−	.015	1.563	56°	5-Isopropyl-4,4-dimethyl-2-pyrazoline · HCl	205
869	+	.021	1.556	70°	2-Isopropyl-5-methylphenoxyethyl-diethylamine · HCl	94
870	−		1.681	37°	Isopropylnitrobenzoic acid	119
871	+	.055	1.465	0°	Isopropyl palmitate	24
872	+	.053	1.468	0°	Isopropyl stearate	25
872 a	+	.036	1.502	64°	Isotemisin	315
873	−	.019	1.450	70°	Isovaleramide	22
874	+	.040	1.466	57°	Isovaleramide	22
875	+ ?	.289	1.615	88°	Isovaler-*p*-bromoanilide	147
876	− ?	.121	1.633	Lg.	Isovalerylsulfanilamide	168
877	+	.058	1.528	0°	Jute	271
878	+	.036	1.532	0°	Jute	271
879	−	.082	1.570	63°	5-Ketorhamnolactone	186
880	−	.331	1.710	60°	2-Ketotetrahydroquinoline	197

No.	Sign	N_Z-N_X	N, N_O, N_Y	2V	Substance	Page
881	+	.031	1.533	0°	Kipawa	271
882	+	.113	1.505	80°	Lactoisocitric acid	190
883	+	>.208	1.532	Sm.	Lactophenine	156
884	−	.038	1.553	21°	α-Lactose·H_2O	268
885	−	.043	1.572	67°	β-Lactose·H_2O	268
886	−	.009	1.482	0°	Lanthanum ethyl sulfate·$18H_2O$	6
886 a	−	.128	1.548	77°	Lanthanum oxalate·$10H_2O$	31
887	+		1.576	84°	Lead acetate·$3H_2O$	17
888	+	.012	1.527	0°	Lead dicalcium propionate	20
888 a	−?	>.335	1.794	?	Lead dicyanoguanidine	42
889	−	.101	1.854	70°	Lead formate	14
890	−	.011	1.633	10°	Lead gluconate	57
890 a	−	.034	1.650	89°	Lead methane disulfonate	60
891	+	.018	1.536	23°	*d*-or *l*-Leucine	69
892	+	.035	1.535	65°	*l*-Leucine	69
893	−	.287	1.717	21°	Leucine diliturate·$3H_2O$	218
894	−	.309	1.645	Lg.	Leucine nitroindandionate	106
895		.000	1.632		Lignite	2
896	+	.025	1.562	53°	Limonin	312
897	+	.010	1.545	51°	Limonin monoacetic acid solvate	312
898	+	.011	1.543	63°	Limonin monomethylene chloride solvate	312
898 a	−	.095	1.631	82°	Linadryl·HCl	252
898 b	+		1.527	35°	Linoleic acid	26
899	+?	.060	1.560	90° *ca.*	Lithium acid malate·$6H_2O$	46
900	+		1.529	82°	Lithium ammonium racemate·H_2O	55
901	+		1.567	87°	Lithium ammonium tartrate·H_2O	50
902	−	.07	>1.505	?	Lithium formate·H_2O	14
903	−	.191	1.638	23°	Lithium 1,5-naphthalenedisulfonate·$2H_2O$	135
904	+	.231	1.53	65°	Lithium oxalate	28
905	+		1.523	74°	Lithium potassium tartrate·H_2O	50
906	−		1.570	81°	Lithium potassium tartrate·H_2O	50
907	−		1.552	57°	Lithium rubidium tartrate·H_2O	50
908	−		1.490	69°	Lithium sodium racemate·$2H_2O$	55
909	+?	>.260	1.718	?	Lonchocarpic acid	311
910	−	.047	1.594	70°	Luminal (metastable)	234
911	+	>.042	1.607	Mod.	Luminal (metastable)	234
912	−?	>.119	1.620	80°	Luminal (stable)	234
912 a	−	<.094	1.567	Lg.	Lupeol acetate	312
912 b	+	.069	1.567	Sm.	Lupeol benzoate	312
913	+		1.570	59°	Lupinine·HCl	283
914	+		1.641	68°	Lupinine thiocyanate·H_2O	283
915	+	.063	1.566	40°	Luteosterone	276
916	−		1.522	80°	Lysidine tartrate	204
917	−	.244	1.699	30°	Lysine di-diliturate·$4H_2O$	218
918	+	.264	1.552	10°	Lysine dinitroindandionate·$6H_2O$	106
919	+	.003	1.492	0°	Lysozyme chloride·nH_2O	312
920	+	.004	1.554	0°	Lysozyme chloride	312

No.	Sign	$N_Z - N_X$	N, N_O, N_Y	2V	Substance	Page
921	−	.017	1.541	83°	α-*D*(−)-Lyxose	259
922	−		1.491	57°	Magnesium acetate·$4H_2O$	17
923	+	.139	1.560	80°	Magnesium dicalcium aconitate·$6H_2O$	37
924	+	.050	1.476	42°	Magnesium formate·$2H_2O$	15
925	−	.028	1.497	48°	Magnesium *l*-malate·$5H_2O$	46
926	−	.119	1.613	52°	Magnesium 1,5-naphthalenedisulfonate·$6H_2O$	135
927	+	.044	1.520	Sm.	Magnesium stearate	24
928	−		1.584	18°	Magnesium tetracyanoplatinate glycerol·$5H_2O$	8
929	+	.3	1.561	?	Maleic acid	3
930	+	.196	1.478	55°	Maleic anhydride	183
930 a	+	.130	1.488	27°	Malonic acid	32
931	−	.075	1.715	55°	Maltose phenylosazone	270
932	+	.259	1.592	78°	Malylureide acid	237
932 a	+	.094	1.564	84°	Mandelic acid	44
933	+	.049	1.525	0°	Manila hemp	271
934	+	.035	1.529	0°	Manila hemp	271
935	−	.018	1.545	60°	*d*-Mannitol	10
936	−	.042	1.553	44°	*d*-Mannitol	10
936 a	+	.007	1.551	85°	*d*-Mannitol	10
937	−	.011	1.545	Lg.	*D*-α-Mannoheptitol	11
938	+ ?	.012	1.54 *ca.*	?	*D*-β-Mannoheptitol	11
939	+	.048	1.570	89°	Mannoketoheptose	268
940	+	.034	1.536	55°	β-*D*-(+)-Mannose	263
940 a	−	.055	1.615	77°	Mannoseanil sulfanilamide	264
941	+	.22 *ca.*	1.650	Lg.	*D* or *L*-Mannose phenylhydrazone	264
942	−	.057	1.610	65°	Mebaral	235
943	+	.098	1.532	40°	Medinal	227
944	−	.382	1.743	70°	Melamine	244
945	−	.300	1.745	47°	Melamine·HCl	245
946	−	.010	1.548	50°	Melezitose·$2H_2O$	270
947	+	.034	1.541	Lg.	Melibiose·$2H_2O$	269
948	−	.021	1.497	0°	α-Menthol	84
949	−	.147	1.615	18°	Menthyl *p*-nitrobenzoate	114
950	−	.140	1.597	85°	Menthylxanthic anhydride	84
951	−	.4	1.965	50°	2-Mercaptobenzothiazole	253
952	+	.054	1.517	0°	Mercerized flax	271
953	+	.060	1.524	0°	Mercerized ramie	271
954	+	.049	1.532	0°	Mercerized ramie	271
955	−	$>$.295	1.690	$<$50°	Mesaconic acid	36
956	+	.097	1.610	65°	Mesaconic dihydrazide	36
957	+ ?	.030	1.59	90° *ca.*	Mescaline sulfate ($2H_2O$?)	160
957 a	−	.035	1.600	33°	Mesantoin	213
958	−	.15	1.62	89°	Mesitol	94
959	− ?	.076	1.516 *ca.*	90° *ca.*	Mesotartaric acid·H_2O	56
960	−	.100	1.530	0°	Metaldehyde	12
961	−	.128	1.678	89°	Metanilamidochloropyrimidine	240

No.	Sign	N_Z-N_X	N, N_O, N_Y	2V	Substance	Page
962	+	.091	1.658	62°	Metanilamidopyrimidine	239
963	+	⟩.324	1.656	81°	Methacryl-*p*-bromoanilide	147
963 a	−	.065	1.623	52°	Methadon·HCl	161
964	+	.031	1.487	0°	Methanetetra-acetic acid	37
965	+	.33	1.620	85°	Methoxyacet-*p*-bromoanilide	147
966	−	.065	1.580	45°	Methoxyacetylhelenalin	311
966 a	+	⟩.294	1.645	?	Methoxybenzylidene sulfanilamide	168
967	+		1.503	78°	Methoxyhydratropic acid	130
968	−	.093	1.650	72°	5-Methoxy-3-methyl-1-phenyl-1,2-diazole-2-methiodide	206
969	−	.209	1.692	75°	5-(4-Methoxyphenyl)tetrazole	246
970	+	.086	1.576	51°	*N*-Methylacetanilide	141
971		.00	1.74		Methylamine chloroplatinate	61
972	−	⟩.359	1.696	⟩60°	Methylamine diliturate	216
973	+	.070*ca.*	1.523	Sm.	Methyl-3-amino-4-hydroxybenzoate	164
974	−	.036	1.658	0°	Methyl-3-amino-4-hydroxybenzoate	164
975	−	.186	1.607	81°	*p*-Methylaminophenol sulfate	155
975 a	+	.066	1.656	63°	Methylammonium chloroiridate	61
975 b	+	.020	1.680	79°	Methylammonium chlororhodate	61
976	+	.022	1.529	71°	*β*-Methyl *l*-arabinopyranoside	258
977	−	.039	1.546	14°	Methylarsenic acid	72
977 a	−	.048	1.606	32°	Methylbenzhydryldimethylethanolamine·HCl	157
978	−		1.674	70°	Methylbenzohydroxamate benzoate	113
978 a	+	⟩.338	1.661	?	Methylbenzilidene sulfanilamide	168
979	−		1.646	33°	Methylbornylxanthate	85
980	−	.15*ca.*	1.588	Lg.	Methylbutyl 3,5-dinitrobenzoate	115
981	−	.05	1.58	Lg.	Methylcapsaicin	159
982	+	.08*ca.*	1.640	60° *ca.*	3-Methylcholanthrene I	83
983	+	.24	1.63 *ca.*	75°	3-Methylcholanthrene III	83
984	−	.128	1.605	53°	3-Methyl-1,2-diazole-4-sulfonic acid	238
985	−	.040	1.560	49°	Methyl dihydroabietate	120
986	−	.455	1.780	40°	Methyl-3,5-dinitrobenzoate	115
987	−	.020	1.660	65°	8-Methyldiphenyldesoxycaffeine	247
988	+	.10	1.68	68°	Methyldiphenylmethyldichloramine	153
989	−		1.598	63°	Methylenecamphor-phenylhydroxylamine	171
990	+	.08	1.602	61°	*d,l*-Methylethylacetbromoanilide	147
991	+?	.025	1.49 *ca.*	Sm.?	α-Methyl-*l*-fucopyranoside	260
992	−	.005	1.584	Lg.	α-Methylgalactopyranoside-6-bromide	265
993	+	.007	1.523	53°	α-Methyl-*d*-galactopyranoside·H_2O	265
994	+		1.543	85°	α-Methyl-*d*-glucoside	262
995	−	.016	1.529	0°	*β*-Methyl-*d*-glucoside	262
996	+?	⟩.085	1.520	Mod.	3-Methylhydantoincarboxymethylamide	236
996 a	−	.105	1.688	36°	Methyl *p*-hydroxybenzoate	128
997	+	.177	1.513	40°	1-Methyl-5-hydroxy-5-hydantoin-carboxylic acid ω-methylureide	236
998	−	⟩.369	1.702	⟩55°	α-Methylhydroxylamine diliturate	219
999	−	.26	1.74	45°	α-1-Methylisatin	199

No.	Sign	N_Z-N_X	N, N_O, N_Y	2V	Substance	Page
1000	−	.18	1.71	45°	β-1-Methylisatin	199
1001	+	.30	1.639	85°	*o*-Methylisatin	199
1002	+	.26	1.68	80°	Methylisatoid	309
1003	−	.031	1.54 *ca.*	Mod.	α-Methyl-*D*-mannofuranoside	264
1004	+	.009	1.529	47°	α-Methyl-*d*-mannoside	264
1005	−	.276	1.640	81°	2-Methylnaphthalene	78
1006	−	.15	1.55	70°	Methyl oxalate	32
1007	+	.076	1.595	0°	1-Methyl-5-phenylbiuret	142
1008	+	.072	1.585	Lg.	1-Methyl-3-phenyl-5-hydantoin-carboxymethylamide	237
1009	+	.068	1.695	88°	*N*-Methyl-*N'*-phenylthiourea	143
1010	+	.041	1.606	26°	Methylpropyl(carboxymethyl)arsine sulfide	73
1011	−	.16 *ca.*	1.585	Lg.	2-Methyl-2-propyl 3,5-dinitrobenzoate	115
1012	−	.005	1.540	36°	α-Methylrhamnopyranoside	260
1013	+	.114	1.562	23°	Methylsandaraco-pimarate	121
1014	−		1.524	75°	Methyl santonate	133
1015	−	.025	1.536	11°	α-Methyltetrahydroxyadipic acid I dilactone	192
1016	−	.045	1.547	0°	α-Methyltetrahydroxyadipic acid II dilactone·$0.5H_2O$	192
1017	+	.035	1.515	80°	Methyltetronic acid lactone	185
1018	+	.056	1.530	74°	Methyltetronamide	45
1019	−	.100	1.560	50°	Methyl undecil ketone semicarbazone	42
1020	−		1.524	35°	Methyl xylopyranoside	259
1020 a	+	.07	1.573	76°	Mibulactone	312
1021	+	.03	1.53	70°	Molybdenum oxalate·H_2O	29
1022	+	⟩.193	1.633	85°	Monoacetate of dihydrodesoxytoxicarol	317
1023	+	.035	1.537	50°	Monoacetate of methyl ursolate	317
1024	−	.143	1.617	30°	*dl*-Monochlorotyrosine	165
1025	−	.547	1.900	40°	Monoethylamine picrate	88
1026	+	.16	1.628	75°	Monoguanylmelamine·2HCl·nH_2O	246
1027	−	.514	1.878	42°	Monomethylamine picrate	88
1028	−	.093	1.562	60°	Monomethylaniline hexafluorogermanate	139
1029	+	.134	1.460	70°	Monomethyl oxalate	32
1030	−	.057	1.625	32°	Morphine I	296
1031	+	.018	1.657	56°	Morphine II	296
1032	−	.065	1.625	66°	Morphine·H_2O	296
1033	−	.095	1.590	Lg.	Morphine·HCl·H_2O	296
1034	−	.422	1.852	42°	Morpholine picrate	252
1035	−	.087	1.620	40°	Morphine·H_2SO_4·$7H_2O$	296
1036	−	.120	1.600	Mod.	Mucic acid	59
1037	−	.490	1.775	83°	Naphthalene	77
1038	+	⟩.13	1.604	10°	α-Naphthalene acetic acid	121
1039	−	.258	1.766	30°	Naphthalene tetrachloride	78
1040	+	⟩.150	1.684	⟨70°	α-Naphthylamine diliturate I	222
1041	−	⟩.135	1.783	⟩10°	α-Naphthylamine diliturate II	222
1042	−	.247	1.675	55°	1,5-Naphthalenedisulfonic acid·$4H_2O$	134

No.	Sign	N_Z-N_X	N, N_O, N_Y	2V	Substance	Page
1043	−	.237	1.614	79°	1,6-Naphthalene disulfonic acid·$4H_2O$	136
1043 a	+	>.180	1.619	<70°	Naphthazoline nitrate	204
1044	+	.124	1.577	30°	*β*-Naphthol	95
1045	−	>.135	1.758	>35°	*β*-Naphthylamine diliturate	222
1046	−	.187	1.730	Lg.	α-Naphthylamine-1,6-naphthalene-disulfonate	152
1047	−	.107	1.640	Lg.	α-Naphthylamine-2,6-naphthalene-disulfonate	152
1048	+	.115	1.650	55°	α-Naphthylamine-2,7-naphthalene-disulfonate	152
1049	+	>.23	1.670	48°	*β*-Naphthylamine-1-naphthalenesulfonate	152
1050	+	.124	1.647	40°	*β*-Naphthylamine-1,5-naphthalene-disulfonate	152
1051	−	.205	1.700	Lg.	*β*-Naphthylamine-1,6-naphthalene-disulfonate	153
1052	+	.220	1.634	40°	*β*-Naphthylamine-2,6-naphthalene-disulfonate	153
1053	−	.210	1.700	Lg.	*β*-Naphthylamine-2,7-naphthalene-disulfonate	153
1054	+	.125	1.650	80°	α-Naphthylamine-2-naphthalene-sulfonate	152
1055	+	.23	1.691	59°	*β*-Naphthylamine-1-sulfonic acid	169
1056	+	>.250	1.615	Lg.	α-Naphthyl-3,5-dinitrobenzoate	116
1057	+	>.265	1.740	?	*β*-Naphthyl-3,5-dinitrobenzoate	117
1058	−?	.04	1.57	Lg.	Narceine·HCl	294
1059	−	.172	1.687	22°	Narcotine	294
1060	−	.188	1.625	60°	Naringin·$2H_2O$	268
1061	−	.008	1.487	0°	Neodymium ethyl sulfate·$18H_2O$	6
1062	−	.079	1.679	45°	Neoheteramine·HCl	239
1063	−	.096	1.520	72°	Neonal	229
1064	−	.083	1.590 *ca.*	73°	*p*-Neopentylbenzenesulfonanilide	144
1065	−	.128	1.636	58°	Nickel 1,5-naphthalenedisulfonate·$6H_2O$	136
1066		.00	1.605		Nickel phthalate	122
1067		.00	1.602		Nickel tripyrocatecholarsenate·$8H_2O$	98
1068	−	.03	1.74	32°	Nicotinamide	277
1068 a	−	.245	1.685	23°	Nicotinamide with ethylene glycol	277
1068 b	+	.33	1.47 *ca.*	50°	Nicotinamide with HNO_3	277
1068 c	−	>.326	1.717	46°	Nicotinic acid	277
1069	+	.030	1.518	0°	Nitrate silk	272
1070	+	.214	1.629	16°	α-Nitroacetanilide	148
1071	−		1.74	42°	Nitroaminoguanidine	43
1072	−	>.10	1.73 *ca.*	Sm.	*m*-Nitroaniline	147
1072 a	+?		>1.78	80° *ca.*	*p*-Nitroaniline	148
1073	−	>.223	1.762	>45°	*m*-Nitroaniline diliturate I	220
1074	+	.264	1.650	87°	*m*-Nitroaniline diliturate II	220
1075	−	>.245	1.714	>67°	*o*-Nitroaniline diliturate	220
1076	+	>.170	1.698	<88°	*p*-Nitroaniline diliturate	220
1077	+	.083	1.661	30°	*cis*-Nitroaquodiethylamine cobaltinaphthionate·$3H_2O$ I	170

No.	Sign	N_Z-N_X	N, N_O, N_Y	2V	Substance	Page
1077 a	+	.080	1.665	37°	*cis*-Nitroaquodiethylamine cobaltinaphthionate·$3H_2O$ II	170
1078	+		1.76	60°	*m*-Nitrobenzoic acid	114
1079	−	.140	1.706	60°	*o*-Nitrobenzoic acid	114
1080	−	.070	1.706	60°	*p*-Nitrobenzoic acid	114
1081	−	.076	1.520	30°	*o*-Nitrobenzoic acid menthyl ester	114
1082	+	.098	1.602	66°	*p*-Nitrobenzyl alurate	231
1083	−	.146	1.640	38°	Nitrobenzyl amytal	230
1084	−	.188	1.658	55°	Nitrobenzyldiallylbarbiturate	232
1085	−	.099	1.621	67°	*p*-Nitrobenzyl evipal	234
1086	−	.178	1.576	70°	*m*-Nitrobenzylidene diacetate	104
1086 a	−	>.129	1.676	?	*m*-Nitrobenzylidene sulfanilamide	167
1086 b	−	>.227	1.690	?	*o*-Nitrobenzylidene sulfanilamide	167
1086 c	−	>.179	1.703+	?	*p*-Nitrobenzylidene sulfanilamide	167
1087	+	.070	1.627	60°	*p*-Nitrobenzyl mesaconate	93
1088	+	.159	1.556	25°	Nitrobenzyl neonal	229
1089	+	.138	1.593	20°	Nitrobenzyl nostal	232
1090	−	.108	1.684	88°	*p*-Nitrobenzyl phanodorn	233
1091	+	.157	1.559	20°	Nitrobenzyl sandoptal	231
1092	+	.039	1.528	0°	Nitrocellulose (with 5.6%N)	273
1093	−	.002	1.511	0°	Nitrocellulose (with 13.7%N)	273
1094	+	>.180	1.680	<80°	3-Nitro-4-chloroaniline diliturate	220
1095	+	.354	1.693	55°	2-Nitrodiphenyl sulfide	92
1096	−	.33	1.715	74°	Nitroguanidine	43
1097	−?	>.25	1.668	Lg.	Nitroguanidine	43
1098	−	>.192	1.770	Lg.	Nitroindandion	43
1099	−	.139	1.752	80°	2-Nitro-5-methyl-diphenylsulfide	93
1100	−		1.703	60°	Nitrophthalimide	125
1101	+	.153	1.636	83°	3-Nitrophthalic acid-2-benzyl ester	124
1102	−	.099	1.589	Lg.	3-Nitrophthalic acid 2-*n*-butyl ester	124
1103	−	.211	1.638	20° *ca.*	3-Nitrophthalic acid 2-ethyl ester	124
1104	−	.231	1.665	22°	4-Nitrophthalic acid 1-ethyl ester	125
1105	−	.101	1.601	Lg.	3-Nitrophthalic acid 2-*n*-hexyl ester	124
1106	−	.165	1.580	Lg.	3-Nitrophthalic acid 2-isoamyl ester	124
1107	−	.103	1.609	Lg.	3-Nitrophthalic acid 2-isobutyl ester	124
1108	−	.141	1.659	Lg.	3-Nitrophthalic acid 2-isopropyl ester	124
1109	−	.232	1.637	15° *ca.*	3-Nitrophthalic acid 2-methyl ester·H_2O	123
1110	−	.148	1.530	Lg.	4-Nitrophthalic acid 1-methyl ester	125
1111	−	.075	1.601	Lg.	3-Nitrophthalic acid 2-*n*-propyl ester	124
1111 a	−		1.703	60°	4-Nitrophthalimide	125
1112	−	>.245	1.650	Sm.	5-Nitropyrogallol·$0.5H_2O$	101
1113	+		1.567	83°	Nitrosoamylene nitroaniline	144
1114	+	.169	1.409	60°	Nitrotetronic acid·$2H_2O$	182
1115	+?		1.600	90° *ca.*	Nonylnitrophthalimide	126
1115 a	+	>.308	1.659	Lg.	5-Nitrouracil	214
1116	−	.235	1.670	48°	*p*-Nitrotoluene	75
1117	+	.033	1.510	18°	*d*-or *l*-Norleucine	68
1118	−	.109	1.598	70°	Nostal	232
1119	+	.060	1.520	0°	Nylon	272

No.	Sign	N_Z-N_X	N, N_O, N_Y	2V	Substance	Page
1120	+	.086	1.646	58°	β-Octachlorocyclohexenone	103
1121	−	.077	1.688	37°	γ-Octachlorocyclohexenone	103
1122	+		1.580	45–50°	Octylnitrophthalimide	125
1122 a	−	.076	1.519	76°	Ortal	230
1122 b	−	.002	1.525	0°	Ouabain I	132
1122 c	+	.047	1.547	67°	Ouabain II	132
1123	+?	.190	1.540	90° *ca.*	α-Oxalic acid	26
1124	+	.186	1.523	80°	β-Oxalic acid	26
1125	−	.125	1.495	68°	Oxalic acid $\cdot 2H_2O$	26
1125 a	+	.172	1.59 *ca.*	Lg.	Oxedrine tartrate	160
1126	+	>.250	1.595	75°	Oxydehydrodeguelin	311
1127	−	.11	1.525	74°	Oxydiethanoic acid $\cdot H_2O$	44
1128	−	.066	1.663	46°	Oxydiphenyldesoxycaffeine	250
1129	+	>.106	1.68 *ca.*	87°	Papaverine	293
1130	+	>.106	1.68	87°	Papaverine · HCl	294
1131	+	.046	1.496	0°	Paraffin	4
1132	+	.047	1.504	0°	Paraffin	4
1133	+	.04 *ca.*	1.50	13°	Paraffin	4
1134	+	.04 *ca.*	1.52	26°	Paraffin	4
1134 a	−	>.330	1.731	>45°	Paredrine diliturate	224
1134 b	−	.174	1.680	70°	Paredrine · HBr	155
1134 c	+	>.09	1.550	0°	Parthenyl cinnamate	121
1135	−	.006	1.533	0°	Pectic acid	273
1136	−	.001	1.504	0°	Pectin	273
1137	+	.037	1.602	5° *ca.*	Penicillamine	255
1138	−	.062	1.500	45°	Penta-acetyl-*D*-arabinose methyl hemiacetyl I	258
1139	+	.035	1.464	60°	Penta-acetyl-*D*-arabinose methyl hemiacetyl II	258
1139 a	−	.028	1.539	0°	Pentaerythritol	9
1140	−	.041	1.556	0°	Pentaerythritol	9
1141	+	.012	1.471	0°	Pentaerythritol tetra-acetate	9
1142	+	.050	1.433	0°	Pentaerythritol tetra-acetate	9
1143	−	.039	1.630	80°	Pentaerythritol tetrakis(*p*-chlorophenyl)-ether	86
1144	−	.001	1.554	0°	Pentaerythritoltetranitrate	9
1145	+	.006	1.593	0°	Pentaerythritol tetraphenyl ether	85
1146	+	.007	1.550	0°	Pentaerythritol tetra-*tert*-butyl-thioether II	9
1147	−	.013	1.559	0°	Pentaerythritol tetra-*tert*-butylthioether I	9
1148	+	.070	1.586	81°	Pentamethylbenzene	77
1149	−	.100	1.528	80°	Pentobarbitol	229
1149 a	−	.116	1.634	45°	Pentothal	230
1149 b	−	.055	1.660	Sm.	Perazil · 2HCl	204
1150	−	.055 *ca.*	1.572	87°	Perhydroretene	74
1151	+	.018	1.58	Mod.	Pethedine with HNO_3	201
1152	+	.105	1.553	70°	Phanodorn	233

No.	Sign	$N_Z - N_X$	N, N_O, N_Y	2V	Substance	Page
1153	−	>.227 <.267	1.627	90° *ca.*	Phenacetin	155
1154	−	.372	1.724	83°	Phenanthrene	81
1154 a	+	.067	1.675	Sm.	Phenergan·HBr	256
1154 b	−?	.116	1.691	73°	Phenergan·HCl	256
1155	−	.099	1.668	60°	Phenobarbital-*m*-bromobenzyl	234
1156	+	.115	1.620	40°	Phenobarbital-*o*-bromobenzyl	234
1157	+	.104	1.656	85°	Phenobarbital-*p*-bromophenacyl	235
1158	−	.101	1.660	55°	Phenobarbital-*m*-chlorobenzyl	235
1159	+	.145	1.593	25°	Phenobarbital-*p*-chlorobenzyl	235
1160	−	>.16 <.30	1.730	?	Phenobarbital-*p*-iodobenzyl	235
1161	−	.177	1.652	75°	Phenobarbital-*m*-nitrobenzyl	235
1162	−	.206	1.666	75°	Phenobarbital-*p*-nitrobenzyl	235
1162 a	+	.21	1.74	81°	Phenoxselenine	191
1162 b	+	.34	1.73	81°	Phenothiazine	252
1162 c	+	.113	1.569	39°	Phenylacetic acid	117
1163	+	.08	1.73	67°	9-Phenylacridine sulfate I	196
1164	−	.64	1.72	42°	9-Phenylacridine sulfate II	196
1165	+	.075	1.610	40°	*β*-Phenylalanine	164
1166	−	.326	1.777	32°	Phenylalanine diliturate·$2H_2O$ I	225
1167	−	.263	1.695	20°	Phenylalanine diliturate·$2H_2O$ II	225
1168	+	>.05	1.581	Mod.	1-Phenyl-2-aminoethanol sulfate	156
1169	+	.31	1.620	34°	Phenylbiguanide	143
1169 a	−	.20	1.684	75° *ca.*	Phenylbiguanide·HCl	143
1169 b	+	.238	1.747	45°	Phenylbiguanide mercaptobenzothiazole	254
1170	−	.020	1.665	0°	*ω*-Phenylbiuret	142
1171	−	.031	1.581	0°	*cis*-4-Phenylcyclohexanol	94
1172	+	.139	1.595	80° *ca.*	*trans*-4-Phenylcyclohexanol	94
1173	+	.425	1.755	Lg.	Phenyldibromosulfide	92
1174	−?	>.235	1.690	?	Phenyl-3,5-dinitrobenzoate	115
1175	+	.106	1.669	76°	8-Phenyldiphenyldesoxycaffeine	247
1176	−	.292	1.683	>74°	*m*-Phenylenediamine diliturate	223
1177	−	.334	1.737	35°	*o*-Phenylenediamine diliturate	223
1178	−	>.284	1.716	>60°	*p*-Phenylenediamine diliturate	223
1179	−	.092	1.663	22°	Phenylguanidine carbonate	143
1180	+	>.292	<1.776	?	1-Phenyl-3-iminotriazoline·HCl·H_2O	243
1181	−	.200 *ca.*	1.763	32°	Phenyl melamine	246
1182	+	.46 *ca.*	1.683	65° *ca.*	Phenylmercuric acetate	181
1182 a	−	.284	1.82	65°	Phenyl-2-naphthylamine	139
1183	+	.045	1.700	56°	*N*-Phenyl-*N′*-propylthiourea	143
1184	+	>.189	1.575	<45°	2-Phenylquinoline-4-carboxylic acid I	201
1185	+	.099	1.657	88°	3-Phenylsulfonyl-1,1-diphenyl-2-propen-1-ol	92
1186	−	.345	1.598	46°	α-(Phenylsulfonyl)butyric acid	92
1187	−	.209	1.696	80°	3-Phenyl-2,4-thiazolidenedione (high temp.)	254
1188	−	.230	1.693	83°	3-Phenyl-2,4-thiazolidinedione (stable)	254
1189	−	.154	1.717	0°	Phenyl-*p*-tolyl ketone	105

No.	Sign	N_Z-N_X	N, N_O, N_Y	2V	Substance	Page
1190	+	.085*ca.*	1.663	35°	*N*-Phenyl-*N′*-*o*-tolylthiourea	149
1191	+	.190*ca.*	1.675	63°	*N*-Phenyl-*N′*-*p*-tolylthiourea	151
1192	+	.024	1.615	Lg.	Phlorizoside · $2H_2O$	263
1192 a	+	2.39	1.617	65°	1,3,5-Phloroglucinol	101
1193	−	.300	1.696	31°	Phthalic acid	122
1193 a	−	.34	1.762	34° *ca.*	Phthalic acid	122
1194	−	.268	1.685	70°	Phthalic anhydride	182
1194 a	+	.254	1.519	25°	Phthalimide	199
1194 b	−	.399	1.802	36°	Phthiocol	109
1195	+	.12	1.55	20°	Physostigmine	304
1196	+	>.445	1.54	Sm.	Picramic acid	155
1197	+	.06*ca.*	1.71 *ca.*	83°	Picric acid	87
1198	+	.02	1.555 *ca.*	60°	Picrotoxinin	313
1199	−	.619	1.800	86°	Picrylaniline	148
1199 a	+	.37	1.750	81°	*N*-Picryl-*p*-iodoaniline I	148
1199 b	+	.34	1.740	56°	*N*-Picryl-*p*-iodoaniline II	148
1199 c	+	.60	1.743	39°	*N*-Picryl-*p*-iodoaniline III	148
1200	−	.484	1.769	85°	Picryl-*p*-toluidine (red)	150
1201	+	.472	1.747	84°	Picryl-*p*-toluidine (yellow)	150
1202	+	.095	1.55	Lg.	Pilocarpine · HBr	303
1203	−	.081	1.570	66°	Pilocarpine · HCl	303
1204	−	.123	1.588	45°	Pilocarpine · HNO_3	303
1205	+	.050	1.564	47°	*d*-Pimaric acid	120
1206	−		1.600	62°	Pimaric acid	120
1207	+	.120	1.492	67°	Pimelic acid	35
1208	+	.531	1.942	53°	Pinastric acid	313
1209	+	.42	>1.75	?	Pinaverdol	206
1210	+	.044	1.532	70°	Pinoresinol	313
1210 a	+	.047	1.636	72°	Piperidinediphenylbutene · HCl	196
1210 b	−	.236	1.675	32°	2,5-Piperazinedione	213
1211	−	.387	1.832	50°	Piperazine picrate	204
1212	+ ?	.120	1.685	90° *ca.*	2-(1-Piperidino)-5-bromo-5,6-dihydro-1,3-thiazine	256
1213	−	.003	1.520	0°	Polyacrilonitrile	272
1214	−	.145	1.536	46°	Potassium acid dioxalate · $2H_2O$	27
1215	−	.150	1.545	52°	Potassium acid oxalate	26
1216	−	.191	1.553	40°	Potassium acid oxalate	26
1217	−	.165	1.659	16°	Potassium acid phthalate	123
1218	−	.103	1.571	45°	Potassium acid *D*-saccharate	59
1219	−	.116	1.530	Sm.	Potassium acid succinate · $2H_2O$	33
1220	−	.080	1.550	88°	Potassium acid tartrate	48
1221	+	.01	1.493	71°	Potassium aluminum oxalate · $6H_2O$	30
1222	−	.305	1.735	Sm.	Potassium ammeline	244
1223	−	.018	1.636	75°	Potassium antimonyl tartrate · H_2O	49
1224	−	.054	1.51	87°	Potassium boromalate · H_2O	46
1225	−	.009	1.552	0°	Potassium bromomethanetrisulfonate · H_2O	61
1226	−		1.593	43°	Potassium carboxybenzene sulfonate	139
1227	−	.042	1.531	69°	Potassium chloromethanedisulfonate	60

No.	Sign	N_Z-N_X	N, N_O, N_Y	2V	Substance	Page
1227 a	−	.175	1.552	0°	Potassium cyanate	38
1228	+	.2 *ca.*	1.65	Lg.	Potassium *trans*-diaminodinitro-oxalato-cobaltiate·H_2O	31
1228 a	−	.395	1.638	75°	Potassium dicyanoguanidine	42
1229	−	.094	1.556	79°	Potassium ferric oxalate·$6H_2O$	30
1230	+	.042	1.548	80°	Potassium gluconate	57
1231	+	.111	1.552	Mod.	Potassium guaiacol sulfate·$2H_2O$	98
1232	+		1.592	76°	Potassium iridium chloro-oxalate·H_2O	31
1233	+	.100	1.579	39°	Potassium iridium dichlorodinitrito-oxalate·$2H_2O$	31
1234	−	.118	1.568	0°	Potassium iridium oxalate·KCl·$8H_2O$	31
1235	−?		1.539	72°	Potassium methane disulfonate	59
1236	−	.014	1.524	52°	Potassium methanetrisulfonate·H_2O	60
1237	−	.212	1.669	38°	Potassium 1,5-naphthalene disulfonate·$2H_2O$	135
1238	−	>.275	>1.743	Mod.	Potassium nitranilate I	109
1239	+	.126	1.493	83°	Potassium oxalate·H_2O	28
1240	+	.061	1.515 *ca.*	Mod.	Potassium palmitate	23
1241	−	.08	1.607	65°	Potassium 1-phenol-2,4-disulfonate·H_2O	137
1242	+	.123	1.608	68°	Potassium 1-phenol-4-sulfonate	136
1243	+	.120	1.568	70°	Potassium 1-phenol-2-sulfonate·$2H_2O$	136
1244	−	.425	1.903	33°	Potassium picrate	87
1245	+	.215	1.641	89°	Potassium platinum nitrito-oxalate·H_2O	31
1246	+	.337	1.555	81°	Potassium platinum oxalate·$2H_2O$	32
1247	−	.025	1.605	0°	*d*-Potassium rhodium oxalate·H_2O	29
1248	−	.015?	1.526	62°	Potassium tartrate·$0.5H_2O$	49
1248 a	−	.075	1.724	70°	Potassiumtrichloroplatinumbutylene	5
1249	+	.010	1.477	0°	Potassium zinc uranyl acetate·$6H_2O$	18
1250	−	.007	1.486	0°	Praseodymium ethyl sulfate·$18H_2O$	6
1251	+	.105	1.502	20°	Procaine borate	163
1252	+	.121	1.554	40°	α-Progesterone	276
1253	+	.149	1.575	70°	β-Progesterone	276
1254	−	.124	1.611	75°	Proline diliturate·$2H_2O$	226
1255	+	>.346	1.678	Lg.	Proline nitroindandionate	200
1255 a	−	.247	1.678	40°	Propadrine diliturate I	225
1255 b	−	.214	1.663	35°	Propadrine diliturate II	225
1256	−	.533	1.917	24°	Propionaldehyde-2,4-dinitrophenyl-hydrazone	174
1257	+	.165	1.653	78°	Propion-*p*-bromoanilide I	145
1258	−	.021	1.660	72°	Propion-*p*-bromoanilide II	145
1259	+	.095	1.619	40°	*n*-Propylamine diliturate	216
1260	−	.373	1.790	30°	Propylamine picrate	89
1261	−	.163	1.674	33°	*p*-Propylbenzamide	119
1262	−	>.333	>1.785	?	Propylenediamine diliturate	217
1262 a	−	.280	1.650	70°	*n*-Propyl *p*-hydroxybenzoate	128
1263	−		1.635	73°	Propylnitrophthalimide	125
1264	+	.053	1.464	0°	Propyl palmitate	24
1265	+	.391	1.529	0°	Propylphenylbenzalaminoethyl cinnamate I	164

No.	Sign	N_Z-N_X	N, N_O, N_Y	2V	Substance	Page
1266	–?		1.527	0°	Propylphenylbenzalaminoethyl-cinnamate II	164
1267	+?		1.562	0°	Propylphenylbenzalaminoethyl-cinnamate III	164
1268	+	.055	1.465	0°	Propyl stearate	25
1269	–	.115	1.658	45°	Prostigmine bromide	155
1270	+	.061	1.525	35°	Prostigmine methyl sulfate	156
1271	+	.073	1.602	77°	Pseudocodeine	298
1272	+	.072	1.573 *ca.*	0° *ca.*	Pseudoergotinine	302
1272 a	±?	.034	1.566	90°	Pseudotropine	197
1273	–	.084	1.642	80°	Pseudoyohimbine	305
1274	–	.210	1.604?	80°?	Pyramidone	240
1275	+	⟨.18	1.633	Lg.	Pyramidone salicylate	240
1276	–	.125	1.655	80°	Pyribenzamine·HCl	202
1277	+	.164	1.557	52°	Pyridinebetaine·HCl	94
1278	–	.122	1.639	25°	Pyridinebetaine·H_2O	194
1278 a	–	.100	1.756	78°	Pyridinebutylenedichloroplatinum	193
1279	–	.306	1.705	41°	α-Pyridinecarboxylic acid·HCl	200
1279 a	+	.288	1.704	28°	Pyridineethylenedichloroplatinum	194
1280	–	.448	1.893	50°	Pyridine picrate	194
1281	–	.23	1.650	83°	α-Pyridinesulfonic acid	201
1282	–	.206	1.670	67°	β-Pyridinesulfonic acid	201
1283	–	.178	1.630	49°	Pyridinium sulfamate	193
1283 a	–	.126	1.696	78°	Pyridinoamminodinitroplatinum	193
1283 b	–	.254	1.706	33°	Pyridoxin·HCl	197
1284	–	⟩.31	1.608	63°	Pyruv-*p*-bromoanilide	146
1285	+	.05	1.59	Lg.	Quassin	313
1286	+	.026	1.552	70°	Quebrachitol	102
1287	–?	⟩.179	1.734	?	Quercetin dihydrate	187
1288	+	⟩.226	1.508	0°	Quercitrin dihydrate	187
1289	–		1.785	67°	Quinaldine iodoethylate	196
1290	–	.110	1.665	55°	Quinidine	292
1291	+	.110	1.595	50°	Quinidine benzene solvate	292
1292	+	.140	1.570	48°	Quinidine ethyl alcohol solvate	293
1293	+	.10	1.60	55°	Quinidine·HBr	293
1294	–	.146	1.641	55°	Quinidine-2-phenylpyridine-2′,3-dicarboxylate	293
1295	+	.06	1.61	60°	Quinidine·H_2SO_4·$2H_2O$	292
1296	+?	⟩.185	1.643	Lg.	Quinidine thiocyanate	292
1297	+	.093	1.624	65°	Quinine	288
1298	+	.08	1.62	42°	Quinine·H_3AsO_4	290
1299	+	.007	1.611	Lg.	Quinine benzene solvate I	288
1300	–	.130	1.630	61°	Quinine benzene solvate II	288
1301	–	.09	1.66	70°	Quinine benzoate	290
1302	–	.04	1.61	60°	Quinine camphorate	290
1303	+	.14	1.64	80°	Quinine carbamate·2HCl	290
1304	+	.07	1.64	65°	Quinine·$HClO_3$	290
1305	–	.11	1.61	60°	Quinine·2HBr	290

No.	Sign	N_Z-N_X	N, N_O, N_Y	2V	Substance	Page
1306	+	.07	1.63	65°	Quinine·HBr	289
1307	+	.08	1.61	70°	Quinine·HCl	289
1308	+	.06	1.58	70°	Quinine·H_2SiF_6	291
1309	+	.05	1.62	80°	Quinine·$H_4P_2O_6$	291
1310	+	.072	1.588	0°	Quinine lactate(*d* or *l*)	289
1311	+	.047	1.608	0°	Quinine *dl*-lactate	289
1312	−	.08	1.61	75°	Quinine·HNO_3	291
1313	+	.09	1.61	35°	Quinine oxalate	291
1314	−	.084	1.665	17°	Quinine 2-phenylpyridine-2′,3-dicarboxylate	289
1315	+	.08	1.62	40°	Quinine phthalate	290
1316	+	.080	1.595	Mod.	Quinine phosphate	290
1317	+	.11	1.64	60°	Quinine picrate	291
1318	+	.05	1.63	50°	Quinine salicylate	289
1319	+	.080	1.620	Mod.	Quinine salicylate	289
1320	+	.09	1.63	Lg.	Quinine succinate	289
1321	+	.05	1.63	50°	Quinine·H_2SO_4 (anhydrous ?)	288
1321 a	+	.095	1.635	80°	Quinine·H_2SO_4·$7H_2O$	288
1321 b	−	.072	1.657	83°	Quinine sulfanilamide sulfate	292
1321 c	+	$>$.129	1.618	$<$72°	Quinine sulfanilamide sesquisulfate	292
1321 d	+	.083	1.614	40°	Quinine thiocyanate·H_2O	291
1321 e	+?	.01	1.625	90°	Quinine trihydrate	288
1322	−	.02	1.632	0°	Quinol acetylene	99
1322 a	−	.009	1.632	0°	Quinol hydrochloride	99
1322 b	−	.001	1.630	0°	Quinol hydrochloride sulfur dioxide	99
1322 c	−	.016	1.651	0°	Quinol hydrogen sulfide	99
1322 d	+	.060	1.606	0°	Quinol methyl cyanide	99
1322 e	+	.021	1.568	0°	Quinuclidinium hydrobromide	193
1322 f	+	.026	1.569	50°	Quinuclidinium hydrochloride	193
1322 g	−	.194	1.662	75°	Racephedrine	225
1323	−	.015	1.529	87°	Raffinose·$5H_2O$	270
1324	+	.046	1.525	0°	Ramie	270
1325	+	.062	1.533	0°	Ramie	270
1326	−	.049	1.620	46°	Resorcinol	98
1327	−	.063	1.492	53°	*l*-Rhamnitol·$3H_2O$	9
1328	−	.035	1.525	50°	Rhamnono-1,4-lactone	185
1329	+	.078	1.546	82°	Rhamnono-1,5-lactone	185
1330	−	.011	1.531	58°	*L*(+)-Rhamnose·H_2O	260
1331	−		1.606	0°	Rhodium cyclohexanediamine·Cl_3·$3H_2O$	153
1331 a	+	.478	1.651	82°	Riboflavine I	252
1331 b	+	.10	1.78	50°	Riboflavine II	252
1332	+	.037	1.549	80°	*d*(−)-Ribose	257
1333	−	.212	1.612	80°	α-Robinin	314
1334	−	.085	1.650	65°	Rotenone I	314
1335	+	.046	1.635	Lg.	Rotenone II	314
1336	−	.139	1.523	39°	Rubidium acid dioxalate·$2H_2O$	27
1337	−	.197	1.555	40°	Rubidium acid oxalate	27
1338	−	.157	1.652	24°	Rubidium acid phthalate	123

No.	Sign	N_Z-N_X	N, N_O, N_Y	2V	Substance	Page
1339	−	.073	1.550	84°	Rubidium acid tartrate	48
1340	−		1.494	81°	Rubidium aluminum oxalate·$6H_2O$	30
1341	−	.007	1.549	0°	Rubidium bromoethanetrisulfonate·H_2O	61
1342	−		1.510	75°	Rubidium mesotartrate·H_2O	56
1343	−	.012*ca.*	1.528	80°	Rubidium methanetrisulfonate·H_2O	60
1344	+	.119	1.485	80°	Rubidium oxalate·H_2O	28
1345	−		1.488	56°	Rubidium racemate·$2H_2O$	56
1346	−?	>.226	1.734	?	Rutin·$2H_2O$	187
1347		.00	1.54		Sabadine·H_2SO_4	305
1348	+	.020	1.56	Lg.	Sabadinine·$2H_2SO_4$	305
1349	−	>.198	1.690	Mod.	Saccharine	253
1350	−	.075	1.69 *ca.*	Sm.	Saccharinic acid lactone	186
1351	−	.098	1.590	45°	Salicin	263
1352	−	.009	1.490	0°	Samarium ethyl sulfate·$18H_2O$	6
1353	+	.062	1.551	43°	Sandaraco-pimaric acid	120
1354	−	.073	1.574	42°	Sandoptal	231
1355	+	.050	1.592	25°	α-Santonin	314
1355 a	−	.173	1.640	70°	β-Santonin	314
1356	−	.083	1.588	62°	*l*-Sapietic acid	120
1357	+	.035	1.550	Lg.	Sapogenin	275
1358	−	>.10	1.573	>67°	Scandium basic formate·H_2O	15
1359	+	.04	1.61	60°	Scopolamine·HI·$0.5H_2O$	280
1360	+	.095	1.510	59°	Sebacic acid	35
1360 a	−	.076	1.557	31°	Seconal	232
1361	+	.012	1.555	80°	*D*-α-Sedoheptitol	11
1362	+	.020	1.570	65°	*D*-β-Sedoheptitol	11
1363	−	.071	1.575	45°	*l*-Serine	71
1364	−	.249	1.694	15°	Serine diliturate·$1.5H_2O$	219
1365	+	.176	1.705	Lg.	Serine nitroindandionate	107
1366	+		1.586	55°	Shellolic acid dimethyl ester	315
1367	−	.115	1.583	80°	Sigmodal	232
1368	−	.059	1.750	41°	Silicon tetrakis(phenylmercaptide)	93
1369	+	.055	1.529	0°	Silk	272
1370	+	.057	1.538	0°	Silk	272
1371	−	.042	1.551	65°	Sodium abietate	119
1372	−	.065	1.463	63°	Sodium acetate·$3H_2O$	17
1373		.00	1.457		Sodium acid acetate	16
1374	−	.092	1.550	63°	Sodium acid *l*-glutamate·H_2O	70
1375	−	.134	1.524	39°	Sodium acid malonate·H_2O	32
1376	−	.190	1.553	52°	Sodium acid oxalate·H_2O	27
1377	+	.064	1.513	49°	Sodium acid palmitate	23
1378	−	.183	1.661	20°	Sodium acid phthalate	123
1379	+	.053	1.517	49°	Sodium acid stearate I	25
1380	+	.092	1.510	42°	Sodium acid stearate II	25
1381	+	.070	1.54	52°	Sodium acid tartrate·H_2O	48
1382	+	>.392	1.75	?	Sodium acid urate·H_2O	249
1383	−	.03	1.48	77°	Sodium ammonium aluminum oxalate·$7H_2O$	30

No.	Sign	$N_Z - N_X$	N, N_O, N_Y	2V	Substance	Page
1384	−	.035	1.48	79°	Sodium ammonium aluminum oxalate· $6H_2O$	30
1385	−		1.473	44°	Sodium ammonium racemate·H_2O	56
1386	−	.004	1.499	60°	Sodium ammonium tartrate·$4H_2O$	50
1387	+	.173	1.642	87°	Sodium-*o*-benzosulfimide·$2H_2O$	253
1388	−		1.511	63°	Sodium biglutamate	70
1388 a	+	.072	1.490	40°	Sodium bromocarbamide·H_2O-I	38
1388 b	+	.065	1.490	0°	Sodium bromocarbamide·H_2O-II	38
1389	+	.009	1.387	0°	Sodium-*n*-butyrate	22
1390	+	.127	1.584	75°	Sodium carbamate	37
1391	−	.097	1.446	44°	Sodium carbamate·$3H_2O$	37
1391 a	+	.064	1.485	36°	Sodium chlorocarbamide·H_2O	38
1392	+	.34	1.489	55°	Sodium dicyanimide	40
1393	−	>.30	1.750	50°	Sodium dinitrocresol	92
1394	−	.156	1.547	84°	Sodium dipyrocatchol nickel acid·$18H_2O$	98
1395	−		1.537	30°	Sodium ferric oxalate·$10H_2O$	31
1396	−?	.159*ca.*	1.462 *ca.*	Lg.	Sodium formate	13
1397	−	.218	1.620	40°	Sodium fumarate	35
1398	−	.066	1.569	70°	Sodium gluconate	57
1399	+	.024	1.455	85°	Sodium α-glycerophosphate·$6H_2O$	8
1400	−	.025	1.489	79°	Sodium β-glycerophosphate·$5H_2O$	8
1401	−	.109	1.527	70°	Sodium maleate	36
1402	+	.062	1.636	24°	Sodium 1,5-naphthalene-disulfonate· $2H_2O$	135
1403	+	.084	1.599	69°	Sodium 1-naphthylamine-4-sulfonate· $4H_2O$	169
1404	−	.177	1.528	70°	Sodium oxalate	28
1405	+	.065	1.52 *ca.*	50°	Sodium palmitate ($0.5H_2O$?)	23
1406	−	.070	1.609	45°	Sodium penicillin G	309
1407	+	.005	1.492	72°	Sodium potassium tartrate·$4H_2O$	51
1408	−	.007	1.495	50°	Sodium rubidium tartrate·$4H_2O$	52
1409	+	.257	1.445	32°	Sodium salicylate	127
1410	−	.161	1.584	80°	Sodium salt of 2-ethoxy-4-hydroxy-pyrimidine	213
1411	−	.138	1.572	74°	Sodium salt of 4-ethoxy-2-hydroxy-pyrimidine	214
1412	+	.022	1.577	75°	Sodium (and silver) methanedisulfonate· $2H_2O$	60
1413	+	.113	1.567	65°	Sodium sulfanilate·$2H_2O$	166
1414	+	.138	1.660	Lg.	Sodium sulfapyridine	202
1415	+	>.107	1.672	?	Sodium sulfathiazole	255
1416	+	.044	1.551	45° *ca.*	Sodium tetra-abietate	119
1417	+	.14	1.69	67°	Sodium *dl*-thyroxine·$5H_2O$	166
1418		.00	1.501		Sodium uranyl acetate	16
1419	+	.001	1.404	0°	Sodium *i*-valerate	21
1420	+	.012	1.398	0°	Sodium-*n*-valerate	21
1420 a	−	.262	1.648	41°	Sodium xanthinate·$3.5H_2O$	248
1421	−	.005	1.479	0°	Soluble acetate rayon	272

No.	Sign	N_Z-N_X	N, N_O, N_Y	2V	Substance	Page
1422	−	.019	1.566	70°	*d*-Sorbose	266
1423	+	.02 *ca.*	1.645 *ca.*	Sm.	Sparteine·HI	283
1424	+	.039	1.542	0°	Spinning silk	272
1424 a	+	.165	1.58 *ca.*	Sm.	Spirobihydantoin	251
1425	−		1.53	0°	Starch	270
1426	+	.025	1.52 *ca.*	Mod.	*β*-Stearic acid	24
1427	+	.010	1.508	0°	Stearopten	315
1428	+	.142	1.732	52°	*trans*-Stilbene	82
1429	−	.100	1.620	34°	Stovaine	112
1430	+	.024	1.542	0°	Straw	271
1431	+	.051	1.524	0°	Straw	271
1432	−	.095	1.683	0°	Strontium antimonyl tartrate	49
1433	+	.080	1.520	60°	Strontium copper formate·$8H_2O$	15
1434	+	.009	1.487	0°	Strontium dicalcium propionate	20
1435	−	.013	1.505	75°	Strontium ethyl sulfate·$2H_2O$	6
1436	+	.039	1.574	74°	Strontium formate	13
1437	−	.054	1.521	67°	Strontium formate·$2H_2O$	15
1438	−	.254	1.637	30°	α-Strontium nitrotetronate·nH_2O	183
1439	+	.018	1.517	0°	Strontium oxalate·$2.5H_2O$	29
1440	+	.13	1.653–1.68	Lg.	Strychnine	306
1441	+	.073	1.603	45°	Strychnine bioxalate·$1.5H_2O$	308
1442	−	.074	1.646 *ca.*	55°	Strychnine bisuccinate·H_2O	308
1443	+	.036	1.603	52°	Strychnine bitartrate·$3H_2O$	308
1444	+	.084 *ca.*	1.650	20°	Strychnine·HBr·H_2O	306
1445	+	.058	1.611	37°	Strychnine·$HClO_3$·H_2O	307
1446	+	.053	1.627	72°	Strychnine·HCl·$2H_2O$	306
1447	+	.069	1.665	30°	Strychnine·HI·H_2O	306
1448	+ ?	.123	1.598	85°	Strychnine maleate·H_2O	308
1449	−		1.610	0°	Strychnine malonate·$6H_2O$	308
1450	+	.065	1.624	54°	Strychnine·HNO_3	307
1451	+	.070 *ca.*	1.598	35°	Strychnine oxalate·$4.5H_2O$	307
1452	+	.065	1.598	45°	Strychnine·$HClO_4$·H_2O	307
1453	+	.066	1.597	38°	Strychnine·H_3PO_4·$2H_2O$	307
1454	+	.125	1.596	60°	Strychnine phthalate·H_2O	308
1455	+	.063	1.600	6°	Strychnine·H_2SeO_4·$5H_2O$	307
1456	−	.020	1.613	0° *ca.*	Strychnine·H_2SO_4·$6H_2O$	307
1457	+	.069	1.597	10°	Strychnine·H_2SO_4·$5H_2O$	307
1458	+	.044	1.654	35°	Strychnine·HCNS·H_2O	307
1458 a	−	$>$.122	$>$1.79	45°	Styreneamminodichloroplatinum	77
1458 b	+	.118	1.507	72°	Suberic acid	35
1459	−	.160	1.534	87°	*β*-Succinic acid	33
1459 a		.00	1.440		Succinonitrile	34
1460	−	.032	1.567	42°	Sucrose	269
1460 a	−	.011	1.526	51°	Sucrose·$2.5H_2O$	269
1460 b	−	.007	1.519	52°	Sucrose·$3.5H_2O$	269
1461	−	.030	1.488	80°	Sucrose octa-acetate I	269
1462	+	.018	1.462	77°	Sucrose octa-acetate II	269
1463	+	.168	1.564	21°	Sulfacetamide	169
1464	−	.355 ?	1.659	Lg.	Sulfacetimide diliturate·$1.5H_2O$	226

No.	Sign	N_Z-N_X	N, N_O, N_Y	2V	Substance	Page
1465	+	.108	1.695	45°	Sulfadiazine	239
1466	+	.211	1.673	77°	Sulfadiazine	239
1467	–		1.714	15–60°	Sulfadiazine diliturate·$2H_2O$	226
1468	+	.128	1.663	85°	Sulfaguanidine	168
1469	+	.145	1.649	85°	Sulfaguanidine·H_2O	168
1469 a	+	.117	1.648	85°	Sulfaguanidine·H_2O	168
1470	+	.282	1.688	87°	Sulfaguanidine diliturate	226
1471	–	.109	1.658	55°	Sulfamerazine	240
1472	–	.249	1.720	40°	Sulfamerazine diliturate·H_2O	226
1473	+	.340	1.674	90° *ca.*	Sulfanilamide I	166
1474	+	.270	1.674	85°	Sulfanilamide II	166
1475	+	.262	1.623	71°	Sulfanilamide III	166
1476	+	.214	1.615	24°	Sulfanilamide IV	166
1477	+	.218	1.636	89°	Sulfanilamide·H_2O	167
1478	–	.208	1.724	51°	Sulfanilamide diliturate·H_2O	225
1479	+		1.685	70° *ca.*	Sulfanilamidochloropyrimidine	240
1480	–?	.097	1.733	Lg.	Sulfanilamidopyridine I	239
1481	–	.154	1.722	36°	Sulfanilamidopyridine II	239
1482	+	.04	1.697	Lg.	Sulfanilamidopyridine III	239
1483	+	.210	1.693	74°	Sulfanilamidopyridine IV	239
1484	–	⟩.14?	1.745	Sm.	Sulfanilamidopyridine V	239
1485	–	.257	1.785	24°	Sulfapyridine diliturate·H_2O	226
1486	+	.19	1.61 *ca.*	80°	Sulfasuxidine I	255
1486 a	–	.132	1.676	58°	Sulfasuxidine II	255
1487	+	.085	1.685	Sm.	Sulfathiazole I	255
1488	–?	⟩.128	1.733	?	Sulfathiazole II	255
1489	–	.220	1.716	63°	Sulfathiazole diliturate·$2H_2O$	255
1490	–	.013	1.720	0°	Sulfobenzene trisulfide	133
1491	+	.054	1.541	80°	Sulfonal	11
1492	–	.043	1.706	0°	*p*-Sulfotoluene trisulfide	134
1493	–	.458	2.253	0°	Sulfur iodoform solvate	3
1494	–	.216	1.716	40°	Sumatrol	315
1494 a	–	.161	1.604	80°	Supriphen hydrochloride	160
1494 b	+	.062	1.603	70°	Tagathen	204
1495	+	.109	1.535	78°	Tartaric acid	47
1495 a	–	.082	1.540	80°	Temisin	315
1496	–	.170	1.68 *ca.*	Lg.	Tephrosin	316
1497	–	.270	1.616	63°	Terephthalic acid	126
1498	+	.021	1.529	80°	Terpin (terpinol)	96
1499	+	.019	1.512	77°	*cis*-Terpin·H_2O	97
1499 a	+	⟩.066	1.646	28°	Terramycin·$2H_2O$	310
1500	+	.021	1.49	Lg.	Tetra-acetyl-*D*-glucopyranose	261
1501	+	.079	1.499	45°	Tetra-acetylhydrazine	72
1502	–?	⟩.245	1.733	?	Tetracaine·HCl	163
1503		.00	1.518		Tetracalcium butyrate pentalead propionate·$12H_2O$	21
1503 a	+	.268	1.737	87°	Tetrachlorophthalic anhydride	184
1504	–	.343	1.774	56°	Tetraethylammonium picrate	89

No.	Sign	$N_Z - N_X$	N, N_O, N_Y	2V	Substance	Page
1504 a	+	.008	1.660	0°	Tetraethylphosphonium oidide	72
1505	+	.025	1.550	55°	Tetrahydrohelenalin	311
1506	−	.131	1.651	12°	Tetrahydro-4-hydroxy-2-keto-5-phenyl-furan	188
1507	−		1.516	57°	Tetrahydrohydroxyisopropylketo-dimethylfuran	184
1508	−	.036	1.540	25°	Tetrahydro-*d*-pimaric acid	111
1508 a	+	.008	1.523	81°	α-Tetrahydrotemisol	316
1509	−	.356	1.725	66°	1,2,3,4-Tetrahydro-1,4,5-triphenyl-pyrazine	205
1509 a	+	.117	1.545	29°	2,2,5,5-Tetrahydroxymethylcyclo-pentanone	9
1510		.00	1.712		Tetramethyl alcohol cobalt chloride	5
1511	−	.372	1.789	32°	Tetramethylammonium picrate	88
1512	+		1.544	49°	Tetramethoxybenzene	102
1513	−		1.615	87°	Tetramethylbenzene	76
1514	−	.02	1.52	90° *ca.*	1,3,4,5-Tetramethyl-*β*-*d*-fructopyranose	266
1515	+	.216	1.609	75°	1,3,7,9-Tetramethyluric acid	250
1516	−	.220	1.760	Lg.	2,3,4,6-Tetranitroaniline	148
1517	−	.07	1.52	80°	Tetrapotassium trioxalate·$2H_2O$	28
1518	−	.020	1.775	0°	Tetrathioacetamide·CuCl	20
1518 a	−	.272	1.595	51°	Tetrazole	246
1519	−	.144	1.632	44°	Thallous acid dioxalate·$2H_2O$	28
1520	−	.044	1.687	79°	Thallous acid tartrate	48
1521	−	.051	1.734	47°	Thallous chloromethanedisulfonate	60
1522	+		1.707	74°	Thallous mesotartrate	56
1523	+		1.739	24°	Thallous methanetrisulfonate·H_2O	60
1524	+		1.81	88°	Thallous racemate	55
1525	−	.044	1.768	0°	Thallous *d*-tartrate	49
1526	+	.06	1.63 *ca.*	Lg.	Thebaine	298
1527	−	>.305	1.74	Mod.	Theobromine	247
1527 a	+	>.153	1.76	Sm.	2-Thio-5-iodouracil	214
1528	−	.64	1.805	89°	2-Thiouracil	214
1529	−	.13	1.742	32°	Thiourea	43
1529 a	−	.079	1.591	37°	Threonine	71
1530	−	.006	1.492	0°	Thulium ethyl sulfate·$18H_2O$	7
1530 a	−	.322	1.726	14°	Thymine	214
1531	+	.084	1.525	0°	Thymol	94
1532	−	.225	1.625	80°	Thymol-3,5-dinitrobenzoate	116
1533	−		1.645	85°	Tolanisbenzhydroxylamine	129
1534	+		1.579	64°	Tolanishydroxamic acid	129
1535	−		1.694	69°	Tolbenzanishydroxylamine	128
1536	+	>.195	1.705	<80°	Tolidine diliturate	225
1537	−	.284	1.737	20°	*m*-Toluamide	118
1538	−	.291	1.715	44°	*o*-Toluamide	118
1539	−	.224	1.708	36°	*p*-Toluamide	118
1540	+	>.218	1.675	<84°	*m*-Toluidine diliturate	221
1541	+	.214	1.632	75°	*o*-Toluidine diliturate	221
1542	+	.064	1.680	45°	*p*-Toluidine diliturate	221

No.	Sign	N_Z-N_X	N, N_O, N_Y	2V	Substance	Page
1543	−		1.667	83°	Toluidine·HBr	148
1544	+	.334	1.662	32°	α-*p*-Toluylacetophenone enol	109
1544 a	−	.113	1.666	45°	*o*-Tolylbiguanide·HCl	149
1545	+	.005	1.529	50°	Trehalose·$2H_2O$	268
1546	+	>.20	1.645	Lg.	Triacetate of apotoxicarol	317
1547	+	.028	1.569	36°	Triacetonediamine·2HCl·$ZnCl_2$·$3H_2O$	66
1548	+		1.500	77°	Triacetone mannitol	193
1549	−	.014	1.595 *ca.*	0°	Triasaminoethylamine·4HCl·H_2O	65
1549 a	−	>.205	>1.785	0°	Tribromocarbonylplatinum pyridinium·H_2O	194
1550	−	.217	1.641	51°	Tributylamine picrate	90
1551	+	.011	1.589	0°	Tributylmonoisopropyl tetrathiosilicate	8
1552	+	.030	1.602	80°	Tricadmium aconitate·$6H_2O$	37
1553	+	.123	1.545	80°	Tricalcium aconitate·$6H_2O$	37
1554	+	.097	1.558	36°	Trichloracetamide	19
1555	+	.045	1.512	<10°	Trichloroacetic acid	19
1556	+	.137	1.626	30°	Trichlorochlorophenylethane I (or DDT)	80
1557	+	.10	1.639	52°	Trichlorochlorophenylethane III	80
1558	+		1.562	57°	Trichloronaphthalenone	104
1559	+	.22	1.740	85°	Trichlorophenylbenzene	83
1560	−		1.57	0°	Tricyclohexanediamine cobaltic chlorate·$3H_2O$	154
1561	−		1.563	0°	Tricyclohexanediamine cobaltic perchlorate·$3H_2O$	154
1562	−	.009	1.583	0°	Tricyclohexanediamine cobaltic nitrate·$3H_2O$	154
1563	+	.208	1.651	80°	Triethanolamine picrate	91
1564		.000	1.459		Triethylamine aluminum sulfate·$12H_2O$	63
1565	+	.026	1.585	Lg.	Triethylamine hexachlorostannate	63
1566	−	.278	1.735	19°	Triethylamine picrate	89
1567	−	.367	1.865	14°	Triethylenetetramine picrate	91
1568	+	.06 *ca.*	1.59	0°	Triethylphosphine sulfide	72
1569	−	.31	1.69	36°	1,3,5-Trihydroxybenzene·$2H_2O$	101
1570	−	.178	1.648	20° *ca.*	1,3,5-Trihydroxybenzene·$2H_2O$	101
1571	−	.04 *ca.*	1.78 *ca.*	0°	2,6,8-Trihydroxy-9-(2-propenyl)purine	251
1571 a	−	.21	1.69	0°	*s*-Trimesic acid ethyl ester	126
1572	+	.138	1.590	50°	Trimethylacet-*p*-bromoanilide	146
1573		.00	1.453		Trimethylamine aluminum sulfate·$12H_2O$	62
1574		.00	1.600		Trimethylamine chloroplatinate	62
1575	−	.358	1.790	27°	Trimethylamine picrate	88
1576		.00	1.535		Trimethylamine·$SnCl_6$	62
1576 a	+	.89	1.673	61°	3,3′,5-Trimethyl-2′-amino-5′-chlorobiphenyl	140
1577	−	.091	1.601 *ca.*	61°	Trimethylbenzylsilicon-*p*-sulfonanilide	144
1578	−	.019	1.503	0°	2,5,5-Trimethyl-1,3-cyclohexandiol	96
1579	−	.025	1.597	53°	Trimethylenetrinitramine	243
1580	−	.035	1.52 *ca.*	18°	1,3,4-Trimethyl-*D*-fructose	266
1581	−	.086	1.648	24°	1,3,3-Trimethyl-2-methyleneindoline·HI	195
1581 a	−	.118	1.653	66°	2,4,6′-Trimethyl-2′-nitrobiphenyl	81

No.	Sign	N_Z-N_X	N, N_O, N_Y	2V	Substance	Page
1582	−	.105	1.670	0°	1,3,7-Trimethyl-9-phenyluric acid	251
1583	+	.026	1.560	⟨80°	Trimorpholine	256
1584	−	.007	1.567	?	Trimorpholine·HCl	257
1585	+	.798	1.854	81°	1,6,8-Trinitro-2-ethylaminonaphthalene	153
1586	−	⟩.097	⟩1.70	0°	Trinitroresorcinol II	99
1586 a	−	.174	1.674	60°	2,4,6-Trinitrotoluene	76
1587	−	.084?	1.751?	25°	Triphenylarsine	180
1588	−	.348	1.867	10°	1,3,5-Triphenylbenzene	83
1589	+	.097	1.782	66°	Triphenylbismuthine	180
1590	+	.060	1.734	36°	Triphenylbismuthine dichloride	181
1591	−	.222	1.674	17°	Tripropylamine picrate	89
1592	+	.012	1.656	50°	Triphenylcarbinol	95
1593	+	.043	1.655	70°	Triphenylmethane	82
1594	+	.050	1.636	60°	Triphenylmethylethyl ether	96
1595	+	.050	1.641	60°	Triphenylmethylisopropyl ether	96
1596	+	.050	1.676	60°	Triphenylmethylmethyl ether	96
1597	−	.042	1.660	80°	Triphenylmethyl-2-phenylether ether	96
1598	−	.018	1.658	55°	Triphenylmethylpropyl ether	96
1599	+		1.638	69°	Triphenylpropylpyrrolone I	198
1600	+	.047	1.582	80°	Tripyrocatechol arsenate·$4H_2O$	97
1601	−	.014	1.772	0°	Trithiocarbamide·CuCl	43
1602	−	.08	1.46	0°	Trithiourea·$BiCl_3$	44
1603	−	.023	1.650	50°	Tropine chloroplatinate	281
1603 a	+	.010	1.458	0°	*l*-Tuamine sulfate	64
1604	+	.130	1.600	65°	*l*-Tyrosine	165
1605		.00	1.712		Tryptophan picrolonate	212
1606	+	.118	1.484	0°	Urea	38
1607	+	.070	1.500	65°	Urea hydrogen peroxide	38
1608	−	.279	1.647	14°	Urea nitrate	38
1609	−	.228	1.612	19°	Urea oxalate	39
1610	−	.034	1.533	50°	Urea phosphate	38
1611	+	.03	1.56	70°	Ursolic acid	317
1612	−	.161	1.710	60°	Usnic acid	318
1613	+	.064	1.488	74°	Valeramide	22
1614	+?	.291	1.617	85°	Valer-*p*-bromoanilide	147
1615	+	.077	1.494	0°	Valerolactone-α,α-spiran	192
1616	−	.213	1.646	15°	Valine dilituraté·$2H_2O$ I	218
1617	−	.103	1.627	82°	Valine dilituraté·$2H_2O$ II	218
1618	−	⟩.303	1.678	Lg.	Valine nitroindandionate	106
1618 a	−	.249	1.694	75°	Vanillin	108
1619	+	.135	1.585	62°	*N*-Vanillylacetamide	158
1620	−	.225	1.705	39°	Vanillylamine·HCl	158
1621	−	.105	1.675	48°	*N*-Vanillylbenzamide	160
1622	+	.140	1.580	Lg.	*N*-Vanillylbutyramide	158
1623	+	.220	1.605	Lg.	*N*-Vanillylcrotonamide	159
1624	+	.075	1.555	Sm.	*N*-Vanillyldecanamide	159
1625	+	.08	1.54	Mod.	*N*-Vanillyldodecanamide	159
1626	−	.110	1.595	62°	*N*-Vanillylenanthamide	158

No.	Sign	N_Z-N_X	N, N_O, N_Y	2V	Substance	Page
1627	−	.170	1.633	11°	*N*-Vanillylisobutyramide	158
1628	−	.185	1.635	56°	*N*-Vanillylpropionamide	158
1629	+	.100	1.540	64°	*N*-Vanillylundecanamide	159
1630	+	.08	1.60	Lg.	*N*-Vanillylundecenamide	160
1631	+	.044	1.526	0°	Veronal I	226
1632	−	.143	1.558	45°	Veronal II	226
1633	−	.113	1.550	36°	Veronal III	226
1634	+	very weak	1.536	0°	Vinyon	272
1635	+	.025	1.516	0°	Viscose rayon (thick skin)	273
1636	+	.022	1.534	0°	Viscose rayon	273
1637	+	.035	1.532	0°	Viscose rayon with little alkali and 70% stretch	273
1638	+	.045	1.528	0°	Viscose rayon with high alkali and 120% stretch	273
1639	+	.025	1.523	0°	Viscose silk	272
1640	+	.015	1.530	0°	Viscose with urea formaldehyde resin	273
1640 a	+	.63	1.634	50°	Vitamin A	94
1641	−	.048	1.652	Mod.	Vitamin B_{12}	310
1641 a	−	.074	1.640	Mod.	Vitamin B_{12a}	310
1642		.000	1.67		Vitrain	1
1643		.000	1.91		Vitrain	1
1644		.010	1.545	0°	Wool	272
1644 a	−	.352	1.772	12°	Xanthine·HCl	248
1664 b	−	.044	1.734	43°	Xanthotoxin I	191
1645	+	.029	1.521	32°	Xylitol I	10
1646	+	.017	1.551	38°	Xylitol II	10
1647	−	.029	1.544	32°	Xylopyranose	258
1648	+	.080	1.760	Lg.	Xylosazone	259
1649	+	.710	1.638	62°	Yangonin	186
1650	+	.140	1.563	42°	Yohimbine	299
1651	+	.05 *ca.*	1.595 *ca.*	Mod.	Yohimbine·HCl	299
1652	+	.124	1.542	35°	Yohimbine chloroacetate	299
1653	−	.012	1.494	0°	Ytterbium ethyl sulfate·$18H_2O$	7
1654	−	.013	1.493	0°	Yttrium ethyl sulfate·$18H_2O$	6
1655	+	.138	1.618	50°	Yttrium *m*-nitrobenzenesulfonate·$7H_2O$	133
1656	+	.007	1.532	0°	Zealon	271
1657	+	.006	1.540	0°	Zeorin	318
1658	+	.121	1.492	87°	Zinc acetate·$2H_2O$	16
1659	+		1.494	85°	Zinc acetate·$3H_2O$	17
1660	−		1.474	71°	Zinc bromomesaconate·$8H_2O$	36
1661	−	.257	1.698	14°	Zinc dicyanimide	40
1662	+	.050	1.500	80°	Zinc butyrate	22
1663	+	.043	1.526	38°	Zinc formate·$2H_2O$	15
1664	+	.065	1.497	75°	Zinc *d*-(or *l*-)lactate·$3H_2O$	45
1665	−	.025	1.535	27°	Zinc *dl*-lactate·$3H_2O$	45
1666	−	.128	1.625	59°	Zinc 1,5-naphthalenedisulfonate·$6H_2O$	135